Developmental Mathematics

CUSTOM EDITION FOR BRISTOL COMMUNITY COLLEGE

Taken from:

Developmental Mathematics
by Elayn Martin-Gay

Learning Solutions

New York   Boston   San Francisco
London   Toronto   Sydney   Tokyo   Singapore   Madrid
Mexico City   Munich   Paris   Cape Town   Hong Kong   Montreal

Cover Art: Courtesy of PhotoDisc/Getty Images

Taken from:

Developmental Mathematics
by Elayn Martin-Gay
Copyright © 2007 by Pearson Education, Inc.
Published by Prentice Hall
Upper Saddle River, New Jersey 07458

This special edition published in cooperation with Pearson Learning Solutions.

All trademarks, service marks, registered trademarks, and registered service marks are the property of their respective owners and are used herein for identification purposes only.

Pearson Learning Solutions, 501 Boylston Street, Suite 900, Boston, MA 02116
A Pearson Education Company
www.pearsoned.com

Printed in the United States of America

5 6 7 8 9 10 V011 15 14 13 12 11

000200010270584142

JL

ISBN 10: 0-558-76240-9
ISBN 13: 978-0-558-76240-7

*To my mother, Barbara M. Miller,
and her husband, Leo Miller, and to the memory of
my father, Robert J. Martin*

Contents

4 Decimals   249

5 Percent   320

6 Geometry   406

7 Statistics and Probability   487

8 Real Numbers and Introduction to Algebra   537

9 Equations, Inequalities, and Problem Solving   621

10 Graphing Equations and Inequalities 710

12 Exponents and Polynomials 868

13 Factoring Polynomials 944

14 Rational Expressions   1014

Appendix B   Tables   1245

Appendix C   The Bigger Picture   1248

Appendix D   Further Geometric Topics   1254

Tools to Help Students Succeed

Your textbook includes a number of features designed to help you succeed in this math course—as well as the next math course you take. These features include:

Feature	Benefit	Page
Well-crafted Exercise Sets: We learn math by doing math	The exercise sets in your text offer an ample number of exercises carefully ordered so you can master basic mathematical skills and concepts while developing all-important problem solving skills. Exercise sets include Mixed Practice exercises to help you master multiple key concepts, as well as Mental Math, Writing, Applications, Concept Check, Concept Extension, and Review exercises.	183–186
Study Skills Builders: Maximize your chances for success	Study Skills Builders reinforce the material in *Section 1.1—Tips for Success in Mathematics.* Study Skills Builders are a great resource for study ideas and self-assessment to maximize your opportunity for success in this course. Take your new study skills with you to help you succeed in your next math course.	203
The Bigger Picture: Succeed in this math course and the next one you take	The Bigger Picture focuses on the key concepts of this course—operations on numbers, simplifying expressions, and solving equations and inequalities—and asks you to keep an ongoing outline so you can recognize and solve different types of equations and inequalities. A strong foundation in these topics will help you succeed in this algebra course, as well as the next math course you take.	216, 696
Examples: Step-by-step instruction for you	Examples in the text provide you with clear, concise step-by-step instructions to help you learn. Annotations in the examples provide additional instruction.	195
Helpful Hints: Help where you'll need it most	Helpful Hints provide tips and advice at exact locations where students need it most. Strategically placed where you might have the most difficulty, Helpful Hints will help you work through common trouble spots.	191
Practice Problems: Immediate reinforcement	Practice Problems offer immediate reinforcement after every example. Try each Practice Problem after studying the corresponding example to make sure you have a good working knowledge of the concept.	195
Integrated Review: Mid-chapter progress check	To ensure that you understand the key concepts covered in the first sections of the chapter, work the exercises in the Integrated Review before you continue with the rest of the chapter.	204
Vocabulary Check: Key terms and vocabulary	Make sure you understand key terms and vocabulary in each chapter with the Vocabulary Check.	236
Chapter Highlights: Study smart	Chapter Highlights outline the key concepts of the chapter along with examples to help you focus your studying efforts as you prepare for your test.	236
Chapter Test: Take a practice test	In preparation for your classroom test, take this practice test to make sure you understand the key topics in the chapter. Be sure to use the **Chapter Test Prep Video CD** included with this text to see the author present a fully worked-out solution to each exercise in the Chapter Test.	244

Martin-Gay's CD VIDEO RESOURCES Help Students Succeed

Martin-Gay's **Chapter Test Prep Video CD (available with this text)**

- Provides students with help during their most "teachable moment"—while they are studying for a test.

- Text author Elayn Martin-Gay presents step-by-step solutions to the exact exercises found in each Chapter Test in the book.

- Easy video navigation allows students to instantly access the worked-out solutions to the exercises they want to review.

- A close-captioned option for the hearing impaired is provided.

Martin-Gay's **CD Lecture Series (with Tips for Success in Mathematics)**

- Text author Elayn Martin-Gay presents the key concepts from every section of the text in 10–15 minute mini-lectures.

- Students can easily review a section or a specific topic before a homework assignment, quiz, or test.

- Includes fully worked-out solutions to exercises marked with a CD Video icon ( ) in each section.

- Includes *Section 1.1, Tips for Success in Mathematics.*

- A close-captioned option for the hearing impaired is provided.

- Ask your bookstore for information about Martin-Gay's *Developmental Mathematics,* CD Lecture Series, or visit www.prenhall.com.

Martin-Gay's **Instructor-to-Instructor CD Videos**

- Text author Elayn Martin-Gay presents tips, hints, and suggestions for engaging students and presenting key topics.

- Available as part of the Martin-Gay Instructor/Adjunct Resource Kit.

- Contact your local Prentice Hall representative for more information.

Additional Resources to Help You Succeed

Student Study Pack

A single, easy-to-use package—available bundled with your textbook or by itself—for purchase through your bookstore. This package contains the following resources to help you succeed:

Student Solutions Manual
- Contains worked-out solutions to odd-numbered exercises from each section exercise set, Practice Problems, Mental Math exercises, and all exercises found in the Chapter Review and Chapter Tests.

Prentice Hall Math Tutor Center
- Staffed by qualified math instructors who provide students with tutoring on examples and odd-numbered exercises from the textbook. Tutoring is available via telephone, fax, email, or the Internet.

Martin-Gay's CD Lecture Series
- Text author Elayn Martin-Gay presents the key concepts from every section of the text with 10–15 minute mini-lectures. Students can easily review a section or a specific topic before a homework assignment, quiz, or test.
- Includes fully worked-out solutions to exercises marked with a CD Video icon (◉) in each section. Also includes *Section 1.1, Tips for Success in Mathematics.*
- A close-captioned option for the hearing impaired is provided.

Online Homework and Tutorial Resources

MyMathLab *MyMathLab*
MyMathLab

MyMathLab is a series of text specific, easily customizable, online courses for Prentice Hall textbooks in mathematics and statistics. MyMathLab is powered by Course Compass™—Pearson Education's online teaching and learning environment—and by MathXL®—our online homework, tutorial, and assessment system. MyMathLab gives instructors the tools they need to deliver all or a portion of their course online, whether students are in a lab setting or working from home. MyMathLab provides a rich and flexible set of course materials, featuring free-response exercises that are algorithmically generated for unlimited practice and mastery. Students can also use online tools, such as video lectures, animations, and a multimedia textbook, to independently improve their understanding and performance. MyMathLab is available to qualified adopters. For more information, visit our Web site at www.mymathlab.com or contact your Prentice Hall sales representative. (MyMathLab must be set up and assigned by your instructor.)

MathXL® www.mathxl.com *Math XL*
MathXL®

MathXL is a powerful online homework, tutorial, and assessment system that accompanies the text. With MathXL, instructors can create, edit, and assign online homework and tests using algorithmically generated exercises correlated to your textbook. All student work is tracked in MathXL's online gradebook. Students can take chapter tests in MathXL and receive personalized study plans based on their test results. The study plan diagnoses weaknesses and links students directly to tutorial exercises for the objectives they need to study and retest. Students can also access supplemental animations and video clips directly from selected exercises. MathXL is available to qualified adopters. For more information, visit our Web site at www.mathxl.com, or contact your Prentice Hall sales representative for a product demonstration. (MathXL must be set up and assigned by your instructor.)

Preface

Developmental Mathematics was written to provide a solid foundation in arithmetic and algebra as well as to develop problem solving skills. It is intended for basic math and introductory algebra courses; however, all of the necessary intermediate topics are included in the appendices for those wishing to extend the course to intermediate algebra. Specific care was taken to make sure students have the most up-to-date relevant text preparation for their next mathematics course or for non-mathematical courses that require an understanding of algebraic fundamentals. I have tried to achieve this by writing a user-friendly text that is keyed to objectives and contains many worked-out examples. As suggested by AMATYC and the NCTM Standards (plus Addenda), real-life and real-data applications, data interpretation, conceptual understanding, problem solving, writing, cooperative learning, appropriate use of technology, mental mathematics, number sense, estimation, critical thinking, and geometric concepts are emphasized and integrated throughout the book.

Highlights of *Developmental Mathematics*

Exercise Sets

- Three forms of mixed sections of exercises are included:
  - **Mixed Practice** exercises combining objectives within a section
  - **Mixed Practice** exercises combining previous sections
  - **Mixed Review** exercises included at the end of the Chapter Review

  These exercises require students to determine the problem type and strategy needed in order to solve it. In doing so, students need to think about key concepts to proceed with a correct method of solving—just as they would need to do on a test.

- **Concept Check exercises** are included in the section exercise sets. These exercises are related to the Concept Check(s) found within the section. They help students measure their understanding of key concepts by focusing on common trouble areas. These exercises may ask students to identify a common error, and/or provide an explanation.

- **Concept Extensions** These exercises extend the concepts and require students to combine several skills or concepts to solve the exercises in this section.

Emphasis on Study Skills and Student Success

- **Study Skills Builders** Found at the end of many exercise sets, Study Skills Builders allow instructors to assign exercises that will help students improve their study skills and take responsibility for their part of the learning process. Study Skills Builders reinforce the material found in Section 1.1, "Tips for Success in Mathematics," and serve as an excellent tool for self-assessment.

- **The Bigger Picture** is a recurring feature beginning in Section 1.7, that focuses on the key concepts of the course—operations on numbers, simplifying expressions and solving equations and inequalities. It helps students develop a study guide throughout the course. By working the exercises and developing this outline throughout the text, students can begin to transition from thinking "section by section" to thinking about how the mathematics in this course is part of the "bigger picture" of mathematics in general. A completed outline is provided in Appendix C so students have a model for their work.

- **Chapter Test Prep Video CD** provides students with help during their most "teachable moment"—while they are studying for a test. Included with every copy of the student edition of the text, this video CD provides fully worked-out solutions by the author to every exercise from each Chapter Test in the text. The easy video navigation allows students to instantly access the solutions to the exercises they want to review. The problems are solved by the author in the same manner as in the text.

■ **Chapter Test files in TestGen** provide algorithms specific to each exercise from each Chapter Test in the text. Allows for easy replication of Chapter Tests with consistent, algorithmically generated problem types for additional assignments or assessment purposes.

Key Pedagogical Features

The following key features are found throughout the text:

Problem Solving Process   This is formally introduced in Chapter 1 with a four-step process that is integrated throughout the text. The four steps are **Understand, Translate, Solve,** and **Interpret.** The repeated use of these steps in a variety of examples shows their wide applicability. Reinforcing the steps can increase students' comfort level and confidence in tackling problems.

Exercise Sets   Special focus was placed on making sure that even- and odd-numbered exercises are paired.

Examples   Detailed step-by-step examples are included. Many of these reflect real life. Additional instructional support is provided in the annotated examples.

Practice Problems   Throughout the text, each worked-out example has a parallel Practice Problem. These invite students to be actively involved in the learning process. Students should try each Practice Problem after finishing the corresponding example. Learning by doing will help students grasp ideas before moving on to other concepts. Answers to the Practice Problems are provided at the bottom of each page.

Helpful Hints   Helpful Hints contain practical advice on applying mathematical concepts. Strategically placed where students are most likely to need immediate reinforcement, Helpful Hints help students avoid common trouble areas and mistakes.

Concept Checks   This feature allows students to gauge their grasp of an idea as it is being presented in the text. Concept Checks stress conceptual understanding at the point-of-use and help suppress misconceived notions before they start. Answers appear at the bottom of the page. Exercises related to Concept Checks are included in the exercise sets.

Integrated Reviews   A unique, mid-chapter exercise set that helps students assimilate new skills and concepts that they have learned separately over several sections. These reviews provide yet another opportunity for students to work with "mixed" exercises as they master the topics.

Vocabulary Check   Provides an opportunity for students to become more familiar with the use of mathematical terms as they strengthen their verbal skills. These appear at the end of each chapter before the Chapter Highlights.

Chapter Highlights   Found at the end of every chapter, these contain key definitions and concepts with examples to help students understand and retain what they have learned and help them organize their notes and study for tests.

Chapter Review   The end of every chapter contains a comprehensive review of topics introduced in the chapter. The Chapter Review offers exercises keyed to every section in the chapter, as well as Mixed Review exercises that are not keyed to sections.

Chapter Test and Chapter Test Prep Video CD   The Chapter Test is structured to include those problems that involve common student errors. The **Chapter Test Prep Video CD** gives students instant author access to a step-by-step video solution of each exercise in the Chapter Test.

Cumulative Review   Follows every chapter in the text (except Chapter 1). Each odd-numbered exercise contained in the Cumulative Review is an earlier worked example in the text that is referenced in the back of the book along with the answer. The even exercises are new.

Mental Math   Found at the beginning of an exercise set, these mental warm-ups reinforce concepts found in the accompanying section and increase student's confidence before they tackle an exercise set.

Writing Exercises   These exercises occur in almost every exercise set and require students to provide a written response to explain concepts or justify their thinking.

Applications   Real-world and real-data applications have been thoroughly updated and many new applications are included. These exercises occur in almost every exercise set and show the relevance of mathematics and help students gradually, and continuously develop their problem solving skills.

Review Exercises   These exercises occur in each exercise set (except in Chapter 1) and are keyed to earlier sections. They review concepts learned earlier in the text that will be needed in the next section or chapter.

Exercise Set Resource Icons at the opening of each exercise set remind students of the resources available for extra practice and support:

CD/Video for Review   MyMathLab   MathXL®

PH Math/Tutor Center   Student Solutions Manual

See Student Resource descriptions pages xx–xxi for details on the individual resources available.

Exercise Icons   These icons facilitate the assignment of specialized exercises and let students know what resources can support them.
  CD Video icon: exercise worked on Martin-Gay's CD Lecture Series.
△ Triangle icon: identifies exercises involving geometric concepts.
  Pencil icon: indicates a written response is needed.
  Calculator icons: optional exercises intended to be solved using a scientific or graphing calculator.

Group Activities   Found at the end of each chapter, these activities are for individual or group completion, and are usually hands-on or data-based activities that extend the concepts found in the chapter allowing students to make decisions and interpretations and to think and write about algebra.

Optional: Calculator Exploration Boxes and Calculator Exercises   The optional Calculator Explorations provide key strokes and exercises at appropriate points to provide an opportunity for students to become familiar with these tools. Section exercises that are best completed by using a calculator are identified by 📱 or 📱 for ease of the assignment.

A Word about Textbook Design and Student Success

The design of developmental mathematics textbooks has become increasingly important. As students and instructors have told Prentice Hall in focus groups and market research surveys, these textbooks cannot look "cluttered" or "busy." A "busy" design can distract a student from what is most important in the text. It can also heighten math anxiety.

As a result of the conversations and meetings we have had with students and instructors, we concluded the design of this text should be understated and focused on the most important pedagogical elements. Students and instructors helped us to identify the primary elements that are central to student success. These primary elements include:

- Exercise Sets

- Examples and Practice Problems

- Helpful Hints

- Rules, Property, and Definition boxes

As you will notice in this text, these primary features are the most prominent elements in the design. We have made every attempt to make sure these elements are the features the eye is drawn to. The remaining features, the secondary elements in the design, blend into the "fabric" or "grain" of the overall design. These secondary elements complement the primary elements without becoming distractions.

Prentice Hall's thanks goes to all of the students and instructors (as noted by the author in Acknowledgments) who helped us develop the design of this text. At every step in the design process, their feedback proved valuable in helping us to make the right decisions. Thanks to your input, we're confident the design of this text will be both practical and engaging as it serves its educational and learning purposes.

Sincerely,

Paul Murphy

Executive Editor
Developmental Mathematics
Prentice Hall

Instructor and Student Resources

The following resources are available to help instructors and students use this text more effectively.

Instructor Resources

Annotated Instructor's Edition (0-13-229091-X)

- Answers to all exercises printed on the same text page

- Teaching Tips throughout the text placed at key points

- Includes Vocabulary Check at the beginning of relevant sections

- General tips and suggestions for classroom or group activities

Instructor Solutions Manual (0-13-229069-3)

- Solutions to the even- and odd-numbered exercises

- Solutions to every Mental Math exercise

- Solutions to every Practice Problem

- Solutions to every exercise in the Integrated Reviews, Chapter Reviews, Chapter Tests, and Cumulative Reviews

Instructor's Resource Manual with Tests (0-13-229070-7)

- Includes Mini-Lectures for every section from the text
- Group Activities
- Free Response Test Forms, Multiple Choice Test Forms, Cumulative Tests, and Additional Exercises
- Answers to all items

TestGen (0-13-229072-3)

- Enables instructors to build, edit, print, and administer tests
- Features a computerized bank of questions developed to cover all text objectives
- Available on dual-platform Windows/Macintosh CD-Rom

Instructor Adjunct Resource Kit (0-13-229094-4)

The Martin-Gay Instructor/Adjunct Resource Kit (IARK) contains tools and resources to help adjuncts and instructors succeed in the classroom. The IARK includes:

- Instructor-to-Instructor CD Videos that offer tips, suggestions, and strategies for engaging students and presenting key topics
- PDF files of the Instructor Solutions Manual and the Instructor's Resource Manual
- TestGen

MyMathLab Instructor Version (0-13-147898-2)
MyMathLab www.mymathlab.com

MyMathLab is a series of text specific, easily customizable, online courses for Prentice Hall textbooks in mathematics and statistics. MyMathLab is powered by Course Compass™—Pearson Education's online teaching and learning environment—and by MathXL®—our online homework, tutorial, and assessment system. MyMathLab gives instructors the tools they need to deliver all or a portion of their course online, whether students are in a lab setting or working from home. MyMathLab provides a rich and flexible set of course materials, featuring free-response exercises that are algorithmically generated for unlimited practice and mastery. Students can also use online tools, such as video lectures, animations, and a multimedia textbook, to independently improve their understanding and performance. Instructors can use MyMathLab's homework and test managers to select and assign online exercises correlated directly to the text, and they can import TestGen tests into MyMathLab for added flexibility. MyMathLab's online gradebook—designed specifically for mathematics and statistics—automatically tracks students' homework and test results and gives the instructor control over how to calculate final grades. Instructors can also add offline (paper-and-pencil) grades to the gradebook. MyMathLab is available to qualified adopters. For more information, visit our website at www.mymathlab.com or contact your Prentice Hall sales representative.

MathXL Instructor Version (0-13-147895-8)
MathXL® www.mathxl.com

MathXL is a powerful online homework, tutorial, and assessment system that accompanies the text. With MathXL, instructors can create, edit, and assign online homework and tests using algorithmically generated exercises correlated to your textbook. All student work is tracked in MathXL's online gradebook. Students can take chapter tests in MathXL and receive personalized study plans based on their test results. The study plan diagnoses weaknesses and links students directly to tutorial exercises for the objectives they need to study and retest. Students can also access supplemental animations and video clips directly from selected exercises. MathXL is available to qualified adopters. For more information, visit our Web site at www.mathxl.com, or contact your Prentice Hall sales representative for a product demonstration.

Interact Math® Tutorial Web site www.interactmath.com

Get practice and tutorial help online! This interactive tutorial Web site provides algorithmically generated practice exercises that correlate directly to the exercises in your textbook. You can retry an exercise as many times as you like with new values each time for unlimited practice and mastery. Every exercise is accompanied by an interactive guided solution that gives you helpful feedback if you enter an incorrect answer, and you can also view a worked-out sample problem that steps you through an exercise similar to the one you're working on.

Student Resources

Student Solutions Manual (0-13-229102-9)

- Solutions to the odd-numbered section exercises
- Solutions to the Practice Problems
- Solutions to every Mental Math exercise
- Solutions to every exercise found in the Chapter Reviews and Chapter Tests

Martin-Gay's CD Lecture Series (0-13-229098-7)

- Perfect for review of a section or a specific topic, these mini-lectures by Elayn Martin-Gay cover the key concepts from each section of the text in approximately 10–15 minutes.
- Includes fully worked-out solutions to exercises in each section marked with a
- Includes coverage of Section 1.1, "Tips for Success Mathematics"
- Closed-captioned for the hearing impaired

Prentice Hall Math Tutor Center (0-13-064604-0)

- Staffed by qualified math instructors who provide students with tutoring on examples and odd-numbered exercises from the textbook
- Tutoring is available via telephone, fax, e-mail, or the Internet
- Whiteboard technology allows tutors and students to see problems worked while they "talk" in real time over the Internet during tutoring sessions

Developmental Mathematics, Student Study Pack

The Student Study Pack includes:

- Martin-Gay's CD Lecture Series
- Student Solutions Manual
- Prentice Hall Math Tutor Center access code

Chapter Test Prep Video CD—Standalone (0-13-229093-6)

- Includes fully worked-out solutions to every problem from each Chapter Test in the text.

MathXL Tutorials on CD—Standalone (0-13-229101-0)

- Provides algorithmically generated practice exercises that correlate to exercises at the end of sections.
- Every exercise is accompanied by an example and a guided solution, selected exercises include a video clip.
- The software recognizes student errors and provides feedback. It can also generate printed summaries of student's progress.

Interact Math® Tutorial Web Site www.interactmath.com

Get practice and tutorial help online! This interactive tutorial Web site provides algorithmically generated practice exercises that correlate directly to the exercises in your textbook. You can retry an exercise as many times as you like with new values each time for unlimited practice and mastery. Every exercise is accompanied by an interactive guided solution that gives you helpful feedback if you enter an incorrect answer, and you can also view a worked-out sample problem that steps you through an exercise similar to the one you're working on.

Acknowledgments

There are many people who helped me develop this text, and I will attempt to thank some of them here. Cindy Trimble and Carrie Green were *invaluable* for contributing to the overall accuracy of the text. Chris Callac, Laura Wheel, Lori Mancuso, Suellen Robinson, Gail Burkett, and Nancy Lange were *invaluable* for their many suggestions and contributions during the development and writing of this text. Ingrid Benson provided guidance throughout the production process.

A special thanks to my editor, Paul Murphy, for all of his assistance, support, and contributions to this project. A very special thank you goes to my project manager, Mary Beckwith, for being there 24/7/365, as my students say. Last, my thanks to the staff at Prentice Hall for all their support: Linda Behrens, Alan Fischer, Patty Burns, Tom Benfatti, Paul Belfanti, Maureen Eide, Suzanne Behnke, Kate Valentine, Patrice Jones, Chris Hoag, Paul Corey, and Tim Bozik.

I would like to thank the following reviewers for their input and suggestions:

Anita Aikman, *Collin County Community College*

Sheila Anderson, *Housatonic Community College*

Adrianne Arata, *College of the Siskyous*

Cedric Atkins, *Mott Community College*

Laurel Berry, *Bryant & Stratton College*

Tom Blackburn, *Northeastern Illinois University*

Connie Buller, *Metropolitan Community College*

Gail Burket, *Palm Beach Community College*

James Butterbach, *Joliet Junior College*

Laura Dyer, *South West Illinois College*

Sharon Edgemon, *Bakersfield College*

Hope Essien, *Olive-Harvey College*

Lisa Feintech, *Cabrillo College*

Chris Ford, *Shasta College*

Cindy Fowler, *Central Piedmont Community College*

Pam Gerszewski, *College of the Albemarle*

Doug Harley, *Del Mar College*

Sonya Johnson, *Central Piedmont Community College*

Deborah Jones, *High Tech College*

Randa Kress, *Idaho State University*

Ted Lai, *Hudson Community College*

Nicole Lang, *North Hennepin Community College*

Nancy Lange, *Inver Hills Community College*

Lee LaRue, *Paris Junior College*

Paul Laverty, *Wachusett Community College*

Jeri Lee, *Des Moines Area Community College*

Jean McArthur, *Joliet Junior College*

Donna Martin, *Florida Community College–Jacksonville*

Robbin Miller, *Erie Community College*

Michael Montano, *Riverside Community College*

Kris Mundunuri, *Long Beach City College*

Lisa J. Music, *Big Sandy Community and Technical College*

Linda Padilla, *Joliet Junior College*

Scott Perkins, *Lake Sumter Community College*

Gary Piercy, *Moraine Valley Community College*

Marilyn Platt, *Gaston Community College*

Carolyn Poos, *Southwestern Illinois Community College*

Johnny Reaves, *Central Piedmont Community College*

Mary Lee Seitz, *Erie Community College*

Sandy Spears, *Jefferson Community College*

Ping Charlene Tintera, *Texas A & M University*

Jane Wampler, *Housatonic Community College*

Rhonda Watts, *College of the Albemarle*

Carol Williams, *Des Moines Area Community College*

Peter Zimmer, *West Cheseter University*

I would also like to thank the following dedicated group of instructors who participated in our focus groups, Martin-Gay Summits, and our design review for this text. Their feedback and insights have helped to strengthen this text. These instructors include:

Cedric Atkins, *Mott Community College*

Laurel Berry, *Bryant & Stratton*

Bob Brown, *Community College of Baltimore County–Essex*

Lisa Brown, *Community College of Baltimore County–Essex*

Gail Burkett, *Palm Beach Community College*

Cheryl Cantwell, *Seminole Community College*

Jackie Cohen, *Augusta State College*

Janice Ervin, *Central Piedmont Community College*

Pauline Hall, *Iowa State College*

Sonya Johnson, *Central Piedmont Community College*

Irene Jones, *Fullerton College*

Nancy Lange, *Inver Hills Community College*

Jean McArthur, *Joliet Junior College*

Marica Molle, *Metropolitan Community College*

Linda Padilla, *Joliet Junior College*

Carole Shapero, *Oakton Community College*

Jennifer Strehler, *Oakton Community College*

Tanomo Taguchi, *Fullerton College*

Leigh Ann Wheeler, *Greenville Technical Community College*

Valerie Wright, *Central Piedmont Community College*

A special thank you to those students who participated in our design review: Katherine Browne, Mike Bulfin, Nancy Canipe, Ashley Carpenter, Jeff Chojnachi, Roxanne Davis, Mike Dieter, Amy Dombrowski, Kay Herring, Todd Jaycox, Kaleena Levan, Matt Montgomery, Tony Plese, Abigail Polkinghorn, Harley Price, Eli Robinson, Avery Rosen, Robyn Schott, Cynthia Thomas, and Sherry Ward.

Additional Acknowledgments

As usual, I would like to thank my husband, Clayton, for his constant encouragement. I would also like to thank my children, Eric and Bryan, for providing most of the cooking and humor in our household. I would also like to thank my extended family for their help and wonderful sense of humor. Their contributions are too numerous to list. They are Rod and Karen Pasch; Peter, Michael, Christopher, Matthew, and Jessica Callac; Stuart and Earline Martin; Josh, Mandy, Bailey, Ethan, and Avery Barnes; Mark, Sabrina, and Madison Martin; Leo and Barbara Miller; and Jewett Gay.

Elayn Martin-Gay

About the Author

Elayn Martin-Gay has taught mathematics at the University of New Orleans for more than 25 years. Her numerous teaching awards include the local University Alumni Association's Award for Excellence in Teaching, and Outstanding Developmental Educator at University of New Orleans, presented by the Louisiana Association of Developmental Educators.

Prior to writing textbooks, Elayn Martin-Gay developed an acclaimed series of lecture videos to support developmental mathematics students in their quest for success. These highly successful videos originally served as the foundation material for her texts. Today, the videos are specific to each book in the Martin-Gay series. The author has also created Chapter Test Prep Videos to help students during their most "teachable moment"—as they prepare for a test, along with Instructor-to-Instructor videos that provide teaching tips, hints, and suggestions for each developmental mathematics course, including basic mathematics, prealgebra, beginning algebra, and intermediate algebra.

Elayn is the author of 10 published textbooks as well as multimedia interactive mathematics, all specializing in developmental mathematics courses. She has participated as an author across the broadest range of educational materials: textbooks, videos, tutorial software, and Interactive Math courseware. All of these components are designed to work together. This offers an opportunity of various combinations for an integrated teaching and learning package offering great consistency for the student.

Applications Index

1

The Whole Numbers

Whole numbers are the basic building blocks of mathematics. The whole numbers answer the question "How many?"

This chapter covers basic operations on whole numbers. Knowledge of these operations provides a good foundation on which to build further mathematical skills.

Yosemite National Park was established on October 1, 1890, and it is a favorite tourist destination in the Sierra Nevada Mountains in central California. Its nearly 750,000 acres are home to many of nature's most beautiful sites, including rock formations, giant sequoias, and waterfalls. In Exercise 65, Section 1.3, we will see how whole numbers can be used to measure the height of Yosemite Falls, the highest waterfall in the United States.

Highest U.S. Waterfalls

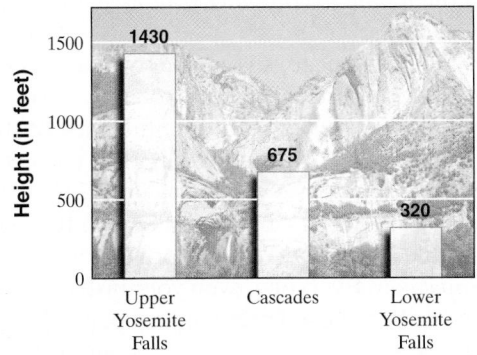

1

A Get Ready for This Course.

B Understand Some General Tips for Success.

C Understand How to Use This Text.

D Get Help As Soon As You Need It.

E Learn How to Prepare for and Take an Exam.

F Develop Good Time Management.

1.1 TIPS FOR SUCCESS IN MATHEMATICS

Before reading this section, remember that your instructor is your best source of information. Please see your instructor for any additional help or information.

Objective A Getting Ready for This Course

Now that you have decided to take this course, remember that a *positive attitude* will make all the difference in the world. Your belief that you can succeed is just as important as your commitment to this course. Make sure that you are ready for this course by having the time and positive attitude that it takes to succeed.

Next, make sure that you have scheduled your math course at a time that will give you the best chance for success. For example, if you are also working, you may want to check with your employer to make sure that your work hours will not conflict with your course schedule.

On the day of your first class period, double-check your schedule and allow yourself extra time to arrive on time in case of traffic problems or difficulty locating your classroom. Make sure that you bring at least your textbook, paper, and a writing instrument. Are you required to have a lab manual, graph paper, calculator, or some other supply besides this text? If so, also bring this material with you.

Objective B General Tips for Success

Below are some general tips that will increase your chance for success in a mathematics class. Many of these tips will also help you in other courses you may be taking.

Exchange names and phone numbers or e-mail addresses with at least one other person in class. This contact person can be a great help if you miss an assignment or want to discuss math concepts or exercises that you find difficult.

Choose to attend all class periods. If possible, sit near the front of the classroom. This way, you will see and hear the presentation better. It may also be easier for you to participate in classroom activities.

Do your homework. You've probably heard the phrase "practice makes perfect" in relation to music and sports. It also applies to mathematics. You will find that the more time you spend solving mathematics exercises, the easier the process becomes. Be sure to schedule enough time to complete your assignments before the next class period.

Check your work. Review the steps you made while working a problem. Learn to check your answers in the original problems. You may also compare your answers with the answers to selected exercises section in the back of the book. If you have made a mistake, try to figure out what went wrong. Then correct your mistake. If you can't find what went wrong, don't erase your work or throw it away. Bring your work to your instructor, a tutor in a math lab, or a classmate. It is easier for someone to find where you had trouble if they look at your original work.

Learn from your mistakes. Everyone, even your instructor, makes mistakes. Use your errors to learn and to become a better math student. The key is finding and understanding your errors. Was your mistake a careless one, or did you make it because you can't read your own math writing? If so, try to work more slowly or write more neatly and make a conscious effort to carefully check your work. Did you make a mistake because you don't understand a concept? If so, take the time to review the concept or ask questions to better understand it.

Know how to get help if you need it. It's all right to ask for help. In fact, it's a good idea to ask for help whenever there is something that you don't understand. Make sure you know when your instructor has office hours and how to find his or her

office. Find out whether math tutoring services are available on your campus. Check on the hours, location, and requirements of the tutoring service. Know whether software is available and how to access this resource.

Organize your class materials, including homework assignments, graded quizzes and tests, and notes from your class or lab. All of these items will make valuable references throughout your course and when studying for upcoming tests and the final exam. Make sure that you can locate these materials when you need them.

Read your textbook before class. Reading a mathematics textbook is unlike reading a novel or a newspaper. Your pace will be much slower. It is helpful to have paper and a pencil with you when you read. Try to work out examples on your own as you encounter them in your text. You should also write down any questions that you want to ask in class. When you read a mathematics textbook, sometimes some of the information in a section will be unclear. But after you hear a lecture or watch a videotape on that section, you will understand it much more easily than if you had not read your text beforehand.

Don't be afraid to ask questions. You are not the only person in class with questions. Other students are normally grateful that someone has spoken up.

Hand in assignments on time. This way you can be sure that you will not lose points for being late. Show every step of a problem and be neat and organized. Also be sure that you understand which problems are assigned for homework. If allowed, you can always double-check the assignment with another student in your class.

Objective C Using This Text

There are many helpful resources that are available to you in this text. It is important that you become familiar with and use these resources. They should increase your chances for success in this course.

- *Practice Problems.* Each example in every section has a parallel Practice Problem. As you read a section, try each Practice Problem after you've finished the corresponding example. This "learn-by-doing" approach will help you grasp ideas before you move on to other concepts.

- *Chapter Test Prep Video CD.* This book contains a CD. This CD contains all of the Chapter Test exercises worked out by the author. This supplement is very helpful before a classroom chapter test.

- *Lecture Video CDs.* Exercises marked with a ⊚ are fully worked out by the author on video CDs. Check with your instructor for the availability of these video CDs.

- *Symbols at the beginning of an exercise set.* If you need help with a particular section, the symbols listed at the beginning of each exercise set will remind you of the numerous supplements available.

- *Objectives.* The main section of exercises in each exercise set is referenced by an objective, such as A or B, and also an example(s). There is also often a section of exercises entitled "Mixed Practice," which is referenced by two or more objectives or sections. These are mixed exercises written to prepare you for your next exam. Use all of this referencing if you have trouble completing an assignment from the exercise set.

- *Icons (Symbols).* Make sure that you understand the meaning of the icons that are beside many exercises. ⊚ tells you that the corresponding exercise may be viewed on the video segment that corresponds to that section. ✎ tells you that this exercise is a writing exercise in which you should answer in complete sentences. △ icon tells you that the exercise involves geometry.

- *Integrated Reviews.* Found in the middle of each chapter, these reviews offer you a chance to practice—in one place—the many concepts that you have learned separately over several sections.

- *End of Chapter Opportunities.* There are many opportunities at the end of each chapter to help you understand the concepts of the chapter.

  Chapter Highlights contain chapter summaries and examples.

  Chapter Reviews contain review problems. The first part is organized section by section and the second part contains a set of mixed exercises.

  Chapter Tests are sample tests to help you prepare for an exam. The Chapter Test Prep Video CD, found in this text, contains all the Chapter Test exercises worked by the author.

  Cumulative Reviews are reviews consisting of material from the beginning of the book to the end of that particular chapter.

- *Study Skills Builder.* This feature is found at the end of many exercise sets. In order to increase your chance of success in this course, please read and answer the questions in the Study Skills Builder.

- *The Bigger Picture.* This feature contains the directions for building an outline to be used throughout the course. The purpose of this outline is to help you make the transition from thinking "section by section" to thinking about how the mathematics in this course is part of a bigger picture.

See the Preface at the beginning of this text for a more thorough explanation of the features of this text.

Objective **D** Getting Help

If you have trouble completing assignments or understanding the mathematics, get help as soon as you need it! This tip is presented as an objective on its own because it is so important. In mathematics, usually the material presented in one section builds on your understanding of the previous section. This means that if you don't understand the concepts covered during a class period, there is a good chance that you will not understand the concepts covered during the next class period. If this happens to you, get help as soon as you can.

Where can you get help? Many suggestions have been made in this section on where to get help, and now it is up to you to do it. Try your instructor, a tutoring center, or a math lab, or you may want to form a study group with fellow classmates. If you do decide to see your instructor or go to a tutoring center, make sure that you have a neat notebook and are ready with your questions.

Objective **E** Preparing for and Taking an Exam

Make sure that you allow yourself plenty of time to prepare for a test. If you think that you are a little "math anxious," it may be that you are not preparing for a test in a way that will ensure success. The way that you prepare for a test in mathematics is important. To prepare for a test:

1. Review your previous homework assignments.
2. Review any notes from class and section-level quizzes you have taken. (If this is a final exam, also review chapter tests you have taken.)
3. Review concepts and definitions by reading the Highlights at the end of each chapter.
4. Practice working out exercises by completing the Chapter Review found at the end of each chapter. (If this is a final exam, go through a Cumulative Review. There is one found at the end of each chapter except Chapter 1. Choose the review found at the end of the latest chapter that you have covered in your course.) *Don't stop here!*
5. It is important that you place yourself in conditions similar to test conditions to find out how you will perform. In other words, as soon as you feel that you know the material, get a few blank sheets of paper and take a sample test. There is a Chapter Test available at the end of each chapter, or you can work selected

problems from the Chapter Review. Your instructor may also provide you with a review sheet. During this sample test, do not use your notes or your textbook. Then check your sample test. If you are not satisfied with the results, study the areas that you are weak in and try again.

6. On the day of the test, allow yourself plenty of time to arrive at where you will be taking your exam.

When taking your test:

1. Read the directions on the test carefully.
2. Read each problem carefully as you take the test. Make sure that you answer the question asked.
3. Watch your time and pace yourself so that you can attempt each problem on your test.
4. If you have time, check your work and answers.
5. Do not turn your test in early. If you have extra time, spend it double-checking your work.

Objective F Managing Your Time

As a college student, you know the demands that classes, homework, work, and family place on your time. Some days you probably wonder how you'll ever get everything done. One key to managing your time is developing a schedule. Here are some hints for making a schedule:

1. Make a list of all of your weekly commitments for the term. Include classes, work, regular meetings, extracurricular activities, etc. You may also find it helpful to list such things as laundry, regular workouts, grocery shopping, etc.
2. Next, estimate the time needed for each item on the list. Also make a note of how often you will need to do each item. Don't forget to include time estimates for the reading, studying, and homework you do outside of your classes. You may want to ask your instructor for help estimating the time needed.
3. In the exercise set that follows, you are asked to block out a typical week on the schedule grid given. Start with items with fixed time slots like classes and work.
4. Next, include the items on your list with flexible time slots. Think carefully about how best to schedule items such as study time.
5. Don't fill up every time slot on the schedule. Remember that you need to allow time for eating, sleeping, and relaxing! You should also allow a little extra time in case some items take longer than planned.
6. If you find that your weekly schedule is too full for you to handle, you may need to make some changes in your workload, classload, or in other areas of your life. You may want to talk to your advisor, manager or supervisor at work, or someone in your college's academic counseling center for help with such decisions.

1.1 EXERCISE SET

 Student Solutions Manual    PH Math/Tutor Center    CD/Video for Review    MathXL®    MyMathLab

1. What is your instructor's name?

2. What are your instructor's office location and office hours?

3. What is the best way to contact your instructor?

4. Do you have the name and contact information of at least one other student in class?

5. Will your instructor allow you to use a calculator in this class?

6. Is tutorial software available to you? If so, what type and where?

7. Is there a tutoring service available on campus? If so, what are its hours? What services are available?

8. Have you attempted this course before? If so, write down ways that you might improve your chances of success during this second attempt.

9. List some steps that you can take if you begin having trouble understanding the material or completing an assignment.

10. How many hours of studying does your instructor advise for each hour of instruction?

11. What does the ✎ icon in this text mean?

12. What does the ⊙ icon in this text mean?

13. What does the △ icon in this text mean?

14. Search the minor columns in your text. What are Practice Problems?

15. When might be the best time to work a Practice Problem?

16. Where are the answers to Practice Problems?

17. What answers are contained in this text and where are they?

18. What solutions are contained in this text and where are they?

19. What and where are Integrated Reviews?

20. What video CD is contained in this book, where is it, and what material is on it?

21. Chapter Highlights are found at the end of each chapter. Find the Chapter 1 Highlights and explain how you might use it and how it might be helpful.

22. Chapter Reviews are found at the end of each chapter. Find the Chapter 1 Review and explain how you might use it and how it might be useful.

23. Chapter Tests are found at the end of each chapter. Find the Chapter 1 Test and explain how you might use it and how it might be helpful when preparing for an exam on Chapter 1. Include how the Chapter Test Prep Video in this book may help.

24. Read or reread objective **F** and fill out the schedule grid below.

	Monday	Tuesday	Wednesday	Thursday	Friday	Saturday	Sunday
7:00 a.m.							
8:00 a.m.							
9:00 a.m.							
10:00 a.m.							
11:00 a.m.							
12:00 a.m.							
1:00 p.m.							
2:00 p.m.							
3:00 p.m.							
4:00 p.m.							
5:00 p.m.							
6:00 p.m.							
7:00 p.m.							
8:00 p.m.							
9:00 p.m.							

1.2 PLACE VALUE AND NAMES FOR NUMBERS

Objectives

A Find the Place Value of a Digit in a Whole Number.

B Write a Whole Number in Words and in Standard Form.

C Write a Whole Number in Expanded Form.

D Read Tables.

The **digits** 0, 1, 2, 3, 4, 5, 6, 7, 8, and 9 can be used to write numbers. For example, the **whole numbers** are

0, 1, 2, 3, 4, 5, 6, 7, 8, 9, 10, 11, . . .

The three dots (. . .) after the 11 mean that this list continues indefinitely. That is, there is no largest whole number. The smallest whole number is 0.

Objective **A** Finding the Place Value of a Digit in a Whole Number

The position of each digit in a number determines its **place value.** For example, the distance (in miles) between the planet Mercury and the planet Earth can be represented by the whole number 48,337,000.

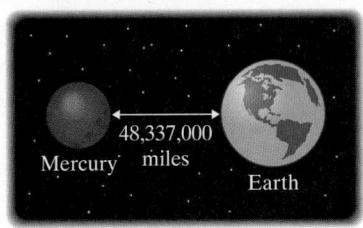

Below is a place-value chart for this whole number.

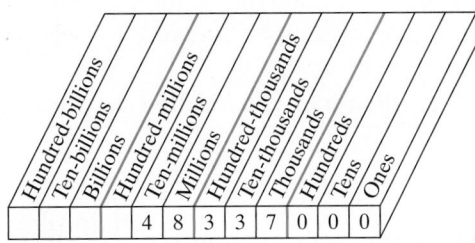

The two 3s in 48,337,000 represent different amounts because of their different placements. The place value of the 3 on the left is hundred-thousands. The place value of the 3 on the right is ten-thousands.

EXAMPLES Find the place value of the digit 4 in each whole number.

1. 48,761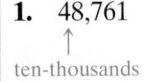
ten-thousands

2. 249
tens

3. 524,007,656
millions

■ **Work Practice Problems 1–3**

Objective **B** Writing a Whole Number in Words and in Standard Form

A whole number such as 1,083,664,500 is written in **standard form.** Notice that commas separate the digits into groups of three, starting from the right. Each group of three digits is called a **period.** The names of the first four periods are shown in blue.

PRACTICE PROBLEMS 1–3

Find the place value of the digit 7 in each whole number.

1. 72,589,620

2. 67,890

3. 50,722

Answers

1. ten-millions, **2.** thousands, **3.** hundreds

7

Periods			
Billions	Millions	Thousands	Ones

Hundred-billions	Ten-billions	Billions	Hundred-millions	Ten-millions	Millions	Hundred-thousands	Ten-thousands	Thousands	Hundreds	Tens	Ones
	1	0	8	3	6	6	4	5	0	0	

Writing a Whole Number in Words

To write a whole number in words, write the number in each period followed by the name of the period. (The ones period is usually not written.) This same procedure can be used to read a whole number.

For example, we write 1,083,664,500 as

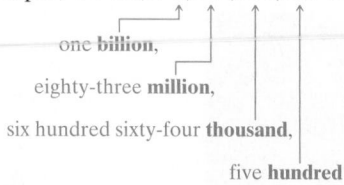

one **billion**,

eighty-three **million**,

six hundred sixty-four **thousand**,

five **hundred**

Helpful Hint Notice the commas after the name of each period.

Helpful Hint The name of the ones period is not used when reading and writing whole numbers. For example,

9,265

is read as

"nine **thousand**, two **hundred** sixty-five."

PRACTICE PROBLEMS 4–6

Write each number in words.

4. 67

5. 395

6. 12,804

EXAMPLES Write each number in words.

4. 85   eighty-five

5. 126   one hundred twenty-six

6. 27,034   twenty-seven thousand, thirty-four

▧ **Work Practice Problems 4–6**

Helpful Hint The word "and" is *not* used when reading and writing whole numbers. It is used when reading and writing mixed numbers and some decimal values, as shown later in this text.

PRACTICE PROBLEM 7

Write 321,670,200 in words.

EXAMPLE 7 Write 106,052,447 in words.

Solution: 106,052,447 is written as

one hundred six **million**, fifty-two **thousand**, four **hundred** forty-seven

▧ **Work Practice Problem 7**

Answers

4. sixty-seven,   **5.** three hundred ninety-five,   **6.** twelve thousand, eight hundred four,   **7.** three hundred twenty-one million, six hundred seventy thousand, two hundred

✔ **Concept Check Answer**

false

✔ **Concept Check** True or false? When writing a check for $2600, the word name we write for the dollar amount of the check is "two thousand sixty." Explain your answer.

Writing a Whole Number in Standard Form

To write a whole number in standard form, write the number in each period, followed by a comma.

EXAMPLES Write each number in standard form.

8. sixty-one   61

9. eight hundred five   805

10. two million, five hundred sixty-four thousand, three hundred fifty

2,564,350

11. nine thousand, three hundred eighty-six

9,386   or   9386

🖳 **Work Practice Problems 8–11**

Helpful Hint
A comma may or may not be inserted in a four-digit number. For example, both

9,386   and   9386

are acceptable ways of writing nine thousand, three hundred eighty-six.

PRACTICE PROBLEMS 8–11

Write each number in standard form.

8. twenty-nine

9. seven hundred ten

10. twenty-six thousand, seventy-one

11. six thousand, five hundred seven

Objective C Writing a Whole Number in Expanded Form

The place value of a digit can be used to write a number in expanded form. The **expanded form** of a number shows each digit of the number with its place value. For example, 5672 is written in expanded form as

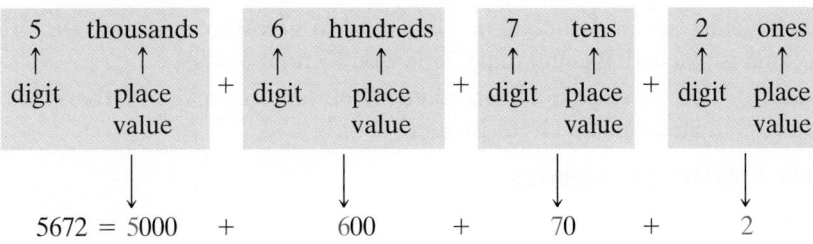

$$5672 = 5000 + 600 + 70 + 2$$

EXAMPLE 12 Write 706,449 in expanded form.

Solution: $700,000 + 6000 + 400 + 40 + 9$

🖳 **Work Practice Problem 12**

PRACTICE PROBLEM 12

Write 1,047,608 in expanded form.

Objective D Reading Tables

Now that we know about place value and names for whole numbers, we introduce one way that whole number data may be presented. **Tables** are often used to organize and display facts that involve numbers. The following table shows the countries that won the most medals during the 2004 Olympic summer games. (Although the medals are truly won by athletes from the various countries, for simplicity we will state that countries have won the medals.)

Answers

8. 29, **9.** 710, **10.** 26,071, **11.** 6507,
12. 1,000,000 + 40,000 + 7000 + 600 + 8

Most Medals—2004 Olympic Summer Games

Country	Gold	Silver	Bronze	Total	Country	Gold	Silver	Bronze	Total
United States	35	39	27	101	Italy	10	11	11	32
Russia	27	27	38	92	Great Britain	9	9	12	30
China	32	17	14	63	South Korea	9	12	9	30
Australia	17	16	16	49	Cuba	9	7	11	27
Germany	14	16	18	48	Ukraine	9	5	9	23
Japan	16	9	12	37	Netherlands	4	9	9	22
France	11	9	13	33					

(*Source:* ESPN.com)

For example, by reading from left to right along the row marked "U.S." we find that the United States won 35 gold, 39 silver, and 27 bronze medals during the 2004 Summer Games.

PRACTICE PROBLEM 13

Use the Summer Games table to answer the following questions:

a. How many bronze medals did Australia win during the Summer Games of the 2004 Olympics?

b. Which countries shown won more than 30 gold medals?

EXAMPLE 13 Use the Summer Games table to answer each question.

a. How many total medals did China win during the 2004 Summer Games of the Olympics?

b. Which country shown won fewer gold medals than Great Britain?

Solution:

a. Find "China" in the left column. Then read from left to right until the "Total" column is reached. We find that China won 63 total medals.

b. Great Britain won 9 gold medals while Netherlands won 4, so Netherlands won fewer gold medals than Great Britain.

■ **Work Practice Problem 13**

Answers

13. a. 16, **b.** United States and China

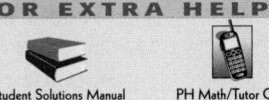

Objective **A** *Determine the place value of the digit 5 in each whole number. See Examples 1 through 3.*

1. 352

2. 905

3. 5890

4. 6527

5. 62,500,000

6. 79,050,000

7. 5,070,099

8. 51,682,700

Objective **B** *Write each whole number in words. See Examples 4 through 7.*

9. 542

10. 316

11. 7896

12. 5445

13. 26,990

14. 42,009

15. 1,620,000

16. 3,204,000

17. 53,520,170

18. 47,033,107

Write each number in the sentence in words. See Examples 4 through 7.

19. At this writing, the population of Bermuda is 64,482. (*Source:* 2004 *World Almanac*)

20. Each Home Depot store in the United States and Canada stocks at least 40,000 different kinds of building materials, home improvement supplies, and lawn and garden products. (*Source:* The Home Depot, Inc.)

21. The world's tallest building, the Taipei 101 building in Taiwan is 1679 feet tall. (*Source:* Council on Tall Buildings and Urban Habitat)

22. In a recent year, there were 3895 patients in the United States waiting for a heart transplant. (*Source:* United Network for Organ Sharing)

23. Each day, UPS delivers 13,600,000 packages and documents worldwide. (*Source:* United Parcel Service of America, Inc.)

24. Liz Harold has the number 16,820,409 showing on her calculator display.

25. The highest point in Idaho is at Granite Peak, at an elevation of 12,662 feet. (*Source:* U.S. Geological Survey)

26. The highest point in New Mexico is Wheeler Peak, at an elevation of 13,161 feet. (*Source:* U.S. Geological Survey)

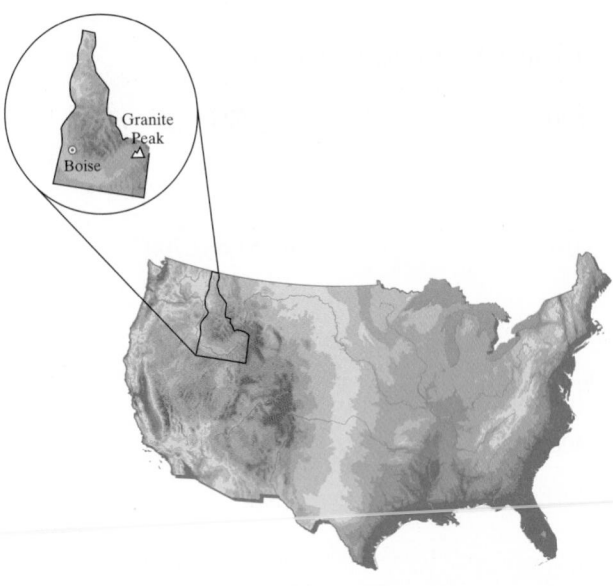

27. The Goodyear blimp *Eagle* holds 202,700 cubic feet of helium. (*Source:* The Goodyear Tire & Rubber Company)

28. In a recent year, zinc mines in the United States mined 799,000 metric tons of zinc. (*Source:* U.S. Dept. of Interior)

Write each whole number in standard form. See Examples 8 through 11.

29. Six thousand, five hundred eighty-seven

30. Three thousand, three hundred seventy-nine

31. Twenty-nine thousand, nine hundred

32. Forty-two thousand, six

33. Sixteen million, five hundred four thousand, nineteen

34. Ten million, thirty-seven thousand, sixteen

35. Three million, fourteen

36. Seven million, twelve

Write the whole number in each sentence in standard form. See Examples 8 through 11.

37. The International Space station orbits above Earth at an altitude of two hundred twenty miles. (*Source:* NASA)

38. The average distance between the surfaces of the Earth and the Moon is about two hundred thirty-four thousand miles.

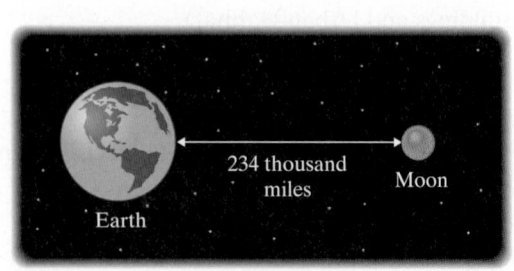

39. The price for a 2005 Porsche Carrera GT is four hundred forty thousand, two hundred seventy-six dollars. (*Source:* Porsche Cars North America)

40. You might know that the zip code for Beverly Hills, California, is 90210, but did you know that one of its area codes is three hundred ten?

41. The Disney/Pixar film *Finding Nemo* set the world record for opening weekend income when it took in seventy million, two hundred fifty-one thousand, seven hundred ten dollars during the weekend of May 30, 2003. (*Source: Guinness Book,* 2005)

42. In 2004, there were one hundred eight million, four hundred thousand U.S. households that owned at least one television set. (*Source:* Nielsen Media Research)

43. The world's tallest self-supporting structure is the CN Tower in Toronto, Canada. It is one thousand, eight hundred fifteen feet tall. (*Source: The World Almanac,* 2005)

44. As of 2004, there were one thousand, eight hundred twenty-four species classified as either threatened or endangered in the United States. (*Source:* U.S. Fish & Wildlife Service)

45. Hank Aaron holds the career record for home runs in Major League baseball since 1974, with a total of seven hundred fifty-five home runs. (*Source:* Major League Baseball)

46. Barry Bonds is approaching Hank Aaron's career record for home runs in Major League baseball (see Exercise 45). Barry has seven hundred three home runs through 2004.

Objective **C** *Write each whole number in expanded form. See Example 12.*

47. 406

48. 789

49. 5290

50. 6040

51. 62,407

52. 20,215

53. 30,680

54. 99,032

55. 39,680,000

56. 47,703,029

Objectives **B** **C** **D** **Mixed Practice** *The table shows the six tallest mountains in New England and their elevations. Use this table to answer Exercises 57 through 62. See Example 13.*

Mountain (State)	Elevation (in feet)
Boott Spur (NH)	5492
Mt. Adams (NH)	5774
Mt. Clay (NH)	5532
Mt. Jefferson (NH)	5712
Mt. Sam Adams (NH)	5584
Mt. Washington (NH)	6288
Source: U.S. Geological Survey	

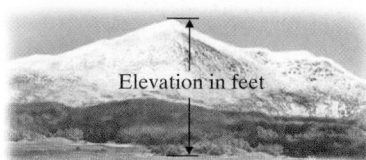

Elevation in feet

57. Write the elevation of Mt. Clay in standard form and then in words.

58. Write the elevation of Mt. Washington in standard form and then in words.

59. Write the height of Boott Spur in expanded form.

60. Write the height of Mt. Jefferson in expanded form.

61. Which mountain is the tallest in New England?

62. Which mountain is the second tallest in New England?

The table shows the top ten popular breeds of dogs in 2003 according to the American Kennel Club. Use this table to answer Exercises 63 through 68. See Example 13.

Top Ten American Kennel Club Registrations in 2003			
Breed	Number of Registered Dogs	Average Dog Maximum Height (in inches)	Average Dog Maximum Weight (in pounds)
Beagle	45,033	15	30
Boxer	34,136	25	70
Chihuahua	24,930	9	6
Dachshund	39,473	9	25
German shepherd dog	43,950	26	95
Golden retriever	52,530	24	80
Labrador retriever	144,934	25	75
Poodle (standard, miniature, and toy)	32,176	standard: 26	standard: 70
Shih Tzu	26,935	11	16
Yorkshire terrier	38,256	9	7

(*Source:* American Kennel Club)

63. Which breed has more dogs registered, Chihuahua or Golden retriever?

64. Which breed has fewer dogs registered, Beagle or Yorkshire terrier?

65. Which breed has the most American Kennel Club registrations? Write the number of registrations for this breed in words.

66. Which of the listed breeds has the fewest registrations? Write the number of registered dogs for this breed in words.

67. What is the maximum weight of an average-size Dachshund?

68. What is the maximum height of an average-size Yorkshire terrier?

Concept Extensions

69. Write the largest four-digit number that can be made from the digits 3, 6, 7, and 2 if each digit must be used once.

_____ _____ _____ _____

70. Write the largest five-digit number that can be made using the digits 4, 5, and 3 if each digit must be used at least once.

_____ _____, _____ _____ _____

Check to see whether each number written in standard form matches the number written in words. If not, correct the number in words. See the Concept Check in this section.

71.

60-8124/7233
1000613331
1401

DATE _____

PAY TO
THE ORDER OF _____ $ 105.00

One Hundred Fifty and 00/100 ~~~~ DOLLARS

FIRST STATE BANK
OF FARTHINGTON
FARTHINGTON, IL 64422

MEMO _____

⑆621497260⑆ 1000613331⑈ 1401

72.

60-8124/7233
1000613331
1402

DATE _____

PAY TO
THE ORDER OF _____ $ 7030.00

Seven Thousand Thirty and 00/100 ~~~ DOLLARS

FIRST STATE BANK
OF FARTHINGTON
FARTHINGTON, IL 64422

MEMO _____

⑆621497260⑆ 1000613331⑈ 1402

73. If a number is given in words, describe the process used to write this number in standard form.

74. If a number is written in standard form, describe the process used to write this number in expanded form.

75. The Pro-Football Hall of Fame was established on September 7, 1963, in this town. Use the information and the diagram to the right to find the name of the town.

- Alliance is east of Massillon.
- Dover is between Canton and New Philadelphia.
- Massillon is not next to Alliance.
- Canton is north of Dover.

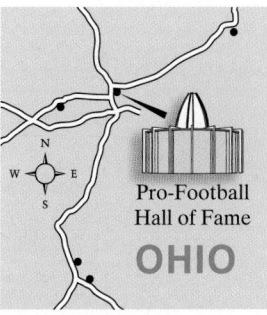

Pro-Football
Hall of Fame

OHIO

76. The world's fastest super computer is Japan's Earth Simulator, which is programmed to simulate weather patterns and other massive systems. It can perform thirty-five trillion calculations in a second. Look up "trillion" in a dictionary and use the definition to write this number in standard form. (*Source: 2005 World Almanac*)

1.3 ADDING WHOLE NUMBERS AND PERIMETER

Objective **A** Adding Whole Numbers

The iPod is a hard drive–based portable audio player. As of 2004, it is the most popular digital music player in the United States.

Suppose that a small computer store received a shipment of two iPods one day and an additional four iPods the next day. The **total** shipment in the two days can be found by adding 2 and 4.

$$2 \text{ iPods} + 4 \text{ iPods} = 6 \text{ iPods}$$

The **sum** (or total) is 6 iPods. Each of the numbers 2 and 4 is called an **addend,** and the process of finding the sum is called **addition.**

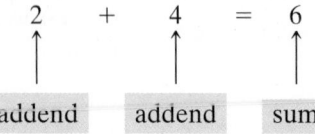

$$2 \quad + \quad 4 \quad = \quad 6$$

addend   addend   sum

To add whole numbers, we add the digits in the ones place, then the tens place, then the hundreds place, and so on. For example, let's add $2236 + 160$.

```
  2236
+ 160
  2396
```

Line up numbers vertically so that the place values correspond. Then add digits in corresponding place values, starting with the ones place.

    sum of ones
    sum of tens
    sum of hundreds
    sum of thousands

PRACTICE PROBLEM 1

Add: $7235 + 542$

EXAMPLE 1 Add: $23 + 136$

Solution:
```
   23
+ 136
  159
```

▦ **Work Practice Problem 1**

When the sum of digits in corresponding place values is more than 9, **carrying** is necessary. For example, to add $365 + 89$, add the ones-place digits first.

Carrying
```
   ¹
  365
+  89
    4
```
5 ones + 9 ones = **14 ones** or **1 ten** + **4 ones**
Write the 4 ones in the ones place and carry the 1 ten to the tens place.

Next, add the tens-place digits.
```
  ¹ ¹
  365
+  89
   54
```
1 ten + 6 tens + 8 tens = **15 tens** or **1 hundred** + **5 tens**
Write the 5 tens in the tens place and carry the 1 hundred to the hundreds place.

Next, add the hundreds-place digits.
```
  ¹ ¹
  365
+  89
  454
```
1 hundred + 3 hundreds = **4 hundreds**
Write the 4 hundreds in the hundreds place.

Answer

1. 7777

EXAMPLE 2 Add: 34,285 + 149,761

Solution:

$$\begin{array}{r}{}^{1\,1\ 1}\\ 34{,}285\\ +\ 149{,}761\\ \hline 184{,}046\end{array}$$

◼ **Work Practice Problem 2**

PRACTICE PROBLEM 2
Add: 27,364 + 92,977

✔**Concept Check** What is wrong with the following computation?

$$\begin{array}{r}394\\ +283\\ \hline 577\end{array}$$

Before we continue adding whole numbers, let's review some properties of addition that you may have already discovered. The first property that we will review is the **addition property of 0.** This property reminds us that the sum of 0 and any number is that same number.

Addition Property of 0

The sum of 0 and any number is that number. For example,

$$7 + 0 = 7$$
$$0 + 7 = 7$$

Next, notice that we can add any two whole numbers in any order and the sum is the same. For example,

$$4 + 5 = 9 \quad \text{and} \quad 5 + 4 = 9$$

We call this special property of addition the **commutative property of addition.**

Commutative Property of Addition

Changing the **order** of two addends does not change their sum. For example,

$$2 + 3 = 5 \quad \text{and} \quad 3 + 2 = 5$$

Another property that can help us when adding numbers is the **associative property of addition.** This property states that when adding numbers, the grouping of the numbers can be changed without changing the sum. We use parentheses to group numbers. They indicate which numbers to add first. For example, let's use two different groupings to find the sum of $2 + 1 + 5$.

$$(2 + 1) + 5 = 3 + 5 = 8$$

Also,

$$2 + (1 + 5) = 2 + 6 = 8$$

Both groupings give a sum of 8.

Answer
2. 120,341

✔ Concept Check Answer
forgot to carry 1 hundred to the hundreds place

Associative Property of Addition

Changing the **grouping** of addends does not change their sum. For example,

$$3 + \underbrace{(5 + 7)} = 3 + 12 = 15 \quad \text{and} \quad \underbrace{(3 + 5)} + 7 = 8 + 7 = 15$$

The commutative and associative properties tell us that we can add whole numbers using any order and grouping that we want.

When adding several numbers, it is often helpful to look for two or three numbers whose sum is 10, 20, and so on. Why? Adding multiples of 10 such as 10 and 20 is easier.

PRACTICE PROBLEM 3

Add: $11 + 7 + 8 + 9 + 13$

EXAMPLE 3   Add: $13 + 2 + 7 + 8 + 9$

Solution: $13 + 2 + 7 + 8 + 9 = 39$

$$20 + 10 + 9$$

$$39$$

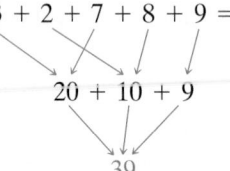

▣ **Work Practice Problem 3**

Feel free to use the process of Example 3 anytime when adding.

PRACTICE PROBLEM 4

Add: $19 + 5042 + 638 + 526$

EXAMPLE 4   Add: $1647 + 246 + 32 + 85$

Solution:

$$
\begin{array}{r}
^{1\,2\,2} \\
1647 \\
246 \\
32 \\
+85 \\
\hline
2010
\end{array}
$$

▣ **Work Practice Problem 4**

Objective ▣ Finding the Perimeter of a Polygon

In geometry addition is used to find the perimeter of a polygon. A **polygon** can be described as a flat figure formed by line segments connected at their ends. Geometric figures such as triangles, squares, and rectangles are called polygons.

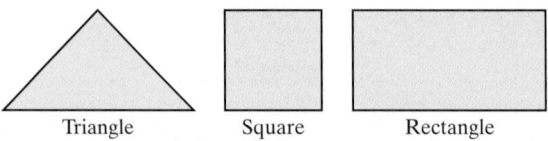

Triangle   Square   Rectangle

The **perimeter** of a polygon is the *distance around* the polygon. This means that the perimeter of a polygon is the sum of the lengths of its sides.

Answers

3. 48,   **4.** 6225

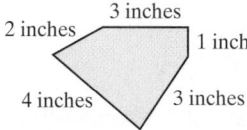 Find the perimeter of the polygon shown.

Solution: To find the perimeter (distance around), we add the lengths of the sides.

2 in. + 3 in. + 1 in. + 3 in. + 4 in. = 13 in.

The perimeter is 13 inches.

◻ **Work Practice Problem 5**

To make the addition appear simpler, we will often not include units with the addends. If you do this, make sure units are included in the final answer.

EXAMPLE 6 **Calculating the Perimeter of a Building**

The largest commercial building in the world under one roof is the flower auction building of the cooperative VBA in Aalsmeer, Netherlands. The floor plan is a rectangle that measures 776 meters by 639 meters. Find the perimeter of this building. (A meter is a unit of length in the metric system.) (*Source: The Handy Science Answer Book,* Visible Ink Press)

Solution: Recall that opposite sides of a rectangle have the same length. To find the perimeter of this building, we add the lengths of the sides. The sum of the lengths of its sides is

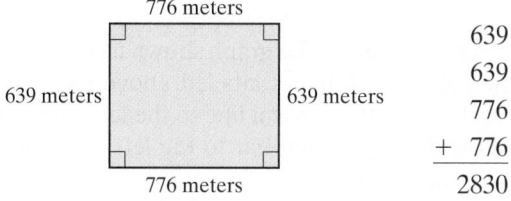

$$\begin{array}{r} 639 \\ 639 \\ 776 \\ +\ 776 \\ \hline 2830 \end{array}$$

The perimeter of the building is 2830 meters.

◻ **Work Practice Problem 6**

Objective ◉ Solving Problems by Adding

Often, real-life problems occur that can be solved by writing an addition statement. The first step in solving any word problem is to *understand* the problem by reading it carefully. Descriptions of problems solved through addition *may* include any of these key words or phrases:

Key Words or Phrases	Example	Symbols
added to	5 added to 7	7 + 5
plus	0 plus 78	0 + 78
increased by	12 increased by 6	12 + 6
more than	11 more than 25	25 + 11
total	the total of 8 and 1	8 + 1
sum	the sum of 4 and 133	4 + 133

To solve a word problem that involves addition, we first use the facts given to write an addition statement. Then we write the corresponding solution of the real-life

PRACTICE PROBLEM 5

Find the perimeter of the polygon shown. (A centimeter is a unit of length in the metric system.)

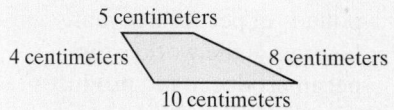

PRACTICE PROBLEM 6

A new shopping mall has a floor plan in the shape of a triangle. Each of the mall's three sides is 532 feet. Find the perimeter of the building.

Answers
5. 27 cm, **6.** 1596 ft

problem. It is sometimes helpful to write the statement in words (brief phrases) and then translate to numbers.

PRACTICE PROBLEM 7

Texas produces 90 million pounds of pecans per year. Georgia is the world's top pecan producer and produces 15 million pounds more pecans than Texas. How much does Georgia produce? (*Source: Absolute Trivia.com*)

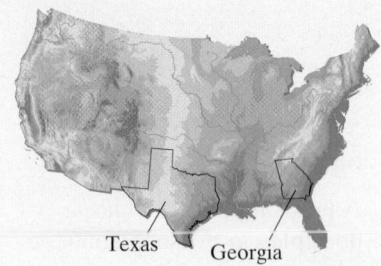

EXAMPLE 7 Finding a Salary

The governor's salary in the state of Alabama was recently increased by $1706. If the old salary was $94,655, find the new salary. (*Source: The World Almanac and Book of Facts*, 2003 and 2005)

Montgomery

Solution: The key phrase here is "increased by," which suggests that we add. To find the new salary, we add the increase, $1706, to the old salary.

In Words		Translate to Numbers
old salary	$\rightarrow$	94,655
+ increase	$\rightarrow$	+ 1 706
new salary	$\rightarrow$	96,361

The Alabama governor's salary is now $96,361.

🔲 **Work Practice Problem 7**

Graphs can be used to visualize data. The graph shown next is called a **bar graph.** For this bar graph, the height of each bar is labeled above the bar. To check this height, follow the top of each bar to the vertical line to the left. For example, the second bar is labeled 15. Follow the top of that bar to the left until the vertical line is reached, halfway between 10 and 20, or 15.

PRACTICE PROBLEM 8

Use the graph in Example 8 to answer the following:

a. Which rating had the least number of Best Picture nominees?

b. Find the total number of Best Picture nominees that were rated PG, PG-13, or R.

EXAMPLE 8 Reading a Bar Graph

The graph below shows the ratings of Best Picture nominees since PG-13 was introduced in 1984. In this graph, each bar represents a different rating, and the height of each bar represents the number of Best Picture nominees for that rating.

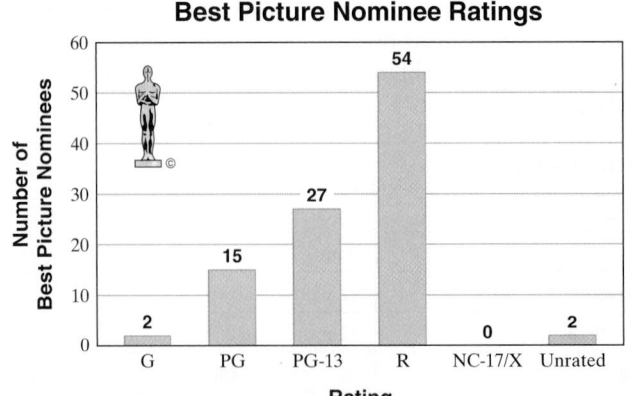

Best Picture Nominee Ratings

Source: Academy of Motion Picture Arts and Sciences; Internet Movie Database

a. Which rating did most Best Picture nominees have?

b. Find the total number of Best Picture nominees that were rated G, PG, or PG-13.

Solution:

a. The rating for most Best Picture nominees is the one corresponding to the highest bar, which is an R rating.

b. The key word here is "total." To find the total number of Best Picture nominees that were rated G, PG, or PG-13, we add.

In Words		Translate to Numbers
G-rated nominees	$\rightarrow$	2
PG-rated nominees	$\rightarrow$	15
PG-13–rated nominees	$\rightarrow$	+ 27
Total		44

The number of Best Picture nominees rated G, PG, or PG-13 is 44.

▣ **Work Practice Problem 8**

▦ **CALCULATOR EXPLORATIONS** Adding Numbers

To add numbers on a calculator, find the keys marked ⊞ and ⊟ or ⎡ENTER⎤.

For example, to add 5 and 7 on a calculator, press the keys ⎡5⎤ ⎡+⎤ ⎡7⎤ ⎡=⎤ or ⎡ENTER⎤.

The display will read ⎡ 12 ⎤.
Thus, $5 + 7 = 12$.

To add 687, 981, and 49 on a calculator, press the keys ⎡687⎤ ⎡+⎤ ⎡981⎤ ⎡+⎤ ⎡49⎤ ⎡=⎤ or ⎡ENTER⎤.
The display will read ⎡ 1717 ⎤.

Thus, $687 + 981 + 49 = 1717$. (Although entering 687, for example, requires pressing more than one key, here numbers are grouped together for easier reading.)

Use a calculator to add.

1. $89 + 45$ **2.** $76 + 97$

3. $285 + 55$ **4.** $8773 + 652$

5.
```
    985
   1210
    562
 +   77
```

6.
```
    465
   9888
    620
 + 1550
```

Mental Math

Find each sum.

1. 9 + 7   **2.** 20 + 30   **3.** 5000 + 4000   **4.** 4300 + 26   **5.** 1620 + 0   **6.** 6 + 126 + 4

1.3 EXERCISE SET

Objective A *Add. See Examples 1 through 4.*

1.
$$\begin{array}{r} 14 \\ +22 \\ \hline \end{array}$$

2.
$$\begin{array}{r} 27 \\ +31 \\ \hline \end{array}$$

3.
$$\begin{array}{r} 62 \\ +230 \\ \hline \end{array}$$

4.
$$\begin{array}{r} 37 \\ +542 \\ \hline \end{array}$$

5.
$$\begin{array}{r} 12 \\ 13 \\ +24 \\ \hline \end{array}$$

6.
$$\begin{array}{r} 23 \\ 45 \\ +30 \\ \hline \end{array}$$

7.
$$\begin{array}{r} 5267 \\ +\ 132 \\ \hline \end{array}$$

8.
$$\begin{array}{r} 236 \\ +6243 \\ \hline \end{array}$$

9. 53 + 64

10. 41 + 74

11. 22 + 490   **12.** 35 + 470   **13.** 22,781 + 186,297   **14.** 17,427 + 821,059

15.
$$\begin{array}{r} 8 \\ 9 \\ 2 \\ 5 \\ +1 \\ \hline \end{array}$$

16.
$$\begin{array}{r} 3 \\ 5 \\ 8 \\ 5 \\ +7 \\ \hline \end{array}$$

17.
$$\begin{array}{r} 6 \\ 21 \\ 14 \\ 9 \\ +12 \\ \hline \end{array}$$

18.
$$\begin{array}{r} 12 \\ 4 \\ 8 \\ 26 \\ +10 \\ \hline \end{array}$$

19.
$$\begin{array}{r} 81 \\ 17 \\ 23 \\ 79 \\ +12 \\ \hline \end{array}$$

20.
$$\begin{array}{r} 64 \\ 28 \\ 56 \\ 25 \\ +32 \\ \hline \end{array}$$

21. 62 + 18 + 14

22. 23 + 49 + 18

23. 40 + 800 + 70   **24.** 30 + 900 + 20   **25.** 7542 + 49 + 682

26. 1624 + 32 + 976   **27.** 24 + 9006 + 489 + 2407   **28.** 16 + 1056 + 748 + 7770

29. 627
628
+ 629

30. 427
383
+ 229

31. 6820
4271
+ 5626

32. 6789
4321
+ 5555

33. 507
593
+ 10

34. 864
33
+ 356

35. 4200
2107
+ 2692

36. 5000
1400
+ 3021

37. 49
628
5 762
+ 29,462

38. 26
582
4 763
+ 62,511

39. 121,742
57,279
26,586
+ 426,782

40. 504,218
321,920
38,507
+ 594,687

Objective **B** *Find the perimeter of each figure. See Examples 5 and 6.*

△ **41.**

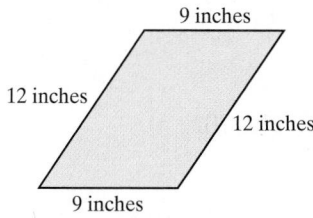

9 inches
12 inches
12 inches
9 inches

△ **42.**

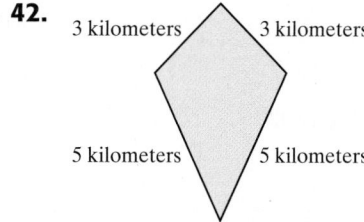

3 kilometers   3 kilometers
5 kilometers   5 kilometers

◉
△ **43.**

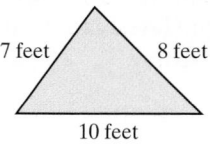

7 feet   8 feet
10 feet

△ **44.**

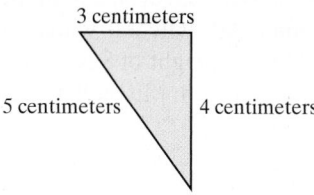

3 centimeters
5 centimeters   4 centimeters

△ **45.**

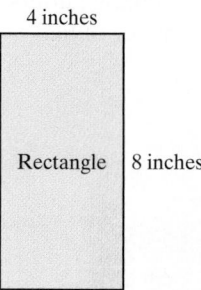

4 inches
Rectangle   8 inches

△ **46.**

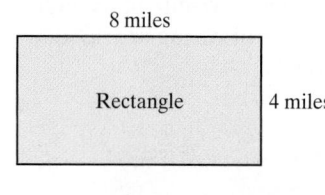

8 miles
Rectangle   4 miles

△ **47.**

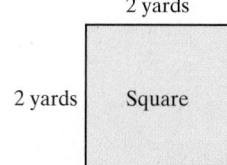

2 yards
2 yards   Square

△ **48.**

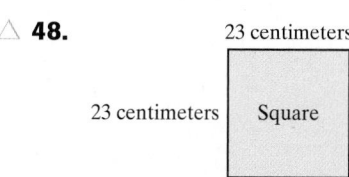

23 centimeters
23 centimeters   Square

△ **49.**

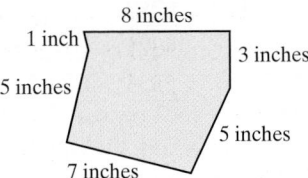

△ **50.**

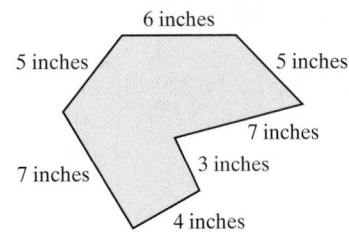

Objectives Ⓐ Ⓑ Ⓒ **Mixed Practice** *Solve. See Examples 1 through 8.*

51. Find the sum of 297 and 1796.

52. Find the sum of 802 and 6487.

53. Find the total of 76, 39, 8, 17, and 126.

54. Find the total of 89, 45, 2, 19, and 341.

55. What is 452 increased by 92?

56. What is 712 increased by 38?

57. What is 2686 plus 686 plus 80?

58. What is 3565 plus 565 plus 70?

59. The highest point in South Carolina is Sassafras Mountain at 3560 feet above sea level. The highest point in North Carolina is Mt. Mitchell, whose peak is 3124 feet increased by the height of Sassafras Mountain. Find the height of Mt. Mitchell. (*Source: U.S. Geological Survey*)

60. The distance from Kansas City, Kansas, to Hays, Kansas, is 285 miles. Colby, Kansas, is 98 miles farther from Kansas City than Hays. Find the total distance from Kansas City to Colby.

△ **61.** Leo Callier is installing an invisible fence in his backyard. How many feet of wiring are needed to enclose the yard below?

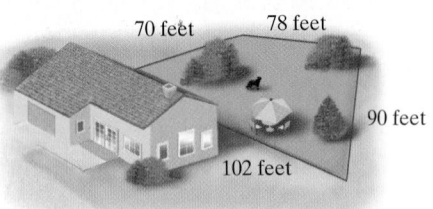

△ **62.** A homeowner is considering installing gutters around her home. Find the perimeter of her rectangular home.

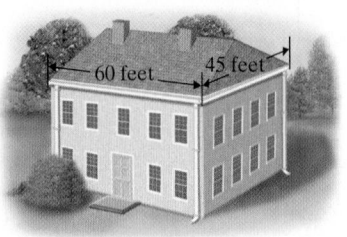

63. In 2003, Harley-Davidson sold 228,400 of its motorcycles domestically. In addition, 62,747 Harley-Davidson motorcycles were sold internationally. What was the total number of Harley-Davidson motorcycles sold in 2003? (*Source:* Harley-Davidson, Inc.)

64. Dan Marino holds the NFL career record for most passes completed. He completed 2305 passes from the beginning of his NFL career in 1983 through 1989. He completed another 2662 passes from 1990 through 1999, his last season before retiring from professional football. How many total passes did he complete during his NFL career? (*Source:* National Football League)

65. The highest waterfall in the United States is Yosemite Falls in Yosemite National Park in California. Yosemite Falls is made up of three sections, as shown in the graph. What is the total height of Yosemite Falls? (*Source:* U.S. Department of the Interior)

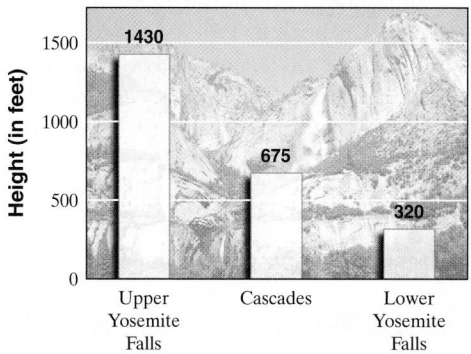

Highest U.S. Waterfalls

Height (in feet)

- Upper Yosemite Falls: 1430
- Cascades: 675
- Lower Yosemite Falls: 320

66. Jordan White, a nurse at Mercy Hospital, is recording fluid intake on a patient's medical chart. During his shift, the patient had the following types and amounts of intake measured in cubic centimeters (cc). What amount should Jordan record as the total fluid intake for this patient?

Oral	Intravenous	Blood
240	500	500
100	200	
355		

67. The State of Alaska has 1795 miles of urban highways and 11,460 miles of rural highways. Find the total highway mileage in Alaska. (*Source:* U.S. Federal Highway Administration)

68. The state of Hawaii has 1851 miles of urban highways and 2291 miles of rural highways. Find the total highway mileage in Hawaii. (*Source:* U.S. Federal Highway Administration)

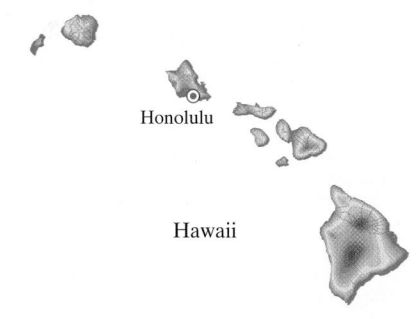

69. The largest permanent Monopoly board is made of granite and located in San Jose, California. Find the perimeter of the square playing board.

31 ft

31 ft

70. The smallest commercially available jigsaw puzzle is a 1000-piece puzzle manufactured in Spain. Find the perimeter of this rectangular-shaped puzzle.

12 in.

18 in.

71. The two top-selling automobiles in the United States are the Honda Accord, with sales of 397,750 and the Toyota Camry with sales of 369,562 in 2003. What is the total amount of Accords and Camrys sold in 2003? (*Source:* J. D. Power and Associates)

72. In the country of New Zealand, there are 40,748,693 more sheep than there are people. If the human population of New Zealand is 3,951,307, what is the sheep population? (*Source:* Food and Agricultural Organization of the United States)

73. In 2004, there were 5670 Blockbuster video rental stores located in the United States and 3197 located outside the United States. How many Blockbuster rental stores were located worldwide? (*Source:* Blockbuster Inc.)

74. Wilma Rudolph, who won three gold medals in track and field events in the 1960 Summer Olympics, was born in 1940. Marion Jones, who also won three gold medals in track and field events but in the 2000 Summer Olympics, was born 35 years later. In what year was Marion Jones born?

The table shows the number of Target stores in ten states. Use this table to answer Exercises 75 through 80.

The Top States for Target Stores in 2003	
State	**Number of Stores**
Arizona	36
California	184
Florida	78
Georgia	38
Illinois	62
New York	37
Michigan	51
Minnesota	65
Ohio	44
Texas	104
(*Source:* Target Corporation)	

75. Which state has the most Target stores?

76. Which of the states listed in the table has the fewest number of Target stores?

77. What is the total number of Target stores located in the three states with the most Target stores?

78. How many Target stores are located in the ten states listed in the table?

79. Which pair of neighboring states have more Target stores combined, Florida and Georgia or Michigan and Ohio?

80. Target operates stores in 47 states. There are 526 Target stores located in the states not listed in the table. How many Target stores are in the United States?

Concept Extensions

81. In your own words, explain the commutative property of addition.

82. In your own words, explain the associative property of addition.

83. Give any three whole numbers whose sum is 100.

84. Give any four whole numbers whose sum is 25.

85. Find the perimeter of the figure.

8 ft

3 ft

4 ft

?

5 ft

?

86. Add: $78,962 + 129,968,350 + 36,462,880$

87. Add: $56,468,980 + 1,236,785 + 986,768,000$

Check each addition below. If it is incorrect, find the correct answer. See the Concept Check in this section.

88.
```
  566
  932
+ 871
─────
 2369
```

89.
```
  773
  659
+ 481
─────
 1913
```

90.
```
   14
  173
   86
+ 257
─────
  520
```

91.
```
   19
  214
   49
+ 651
─────
  923
```

 STUDY SKILLS BUILDER

Learning New Terms?

Many of the terms used in this text may be new to you. It will be helpful to make a list of new mathematical terms and symbols as you encounter them and to review them frequently. Placing these new terms (including page references) on 3 × 5 index cards might help you later when you're preparing for a quiz.

Answer the following.

1. Name one way you might place a word and its definition on a 3 × 5 card.

2. How do new terms stand out in this text so that they can be found?

1.4 SUBTRACTING WHOLE NUMBERS

Objective **A** Subtracting Whole Numbers

If you have $5 and someone gives you $3, you have a total of $8, since $5 + 3 = 8$. Similarly, if you have $8 and then someone borrows $3, you have $5 left. **Subtraction** is finding the **difference** of two numbers.

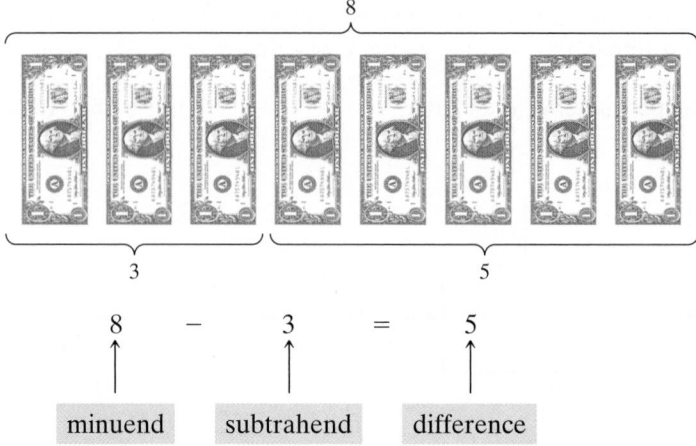

Notice that addition and subtraction are very closely related. In fact, subtraction is defined in terms of addition.

$$8 - 3 = 5 \text{ because } 5 + 3 = 8$$

This means that subtraction can be *checked* by addition, and we say that addition and subtraction are reverse operations.

PRACTICE PROBLEM 1

Subtract. Check each answer by adding.
a. $14 - 9$
b. $20 - 8$
c. $9 - 9$
d. $4 - 0$

EXAMPLE 1 Subtract. Check each answer by adding.

a. $12 - 9$ **b.** $11 - 6$ **c.** $5 - 5$ **d.** $7 - 0$

Solution:

a. $12 - 9 = 3$ because $3 + 9 = 12$
b. $11 - 6 = 5$ because $5 + 6 = 11$
c. $5 - 5 = 0$ because $0 + 5 = 5$
d. $7 - 0 = 7$ because $7 + 0 = 7$

□ **Work Practice Problem 1**

Look again at Examples 1(c) and 1(d).

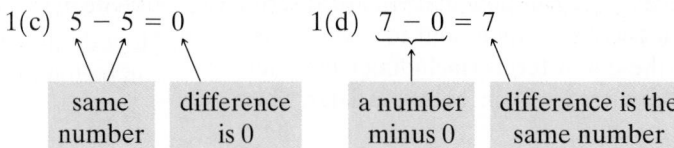

These two examples illustrate the subtraction properties of 0.

Subtraction Properties of 0

The difference of any number and that same number is 0. For example,

$$11 - 11 = 0$$

The difference of any number and 0 is that same number. For example,

$$45 - 0 = 45$$

To subtract whole numbers we subtract the digits in the ones place, then the tens place, then the hundreds place, and so on. When subtraction involves numbers of two or more digits, it is more convenient to subtract vertically. For example, to subtract $893 - 52$,

$$
\begin{array}{r}
893 \\
-52 \\
\hline
841
\end{array}
$$

893 ⟵ minuend
−52 ⟵ subtrahend
841 ⟵ difference

3 − 2
9 − 5
8 − 0

Line up the numbers vertically so that the minuend is on top and the place values correspond. Subtract in corresponding places, starting with the ones place.

To check, add.

difference   or   841
+ subtrahend   + 52
—————   —————
minuend   893 ⟵ Since this is the original minuend, the problem checks.

EXAMPLE 2 Subtract: $7826 - 505$. Check by adding.

Solution:
$$
\begin{array}{r}
7826 \\
-505 \\
\hline
7321
\end{array}
$$

Check:
$$
\begin{array}{r}
7321 \\
+505 \\
\hline
7826
\end{array}
$$

▣ **Work Practice Problem 2**

Objective B Subtracting with Borrowing

When subtracting vertically, if a digit in the second number (subtrahend) is larger than the corresponding digit in the first number (minuend), **borrowing** is necessary. For example, consider

$$
\begin{array}{r}
8\,|1 \\
-6\,|3
\end{array}
$$

Since the 3 in the ones place of 63 is larger than the 1 in the ones place of 81, borrowing is necessary. We borrow 1 ten from the tens place and add it to the ones place.

Borrowing

$$
\begin{array}{cccc}
8 & - & 1 & = & 7 & \rightarrow \\
\text{tens} & & \text{ten} & & \text{tens}
\end{array}
$$

7 11 ⟵ 1 ten + 1 one = 11 ones
$$
\begin{array}{r}
\cancel{8}\,\cancel{1} \\
-6\ 3
\end{array}
$$

PRACTICE PROBLEM 2

Subtract. Check by adding.

a. $4689 - 253$

b. $981 - 630$

Now we subtract the ones-place digits and then the tens-place digits.

$$
\begin{array}{r}
\overset{7\ 11}{8\cancel{1}} \\
-63 \\
\hline
18
\end{array}
\begin{array}{l}
\leftarrow 11 - 3 = 8 \\
 7 - 6 = 1
\end{array}
$$

Check:

$$
\begin{array}{r}
18 \\
+63 \\
\hline
81
\end{array}
$$
The original minuend

PRACTICE PROBLEM 3

Subtract. Check by adding.

a. $\begin{array}{r} 227 \\ -175 \\ \hline \end{array}$

b. $\begin{array}{r} 1136 \\ -\ 914 \\ \hline \end{array}$

c. $\begin{array}{r} 8627 \\ -4119 \\ \hline \end{array}$

EXAMPLE 3 Subtract: $543 - 29$. Check by adding.

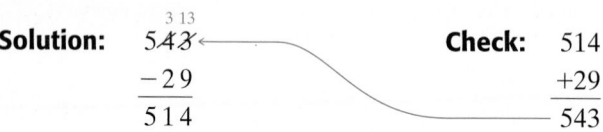

Solution:
$$
\begin{array}{r}
\overset{3\ 13}{54\cancel{3}} \\
-29 \\
\hline
514
\end{array}
$$

Check:
$$
\begin{array}{r}
514 \\
+29 \\
\hline
543
\end{array}
$$

■ **Work Practice Problem 3**

Sometimes we may have to borrow from more than one place. For example, to subtract $7631 - 152$, we first borrow from the tens place.

$$
\begin{array}{r}
76\overset{2\ 11}{\cancel{3}\cancel{1}} \\
-\ 152 \\
\hline
9
\end{array}
\quad \leftarrow 11 - 2 = 9
$$

In the tens place, 5 is greater than 2, so we borrow again. This time we borrow from the hundreds place.

6 hundreds − **1 hundred** = 5 hundreds

$$
\begin{array}{r}
7\overset{5\ \overset{12}{\cancel{2}}\ 11}{\cancel{6}\cancel{3}\cancel{1}} \\
-152 \\
\hline
7479
\end{array}
$$

1 hundred + 2 tens
or
10 tens + 2 tens = 12 tens

Check:

$$
\begin{array}{r}
7479 \\
+\ 152 \\
\hline
7631
\end{array}
$$
The original minuend

PRACTICE PROBLEM 4

Subtract. Check by adding.

a. $\begin{array}{r} 400 \\ -164 \\ \hline \end{array}$

b. $\begin{array}{r} 200 \\ -\ 45 \\ \hline \end{array}$

c. $\begin{array}{r} 1000 \\ -\ 762 \\ \hline \end{array}$

EXAMPLE 4 Subtract: $900 - 174$. Check by adding.

Solution: In the ones place, 4 is larger than 0, so we borrow from the tens place. But the tens place of 900 is 0, so to borrow from the tens place we must first borrow from the hundreds place.

$$
\begin{array}{r}
\overset{8\ \ 10}{\cancel{9}\cancel{0}0} \\
-174 \\
\hline
\end{array}
$$

Answers
3. a. 52, b. 222, c. 4508,
4. a. 236, b. 155, c. 238

Now borrow from the tens place.

$$
\begin{array}{r}
\overset{9}{\cancel{8}}\ \overset{10}{\cancel{}}\ 10 \\
\cancel{9}\ \cancel{0}\ \cancel{0} \\
-\ 1\ 7\ 4 \\
\hline
7\ 2\ 6
\end{array}
$$

Check:

$$
\begin{array}{r}
726 \\
+\ 174 \\
\hline
900
\end{array}
$$

⬛ **Work Practice Problem 4**

Objective C Solving Problems by Subtracting

Descriptions of real-life problems that suggest solving by subtraction include these key words or phrases:

Key Words or Phrases	Examples	Symbols
subtract	subtract 5 from 8	8 − 5
difference	the difference of 10 and 2	10 − 2
less	17 less 3	17 − 3
less than	2 less than 20	20 − 2
take away	14 take away 9	14 − 9
decreased by	7 decreased by 5	7 − 5
subtracted from	9 subtracted from 12	12 − 9

✔**Concept Check** In each of the following problems, identify which number is the minuend and which number is the subtrahend.

a. What is the result when 9 is subtracted from 20?

b. What is the difference of 15 and 8?

c. Find a number that is 15 fewer than 23.

EXAMPLE 5 **Finding the Radius of a Planet**

The radius of Venus is 6052 kilometers. The radius of Mercury is 3612 kilometers less than the radius of Venus. Find the radius of Mercury. (*Source:* National Space Science Data Center)

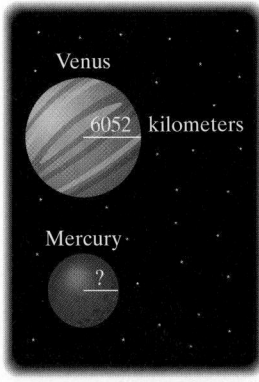

Venus

6052 kilometers

Mercury

?

Continued on next page

Solution:	In Words		Translate to Numbers
	radius of Venus	$\longrightarrow$	6052
	$-\ 3612$	$\longrightarrow$	$-\ 3612$
	radius of Mercury	$\longrightarrow$	2440

The radius of Mercury is 2440 kilometers.

🔲 **Work Practice Problem 5**

PRACTICE PROBLEM 6

During a sale, the price of a new suit is decreased by $47. If the original price was $92, find the sale price of the suit.

EXAMPLE 6 **Calculating Miles per Gallon**

A subcompact car gets 42 miles per gallon of gas. A full-size car gets 17 miles per gallon of gas. Find the difference between the subcompact car miles per gallon and the full-size car miles per gallon.

Solution:	In Words		Translate to Numbers
			$\overset{3\ \ 12}{\not{4}\ \not{2}}$
	subcompact miles per gallon	$\longrightarrow$	
$-$	full-size miles per gallon	$\longrightarrow$	$-\ 1\ 7$
	difference in miles per gallon		$2\ 5$

The difference in the subcompact car miles per gallon and the full-size car miles per gallon is 25 miles per gallon.

🔲 **Work Practice Problem 6**

Helpful Hint

Since subtraction and addition are reverse operations, don't forget that a subtraction problem can be checked by adding.

🔳 **CALCULATOR EXPLORATIONS**   Subtracting Numbers

To subtract numbers on a calculator, find the keys marked
$\boxed{-}$ and $\boxed{=}$ or $\boxed{\text{ENTER}}$.

For example, to find $83 - 49$ on a calculator, press the keys
$\boxed{83}$ $\boxed{-}$ $\boxed{49}$ $\boxed{=}$ or $\boxed{\text{ENTER}}$.

The display will read $\boxed{\qquad 34}$. Thus, $83 - 49 = 34$.

Use a calculator to subtract.

1. $865 - 95$ **2.** $76 - 27$

3. $147 - 38$ **4.** $366 - 87$

5. $9625 - 647$ **6.** $10,711 - 8925$

Answer

6. $45

Mental Math

Find each difference. See Example 1.

1. $9 - 2$ **2.** $6 - 6$ **3.** $5 - 0$ **4.** $44 - 22$ **5.** $93 - 93$

6. $700 - 400$ **7.** $700 - 300$ **8.** $700 - 700$ **9.** $600 - 100$ **10.** $600 - 0$

1.4 EXERCISE SET

FOR EXTRA HELP

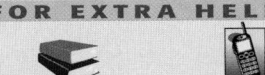

Student Solutions Manual   PH Math/Tutor Center   CD/Video for Review   MathXL®   MyMathLab

Objective A *Subtract. Check by adding. See Examples 1 and 2.*

1. $\begin{array}{r} 67 \\ -23 \end{array}$ **2.** $\begin{array}{r} 72 \\ -41 \end{array}$ **3.** $\begin{array}{r} 389 \\ -124 \end{array}$ **4.** $\begin{array}{r} 572 \\ -321 \end{array}$

5. $\begin{array}{r} 167 \\ -32 \end{array}$ **6.** $\begin{array}{r} 286 \\ -45 \end{array}$ **7.** $2677 - 423$ **8.** $5766 - 324$

9. $6998 - 1453$ **10.** $4912 - 2610$ **11.** $\begin{array}{r} 749 \\ -149 \end{array}$ **12.** $\begin{array}{r} 257 \\ -257 \end{array}$

Objectives A B Mixed Practice *Subtract. Check by adding. See Examples 1 through 4.*

13. $\begin{array}{r} 62 \\ -37 \end{array}$ **14.** $\begin{array}{r} 55 \\ -29 \end{array}$ **15.** $\begin{array}{r} 70 \\ -25 \end{array}$ **16.** $\begin{array}{r} 80 \\ -37 \end{array}$ **17.** $\begin{array}{r} 938 \\ -792 \end{array}$ **18.** $\begin{array}{r} 436 \\ -275 \end{array}$

19. $\begin{array}{r} 922 \\ -634 \end{array}$ **20.** $\begin{array}{r} 674 \\ -299 \end{array}$ **21.** $\begin{array}{r} 600 \\ -432 \end{array}$ **22.** $\begin{array}{r} 300 \\ -149 \end{array}$ **23.** $\begin{array}{r} 142 \\ -36 \end{array}$ **24.** $\begin{array}{r} 773 \\ -29 \end{array}$

25. $\begin{array}{r} 923 \\ -476 \end{array}$ **26.** $\begin{array}{r} 813 \\ -227 \end{array}$ **27.** $\begin{array}{r} 6283 \\ -560 \end{array}$ **28.** $\begin{array}{r} 5349 \\ -720 \end{array}$ **29.** $\begin{array}{r} 533 \\ -29 \end{array}$ **30.** $\begin{array}{r} 724 \\ -16 \end{array}$

31. $\begin{array}{r} 200 \\ -111 \end{array}$ **32.** $\begin{array}{r} 300 \\ -211 \end{array}$ **33.** $\begin{array}{r} 1983 \\ -1904 \end{array}$ **34.** $\begin{array}{r} 1983 \\ -1914 \end{array}$ **35.** $\begin{array}{r} 56,422 \\ -16,508 \end{array}$ **36.** $\begin{array}{r} 76,652 \\ -29,498 \end{array}$

37. 50,000 − 17,289

38. 40,000 − 23,582

39. 7020 − 1979

40. 6050 − 1878

 **41.** 51,111 − 19,898

42. 62,222 − 39,898

Objective **C** *Solve. See Examples 5 and 6.*

43. Subtract 5 from 9.

44. Subtract 9 from 21.

45. Find the difference of 41 and 21.

46. Find the difference of 16 and 5.

47. Subtract 56 from 63.

48. Subtract 41 from 59.

49. Find 108 less 36.

50. Find 25 less 12.

51. Find 12 subtracted from 100.

52. Find 86 subtracted from 90.

53. Dyllis King is reading a 503-page book. If she has just finished reading page 239, how many more pages must she read to finish the book?

54. When Lou and Judy Zawislak began a trip, the odometer read 55,492. When the trip was over, the odometer read 59,320. How many miles did they drive on their trip?

55. In 1997, the hole in the Earth's ozone layer over Antartica was about 21 million square kilometers in size. In 2001, the hole had grown to 25 million square kilometers. By how much has the hole grown from 1997 to 2001? (*Source:* U.S. Environmental Protection Agency EPA)

56. Bamboo can grow to 98 feet while Pacific giant kelp (a type of seaweed) can grow to 197 feet. How much taller is the kelp than the bamboo?

Bamboo   Kelp

57. The peak of Mt. McKinley in Alaska is 20,320 feet above sea level. The peak of Long's Peak in Colorado is 14,255 feet above sea level. How much higher is the peak of Mt. McKinley than Long's Peak? (*Source:* U.S. Geological Survey)

Mt. McKinley, Alaska   Long's Peak, Colorado

58. On one day in May the temperature in Paddin, Indiana, dropped 27 degrees from 2 p.m. to 4 p.m. If the temperature at 2 p.m. was 73° Fahrenheit, what was the temperature at 4 p.m.?

59. During the 2003–2004 regular season, Kevin Garnett of the Minnesota Timberwolves led the NBA in total points scored with 1987. The Sacramento Kings' Predrag Stojakovic placed second for total points scored with 1964. How many more points did Garnett score than Stojakovic during the 2003–2004 regular season? (*Source:* National Basketball Association)

60. In 2002, Americans bought 243,199 Ford Focus cars. In 2003, 13,846 fewer Focuses were sold in the United States. How many Focuses were sold in the United States in 2003? (*Source:* Ford Motor Company)

61. Buhler Gomez has a total of $538 in his checking account. If he writes a check for his electric bill of $129, how much money will be left in his account?

62. Pat Salanki's blood cholesterol level is 243. The doctor tells him it should be decreased to 185. How much of a decrease is this?

63. The distance from Kansas City to Denver is 645 miles. Hays, Kansas, lies on the road between the two and is 287 miles from Kansas City. What is the distance between Hays and Denver?

64. Alan Little is trading his car in on a new car. The new car costs $ 15,425. His car is worth $7998. How much more money does he need to buy the new car?

65. A new VCR with remote control costs $525. Prunella Pasch has $914 in her savings account. How much will she have left in her savings account after she buys the VCR?

66. A stereo that regularly sells for $547 is discounted by $99 in a sale. What is the sale price?

67. The population of Florida grew from 12,937,926 in 1990 to 15,982,378 in 2000. What was Florida's population increase over this time period? (*Source:* U.S. Census Bureau)

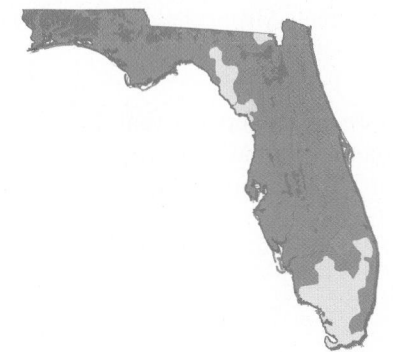

68. The population of El Paso, Texas, was 515,342 in 1990 and 563,662 in 2000. By how much did the population of El Paso grow from 1990 to 2000? (*Source:* U.S. Census Bureau)

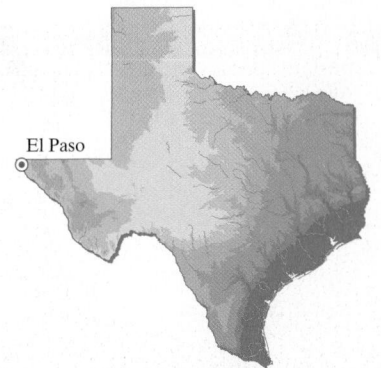

El Paso

69. In 2000, there were 29,393 cocker spaniels registered with the American Kennel Club. In 2003, there were 10,357 fewer cocker spaniels registered. How many cocker spaniels were registered with the AKC in 2003? (*Source:* American Kennel Club)

70. In the United States, there were 41,589 tornadoes from 1950 through 2000. In all, 13,205 of these tornadoes occurred from 1990 through 2000. How many tornadoes occurred during the period prior to 1990? (*Source:* Storm Prediction Center, National Weather Service)

71. Until recently, the world's largest permanent maze was located in Ruurlo, Netherlands. This maze of beech hedges covers 94,080 square feet. A new hedge maze using hibiscus bushes at the Dole Plantation in Wahiawa, Hawaii, covers 100,000 square feet. How much larger is the Dole Plantation maze than the Ruurlo maze? (*Source: The Guinness Book of Records*)

72. There were only 27 California condors in the entire world in 1987. By 2004, the number of California condors had increased to 221. How much of an increase was this? (*Source:* California Department of Fish and Game)

The bar graph shows the top five U.S. airports according to number of passengers arriving and departing in 2003. Use this graph to answer Exercises 73 through 76.

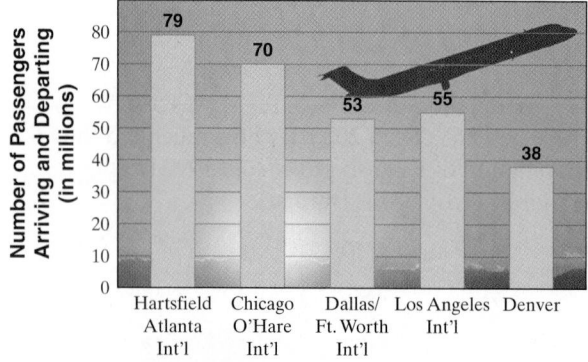

Top Five Airports in U.S.

Number of Passengers Arriving and Departing (in millions)

- Hartsfield Atlanta Int'l: 79
- Chicago O'Hare Int'l: 70
- Dallas/Ft. Worth Int'l: 53
- Los Angeles Int'l: 55
- Denver: 38

Source: Airports Council International

73. Which airport is the busiest?

74. Which airports have fewer than 60 million passengers per year?

75. How many more passengers per year does the Chicago O'Hare International Airport have than the Denver Airport?

76. How many more passengers per year does the Hartsfield Atlanta International Airport have than the Dallas/Ft. Worth International Airport?

The table shows the top ten leading advertisers in the United States in 2003 and the amount of money each spent in that year on advertising. Use this table to answer Exercises 77 through 80.

Advertiser	Amount Spent on Advertising in 2003 (in millions of dollars)
DaimlerChrysler AG	2318
General Motors Corp.	3430
Pfizer	2839
Ford Motor Co.	2234
Johnson & Johnson	1996
Sony Corp.	1815
Walt Disney Co.	2129
Toyota Motor Corp.	1683
Time Warner	3097
Procter & Gamble Co.	3323
Source: Television Bureau of Advertising, Inc.	

77. Which companies spent more than $3000 million on advertising?

78. Which companies shown spent fewer than $2000 million on advertising?

79. How much more money did General Motors Corp. spend on advertising than DaimlerChrysler AG?

80. How much more money did Pfizer spend on advertising than Toyota Motor Corp.?

Mixed Practice (Sections 1.3 and 1.4) *Add or subtract as indicated.*

81.
$$986 + 48$$

82.
$$986 - 48$$

83. $76 - 67$

84. $80 + 93 + 17 + 9 + 2$

85.
$$9000 - 482$$

86.
$$10{,}000 - 1786$$

87.
$$10{,}962$$
$$4851$$
$$+ 7063$$

88.
$$12{,}468$$
$$3211$$
$$+ 1988$$

Concept Extensions

For each exercise, identify which number is the minuend and which number is the subtrahend. See the Concept Check in this section.

89.
$$48 - 1$$

90.
$$2863 - 1904$$

91. Subtract 7 from 70.

92. Find 86 decreased by 25.

Solve.

93. Jo Keen and Trudy Waterbury were candidates for student government president. Who won the election if the votes were cast as follows? By how many votes did the winner win?

Class	Candidate	
	Jo	Trudy
Freshman	276	295
Sophomore	362	122
Junior	201	312
Senior	179	18

94. Two students submitted advertising budgets for a student government fund-raiser.

	Student A	Student B
Radio ads	$600	$300
Newspaper ads	$200	$400
Posters	$150	$240
Handbills	$120	$170

If $1200 is available for advertising, how much excess would each budget have?

Identify each answer as correct or incorrect. Use addition to check. If the answer is incorrect, then write the correct answer.

95.
$$\begin{array}{r} 741 \\ -\ 56 \\ \hline 675 \end{array}$$

96.
$$\begin{array}{r} 478 \\ -\ 89 \\ \hline 389 \end{array}$$

97.
$$\begin{array}{r} 1029 \\ -\ 888 \\ \hline 141 \end{array}$$

98.
$$\begin{array}{r} 7615 \\ -\ 547 \\ \hline 7168 \end{array}$$

Fill in the missing digits in each problem.

99.
$$\begin{array}{r} 526\_ \\ -2\_85 \\ \hline 28\_4 \end{array}$$

100.
$$\begin{array}{r} 10,\_4\_ \\ -\ 8\ 5\ \_ \\ \hline \_710 \end{array}$$

101. Is there a commutative property of subtraction? In other words, does order matter when subtracting? Why or why not?

102. Explain why the phrase "Subtract 7 from 10" translates to "10 − 7."

103. The local college library is having a Million Pages of Reading promotion. The freshmen have read a total of 289,462 pages; the sophomores have read a total of 369,477 pages; the juniors have read a total of 218,287 pages; and the seniors have read a total of 121,685 pages. Have they reached a goal of one million pages? If not, how many more pages need to be read?

1.5 ROUNDING AND ESTIMATING

Objectives

A Round Whole Numbers.

B Use Rounding to Estimate Sums and Differences.

C Solve Problems by Estimating.

Objective A Rounding Whole Numbers

Rounding a whole number means approximating it. A rounded whole number is often easier to use, understand, and remember than the precise whole number. For example, instead of trying to remember the Iowa state population as 2,851,792, it is much easier to remember it rounded to the nearest million: 3 million people.

To understand rounding, let's first understand how we can visualize whole numbers by points on a line. The line below is called a **number line.** This number line has equally spaced marks for each whole number. The arrow to the right simply means that there is no largest whole number.

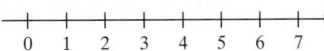

To **graph** a whole number, we darken the point representing the location of the whole number. For example, the number 4 is graphed below.

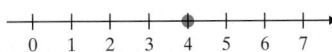

On the number line, the whole number 36 is closer to 40 than 30, so 36 rounded to the nearest ten is 40.

The whole number 52 rounded to the nearest ten is 50 because 52 is closer to 50 than to 60.

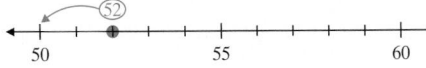

In trying to round 25 to the nearest ten, we see that 25 is halfway between 20 and 30. It is not closer to either number. In such a case, we round to the larger ten, that is, to 30.

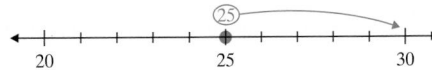

To round a whole number without using a number line, follow these steps:

Rounding Whole Numbers to a Given Place Value

Step 1: Locate the digit to the right of the given place value.

Step 2: If this digit is 5 or greater, add 1 to the digit in the given place value and replace each digit to its right by 0.

Step 3: If this digit is less than 5, replace it and each digit to its right by 0.

PRACTICE PROBLEM 1

Round to the nearest ten.

a. 46

b. 731

c. 125

EXAMPLE 1 Round 568 to the nearest ten.

Solution: 5 6⑧ The digit to the right of the tens place is the ones place,
↑ which is circled.
tens place

5 6⑧ Since the circled digit is 5 or greater, add 1 to the 6 in
↑ the tens place and replace the digit to the right by 0.
Add 1. Replace
with 0.

We find that 568 rounded to the nearest ten is 570.

⊡ **Work Practice Problem 1**

PRACTICE PROBLEM 2

Round to the nearest thousand.

a. 56,702

b. 7444

c. 291,500

EXAMPLE 2 Round 278,362 to the nearest thousand.

Solution:
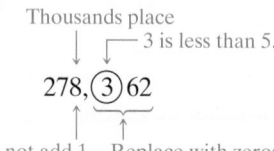
Thousands place
┌─ 3 is less than 5.
278,③62
↑ ↑
Do not add 1. Replace with zeros.

The number 278,362 rounded to the nearest thousand is 278,000.

⊡ **Work Practice Problem 2**

PRACTICE PROBLEM 3

Round to the nearest hundred.

a. 2777

b. 38,152

c. 762,955

EXAMPLE 3 Round 248,982 to the nearest hundred.

Solution:
Hundreds place
┌─ 8 is greater than or equal to 5.
248,9⑧2

Add 1.   9 + 1 = 10, so replace the digit 9 by 0 and carry 1 to the
place value to the left.

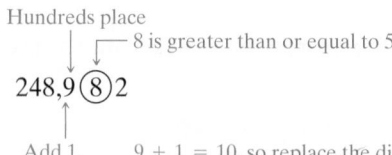
    8+1 0
2 4 8, 9̶ 8 2
       ↑   ↑
    Add 1.   Replace with zeros.

The number 248,982 rounded to the nearest hundred is 249,000.

⊡ **Work Practice Problem 3**

✔**Concept Check** Round each of the following numbers to the nearest *hundred*. Explain your reasoning.

a. 79 **b.** 33

Answers

1. a. 50, **b.** 730, **c.** 130,

2. a. 57,000, **b.** 7000, **c.** 292,000,

3. a. 2800, **b.** 38,200, **c.** 763,000

✔ **Concept Check Answers**

a. 100, **b.** 0

Objective B Estimating Sums and Differences

By rounding addends, we can estimate sums. An estimated sum is appropriate when an exact sum is not necessary. To estimate the sum shown, round each number to the nearest hundred and then add.

768	rounds to	800
1952	rounds to	2000
225	rounds to	200
+ 149	rounds to	+ 100
		3100

The estimated sum is 3100, which is close to the exact sum of 3094.

EXAMPLE 4

Round each number to the nearest hundred to find an estimated sum.

294
625
1071
+ 349

Solution:

294	rounds to	300
625	rounds to	600
1071	rounds to	1100
+ 349	rounds to	+ 300
		2300

The estimated sum is 2300. (The exact sum is 2339.)

Work Practice Problem 4

PRACTICE PROBLEM 4

Round each number to the nearest ten to find an estimated sum.

79
35
42
21
+ 98

EXAMPLE 5

Round each number to the nearest hundred to find an estimated difference.

4725
− 2879

Solution:

4725	rounds to	4700
− 2879	rounds to	− 2900
		1800

The estimated difference is 1800. (The exact difference is 1846.)

Work Practice Problem 5

PRACTICE PROBLEM 5

Round each number to the nearest thousand to find an estimated difference.

4725
− 2879

Objective C Solving Problems by Estimating

Making estimates is often the quickest way to solve real-life problems when solutions do not need to be exact.

Answers
4. 280, **5.** 2000

PRACTICE PROBLEM 6

Tasha Kilbey is trying to estimate how far it is from Grove, Kansas, to Hays, Kansas. Round each given distance on the map to the nearest ten to estimate the total distance.

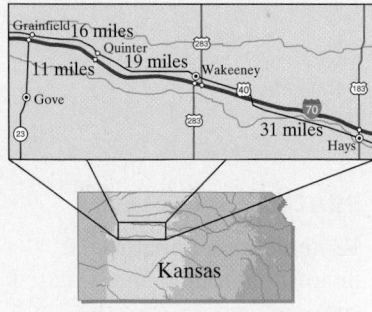

EXAMPLE 6 Estimating Distances

Jose Guillermo is trying to estimate quickly the distance from Temple, Texas, to Brenham, Texas. Round each distance given on the map to the nearest ten to estimate the total distance.

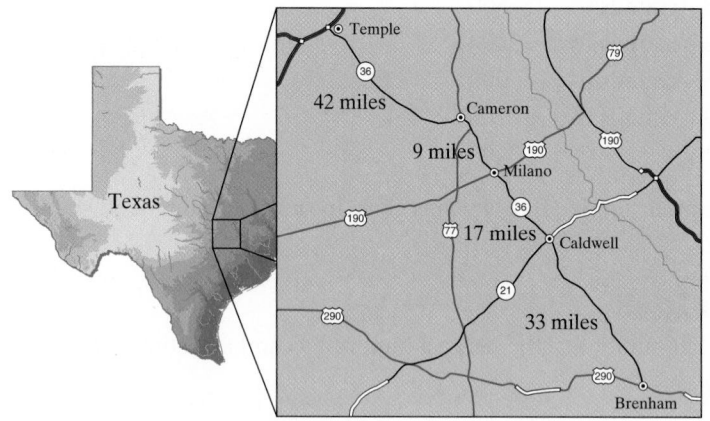

Solution:

Distance		Estimation
42	rounds to	40
9	rounds to	10
17	rounds to	20
+33	rounds to	+ 30
		100

It is approximately 100 miles from Temple to Brenham. (The exact distance is 101 miles.)

■ **Work Practice Problem 6**

PRACTICE PROBLEM 7

In a recent year, there were 120,624 reported cases of chicken pox, 22,866 reported cases of tuberculosis, and 45,970 reported cases of salmonellosis in the United States. Round each number to the nearest ten-thousand to estimate the total number of cases reported for these diseases. (*Source:* Centers for Disease Control and Prevention)

EXAMPLE 7 Estimating Data

In three recent years the numbers of reported cases of mumps in the United States were 906, 1537, and 1692. Round each number to the nearest hundred to estimate the total number of cases reported over this period. (*Source:* Centers for Disease Control and Prevention)

Solution:

Number of Cases		Estimation
906	rounds to	900
1537	rounds to	1500
+ 1692	rounds to	+ 1700
		4100

The approximate number of cases reported over this period was 4100.

■ **Work Practice Problem 7**

Answers

6. 80 mi,   **7.** 190,000

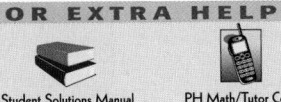 
Objective Ⓐ *Round each whole number to the given place. See Examples 1 through 3.*

1. 632 to the nearest ten

2. 273 to the nearest ten

3. 635 to the nearest ten

4. 275 to the nearest ten

5. 1792 to the nearest hundred

6. 9394 to the nearest hundred

7. 395 to the nearest ten

8. 898 to the nearest ten

9. 51,096 to the nearest thousand

10. 82,198 to the nearest thousand

11. 42,682 to the nearest thousand

12. 42,682 to the nearest ten-thousand

13. 248,695 to the nearest hundred

14. 179,406 to the nearest hundred

15. 36,499 to the nearest thousand

16. 96,501 to the nearest thousand

17. 99,995 to the nearest ten

18. 39,994 to the nearest ten

19. 59,725,642 to the nearest ten-million

20. 39,523,698 to the nearest million

Complete the table by estimating the given number to the given place value.

		Tens	Hundreds	Thousands
21.	5281			
22.	7619			
23.	9444			
24.	7777			
25.	14,876			
26.	85,049			

Round each number to the indicated place.

27. The number of active duty U.S. Air Force personnel in 2004 was 379,884. Round this number to the nearest thousand. (*Source:* U.S. Department of Defense)

28. The number of passengers handled in 2004 by the Hartsfield Atlanta International Airport was 79,086,792. Round this number to the nearest hundred-thousand. (*Source:* Airports Council International)

29. It takes 10,759 days for Saturn to make a complete orbit around the Sun. Round this number to the nearest hundred. (*Source:* National Space Science Data Center)

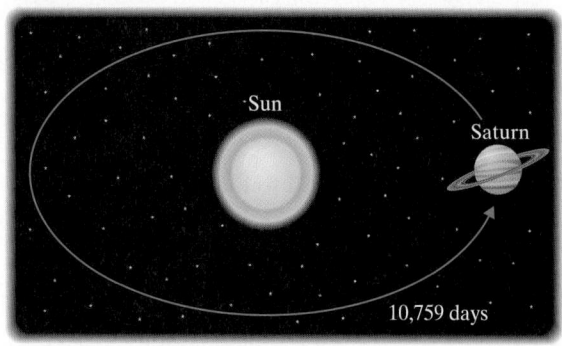

Sun

Saturn

10,759 days

31. The most valuable brand in the world in 2003 was Coca-Cola, with an estimated brand value of $70,450,000,000. Round this to the nearest billion. (*Source: Interbrand/Business Week*)

33. The average salary for a Major League baseball player during the 2004 season was $2,486,609. Round this average salary to the nearest hundred-thousand. (*Source:* Major League Baseball Players Association)

35. The United States currently has 158,722,000 cellular mobile phone users (about 54% of population) while Austria has 7,094,500 users (about 88% of population). Round each of the user numbers to the nearest million. (*Note:* We will study percents in a later chapter.) (*Source:* Siemens AG, International Telecom Statistics, 2003)

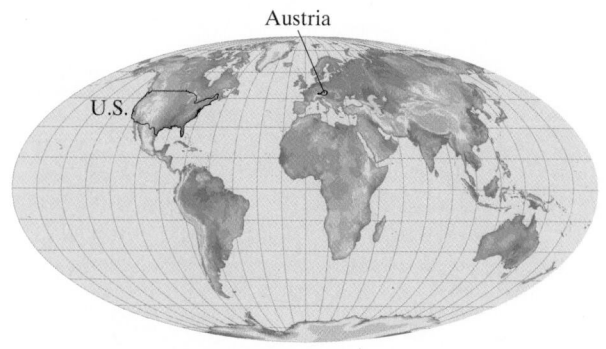

Austria

U.S.

30. Kareem Abdul-Jabbar holds the NBA record for points scored, a total of 38,387 over his NBA career. Round this number to the nearest thousand. (*Source:* National Basketball Association)

32. According to the 2000 U.S. Census, the population of the United States was 281,421,906. Round this population figure to the nearest million. (*Source:* U.S. Census Bureau)

34. In 2004, the Procter & Gamble Company had $51,407,000,000 in sales. Round this sales figure to the nearest billion. (*Source:* The Procter & Gamble Company)

36. In 2003, U.S. farms produced 144,649,000 bushels of oats. Round the oat production figure to the nearest ten-million. (*Source:* U.S. Department of Agriculture)

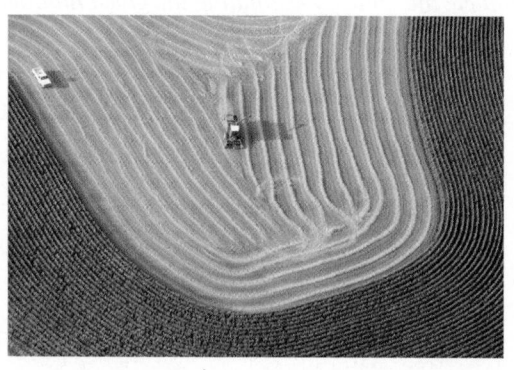

Objective **B** *Estimate the sum or difference by rounding each number to the nearest ten. See Examples 4 and 5.*

37. 29
        35
        42
      + 16

38. 62
        72
        15
      + 19

39. 649
      − 272

40. 555
      − 235

Estimate the sum or difference by rounding each number to the nearest hundred. See Examples 4 and 5.

41.	**42.**	**43.**	**44.**	**45.**	**46.**
1812	2010	1774	1989	2995	799
1776	2001	− 1492	− 1870	1649	1655
+ 1945	+ 1984			+ 3940	+ 271

Two of the given calculator answers below are incorrect. Find them by estimating each sum.

47. 362 + 419   781

48. 522 + 785   1307

49. 432 + 679 + 198   1139

50. 229 + 443 + 606   1278

51. 7806 + 5150   12,956

52. 5233 + 4988   9011

> **Helpful Hint**
>
> Estimation is useful to check for incorrect answers when using a calculator. For example, pressing a key too hard may result in a double digit, while pressing a key too softly may result in the digit not appearing in the display.

Objective **C** *Solve each problem by estimating. See Examples 6 and 7.*

53. Campo Appliance Store advertises three refrigerators on sale at $799, $1299, and $999. Round each cost to the nearest hundred to estimate the total cost.

54. Jared Nuss scored 89, 92, 100, 67, 75, and 89 on his biology tests. Round each score to the nearest ten to estimate his total score.

55. Round each distance given on the map to the nearest ten miles to estimate the total distance from Stockton to LaCrosse.

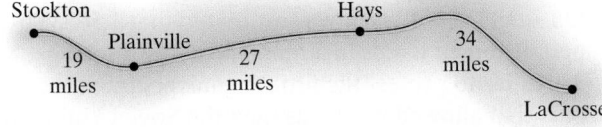

56. The Gonzales family took a trip and traveled 458, 489, 377, 243, 69, and 702 miles on six consecutive days. Round each distance to the nearest hundred to estimate the distance they traveled.

57. The peak of Mt. McKinley, in Alaska, is 20,320 feet above sea level. The top of Mt. Rainier, in Washington, is 14,410 feet above sea level. Round each height to the nearest thousand to estimate the difference in elevation of these two peaks. (*Source:* U.S. Geological Survey)

58. A student is pricing new car stereo systems. One system sells for $1895 and another system sells for $1524. Round each price to the nearest hundred dollars to estimate the difference in price of these systems.

59. In 2003 the population of Chicago was 2,896,121, and the population of Philadelphia was 1,479,339. Round each population to the nearest hundred-thousand to estimate how much larger Chicago was than Philadelphia. (*Source:* U.S. Census Bureau, 2003 census)

60. The distance from Kansas City to Boston is 1429 miles and from Kansas City to Chicago, 530 miles. Round each distance to the nearest hundred to estimate how much farther Boston is from Kansas City than Chicago is.

61. In the 1964 presidential election, Lyndon Johnson received 41,126,233 votes and Barry Goldwater received 27,174,898 votes. Round each number of votes to the nearest million to estimate the number of votes by which Johnson won the election.

62. Enrollment figures at Normal State University showed an increase from 49,713 credit hours in 2003 to 51,746 credit hours in 2004. Round each number to the nearest thousand to estimate the increase.

63. Head Start is a national program that provides developmental and social services for America's low-income preschool children ages three to five. Enrollment figures in Head Start programs showed an increase from 857,664 children in 2000 to 909,608 children in 2003. Round each number of children to the nearest thousand to estimate this increase. (*Source:* Head Start Bureau)

64. In 2002, General Motors produced 244,356 Saturn cars. Similarly, in 2003 only 183,448 Saturns were produced. Round each number of cars to the nearest thousand to estimate the decrease in Saturn production from 2002 to 2003. (*Source:* General Motors Corporation)

Mixed Practice (*Sections 1.2 and 1.5*) *The following table (from Section 1.4) shows a few of the top leading advertisers in the United States for 2003 and the amount of money spent in that year on advertising. Complete this table. The first line is completed for you.*

	Advertiser	Amount Spent on Advertising in 2003 (in millions of dollars)	Amount Written in Standard Form	Standard Form Rounded to Nearest Hundred-Million	Standard Form Rounded to Nearest Billion
	DaimlerChrysler AG	2318	$2,318,000,000	$2,300,000,000	$2,000,000,000
65.	General Motors Corp.	3430			
66.	Pfizer	2839			
67.	Ford Motor Co.	2234			
68.	Johnson & Johnson	1996			
	(*Source:* Television Bureau of Advertising, Inc.)				

Concept Extensions

69. Find one number that when rounded to the nearest hundred is 4600.

70. Find one number that when rounded to the nearest ten is 4600.

71. A number rounded to the nearest hundred is 8600.
   a. Determine the smallest possible number.
   b. Determine the largest possible number.

72. On August 23, 1989, it was estimated that 1,500,000 people joined hands in a human chain stretching 370 miles to protest the fiftieth anniversary of the pact that allowed what was then the Soviet Union to annex the Baltic nations in 1939. If the estimate of the number of people is to the nearest hundred-thousand, determine the largest possible number of people in the chain.

73. In your own words, explain how to round a number to the nearest thousand.

74. Estimate the perimeter of the triangle by first rounding the length of each side to the nearest hundred.

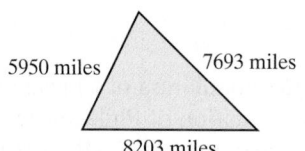

75. Estimate the perimeter of the rectangle by first rounding the length of each side to the nearest ten.

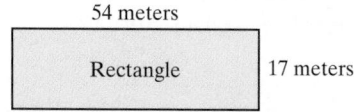

1.6 MULTIPLYING WHOLE NUMBERS AND AREA

Objectives

A Use the Properties of Multiplication.

B Multiply Whole Numbers.

C Multiply by Whole Numbers Ending in Zero(s).

D Find the Area of a Rectangle.

E Solve Problems by Multiplying Whole Numbers.

Multiplication Shown as Repeated Addition Suppose that we wish to count the number of laptops provided in a computer class. The laptops are arranged in 5 rows, and each row has 6 laptops.

6 laptops in each row

1

2

3

⋮

Adding 5 sixes gives the total number of laptops:
$6 + 6 + 6 + 6 + 6 = 30$ laptops. When each addend is the same, we refer to this as **repeated addition.**

Multiplication is repeated addition but with different notation.

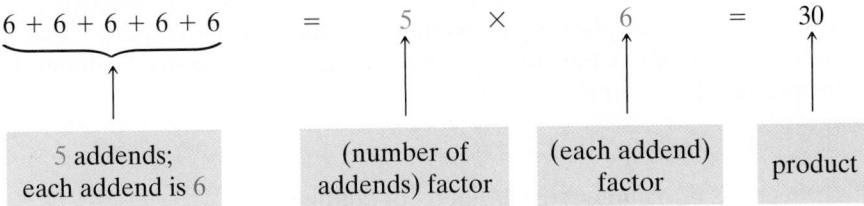

| $6 + 6 + 6 + 6 + 6$ | = | 5 | × | 6 | = | 30 |

| 5 addends; each addend is 6 | (number of addends) factor | (each addend) factor | product |

The × is called a **multiplication sign.** The numbers 5 and 6 are called **factors.** The number 30 is called the **product.** The notation 5×6 is read as "five times six." The symbols · and ( ) can also be used to indicate multiplication.

$$5 \times 6 = 30, \quad 5 \cdot 6 = 30, \quad (5)(6) = 30, \quad \text{and} \quad 5(6) = 30$$

✔ Concept Check

a. Rewrite $4 + 4 + 4 + 4 + 4 + 4 + 4$ using multiplication.

b. Rewrite 3×16 as repeated addition. Is there more than one way to do this? If so, show all ways.

Objective A Using the Properties of Multiplication

As with addition, we memorize products of one-digit whole numbers and then use certain properties of multiplication to multiply larger numbers. Notice that when any number is multiplied by 0, the result is always 0. This is called the **multiplication property of 0.**

✔ **Concept Check Answers**

a. $7 \times 4 = 28$,

b. $16 + 16 + 16 = 48$; yes,
$3 + 3 + 3 + 3 + 3 + 3 + 3 + 3 +$
$3 + 3 + 3 + 3 + 3 + 3 + 3 + 3 = 48$

Multiplication Property of 0

The product of 0 and any number is 0. For example,

$$5 \cdot 0 = 0 \quad \text{and} \quad 0 \cdot 8 = 0$$

Also notice in the appendix that when any number is multiplied by 1, the result is always the original number. We call this result the **multiplication property of 1.**

Multiplication Property of 1

The product of 1 and any number is that same number. For example,

$$1 \cdot 9 = 9 \quad \text{and} \quad 6 \cdot 1 = 6$$

PRACTICE PROBLEM 1

Multiply.
a. 3×0
b. $4(1)$
c. $(0)(34)$
d. $1 \cdot 76$

EXAMPLE 1 Multiply.

a. 6×1 **b.** $0(8)$ **c.** $1 \cdot 45$ **d.** $(75)(0)$

Solution:

a. $6 \times 1 = 6$ **b.** $0(8) = 0$

c. $1 \cdot 45 = 45$ **d.** $(75)(0) = 0$

■ Work Practice Problem 1

Like addition, multiplication is commutative and associative. Notice that when multiplying two numbers, the order of these numbers can be changed without changing the product. For example,

$$3 \cdot 5 = 15 \quad \text{and} \quad 5 \cdot 3 = 15$$

This property is the **commutative property of multiplication.**

Commutative Property of Multiplication

Changing the **order** of two factors does not change their product. For example,

$$9 \cdot 2 = 18 \quad \text{and} \quad 2 \cdot 9 = 18$$

Another property that can help us when multiplying is the **associative property of multiplication.** This property states that when multiplying numbers, the grouping of the numbers can be changed without changing the product. For example,

$$\underline{(2 \cdot 3)} \cdot 4 = 6 \cdot 4 = 24$$

Also,

$$2 \cdot \underline{(3 \cdot 4)} = 2 \cdot 12 = 24$$

Answers

1. a. 0,   **b.** 4,   **c.** 0,   **d.** 76

Both groupings give a product of 24.

Associative Property of Multiplication

Changing the **grouping** of factors does not change their product. From above, we know that for example,

$$(2 \cdot 3) \cdot 4 = 2 \cdot (3 \cdot 4)$$

With these properties, along with the **distributive property,** we can find the product of any whole numbers. The distributive property says that multiplication **distributes** over addition. For example, notice that $3(2 + 5)$ simplifies to the same number as $3 \cdot 2 + 3 \cdot 5$.

$$3(2 + 5) = 3(7) = 21$$

$$3 \cdot 2 + 3 \cdot 5 = 6 + 15 = 21$$

Since $3(2 + 5)$ and $3 \cdot 2 + 3 \cdot 5$ both simplify to 21, then

$$3(2 + 5) = 3 \cdot 2 + 3 \cdot 5$$

Notice in $3(2 + 5) = 3 \cdot 2 + 3 \cdot 5$ that each number inside the parentheses is multiplied by 3.

Distributive Property

Multiplication distributes over addition. For example,

$$2(3 + 4) = 2 \cdot 3 + 2 \cdot 4$$

EXAMPLE 2 Rewrite each using the distributive property.

a. $3(4 + 5)$ **b.** $10(6 + 8)$ **c.** $2(7 + 3)$

Solution: Using the distributive property, we have

a. $3(4 + 5) = 3 \cdot 4 + 3 \cdot 5$
b. $10(6 + 8) = 10 \cdot 6 + 10 \cdot 8$
c. $2(7 + 3) = 2 \cdot 7 + 2 \cdot 3$

Work Practice Problem 2

Objective B Multiplying Whole Numbers

Let's use the distributive property to multiply 7(48). To do so, we begin by writing the expanded form of 48 (see Section 1.2) and then applying the distributive property.

$$7(48) = 7(40 + 8) \quad \text{Write 48 in expanded form.}$$
$$= 7 \cdot 40 + 7 \cdot 8 \quad \text{Apply the distributive property.}$$
$$= 280 + 56 \quad \text{Multiply.}$$
$$= 336 \quad \text{Add.}$$

PRACTICE PROBLEM 2

Rewrite each using the distributive property.
a. $5(2 + 3)$
b. $9(8 + 7)$
c. $3(6 + 1)$

Answers
2. a. $5(2 + 3) = 5 \cdot 2 + 5 \cdot 3$,
  b. $9(8 + 7) = 9 \cdot 8 + 9 \cdot 7$,
  c. $3(6 + 1) = 3 \cdot 6 + 3 \cdot 1$

This is how we multiply whole numbers. When multiplying whole numbers, we will use the following notation.

$$\begin{array}{r} \overset{5}{48} \\ \times\,7 \\ \hline 336 \end{array}$$

$7 \cdot 4 = 28$ and $28 + 5 = 33$

$336 \leftarrow 7 \cdot 8 = 56$ Write 6 in the ones place and carry 5 to the tens place.

PRACTICE PROBLEM 3

Multiply.

a.   36   **b.**   132
     $\times\,4$ $\times\,9$

EXAMPLE 3   Multiply:

a.   25   **b.**   246
     $\times\,8$ $\times\,5$

Solution:

a. $\overset{4}{25}$ **b.** $\overset{2\,3}{246}$
     $\times\,8$ $\times\,5$
     $\overline{200}$ $\overline{1230}$

🔲 **Work Practice Problem 3**

To multiply larger whole numbers, use the following similar notation. Multiply 89×52.

Step 1

$$\begin{array}{r} \overset{1}{89} \\ \times\,52 \\ \hline 178 \end{array} \leftarrow \text{Multiply } 89 \times 2.$$

Step 2

$$\begin{array}{r} \overset{4}{89} \\ \times\,52 \\ \hline 178 \\ 4450 \end{array} \leftarrow \text{Multiply } 89 \times 50.$$

Step 3

$$\begin{array}{r} 89 \\ \times\,52 \\ \hline 178 \\ 4450 \\ \hline 4628 \end{array} \text{ Add.}$$

The numbers 178 and 4450 are called **partial products.** The sum of the partial products, 4628, is the product of 89 and 52.

PRACTICE PROBLEM 4

Multiply.

a.   594   **b.**   306
     $\times\,72$ $\times\,81$

EXAMPLE 4   Multiply: 236×86

Solution:

$$\begin{array}{r} 236 \\ \times\,86 \\ \hline 1\,416 \\ 18\,880 \\ \hline 20{,}296 \end{array}$$

$1\,416 \leftarrow 6(236)$
$18\,880 \leftarrow 80(236)$
$20{,}296$ Add.

🔲 **Work Practice Problem 4**

PRACTICE PROBLEM 5

Multiply.

a.   726   **b.**   288
     $\times\,142$ $\times\,4$

EXAMPLE 5   Multiply: 631×125

Solution:

$$\begin{array}{r} 631 \\ \times\,125 \\ \hline 3\,155 \\ 12\,620 \\ 63\,100 \\ \hline 78{,}875 \end{array}$$

$3\,155 \leftarrow 5(631)$
$12\,620 \leftarrow 20(631)$
$63\,100 \leftarrow 100(631)$
$78{,}875$ Add.

🔲 **Work Practice Problem 5**

Answers

3. a. 144,   **b.** 1188,
4. a. 42,768,   **b.** 24,786,
5. a. 103,092,   **b.** 1152

✔**Concept Check** Find and explain the error in the following multiplication problem.

$$
\begin{array}{r}
102 \\
\times\ 33 \\
\hline
306 \\
306 \\
\hline
612
\end{array}
$$

Objective C Multiplying by Whole Numbers Ending in Zero(s)

Interesting patterns occur when we multiply by a number that ends in zeros. To see these patterns, let's multiply a number, say 34, by 10, then 100, then 1000.

1 zero

$34 \cdot 10 = 340$ 1 zero attached to 34.

2 zeros

$34 \cdot 100 = 3400$ 2 zeros attached to 34.

3 zeros

$34 \cdot 1000 = 34,000$ 3 zeros attached to 34.

These patterns help us develop a shortcut for multiplying by whole numbers ending in zeros.

To multiply by 10, 100, 1000 and so on,
   Form the product by attaching the number of zeros in that number to the other factor.
      For example, $41 \cdot 100 = 4100$.
                      2 zeros

EXAMPLES Multiply.

6. $176 \cdot 1000 = 176,000$ Attach 3 zeros.

7. $2041 \cdot 100 = 204,100$ Attach 2 zeros.

■ **Work Practice Problems 6–7**

We can use a similar format to multiply by any whole number ending in zeros. For example, since

$$15 \cdot 500 = 15 \cdot 5 \cdot 100,$$

we find the product by multiplying 15 and 5, then attaching two zeros to the product.

$$
\begin{array}{r}
\overset{2}{15} \\
\times\ 5 \\
\hline
75
\end{array}
\qquad 15 \cdot 500 = 7500
$$

PRACTICE PROBLEMS 8–9

Multiply.

8. $35 \cdot 3000$

9. $600 \cdot 600$

EXAMPLES Multiply.

8. $25 \cdot 9000 = 225,000$ $\begin{array}{r} \overset{4}{25} \\ \times 9 \\ \hline 225 \end{array}$ Attach 3 zeros.

9. $20 \cdot 7000 = 140,000$ Attach 4 zeros.
$\quad\quad\quad 2 \cdot 7$

■ **Work Practice Problems 8–9**

Objective **D** **Finding the Area of a Rectangle**

A special application of multiplication is finding the area of a region. Area measures the amount of surface of a region. For example, we measure a plot of land or the living space of a home by area. The figures show two examples of units of area measure. (A centimeter is a unit of length in the metric system.)

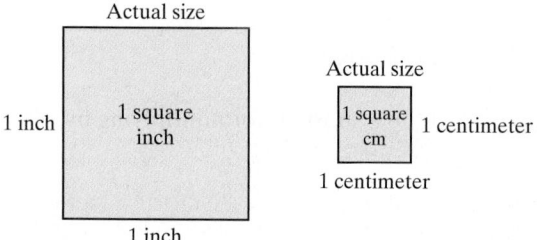

To measure the area of a geometric figure such as the rectangle shown, count the number of square units that cover the region.

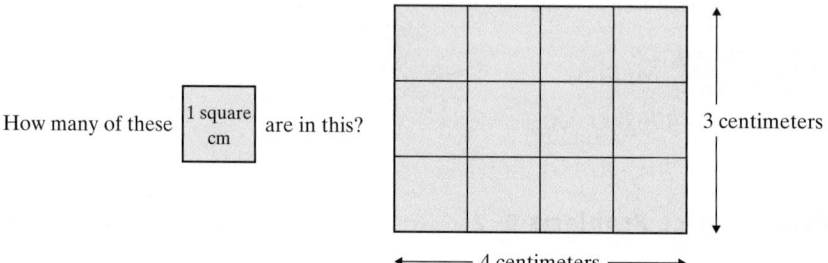

This rectangular region contains 12 square units, each 1 square centimeter. Thus, the area is 12 square centimeters. This total number of squares can be found by counting or by multiplying **4 · 3**(length · width).

$$\begin{aligned} \text{Area of a rectangle} &= \text{length} \cdot \text{width} \\ &= (4 \text{ centimeters})(3 \text{ centimeters}) \\ &= 12 \text{ square centimeters} \end{aligned}$$

In this section, we find the areas of rectangles only. In later sections, we find the areas of other geometric regions.

Answers

8. 105,000,   **9.** 360,000

⚠️ **EXAMPLE 10** **Finding the Area of a State**

The state of Colorado is in the shape of a rectangle whose length is 380 miles and whose width is 280 miles. Find its area.

Solution:

The area of a rectangle is the product of its length and its width.

$$\begin{aligned} \text{Area} &= \text{length} \cdot \text{width} \\ &= (380 \text{ miles})(280 \text{ miles}) \\ &= 106{,}400 \text{ square miles} \end{aligned}$$

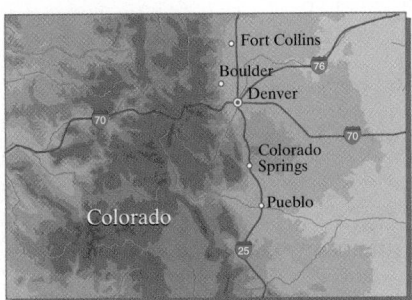

The area of Colorado is 106,400 square miles.

▣ **Work Practice Problem 10**

Objective **E** **Solving Problems by Multiplying**

There are several words or phrases that indicate the operation of multiplication. Some of these are as follows:

Key Words or Phrases	Example	Symbols
multiply	multiply 5 by 7	$5 \cdot 7$
product	the product of 3 and 2	$3 \cdot 2$
times	10 times 13	$10 \cdot 13$

Many key words or phrases describing real-life problems that suggest addition might be better solved by multiplication instead. For example, to find the **total** cost of 8 shirts, each selling for $27, we can either add $27 + 27 + 27 + 27 + 27 + 27 + 27 + 27$, or we can multiply $8(27)$.

EXAMPLE 11 **Finding DVD Space**

A digital video disc (DVD) can hold about 4800 megabytes (MB) of information. How many megabytes can 12 DVDs hold?

Solution:

Twelve DVDs will hold 12×4800 megabytes.

In Words   **Translate to Numbers**

megabytes per disk →	4800
+ _____ DVDs →	× 12
	9600
	48000
total megabytes	57,600

Twelve DVDs will hold 57,600 megabytes.

▣ **Work Practice Problem 11**

PRACTICE PROBLEM 10

The state of Wyoming is in the shape of a rectangle whose length is 360 miles and whose width is 280 miles. Find its area.

PRACTICE PROBLEM 11

A particular computer printer can print 15 pages per minute in color. How many pages can it print in 45 minutes?

Answers

10. 100,800 sq mi, **11.** 675 pages

PRACTICE PROBLEM 12

Softball T-shirts come in two styles: plain at $6 each and striped at $7 each. The team orders 4 plain shirts and 5 striped shirts. Find the total cost of the order.

EXAMPLE 12 **Budgeting Money**

Earline Martin agrees to take her children and their cousins to the San Antonio Zoo. The ticket price for each child is $4 and for each adult, $6. If 8 children and 1 adult plan to go, how much money is needed for admission?

Solution: If the price of one child's ticket is $4, the price for 8 children is $8 \cdot 4 = \$32$. The price of one adult ticket is $6, so the total cost is

In Words		Translate to Numbers
price of 8 children	→	32
+ price of 1 adult	→	+ 6
total cost		38

The total cost is $38.

🖥 **Work Practice Problem 12**

PRACTICE PROBLEM 13

If an average page in a book contains 171 words, estimate, rounding each number to the nearest hundred, the total number of words contained on 395 pages.

EXAMPLE 13 **Estimating Word Count**

The average page of a book contains 259 words. Estimate, rounding each number to the nearest hundred, the total number of words contained on 212 pages.

Solution: The exact number of words is 259×212. Estimate this product by rounding each factor to the nearest hundred.

$$\begin{array}{lcl} 259 & \text{rounds to} & 300 \\ \times 212 & \text{rounds to} & \times 200, \end{array}$$

$$300 \times 200 = 60,000$$
$$3 \cdot 2 = 6$$

There are approximately 60,000 words contained on 212 pages.

🖥 **Work Practice Problem 13**

🖩 **CALCULATOR EXPLORATIONS**   Multiplying Numbers

To multiply numbers on a calculator, find the keys marked ⊠ and ⊟ or ⎡ENTER⎤. For example, to find $31 \cdot 66$ on a calculator, press the keys ⎡31⎤ ⎡×⎤ ⎡66⎤ ⎡=⎤ or ⎡ENTER⎤. The display will read ⎡2046⎤. Thus, $31 \cdot 66 = 2046$.

Use a calculator to multiply.

1. 72×48 **2.** 81×92

3. $163 \cdot 94$ **4.** $285 \cdot 144$

5. $983(277)$ **6.** $1562(843)$

Answers

12. $59,   **13.** 80,000 words

Mental Math

Objective A *Multiply. See Example 1.*

1. $1 \cdot 24$ **2.** $55 \cdot 1$ **3.** $0 \cdot 19$ **4.** $27 \cdot 0$

5. $8 \cdot 0 \cdot 9$ **6.** $7 \cdot 6 \cdot 0$ **7.** $87 \cdot 1$ **8.** $1 \cdot 41$

1.6 EXERCISE SET

FOR EXTRA HELP

 Student Solutions Manual    PH Math/Tutor Center    CD/Video for Review   Math XL MathXL®   MyMathLab MyMathLab

Objective A *Use the distributive property to rewrite each expression. See Example 2.*

1. $4(3 + 9)$ **2.** $5(8 + 2)$ **3.** $2(4 + 6)$ **4.** $6(1 + 4)$ **5.** $10(11 + 7)$ **6.** $12(12 + 3)$

Objective B *Multiply. See Example 3.*

7. $\begin{array}{r} 42 \\ \times\ 6 \\ \hline \end{array}$ **8.** $\begin{array}{r} 79 \\ \times\ 3 \\ \hline \end{array}$ **9.** $\begin{array}{r} 624 \\ \times\ 3 \\ \hline \end{array}$ **10.** $\begin{array}{r} 638 \\ \times\ 5 \\ \hline \end{array}$

11. 277×6 **12.** 882×2 **13.** 1062×5 **14.** 9021×3

Multiply. See Examples 4 and 5.

15. $\begin{array}{r} 98 \\ \times 14 \\ \hline \end{array}$ **16.** $\begin{array}{r} 91 \\ \times 72 \\ \hline \end{array}$ **17.** $\begin{array}{r} 231 \\ \times\ 47 \\ \hline \end{array}$ **18.** $\begin{array}{r} 526 \\ \times\ 23 \\ \hline \end{array}$ **19.** $\begin{array}{r} 809 \\ \times\ 14 \\ \hline \end{array}$ **20.** $\begin{array}{r} 307 \\ \times\ 16 \\ \hline \end{array}$

21. $(620)(40)$ **22.** $(720)(80)$ **23.** $(998)(12)(0)$ **24.** $(593)(47)(0)$ **25.** $(590)(1)(10)$

26. $(240)(1)(20)$ **27.** 1234×48 **28.** 1357×79  **29.** 609×234 **30.** 505×127

31. $\begin{array}{r} 5621 \\ \times\ 324 \\ \hline \end{array}$ **32.** $\begin{array}{r} 1234 \\ \times\ 567 \\ \hline \end{array}$ **33.** $\begin{array}{r} 1941 \\ \times 2035 \\ \hline \end{array}$ **34.** $\begin{array}{r} 1876 \\ \times 1407 \\ \hline \end{array}$ **35.** $\begin{array}{r} 589 \\ \times 110 \\ \hline \end{array}$ **36.** $\begin{array}{r} 426 \\ \times 110 \\ \hline \end{array}$

Objective **C** *Multiply. See Examples 6 through 9.*

37. 8×100 **38.** 6×100 **39.** 11×1000 **40.** 26×1000 **41.** $7406 \cdot 10$ **42.** $9054 \cdot 10$

43. $6 \cdot 4000$ **44.** $3 \cdot 9000$ **45.** $50 \cdot 900$ **46.** $70 \cdot 300$ **47.** $41 \cdot 80{,}000$ **48.** $27 \cdot 50{,}000$

Objectives **D** **E** **Mixed Practice** *Estimate the products by rounding each factor to the nearest hundred. See Example 13.*

49. 576×354 **50.** 982×650 **51.** 604×451 **52.** 111×999

Without actually calculating, mentally round, multiply, and choose the best estimate.

53. $38 \times 42 =$
  a. 16
  b. 160
  c. 1600
  d. 16,000

54. 2872×12
  a. 2872
  b. 28,720
  c. 287,200
  d. 2,872,000

55. $612 \times 29 =$
  a. 180
  b. 1800
  c. 18,000
  d. 180,000

56. 706×409
  a. 280
  b. 2800
  c. 28,000
  d. 280,000

Find the area of each rectangle. See Example 10.

57.
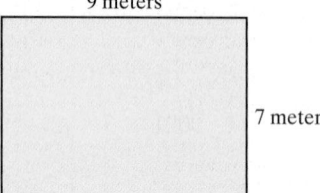
9 meters / 7 meters

58.
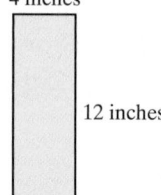
4 inches / 12 inches

59.
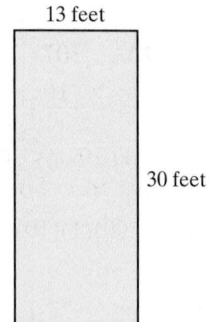
13 feet / 30 feet

60.
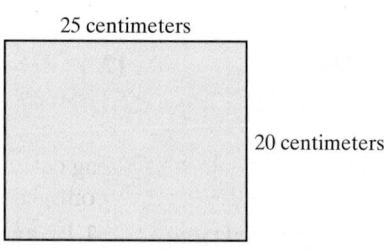
25 centimeters / 20 centimeters

Solve. See Examples 10 through 13.

61. Multiply 70 by 11.

62. Multiply 80 by 12.

63. Find the product of 9 and 600.

64. Find the product of 4 and 400.

65. Find 2 times 2240.

66. Find 3 times 3310.

67. One tablespoon of olive oil contains 125 calories. How many calories are in 3 tablespoons of olive oil? (*Source: Home and Garden Bulletin No. 72*, U.S. Department of Agriculture).

68. One ounce of hulled sunflower seeds contains 14 grams of fat. How many grams of fat are in 6 ounces of hulled sunflower seeds? (*Source: Home and Garden Bulletin No. 72*, U.S. Department of Agriculture).

69. The textbook for a course in Civil War history costs $54. There are 35 students in the class. Find the total cost of the history books for the class.

70. The seats in the mathematics lecture hall are arranged in 12 rows with 34 seats in each row. Find how many seats are in this room.

71. A case of canned peas has *two layers* of cans. In each layer are 8 rows with 12 cans in each row.
   a. How many cans are in 1 layer?
   b. How many cans are in a case?

72. An apartment building has *three floors*. Each floor has five rows of apartments with four apartments in each row.
   a. How many apartments are on 1 floor?
   b. How many apartments are in the building?

△ **73.** A plot of land measures 90 feet by 110 feet. Find its area.

△ **74.** A house measures 45 feet by 60 feet. Find the floor area of the house.

△ **75.** The largest hotel lobby can be found at the Hyatt Regency in San Francisco, CA. It is in the shape of a rectangle that measures 350 feet by 160 feet. Find its area.

△ **76.** Recall from an earlier section that the largest commercial building in the world under one roof is the flower auction building of the cooperative VBA in Aalsmeer, Netherlands. The floor plan is a rectangle that measures 776 meters by 639 meters. Find the area of this building. (A meter is a unit of length in the metric system.) (*Source: The Handy Science Answer Book*, Visible Ink Press)

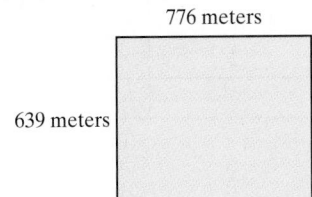

77. A pixel is a rectangular dot on a graphing calculator screen. If a graphing calculator screen contains 62 pixels in a row and 94 pixels in a column, find the total number of pixels on a screen.

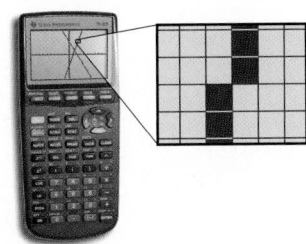

78. A compact disc (CD) can hold 700 megabytes (MB) of information. How many MBs can 17 discs hold?

79. A line of print on a computer contains 60 characters (letters, spaces, punctuation marks). Find how many characters there are in 25 lines.

80. An average cow eats 3 pounds of grain per day. Find how much grain a cow eats in a year. (Assume 365 days in 1 year.)

81. One ounce of Planters® Dry Roasted Peanuts has 160 calories. How many calories are in 8 ounces? (*Source:* RJR Nabisco, Inc.)

82. One ounce of Planters® Dry Roasted Peanuts has 13 grams of fat. How many grams of fat are in 8 ounces? (*Source:* RJR Nabisco, Inc.)

83. The diameter of the planet Saturn is 9 times as great as the diameter of Earth. The diameter of Earth is 7927 miles. Find the diameter of Saturn.

84. The planet Uranus orbits the Sun every 84 Earth years. Find how many Earth days two orbits take. (Assume 365 days in 1 year.)

85. The Thespian club at a local community college is ordering T-shirts. T-shirts size S, M, or L cost $10 each and T-shirts size XL or XXL cost $12 each. Use the table below to find the total cost. (The first row is filled in for you.)

T-Shirt Size	Number of Shirts Ordered	Cost per Shirt	Cost per Size Ordered
S	3	$10	$30
M	5		
L	10		
XL	2		
XXL	2		

Total Cost ____

86. A field trip to the planetarium is planned by the student teacher of a third-grade class. For parent supervisors, the cost is $10 per person. For the third grade students, the cost is $8 per person. For the teacher and student teacher, the cost is $5 per person. Use the table below to find the total cost. (The first row is filled in for you.)

Person	Number of Persons	Cost per Person	Cost per Category
Teacher/ student teacher	2	$5	$10
Third graders	25		
Parents	5		

Total Cost ____

87. Hershey's main chocolate factory in Hershey, Pennsylvania, uses 700,000 quarts of milk each day. How many quarts of milk would be used during the month of March, assuming that chocolate is made at the factory every day of the month? (*Source:* Hershey Foods Corp.)

88. Among older Americans (age 65 years and older), there are about 4 times as many widows as widowers. There were 1,974,000 widowers in 2002. How many widows were there in 2002? (*Sources:* Administration on Aging, U.S. Census Bureau)

Mixed Practice (*Sections 1.3, 1.4, 1.6*) *Perform each indicated operation.*

89.
$$\begin{array}{r} 126 \\ +\ \ 8 \\ \hline \end{array}$$

90.
$$\begin{array}{r} 126 \\ -\ \ 8 \\ \hline \end{array}$$

91.
$$\begin{array}{r} 126 \\ \times\ \ 8 \\ \hline \end{array}$$

92. $47 + 26 + 10 + 231 + 50$

93. Find the sum of 18 and 6.

94. Find the product of 18 and 6.

95. Find the difference of 18 and 6.   **96.** Find the total of 18 and 6.

Concept Extensions

Solve. See the first Concept Check in this section.

97. Rewrite $3 + 3 + 3 + 3 + 3$ using multiplication.

98. Rewrite $11 + 11 + 11 + 11 + 11 + 11$ using multiplication.

99. a. Rewrite $4 \cdot 7$ as repeated addition.
   b. Explain why there is more than one way to do this?

100. a. Rewrite $2 \cdot 5$ as repeated addition.
   b. Explain why there is more than one way to do this.

Find and explain the error in each multiplication problem. See the second Concept Check in this section.

101.
$$
\begin{array}{r}
203 \\
\times\ \ 14 \\
\hline
812 \\
203 \\
\hline
1015
\end{array}
$$

102.
$$
\begin{array}{r}
31 \\
\times\ \ 50 \\
\hline
155
\end{array}
$$

Fill in the missing digits in each problem.

103.
$$
\begin{array}{r}
4\_ \\
\times\ \ \_3 \\
\hline
126 \\
3780 \\
\hline
3906
\end{array}
$$

104.
$$
\begin{array}{r}
\_7 \\
\times\ \ 6\_ \\
\hline
171 \\
3420 \\
\hline
3591
\end{array}
$$

105. Explain how to multiply two 2-digit numbers using partial products.

106. During the NBA's 2003–2004 season, Kevin Garnett of the Minnesota Timberwolves scored 11 three-point field goals, 793 two-point field goals, and 368 free throws (worth one point each). How many points did Garnett score during the 2003–2004 season? (*Source:* National Basketball Association)

107. A window washer in New York City is bidding for a contract to wash the windows of a 23-story building. To write a bid, the number of windows in the building is needed. If there are 7 windows in each row of windows on 2 sides of the building and 4 windows per row on the other 2 sides of the building, find the total number of windows.

1.7 DIVIDING WHOLE NUMBERS

Suppose three people pooled their money and bought a raffle ticket at a local fundraiser. Their ticket was the winner and they won a $60 cash prize. They then divided the prize into three equal parts so that each person received $20.

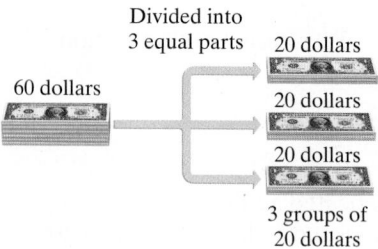

Objective **A** Dividing Whole Numbers

The process of separating a quantity into equal parts is called **division.** The division above can be symbolized by several notations.

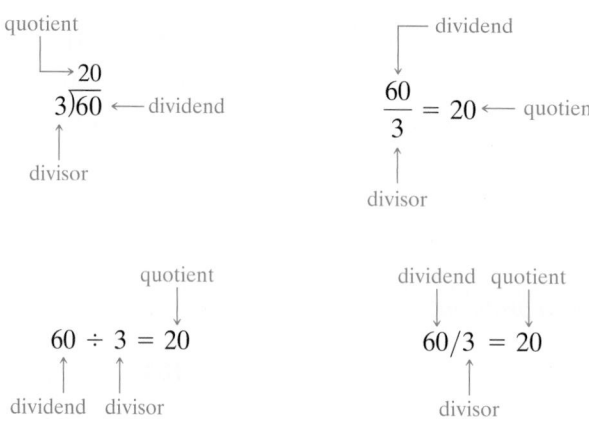

(In the notation $\dfrac{60}{3}$, the bar separating 60 and 3 is called a **fraction bar.**) Just as subtraction is the reverse of addition, division is the reverse of multiplication. This means that division can be checked by multiplication.

$$3\overline{)60}^{\;20} \quad \text{because} \quad 20 \cdot 3 = 60$$

$$\boxed{\text{Quotient}} \cdot \boxed{\text{Divisor}} = \boxed{\text{Dividend}}$$

EXAMPLE 1 Find each quotient. Check by multiplying.

a. $42 \div 7$ **b.** $\dfrac{81}{9}$ **c.** $4\overline{)24}$

Solution:

a. $42 \div 7 = 6$ because $6 \cdot 7 = 42$

b. $\dfrac{81}{9} = 9$ because $9 \cdot 9 = 81$

c. $4\overline{)24}^{\,6}$ because $6 \cdot 4 = 24$

▢ **Work Practice Problem 1**

EXAMPLE 2 Find each quotient. Check by multiplying.

a. $1\overline{)8}$ **b.** $11 \div 1$ **c.** $\dfrac{9}{9}$ **d.** $7 \div 7$ **e.** $\dfrac{10}{1}$ **f.** $6\overline{)6}$

Solution:

a. $1\overline{)8}^{\,8}$ because $8 \cdot 1 = 8$

b. $11 \div 1 = 11$ because $11 \cdot 1 = 11$

c. $\dfrac{9}{9} = 1$ because $1 \cdot 9 = 9$

d. $7 \div 7 = 1$ because $1 \cdot 7 = 7$

e. $\dfrac{10}{1} = 10$ because $10 \cdot 1 = 10$

f. $6\overline{)6}^{\,1}$ because $1 \cdot 6 = 6$

▢ **Work Practice Problem 2**

Example 2 illustrates the important properties of division described next:

Division Properties of 1

The quotient of any number and that same number is 1. For example,

$$8 \div 8 = 1 \qquad \frac{7}{7} = 1 \qquad 4\overline{)4}^{\,1}$$

The quotient of any number and 1 is that same number. For example,

$$9 \div 1 = 9 \qquad \frac{6}{1} = 6 \qquad 1\overline{)3}^{\,3} \qquad \frac{0}{1} = 0$$

EXAMPLE 3 Find each quotient. Check by multiplying.

a. $9\overline{)0}$ **b.** $0 \div 12$ **c.** $\dfrac{0}{5}$ **d.** $\dfrac{3}{0}$

Solution:

a. $9\overline{)0}^{\,0}$ because $0 \cdot 9 = 0$ **b.** $0 \div 12 = 0$ because $0 \cdot 12 = 0$

c. $\dfrac{0}{5} = 0$ because $0 \cdot 5 = 0$

Continued on next page

Find each quotient. Check by multiplying.

a. $8\overline{)48}$

b. $35 \div 5$

c. $\dfrac{49}{7}$

Find each quotient. Check by multiplying.

a. $\dfrac{8}{8}$ **b.** $3 \div 1$

c. $1\overline{)12}$ **d.** $2 \div 1$

e. $\dfrac{5}{1}$ **f.** $11 \div 11$

Find each quotient. Check by multiplying.

a. $\dfrac{0}{7}$ **b.** $5\overline{)0}$

c. $9 \div 0$ **d.** $0 \div 6$

Answers

1. a. 6, **b.** 7, **c.** 7, **2. a.** 1, **b.** 3,
c. 12, **d.** 2, **e.** 5, **f.** 1,
3. a. 0, **b.** 0, **c.** undefined, **d.** 0

d. If $\dfrac{3}{0}$ = a **number,** then the **number** times 0 = 3. Recall from Section 1.6 that any number multiplied by 0 is 0 and not 3. We say, then, that $\dfrac{3}{0}$ is **undefined.**

◼ **Work Practice Problem 3**

Example 3 illustrates important division properties of 0.

Division Properties of 0

The quotient of 0 and any number (except 0) is 0. For example,

$$0 \div 9 = 0 \qquad \frac{0}{5} = 0 \qquad 14\overline{)0}^{\,0}$$

The quotient of any number and 0 is not a number. We say that

$$\frac{3}{0}, \quad 0\overline{)3}, \quad \text{and} \quad 3 \div 0$$

are **undefined.**

Objective **B** **Performing Long Division**

When dividends are larger, the quotient can be found by a process called **long division.** For example, let's divide 2541 by 3.

$$3\overline{)2541}$$

We can't divide 3 into 2, so we try dividing 3 into the first two digits.

$$\begin{array}{r} 8 \\ 3\overline{)2541} \end{array}$$ $25 \div 3 = 8$ with 1 left, so our best estimate is 8. We place 8 over the 5 in 25.

Next, multiply 8 and 3 and subtract this product from 25. Make sure that this difference is less than the divisor.

$$\begin{array}{r} 8 \\ 3\overline{)2541} \\ -24 \\ \hline 1 \end{array}$$ $8(3) = 24$
$25 - 24 = 1$, and 1 is less than the divisor 3.

Bring down the next digit and go through the process again.

$$\begin{array}{r} 84 \\ 3\overline{)2541} \\ -24\downarrow \\ \hline 14 \\ -12 \\ \hline 2 \end{array}$$ $14 \div 3 = 4$ with 2 left
$4(3) = 12$
$14 - 12 = 2$

Once more, bring down the next digit and go through the process.

$$\begin{array}{r} 847 \\ 3\overline{)2541} \\ -24 \\ \hline 14 \\ -12\downarrow \\ \hline 21 \\ -21 \\ \hline 0 \end{array}$$ $21 \div 3 = 7$
$7(3) = 21$
$21 - 21 = 0$

The quotient is 847. To check, see that $847 \times 3 = 2541$.

EXAMPLE 4 Divide: $3705 \div 5$. Check by multiplying.

Solution:

$$
\begin{array}{r}
7 \\
5\overline{)3705} \\
-35\downarrow \\
\hline
20
\end{array}
$$

$37 \div 5 = 7$ with 2 left. Place this estimate, 7, over the 7 in 37.

$7(5) = 35$

$37 - 35 = 2$, and 2 is less than the divisor 5.

— Bring down the 0.

$$
\begin{array}{r}
74 \\
5\overline{)3705} \\
-35 \\
\hline
20 \\
-20\downarrow \\
\hline
05
\end{array}
$$

$20 \div 5 = 4$

$4(5) = 20$

$20 - 20 = 0$, and 0 is less than the divisor 5.

— Bring down the 5.

$$
\begin{array}{r}
741 \\
5\overline{)3705} \\
-35 \\
\hline
20 \\
-20\downarrow \\
\hline
5 \\
-5 \\
\hline
0
\end{array}
$$

$5 \div 5 = 1$

$1(5) = 5$

$5 - 5 = 0$

Check:

$$
\begin{array}{r}
741 \\
\times \quad 5 \\
\hline
3705
\end{array}
$$

🖳 **Work Practice Problem 4**

Helpful Hint Since division and multiplication are reverse operations, don't forget that a division problem can be checked by multiplying.

EXAMPLE 5 Divide and check: $1872 \div 9$

Solution:

$$
\begin{array}{r}
208 \\
9\overline{)1872} \\
-18\downarrow \\
\hline
07 \\
-0\downarrow \\
\hline
72 \\
-72 \\
\hline
0
\end{array}
$$

$2(9) - 18$

$18 - 18 = 0$; bring down the 7.

$0(9) = 0$

$7 - 0 = 7$; bring down the 2.

$8(9) = 72$

$72 - 72 = 0$

Check: $208 \cdot 9 = 1872$

🖳 **Work Practice Problem 5**

Naturally, quotients don't always "come out even." Making 4 rows out of 26 chairs, for example, isn't possible if each row is supposed to have exactly the same number of chairs. Each of 4 rows can have 6 chairs, but 2 chairs are still left over.

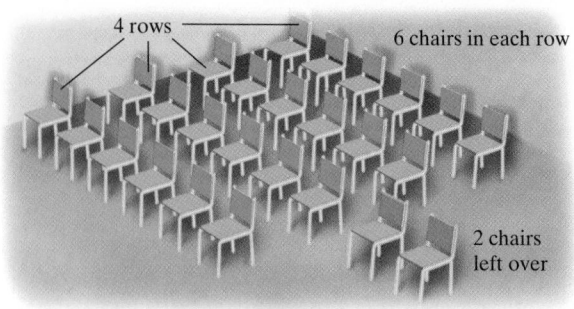

4 rows — 6 chairs in each row

2 chairs left over

We signify "leftovers" or **remainders** in this way:

$$\begin{array}{r} 6 \;\; \text{R}\,2 \\ 4\overline{)26} \end{array}$$

The **whole number part of the quotient** is 6; the **remainder part of the quotient** is 2. Checking by multiplying,

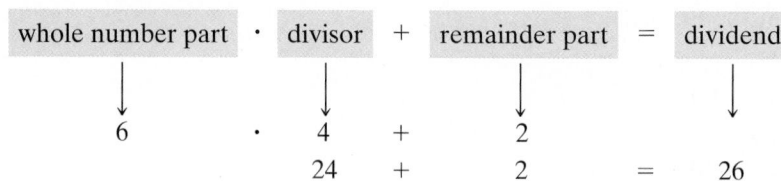

whole number part	·	divisor	+	remainder part	=	dividend

| 6 | · | 4 | + | 2 | | |
| | | 24 | + | 2 | = | 26 |

PRACTICE PROBLEM 6

Divide and check.

a. $5\overline{)949}$

b. $6\overline{)4399}$

EXAMPLE 6 Divide and check: $2557 \div 7$

Solution:

$$\begin{array}{r} 365 \;\; \text{R}\,2 \\ 7\overline{)2557} \\ -21 \\ \hline 45 \\ -42 \\ \hline 37 \\ -35 \\ \hline 2 \end{array}$$

$3(7) = 21$
$25 - 21 = 4$; bring down the 5.
$6(7) = 42$
$45 - 42 = 3$; bring down the 7.
$5(7) = 35$
$37 - 35 = 2$; the remainder is 2.

Check:

365	·	7	+	2	=	2557

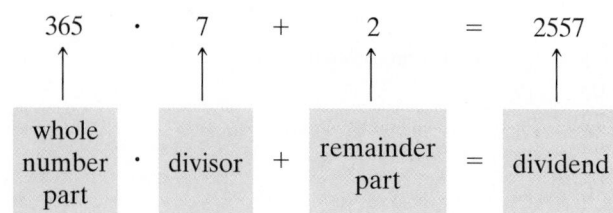

whole number part	·	divisor	+	remainder part	=	dividend

▢ **Work Practice Problem 6**

Answers
6. a. 189 R 4, **b.** 733 R 1

EXAMPLE 7 Divide and check: 56,717 ÷ 8

Solution:

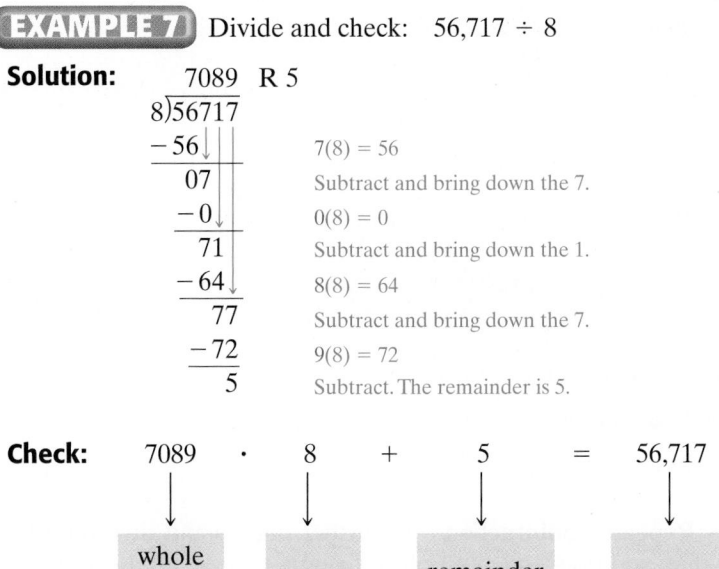

	7089	R 5
8)56717		

$7(8) = 56$
Subtract and bring down the 7.
$0(8) = 0$
Subtract and bring down the 1.
$8(8) = 64$
Subtract and bring down the 7.
$9(8) = 72$
Subtract. The remainder is 5.

Check: 7089 · 8 + 5 = 56,717

whole number part · divisor + remainder part = dividend

🔲 **Work Practice Problem 7**

PRACTICE PROBLEM 7

Divide and check.

a. 5)40,841

b. 7)22,430

When the divisor has more than one digit, the same pattern applies. For example, let's find 1358 ÷ 23.

```
      5      135 ÷ 23 = 5 with 20 left over. Our estimate is 5.
23)1358
  −115↓     5(23) = 115
    208      135 − 115 = 20. Bring down the 8.
```

Now we continue estimating.

```
     59   R 1   208 ÷ 23 = 9 with 1 left over.
23)1358
  −115
    208
  −207          9(23) = 207
      1          208 − 207 = 1. The remainder is 1.
```

To check, see that 59 · 23 + 1 = 1358.

EXAMPLE 8 Divide: 6819 ÷ 17

Solution:

```
      401   R 2
17)6819
  −68↓↓
   01 |       4(17) = 68
  −0↓        Subtract and bring down the 1.
   19         0(17) = 0
  −17        Subtract and bring down the 9.
    2         1(17) = 17
              Subtract. The reminder is 2.
```

To check, see that 401 · 17 + 2 = 6819.

🔲 **Work Practice Problem 8**

PRACTICE PROBLEM 8

Divide: 5740 ÷ 19

Answers

7. a. 8168 R 1, **b.** 3204 R 2,
8. 302 R 2

PRACTICE PROBLEM 9

Divide: $16{,}589 \div 247$

EXAMPLE 9 Divide: $51{,}600 \div 403$

Solution:

$$
\begin{array}{r}
128 \text{ R } 16 \\
403\overline{)51600} \\
-403\!\downarrow \\
\hline
1130 \\
-806\!\downarrow \\
\hline
3240 \\
-3224 \\
\hline
16
\end{array}
$$

$1(403) = 403$
Subtract and bring down the 0.
$2(403) = 806$
Subtract and bring down the 0.
$8(403) = 3224$
Subtract. The remainder is 16.

To check, see that $128 \cdot 403 + 16 = 51{,}600$.

☐ **Work Practice Problem 9**

Division Shown as Repeated Subtraction   To further understand division, recall from Section 1.6 that addition and multiplication are related in the following manner:

$$\underbrace{3 + 3 + 3 + 3}_{\text{4 addends; each addend is 3}} = 4 \times 3 = 12$$

In other words, multiplication is repeated addition. Likewise, division is repeated subtraction.

For example, let's find

$$35 \div 8$$

by repeated subtraction. Keep track of the number of times 8 is subtracted from 35. We are through when we can subtract no more because the difference is less than 8.

$35 \div 8$: Repeated Subtraction

$$
\begin{array}{r}
35 \\
-8
\end{array}\Big\}\ 1 \text{ time}
$$
$$
\begin{array}{r}
27 \\
-8
\end{array}\Big\}\ 2 \text{ times}
$$
$$
\begin{array}{r}
19 \\
-8
\end{array}\Big\}\ 3 \text{ times}
$$
$$
\begin{array}{r}
11 \\
-8
\end{array}\Big\}\ 4 \text{ times}
$$
$$3 \longleftarrow \text{Remainder}$$
(We cannot subtract 8 again.)

$35 \div 8$: Illustration

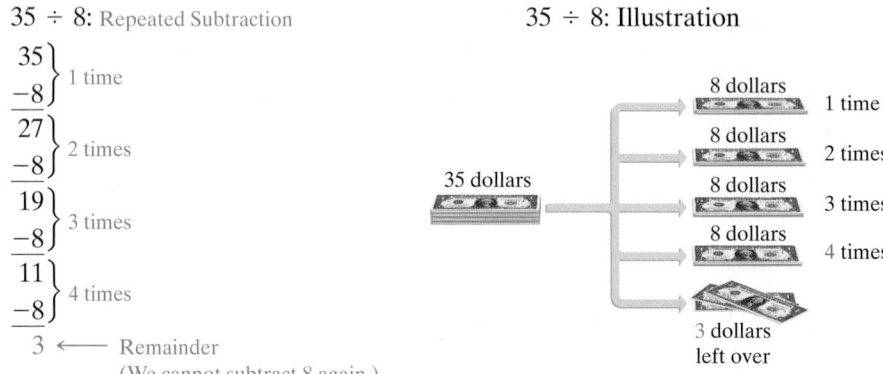

Thus, $35 \div 8 = 4 \text{ R } 3$.

To check, perform the same multiplication as usual, but finish by adding in the remainder.

whole number part of quotient	·	divisor	+	remainder	=	dividend
↓		↓		↓		↓
4	·	8	+	3	=	35

Answer

9. 67 R 40

Objective C Solving Problems by Dividing

Below are some key words and phrases that may indicate the operation of division:

Key Words or Phrases	Examples	Symbols
divide	divide 10 by 5	$10 \div 5$ or $\frac{10}{5}$
quotient	the quotient of 64 and 4	$64 \div 4$ or $\frac{64}{4}$
divided by	9 divided by 3	$9 \div 3$ or $\frac{9}{3}$
divided or **shared equally among**	$100 divided equally among five people	$100 \div 5$ or $\frac{100}{5}$

✔ Concept Check Which of the following is the correct way to represent "the quotient of 20 and 5"? Or are both correct? Explain your answer.

a. $5 \div 20$

b. $20 \div 5$

EXAMPLE 10 Finding Shared Earnings

Zachary, Tyler, and Stephanie McMillan share a paper route to earn money for college expenses. The total in their fund after expenses was $2895. How much is each person's equal share?

Solution:

In words: $\boxed{\text{Each person's share}} = \boxed{\text{total money}} \div \boxed{\text{number of persons}}$

Translate: Each person's share $=$ 2895 $\div$ 3

Then

$$
\begin{array}{r}
965 \\
3\overline{)2895} \\
-27 \\
\hline
19 \\
-18 \\
\hline
15 \\
-15 \\
\hline
0
\end{array}
$$

Each person's share is $965.

■ **Work Practice Problem 10**

PRACTICE PROBLEM 10

Marina, Manual, and Min bought 120 high-density computer diskettes to share equally. How many diskettes did each person get?

Answer

10. 40 diskettes

✔ **Concept Check Answers**

a. incorrect, **b.** correct

PRACTICE PROBLEM 11

Peanut butter and cheese cracker sandwiches come in 6 sandwiches to a package. How many full packages are formed with 195 sandwiches?

PRACTICE PROBLEM 12

Calculators can be packed 24 to a box. If 497 calculators are to be packed but only full boxes are shipped, how many full boxes will be shipped? How many calculators are left over and not shipped?

EXAMPLE 11 Calculating Shipping Needs

How many boxes are needed to ship 56 pairs of Nikes to a shoe store in Texarkana if 9 pairs of shoes will fit in each shipping box?

Solution:

In words: | number of boxes | = | total pairs of shoes | ÷ | how many pairs in a box

Translate: | number or boxes | = | 56 | ÷ | 9

$$\begin{array}{r} 6 \quad R\,2 \\ 9\overline{)56} \\ -54 \\ \hline 2 \end{array}$$

There are 6 full boxes with 2 pairs of shoes left over, so 7 boxes will be needed.

■ **Work Practice Problem 11**

EXAMPLE 12 Dividing Holiday Favors Among Students

Mary Schultz has 48 kindergarten students. She buys 260 stickers as Thanksgiving Day favors for her students. How many stickers will each person receive? How many stickers will be left over?

Solution:

In words: | Number of stickers for each person | = | number of stickers | ÷ | number of students

Translate: | Number of stickers for each person | = | 260 | ÷ | 48

$$\begin{array}{r} 5 \quad R\,20 \\ 48\overline{)260} \\ -240 \\ \hline 20 \end{array}$$

Each student will receive 5 stickers. The stickers cannot be divided equally among her students since there is a nonzero remainder. There will be 20 stickers left over.

■ **Work Practice Problem 12**

Objective **D** **Finding Averages**

A special application of division (and addition) is finding the average of a list of numbers. The **average** of a list of numbers is the sum of the numbers divided by the *number* of numbers.

$$\text{average} = \frac{\text{sum of numbers}}{\textit{number} \text{ of numbers}}$$

Answers

11. 32 full packages,
12. 20 full boxes; 17 calculators left over

EXAMPLE 13 Averaging Scores

Liam Reilly's scores in his mathematics class so far are 93, 86, 71, and 82. Find his average score.

Solution: To find his average score, we find the sum of his scores and divide by 4, the number of scores.

$$
\begin{array}{r}
93 \\
86 \\
71 \\
+82 \\
\hline
332 \text{ sum}
\end{array}
$$

$$
\text{average} = \frac{332}{4} = 83
$$

$$
\begin{array}{r}
83 \\
4\overline{)332} \\
-32 \\
\hline
12 \\
-12 \\
\hline
0
\end{array}
$$

His average score is 83.

■ **Work Practice Problem 13**

PRACTICE PROBLEM 13

To compute a safe time to wait for reactions to occur after allergy shots are administered, a lab technician is given a list of elapsed times between administered shots and reactions. Find the average of the times 5 minutes, 7 minutes, 20 minutes, 6 minutes, 9 minutes, 3 minutes, and 48 minutes.

Answer

13. 14 min

⊞ CALCULATOR EXPLORATIONS Dividing Numbers

To divide numbers on a calculator, find the keys marked ÷ and = or ENTER . For example, to find $435 \div 5$ on a calculator, press the keys 435 ÷ 5 = or ENTER . The display will read 87 . Thus, $435 \div 5 = 87$.

Use a calculator to divide.

1. $848 \div 16$ **2.** $564 \div 12$ **3.** $95\overline{)5890}$ **4.** $27\overline{)1053}$

5. $\dfrac{32,886}{126}$ **6.** $\dfrac{143,088}{264}$ **7.** $0 \div 315$ **8.** $315 \div 0$

Mental Math

Objective **A** *Find each quotient. See Examples 1 through 3.*

1. $40 \div 8$ **2.** $72 \div 9$ **3.** $45 \div 5$ **4.** $24 \div 3$ **5.** $0 \div 5$

6. $0 \div 8$ **7.** $9 \div 1$ **8.** $12 \div 1$ **9.** $\dfrac{16}{16}$ **10.** $\dfrac{49}{49}$

11. $\dfrac{25}{5}$ **12.** $\dfrac{45}{9}$ **13.** $6 \div 0$ **14.** $\dfrac{12}{0}$ **15.** $7 \div 1$

16. $6 \div 6$ **17.** $0 \div 4$ **18.** $7 \div 0$ **19.** $16 \div 2$ **20.** $18 \div 3$

Objective A B Mixed Practice *Divide and then check by multiplying. See Examples 1 through 5.*

1. $3\overline{)78}$ **2.** $5\overline{)85}$ **3.** $6\overline{)222}$ **4.** $8\overline{)640}$ **5.** $3\overline{)1014}$ **6.** $4\overline{)2104}$

7. $\dfrac{20}{0}$ **8.** $\dfrac{0}{20}$ **9.** $48 \div 6$ **10.** $56 \div 8$ **11.** $125 \div 5$ **12.** $121 \div 11$

Divide and then check by multiplying. See Examples 6 and 7.

13. $9\overline{)589}$ **14.** $7\overline{)426}$ **15.** $5\overline{)1129}$ **16.** $3\overline{)1240}$

17. $186 \div 5$ **18.** $167 \div 3$ **19.** $2125 \div 8$ **20.** $3333 \div 4$

Divide and then check by multiplying. See Examples 8 and 9.

21. $23\overline{)1127}$ **22.** $42\overline{)2016}$ **23.** $55\overline{)715}$ **24.** $23\overline{)736}$ **25.** $97\overline{)9449}$

26. $1938 \div 44$ **27.** $3718 \div 18$ **28.** $7224 \div 12$ **29.** $6578 \div 13$ **30.** $5670 \div 14$

31. $9299 \div 46$ **32.** $2539 \div 64$ **33.** $\dfrac{10,620}{236}$ **34.** $\dfrac{5781}{123}$ **35.** $\dfrac{10,194}{103}$

36. $\dfrac{23,048}{240}$ **37.** $20,619 \div 102$ **38.** $40,853 \div 203$ **39.** $244,989 \div 423$ **40.** $164,592 \div 543$

Divide. See Examples 1 through 9.

41. $7\overline{)133}$ **42.** $9\overline{)153}$ **43.** $3\overline{)1540}$ **44.** $5\overline{)3017}$

45. $30\overline{)62,486}$ **46.** $50\overline{)85,747}$ **47.** $139\overline{)699,170}$ **48.** $213\overline{)866,910}$

Objective C *Solve. See Examples 10 through 12.*

49. Find the quotient of 85 and 4.

50. Find the quotient of 90 and 7.

51. Find 100 divided by 35.

52. Find 121 divided by 29.

53. Find the quotient of 62 and 3.

54. Find the quotient of 78 and 5.

55. Kathy Gomez teaches Spanish lessons for $85 per student for a 5-week session. From one group of students, she collects $4930. Find how many students are in the group.

56. Martin Thieme teaches American Sign Language classes for $55 per student for a 7-week session. He collects $1430 from the group of students. Find how many students are in the group.

57. Twenty-one people pooled their money and bought lottery tickets. One ticket won a prize of $5,292,000. Find how many dollars each person received.

58. The gravity of Jupiter is 318 times as strong as the gravity of Earth, so objects on Jupiter weigh 318 times as much as they weigh on Earth. If a person would weigh 52,470 pounds on Jupiter, find how much the person weighs on Earth.

59. A truck hauls wheat to a storage granary. It carries a total of 5810 bushels of wheat in 14 trips. How much does the truck haul each trip if each trip it hauls the same amount?

60. An 18-hole golf course is 5580 yards long. If the distance to each hole is the same, find the distance between holes.

61. The white stripes dividing the lanes on a highway are 25 feet long, and the spaces between them are 25 feet long. Let's call a "lane divider" a stripe followed by a space. Find how many whole "lane dividers" there are in 1 mile of highway. (A mile is 5280 feet.)

62. There is a bridge over highway I-35 every three miles. The first bridge is at the beginning of a 265-mile stretch of highway. Find how many bridges there are over 265 miles of I-35.

63. Wendy Holladay has a piece of rope 185 feet long that she wants to cut into pieces for an experiment in her second-grade class. Each piece of rope is to be 8 feet long. Determine whether she has enough rope for her 22-student class. Determine the amount extra or the amount short.

64. Jesse White is in the requisitions department of Central Electric Lighting Company. Light poles along a highway are placed 492 feet apart. The first light pole is at the beginning of a 1-mile strip. Find how many poles he should order for the 1-mile strip of highway. (A mile is 5280 feet.)

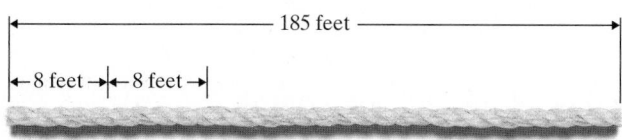

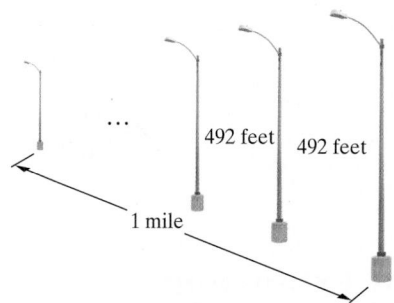

65. Priest Holmes of the Kansas City Chiefs led the NFL in touchdowns during the 2003 football season, scoring a total of 162 points from touchdowns. If a touchdown is worth 6 points, how many touchdowns did Priest make during 2003? (*Source:* National Football League)

66. Broad Peak in Pakistan is the twelfth-tallest mountain in the world. Its elevation is 26,400 feet. A mile is 5280 feet. How many miles tall is Broad Peak? (*Source:* National Geographic Society)

67. Find how many yards are in 1 mile. (A mile is 5280 feet; a yard is 3 feet.)

68. Find how many whole feet are in 1 rod. (A mile is 5280 feet; 1 mile is 320 rods.)

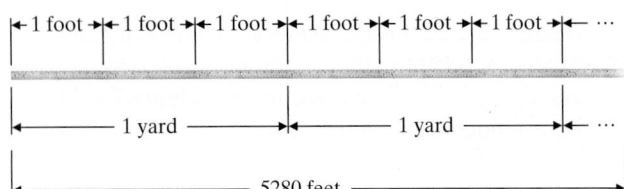

Objective D *Find the average of each list of numbers. See Example 13.*

69. 14, 22, 45, 18, 30, 27

70. 37, 26, 15, 29, 51, 22

71. 204, 968, 552, 268

72. 121, 200, 185, 176, 163

73. 86, 79, 81, 69, 80

74. 92, 96, 90, 85, 92, 79

The normal monthly temperature in degrees Fahrenheit for Minneapolis, Minnesota, is given in the graph. Use this graph to answer Exercises 75 and 76. (Source: National Climatic Data Center)

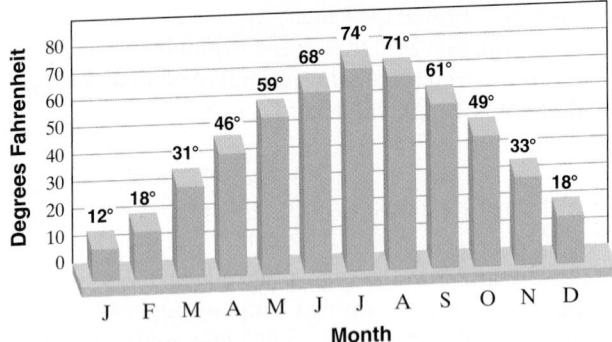

75. Find the average temperature for December, January, and February.

76. Find the average temperature for the entire year.

Mixed Practice (*Sections 1.3, 1.4, 1.6, 1.7*) *Perform each indicated operation. Watch the operation symbol.*

77. 78 + 236 + 42 + 8506

78. 23 + 407 + 92 + 7011

79. $\begin{array}{r} 635 \\ \times\ 46 \end{array}$

80. $\begin{array}{r} 712 \\ \times\ 54 \end{array}$

81. $\begin{array}{r} 635 \\ -\ 46 \end{array}$

82. $\begin{array}{r} 712 \\ -\ 54 \end{array}$

83. $\dfrac{86}{0}$

84. $\dfrac{0}{80}$

85. 211 ÷ 28

86. 304 ÷ 31

Concept Extensions

Match each word phrase to the correct translation. (Not all letter choices will be used.) See the Concept Check in this section.

87. The quotient of 35 and 7

a. 100 ÷ 10

88. The quotient of 100 and 10

b. 10 ÷ 100

89. 100 divided by 10

c. 7 ÷ 35

90. 35 divided by 7

d. 35 ÷ 7

The following table shows the top five leading U.S. advertisers in 2003 and the amount of money spent in that year on advertising. Use this table to answer Exercises 91 and 92.

Company	2003 Advertising Expenditures
General Motors Corp.	$3,430,000,000
DaimlerChrysler AG	$2,318,000,000
Procter & Gamble Co.	$3,323,000,000
Pfizer	$2,839,000,000
Time Warner Inc.	$3,097,000,000
(*Source:* Crain Communications)	

91. Find the average amount of money spent on ads for the year by the top two companies.

92. Find the average amount of money spent on ads by DaimlerChrysler AG, Procter & Gamble Co., Pfizer, and Time Warner Inc.

In Example 13 in this section, we found that the average of 93, 86, 71, and 82 is 83. Use this information to answer Exercises 93 and 94.

93. If the number 71 is removed from the list of numbers, does the average increase or decrease? Explain why.

94. If the number 93 is removed from the list of numbers, does the average increase or decrease? Explain why.

95. Without computing it, tell whether the average of 126, 135, 198, 113 is 86. Explain why it is or why it is not.

96. If the area of a rectangle is 30 square feet and its width is 3 feet, what is its length?

97. Write down any two numbers whose quotient is 15.

98. Find $26 \div 5$ using the process of repeated subtraction.

THE BIGGER PICTURE   Operations on Sets of Numbers

This is a special feature that we begin in this section. Among other concepts introduced later in the text, it is very important for you to be able to perform operations on different sets of numbers. To help you remember these operations, we begin an outline below and continually expand this outline throughout this text. Although suggestions are given, this outline should be in your own words. Once you complete the new portion of your outline, try the exercises below. Remember: Study your outline often as you proceed through this text.

I. Some Operations on Sets of Numbers

  A. Whole Numbers

    1. Add or Subtract:

$$\begin{array}{r} 14 \\ +39 \\ \hline 53 \end{array} \qquad \begin{array}{r} 300 \\ -27 \\ \hline 273 \end{array}$$

2. Multiply or Divide:

$$\begin{array}{r} 238 \\ \times\ 47 \\ \hline 1666 \\ 9520 \\ \hline 11186 \end{array} \qquad \begin{array}{r} 127\ \text{R}\ 2 \\ 7\overline{)891} \\ -7 \\ \hline 19 \\ -14 \\ \hline 51 \\ -49 \\ \hline 2 \end{array}$$

Perform indicated operations.

1. $73 + 45$ **2.** $73 - 45$

3. 73×45 **4.** $2592 \div 29$

5. $0 \cdot 28$ **6.** $0 \div 11$

7. $19 \cdot 1$ **8.** $36 \div 0$

9. $64 \div 1$ **10.** $2000 - 156$

Operations on Whole Numbers

1. _____

2. _____

3. _____

4. _____

5. _____

6. _____

7. _____

8. _____

9. _____

10. _____

11. _____

12. _____

13. _____

14. _____

15. _____

16. _____

17. _____

18. _____

19. _____

20. _____

21. _____

22. _____

23. _____

24. _____

25. _____

26. _____

27. _____

28. _____

29. _____

30. _____

74

Perform each indicated operation.

1.
$$\begin{array}{r} 23 \\ 46 \\ +79 \\ \hline \end{array}$$

2.
$$\begin{array}{r} 7006 \\ -\ 451 \\ \hline \end{array}$$

3.
$$\begin{array}{r} 36 \\ \times 45 \\ \hline \end{array}$$

4. $8\overline{)4496}$

5. $1 \cdot 79$

6. $\dfrac{36}{0}$

7. $9 \div 1$

8. $9 \div 9$

9. $0 \cdot 13$

10. $7 \cdot 0 \cdot 8$

11. $0 \div 2$

12. $12 \div 4$

13. $4219 - 1786$

14. $1861 + 7965$

15. $5\overline{)1068}$

16.
$$\begin{array}{r} 1259 \\ \times\ \ 63 \\ \hline \end{array}$$

17. $3 \cdot 9$

18. $45 \div 5$

19.
$$\begin{array}{r} 207 \\ -\ 69 \\ \hline \end{array}$$

20.
$$\begin{array}{r} 207 \\ +\ 69 \\ \hline \end{array}$$

21. $7\overline{)7695}$

22. $9\overline{)1000}$

23. $32\overline{)21,222}$

24. $65\overline{)70,000}$

25. $4000 - 2976$

26. $10,000 - 101$

27.
$$\begin{array}{r} 303 \\ \times 101 \\ \hline \end{array}$$

28. $(475)(100)$

29. Find the total of 57 and 8.

30. Find the product of 57 and 8.

31. Find the quotient of 57 and 8.

32. Find the difference of 57 and 8.

33. Subtract 14 from 100.

34. Find the difference of 43 and 21.

Complete the table by rounding the given number to the given place value.

		Tens	Hundreds	Thousands
35.	8625			
36.	1553			
37.	10,901			
38.	432,198			

Find the perimeter and area of each figure.

△ **39.**

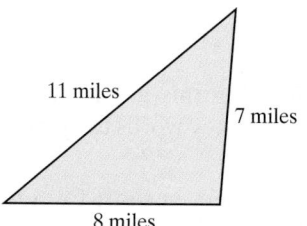

Square   5 feet

△ **40.**

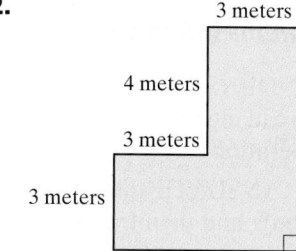

14 inches

Rectangle   7 inches

Find the perimeter of each figure.

△ **41.**

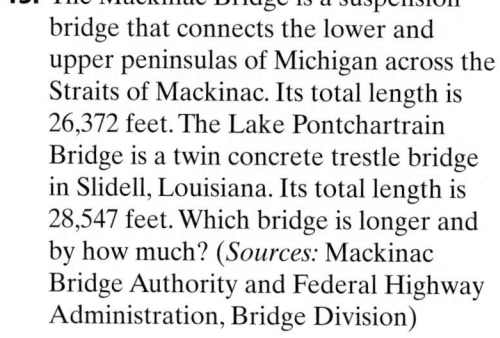

11 miles   7 miles

8 miles

△ **42.**

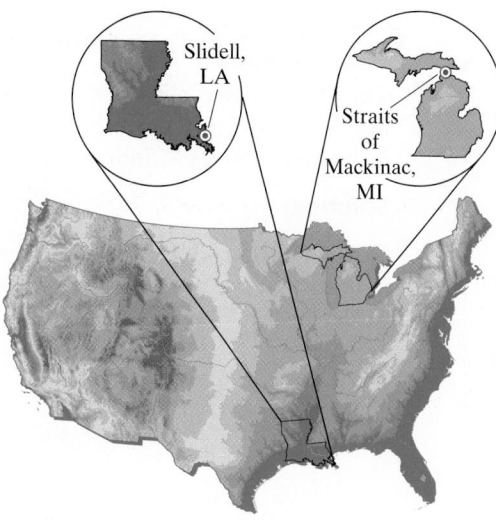

3 meters

4 meters

3 meters

3 meters

Find the average of each list of numbers.

43. 19, 15, 25, 37, 24

44. 108, 131, 98, 159

45. The Mackinac Bridge is a suspension bridge that connects the lower and upper peninsulas of Michigan across the Straits of Mackinac. Its total length is 26,372 feet. The Lake Pontchartrain Bridge is a twin concrete trestle bridge in Slidell, Louisiana. Its total length is 28,547 feet. Which bridge is longer and by how much? (*Sources:* Mackinac Bridge Authority and Federal Highway Administration, Bridge Division)

Slidell, LA

Straits of Mackinac, MI

46. In North America, the average toy expenditure per child is $328 per year. On average, how much is spent on toys for a child by the time he or she reaches age 18? (*Source:* The NPD Group Worldwide)

31. _____

32. _____

33. _____

34. _____

39. _____

40. _____

41. _____

42. _____

43. _____

44. _____

45. _____

46. _____

A Solve Problems by Adding, Subtracting, Multiplying, or Dividing Whole Numbers.

B Solve Problems That Require More Than One Operation.

1.8 AN INTRODUCTION TO PROBLEM SOLVING

Objective **A** Solving Problems Involving Addition, Subtraction, Multiplication, or Division

In this section, we decide which operation to perform in order to solve a problem. Don't forget the key words and phrases that help indicate which operation to use. Some of these are listed below and were introduced earlier in the chapter. Also included are several words and phrases that translate to the symbol "=".

Addition (+)	Subtraction (−)	Multiplication (·)	Division (÷)	Equality (=)
sum	difference	product	quotient	equals
plus	minus	times	divide	is equal to
added to	subtract	multiply	shared equally	is/was
more than	less than	multiply by	among	yields
increased by	decreased by	of	divided by	
total	less	double/triple	divided into	

The following problem-solving steps may be helpful to you:

Problem-Solving Steps

1. UNDERSTAND the problem. Some ways of doing this are to read and reread the problem, construct a drawing and look for key words to identify an operation.

2. TRANSLATE the problem. That is, write the problem in short form using words, and then translate to numbers and symbols.

3. SOLVE the problem. It is helpful to estimate the solution by rounding. Then carry out the indicated operation from Step 2.

4. INTERPRET the results. *Check* the proposed solution in the stated problem and *state* your conclusions. Write your results with the correct units attached.

PRACTICE PROBLEM 1

The Bank of America Building is the second-tallest building in San Francisco, California, at 779 feet. The tallest building in San Francisco is the Transamerica Pyramid, which is 74 feet taller than the Bank of America Building. How tall is the Transamerica Pyramid? (*Source: The World Almanac, 2005*)

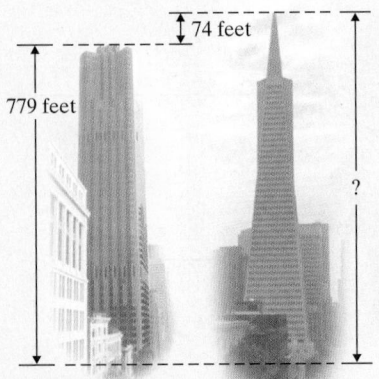

Bank of America   Transamerica Pyramid

Answer

1. 853 ft

EXAMPLE 1 Calculating the Length of a River

The Hudson River in New York State is 306 miles long. The Snake River in the northwestern United States is 732 miles longer than the Hudson River. How long is the Snake River? (*Source:* U.S. Department of the Interior)

Solution:

1. UNDERSTAND. Read and reread the problem, and then draw a picture. Notice that we are told that Snake River is 732 miles longer than the Hudson River. The phrase "longer than" means that we add.

76

2. TRANSLATE.

In words: | Snake River | is | 732 miles | longer than | the Hudson River |

↓ ↓ ↓ ↓ ↓

Translate: Snake River = 732 + 306

3. SOLVE: Let's see if our answer is reasonable by also estimating. We will estimate each addend to the nearest hundred.

$$
\begin{array}{rl}
732 & \text{rounds to} \quad 700 \\
+306 & \text{rounds to} \quad \underline{300} \\
\hline
1038 & \text{exact} \qquad 1000 \quad \text{estimate}
\end{array}
$$

4. INTERPRET. *Check* your work. The answer is reasonable since 1038 is close to our estimated answer of 1000. *State* your conclusion: The Snake River is 1038 miles long.

◼ **Work Practice Problem 1**

EXAMPLE 2 **Filling a Shipping Order**

How many cases can be filled with 9900 cans of jalapeños if each case holds 48 cans? How many cans will be left over? Will there be enough cases to fill an order for 200 cases?

Solution:

1. UNDERSTAND. Read and reread the problem. Draw a picture to help visualize the situation.

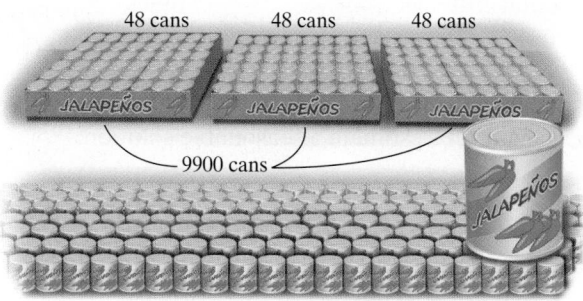

48 cans   48 cans   48 cans

9900 cans

Since each case holds 48 cans, we want to know how many 48s there are in 9900. We find this by dividing.

2. TRANSLATE.

In words: | Number of cases | is | 9900 | divided by | 48 |

↓ ↓ ↓ ↓ ↓

Translate: Number of cases = 9900 ÷ 48

3. SOLVE: Let's estimate a reasonable solution before we actually divide. Since 9900 rounded to the nearest thousand is 10,000 and 48 rounded to the nearest ten is 50, $10,000 \div 50 = 200$. Now find the exact quotient.

$$
\begin{array}{r}
206 \text{ R } 12 \\
48\overline{)9900} \\
\underline{-96} \\
300 \\
\underline{-288} \\
12
\end{array}
$$

Continued on next page

PRACTICE PROBLEM 2

Four friends bought a lottery ticket and won $65,000. If each person is to receive the same amount of money, how much does each person receive?

Answer

2. $16,250

4. INTERPRET. *Check* your work. The answer is reasonable since 206 R 12 is close to our estimate of 200. *State* your conclusion: 206 cases will be filled, with 12 cans left over. There will be enough cases to fill an order for 200 cases.

🔲 **Work Practice Problem 2**

EXAMPLE 3 **Calculating Budget Costs**

The director of a learning lab at a local community college is working on next year's budget. Thirty-three new DVD players are needed at a cost of $187 each. What is the total cost of these DVD players?

Solution:

1. UNDERSTAND. Read and reread the problem, and then draw a diagram.

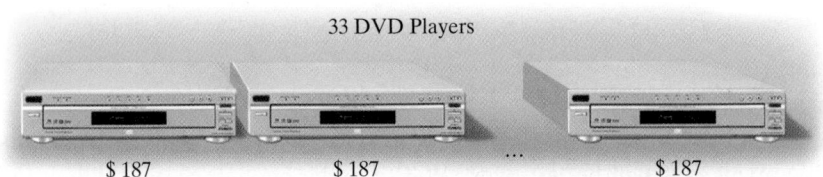

33 DVD Players

$187 $187   ... $187

From the phrase "total cost," we might decide to solve this problem by adding. This would work, but repeated addition, or multiplication, would save time.

2. TRANSLATE.

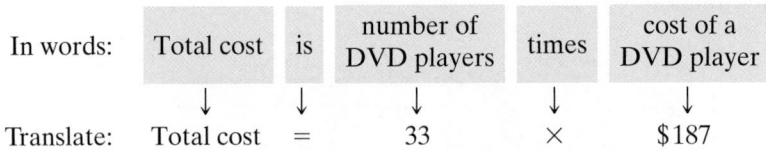

In words:	Total cost	is	number of DVD players	times	cost of a DVD player
	↓	↓	↓	↓	↓
Translate:	Total cost	=	33	×	$187

3. SOLVE: Once again, let's estimate a reasonable solution.

$$
\begin{array}{rl}
187 & \text{rounds to} \quad 200 \\
\times\ 33 & \text{rounds to} \quad \times\ 30 \\
\hline
561 & \qquad\qquad 6000 \quad \text{estimate} \\
5610 & \\
\hline
6171 & \text{exact}
\end{array}
$$

4. INTERPRET. *Check* your work. *State* your conclusion: The total cost of the video players is $6171.

🔲 **Work Practice Problem 3**

EXAMPLE 4 **Calculating a Public School Teacher's Salary**

In 2002, the average salary of a public school teacher in California was $54,300. For the same year, the average salary for a public school teacher in Louisiana was $18,000 less than this. What was the average public school teacher's salary in Louisiana? (*Source:* National Education Association)

Solution:

1. UNDERSTAND. Read and reread the problem. Notice that we are told that the Louisiana salary is $18,000 less than the California salary. The phrase "less than" indicates subtraction.

2. TRANSLATE. Remember that order matters when subtracting, so be careful when translating.

In words:

Louisiana salary	is	California salary	minus	$18,000
↓	↓	↓	↓	↓

Translate: Louisiana salary = 54,300 − 18,000

3. SOLVE: This time, instead of estimating, let's check by adding

$$
\begin{array}{r} 54{,}300 \\ -18{,}000 \\ \hline 36{,}300 \end{array}
\qquad
\textbf{Check:}
\quad
\begin{array}{r} \overset{1}{3}6{,}300 \\ +18{,}000 \\ \hline 54{,}300 \end{array}
$$

4. INTERPRET. *Check* your work. The check is above. *State* your conclusion: The average Louisiana teacher's salary in 2002 was $36,300.

🔲 **Work Practice Problem 4**

Objective **B** Solving Problems That Require More Than One Operation

We must sometimes use more than one operation to solve a problem.

⚠️ **EXAMPLE 5** Planting a New Garden

A gardener bought enough plants to fill a rectangular garden with length 30 feet and width 20 feet. Because of shading problems from a nearby tree, the gardener changed the width of the garden to 15 feet. If the area is to remain the same, what is the new length of the garden?

Solution:

1. UNDERSTAND. Read and reread the problem. Then draw a picture to help visualize the problem.

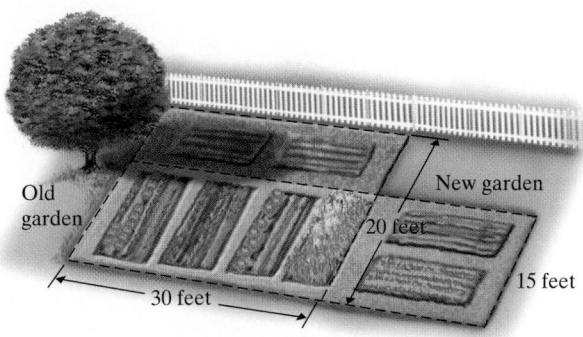

2. TRANSLATE. Since the area of the new garden is to be the same as the area of the old garden, let's find the area of the old garden. Recall that

Area = length × width = 30 feet × 20 feet = 600 square feet

Continued on next page

PRACTICE PROBLEM 5

A gardener is trying to decide how much fertilizer to buy for his yard. He knows that his lot is in the shape of a rectangle that measures 90 feet by 120 feet. He also knows that the floor of his house is in the shape of a rectangle that measures 45 feet by 65 feet. How much area of the lot is not covered by the house?

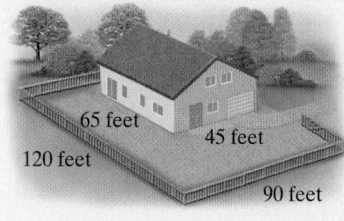

Answer
5. 7875 sq ft

Thus, the area of the new garden is to be 600 square feet. Also, we need to see how many 15s there are in 600. This means division. In other words,

In words:　New length　=　Area of garden　÷　New width

$$\downarrow \qquad\qquad \downarrow \qquad\qquad \downarrow$$

Translate:　New length　=　600　÷　15

Since the area of the new garden is to be 600 square feet also, we need to see how many 15s there are in 600. This means division.

3. SOLVE.

$$\begin{array}{r} 40 \\ 15\overline{)600} \\ -60 \\ \hline 00 \end{array}$$

4. INTERPRET. *Check* your work. *State* your conclusion: The length of the new garden is 40 feet.

▣ Work Practice Problem 5

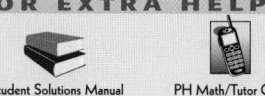   
Objective Ⓐ *Solve. See Examples 1 through 4.*

1. 41 increased by 8 is what number?

2. What is the product of 12 and 9?

3. What is the quotient of 1185 and 5?

4. 78 decreased by 12 is what number?

5. What is the total of 35 and 7?

6. What is the difference of 48 and 8?

7. 60 times 10 is what number?

8. 60 divided by 10 is what number?

△ **9.** A vacant lot in the shape of a rectangle measures 120 feet by 80 feet.
  a. What is the perimeter of the lot?
  b. What is the area of the lot?

△ **10.** A parking lot in the shape of a rectangle measures 100 feet by 150 feet.
  a. What is the perimeter of the lot?
  b. What is the area of the parking lot?

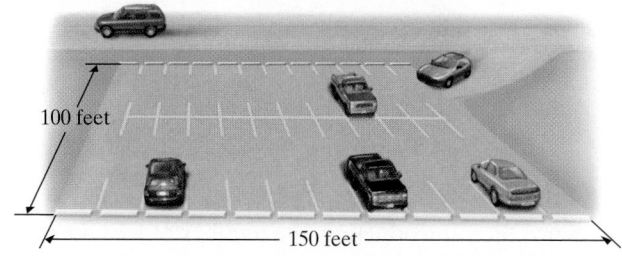

11. The Henrick family bought a house for $85,700 and later sold the house for $101,200. How much money did they make by selling the house?

12. Three people dream of equally sharing a $147 million lottery. How much would each person receive if they have the winning ticket?

13. There are 24 hours in a day. How many hours are in a week?

14. There are 60 minutes in an hour. How many minutes are in a day?

15. The country with the most higher education establishments is India, with 8407 of these establishments. In second place is the United States, with 2649 fewer higher education establishments. Find how many of these establishments there are in the United States.

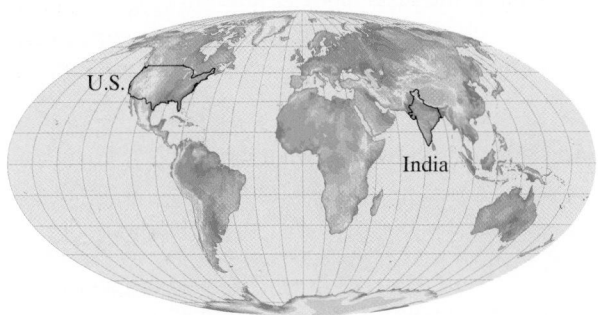

16. The Goodyear Tire & Rubber Company maintains a fleet of five blimps. The *Spirit of Goodyear* can hold 202,700 cubic feet of helium. Its smaller sister, the *Spirit of Europe*, can hold 132,700 fewer cubic feet of helium than *Spirit of Goodyear*. How much helium can *Spirit of Europe* hold? (*Source:* Goodyear Tire & Rubber Company)

17. Yellowstone National Park in Wyoming was the first national park in the United States. It was created in 1872. One of the more recent additions to the National Park System is Governors Island National Monument in New York. It was established in 2001. How much older is Yellowstone than Governors Island? (*Source:* National Park Service)

18. Razor scooters were introduced in 2000. Radio Flyer Wagons were first introduced 83 years earlier. In what year were Radio Flyer Wagons introduced? (*Source:* Toy Industry Association, Inc.)

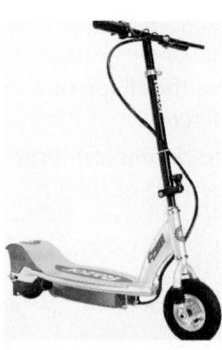

19. Since their introduction, the number of LEGO building bricks that have been sold is equivalent to the world's current population of approximately 6 billion people owning 52 LEGO bricks each. About how many LEGO bricks have been sold since their introduction? (*Source:* LEGO Company)

20. In 2003, the average weekly pay for a production worker in the United States was $517 per week. At that rate, how much would a production worker have earned working a 52-week year? (*Source:* U.S. Bureau of Labor Statistics)

21. The three most common city names in the United States are Fairview, Midway, and Riverside. There are 287 towns named Fairview, 252 named Midway, and 180 named Riverside. Find the total number of towns named Fairview, Midway, and Riverside.

22. In the game of Monopoly, a player must own all properties in a color group before building houses. The yellow color-group properties are Atlantic Avenue, Ventnor Avenue, and Marvin Gardens. These cost $260, $260, and $280, respectively, when purchased from the bank. What total amount must a player pay to the bank before houses can be built on the yellow properties? (*Source:* Hasbro, Inc.)

23. In 2003, the average weekly pay for a Financial Records Processing Supervisor in the United States was $840. If such a supervisor works 40 hours in one week, what is his or her hourly pay? (*Source:* U.S. Bureau of Labor Statistics)

24. In 2003, the average weekly pay for a computer programmer in the United States was $1160. If a computer programmer works 40 hours in one week, what is his or her hourly pay? (*Source:* U.S. Bureau of Labor Statistics)

25. Three ounces of canned tuna in oil has 165 calories. How many calories does 1 ounce have? (*Source: Home and Garden Bulletin No. 72,* U.S. Department of Agriculture)

26. A whole cheesecake has 3360 calories. If the cheesecake is cut into 12 equal pieces, how many calories will each piece have? (*Source: Home and Garden Bulletin No. 72,* U.S. Department of Agriculture)

27. The estimated 2003 U.S. population is 290,800,000 people. Between Memorial Day and Labor Day, 7 billion hot dogs are consumed. Approximately how many hot dogs are consumed per person between Memorial and Labor Days? Divide, but do not give remainder portion of quotient. (*Source:* U.S. Census Bureau, National Hot Dog and Sausage Council)

28. Diana Taurasi of the WNBA's Phoenix Mercury scored an average of 17 points per basketball game during the 2004 regular season. She played a total of 34 games during the season. What was the total number of points she scored during 2004? (*Source:* Women's National Basketball Association)

29. The May Department Stores Company operates Lord & Taylor, Foley's, Filene's, Kaufmann's, and other department stores around the country. It also operates 73 Robinsons-May and Meier & Frank stores in California, Oregon, Nevada, and Arizona. In 2003, Robinsons-May and Meier & Frank had sales of $2,446,000,050. What is the average amount of sales made by each of the 73 stores? (*Source:* The May Department Stores Company)

30. In 2003, the United States Postal Service delivered approximately 859,000,000 pieces of Priority Mail. The total weight of all items sent Priority Mail that year was approximately 1,718,000,000 pounds. What was the average weight of an item sent Priority Mail during 2003? (*Source:* United States Postal Service)

31. The enrollment of all students in elementary and secondary schools in the United States in 2008 is projected to be 54,268,000. Of these students, 16,234,000 are expected to be enrolled in secondary schools. How many students are expected to be enrolled in elementary schools in 2008? (*Source:* National Center for Education Statistics)

32. Kroger now operates convenience stores, food/grocery type stores, and department stores. In 2003, Kroger operated a total of 3774 stores. Of this total, 802 were convenience stores and 2532 were food/grocery type stores. How many department stores did Kroger operate in 2003? (*Source:* The Kroger Company)

33. The length of the southern boundary of the conterminous United States is 1933 miles. The length of the northern boundary of the conterminous United States is 2054 miles longer than this. What is the length of the northern boundary? (*Source:* U.S. Geological Survey)

34. In humans, 14 muscles are required to smile. It takes 29 more muscles to frown. How many muscles does it take to frown?

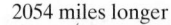
2054 miles longer

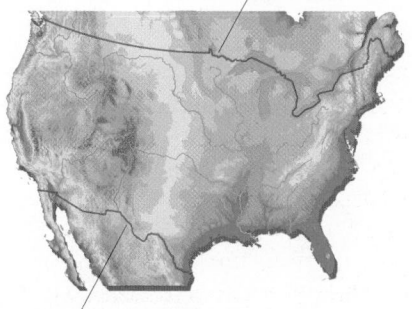
1933 miles

35. Marcel Rockett receives a paycheck every four weeks. Find how many paychecks he receives in a year. (A year has 52 weeks.)

36. A loan of $6240 is to be paid in 48 equal payments. How much is each payment?

Objective **B** *Solve. See Example 5.*

37. Find the total cost of 3 sweaters at $38 each and 5 shirts at $25 each.

38. Find the total cost of 10 computers at $2100 each and 7 boxes of diskettes at $12 each.

39. A college student has $950 in an account. She spends $205 from the account on books and then deposits $300 in the account. How much money is now in the account?

40. The temperature outside was 57°F (degrees Fahrenheit). During the next few hours, it decreased by 18 degrees and then increased by 23 degrees. Find the new temperature.

The table shows the menu from Corky's, a concession stand at the county fair. Use this menu to answer Exercises 41 and 42.

41. A hungry college student is debating between the following two orders:
  a. a hamburger, an order of onion rings, a candy bar, and a soda.
  b. a hot dog, an apple, an order of french fries, and a soda.
  Which order will be cheaper? By how much?

Corky's Concession Stand Menu	
Item	**Price**
Hot dog	$3
Hamburger	$4
Soda	$1
Onion rings	$3
French fries	$2
Apple	$1
Candy bar	$2

42. A family of four is debating between the following two orders:
  a. 6 hot dogs, 4 orders of onion rings, and 4 sodas.
  b. 4 hamburgers, 4 orders of french fries, 2 apples, and 4 sodas.
  Will the family save any money by ordering (b) instead of (a)? If so, how much?

Objectives **A** **B** **Mixed Practice** *Use the bar graph to answer Exercises 43 through 50.*

Top Corporations Receiving U.S. Patents in 2004

Source: United States Patent and Trademark Office

43. Which company listed received the most patents in 2004?

44. Which company listed received the fewest patents in 2004?

45. How many more patents did the company with the most patents receive than the company with the fewest patents?

46. How many more patents did Samsung receive than Sony?

47. How many more patents did Canon receive than Hitachi?

48. Which company received more patents, Matsushita or Fujitsu? How many more patents did it receive?

Find the average number of patents for the companies listed. Do not show remainders. Give whole number answers only.

49. The three companies with the greatest number of patents.

50. The four companies with the least number of patents shown.

Solve.

51. The learning lab at a local university is receiving new equipment. Twenty-two computers are purchased for $615 each and three printers for $408 each. Find the total cost for this equipment.

52. The washateria near the local community college is receiving new equipment. Thirty-six washers are purchased for $585 each and ten dryers are purchased for $388 each. Find the total cost for this equipment.

53. The American Heart Association recommends consuming no more than 2400 milligrams of salt per day. (This is about the amount in 1 teaspoon of salt.) How many milligrams of sodium is this in a week?

54. This semester a particular student pays $1750 for room and board, $709 for a meal ticket plan, and $2168 for tuition. What is her total bill?

△ **55.** The Meish's yard is in the shape of a rectangle and measures 50 feet by 75 feet. In their yard, they have a rectangular swimming pool that measures 15 feet by 25 feet.
  a. Find the area of the entire yard.
  b. Find the area of the swimming pool.
  c. Find the area of the yard that is not part of the swimming pool.

56. The community is planning to construct a rectangular-shaped playground within the local park. The park is in the shape of a square and measures 100 yards on each side. The playground is to measure 15 yards by 25 yards.
  a. Find the area of the entire park.
  b. Find the area of the playground.
  c. Find the area of the park that is not part of the playground.

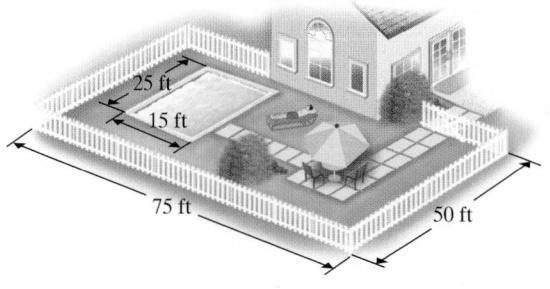

Concept Extensions

57. In 2003, the United States Postal Service issued approximately 202,500,000 money orders worth approximately $48,551,700,000. Round the value of the money orders issued to the nearest hundred-million to estimate the average value of each money order. (*Source:* United States Postal Service)

58. In 2003, there were about 2000 Hilton Hotels worldwide with a total of 348,483 guestrooms. Round the number of guestrooms to the nearest thousand to estimate the average number of guestrooms per hotel. (*Source:* Hilton Hotels Corporation)

59. Write an application of your own that uses the term "bank account" and the numbers 1036 and 524.

 STUDY SKILLS BUILDER

Are You Familiar with Your Textbook Supplements?

There are many student supplements available for additional study. Below, I have listed some of these. See the preface of this text or your instructor for further information.

Chapter Test Prep Video CD. This material is found in your textbook and is fully explained there. The CD contains videos clips solutions to the Chapter Test exercises in this text and are excellent help when studying for chapter tests.

Lecture Video CDs. These video segments are keyed to each section of the text. The material is presented by me, Elayn Martin-Gay, and I have placed a video icon by the exercises in the text that I have worked on the video.

The Student Solutions Manual. This contains worked out solutions to odd-numbered exercises as well as every exercise in the Integrated Reviews, Chapter Reviews, Chapter Tests, and Cumulative Reviews.

Prentice Hall Tutor Center. Mathematics questions may be phoned, faxed, or emailed to this center.

MyMathLab, MathXL, and Interact Math. These are computer and Internet tutorials. This supplement may already be available to you somewhere on campus, for example at your local learning resource lab. Take a moment and find the name and location of any such lab on campus.

As usual, your instructor is your best source of information.

Let's see how you are doing with textbook supplements:

1. Name one way the Chapter Test Prep Video can help you prepare for a chapter test.

2. List any textbook supplements that you have found useful.

3. Have you located and visited a learning resource lab located on your campus?

4. List the textbook supplements that are currently housed in your campus' learning resource lab.

1.9 EXPONENTS, SQUARE ROOTS, AND ORDER OF OPERATIONS

Objectives

Ⓐ Write Repeated Factors Using Exponential Notation.

Ⓑ Evaluate Expressions Containing Exponents.

Ⓒ Evaluate the Square Root of a Perfect Square.

Ⓓ Use the Order of Operations.

Ⓔ Find the Area of a Square.

Objective Ⓐ Using Exponential Notation

In the product $2 \cdot 2 \cdot 2 \cdot 2 \cdot 2$, notice that 2 is a factor several times. When this happens, we can use a shorthand notation, called an **exponent,** to write the repeated multiplication.

$\underbrace{2 \cdot 2 \cdot 2 \cdot 2 \cdot 2}_{\text{2 is a factor 5 times}}$ can be written as

$$\overset{\text{exponent}}{\underset{\text{base}}{2^5}} \quad \text{Read as "two to the fifth power."}$$

This is called **exponential notation.** The **exponent,** 5, indicates how many times the **base,** 2, is a factor.

The table below shows examples of reading exponential notation in words.

Expression	In Words
5^2	"five to the second power" or "five squared."
5^3	"five to the third power" or "five cubed."
5^4	"five to the fourth power."

Usually, an exponent of 1 is not written, so when no exponent appears, we assume that the exponent is 1. For example, $2 = 2^1$ and $7 = 7^1$.

EXAMPLES Write using exponential notation.

1. $4 \cdot 4 \cdot 4 = 4^3$
2. $7 \cdot 7 = 7^2$
3. $5 \cdot 5 \cdot 5 \cdot 5 = 5^4$
4. $6 \cdot 6 \cdot 6 \cdot 8 \cdot 8 \cdot 8 \cdot 8 \cdot 8 = 6^3 \cdot 8^5$

▣ **Work Practice Problems 1–4**

Objective Ⓑ Evaluating Exponential Expressions

To **evaluate** an exponential expression, we write the expression as a product and then find the value of the product.

EXAMPLES Evaluate.

5. $8^2 = 8 \cdot 8 = 64$
6. $9^1 = 9$
7. $2^5 = 2 \cdot 2 \cdot 2 \cdot 2 \cdot 2 = 32$
8. $5 \cdot 6^2 = 5 \cdot 6 \cdot 6 = 180$

▣ **Work Practice Problems 5–8**

PRACTICE PROBLEMS 1–4

Write using exponential notation.

1. $2 \cdot 2 \cdot 2$
2. $3 \cdot 3$
3. $10 \cdot 10 \cdot 10 \cdot 10 \cdot 10 \cdot 10$
4. $5 \cdot 5 \cdot 4 \cdot 4 \cdot 4$

PRACTICE PROBLEMS 5–8

Evaluate.

5. 2^3 6. 5^2
7. 10^1 8. $4 \cdot 5^2$

Answers

1. 2^3, 2. 3^2, 3. 10^6, 4. $5^2 \cdot 4^3$,
5. 8, 6. 25, 7. 10, 8. 100

Example 8 illustrates an important property: An exponent applies only to its base. The exponent 2, in $5 \cdot 6^2$, applies only to its base, 6.

> **Helpful Hint**
> An exponent applies only to its base. For example, $4 \cdot 2^3$ means $4 \cdot 2 \cdot 2 \cdot 2$.

> **Helpful Hint**
> Don't forget that 2^4, for example, is *not* $2 \cdot 4$. The expression 2^4 means repeated multiplication of the same factor.
> $$2^4 = 2 \cdot 2 \cdot 2 \cdot 2 = 16, \quad \text{whereas } 2 \cdot 4 = 8$$

✔ **Concept Check**   Which of the following statements is correct?

a. 3^6 is the same as $6 \cdot 6 \cdot 6$.
b. "Eight to the fourth power" is the same as 8^4.
c. "Ten squared" is the same as 10^3.
d. 11^2 is the same as $11 \cdot 2$.

Objective C Evaluating Square Roots

A **square root** of a number is one of two identical factors of the number. For example,

$$7 \cdot 7 = 49, \text{ so a square root of 49 is 7.}$$

We use this symbol $\sqrt{}$ (called a radical sign) for finding square roots. Since

$$7 \cdot 7 = 49, \text{ then } \sqrt{49} = 7.$$

PRACTICE PROBLEMS 9–11

Find each square root.

9. $\sqrt{100}$
10. $\sqrt{4}$
11. $\sqrt{1}$

> **EXAMPLES**   Find each square root.
>
> **9.** $\sqrt{25} = 5$ because $5 \cdot 5 = 25$
> **10.** $\sqrt{81} = 9$ because $9 \cdot 9 = 81$
> **11.** $\sqrt{0} = 0$ because $0 \cdot 0 = 0$

▣ **Work Practice Problems 9–11**

> **Helpful Hint**
> Make sure you understand the difference between squaring a number and finding the square root of a number.
> $$9^2 = 9 \cdot 9 = 81 \qquad \sqrt{9} = 3 \text{ because } 3 \cdot 3 = 9$$

Not every square root simplifies to a whole number. We will study this more in a later chapter. In this section, we will find square roots of perfect squares only.

A **perfect square** is the product of a whole number multiplied by itself. It may be helpful to study the perfect squares below.

Perfect Squares

$0 = 0 \cdot 0$	$9 = 3 \cdot 3$	$36 = 6 \cdot 6$	$81 = 9 \cdot 9$	$144 = 12 \cdot 12$	$225 = 15 \cdot 15$
$1 = 1 \cdot 1$	$16 = 4 \cdot 4$	$49 = 7 \cdot 7$	$100 = 10 \cdot 10$	$169 = 13 \cdot 13$	$256 = 16 \cdot 16$
$4 = 2 \cdot 2$	$25 = 5 \cdot 5$	$64 = 8 \cdot 8$	$121 = 11 \cdot 11$	$196 = 14 \cdot 14$	$289 = 17 \cdot 17$

Objective D Using the Order of Operations

Suppose that you are in charge of taking inventory at a local bookstore. An employee has given you the number of a certain book in stock as the expression

$3 + 2 \cdot 10$

To calculate the value of this expression, do you add first or multiply first? If you add first, the answer is 50. If you multiply first, the answer is 23.

Contents: 10 books

Contents: 10 books

Mathematical symbols wouldn't be very useful if two values were possible for one expression. Thus, mathematicians have agreed that, given a choice, we multiply first.

$$3 + 2 \cdot 10 = 3 + 20 \quad \text{Multiply.}$$
$$= 23 \quad \text{Add.}$$

This agreement is one of several **order of operations** agreements.

Order of Operations

1. Perform all operations within parentheses ( ), brackets [ ], or other grouping symbols such as fraction bars or square roots.
2. Evaluate any expressions with exponents.
3. Multiply or divide in order from left to right.
4. Add or subtract in order from left to right.

Below we practice using order of operations to simplify expressions.

EXAMPLE 12 Simplify: $2 \cdot 4 - 3 \div 3$

Solution: There are no parentheses and no exponents, so we start by multiplying and dividing, from left to right.

$$2 \cdot 4 - 3 \div 3 = 8 - 3 \div 3 \quad \text{Multiply.}$$
$$= 8 - 1 \quad \text{Divide.}$$
$$= 7 \quad \text{Subtract.}$$

▣ **Work Practice Problem 12**

PRACTICE PROBLEM 12

Simplify: $8 \cdot 2 - 16 \div 4$

Answer
12. 12

PRACTICE PROBLEM 13

Simplify: $36 \div 3 \cdot 2^2$

EXAMPLE 13 Simplify: $4^2 \div 2 \cdot 4$

Solution: We start by evaluating 4^2.

$4^2 \div 2 \cdot 4 = 16 \div 2 \cdot 4$ Write 4^2 as 16.

Next we multiply or divide *in order* from left to right. Since division appears before multiplication from left to right, we divide first, then multiply.

$16 \div 2 \cdot 4 = 8 \cdot 4$ Divide.

$\qquad\qquad = 32$ Multiply.

▣ **Work Practice Problem 13**

PRACTICE PROBLEM 14

Simplify: $(9 - 8)^3 + 3 \cdot 2^4$

EXAMPLE 14 Simplify: $(8 - 6)^2 + 2^3 \cdot 3$

Solution: $(8 - 6)^2 + 2^3 \cdot 3 = 2^2 + 2^3 \cdot 3$ Simplify inside parentheses.

$\qquad\qquad = 4 + 8 \cdot 3$ Write 2^2 as 4 and 2^3 as 8.

$\qquad\qquad = 4 + 24$ Multiply.

$\qquad\qquad = 28$ Add.

▣ **Work Practice Problem 14**

PRACTICE PROBLEM 15

Simplify:
$24 \div [20 - (3 \cdot 4)] + 2^3 - 5$

EXAMPLE 15 Simplify: $4^3 + [3^2 - (10 \div 2)] - 7 \cdot 3$

Solution: Here we begin with the innermost set of parentheses.

$4^3 + [3^2 - (10 \div 2)] - 7 \cdot 3 = 4^3 + [3^2 - 5] - 7 \cdot 3$ Simplify inside parentheses.

$\qquad\qquad = 4^3 + [9 - 5] - 7 \cdot 3$ Write 3^3 as 9.

$\qquad\qquad = 4^3 + 4 - 7 \cdot 3$ Simplify inside brackets.

$\qquad\qquad = 64 + 4 - 7 \cdot 3$ Write 4^3 as 64.

$\qquad\qquad = 64 + 4 - 21$ Multiply.

$\qquad\qquad = 47$ Add and subtract from left to right.

▣ **Work Practice Problem 15**

PRACTICE PROBLEM 16

Simplify: $\dfrac{49 + 4 \cdot 3 - 5^2}{3(1 + 1)}$

EXAMPLE 16 Simplify: $\dfrac{7 - 2 \cdot 3 + 3^2}{5(2 - 1)}$

Solution: Here, the fraction bar is like a grouping symbol. We simplify above and below the fraction bar separately.

$\dfrac{7 - 2 \cdot 3 + 3^2}{5(2 - 1)} = \dfrac{7 - 2 \cdot 3 + 9}{5(1)}$ Evaluate 3^2 and $(2 - 1)$.

$\qquad = \dfrac{7 - 6 + 9}{5}$ Multiply $2 \cdot 3$ in the numerator and add 4 and 1 in the denominator.

$\qquad = \dfrac{10}{5}$ Add and subtract from left to right.

$\qquad = 2$ Divide.

▣ **Work Practice Problem 16**

Answers

13. 48, **14.** 49, **15.** 6, **16.** 6

EXAMPLE 17 Simplify: $64 \div \sqrt{64} \cdot 2 + 4$

Solution: $64 \div \sqrt{64} \cdot 2 + 4 = \underbrace{64 \div 8} \cdot 2 + 4$ Find the square root.

$= \underbrace{8 \cdot 2} + 4$ Divide.

$= 16 + 4$ Multiply.

$= 20$ Add.

■ **Work Practice Problem 17**

PRACTICE PROBLEM 17

Simplify: $81 \div \sqrt{81} \cdot 5 + 7$

Objective **E** Finding the Area of a Square

Since a square is a special rectangle, we can find its area by finding the product of its length and its width.

Area of a rectangle = length · width

By recalling that each side of a square has the same measurement, we can use the following procedure to find its area:

Area of a square = length · width

$= $ side · side

$= (\text{side})^2$

EXAMPLE 18 Find the area of a square whose side measures 5 inches.

Solution: Area of a square $= (\text{side})^2$

$= (5 \text{ inches})^2$

$= 25 \text{ square inches}$

The area of the square is 25 square inches.

■ **Work Practice Problem 18**

PRACTICE PROBLEM 18

Find the area of a square whose side measures 11 centimeters.

Answers

17. 52, **18.** 121 sq cm

🖩 CALCULATOR EXPLORATIONS

Exponents

To evaluate an exponent such as 4^7 on a calculator, find the keys marked $\boxed{y^x}$ or $\boxed{\wedge}$ and $\boxed{=}$ or $\boxed{\text{ENTER}}$. To evaluate 4^7, press the keys $\boxed{4}$ $\boxed{y^x}$ (or $\boxed{\wedge}$) $\boxed{7}$ $\boxed{=}$ or $\boxed{\text{ENTER}}$. The display will read $\boxed{16384}$. Thus, $4^7 = 16,384$.

Use a calculator to evaluate.

1. 3^6 **2.** 5^6 **3.** 4^5

4. 7^6 **5.** 2^{11} **6.** 6^8

Order of Operations

To see whether your calculator has the order of operations built in, evaluate $5 + 2 \cdot 3$ by pressing the keys $\boxed{5}$ $\boxed{+}$ $\boxed{2}$ $\boxed{\times}$ $\boxed{3}$ $\boxed{=}$ or $\boxed{\text{ENTER}}$. If the display reads $\boxed{11}$, your calculator does have the order of operations

built in. This means that most of the time you can key in a problem exactly as it is written and the calculator will perform operations in the proper order. When evaluating an expression containing parentheses, key in the parentheses. (If an expression contains brackets, key in parentheses.) For example, to evaluate $2[25 - (8 + 4)] - 11$, press the keys $\boxed{2}$ $\boxed{\times}$ $\boxed{(}$ $\boxed{25}$ $\boxed{-}$ $\boxed{(}$ $\boxed{8}$ $\boxed{+}$ $\boxed{4}$ $\boxed{)}$ $\boxed{)}$ $\boxed{-}$ $\boxed{11}$ $\boxed{=}$ or $\boxed{\text{ENTER}}$.

The display will read $\boxed{15}$.

Use a calculator to evaluate.

7. $7^4 + 5^3$

8. $12^4 - 8^4$

9. $63 \cdot 75 - 43 \cdot 10$

10. $8 \cdot 22 + 7 \cdot 16$

11. $4(15 \div 3 + 2) - 10 \cdot 2$

12. $155 - 2(17 + 3) + 185$

1.9 EXERCISE SET

FOR EXTRA HELP

 Student Solutions Manual

 PH Math/Tutor Center

 CD/Video for Review

Math*XL*
MathXL®

MyMathLab
MyMathLab

Objective **A** *Write using exponential notation. See Examples 1 through 4.*

1. $3 \cdot 3 \cdot 3 \cdot 3$

2. $5 \cdot 5 \cdot 5$

3. $7 \cdot 7 \cdot 7 \cdot 7 \cdot 7 \cdot 7 \cdot 7 \cdot 7$

4. $6 \cdot 6 \cdot 6 \cdot 6 \cdot 6$

5. $12 \cdot 12 \cdot 12$

6. $10 \cdot 10$

7. $6 \cdot 6 \cdot 5 \cdot 5 \cdot 5$

8. $4 \cdot 4 \cdot 4 \cdot 3 \cdot 3$

9. $9 \cdot 9 \cdot 9 \cdot 8$

10. $7 \cdot 7 \cdot 7 \cdot 4$

11. $3 \cdot 2 \cdot 2 \cdot 2 \cdot 2 \cdot 2$

12. $4 \cdot 6 \cdot 6 \cdot 6 \cdot 6$

13. $3 \cdot 2 \cdot 2 \cdot 5 \cdot 5 \cdot 5$

14. $6 \cdot 6 \cdot 2 \cdot 9 \cdot 9 \cdot 9 \cdot 9$

Objective **B** *Evaluate. See Examples 5 through 8.*

15. 7^2

16. 6^2

17. 5^3

18. 6^3

19. 2^6

20. 2^7

21. 1^{10}

22. 1^{12}

23. 7^1

24. 8^1

25. 3^5

26. 5^4

27. 2^8

28. 3^3

29. 4^3

30. 4^4

31. 9^2

32. 12^2

33. 9^3

34. 8^3

35. 10^2

36. 10^3

37. 20^1

38. 14^1

39. 3^6

40. 4^5

41. $3 \cdot 2^4$

42. $5 \cdot 3^2$

43. $2 \cdot 3^3$

44. $2 \cdot 7^2$

Objective **C** *Find each square root. See Examples 9 through 11.*

45. $\sqrt{9}$ **46.** $\sqrt{36}$ **47.** $\sqrt{64}$ **48.** $\sqrt{121}$

49. $\sqrt{144}$ **50.** $\sqrt{0}$ **51.** $\sqrt{16}$ **52.** $\sqrt{169}$

Objective **D** *Simplify. See Examples 12 through 16. (This section does not contain square roots.)*

53. $15 + 3 \cdot 2$ **54.** $24 + 6 \cdot 3$ **55.** $28 \div 7 \cdot 2 + 3$ **56.** $100 \div 10 \cdot 5 + 4$

57. $28 \div 4 - 3$ **58.** $42 \div 7 - 6$ **59.** $14 + \dfrac{24}{8}$ **60.** $32 + \dfrac{8}{2}$

61. $6 \cdot 5 + 8 \cdot 2$ **62.** $3 \cdot 4 + 9 \cdot 1$ **63.** $\dfrac{6 + 8 \div 2}{1^7}$ **64.** $\dfrac{6 + 9 \div 3}{3^2}$

65. $(3 + 5^2) \div 2 \cdot 3^2$ **66.** $(13 + 6^2) \div 7 \cdot 4^2$ **67.** $6^2 \cdot (10 - 8) + 2^3 + 5^2$

68. $5^3 \div (10 + 15) + 9^2 + 3^3$ **69.** $\dfrac{18 + 6}{2^4 - 2^2}$ **70.** $\dfrac{15 + 17}{5^2 - 3^2}$

71. $(2 + 5) \cdot (8 - 3)$ **72.** $(9 - 7) \cdot (12 + 18)$ **73.** $\dfrac{7(9 - 6) + 3}{3^2 - 3}$

74. $\dfrac{5(12 - 7) - 4}{5^2 - 18}$ **75.** $5 \div 0 + 24$ **76.** $18 - 7 \div 0$

77. $2^3 \cdot 4 - (10 \div 5)$ **78.** $2^4 \cdot 3 - (100 \div 10)$ **79.** $3^4 - [35 - (12 - 6)]$

80. $[40 - (8 - 2)] - 2^5$ **81.** $(7 \cdot 5) + [9 \div (3 \div 3)]$ **82.** $(18 \div 6) + [(3 + 5) \cdot 2]$

83. $8 \cdot [2^2 + (6 - 1) \cdot 2] - 50 \cdot 2$ **84.** $35 \div [3^2 + (9 - 7) - 2^2] + 10 \cdot 3$

85. $\dfrac{9^2 + 2^2 - 1^2}{8 \div 2 \cdot 3 \cdot 1 \div 3}$ **86.** $\dfrac{5^2 - 2^3 + 1^4}{10 \div 5 \cdot 4 \cdot 1 \div 4}$

Simplify. See Examples 12 through 17. (This section does contain square roots.)

87. $6 \cdot \sqrt{9} + 3 \cdot \sqrt{4}$ **88.** $3 \cdot \sqrt{25} + 2 \cdot \sqrt{81}$ **89.** $4 \cdot \sqrt{49} - 0 \div \sqrt{100}$

90. $7 \cdot \sqrt{36} - 0 \div \sqrt{64}$ **91.** $\dfrac{\sqrt{4} + 4^2}{5(20 - 16) - 3^2 - 5}$ **92.** $\dfrac{\sqrt{9} + 9^2}{3(10 - 6) - 2^2 - 1}$

93. $\sqrt{81} \div \sqrt{9} + 4^2 \cdot 2 - 10$ **94.** $\sqrt{100} \div \sqrt{4} + 3^3 \cdot 2 - 20$

95. $[\sqrt{225} \div (11 - 6) + 2^2] + (\sqrt{25} - \sqrt{1})^2$ **96.** $[\sqrt{169} \div (20 - 7) + 2^5] - (\sqrt{4} + \sqrt{9})^2$

97. $7^2 - \{18 - [40 \div (4 \cdot 2) + \sqrt{4}] + 5^2\}$ **98.** $29 - \{5 + 3[8 \cdot (10 - \sqrt{64})] - 50\}$

Objective **E** *Find the area of each square. See Example 18.*

△ **99.**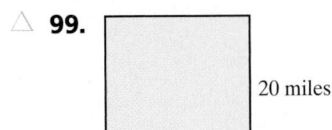

20 miles

△ **100.**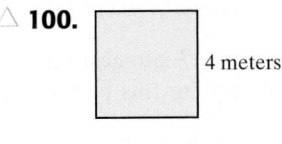

4 meters

△ **101.**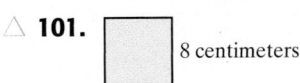

8 centimeters

△ **102.**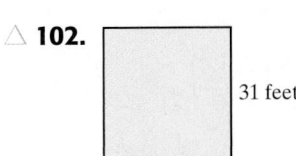

31 feet

Concept Extensions

Answer the following true or false. See the Concept Check in this section.

103. "Five to the sixth power" is the same as 6^5.

104. "Seven cubed" is the same as 7^3.

105. 2^5 is the same as $5 \cdot 5$.

106. 4^9 is the same as $4 \cdot 9$.

Insert grouping symbols (parentheses) so that each given expression evaluates to the given number.

107. $2 + 3 \cdot 6 - 2$; evaluate to 28

108. $2 + 3 \cdot 6 - 2$; evaluate to 20

109. $24 \div 3 \cdot 2 + 2 \cdot 5$; evaluate to 14

110. $24 \div 3 \cdot 2 + 2 \cdot 5$; evaluate to 15

△ **111.** A building contractor is bidding on a contract to install gutters on seven homes in a retirement community, all in the shape shown. To estimate the cost of materials, she needs to know the total perimeter of all seven homes. Find the total perimeter.

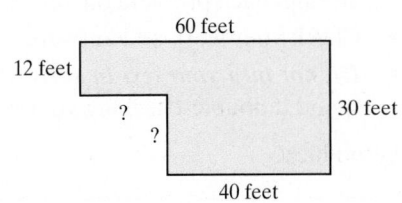

Simplify.

▦ **112.** $25^3 \cdot (45 - 7 \cdot 5) \cdot 5$

▦ **113.** $(7 + 2^4)^5 - (3^5 - 2^4)^2$

114. Explain why $2 \cdot 3^2$ is not the same as $(2 \cdot 3)^2$.

115. Write an expression that simplifies to 5. Use multiplication, division, addition, subtraction, and at least one set of parentheses.

THE BIGGER PICTURE   Operations on Sets of Numbers

Continue your outline started in Section 1.7. Suggestions are once again written to help you complete this part of your outline.

I. **Some Operations on Sets of Numbers**

   A. **Whole Numbers**

      1. **Add or Subtract** (Sections 1.3, 1.4)

      2. **Multiply or Divide** (Sections 1.6, 1.7)

      3. **Exponent:** $3^4 = \overbrace{3 \cdot 3 \cdot 3 \cdot 3}^{\text{4 factors of 3}} = 81$

      4. **Square Root:** $\sqrt{25} = 5 \ because \ 5 \cdot 5 = 25$

      5. **Order of Operations:**

         $24 \div 3 \cdot 2 - (2 + 8)$

         $= 24 \div 3 \cdot 2 - (10)$ Parentheses.

         $= 8 \cdot 2 - 10$ Multiply or divide from left to right.

         $= 16 - 10$ Multiply or divide from left to right.

         $= 6$ Add or subtract from left to right.

Perform the indicated operations.

1. 4^3

2. $2^3 \cdot 6^1$

3. $\sqrt{81}$

4. $\sqrt{9} \cdot \sqrt{25}$

5. $2 + 5(10 - 6)$

6. $20 \div 2 \cdot 5$

7. $867 - 179$

8. $\begin{array}{r} 72 \\ \times\, 30 \\ \hline \end{array}$

9. $626 \div 58$

10. $3[(7 - 3)^2 - (25 - 22)^2] + \sqrt{36}$

 STUDY SKILLS BUILDER

What to Do the Day of an Exam?

Your first exam may be soon. On the day of an exam, don't forget to try the following:

- Allow yourself plenty of time to arrive.
- Read the directions on the test carefully.
- Read each problem carefully as you take your test. Make sure that you answer the question asked.
- Watch your time and pace yourself so that you may attempt each problem on your test.
- Check your work and answers.
- ***Do not turn your test in early.*** If you have extra time, spend it double-checking your work.

Good luck!

Answer the following questions based on your most recent mathematics exam, whenever that was.

1. How soon before class did you arrive?

2. Did you read the directions on the test carefully?

3. Did you make sure you answered the question asked for each problem on the exam?

4. Were you able to attempt each problem on your exam?

5. If your answer to question 4 is no, list reasons why.

6. Did you have extra time on your exam?

7. If your answer to question 6 is yes, describe how you spent that extra time.

CHAPTER 1 Group Activity

Modeling Subtraction of Whole Numbers

A mathematical concept can be represented or modeled in many different ways. For instance, subtraction can be represented by the following symbolic model:

11 − 4

The following verbal models can also represent subtraction of these same quantities:

"Four subtracted from eleven" or
"Eleven take away four"

Physical models can also represent mathematical concepts. In these models, a number is represented by that many objects. For example, the number 5 can be represented by five pennies, squares, paper clips, tiles, or bottle caps.

A physical representation of the number 5

Take-Away Model for Subtraction: 11 − 4

- Start with 11 objects.
- Take 4 objects away.
- How many objects remain?

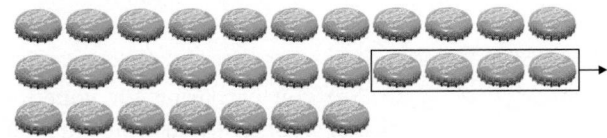

Comparison Model for Subtraction: 11 − 4

- Start with a set of 11 of one type of object and a set of 4 of another type of object.

- Make as many pairs that include one object of each type as possible.

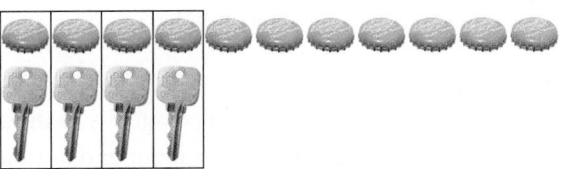

- How many more objects left are in the larger set?

Missing Addend Model for Subtraction: 11 − 4

- Start with 4 objects.
- Continue adding objects until a total of 11 is reached.
- How many more objects were needed to give a total of 11?

Group Activity

Use an appropriate physical model for subtraction to solve each of the following problems. Explain your reasoning for choosing each model.

1. Sneha has assembled 12 computer components so far this shift. If his quota is 20 components, how many more components must he assemble to reach his quota?

2. Yuko has 14 daffodil bulbs to plant in her yard. She planted 5 bulbs in the front yard. How many bulbs does she have left for planting in the backyard?

3. Todd is 19 years old and his sister Tanya is 13 years old. How much older is Todd than Tanya?

Chapter 1 Vocabulary Check

Fill in each blank with one of the words or phrases listed below.

difference	area	square root	addend	divisor	minuend
place value	factor	quotient	subtrahend	exponent	digits
sum	whole numbers	perimeter	dividend	product	

1. The _____ are 0, 1, 2, 3, . . .
2. The _____ of a polygon is its distance around or the sum of the lengths of its sides.
3. The position of each digit in a number determines its _____.
4. An _____ is a shorthand notation for repeated multiplication of the same factor.
5. To find the _____ of a rectangle, multiply length times width.
6. A _____ of a number is one of two identical factors of the number.
7. The _____ used to write numbers are 0, 1, 2, 3, 4, 5, 6, 7, 8, and 9.

Use the facts below for Exercises 8 through 17.

$$2 \cdot 3 = 6 \qquad 4 + 17 = 21 \qquad 20 - 9 = 11 \qquad 5\overset{7}{\overline{)35}}$$

8. The 21 above is called the _____.
9. The 5 above is called the _____.
10. The 35 above is called the _____.
11. The 7 above is called the _____.
12. The 3 above is called a _____.
13. The 6 above is called the _____.
14. The 20 above is called the _____.
15. The 9 above is called the _____.
16. The 11 above is called the _____.
17. The 4 above is called an _____.

Helpful Hint

Are you preparing for your test? Don't forget to take the Chapter 1 Test on page 109. Then check your answers at the back of the text and use the Chapter Test Prep Video CD to see the fully worked-out solutions to any of the exercises you want to review.

1 Chapter Highlights

DEFINITIONS AND CONCEPTS	EXAMPLES
Section 1.2 Place Value and Names for Numbers	

The **whole numbers** are 0, 1, 2, 3, 4, 5, . . .

The position of each digit in a number determines its **place value.** A place-value chart is shown next with the names of the periods given.

Periods			
Billions	Millions	Thousands	Ones

Hundred-billions, Ten-billions, Billions, Hundred-millions, Ten-millions, Millions, Hundred-thousands, Ten-thousands, Thousands, Hundreds, Tens, Ones

0, 14, 968, 5,268,619

DEFINITIONS AND CONCEPTS	**EXAMPLES**

Section 1.2   Place Value and Names for Numbers (*continued*)

To write a whole number in words, write the number in each period followed by the name of the period. (The name of the ones period is not included.)

To write a whole number in standard form, write the number in each period, followed by a comma.

9,078,651,002 is written as nine billion, seventy-eight million, six hundred fifty-one thousand, two.

Four million, seven hundred six thousand, twenty-eight is written as 4,706,028.

Section 1.3   Adding Whole Numbers and Perimeter

To add whole numbers, add the digits in the ones place, then the tens place, then the hundreds place, and so on, carrying when necessary.

Find the sum:

$$
\begin{array}{r}
{\scriptstyle 2\,1\,1} \\
2689 \leftarrow \text{addend} \\
1735 \leftarrow \text{addend} \\
+\ 662 \leftarrow \text{addend} \\
\hline
5086 \leftarrow \text{sum}
\end{array}
$$

The **perimeter** of a polygon is its distance around or the sum of the lengths of its sides.

Find the perimeter of the polygon shown.

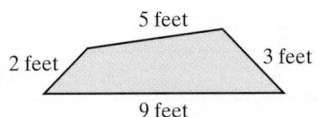

The perimeter is 5 feet + 3 feet + 9 feet + 2 feet = 19 feet.

Section 1.4   Subtracting Whole Numbers

To subtract whole numbers, subtract the digits in the ones place, then the tens place, then the hundreds place, and so on, borrowing when necessary.

Subtract:

$$
\begin{array}{r}
{\scriptstyle 8\ 15} \\
7\,9\,5\,4 \leftarrow \text{minuend} \\
-5\,6\,7\,3 \leftarrow \text{subtrahend} \\
\hline
2\,2\,8\,1 \leftarrow \text{difference}
\end{array}
$$

Section 1.5   Rounding and Estimating

ROUNDING WHOLE NUMBERS TO A GIVEN PLACE VALUE

Step 1. Locate the digit to the right of the given place value.

Step 2. If this digit is 5 or greater, add 1 to the digit in the given place value and replace each digit to its right with 0.

Step 3. If this digit is less than 5, replace it and each digit to its right with 0.

Round 15,721 to the nearest thousand.

15,⑦21   Since the circled digit is 5 or greater, add 1 to the given place value and replace digits to its right with zeros.

Add 1 ⤴   Replace with zeros.

15,721 rounded to the nearest thousand is 16,000.

Section 1.6   Multiplying Whole Numbers and Area

To multiply 73 and 58, for example, multiply 73 and 8, then 73 and 50. The sum of these partial products is the product of 73 and 58. Use the notation to the right.

$$
\begin{array}{r}
73 \leftarrow \text{factor} \\
\times\ 58 \leftarrow \text{factor} \\
\hline
584 \leftarrow 73 \times 8 \\
3650 \leftarrow 73 \times 50 \\
\hline
4234 \leftarrow \text{product}
\end{array}
$$

continued

DEFINITIONS AND CONCEPTS	**EXAMPLES**

Section 1.6   Multiplying Whole Numbers and Area (*continued*)

To find the **area** of a rectangle, multiply length times width.

Find the area of the rectangle shown.

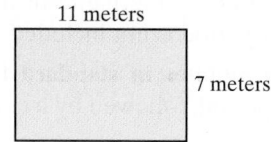

11 meters

7 meters

$$\text{area of rectangle} = \text{length} \cdot \text{width}$$
$$= (11 \text{ meters})(7 \text{ meters})$$
$$= 77 \text{ square meters}$$

To multiply by 10, 100, 1000, and so on, form the product by attaching the number of 0s in that number to the other factor.

$39 \cdot 1000 = 39{,}000$

Attach 3 zeros.

$200 \cdot 4000 = 800{,}000$ Attach 5 zeros.

$2 \cdot 4$

Section 1.7   Dividing Whole Numbers

DIVISION PROPERTIES OF 0

The quotient of 0 and any number (except 0) is 0.

The quotient of any number and 0 is not a number. We say that this quotient is undefined.

$\dfrac{0}{5} = 0$

$\dfrac{7}{0}$ is undefined

To divide larger whole numbers, use the process called **long division** as shown to the right.

$$
\begin{array}{r}
507 \text{ R } 2 \leftarrow \text{quotient} \\
\text{divisor} \rightarrow 14)\overline{7100} \leftarrow \text{dividend} \\
-70 \downarrow \qquad 5(14) = 70 \\
\overline{10} \qquad \text{Subtract and bring down the 0.} \\
-0 \downarrow \qquad 0(14) = 0 \\
\overline{100} \qquad \text{Subtract and bring down the 0.} \\
-98 \qquad 7(14) = 98 \\
\overline{2} \qquad \text{Subtract. The remainder is 2.}
\end{array}
$$

To check, see that $507 \cdot 14 + 2 = 7100$.

The **average** of a list of numbers is

$$\text{average} = \frac{\text{sum of numbers}}{\text{number of numbers}}$$

Find the average of 23, 35, and 38.

$$\text{average} = \frac{23 + 35 + 38}{3} = \frac{96}{3} = 32$$

Section 1.8   An Introduction to Problem Solving

PROBLEM-SOLVING STEPS

1. UNDERSTAND the problem.

Suppose that 225 tickets are sold for each performance of a play. How many tickets are sold for 5 performances?

1. UNDERSTAND. Read and reread the problem. Since we want the number of tickets for 5 performances, we multiply.

DEFINITIONS AND CONCEPTS	EXAMPLES

Section 1.8   An Introduction to Problem Solving (*continued*)

2. TRANSLATE the problem.

2. TRANSLATE.

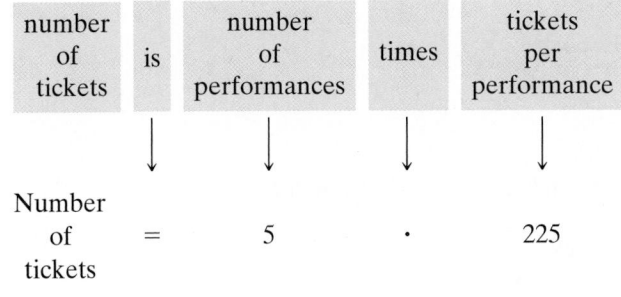

number of tickets	is	number of performances	times	tickets per performance
Number of tickets	=	5	·	225

3. SOLVE the problem.

3. SOLVE: See if the answer is reasonable by also estimating.

$$\begin{array}{r} \overset{1\,2}{225} \\ \times\ \ 5 \\ \hline 1125 \end{array} \text{exact} \qquad \begin{array}{r} 200 \\ \times\ \ 5 \\ \hline 1000 \end{array} \text{estimate}$$

225 rounds to 200

4. INTERPRET the results.

4. INTERPRET. **Check** your work. The product is reasonable since 1125 is close to our estimated answer of 1000, and **state** your conclusion: There are 1125 tickets sold for 5 performances.

Section 1.9   Exponents, Square Roots, and Order of Operations

An **exponent** is a shorthand notation for repeated multiplication of the same factor.

$$3^4 = \underbrace{3 \cdot 3 \cdot 3 \cdot 3}_{\text{4 factors of 3}} = 81$$

exponent, base

A **square root** of a number is one of two identical factors of the number.

$\sqrt{36} = 6$ because $6 \cdot 6 = 36$

$\sqrt{121} = 11$ because $11 \cdot 11 = 121$

$\sqrt{0} = 0$ because $0 \cdot 0 = 0$

ORDER OF OPERATIONS

1. Perform all operations within parentheses ( ), brackets [ ], or other grouping symbols such as square roots or fraction bars.
2. Evaluate any expressions with exponents.
3. Multiply or divide in order from left to right.
4. Add or subtract in order from left to right.

Simplify: $\dfrac{5 + 3^2}{2(7 - 6)}$

Simplify above and below the fraction bar separately.

$$\frac{5 + 3^2}{2(7 - 6)} = \frac{5 + 9}{2(1)} \quad \begin{array}{l}\text{Evaluate } 3^2 \text{ above the fraction bar.} \\ \text{Subtract: } 7 - 6 \text{ below the fraction bar.}\end{array}$$

$$= \frac{14}{2} \quad \text{Add.}$$

$$\quad\quad \text{Multiply.}$$

$$= 7 \quad \text{Divide.}$$

The **area of a square** is $(\text{side})^2$.

Find the area of a square with side length 9 inches.

$$\text{Area of the square} = (\text{side})^2$$
$$= (9 \text{ inches})^2$$
$$= 81 \text{ square inches}$$

1 CHAPTER REVIEW

(1.2) *Determine the place value of the digit 4 in each whole number.*

1. 5480

2. 46,200,120

Write each whole number in words.

3. 5480

4. 46,200,120

Write each whole number in expanded form.

5. 6279

6. 403,225,000

Write each whole number in standard form.

7. Fifty-nine thousand, eight hundred

8. Six billion, three hundred four million

The following table shows the populations of the ten largest cities in the United States. Use this table to answer Exercises 9 and 10 and other exercises throughout this review.

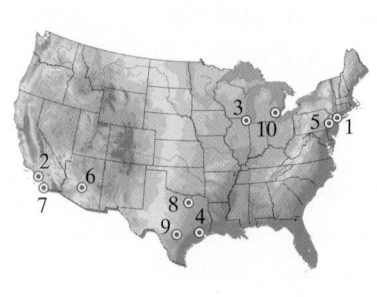

Rank	City	2000	1990	1980
1	New York, NY	8,008,278	7,322,564	7,071,639
2	Los Angeles, CA	3,694,820	3,485,398	2,968,528
3	Chicago, IL	2,896,016	2,783,726	3,005,072
4	Houston, TX	1,953,631	1,630,553	1,595,138
5	Philadelphia, PA	1,517,550	1,585,577	1,688,210
6	Phoenix, AZ	1,321,045	983,403	789,704
7	San Diego, CA	1,223,400	1,110,549	875,538
8	Dallas, TX	1,188,580	1,006,877	904,599
9	San Antonio, TX	1,144,646	935,933	785,940
10	Detroit, MI	951,270	1,027,974	1,203,368

(*Source:* U.S. Census Bureau)

9. Find the population of Houston, Texas, in 1990.

10. Find the population of Los Angeles, California, in 1980.

11. Which city had the smallest population in 1990?

12. Which city had the largest population in 1990?

(1.3) *Add.*

13. 17 + 46   **14.** 28 + 39   **15.** 25 + 8 + 15   **16.** 27 + 9 + 41   **17.** 932 + 24

18. 819 + 21   **19.** 567 + 7383   **20.** 463 + 6787   **21.** 91 + 3623 + 497   **22.** 82 + 1647 + 238

Solve.

23. Find the sum of 86, 331, and 909.

24. Find the sum of 49, 529, and 308.

25. What is 26,481 increased by 865?

26. What is 38,556 increased by 744?

27. The distance from Chicago to New York City is 714 miles. The distance from New York City to New Delhi, India, is 7318 miles. Find the total distance from Chicago to New Delhi if traveling by air through New York City.

28. Susan Summerline earned salaries of $62,589, $65,340, and $69,770 during the years 2002, 2003, and 2004, respectively. Find her total earnings during those three years.

Find the perimeter of each figure.

△ **29.**

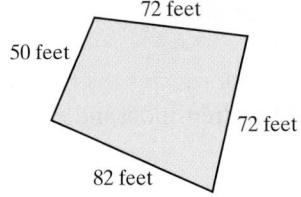

72 feet
50 feet
72 feet
82 feet

△ **30.**

11 kilometers   20 kilometers
35 kilometers

(1.4) *Subtract and then check.*

31. 93 − 79   **32.** 61 − 27   **33.** 462 − 397   **34.** 583 − 279   **35.** 4000 − 86   **36.** 8000 − 92

Solve.

37. Subtract 7965 from 25,862.

38. Subtract 4349 from 39,007.

Use the city population table for Exercises 39 and 40.

39. Find the increase in population for Phoenix, Arizona, from 1980 to 2000.

40. Find the decrease in population for Detroit, Michigan, from 1990 to 2000.

41. Bob Roma is proofreading the Yellow Pages for his county. If he has finished 315 pages of the total 712 pages, how many pages does he have left to proofread?

42. Shelly Winters bought a new car listed at $28,425. She received a discount of $1599 and a factory rebate of $1200. Find how much she paid for the car.

The following bar graph shows the monthly savings account balance for a freshman attending a local community college. Use this graph to answer Exercises 43 through 46.

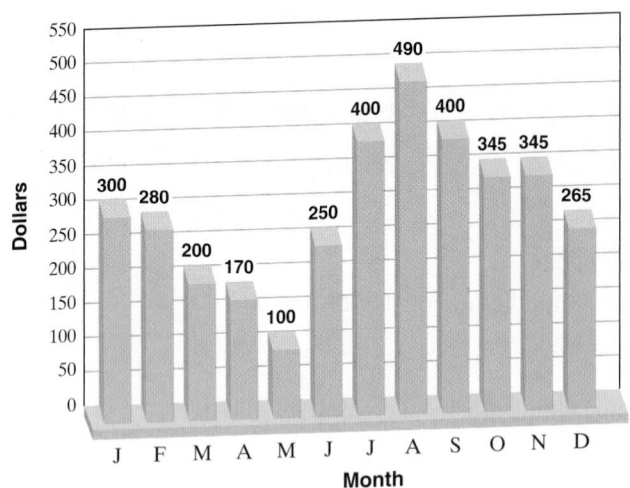

43. During what month was the balance the least?

44. During what month was the balance the greatest?

45. By how much did his balance decrease from February to April?

46. By how much did his balance increase from June to August?

(1.5) *Round to the given place.*

47. 93 to the nearest ten

48. 45 to the nearest ten

49. 467 to the nearest ten

50. 493 to the nearest hundred

51. 4832 to the nearest hundred

52. 57,534 to the nearest thousand

53. 49,683,712 to the nearest million

54. 768,542 to the nearest hundred-thousand

55. In 2003, there were 73,365,880 households in the United States subscribing to cable television services. Round this number to the nearest million. (*Source:* Nielsen Media Research-NTI)

56. In 2003, the total number of employees working for U.S. airlines was 570,868. Round this number to the nearest thousand. (*Source:* The Air Transport Association of America, Inc.)

Estimate the sum or difference by rounding each number to the nearest hundred.

57. $4892 + 647 + 1876$

58. $5925 - 1787$

59. A group of students took a week-long driving trip and traveled 628, 290, 172, 58, 508, 445, and 383 miles on seven consecutive days. Round each distance to the nearest hundred to estimate the distance they traveled.

60. According to the city population table, the 2000 population of Los Angeles was 3,694,820, and for Dallas it was 1,188,580. Round each number to the nearest hundred-thousand and estimate how much larger Los Angeles is than Dallas.

(1.6) *Multiply.*

61. 273
      $\times\ 7$

62. 349
      $\times\ 4$

63.   47
      $\times 30$

64.   69
      $\times 42$

65. $20(8)(5)$

66. $25(9)(4)$

67. $\begin{array}{r} 48 \\ \times\ 77 \\ \hline \end{array}$

68. $\begin{array}{r} 77 \\ \times\ 22 \\ \hline \end{array}$

69. $49 \cdot 49 \cdot 0$

70. $62 \cdot 88 \cdot 0$

71. $\begin{array}{r} 586 \\ \times\ 29 \\ \hline \end{array}$

72. $\begin{array}{r} 242 \\ \times\ 37 \\ \hline \end{array}$

73. $\begin{array}{r} 642 \\ \times\ 177 \\ \hline \end{array}$

74. $\begin{array}{r} 347 \\ \times\ 129 \\ \hline \end{array}$

75. $\begin{array}{r} 1026 \\ \times\ 401 \\ \hline \end{array}$

76. $\begin{array}{r} 2107 \\ \times\ 302 \\ \hline \end{array}$

77. $375 \cdot 1000$

78. $108 \cdot 1000$

79. $30 \cdot 400$

80. $50 \cdot 700$

81. $1700 \cdot 3000$

82. $1900 \cdot 4000$

Solve.

83. Find the product of 5 and 230.

84. Find the product of 6 and 820.

85. Multiply 9 and 12.

86. Multiply 8 and 14.

87. One ounce of Swiss cheese contains 8 grams of fat. How many grams of fat are in 3 ounces of Swiss cheese? (*Source: Home and Garden Bulletin No. 72*, U.S. Department of Agriculture)

88. There were 5283 students enrolled at Weskan State University in the fall semester. Each paid $927 in tuition. Find the total tuition collected.

Find the area of each rectangle.

△ **89.**

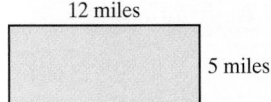

12 miles

5 miles

△ **90.** 20 centimeters

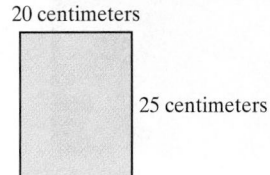

25 centimeters

(1.7) *Divide and then check.*

91. $\dfrac{18}{6}$

92. $\dfrac{36}{9}$

93. $42 \div 7$

94. $35 \div 5$

95. $27 \div 5$

96. $18 \div 4$

97. $16 \div 0$

98. $0 \div 8$

99. $9 \div 9$

100. $10 \div 1$

101. $918 \div 0$ **102.** $0 \div 668$ **103.** $5\overline{)167}$ **104.** $8\overline{)159}$ **105.** $26\overline{)626}$

106. $19\overline{)680}$ **107.** $47\overline{)23{,}792}$ **108.** $53\overline{)48{,}111}$ **109.** $207\overline{)578{,}291}$ **110.** $306\overline{)615{,}732}$

Solve.

111. Find the quotient of 92 and 5.

112. Find the quotient of 86 and 4.

113. One foot is 12 inches. Find how many feet there are in 5496 inches.

114. One mile is 1760 yards. Find how many miles there are in 22,880 yards.

115. Find the average of the numbers 76, 49, 32, and 47.

116. Find the average of the numbers 23, 85, 62, and 66.

(1.8) *Solve.*

117. A box can hold 24 cans of corn. How many boxes can be filled with 648 cans of corn?

118. If a ticket to a movie costs $6, how much do 32 tickets cost?

119. Aspirin was 100 years old in 1997 and was the first U.S. drug made in tablet form. Today, people take 11 billion tablets a year for heart disease prevention and 4 billion tablets a year for headaches. How many more tablets are taken a year for heart disease prevention? (*Source:* Bayer Market Research)

120. The cost to banks when a person uses an ATM (Automatic Teller Machine) is 27¢. The cost to banks when a person deposits a check with a teller is 48¢ more. How much is this cost?

121. A golf pro orders shirts for the company sponsoring a local charity golfing event. Shirts size large cost $32 while shirts size extra-large cost $38. If 15 large shirts and 11 extra-large shirts are ordered, find the cost.

122. Two rectangular pieces of land are purchased: one that measures 65 feet by 110 feet and one that measures 80 feet by 200 feet. Find the total area of land purchased. (*Hint:* Find the area of each rectangle, then add.)

200 feet   65 feet   80 feet   110 feet

(1.9) *Simplify.*

123. 7^2 **124.** 5^3 **125.** $5 \cdot 3^2$ **126.** $4 \cdot 10^2$

127. $18 \div 3 + 7$ **128.** $12 - 8 \div 4$ **129.** $\dfrac{5(6^2 - 3)}{3^2 + 2}$ **130.** $\dfrac{7(16 - 8)}{2^3}$

131. $48 \div 8 \cdot 2$

132. $27 \div 9 \cdot 3$

133. $2 + 3[1^5 + (20 - 17) \cdot 3] + 5 \cdot 2$

134. $21 - [2^4 - (7 - 5) - 10] + 8 \cdot 2$

Simplify. These exercises contain roots.

135. $\sqrt{81}$

136. $\sqrt{4}$

137. $\sqrt{1}$

138. $\sqrt{0}$

139. $4 \cdot \sqrt{25} - 2 \cdot 7$

140. $8 \cdot \sqrt{49} - 3 \cdot 9$

141. $\left(\sqrt{36} - \sqrt{16}\right)^3 \cdot [10^2 \div (3 + 17)]$

142. $\left(\sqrt{49} - \sqrt{25}\right)^3 \cdot [9^2 \div (2 + 7)]$

143. $\dfrac{5 \cdot 7 - 3 \cdot \sqrt{25}}{2\left(\sqrt{121} - 3^2\right)}$

144. $\dfrac{4 \cdot 8 - 1 \cdot \sqrt{121}}{3\left(\sqrt{81} - 2^3\right)}$

Find the area of each square.

△ **145.** A square with side length of 7 meters.

△ **146.**

3 inches

Mixed Review

Perform the indicated operations.

147. $375 - 68$

148. $729 - 47$

149. 723×3

150. 629×4

151. $264 + 39 + 598$

152. $593 + 52 + 766$

153. $13\overline{)5962}$

154. $18\overline{)4267}$

155. 1968×36

156. 5324×18

157. $2000 - 356$

158. $9000 - 519$

Round to the given place.

159. 736 to the nearest ten

160. 258,371 to the nearest thousand

161. 1999 to the nearest hundred

162. 44,499 to the nearest ten thousand

Write each whole number in words.

163. 36,911

164. 154,863

Write each whole number in standard form.

165. Seventy thousand, nine hundred forty-three

166. Forty-three thousand, four hundred one

Simplify.

167. 4^3

168. 5^3

169. $\sqrt{144}$

170. $\sqrt{100}$

171. $24 \div 4 \cdot 2$

172. $\sqrt{256} - 3 \cdot 5$

173. $\dfrac{8(7-4)-10}{4^2-3^2}$

174. $\dfrac{(15+\sqrt{9})\cdot(8-5)}{2^3+1}$

Solve.

175. 36 divided by 9 is what number?

176. What is the product of 2 and 12?

177. 16 increased by 8 is what number?

178. 7 subtracted from 21 is what number?

The following table shows the top-grossing movies for 2003 and 2004. Use this table to answer Exercises 179 and 180.

Movie (2003)	Gross	Movie (2004)	Gross
The Lord of the Rings: The Return of the King	$377,019,000	Shrek 2	$436,471,000
Finding Nemo	$339,714,000	Spider-Man 2	$373,378,000
Pirates of the Caribbean: The Curse of the Black Pearl	$305,389,000	The Passion of the Christ	$370,275,000
The Matrix Reloaded	$281,492,000	Harry Potter and the Prisoner of Azkaban	$249,359,000
Bruce Almighty	$242,590,000	The Incredibles	$242,426,000
(*Source:* Internet Movie Database)			

179. How much more did the top grossing film in 2004 make than the top-grossing film in 2003?

180. Find the total gross of the animated films *Finding Nemo* and *The Incredibles*.

181. A manufacturer of drinking glasses ships his delicate stock in special boxes that can hold 32 glasses. If 1714 glasses are manufactured, how many full boxes are filled? Are there any glasses left over?

182. A teacher orders 2 small white boards for $27 each and 8 boxes of dry erase pens for $4 each. What is her total bill before taxes?

CHAPTER TEST

 Use the Chapter Test Prep Video CD to see the fully worked-out solutions to any of the exercises you want to review.

Answers

Simplify.

1. Write 82,426 in words.

2. Write "four hundred two thousand, five hundred fifty" in standard form.

3. $59 + 82$

4. $600 - 487$

5. $\begin{array}{r} 496 \\ \times\ \ 30 \\ \hline \end{array}$

6. $52,896 \div 69$

7. $2^3 \cdot 5^2$

8. $\sqrt{4} \cdot \sqrt{25}$

9. $0 \div 49$

10. $62 \div 0$

11. $(2^4 - 5) \cdot 3$

12. $16 + 9 \div 3 \cdot 4 - 7$

13. $\dfrac{64 \div 8 \cdot 2}{\left(\sqrt{9} - \sqrt{4}\right)^2 + 1}$

14. $2[(6 - 4)^2 + (22 - 19)^2] + 10$

15. $5698 \cdot 1000$

16. $8000 \cdot 1400$

17. Round 52,369 to the nearest thousand.

Estimate each sum or difference by rounding each number to the nearest hundred.

18. $6289 + 5403 + 1957$

19. $4267 - 2738$

1. _____

2. _____

3. _____

4. _____

5. _____

6. _____

7. _____

8. _____

9. _____

10. _____

11. _____

12. _____

13. _____

14. _____

15. _____

16. _____

17. _____

18. _____

19. _____

Solve.

20. _____

20. Subtract 15 from 107.

21. Find the sum of 15 and 107.

21. _____

22. _____

22. Find the product of 15 and 107.

23. Find the quotient of 107 and 15.

23. _____

24. _____

24. Twenty-nine cans of Sherwin-Williams paint cost $493. How much was each can?

25. Jo McElory is looking at two new refrigerators for her apartment. One costs $599 and the other costs $725. How much more expensive is the higher-priced one?

25. _____

26. _____

26. One tablespoon of white granulated sugar contains 45 calories. How many calories are in 8 tablespoons of white granulated sugar? (*Source: Home and Garden Bulletin No. 72*, U.S. Department of Agriculture)

27. A small business owner recently ordered 16 digital cameras that cost $430 each and 5 printers that cost $205 each. Find the total cost for these items.

27. _____

28. _____

Find the perimeter and the area of each figure.

△ **28.**

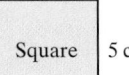

Square | 5 centimeters

△ **29.**   20 yards

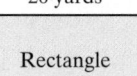

Rectangle | 10 yards

29. _____

2

Multiplying and Dividing Fractions

Fractions are numbers, and like whole numbers, they can be added, subtracted, multiplied, and divided. Fractions are very useful and appear frequently in everyday language, in common phrases like "half an hour," "quarter of a pound," and "third of a cup." This chapter introduces the concept of fractions, presents some basic vocabulary, and demonstrates how to multiply and divide fractions.

S ales of digital cameras are increasing as prices decrease and quality and ease of use increase.
    In Section 2.4, Exercise 89, we calculate the face area of the currently smallest digital camera.

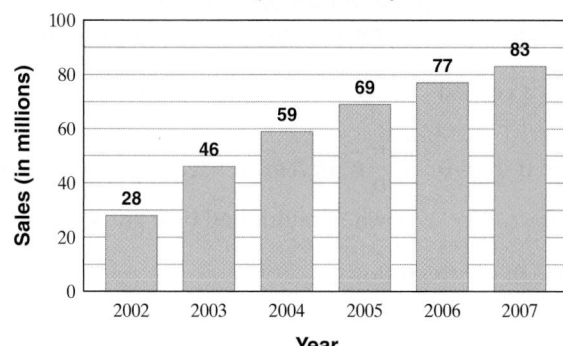

World-wide Sales of Digital Cameras (in millions)

Source: IDC; '05, '06, '07 are projected

A Identify the Numerator and the Denominator of a Fraction and Review Division Properties for 0 and 1.

B Write a Fraction to Represent the Shaded Part of a Figure.

C Identify Proper Fractions, Improper Fractions, and Mixed Numbers.

D Write Mixed Numbers as Improper Fractions.

E Write Improper Fractions as Mixed Numbers or Whole Numbers.

2.1 INTRODUCTION TO FRACTIONS AND MIXED NUMBERS

Objective **A** Identifying Numerators and Denominators and Reviewing Division Properties for 0 and 1

Whole numbers are used to count whole things or units, such as cars, horses, dollars, and people. To refer to a part of a whole, fractions can be used. Here are some examples of **fractions.** Study these examples for a moment.

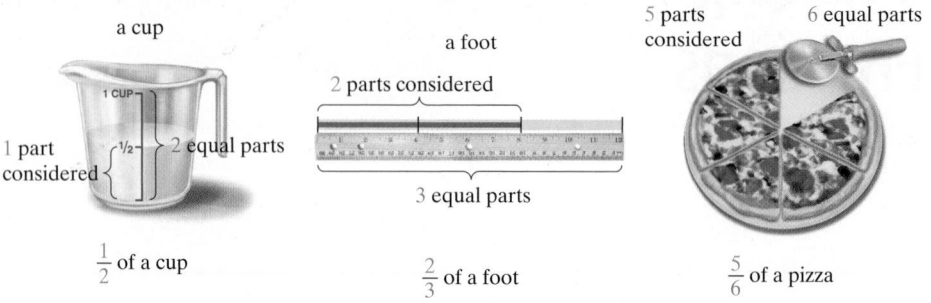

| a cup | a foot | 5 parts considered | 6 equal parts |

1 part considered
$\frac{1}{2}$ of a cup

2 parts considered
3 equal parts
$\frac{2}{3}$ of a foot

$\frac{5}{6}$ of a pizza

In a fraction, the top number is called the **numerator** and the bottom number is called the **denominator.** The bar between the numbers is called the **fraction bar.**

Names	Fraction	Meaning
numerator $\longrightarrow$	$\frac{5}{6}$	$\longleftarrow$ number of parts being considered
denominator $\longrightarrow$		$\longleftarrow$ number of equal parts in the whole

EXAMPLES Identify the numerator and the denominator of each fraction.

1. $\frac{3}{7}$ $\leftarrow$ numerator
$\leftarrow$ denominator

2. $\frac{13}{5}$ $\leftarrow$ numerator
$\leftarrow$ denominator

> **Helpful Hint** Notice the fraction $\frac{11}{1} = 11$, or also $11 = \frac{11}{1}$.

☐ **Work Practice Problems 1–2**

Before we continue further, don't forget from Section 1.7 that the fraction bar indicates division. Let's review some division properties for 1 and 0.

$\frac{9}{9} = 1$ because $1 \cdot 9 = 9$ $\frac{11}{1} = 11$ because $11 \cdot 1 = 11$

$\frac{0}{6} = 0$ because $0 \cdot 6 = 0$ $\frac{6}{0}$ *is undefined* because there is no number that when multiplied by 0 gives 6.

In general, we can say the following.

Let n be any whole number except 0.

$$\frac{n}{n} = 1 \qquad \frac{0}{n} = 0$$

$$\frac{n}{1} = n \qquad \frac{n}{0} \text{ is undefined.}$$

Answers
1. numerator = 9, denominator = 2,
2. numerator = 10, denominator = 17

EXAMPLES Simplify.

3. $\frac{5}{5} = 1$ **4.** $\frac{0}{7} = 0$ **5.** $\frac{10}{1} = 10$ **6.** $\frac{3}{0}$ is undefined

■ **Work Practice Problems 3–6**

PRACTICE PROBLEMS 3–6

Simplify.

3. $\frac{0}{2}$ **4.** $\frac{8}{8}$

5. $\frac{4}{0}$ **6.** $\frac{20}{1}$

Objective B Writing Fractions to Represent Shaded Areas of Figures

One way to become familiar with the concept of fractions is to visualize fractions with shaded figures. We can then write a fraction to represent the shaded area of the figure.

EXAMPLES Write a fraction to represent the shaded part of each figure.

7. In this figure, 2 of the 5 equal parts are shaded. Thus, the fraction is $\frac{2}{5}$.

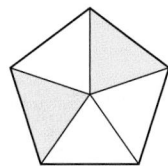

$\frac{2}{5}$ ← number of parts shaded
← number of equal parts

8. In this figure, 3 of the 10 rectangles are shaded. Thus, the fraction is $\frac{3}{10}$.

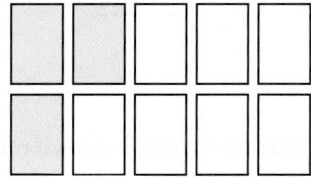

$\frac{3}{10}$ ← number of parts shaded
← number of equal parts

■ **Work Practice Problems 7–8**

PRACTICE PROBLEMS 7–8

Write a fraction to represent the shaded part of each figure.

7.

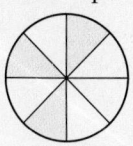

8.

EXAMPLES Write a fraction to represent the shaded part of the diagram.

9.

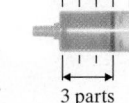

The fraction is $\frac{3}{10}$.

10.

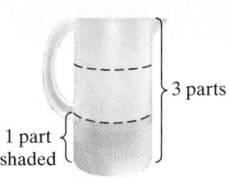

The fraction is $\frac{1}{3}$.

■ **Work Practice Problems 9–10**

PRACTICE PROBLEMS 9–10

Write a fraction to represent the part of the whole shown.

9. Just consider this part of the syringe

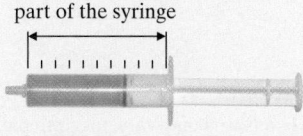

10.

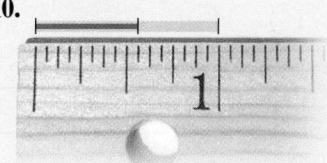

Answers

3. 0, **4.** 1, **5.** undefined, **6.** 20,

7. $\frac{3}{8}$, **8.** $\frac{1}{6}$, **9.** $\frac{7}{10}$, **10.** $\frac{9}{16}$

PRACTICE PROBLEMS 11–12

Draw and shade a part of a figure to represent each fraction.

11. $\frac{2}{3}$ of a figure

12. $\frac{7}{11}$ of a figure

EXAMPLES Draw a figure and then shade a part of it to represent each fraction.

11. $\frac{5}{6}$ of a figure

We will use a geometric figure such as a rectangle. Since the denominator is 6, we divide it into 6 equal parts. Then we shade 5 of the equal parts.

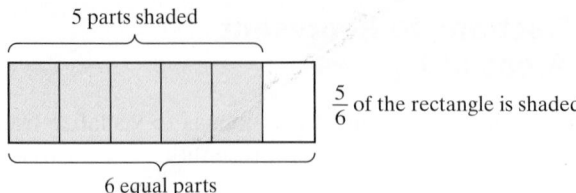

5 parts shaded

$\frac{5}{6}$ of the rectangle is shaded

6 equal parts

12. $\frac{3}{8}$ of a figure

If you'd like, our figure can consist of 8 triangles of the same size. We will shade 3 of the triangles.

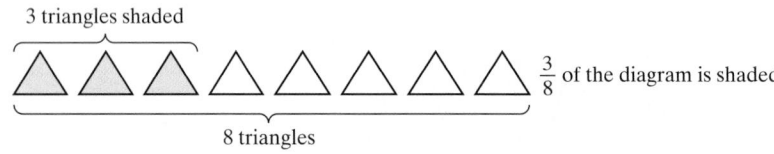

3 triangles shaded

$\frac{3}{8}$ of the diagram is shaded

8 triangles

Work Practice Problems 11–12

✔ **Concept Check** If 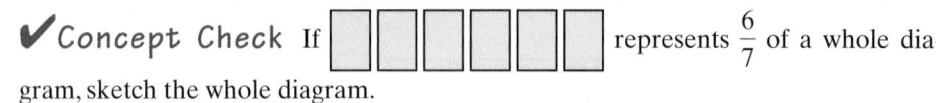 represents $\frac{6}{7}$ of a whole diagram, sketch the whole diagram.

PRACTICE PROBLEM 13

Of the nine planets in our solar system, seven are farther from the Sun than Venus is. What fraction of the planets are farther from the Sun than Venus is?

EXAMPLE 13 Writing Fractions from Real-Life Data

Of the nine planets in our solar system, two are closer to the Sun than Earth is. What fraction of the planets are closer to the Sun than Earth is?

Solution: The fraction of planets closer to the Sun than Earth is:

$\frac{2}{9}$ ← number of planets closer
   ← number of planets in our solar system

Thus, $\frac{2}{9}$ of the planets in our solar system are closer to the Sun than the Earth is.

Work Practice Problem 13

Answers

11. answers may vary; for example,

12. answers may vary; for example,

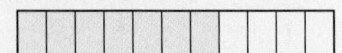

13. $\frac{7}{9}$

✔ **Concept Check Answer**

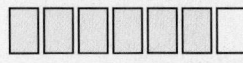

Objective **C** Identifying Proper Fractions, Improper Fractions, and Mixed Numbers

A **proper fraction** is a fraction whose numerator is less than its denominator. Proper fractions are less than 1. For example, the shaded portion of the triangle's area is represented by $\frac{2}{3}$.

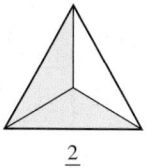

$\frac{2}{3}$

An **improper fraction** is a fraction whose numerator is greater than or equal to its denominator. Improper fractions are greater than or equal to 1. The shaded part of the group of circles' area below is $\frac{9}{4}$. The shaded part of the rectangle's area is $\frac{6}{6}$. (Recall from earlier that $\frac{6}{6}$ simplifies to 1 and notice that 1 whole figure or rectangle is shaded below.)

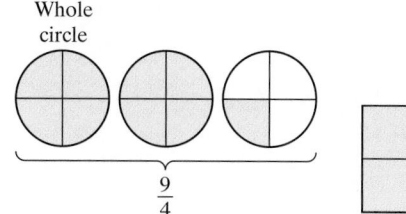

Whole circle

$\frac{9}{4}$

$\frac{6}{6}$

A **mixed number** contains a whole number and a fraction. Mixed numbers are greater than 1. Earlier, we wrote the shaded part of the group of circles below as the improper fraction $\frac{9}{4}$. Now let's write the shaded part as a mixed number. The shaded part of the group of circles' area is $2\frac{1}{4}$. (Read "two and one-fourth.")

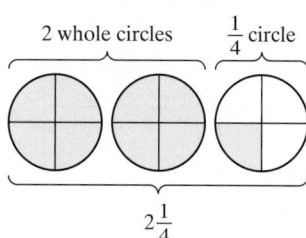

2 whole circles $\frac{1}{4}$ circle

$2\frac{1}{4}$

EXAMPLE 14 Identify each number as a proper fraction, improper fraction, or mixed number.

a. $\frac{6}{7}$ is a proper fraction

b. $\frac{13}{12}$ is an improper fraction

c. $\frac{2}{2}$ is an improper fraction

d. $\frac{99}{101}$ is a proper fraction

e. $1\frac{7}{8}$ is a mixed number

f. $\frac{93}{74}$ is an improper fraction

📖 **Work Practice Problem 14**

☁ **Helpful Hint**

The mixed number $2\frac{1}{4}$ represents $2 + \frac{1}{4}$.

PRACTICE PROBLEM 14

Identify each number as a proper fraction, improper fraction, or mixed number.

a. $\frac{5}{8}$ **b.** $\frac{7}{7}$

c. $\frac{14}{13}$ **d.** $\frac{13}{14}$

e. $5\frac{1}{4}$ **f.** $\frac{100}{49}$

Answers

14. a. proper fraction, **b.** improper fraction, **c.** improper fraction, **d.** proper fraction, **e.** mixed number, **f.** improper fraction

PRACTICE PROBLEMS 15–16

Represent the shaded part of each figure group as both an improper fraction and a mixed number.

15.

16.

EXAMPLES Represent the shaded part of each figure group's area as both an improper fraction and a mixed number.

15. Whole object

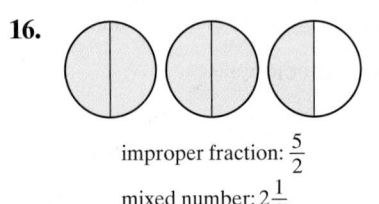

improper fraction: $\frac{4}{3}$

mixed number: $1\frac{1}{3}$

16.

improper fraction: $\frac{5}{2}$

mixed number: $2\frac{1}{2}$

■ **Work Practice Problems 15–16**

✔ **Concept Check** If you were to estimate $2\frac{1}{8}$ by a whole number, would you choose 2 or 3? Why?

Objective D Writing Mixed Numbers as Improper Fractions

Notice from Examples 15 and 16 that mixed numbers and improper fractions were both used to represent the shaded area of the figure groups. For example,

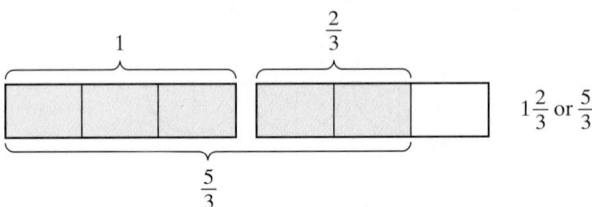

$1\frac{2}{3}$ or $\frac{5}{3}$

$\frac{5}{3}$

The following steps may be used to write a mixed number as an improper fraction:

Writing a Mixed Number as an Improper Fraction

To write a mixed number as an improper fraction:

Step 1: Multiply the denominator of the fraction by the whole number.

Step 2: Add the numerator of the fraction to the product from Step 1.

Step 3: Write the sum from Step 2 as the numerator of the improper fraction over the original denominator.

For example,

Step 1 Step 2

$$1\frac{2}{3} = \frac{3 \cdot 1 + 2}{3} = \frac{3+2}{3} = \frac{5}{3}$$

Step 3

Answers

15. $\frac{8}{3}, 2\frac{2}{3}$, 16. $\frac{5}{4}, 1\frac{1}{4}$

✔ **Concept Check Answer**

2, answers may vary

EXAMPLE 17 Write each as an improper fraction.

a. $4\frac{2}{9} = \frac{9 \cdot 4 + 2}{9} = \frac{36 + 2}{9} = \frac{38}{9}$

b. $1\frac{8}{11} = \frac{11 \cdot 1 + 8}{11} = \frac{11 + 8}{11} = \frac{19}{11}$

■ Work Practice Problem 17

Objective **E** Writing Improper Fractions as Mixed Numbers or Whole Numbers

Just as there are times when an improper fraction is preferred, sometimes a mixed or a whole number better suits a situation. To write improper fractions as mixed or whole numbers, we use division. Recall once again from Section 1.7 that the fraction bar means division. This means that the fraction

$\frac{5}{3}$ numerator denominator   means $3\overline{)5}$
↑ ↑
numerator
denominator

Writing an Improper Fraction as a Mixed Number or a Whole Number

To write an improper fraction as a mixed number or a whole number:

Step 1: Divide the denominator into the numerator.

Step 2: The whole number part of the mixed number is the quotient. The fraction part of the mixed number is the remainder over the original denominator.

$$\text{quotient} \frac{\text{remainder}}{\text{original denominator}}$$

For example,

Step 1

$\frac{5}{3} : \begin{array}{r} 1 \\ 3\overline{)5} \\ \underline{3} \\ 2 \end{array}$

Step 2

$\frac{5}{3} = 1\frac{2}{3}$ ← remainder
← original denominator
↑
quotient

EXAMPLE 18 Write each as a mixed number or a whole number.

a. $\frac{30}{7}$ b. $\frac{16}{15}$ c. $\frac{84}{6}$

Solution:

a. $\frac{30}{7} : \begin{array}{r} 4 \\ 7\overline{)30} \\ \underline{28} \\ 2 \end{array}$ $\frac{30}{7} = 4\frac{2}{7}$

Continued on next page

PRACTICE PROBLEM 17

Write each as an improper fraction.

a. $2\frac{5}{7}$ b. $5\frac{1}{3}$

c. $9\frac{3}{10}$ d. $1\frac{1}{5}$

PRACTICE PROBLEM 18

Write each as a mixed number or a whole number.

a. $\frac{8}{5}$ b. $\frac{17}{6}$ c. $\frac{48}{4}$

d. $\frac{75}{13}$ e. $\frac{51}{7}$ f. $\frac{21}{20}$

Answers

17. a. $\frac{19}{7}$, b. $\frac{16}{3}$, c. $\frac{93}{10}$, d. $\frac{6}{5}$,

18. a. $1\frac{3}{5}$, b. $2\frac{5}{6}$, c. 12,

d. $5\frac{10}{13}$, e. $7\frac{2}{7}$, f. $1\frac{1}{20}$

b. $\dfrac{16}{15}$ $15\overline{)16}$ $\dfrac{16}{15} = 1\dfrac{1}{15}$

$\phantom{15\overline{)}}\dfrac{15}{1}$

c. $\dfrac{84}{6}$ $6\overline{)84}$ $\dfrac{84}{6} = 14$ Since the remainder is 0, the result is the whole number 14.

$\phantom{6\overline{)}}\dfrac{6}{24}$

$\phantom{6\overline{)}24}\dfrac{24}{0}$

▥ **Work Practice Problem 18**

Helpful Hint

When the remainder is 0, the improper fraction is a whole number.
For example, $\dfrac{92}{4} = 23$.

$4\overline{)92}$
$\dfrac{8}{12}$
$\dfrac{12}{0}$

Mental Math

Objective Ⓐ **Mixed Practice** *Identify the numerator and the denominator of each fraction and identify each fraction as proper or improper. See Examples 1, 2, and 14.*

1. $\dfrac{1}{2}$

2. $\dfrac{1}{4}$

3. $\dfrac{10}{3}$

4. $\dfrac{53}{21}$

5. $\dfrac{15}{15}$

6. $\dfrac{26}{26}$

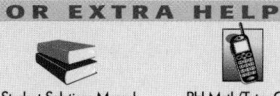
Objective A *Simplify. See Examples 3 through 6.*

1. $\dfrac{21}{21}$ **2.** $\dfrac{14}{14}$ **3.** $\dfrac{5}{0}$ **4.** $\dfrac{1}{0}$ **5.** $\dfrac{13}{1}$ **6.** $\dfrac{14}{1}$

7. $\dfrac{0}{20}$ **8.** $\dfrac{0}{17}$ **9.** $\dfrac{10}{0}$ **10.** $\dfrac{0}{18}$ **11.** $\dfrac{16}{1}$ **12.** $\dfrac{18}{18}$

Objective B *Write a fraction to represent the shaded part of each. See Examples 7 through 10.*

13.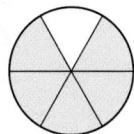

 **14.**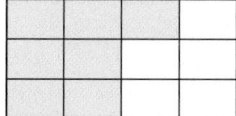

15.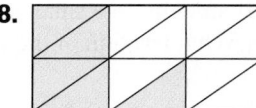

16.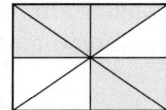

17.

18.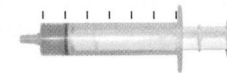

19.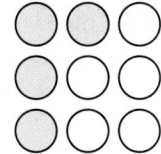

20.

21.

22.

23.

1 mile

24.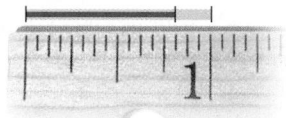

119

Draw and shade a part of a diagram to represent each fraction. See Examples 11 and 12.

25. $\frac{1}{5}$ of a diagram

26. $\frac{1}{16}$ of a diagram

27. $\frac{7}{8}$ of a diagram

28. $\frac{3}{5}$ of a diagram

29. $\frac{6}{7}$ of a diagram

30. $\frac{7}{9}$ of a diagram

31. $\frac{4}{4}$ of a diagram

32. $\frac{6}{6}$ of a diagram

Write each fraction. See Example 13.

33. Of the 131 students at a small private school, 42 are freshmen. What fraction of the students are freshmen?

34. Of the 78 executives at a private accounting firm, 61 are women. What fraction of the executives are women?

35. Use Exercise 33 to answer a and b.
   a. How many students are *not* freshmen?
   b. What fraction of the students are *not* freshmen?

36. Use Exercise 34 to answer a and b.
   a. How many of the executives are men?
   b. What fraction of the executives are men?

37. As of 2005, the United States has had 43 different presidents. A total of eight U.S. presidents were born in the state of Virginia, more than any other state. What fraction of U.S. presidents were born in Virginia? (*Source: 2005 World Almanac and Book of Facts*)

38. Of the nine planets in our solar system, four have days that are longer than the 24-hour Earth day. What fraction of the planets have longer days than Earth has? (*Source:* National Space Science Data Center)

Eight U.S. Presidents

39. The hard drive in Aaron Hawn's Computer can hold 70 gigabytes of information. He has currently used 27 gigabytes. What fraction of his hard drive has he used?

40. There are 12 inches in a foot. What fractional part of a foot does 5 inches represent?

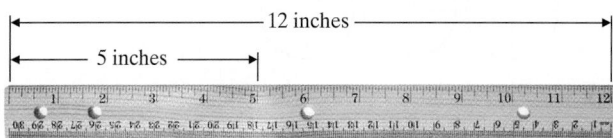

41. There are 31 days in the month of March. What fraction of the month does 11 days represent?

42. There are 60 minutes in an hour. What fraction of an hour does 37 minutes represent?

Mon.	Tue.	Wed.	Thu.	Fri.	Sat.	Sun.
					1	2
3	4	5	6	7	8	9
10	11	12	13	14	15	16
17	18	19	20	21	22	23
24	25	26	27	28	29	30
31						

43. In a basic college mathematics class containing 31 students, there are 18 freshmen, 10 sophomores, and 3 juniors. What fraction of the class is sophomores?

44. In a family with 11 children, there are 4 boys and 7 girls. What fraction of the children is girls?

45. Thirty-three states in the United States contain federal Indian reservations.
  a. What fraction of the states contain Indian reservations?
  b. How many states do not contain Indian reservations?
  c. What fraction of the states do not contain Indian reservations? (*Source:* Tiller Research, Inc., Albuquerque, NM)

46. Consumer fireworks are legal in 40 states in the United States.
  a. In what fraction of the states are consumer fireworks legal?
  b. In how many states are consumer fireworks illegal?
  c. In what fraction of the states are consumer fireworks illegal? (*Source:* United States Fireworks Safety Council)

47. A bag contains 50 red or blue marbles. If 21 marbles are blue,
  a. What *fraction* of the marbles are blue?
  b. How many marbles are red?
  c. What *fraction* of the marbles are red?

48. An art dealer is taking inventory. His shop contains a total of 37 pieces, which are all sculptures, watercolor paintings, or oil paintings. If there are 15 watercolor paintings and 17 oil paintings, answer each question.
  a. What fraction of the inventory is watercolor paintings?
  b. What fraction of the inventory is oil paintings?
  c. How many sculptures are there?
  d. What fraction of the inventory is sculptures?

Objective **C** *Write the shaded area in each figure group as (a) an improper fraction and (b) a mixed number. See Examples 15 and 16.*

49.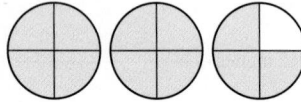

50.

51.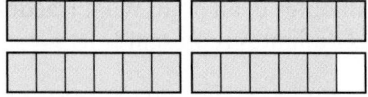

52.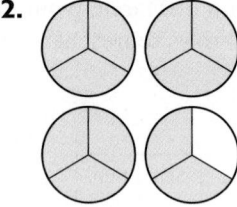

53.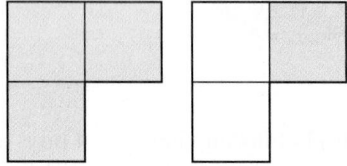

54.

55.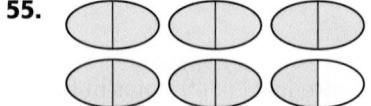

56.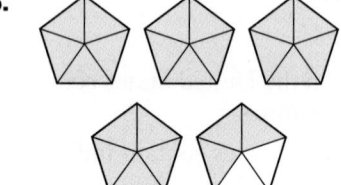

Objective **D** *Write each mixed number as an improper fraction. See Example 17.*

57. $2\frac{1}{3}$ **58.** $6\frac{3}{4}$ **59.** $3\frac{3}{5}$ **60.** $2\frac{5}{9}$ **61.** $6\frac{5}{8}$ **62.** $7\frac{3}{8}$

63. $2\frac{11}{15}$ **64.** $1\frac{13}{17}$ **65.** $11\frac{6}{7}$ **66.** $12\frac{2}{5}$ **67.** $6\frac{6}{13}$ **68.** $8\frac{9}{10}$

69. $4\dfrac{13}{24}$ **70.** $5\dfrac{17}{25}$ **71.** $17\dfrac{7}{12}$ **72.** $12\dfrac{7}{15}$ **73.** $9\dfrac{7}{20}$ **74.** $10\dfrac{14}{27}$

75. $2\dfrac{51}{107}$ **76.** $3\dfrac{27}{125}$ **77.** $166\dfrac{2}{3}$ **78.** $114\dfrac{2}{7}$

Objective **E** *Write each improper fraction as a mixed number or a whole number. See Example 18.*

79. $\dfrac{17}{5}$ **80.** $\dfrac{13}{7}$ **81.** $\dfrac{37}{8}$ **82.** $\dfrac{64}{9}$ **83.** $\dfrac{47}{15}$ **84.** $\dfrac{65}{12}$

85. $\dfrac{46}{21}$ **86.** $\dfrac{67}{17}$ **87.** $\dfrac{198}{6}$ **88.** $\dfrac{112}{7}$ **89.** $\dfrac{225}{15}$ **90.** $\dfrac{196}{14}$

91. $\dfrac{200}{3}$ **92.** $\dfrac{300}{7}$ **93.** $\dfrac{247}{23}$ **94.** $\dfrac{437}{53}$ **95.** $\dfrac{319}{18}$ **96.** $\dfrac{404}{21}$

97. $\dfrac{182}{175}$ **98.** $\dfrac{149}{143}$ **99.** $\dfrac{737}{112}$ **100.** $\dfrac{901}{123}$

Review

Simplify. See Section 1.9.

101. 3^2 **102.** 4^3 **103.** 5^3 **104.** 3^4

Write each using exponents.

105. $7 \cdot 7 \cdot 7 \cdot 7 \cdot 7$ **106.** $5 \cdot 5 \cdot 5 \cdot 5$ **107.** $2 \cdot 2 \cdot 2 \cdot 3$ **108.** $4 \cdot 4 \cdot 10 \cdot 10 \cdot 10$

Concept Extensions

Write each fraction.

109. In your own words, explain how to write an improper fraction as a mixed number.

110. In your own words, explain how to write a mixed number as an improper fraction.

Identify the larger fraction for each pair.

111. $\frac{1}{2}$ or $\frac{2}{3}$ (*Hint:* Represent each fraction by the shaded part of equivalent figures. Then compare the shaded areas.)

112. $\frac{7}{4}$ or $\frac{3}{5}$ (*Hint:* Identify each as a proper fraction or an improper fraction.)

Solve. See the Concept Check in this section.

113. If  represents $\frac{4}{9}$ of a whole diagram, sketch the whole diagram.

114. If △ △ represents $\frac{1}{3}$ of a whole diagram, sketch the whole diagram.

115. The Wendy's Corporation owns restaurants with five different names, as shown on the bar graph. What fraction of restaurants owned by Wendy's corporation are named "Wendy's" restaurants? (*Source:* The Wendy's Corporation)

116. The Public Broadcasting Service (PBS) provides programming to the noncommercial public TV stations of the United States. The table shows a breakdown of the public television licensees by type. Each licensee operates one or more PBS member TV stations. What fraction of the public television licensees are universities or colleges? (*Source:* The Public Broadcast Service)

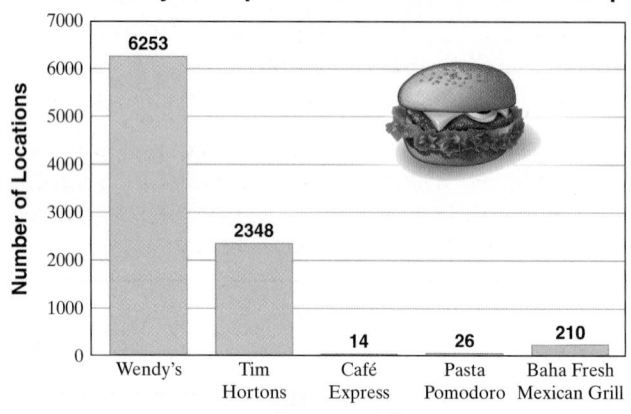

Wendy's Corporation Restaurant Ownership

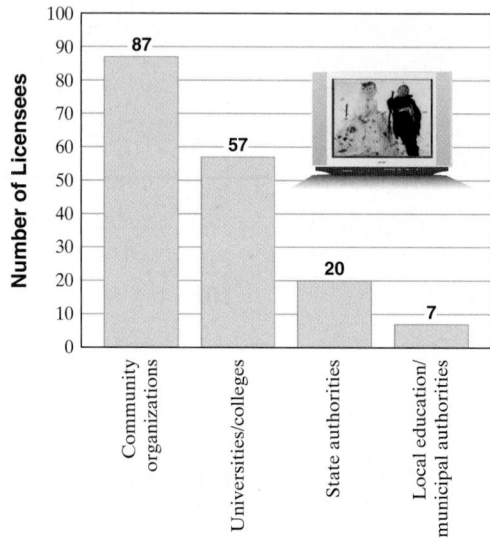

Public Television Licensees

117. Habitat for Humanity is a nonprofit organization that helps provide affordable housing to families in need. Habitat for Humanity does its work of building and renovating houses through 1651 local affiliates in the United States and 634 international affiliates. What fraction of the total Habitat for Humanity affiliates are located in the United States? (*Hint:* First find the total number of affiliates.) (*Source:* Habitat for Humanity International)

118. The United States Marine Corps (USMC) has five principal training centers in California, three in North Carolina, two in South Carolina, one in Arizona, one in Hawaii, and one in Virginia. What fraction of the total USMC principal training centers are located in California? (*Source:* U.S. Department of Defense)

 STUDY SKILLS BUILDER

Have You Decided to Complete This Course Successfully?

Ask yourself if one of your current goals is to complete this course successfully.

If it is not a goal of yours, ask yourself why? One common reason is fear of failure. Amazingly enough, fear of failure alone can be strong enough to keep many of us from doing our best in any endeavor.

Another common reason is that you simply haven't taken the time to make successfully completing this course one of your goals. How do you do this? Start by writing this goal in your mathematics notebook. Then list steps you will take to ensure success. A great first step is to read or reread Section 1.1 and make a commitment to try the suggestions in that section.

Good luck, and don't forget that a positive attitude will make a big difference.

Let's see how you are doing.

1. Have you decided to make "successfully completing this course" a goal of yours? If no, please list reasons why this has not happened. Study your list and talk to your instructor about this.

2. If your answer to question 1 is yes, take a moment and list in your notebook further specific goals that will help you achieve this major goal of successfully completing this course. (For example, "My goal this semester is not to miss any of my mathematics classes.")

3. Rate your commitment to this course with a number between 1 and 5. Use the diagram below to help.

High Commitment		Average Commitment		Not committed at all
5	4	3	2	1

4. If you have rated your personal commitment level (from the exercise above) as a 1, 2, or 3, list the reasons why this is so. Then determine whether it is possible to increase your commitment level to a 4 or 5.

2.2 FACTORS AND PRIME FACTORIZATION

To perform many operations with fractions, it is necessary to be able to factor a number. In this section, only the **natural numbers**—1, 2, 3, 4, 5, and so on—will be considered.

✔**Concept Check** How are the natural numbers and the whole numbers alike? How are they different?

Objective **A** Finding Factors of Numbers

Recall that when numbers are multiplied to form a product, each number is called a factor. Since $5 \cdot 9 = 45$, both 5 and 9 are **factors** of 45, and $5 \cdot 9$ is called a **factorization** of 45.

The two-number factorizations of 45 are

$1 \cdot 45 \quad 3 \cdot 15 \quad 5 \cdot 9$

Thus, we say that the factors of 45 are $1, 3, 5, 9, 15,$ and 45.

> **Helpful Hint**
>
> From our definition of factor above, notice that a **factor** of a number divides the number evenly (with a remainder of 0). For example,
>
> $$\frac{45}{1)\overline{45}} \quad \frac{15}{3)\overline{45}} \quad \frac{9}{5)\overline{45}} \quad \frac{5}{9)\overline{45}} \quad \frac{3}{15)\overline{45}} \quad \frac{1}{45)\overline{45}}$$

PRACTICE PROBLEM 1

Find all the factors of each number.

a. 15   **b.** 7   **c.** 24

EXAMPLE 1 Find all the factors of 20.

Solution: First we write all the two-number factorizations of 20.

$1 \cdot 20 = 20$

$2 \cdot 10 = 20$

$4 \cdot 5 = 20$

The factors of 20 are $1, 2, 4, 5, 10,$ and 20.

Work Practice Problem 1

Objective **B** Identifying Prime and Composite Numbers

Of all the ways to factor a number, one special way is called the **prime factorization.** To help us write prime factorizations, we first review prime and composite numbers.

> **Prime Numbers**
>
> A **prime number** is a natural number that has exactly two different factors, 1 and itself.

The first several prime numbers are

$2, 3, 5, 7, 11, 13, 17$

It would be helpful to memorize these.

If a natural number other than 1 is not a prime number, it is called a **composite number.**

Answers

1. a. $1, 3, 5, 15,$ **b.** $1, 7,$
c. $1, 2, 3, 4, 6, 8, 12, 24$

✔ **Concept Check Answer**

answers may vary

Composite Numbers

A **composite number** is any natural number, other than 1, that is not prime.

 **Helpful Hint**

The natural number 1 is neither prime nor composite.

EXAMPLE 2 Determine whether each number is prime or composite. Explain your answers.

3, 9, 11, 17, 26

Solution: The number 3 is prime. Its only factors are 1 and 3 (itself).
The number 9 is composite. It has more than two factors: 1, 3, and 9.
The number 11 is prime. Its only factors are 1 and 11.
The number 17 is prime. Its only factors are 1 and 17.
The number 26 is composite. Its factors are 1, 2, 13, and 26.

▣ **Work Practice Problem 2**

Objective **C** Finding Prime Factorizations

Now we are ready to find **prime factorizations** of numbers.

Prime Factorization

The **prime factorization** of a number is the factorization in which all the factors are prime numbers.

For example, the prime factorization of 12 is $2 \cdot 2 \cdot 3$ because

$12 = 2 \cdot 2 \cdot 3$ and each number is a prime number.

There is only one prime factorization for any given number. In other words, the prime factorization of a number is unique.

Helpful Hint

Don't forget that multiplication is commutative, so $2 \cdot 2 \cdot 3$ can also be written as $2 \cdot 3 \cdot 2$ or $3 \cdot 2 \cdot 2$ or $2^2 \cdot 3$. Any one of these can be called *the prime factorization of* 12.

EXAMPLE 3 Find the prime factorization of 45.

Solution: The first prime number, 2, does not divide 45 evenly (with a remainder of 0). The second prime number, 3, does, so we divide 45 by 3.

$$\begin{array}{r} 15 \\ 3\overline{)45} \end{array}$$

Because 15 is not prime and 3 also divides 15 evenly, we divide by 3 again.

$$\begin{array}{r} 5 \\ 3\overline{)15} \\ 3\overline{)45} \end{array}$$

Continued on next page

PRACTICE PROBLEM 2

Determine whether each number is prime or composite. Explain your answers.

21, 13, 18, 29, 39

PRACTICE PROBLEM 3

Find the prime factorization of 28.

Answers

2. 13, 29 are prime. 21, 18, and 39 are composite.   **3.** $2^2 \cdot 7$

The quotient, 5, is a prime number, so we are finished. The prime factorization of 45 is

$$45 = 3 \cdot 3 \cdot 5 \quad \text{or} \quad 45 = 3^2 \cdot 5,$$

using exponents.

Work Practice Problem 3

There are a few quick **divisibility tests** to determine whether a number is divisible by the primes 2, 3, or 5. (A number is divisible by 2, for example, if 2 divides it evenly.)

Divisibility Tests

A whole number is divisible by:

- **2** if the last digit is 0, 2, 4, 6, or 8.

    132 is divisible by 2 since the last digit is a 2.

- **3** if the sum of the digits is divisible by 3.

    144 is divisible by 3 since $1 + 4 + 4 = 9$ is divisible by 3.

- **5** if the last digit is 0 or 5.

    1115 is divisible by 5 since the last digit is a 5.

Helpful Hint

Here are a few other divisibility tests you may find interesting. A whole number is divisible by:

- **4** if its last two digits are divisible by 4.

    1712 is divisible by 4.

- **6** if it's divisible by 2 and 3.

    9858 is divisible by 6.

- **9** if the sum of its digits is divisible by 9.

    5238 is divisible by 9 since $5 + 2 + 3 + 8 = 18$ is divisible by 9.

For the next few examples, we will begin the division process with the smallest prime number factor of the given number. Remember that since multiplication is commutative, this is not necessary. As long as the divisor is a prime number factor, this process works.

PRACTICE PROBLEM 4

Find the prime factorization of 120.

EXAMPLE 4 Find the prime factorization of 180.

Solution: We divide 180 by 2 and continue dividing until the quotient is no longer divisible by 2. We then divide by the next largest prime number, 3, until the quotient is no longer divisible by 3. We continue this process until the quotient is a prime number.

$$
\begin{array}{r}
5 \\
3\overline{)15} \\
3\overline{)45} \\
2\overline{)90} \\
2\overline{)180}
\end{array}
$$

Answer

4. $2^3 \cdot 3 \cdot 5$

Thus, the prime factorization of 180 is

$$180 = 2 \cdot 2 \cdot 3 \cdot 3 \cdot 5 \quad \text{or} \quad 180 = 2^2 \cdot 3^2 \cdot 5,$$

using exponents.

Work Practice Problem 4

EXAMPLE 5 Find the prime factorization of 945.

Solution: This number is not divisible by 2 but is divisible by 3. We will begin by dividing 945 by 3.

$$
\begin{array}{r}
7 \\
5)\overline{35} \\
3)\overline{105} \\
3)\overline{315} \\
3)\overline{945}
\end{array}
$$

Thus, the prime factorization of 945 is

$$945 = 3 \cdot 3 \cdot 3 \cdot 5 \cdot 7 \quad \text{or} \quad 945 = 3^3 \cdot 5 \cdot 7$$

Work Practice Problem 5

Another way to find the prime factorization is to use a factor tree, as shown in the next example.

EXAMPLE 6 Use a factor tree to find the prime factorization of 18.

Solution: We begin by writing 18 as a product of two natural numbers greater than 1, say $2 \cdot 9$.

$$
\begin{array}{c}
18 \\
\diagup \diagdown \\
2 \cdot 9
\end{array}
$$

The number 2 is prime, but 9 is not. So we write 9 as $3 \cdot 3$.

$$
\begin{array}{c}
18 \\
\diagup \diagdown \\
2 \cdot 9 \\
\downarrow \quad \downarrow \diagdown \\
2 \cdot 3 \cdot 3
\end{array}
$$

Each factor is now prime, so the prime factorization is

$$18 = 2 \cdot 3 \cdot 3 \quad \text{or} \quad 18 = 2 \cdot 3^2,$$

using exponents.

Work Practice Problem 6

In this text, we will write the factorization of a number from the smallest factor to the largest factor.

PRACTICE PROBLEM 5

Find the prime factorization of 756.

PRACTICE PROBLEM 6

Use a factor tree to find the prime factorization of 70.

Answers

5. $2^2 \cdot 3^3 \cdot 7$, **6.** $2 \cdot 5 \cdot 7$

PRACTICE PROBLEM 7

Use a factor tree to find the prime factorization of each number.

a. 30   **b.** 56   **c.** 72

EXAMPLE 7 Use a factor tree to find the prime factorization of 24.

Solution:

$$24$$
$$4 \cdot 6$$
$$2 \cdot 2 \cdot 2 \cdot 3$$

The prime factorization of 24 is

$$24 = 2 \cdot 2 \cdot 2 \cdot 3 \quad \text{or} \quad 2^3 \cdot 3,$$

using exponents.

◻ **Work Practice Problem 7**

✔**Concept Check** True or false? Two different numbers can have exactly the same prime factorization. Explain your answer.

Helpful Hint

When using a factor tree, we arrive at the same prime factorization of a number no matter what original factors we use. For example, let's factor 24 again from Example 7.

Still, $24 = 2^3 \cdot 3$.

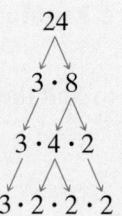

$$24$$
$$3 \cdot 8$$
$$3 \cdot 4 \cdot 2$$
$$3 \cdot 2 \cdot 2 \cdot 2$$

PRACTICE PROBLEM 8

Use a factor tree to find the prime factorization of 117.

EXAMPLE 8 Use a factor tree to find the prime factorization of 175.

Solution: We begin by writing 175 as a product of two numbers greater than 1, say $7 \cdot 25$.

$$175$$
$$7 \cdot 25$$
$$7 \cdot 5 \cdot 5$$

The prime factorization of 175 is

$$175 = 5 \cdot 5 \cdot 7 \quad \text{or} \quad 175 = 5^2 \cdot 7$$

◻ **Work Practice Problem 8**

Answers

7. **a.** $2 \cdot 3 \cdot 5$, **b.** $2^3 \cdot 7$, **c.** $2^3 \cdot 3^2$

8. $3^2 \cdot 13$

✔ **Concept Check Answer**

false; answers may vary

Objective A *List all the factors of each number. See Example 1.*

1. 8   **2.** 6   **3.** 25   **4.** 30   **5.** 4   **6.** 9

7. 18   **8.** 48   **9.** 29   **10.** 37   **11.** 80   **12.** 100

13. 12   **14.** 28   **15.** 34   **16.** 26

Objective B *Identify each number as prime or composite. See Example 2.*

17. 7   **18.** 5   **19.** 4   **20.** 10   **21.** 23   **22.** 13

23. 49   **24.** 45   **25.** 67   **26.** 89   **27.** 39   **28.** 21

29. 31   **30.** 27   **31.** 63   **32.** 51   **33.** 119   **34.** 147

Objective C *Find the prime factorization of each number. Write any repeated factors using exponents. See Examples 3 through 8.*

35. 32   **36.** 80   **37.** 15   **38.** 21   **39.** 40   **40.** 63

41. 36   **42.** 64   **43.** 39   **44.** 56   **45.** 60   **46.** 84

47. 110   **48.** 130   **49.** 85   **50.** 93   **51.** 128   **52.** 81

53. 154   **54.** 198   **55.** 300   **56.** 360   **57.** 240   **58.** 836

59. 828   **60.** 504   **61.** 882   **62.** 405   **63.** 637   **64.** 539

Objectives **B** **C** **Mixed Practice** *Find the prime factorization of each composite number. Write prime if the number is prime.*

65. 33   **66.** 48   **67.** 98   **68.** 54   **69.** 67   **70.** 59

71. 459   **72.** 208   **73.** 97   **74.** 103   **75.** 700   **76.** 1000

Review

Round each whole number to the indicated place value. See Section 1.5.

77. 4267 hundreds   **78.** 7,658,240 ten-thousands   **79.** 4,286,340 tens

80. 19,764 thousands   **81.** 10,292,876 millions

With all the recent low-carbohydrate diets, the number of new no- and low-carb ice cream products has greatly increased. Use this bar graph to answer the questions below. See Section 2.1.

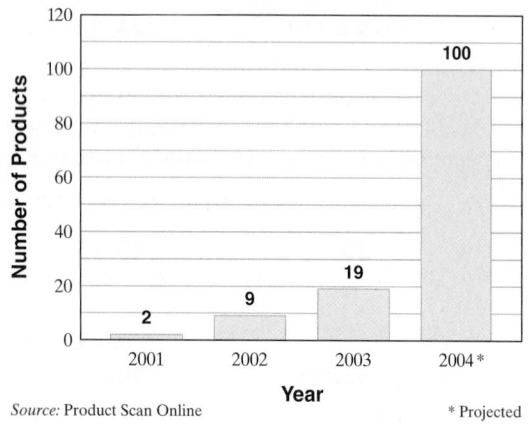

New No-Carb and Low-Carb Ice Cream Product

Source: Product Scan Online   * Projected

82. Find the total number of new products for the years shown.

83. What fraction of new products were introduced in 2003?

84. What fraction of new products were introduced in 2002?

Concept Extensions

Find the prime factorization of each number.

85. 34,020

86. 131,625

 87. In your own words, define a prime number.

88. The number 2 is a prime number. All other even natural numbers are composite numbers. Explain why.

89. Why are we interested in the prime factorization of nonzero whole numbers only?

90. Two students have different prime factorizations for the same number. Is this possible? Explain.

STUDY SKILLS BUILDER

Organizing a Notebook

It's never too late to get organized. If you need ideas about organizing a notebook for your mathematics course, try some of these:

- Use a spiral or ring binder notebook with pockets and use it for mathematics only.
- Start each page by writing the book's section number you are working on at the top.
- When your instructor is lecturing, take notes. *Always* include any examples your instructor works for you.
- Place your worked-out homework exercises in your notebook immediately after the lecture notes from that section. This way, a section's worth of material is together.
- Homework exercises: Attempt all assigned homework. For odd-numbered exercises, you are not through until you check your answers against the back of the book. Correct any exercises with incorrect answers. You may want to place a "?" by any homework exercises or notes that you need to ask questions about. Also, consider placing a "!" by any notes or exercises you feel are important.

- Place graded quizzes in the pockets of your notebook. If you are using a binder, you can place your quizzes in a special section of your binder.

Let's check your notebook organization by answering the following questions.

1. Do you have a spiral or ring binder notebook for your mathematics course only?

2. Have you ever had to flip through several sheets of notes and work in your mathematics notebook to determine what section's work you are in?

3. Are you now writing the textbook's section number at the top of each notebook page?

4. Have you ever lost or had trouble finding a graded quiz or test?

5. Are you now placing all your graded work in a dedicated place in your notebook?

6. Are you attempting all of your homework and placing all of your work in your notebook?

7. Are you checking and correcting your homework in your notebook? If not, why not?

8. Are you writing in your notebook the examples your instructor works for you in class?

2.3 SIMPLEST FORM OF A FRACTION

Objective **A** Writing Fractions in Simplest Form

Fractions that represent the same portion of a whole are called **equivalent fractions.**

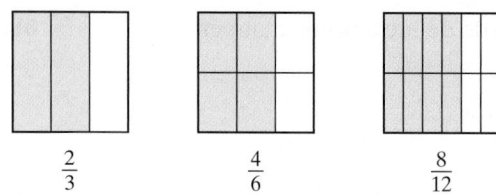

$$\frac{2}{3} \qquad \frac{4}{6} \qquad \frac{8}{12}$$

For example, $\frac{2}{3}$, $\frac{4}{6}$, and $\frac{8}{12}$ all represent the same shaded portion of the rectangle's area, so they are equivalent fractions.

$$\frac{2}{3} = \frac{4}{6} = \frac{8}{12}$$

A special form of a fraction is called **simplest form.**

Simplest Form of a Fraction

A fraction is written in **simplest form** or **lowest terms** when the numerator and the denominator have no common factors other than 1.

For example, the fraction $\frac{2}{3}$ is in simplest form because 2 and 3 have no common factor other than 1. The fraction $\frac{4}{6}$ is *not* in simplest form because 4 and 6 both have a factor of 2. That is, 2 is a common factor of 4 and 6. The process of writing a fraction in simplest form is called **simplifying** the fraction.

To simplify $\frac{4}{6}$ and write it as $\frac{2}{3}$, let's first study a few properties. Recall from Section 2.1 that any nonzero whole number n divided by itself is 1.

Any nonzero number n divided by itself is 1.

$$\frac{5}{5} = 1, \quad \frac{17}{17} = 1, \quad \frac{24}{24} = 1, \text{ or, in general, } \frac{n}{n} = 1$$

Also, in general, if $\frac{a}{b}$ and $\frac{c}{d}$ are fractions (with b and d not 0), the following is true.

$$\frac{a \cdot c}{b \cdot d} = \frac{a}{b} \cdot \frac{c}{d}^{*}$$

These properties allow us to do the following:

$$\frac{4}{6} = \frac{2 \cdot 2}{2 \cdot 3} = \frac{2}{2} \cdot \frac{2}{3} = 1 \cdot \frac{2}{3} = \frac{2}{3}$$
$$\underset{\llcorner \text{This is 1}}{}$$

When 1 is multiplied by a number, the result is the same number.

Note: We will study this concept further in the next section.

EXAMPLE 1 Write in simplest form: $\dfrac{12}{20}$

Solution: Notice that 12 and 20 have a common factor of 4.

$$\frac{12}{20} = \frac{4 \cdot 3}{4 \cdot 5} = \frac{4}{4} \cdot \frac{3}{5} = 1 \cdot \frac{3}{5} = \frac{3}{5}$$

Since 3 and 5 have no common factors (other than 1), $\dfrac{3}{5}$ is in simplest form.

🔲 **Work Practice Problem 1**

If you have trouble finding common factors, write the prime factorization of the numerator and the denominator.

EXAMPLE 2 Write in simplest form: $\dfrac{42}{66}$

Solution: Let's write the prime factorizations of 42 and 66.

$$\frac{42}{66} = \frac{2 \cdot 3 \cdot 7}{2 \cdot 3 \cdot 11} = \frac{2}{2} \cdot \frac{3}{3} \cdot \frac{7}{11} = 1 \cdot 1 \cdot \frac{7}{11} = \frac{7}{11}$$

🔲 **Work Practice Problem 2**

In the example above, you may have saved time by noticing that 42 and 66 have a common factor of 6.

$$\frac{42}{66} = \frac{6 \cdot 7}{6 \cdot 11} = \frac{6}{6} \cdot \frac{7}{11} = 1 \cdot \frac{7}{11} = \frac{7}{11}$$

Helpful Hint
Writing the prime factorizations of the numerator and the denominator is helpful in finding any common factors.

EXAMPLE 3 Write in simplest form: $\dfrac{10}{27}$

Solution:

$$\frac{10}{27} = \frac{2 \cdot 5}{3 \cdot 3 \cdot 3} \qquad \text{Prime factorizations of 10 and 27.}$$

Since 10 and 27 have no common factors, $\dfrac{10}{27}$ is already in simplest form.

🔲 **Work Practice Problem 3**

EXAMPLE 4 Write in simplest form: $\dfrac{30}{108}$

Solution:

$$\frac{30}{108} = \frac{2 \cdot 3 \cdot 5}{2 \cdot 2 \cdot 3 \cdot 3 \cdot 3} = \frac{2}{2} \cdot \frac{3}{3} \cdot \frac{5}{2 \cdot 3 \cdot 3} = 1 \cdot 1 \cdot \frac{5}{18} = \frac{5}{18}$$

🔲 **Work Practice Problem 4**

We can use a shortcut procedure with common factors when simplifying.

$$\frac{4}{6} = \frac{\overset{1}{\cancel{2}} \cdot 2}{\underset{1}{\cancel{2}} \cdot 3} = \frac{1 \cdot 2}{1 \cdot 3} = \frac{2}{3} \qquad \text{Divide out the common factor of 2 in the numerator and denominator.}$$

PRACTICE PROBLEM 1
Write in simplest form: $\dfrac{30}{45}$

PRACTICE PROBLEM 2
Write in simplest form: $\dfrac{39}{51}$

PRACTICE PROBLEM 3
Write in simplest form: $\dfrac{9}{50}$

PRACTICE PROBLEM 4
Write in simplest form: $\dfrac{49}{112}$

Answers
1. $\dfrac{2}{3}$, 2. $\dfrac{13}{17}$, 3. $\dfrac{9}{50}$, 4. $\dfrac{7}{16}$

This procedure is possible because dividing out a common factor in the numerator and denominator is the same as removing a factor of 1 in the product.

Writing a Fraction in Simplest Form

To write a fraction in simplest form, write the prime factorization of the numerator and the denominator and then divide both by all common factors.

PRACTICE PROBLEM 5

Write in simplest form: $\dfrac{64}{20}$

EXAMPLE 5 Write in simplest form: $\dfrac{72}{26}$

Solution:

$$\frac{72}{26} = \frac{\overset{1}{\cancel{2}} \cdot 2 \cdot 2 \cdot 3 \cdot 3}{\underset{1}{\cancel{2}} \cdot 13} = \frac{1 \cdot 2 \cdot 2 \cdot 3 \cdot 3}{1 \cdot 13} = \frac{36}{13},$$

which can also be written as

$$2\frac{10}{13}$$

◻ **Work Practice Problem 5**

✔ **Concept Check** Which is the correct way to simplify the fraction $\dfrac{15}{25}$? Or are both correct? Explain.

a. $\dfrac{15}{25} = \dfrac{3 \cdot \overset{1}{\cancel{5}}}{5 \cdot \underset{1}{\cancel{5}}} = \dfrac{3}{5}$ **b.** $\dfrac{1\overset{1}{\cancel{5}}}{2\underset{1}{\cancel{5}}} = \dfrac{11}{21}$

PRACTICE PROBLEM 6

Write in simplest form: $\dfrac{8}{56}$

EXAMPLE 6 Write in simplest form: $\dfrac{6}{60}$

Solution:

$$\frac{6}{60} = \frac{\overset{1}{\cancel{2}} \cdot \overset{1}{\cancel{3}}}{\underset{1}{\cancel{2}} \cdot 2 \cdot \underset{1}{\cancel{3}} \cdot 5} = \frac{1 \cdot 1}{1 \cdot 2 \cdot 1 \cdot 5} = \frac{1}{10}$$

◻ **Work Practice Problem 6**

> **Helpful Hint**
>
> Be careful when all factors of the numerator or denominator are divided out. In Example 6, the numerator was $1 \cdot 1 = 1$, so the final result was $\dfrac{1}{10}$.

In the fraction of Example 6, $\dfrac{6}{60}$, you may have immediately noticed that the largest common factor of 6 and 60 is 6. If so, you may simply divide out that common factor.

$$\frac{6}{60} = \frac{\overset{1}{\cancel{6}}}{\underset{1}{\cancel{6}} \cdot 10} = \frac{1}{1 \cdot 10} = \frac{1}{10} \qquad \text{Divide out the common factor of 6.}$$

Notice that the result, $\dfrac{1}{10}$, is in simplest form. If it were not, we would repeat the same procedure until the result was in simplest form.

Answers

5. $\dfrac{16}{5}$ or $3\dfrac{1}{5}$, **6.** $\dfrac{1}{7}$

✔ **Concept Check Answers**

a. correct, **b.** incorrect

EXAMPLE 7 Write in simplest form: $\dfrac{45}{75}$

Solution: You may write the prime factorizations of 45 and 75 or you may notice that these two numbers have a common factor of 15.

$$\frac{45}{75} = \frac{3 \cdot \overset{1}{\cancel{15}}}{5 \cdot \cancel{15}} = \frac{3 \cdot 1}{5 \cdot 1} = \frac{3}{5}$$

The numerator and denominator of $\dfrac{3}{5}$ have no common factors other than 1, so $\dfrac{3}{5}$ is in simplest form.

☐ **Work Practice Problem 7**

Objective B Determining Whether Two Fractions Are Equivalent

Recall that two fractions are equivalent if they represent the same part of a whole. One way to determine whether two fractions are equivalent is to see whether they simplify to the same fraction.

EXAMPLE 8 Determine whether $\dfrac{16}{40}$ and $\dfrac{10}{25}$ are equivalent.

Solution: Simplify each fraction.

$$\frac{16}{40} = \frac{\overset{1}{\cancel{8}} \cdot 2}{\underset{1}{\cancel{8}} \cdot 5} = \frac{1 \cdot 2}{1 \cdot 5} = \frac{2}{5}$$

$$\frac{10}{25} = \frac{2 \cdot \overset{1}{\cancel{5}}}{5 \cdot \underset{1}{\cancel{5}}} = \frac{2 \cdot 1}{5 \cdot 1} = \frac{2}{5}$$

Since these fractions are the same, $\dfrac{16}{40} = \dfrac{10}{25}$.

☐ **Work Practice Problem 8**

There is a shortcut method you may use to check or test whether two fractions are equivalent. In the example above, we learned that the fractions are equivalent, or

$$\frac{16}{40} = \frac{10}{25}$$

In this example above, we call $25 \cdot 16$ and $40 \cdot 10$ **cross products** because they are the products one obtains by multiplying across.

Cross Products

$$25 \cdot 16 \qquad 40 \cdot 10$$

$$\frac{16}{40} = \frac{10}{25}$$

Notice that these cross products are equal

$$25 \cdot 16 = 400, \quad 40 \cdot 10 = 400$$

PRACTICE PROBLEM 7

Write in simplest form: $\dfrac{42}{48}$

PRACTICE PROBLEM 8

Determine whether $\dfrac{7}{9}$ and $\dfrac{21}{27}$ are equivalent.

Answers

7. $\dfrac{7}{8}$, **8.** equivalent

In general, this is true for equivalent fractions.

Equality of Fractions

$$8 \cdot 6 \qquad\qquad\qquad 24 \cdot 2$$

$$\frac{6}{24} \overset{?}{=} \frac{2}{8}$$

Since the cross products ($8 \cdot 6 = 48$ and $24 \cdot 2 = 48$) are equal, the fractions are equal.

Note: If the cross products are not equal, the fractions are not equal.

PRACTICE PROBLEM 9

Determine whether $\frac{4}{13}$ and $\frac{5}{18}$ are equivalent.

EXAMPLE 9 Determine whether $\frac{8}{11}$ and $\frac{19}{26}$ are equivalent.

Solution: Let's check cross products.

$$26 \cdot 8 = 208 \qquad \frac{8}{11} \overset{?}{=} \frac{19}{26} \qquad 11 \cdot 19 = 209$$

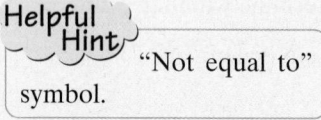

Helpful Hint

"Not equal to" symbol.

Since $208 \ne 209$, then $\frac{8}{11} \ne \frac{19}{26}$.

■ **Work Practice Problem 9**

Objective **C** **Solving Problems by Writing Fractions in Simplest Form**

Many real-life problems can be solved by writing fractions. To make the answers clearer, these fractions should be written in simplest form.

PRACTICE PROBLEM 10

Eighty pigs were used in a recent study of olestra, a calorie-free fat substitute. A group of 12 of these pigs were fed a diet high in fat. What fraction of the pigs were fed the high-fat diet in this study? Write your answer in simplest form. (*Source:* from a study conducted by the Procter & Gamble Company)

EXAMPLE 10 **Calculating the Fraction of Memorials in Washington, D.C.**

There are 28 national memorials in the United States. Seven of these are located in Washington, D.C. What fraction of the national memorials in the United States can be found in Washington, D.C.? Write the fraction in simplest form.
(*Source:* National Park Service)

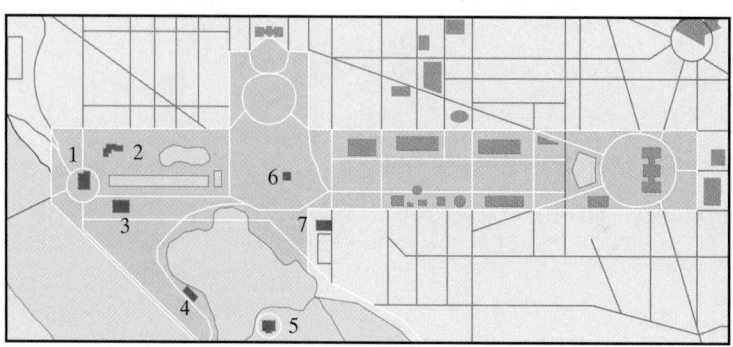

Answers

9. not equivalent,   **10.** $\frac{3}{20}$

Solution: First we determine the fraction of national memorials located in Washington, D.C.

$$\frac{7}{28} \begin{array}{l} \leftarrow \text{ number of national memorials in Washington, D.C.} \\ \leftarrow \text{ total number of national memorials in U.S.} \end{array}$$

Next we simplify the fraction.

$$\frac{7}{28} = \frac{\overset{1}{\cancel{7}}}{\underset{1}{\cancel{7}} \cdot 4} = \frac{1}{1 \cdot 4} = \frac{1}{4}$$

Thus, $\frac{1}{4}$ of the United States' national memorials are in Washington, D.C.

Work Practice Problem 10

CALCULATOR EXPLORATIONS Simplifying Fractions

Scientific Calculator

Many calculators have a fraction key, such as $\boxed{a\ b/c}$, that allows you to simplify a fraction on the calculator. For example, to simplify $\frac{324}{612}$, enter

The display will read

$$\boxed{\quad 9 \mid 17 \quad}$$

which represents $\frac{9}{17}$, the original fraction simplified.

> **Helpful Hint**
>
> The Calculator Explorations boxes in this chapter provide only an introduction to fraction keys on calculators. Any time you use a calculator, there are both advantages and limitations to its use. Never rely solely on your calculator. It is very important that you understand how to perform all operations on fractions by hand in order to progress through later topics. For further information, talk to your instructor.

Use your calculator to simplify each fraction.

1. $\frac{128}{224}$ 2. $\frac{231}{396}$ 3. $\frac{340}{459}$ 4. $\frac{999}{1350}$

5. $\frac{810}{432}$ 6. $\frac{315}{225}$ 7. $\frac{243}{54}$ 8. $\frac{689}{455}$

Objective **A** *Write each fraction in simplest form. See Examples 1 through 7.*

1. $\dfrac{3}{12}$

2. $\dfrac{5}{30}$

3. $\dfrac{4}{42}$

4. $\dfrac{9}{48}$

5. $\dfrac{14}{16}$

6. $\dfrac{22}{34}$

7. $\dfrac{20}{30}$

8. $\dfrac{70}{80}$

9. $\dfrac{35}{50}$

10. $\dfrac{25}{55}$

11. $\dfrac{63}{81}$

12. $\dfrac{21}{49}$

13. $\dfrac{24}{40}$

14. $\dfrac{36}{54}$

15. $\dfrac{27}{64}$

16. $\dfrac{32}{63}$

17. $\dfrac{25}{40}$

18. $\dfrac{36}{42}$

19. $\dfrac{40}{64}$

20. $\dfrac{28}{60}$

21. $\dfrac{56}{68}$

22. $\dfrac{39}{42}$

23. $\dfrac{36}{24}$

24. $\dfrac{60}{36}$

25. $\dfrac{90}{120}$

26. $\dfrac{60}{150}$

27. $\dfrac{70}{196}$

28. $\dfrac{98}{126}$

29. $\dfrac{66}{308}$

30. $\dfrac{65}{234}$

31. $\dfrac{55}{85}$

32. $\dfrac{78}{90}$

33. $\dfrac{75}{350}$

34. $\dfrac{72}{420}$

35. $\dfrac{189}{216}$

36. $\dfrac{144}{162}$

37. $\dfrac{288}{480}$

38. $\dfrac{135}{585}$

39. $\dfrac{224}{16}$

40. $\dfrac{270}{15}$

Objective **B** *Determine whether each pair of fractions is equivalent. See Examples 8 and 9.*

41. $\dfrac{3}{6}$ and $\dfrac{4}{8}$

42. $\dfrac{3}{9}$ and $\dfrac{2}{6}$

43. $\dfrac{7}{11}$ and $\dfrac{5}{8}$

44. $\dfrac{2}{5}$ and $\dfrac{4}{11}$

45. $\dfrac{10}{15}$ and $\dfrac{6}{9}$

46. $\dfrac{4}{10}$ and $\dfrac{6}{15}$

47. $\dfrac{3}{9}$ and $\dfrac{6}{18}$

48. $\dfrac{2}{8}$ and $\dfrac{7}{28}$

49. $\frac{10}{13}$ and $\frac{12}{15}$ **50.** $\frac{16}{20}$ and $\frac{9}{12}$ **51.** $\frac{8}{18}$ and $\frac{12}{24}$ **52.** $\frac{6}{21}$ and $\frac{14}{35}$

Objective **C** *Solve. Write each fraction in simplest form. See Example 10.*

53. A work shift for an employee at McDonald's consists of 8 hours. What fraction of the employee's work shift is represented by 2 hours?

54. Two thousand baseball caps were sold one year at the U.S. Open Golf Tournament. What fractional part of this total does 200 caps represent?

55. There are 5280 feet in a mile. What fraction of a mile is represented by 2640 feet?

56. There are 100 centimeters in 1 meter. What fraction of a meter is 20 centimeters?

57. Fifteen states in the United States have Ritz-Carlton hotels. (*Source:* Ritz-Carlton Hotel Company, LLC)

     a. What fraction of states can claim at least one Ritz-Carlton hotel?

     b. How many states do not have a Ritz-Carlton hotel?

     c. Write the fraction of states without a Ritz-Carlton hotel.

58. There were 74 national monuments in the United States. Ten of these monuments are located in New Mexico. (*Source:* National Park Service)

     a. What fraction of the national monuments in the United States can be found in New Mexico?

     b. How many of the national monuments in the United States are found outside New Mexico

     c. Write the fraction of national monuments found in states other than New Mexico.

59. The outer wall of the Pentagon is 24 inches wide. Ten inches is concrete, 8 inches is brick, and 6 inches is limestone. What fraction of the wall is concrete? (*Source: USA Today,* 1/28/2000)

60. There are 35 students in a biology class. If 10 students made an A on the first test, what fraction of the students made an A?

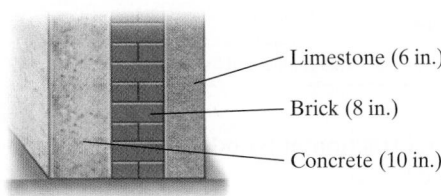

Limestone (6 in.)

Brick (8 in.)

Concrete (10 in.)

61. As Internet usage grows in the United States, more and more state governments are placing services online. Twenty-eight states have Web sites that allow residents to pay their state income tax online.

     a. How many states do not have this type of Web site?

     b. What fraction of states do not have this type of Web site? (*Source:* Center for Digital Government)

62. Chris Callac just bought a brand new 2005 Toyota Camry for $22,000. His old car was traded in for $10,000.

     a. How much of his purchase price was not covered by his trade-in?

     b. What fraction of the purchase price was not covered by the trade-in?

Review

Multiply. See Section 1.6.

63.   91
         $\times\ 4$

64.   73
         $\times\ 8$

65.   387
         $\times\ 6$

66.   562
         $\times\ 9$

67.   72
         $\times\ 35$

68.   238
         $\times\ 26$

Concept Extensions

69. In your own words, define equivalent fractions.

70. Given a fraction, say $\frac{3}{8}$, how many fractions are there that are equivalent to it? Explain your answer.

Write each fraction in simplest form.

71. $\dfrac{3975}{6625}$

72. $\dfrac{9506}{12{,}222}$

There are generally considered to be eight basic blood types. The table shows the number of people with the various blood types in a typical group of 100 blood donors. Use the table to answer Exercises 73 through 77. Write each answer in simplest form.

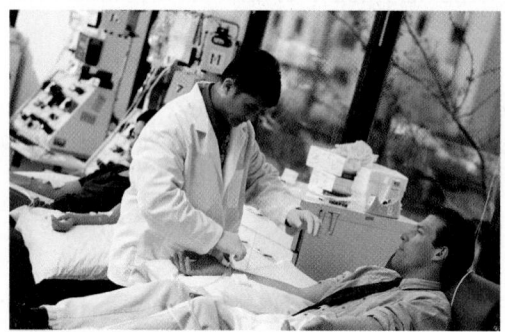

Distribution of Blood Types in Blood Donors	
Blood Type	**Number of People**
O Rh-positive	37
O Rh-negative	7
A Rh-positive	36
A Rh-negative	6
B Rh-positive	9
B Rh-negative	1
AB Rh-positive	3
AB Rh-negative	1
(*Source:* American Red Cross Biomedical Services)	

73. What fraction of blood donors have blood type A Rh-positive?

74. What fraction of blood donors have an O blood type?

75. What fraction of blood donors have an AB blood type?

76. What fraction of blood donors have a B blood type?

77. What fraction of blood donors have the negative Rh-factor?

The following graph is called a circle graph or pie chart. Each sector (shaped like a piece of pie) shows the fraction of entering college freshmen who expect to major in each discipline shown. The whole circle represents the entire class of college freshmen. Use this graph to answer Exercises 78 through 81.

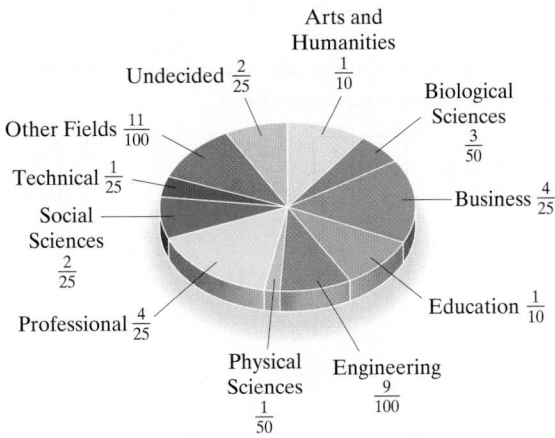

Source: Higher Education Research Institute

78. What fraction of entering college freshmen plan to major in education?

79. What fraction of entering college freshmen plan to major in social sciences?

80. Why is the Professional sector the same size as the Business sector?

81. Why is the Physical Sciences sector smaller than the Biological Sciences sector?

Summary on Fractions, Mixed Numbers, and Factors

Use a fraction to represent the shaded area of each figure. If the fraction is improper, also write the fraction as a mixed number.

1.

2.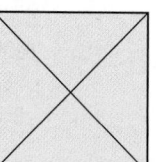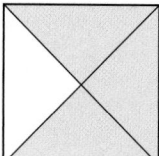

Solve.

3. In a survey, 73 people out of 85 get fewer than 8 hours of sleep each night. What fraction of people in the survey get fewer than 8 hours of sleep?

4. Sketch a diagram to represent $\frac{9}{13}$.

Simplify.

5. $\frac{11}{11}$ **6.** $\frac{17}{1}$ **7.** $\frac{0}{3}$ **8.** $\frac{7}{0}$

Write each mixed number as an improper fraction.

9. $3\frac{1}{8}$ **10.** $5\frac{3}{5}$ **11.** $9\frac{6}{7}$ **12.** $20\frac{1}{7}$

Write each improper fraction as a mixed number or a whole number.

13. $\frac{20}{7}$ **14.** $\frac{55}{11}$ **15.** $\frac{39}{8}$ **16.** $\frac{98}{11}$

List the factors of each number.

17. 35 **18.** 40

Determine whether each number is prime or composite.

19. 72 **20.** 13

Answers

1. _____

2. _____

3. _____

4. _____

5. _____

6. _____

7. _____

8. _____

9. _____

10. _____

11. _____

12. _____

13. _____

14. _____

15. _____

16. _____

17. _____

18. _____

19. _____

20. _____

Write the prime factorization of each composite number. Write prime if the number is prime.
Write any repeated factors using exponents.

21. 65   **22.** 70   **23.** 96   **24.** 132

25. 252   **26.** 31   **27.** 315   **28.** 441

29. 286   **30.** 41

Write each fraction in simplest form.

31. $\dfrac{2}{14}$ **32.** $\dfrac{24}{20}$ **33.** $\dfrac{18}{38}$ **34.** $\dfrac{42}{110}$

35. $\dfrac{56}{60}$ **36.** $\dfrac{72}{80}$ **37.** $\dfrac{54}{135}$ **38.** $\dfrac{90}{240}$

39. $\dfrac{165}{210}$ **40.** $\dfrac{245}{385}$

Determine whether each pair of fractions is equivalent.

41. $\dfrac{7}{8}$ and $\dfrac{9}{10}$ **42.** $\dfrac{10}{12}$ and $\dfrac{15}{18}$

43. Of the 50 states, 2 states are not adjacent to any other states.
    a. What fraction of the states are not adjacent to other states?
    b. How many states are adjacent to other states.
    c. What fraction of the states are adjacent to other states?

44. In a recent year, 460 films were released and rated. Of these, 275 were rated PG-13.
    (*Source:* Motion Picture Association)
    a. What fraction were rated PG-13?
    b. How many films were rated other than PG-13?
    c. What fraction of films were rated other than PG-13?

---

21. _____

22. _____

23. _____

24. _____

25. _____

26. _____

27. _____

28. _____

29. _____

30. _____

31. _____

32. _____

33. _____ **34.** _____

35. _____ **36.** _____

37. _____ **38.** _____

39. _____ **40.** _____

41. _____

42. _____

43. a. _____

    b. _____

    c. _____

44. a. _____

    b. _____

    c. _____

2.4 MULTIPLYING FRACTIONS

Objective **A** Multiplying Fractions

Let's use a diagram to discover how fractions are multiplied. For example, to multiply $\frac{1}{2}$ and $\frac{3}{4}$, we find $\frac{1}{2}$ of $\frac{3}{4}$. To do this, we begin with a diagram showing $\frac{3}{4}$ of a rectangle's area shaded.

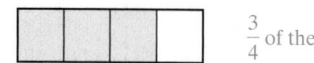

$\frac{3}{4}$ of the rectangle's area is shaded.

To find $\frac{1}{2}$ of $\frac{3}{4}$, we heavily shade $\frac{1}{2}$ of the part that is already shaded.

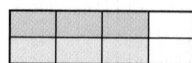

By counting smaller rectangles, we see that $\frac{3}{8}$ of the larger rectangle is now heavily shaded, so that

$$\frac{1}{2} \text{ of } \frac{3}{4} \text{ is } \frac{3}{8}, \text{ or } \frac{1}{2} \cdot \frac{3}{4} = \frac{3}{8} \quad \text{Notice that } \frac{1}{2} \cdot \frac{3}{4} = \frac{1 \cdot 3}{2 \cdot 4} = \frac{3}{8}.$$

Multiplying Fractions

To multiply two fractions, multiply the numerators and multiply the denominators.

If a, b, c, and d represent positive whole numbers, we have

$$\frac{a}{b} \cdot \frac{c}{d} = \frac{a \cdot c}{b \cdot d}$$

PRACTICE PROBLEMS 1–2

Multiply.

1. $\frac{3}{8} \cdot \frac{5}{7}$ **2.** $\frac{1}{3} \cdot \frac{1}{6}$

EXAMPLES Multiply.

1. $\frac{2}{3} \cdot \frac{5}{11} = \frac{2 \cdot 5}{3 \cdot 11} = \frac{10}{33}$

This fraction is in simplest form since 10 and 33 have no common factors other than 1.

2. $\frac{1}{4} \cdot \frac{1}{2} = \frac{1 \cdot 1}{4 \cdot 2} = \frac{1}{8}$

▨ **Work Practice Problems 1–2**

Answers

1. $\frac{15}{56}$, **2.** $\frac{1}{18}$

EXAMPLE 3 Multiply and simplify: $\dfrac{6}{7} \cdot \dfrac{14}{27}$

Solution:

$$\frac{6}{7} \cdot \frac{14}{27} = \frac{6 \cdot 14}{7 \cdot 27}$$

We can simplify by finding the prime factorizations and using our shortcut procedure of dividing out common factors in the numerator and denominator.

$$\frac{6 \cdot 14}{7 \cdot 27} = \frac{2 \cdot \overset{1}{\cancel{3}} \cdot 2 \cdot \overset{1}{\cancel{7}}}{\underset{1}{\cancel{7}} \cdot \underset{1}{\cancel{3}} \cdot 3 \cdot 3} = \frac{2 \cdot 2}{3 \cdot 3} = \frac{4}{9}$$

■ **Work Practice Problem 3**

Helpful Hint　　Remember that the shortcut procedure above is the same as removing factors of 1 in the product.

$$\frac{6 \cdot 14}{7 \cdot 27} = \frac{2 \cdot 3 \cdot 2 \cdot 7}{7 \cdot 3 \cdot 3 \cdot 3} = \frac{7}{7} \cdot \frac{3}{3} \cdot \frac{2 \cdot 2}{3 \cdot 3} = 1 \cdot 1 \cdot \frac{4}{9} = \frac{4}{9}$$

Helpful Hint　　In simplifying a product, don't forget that it may be possible to identify common factors without actually writing the prime factorization. For example,

$$\frac{10}{11} \cdot \frac{1}{20} = \frac{10 \cdot 1}{11 \cdot 20} = \frac{\overset{1}{\cancel{10}} \cdot 1}{11 \cdot \underset{1}{\cancel{10}} \cdot 2} = \frac{1}{11 \cdot 2} = \frac{1}{22}$$

EXAMPLE 4 Multiply and simplify: $\dfrac{23}{32} \cdot \dfrac{4}{7}$

Solution: Notice that 4 and 32 have a common factor of 4.

$$\frac{23}{32} \cdot \frac{4}{7} = \frac{23 \cdot 4}{32 \cdot 7} = \frac{23 \cdot \overset{1}{\cancel{4}}}{\underset{1}{\cancel{4}} \cdot 8 \cdot 7} = \frac{23}{8 \cdot 7} = \frac{23}{56}$$

■ **Work Practice Problem 4**

After multiplying two fractions, always check to see whether the product can be simplified.

EXAMPLES Multiply.

5. $\dfrac{3}{4} \cdot \dfrac{8}{5} = \dfrac{3 \cdot 8}{4 \cdot 5} = \dfrac{3 \cdot \overset{1}{\cancel{4}} \cdot 2}{\underset{1}{\cancel{4}} \cdot 5} = \dfrac{6}{5}$

6. $\dfrac{6}{13} \cdot \dfrac{26}{30} = \dfrac{6 \cdot 26}{13 \cdot 30} = \dfrac{\overset{1}{\cancel{6}} \cdot \overset{1}{\cancel{13}} \cdot 2}{\underset{1}{\cancel{13}} \cdot \underset{1}{\cancel{6}} \cdot 5} = \dfrac{2}{5}$

7. $\dfrac{1}{3} \cdot \dfrac{2}{5} \cdot \dfrac{9}{16} = \dfrac{1 \cdot 2 \cdot 9}{3 \cdot 5 \cdot 16} = \dfrac{1 \cdot \overset{1}{\cancel{2}} \cdot \overset{1}{\cancel{3}} \cdot 3}{\underset{1}{\cancel{3}} \cdot 5 \cdot \underset{1}{\cancel{2}} \cdot 8} = \dfrac{3}{40}$

■ **Work Practice Problems 5–7**

PRACTICE PROBLEM 3

Multiply and simplify: $\dfrac{6}{55} \cdot \dfrac{5}{8}$

PRACTICE PROBLEM 4

Multiply and simplify: $\dfrac{4}{15} \cdot \dfrac{3}{8}$

PRACTICE PROBLEMS 5–7

Multiply.

5. $\dfrac{2}{5} \cdot \dfrac{20}{7}$

6. $\dfrac{4}{11} \cdot \dfrac{33}{16}$

7. $\dfrac{1}{6} \cdot \dfrac{3}{10} \cdot \dfrac{25}{16}$

Answers

3. $\dfrac{3}{44}$, **4.** $\dfrac{1}{10}$, **5.** $\dfrac{8}{7}$, **6.** $\dfrac{3}{4}$, **7.** $\dfrac{5}{64}$

Objective B Multiplying Fractions and Mixed Numbers or Whole Numbers

When multiplying a fraction and a mixed or a whole number, remember that mixed and whole numbers can be written as fractions.

Multiplying Fractions and Mixed Numbers or Whole Numbers

To multiply with mixed numbers or whole numbers, first write any mixed or whole numbers as fractions and then multiply as usual.

PRACTICE PROBLEM 8

Multiply and simplify: $2\dfrac{1}{2} \cdot \dfrac{8}{15}$

EXAMPLE 8 Multiply: $3\dfrac{1}{3} \cdot \dfrac{7}{8}$

Solution: The mixed number $3\dfrac{1}{3}$ can be written as the fraction $\dfrac{10}{3}$. Then,

$$3\frac{1}{3} \cdot \frac{7}{8} = \frac{10}{3} \cdot \frac{7}{8} = \frac{\overset{1}{\cancel{2}} \cdot 5 \cdot 7}{3 \cdot \underset{1}{\cancel{2}} \cdot 4} = \frac{35}{12} \quad \text{or} \quad 2\frac{11}{12}$$

🔲 **Work Practice Problem 8**

Don't forget that a whole number can be written as a fraction by writing the whole number over 1. For example,

$$20 = \frac{20}{1} \qquad \text{and} \qquad 7 = \frac{7}{1}$$

PRACTICE PROBLEM 9

Multiply.

9. $\dfrac{2}{3} \cdot 18$

EXAMPLE 9 Multiply.

$$\frac{3}{4} \cdot 20 = \frac{3}{4} \cdot \frac{20}{1} = \frac{3 \cdot 20}{4 \cdot 1} = \frac{3 \cdot \overset{1}{\cancel{4}} \cdot 5}{\underset{1}{\cancel{4}} \cdot 1} = \frac{15}{1} \quad \text{or} \quad 15$$

🔲 **Work Practice Problem 9**

When both numbers to be multiplied are mixed or whole numbers, it is a good idea to estimate the product to see if your answer is reasonable. To do this, we first practice rounding mixed numbers to the nearest whole. If the fraction part of the mixed number is $\dfrac{1}{2}$ or greater, we round the whole number part up. If the fraction part of the mixed number is less than $\dfrac{1}{2}$, then we do not round the whole number part up. Study the table below for examples.

Mixed Number	Rounding
$5\dfrac{1}{4}$ $\dfrac{1}{4}$ is less than $\dfrac{1}{2}$	Thus, $5\dfrac{1}{4}$ rounds to 5.
$3\dfrac{9}{16}$ ← 9 is greater than 8. → Half of 16 is 8.	Thus, $3\dfrac{7}{16}$ rounds to 4.
$1\dfrac{3}{7}$ ← 3 is less than $3\dfrac{1}{2}$. → Half of 7 is $3\dfrac{1}{2}$.	Thus, $1\dfrac{3}{7}$ rounds to 1.

Answers

8. $\dfrac{4}{3}$ or $1\dfrac{1}{3}$, **9.** 12

EXAMPLES Multiply. Check by estimating.

10. $1\frac{2}{3} \cdot 2\frac{1}{4} = \frac{5}{3} \cdot \frac{9}{4} = \frac{5 \cdot 9}{3 \cdot 4} = \frac{5 \cdot \overset{1}{\cancel{3}} \cdot 3}{\underset{1}{\cancel{3}} \cdot 4} = \frac{15}{4}$ or $3\frac{3}{4}$ Exact

PRACTICE PROBLEMS 10–11

Multiply.

10. $3\frac{1}{5} \cdot 2\frac{3}{4}$ **11.** $5 \cdot 3\frac{11}{15}$

Let's check by estimating.

$1\frac{2}{3}$ rounds to 2, $2\frac{1}{4}$ rounds to 2, and $2 \cdot 2 = 4$ Estimate

The estimate is close to the exact value, so our answer is reasonable.

11. $7 \cdot 2\frac{11}{14} = \frac{7}{1} \cdot \frac{39}{14} = \frac{7 \cdot 39}{1 \cdot 14} = \frac{\overset{1}{\cancel{7}} \cdot 39}{1 \cdot 2 \cdot \underset{1}{\cancel{7}}} = \frac{39}{2}$ or $19\frac{1}{2}$ Exact

To estimate,

$2\frac{11}{14}$ rounds to 3 and $7 \cdot 3 = 21$.   Estimate

The estimate is close to the exact value, so our answer is reasonable.

▣ **Work Practice Problems 10–11**

Recall from Section 1.6 that 0 multiplied by any number is 0. This is true of fractions and mixed numbers also.

EXAMPLES Multiply.

12. $0 \cdot \frac{3}{5} = 0$

13. $2\frac{3}{8} \cdot 0 = 0$

▣ **Work Practice Problems 12–13**

PRACTICE PROBLEMS 12–13

Multiply.

12. $\frac{9}{11} \cdot 0$ **13.** $0 \cdot 4\frac{1}{8}$

✔**Concept Check**

Find the error.

$2\frac{1}{4} \cdot \frac{1}{2} = 2\frac{1 \cdot 1}{4 \cdot 2} = 2\frac{1}{8}$

Objective **C** Solving Problems by Multiplying Fractions

To solve real-life problems that involve multiplying fractions, we use our four problem-solving steps from Chapter 1. In Example 14, a new key word that implies multiplication is used. That key word is "**of.**"

Helpful Hint

"of" usually translates to multiplication.

Answers

10. $\frac{44}{5}$ or $8\frac{4}{5}$, **11.** $\frac{56}{3}$ or $18\frac{2}{3}$, **12.** 0,

13. 0

✔ **Concept Check Answer**

forgot to change mixed number to fraction

PRACTICE PROBLEM 14

About $\frac{1}{3}$ of all plant and animal species in the United States are at risk of becoming extinct. There are 20,439 known species of plants and animals in the United States. How many species are at risk of extinction? (*Source:* The Nature Conservancy)

EXAMPLE 14 **Finding the Number of Roller Coasters in an Amusement Park**

Cedar Point is an amusement park located in Sandusky, Ohio. Its collection of 68 rides is the largest in the world. Of the rides, $\frac{7}{34}$ are roller coasters. How many roller coasters are in Cedar Point's collection of rides? (*Source:* Cedar Fair, L.P.)

Solution:

1. UNDERSTAND the problem. To do so, read and reread the problem. We are told that $\frac{7}{34}$ of Cedar Point's rides are roller coasters. The word "of" here means multiplication.

2. TRANSLATE.

In words:	Number of roller coasters	is	$\frac{7}{34}$	of	total rides at Cedar Point
	↓	↓	↓	↓	↓
Translate:	Number of roller coasters	=	$\frac{7}{34}$	·	68

3. SOLVE: Before we solve, let's estimate a reasonable answer. The fraction $\frac{7}{34}$ is less than $\frac{1}{2}$ (draw a diagram, if needed), and $\frac{1}{2}$ of 68 rides is 34 rides, so the number of roller coasters should be less than 34.

$$\frac{7}{34} \cdot 68 = \frac{7}{34} \cdot \frac{68}{1} = \frac{7 \cdot 68}{34 \cdot 1} = \frac{7 \cdot \overset{1}{\cancel{34}} \cdot 2}{\underset{1}{\cancel{34}} \cdot 1} = \frac{14}{1} \quad \text{or} \quad 14$$

4. INTERPRET. *Check* your work. From our estimate, our answer is reasonable. *State* your conclusion: The number of roller coasters at Cedar Point is 14.

■ **Work Practice Problem 14**

> **Helpful Hint**
>
> To help visualize a fractional part of a whole number, look at the diagram below.
>
> $\frac{1}{5}$ of 60 = ?
>
>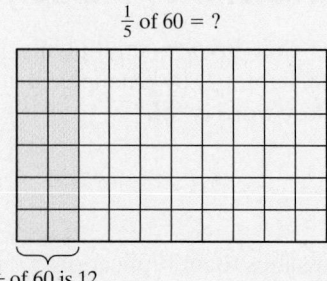
>
> $\frac{1}{5}$ of 60 is 12.

Answer

14. 6813 species

Mental Math

Round each mixed number to the nearest whole number.

1. $7\frac{7}{8}$

2. $11\frac{3}{4}$

3. $6\frac{1}{5}$

4. $4\frac{1}{9}$

5. $8\frac{5}{22}$

6. $9\frac{7}{24}$

7. $19\frac{11}{20}$

8. $18\frac{12}{22}$

2.4 EXERCISE SET

FOR EXTRA HELP

Student Solutions Manual · PH Math/Tutor Center · CD/Video for Review · MathXL® · MyMathLab

Objective A *Multiply. Write each answer in simplest form. See Examples 1 through 7 and 12.*

1. $\frac{1}{3} \cdot \frac{2}{5}$

2. $\frac{2}{3} \cdot \frac{4}{7}$

3. $\frac{6}{5} \cdot \frac{1}{7}$

4. $\frac{7}{3} \cdot \frac{1}{4}$

5. $\frac{3}{10} \cdot \frac{3}{8}$

6. $\frac{2}{5} \cdot \frac{7}{11}$

7. $\frac{2}{7} \cdot \frac{5}{8}$

8. $\frac{7}{8} \cdot \frac{2}{3}$

9. $\frac{16}{5} \cdot \frac{3}{4}$

10. $\frac{8}{3} \cdot \frac{5}{12}$

11. $\frac{5}{28} \cdot \frac{2}{25}$

12. $\frac{4}{35} \cdot \frac{5}{24}$

13. $0 \cdot \frac{8}{9}$

14. $\frac{11}{12} \cdot 0$

15. $\frac{1}{10} \cdot \frac{1}{11}$

16. $\frac{1}{9} \cdot \frac{1}{13}$

17. $\frac{18}{20} \cdot \frac{36}{99}$

18. $\frac{5}{32} \cdot \frac{64}{100}$

19. $\frac{3}{8} \cdot \frac{9}{10}$

20. $\frac{4}{5} \cdot \frac{8}{25}$

21. $\frac{11}{20} \cdot \frac{1}{7} \cdot \frac{5}{22}$

22. $\frac{27}{32} \cdot \frac{10}{13} \cdot \frac{16}{30}$

23. $\frac{1}{3} \cdot \frac{2}{7} \cdot \frac{1}{5}$

24. $\frac{3}{5} \cdot \frac{1}{2} \cdot \frac{3}{7}$

25. $\frac{9}{20} \cdot 0 \cdot \frac{4}{19}$

26. $\frac{8}{11} \cdot \frac{4}{7} \cdot 0$

27. $\frac{3}{14} \cdot \frac{6}{25} \cdot \frac{5}{27} \cdot \frac{7}{6}$

28. $\frac{7}{8} \cdot \frac{9}{20} \cdot \frac{12}{22} \cdot \frac{11}{14}$

Objective B *Multiply. Write each answer in simplest form. For those exercises marked, find both an exact product and an estimated product. See Examples 8 through 11 and 13.*

29. $12 \cdot \frac{1}{4}$

30. $\frac{2}{3} \cdot 6$

31. $\frac{5}{8} \cdot 4$

32. $10 \cdot \frac{7}{8}$

33. $1\frac{1}{4} \cdot \frac{4}{25}$

151

34. $\dfrac{3}{22} \cdot 3\dfrac{2}{3}$ **35.** $\dfrac{2}{5} \cdot 4\dfrac{1}{6}$ **36.** $2\dfrac{1}{9} \cdot \dfrac{6}{7}$ **37.** $\dfrac{2}{3} \cdot 1$ **38.** $1 \cdot \dfrac{5}{9}$

39. $2\dfrac{1}{5} \cdot 3\dfrac{1}{2}$ **40.** $2\dfrac{1}{4} \cdot 7\dfrac{1}{8}$ **41.** $3\dfrac{4}{5} \cdot 6\dfrac{2}{7}$ **42.** $5\dfrac{5}{6} \cdot 7\dfrac{3}{5}$ **43.** $5 \cdot 2\dfrac{1}{2}$

Exact: Exact: Exact: Exact:

Estimate: Estimate: Estimate: Estimate:

44. $6 \cdot 3\dfrac{1}{3}$ **45.** $1\dfrac{1}{5} \cdot 12\dfrac{1}{2}$ **46.** $1\dfrac{1}{6} \cdot 7\dfrac{1}{5}$ **47.** $\dfrac{3}{4} \cdot 16 \cdot \dfrac{1}{2}$ **48.** $\dfrac{7}{8} \cdot 24 \cdot \dfrac{1}{3}$

49. $\dfrac{3}{10} \cdot 15 \cdot 2\dfrac{1}{2}$ **50.** $\dfrac{11}{20} \cdot 12 \cdot 3\dfrac{1}{3}$ **51.** $3\dfrac{1}{2} \cdot 1\dfrac{3}{4} \cdot 2\dfrac{2}{3}$ **52.** $4\dfrac{1}{2} \cdot 2\dfrac{1}{9} \cdot 1\dfrac{1}{5}$

Objectives **A** **B** **Mixed Practice** *Multiply and simplify. See Examples 1 through 13.*

53. $\dfrac{1}{4} \cdot \dfrac{2}{15}$ **54.** $\dfrac{3}{8} \cdot \dfrac{5}{12}$ **55.** $\dfrac{19}{37} \cdot 0$ **56.** $0 \cdot \dfrac{3}{31}$ **57.** $2\dfrac{4}{5} \cdot 1\dfrac{1}{7}$

58. $3\dfrac{1}{5} \cdot 2\dfrac{11}{32}$ **59.** $\dfrac{3}{2} \cdot \dfrac{7}{3}$ **60.** $\dfrac{15}{2} \cdot \dfrac{3}{5}$ **61.** $\dfrac{6}{15} \cdot \dfrac{5}{16}$ **62.** $\dfrac{9}{20} \cdot \dfrac{10}{90}$

63. $\dfrac{7}{72} \cdot \dfrac{9}{49}$ **64.** $\dfrac{3}{80} \cdot \dfrac{2}{27}$ **65.** $20 \cdot \dfrac{11}{12}$ **66.** $30 \cdot \dfrac{8}{9}$ **67.** $9\dfrac{5}{7} \cdot 8\dfrac{1}{5} \cdot 0$

68. $4\dfrac{11}{13} \cdot 0 \cdot 12\dfrac{1}{13}$ **69.** $12\dfrac{4}{5} \cdot 6\dfrac{7}{8} \cdot \dfrac{26}{77}$ **70.** $14\dfrac{2}{5} \cdot 8\dfrac{1}{3} \cdot \dfrac{11}{16}$

Objective **C** *Solve. Write each answer in simplest form. For Exercises 71 through 74, recall that "of" translates to multiplication. See Example 14.*

71. Find $\dfrac{1}{4}$ of 200.   **72.** Find $\dfrac{1}{5}$ of 200.   **73.** Find $\dfrac{5}{6}$ of 24.   **74.** Find $\dfrac{5}{8}$ of 24.

75. Each turn of a screw sinks it $\frac{3}{16}$ of an inch deeper into a piece of wood. Find how deep the screw is after 8 turns.

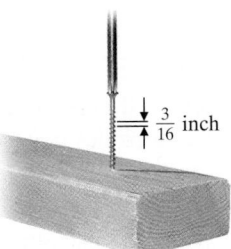

$\frac{3}{16}$ inch

76. A veterinarian's dipping vat holds 36 gallons of liquid. She normally fills it $\frac{5}{6}$ full of a medicated flea dip solution. Find how many gallons of solution are normally in the vat.

36 gallons
$\frac{5}{6}$ full

77. The Oregon National Historic Trail is 2,170 miles long. It begins in Independence, Missouri, and ends in Oregon City, Oregon. Manfred Coulon has hiked $\frac{2}{5}$ of the trail before. How many miles has he hiked? (*Source:* National Park Service)

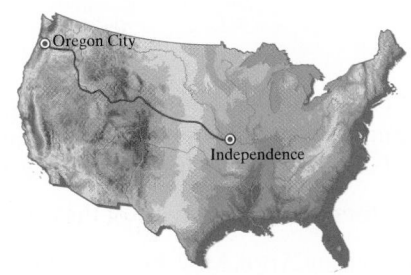

Oregon City

Independence

78. Movie theater owners received a total of $7660 million in movie admission tickets, about $\frac{7}{10}$ of this amount was for R-rated movies. Find the amount of money received from R-rated movies. (*Source:* Motion Picture Association of America)

79. An estimate for the measure of an adult's wrist is $\frac{1}{4}$ of the waist size. If Jorge has a 34-inch waist, estimate the size of his wrist.

80. An estimate for an adult's waist measurement is found by multiplying the neck size (in inches) by 2. Jock's neck measures $\frac{36}{2}$ inches. Estimate his waist measurement.

81. The radius of a circle is one-half of its diameter as shown. If the diameter of a circle is $\frac{3}{8}$ of an inch, what is its radius?

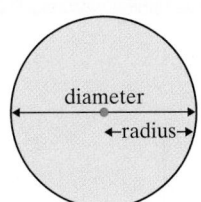

diameter

←radius→

82. The plans for a deck call for $\frac{2}{5}$ of a 4-foot post to be underground. Find the length of the post that is to be buried.

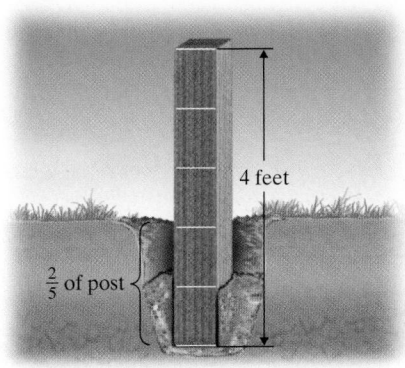

4 feet

$\frac{2}{5}$ of post

83. A patient was told that no more than $\frac{1}{5}$ of his calories should come from fat. If his diet consists of 3000 calories a day, how many of these calories can come from fat?

84. A recipe calls for $\frac{1}{3}$ of a cup of flour. How much flour should be used if only $\frac{1}{2}$ of the recipe is being made?

85. A special on a cruise to the Bahamas is advertised to be $\frac{2}{3}$ of the regular price. If the regular price is $2757, what is the sale price?

86. The Gonzales recently sold their house for $102,000, but $\frac{3}{50}$ of this amount goes to the real estate companies that helped them sell their house. How much money do the Gonzales pay to the real estate companies?

87. A sidewalk is built 6 bricks wide by laying each brick side by side. How many inches wide is the sidewalk if each brick measures $3\frac{1}{4}$ inches wide?

88. The nutrition label on a can of crushed pineapple shows 9 grams of carbohydrates for each cup of pineapple. How many grams of carbohydrates are in a $2\frac{1}{2}$-cup can?

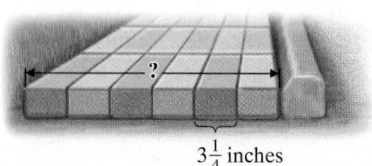

$3\frac{1}{4}$ inches

89. At this writing, the smallest digital camera is the SPYZ camera from a Japanese company called Che-ez! The face of the camera measures $2\frac{9}{25}$ inches by $1\frac{13}{25}$ inches and is slightly bigger than a Zippo lighter. Find the area of the face of this camera. (Area = length · width)

90. As part of his research, famous tornado expert Dr. T. Fujita studied approximately 31,050 tornadoes that occurred in the United States between 1916 and 1985. He found that roughly $\frac{7}{10}$ of these tornadoes occurred during April, May, June, and July. How many of these tornadoes occurred during these four months? (*Source: U.S. Tornadoes Part 1*, T. Fujita, University of Chicago)

$1\frac{13}{25}$ in.

$2\frac{9}{25}$ in.

Find the area of each rectangle. Recall that area = length · width.

△ **91.**

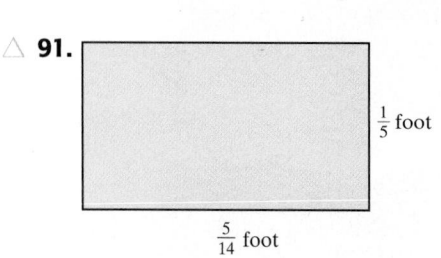

$\frac{1}{5}$ foot

$\frac{5}{14}$ foot

△ **92.**

$\frac{1}{2}$ mile

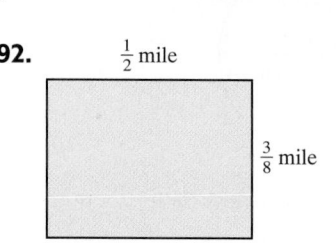

$\frac{3}{8}$ mile

△ **93.**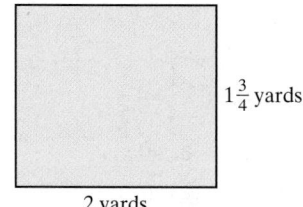

$1\frac{3}{4}$ yards

2 yards

△ **94.**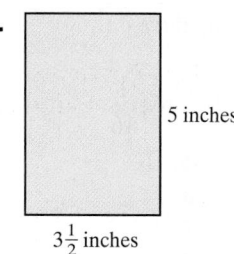

5 inches

$3\frac{1}{2}$ inches

*The following graph is called a **circle graph** or **pie chart**. Each sector (shaped like a piece of pie) shows the fractional part of a car's total mileage that falls into a particular category. The whole circle represents a car's total mileage.*

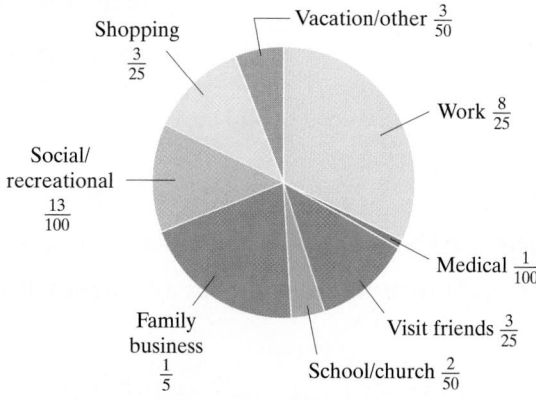

Shopping $\frac{3}{25}$

Vacation/other $\frac{3}{50}$

Work $\frac{8}{25}$

Social/recreational $\frac{13}{100}$

Medical $\frac{1}{100}$

Family business $\frac{1}{5}$

Visit friends $\frac{3}{25}$

School/church $\frac{2}{50}$

Source: The American Automobile Manufacturers Association and The National Automobile Dealers Association

In one year, a family drove 12,000 miles in the family car. Use the circle graph to determine how many of these miles might be expected to fall in the categories shown in Exercises 95 through 98.

95. Work

96. Shopping

97. Family business

98. Medical

Review

Divide. See Section 1.7.

99. $8\overline{)1648}$

100. $7\overline{)3920}$

101. $23\overline{)1300}$

102. $31\overline{)2500}$

Concept Extensions

103. In your own words, explain how to multiply
  a. fractions
  b. mixed numbers

104. In your own words, explain how to round a mixed number to the nearest whole number.

Solve. See the Concept Check in this section.

105. A student asked you to check his work below. Is it correct? If not, where is the error?

$$3\frac{2}{3} \cdot 1\frac{1}{7} = 3\frac{2}{21}$$

Choose the best estimate for each product.

106. $3\frac{1}{5} \cdot 4\frac{5}{8}$

    a. 7
    b. 15
    c. 8
    d. $12\frac{1}{8}$

107. $\frac{11}{12} \cdot 4\frac{1}{16}$

    a. 16
    b. 1
    c. 4
    d. 8

108. $9 \cdot \frac{10}{11}$

    a. 9
    b. 90
    c. 99
    d. 0

109. $7\frac{1}{4} \cdot 4\frac{1}{5}$

    a. 40
    b. $\frac{7}{5}$
    c. 35
    d. 28

110. If $\frac{3}{4}$ of 36 students on a first bus are girls and $\frac{2}{3}$ of the 30 students on a second bus are *boys,* how many students on the two buses are girls.

111. According to the 2000 census, in that year there were 34,800,000 Americans age 65 or older. About $\frac{11}{20}$ of these older Americans had annual incomes *under* $15,000. How many older Americans had incomes greater than or equal to $15,000? (*Source:* U.S. Census Bureau)

112. In 2004, there were approximately 10,600 commercial radio stations broadcasting in the United States. Of these stations, $\frac{32}{265}$ were news/talk stations. How many radio stations were news/talk stations in 2004? (*Source:* Corporation for Public Broadcasting)

 STUDY SKILLS BUILDER

How Are Your Homework Assignments Going?

It is very important in mathematics to keep up with homework. Why? Many concepts build on each other. Often your understanding of a day's concepts depends on an understanding of the previous day's material.

Remember that completing your homework assignment involves a lot more than attempting a few of the problems assigned.

To complete a homework assignment, remember these four things:

- Attempt all of it.
- Check it.
- Correct it.
- If needed, ask questions about it.

Take a moment and review your completed homework assignments. Answer the questions below based on this review.

1. Approximate the fraction of your homework you have attempted.

2. Approximate the fraction of your homework you have checked (if possible).

3. If you are able to check your homework, have you corrected it when errors have been found?

4. When working homework, if you do not understand a concept, what do you do?

2.5 DIVIDING FRACTIONS

Objective A Finding Reciprocals of Fractions

Before we can divide fractions, we need to know how to find the **reciprocal** of a fraction or whole number.

Objectives

A Find the Reciprocal of a Fraction.

B Divide Fractions.

C Divide Fractions and Mixed Numbers or Whole Numbers.

D Solve Problems by Dividing Fractions.

Reciprocal of a Number

Two numbers are **reciprocals** of each other if their product is 1.

For example,

$$\frac{2}{3} \cdot \frac{3}{2} = \frac{2 \cdot 3}{3 \cdot 2} = \frac{6}{6} = 1 \qquad \text{so } \frac{2}{3} \text{ and } \frac{3}{2} \text{ are reciprocals.}$$

$$4 \cdot \frac{1}{4} = \frac{4}{1} \cdot \frac{1}{4} = \frac{4 \cdot 1}{1 \cdot 4} = \frac{4}{4} = 1 \qquad \text{so } 4 \text{ and } \frac{1}{4} \text{ are reciprocals.}$$

Finding the Reciprocal of a Fraction

To find the reciprocal of a fraction, interchange its numerator and denominator.

For example, the reciprocal of $\frac{6}{11}$ is $\frac{11}{6}$.

EXAMPLES Find the reciprocal of each number.

1. The reciprocal of $\frac{5}{6}$ is $\frac{6}{5}$. $\quad \frac{5}{6} \cdot \frac{6}{5} = \frac{5 \cdot 6}{6 \cdot 5} = \frac{30}{30} = 1$

2. The reciprocal of $\frac{11}{8}$ is $\frac{8}{11}$. $\quad \frac{11}{8} \cdot \frac{8}{11} = \frac{11 \cdot 8}{8 \cdot 11} = \frac{88}{88} = 1$

3. The reciprocal of $\frac{1}{3}$ is $\frac{3}{1}$ or 3. $\quad \frac{1}{3} \cdot \frac{3}{1} = \frac{1 \cdot 3}{3 \cdot 1} = \frac{3}{3} = 1$

4. The reciprocal of 5, or $\frac{5}{1}$, is $\frac{1}{5}$. $\quad \frac{5}{1} \cdot \frac{1}{5} = \frac{5 \cdot 1}{1 \cdot 5} = \frac{5}{5} = 1$

Work Practice Problems 1–4

Helpful Hint

Every number except 0 has a reciprocal. The number 0 has no reciprocal because there is no number that when multiplied by 0 gives a result of 1.

PRACTICE PROBLEMS 1–4

Find the reciprocal of each number.

1. $\frac{4}{9}$ 2. $\frac{15}{7}$

3. 7   4. $\frac{1}{8}$

Answers

1. $\frac{9}{4}$, 2. $\frac{7}{15}$, 3. $\frac{1}{7}$, 4. 8

Objective B Dividing Fractions

Division of fractions has the same meaning as division of whole numbers. For example,

$10 \div 5$ means: How many 5s are there in 10?

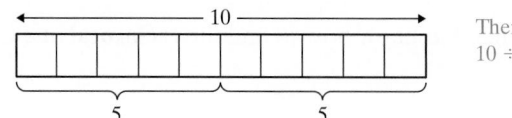

There are two 5s in 10, so
$10 \div 5 = 2$

$\frac{3}{4} \div \frac{1}{8}$ means: How many $\frac{1}{8}$s are there in $\frac{3}{4}$?

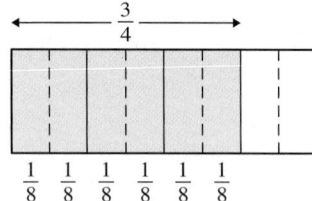

There are six $\frac{1}{8}$s in $\frac{3}{4}$,

so $\frac{3}{4} \div \frac{1}{8} = 6$

We can use reciprocals to divide fractions.

Dividing Fractions

To divide two fractions, multiply the first fraction by the reciprocal of the second fraction.

If a, b, c, and d represent positive whole numbers, then

$$\frac{a}{b} \div \underbrace{\frac{c}{d}}_{\text{reciprocal}} = \frac{a}{b} \cdot \frac{d}{c} = \frac{a \cdot d}{b \cdot c}$$

For example,

$$\frac{3}{4} \overset{\text{multiply by reciprocal}}{\div \frac{1}{8}} = \frac{3}{4} \cdot \frac{8}{1} = \frac{3 \cdot 8}{4 \cdot 1} = \frac{3 \cdot 2 \cdot \overset{1}{\cancel{4}}}{\underset{1}{\cancel{4}} \cdot 1} = \frac{6}{1} \text{ or } 6$$

Just as when you are multiplying fractions, always check to see whether your answer can be simplified when you divide fractions.

EXAMPLES Divide and simplify.

5. $\dfrac{7}{8} \div \dfrac{2}{9} = \dfrac{7}{8} \cdot \dfrac{9}{2} = \dfrac{7 \cdot 9}{8 \cdot 2} = \dfrac{63}{16}$

6. $\dfrac{5}{16} \div \dfrac{3}{4} = \dfrac{5}{16} \cdot \dfrac{4}{3} = \dfrac{5 \cdot 4}{16 \cdot 3} = \dfrac{5 \cdot \overset{1}{\cancel{4}}}{\underset{1}{\cancel{4}} \cdot 4 \cdot 3} = \dfrac{5}{12}$

7. $\dfrac{2}{5} \div \dfrac{1}{2} = \dfrac{2}{5} \cdot \dfrac{2}{1} = \dfrac{2 \cdot 2}{5 \cdot 1} = \dfrac{4}{5}$

Work Practice Problems 5–7

Helpful Hint

When dividing fractions, do *not* look for common factors to divide out until you rewrite the division as multiplication.

Do not try to divide out these two 2s.

$$\frac{1}{2} \div \frac{2}{3} = \frac{1}{2} \cdot \frac{3}{2} = \frac{3}{4}$$

Objective C Dividing Fractions and Mixed Numbers or Whole Numbers

Just as with multiplying, mixed or whole numbers should be written as fractions before you divide them.

Dividing Fractions and Mixed Numbers or Whole Numbers

To divide with a mixed number or a whole number, first write the mixed or whole number as a fraction and then divide as usual.

EXAMPLES Divide.

8. $\frac{3}{4} \div 5 = \frac{3}{4} \div \frac{5}{1} = \frac{3}{4} \cdot \frac{1}{5} = \frac{3 \cdot 1}{4 \cdot 5} = \frac{3}{20}$

9. $\frac{11}{18} \div 2\frac{5}{6} = \frac{11}{18} \div \frac{17}{6} = \frac{11}{18} \cdot \frac{6}{17} = \frac{11 \cdot 6}{18 \cdot 17} = \frac{11 \cdot \cancel{6}}{\cancel{6} \cdot 3 \cdot 17} = \frac{11}{51}$

10. $5\frac{2}{3} \div 2\frac{5}{9} = \frac{17}{3} \div \frac{23}{9} = \frac{17}{3} \cdot \frac{9}{23} = \frac{17 \cdot 9}{3 \cdot 23} = \frac{17 \cdot \cancel{3} \cdot 3}{\cancel{3} \cdot 23} = \frac{51}{23} \text{ or } 2\frac{5}{23}$

Work Practice Problems 8–10

Recall from Section 1.7 that the quotient of 0 and any number (except 0) is 0. This is true of fractions and mixed numbers also. For example,

$$0 \div \frac{7}{8} = 0 \cdot \frac{8}{7} = 0 \qquad \text{Recall that 0 multiplied by any number is 0.}$$

Also recall from Section 1.7 that the quotient of any number and 0 is not a number. This is also true of fractions and mixed numbers. For example, to find $\frac{7}{8} \div 0$, or $\frac{7}{8} \div \frac{0}{1}$, we would need to find the reciprocal of 0 $\left(\text{or } \frac{0}{1}\right)$. As we mentioned in the helpful hint at the beginning of this section, 0 has no reciprocal because there is no number that when multiplied by 0 gives a result of 1. Thus,

$$\frac{7}{8} \div 0 \text{ is undefined.}$$

PRACTICE PROBLEMS 8–10

Divide.

8. $\frac{4}{9} \div 7$ **9.** $\frac{8}{15} \div 3\frac{4}{5}$

10. $3\frac{2}{7} \div 2\frac{3}{14}$

Answers

8. $\frac{4}{63}$, **9.** $\frac{8}{57}$, **10.** $\frac{46}{31}$ or $1\frac{15}{31}$

PRACTICE PROBLEMS 11–12

Divide.

11. $\dfrac{14}{17} \div 0$　　　　**12.** $0 \div 2\dfrac{1}{8}$

EXAMPLES Divide.

11. $0 \div \dfrac{2}{21} = 0 \cdot \dfrac{21}{2} = 0$　　　　**12.** $1\dfrac{3}{4} \div 0$ is undefined.

◻ Work Practice Problems 11–12

✔ Concept Check Which of the following is the correct way to divide $\dfrac{2}{5}$ by $\dfrac{3}{4}$? Or are both correct? Explain.

a. $\dfrac{5}{2} \cdot \dfrac{3}{4}$　　　　**b.** $\dfrac{2}{5} \cdot \dfrac{4}{3}$

Objective D Solving Problems by Dividing Fractions

To solve real-life problems that involve dividing fractions, we continue to use our four problem-solving steps.

EXAMPLE 13 Calculating Manufacturing Materials Needed

In a manufacturing process, a metal-cutting machine cuts strips $1\dfrac{3}{5}$ inches long from a piece of metal stock. How many such strips can be cut from a 48-inch piece of stock?

PRACTICE PROBLEM 13

A designer of women's clothing designs a woman's dress that requires $2\dfrac{1}{7}$ yards of material. How many dresses can be made from a 30-yard bolt of material?

Solution:

1. UNDERSTAND the problem. To do so, read and reread the problem. Then draw a diagram:

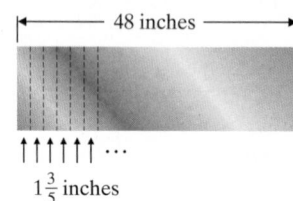

We want to know how many $1\dfrac{3}{5}$s there are in 48.

2. TRANSLATE.

In words:	Number of strips	is	48	divided by	$1\dfrac{3}{5}$
	↓	↓	↓	↓	↓
Translate:	Number of strips	=	48	÷	$1\dfrac{3}{5}$

3. SOLVE: Let's estimate a reasonable answer. The mixed number $1\dfrac{3}{5}$ rounds to 2 and $48 \div 2 = 24$.

$$48 \div 1\dfrac{3}{5} = 48 \div \dfrac{8}{5} = \dfrac{48}{1} \cdot \dfrac{5}{8} = \dfrac{48 \cdot 5}{1 \cdot 8} = \dfrac{\overset{1}{\cancel{8}} \cdot 6 \cdot 5}{1 \cdot \cancel{8}} = \dfrac{30}{1} \text{ or } 30$$

4. INTERPRET. *Check* your work. Since the exact answer of 30 is close to our estimate of 24, our answer is reasonable. *State* your conclusion: Thirty strips can be cut from the 48-inch piece of stock.

◻ Work Practice Problem 13

Answers

11. undefined, **12.** 0, **13.** 14 dresses

✔ Concept Check Answers

a. incorrect, **b.** correct

2.5 EXERCISE SET

FOR EXTRA HELP

Student Solutions Manual

PH Math/Tutor Center

CD/Video for Review

MathXL
MathXL®

MyMathLab
MyMathLab

Objective A *Find the reciprocal of each number. See Examples 1 through 4.*

1. $\dfrac{4}{7}$

2. $\dfrac{9}{10}$

3. $\dfrac{1}{11}$

4. $\dfrac{1}{20}$

5. 15

6. 13

7. $\dfrac{12}{7}$

8. $\dfrac{10}{3}$

Objective B *Divide. Write each answer in simplest form. See Examples 5 through 7 and 11.*

9. $\dfrac{2}{3} \div \dfrac{5}{6}$

10. $\dfrac{5}{8} \div \dfrac{2}{3}$

11. $\dfrac{8}{9} \div \dfrac{1}{2}$

12. $\dfrac{10}{11} \div \dfrac{4}{5}$

13. $\dfrac{3}{7} \div \dfrac{5}{6}$

14. $\dfrac{16}{27} \div \dfrac{8}{15}$

15. $\dfrac{3}{5} \div \dfrac{4}{5}$

16. $\dfrac{11}{16} \div \dfrac{13}{16}$

17. $\dfrac{1}{10} \div \dfrac{10}{1}$

18. $\dfrac{3}{13} \div \dfrac{13}{3}$

19. $\dfrac{7}{9} \div \dfrac{7}{3}$

20. $\dfrac{6}{11} \div \dfrac{6}{5}$

21. $\dfrac{5}{8} \div \dfrac{3}{8}$

22. $\dfrac{7}{8} \div \dfrac{5}{6}$

23. $\dfrac{7}{45} \div \dfrac{4}{25}$

24. $\dfrac{14}{52} \div \dfrac{1}{13}$

25. $\dfrac{2}{37} \div \dfrac{1}{7}$

26. $\dfrac{100}{158} \div \dfrac{10}{79}$

27. $\dfrac{3}{25} \div \dfrac{27}{40}$

28. $\dfrac{6}{15} \div \dfrac{7}{10}$

29. $\dfrac{11}{12} \div \dfrac{11}{12}$

30. $\dfrac{7}{13} \div \dfrac{7}{13}$

31. $\dfrac{8}{13} \div 0$

32. $0 \div \dfrac{4}{11}$

33. $0 \div \dfrac{7}{8}$

34. $\dfrac{2}{3} \div 0$

35. $\dfrac{25}{126} \div \dfrac{125}{441}$

36. $\dfrac{65}{495} \div \dfrac{26}{231}$

Objective [C] *Divide. Write each answer in simplest form. See Examples 8 through 10 and 12.*

37. $\dfrac{2}{3} \div 4$ **38.** $\dfrac{5}{6} \div 10$ **39.** $8 \div \dfrac{3}{5}$ **40.** $7 \div \dfrac{2}{11}$ **41.** $2\dfrac{1}{2} \div \dfrac{1}{2}$

42. $4\dfrac{2}{3} \div \dfrac{2}{5}$ **43.** $\dfrac{5}{12} \div 2\dfrac{1}{3}$ **44.** $\dfrac{4}{15} \div 2\dfrac{1}{2}$ **45.** $3\dfrac{3}{7} \div 3\dfrac{1}{3}$ **46.** $2\dfrac{5}{6} \div 4\dfrac{6}{7}$

47. $1\dfrac{4}{9} \div 2\dfrac{5}{6}$ **48.** $3\dfrac{1}{10} \div 2\dfrac{1}{5}$ **49.** $0 \div 15\dfrac{4}{7}$ **50.** $\dfrac{33}{50} \div 1$ **51.** $1 \div \dfrac{13}{17}$

52. $0 \div 7\dfrac{9}{10}$ **53.** $1 \div \dfrac{18}{35}$ **54.** $\dfrac{17}{75} \div 1$ **55.** $10\dfrac{5}{9} \div 16\dfrac{2}{3}$ **56.** $20\dfrac{5}{6} \div 137\dfrac{1}{2}$

Objectives [B] [C] **Mixed Practice** *Divide. Write each answer in simplest form. See Examples 5 through 12.*

57. $\dfrac{6}{15} \div \dfrac{12}{5}$ **58.** $\dfrac{4}{15} \div \dfrac{8}{3}$ **59.** $\dfrac{11}{20} \div \dfrac{3}{11}$ **60.** $\dfrac{9}{20} \div \dfrac{2}{9}$

61. $12 \div \dfrac{1}{8}$ **62.** $9 \div \dfrac{1}{6}$ **63.** $\dfrac{3}{7} \div \dfrac{4}{7}$ **64.** $\dfrac{3}{8} \div \dfrac{5}{8}$

65. $2\dfrac{3}{8} \div 0$ **66.** $20\dfrac{1}{5} \div 0$ **67.** $\dfrac{11}{85} \div \dfrac{7}{5}$ **68.** $\dfrac{13}{84} \div \dfrac{3}{16}$

69. $4\dfrac{5}{11} \div 1\dfrac{2}{5}$ **70.** $8\dfrac{2}{7} \div 3\dfrac{1}{7}$ **71.** $\dfrac{27}{100} \div \dfrac{3}{20}$ **72.** $\dfrac{25}{128} \div \dfrac{5}{32}$

Objective [D] *Solve. Write each answer in simplest form. See Example 13.*

73. A patient is to take $3\dfrac{1}{3}$ tablespoons of medicine per day in 4 equally divided doses. How much medicine is to be taken in each dose?

74. If there are $13\dfrac{1}{3}$ grams of fat in 4 ounces of lean hamburger meat, how many grams of fat are in an ounce?

75. A heart attack patient in rehabilitation walked on a treadmill $12\frac{3}{4}$ miles over 4 days. How many miles is this per day?

76. A local restaurant is selling hamburgers from a booth on Memorial Day. A total of $27\frac{3}{4}$ pounds of hamburger have been ordered. How many quarter-pound hamburgers can this make?

77. The record for rainfall during a 24-hour period in Alaska is $15\frac{1}{5}$ inches. This record was set in Angoon, Alaska, in October 1982. How much rain fell per hour on average? (*Source:* National Climatic Data Center)

78. An order for 125 custom-made candle stands was placed with Mr. Levi, the manager of Just For You, Inc. The worker assigned to the job can produce $2\frac{3}{5}$ candle stands per hour. Using this worker, how many work hours will be required to complete the order?

79. In October, 2004, the average price of aluminum was $83\frac{1}{2}$¢ per pound. During that time, Severo Gutierrez received 1169¢ for aluminum cans that he sold for recycling at a scrap metal center. Assuming that he received the average price, how many pounds of aluminum cans did Severo recycle? (*Source:* London Metal Exchange)

80. Yoko's Fine Jewelry sells a $\frac{3}{4}$-carat gem for $450. At this price, what is the cost of one carat?

△ **81.** The area of the rectangle below is 12 square meters. If its width is $2\frac{4}{7}$ meters, find its length.

Rectangle $2\frac{4}{7}$ meters

△ **82.** The perimeter of the square below is $23\frac{1}{2}$ feet. Find the length of each side.

Square

Mixed Practice (*Sections 2.4, 2.5*) *Perform the indicated operation.*

83. $\frac{2}{5} \cdot \frac{4}{7}$

84. $\frac{2}{5} \div \frac{4}{7}$

85. $2\frac{2}{3} \div 1\frac{1}{16}$

86. $2\frac{2}{3} \cdot 1\frac{1}{16}$

87. $5\frac{1}{7} \cdot \frac{2}{9} \cdot \frac{14}{15}$

88. $8\frac{1}{6} \cdot \frac{3}{7} \cdot \frac{18}{25}$

89. $\frac{11}{20} \div \frac{20}{11}$

90. $2\frac{1}{5} \div 1\frac{7}{10}$

Review

Perform each indicated operation. See Sections 1.3 and 1.4.

91.   27
           76
        + 98

92.   811
            42
         + 69

93.   968
         − 772

94.   882
         − 773

95.   2000
        − 431

96.   500
         − 92

Concept Extensions

Solve. See the Concept Check in this section.

97. A student asked you to check her work below. Is it correct? If not, where is the error?

$$20\frac{2}{3} \div 10\frac{1}{2} = 2\frac{1}{3}.$$

Choose the best estimate for each quotient.

98. $10\frac{1}{4} \div 2\frac{1}{16}$

    a. 8   **b.** 5   **c.** 20   **d.** 12

99. $20\frac{1}{4} \div \frac{5}{6}$

    a. 5   **b.** $5\frac{1}{8}$ **c.** 20   **d.** 10

100. $\frac{11}{12} \div 16\frac{1}{5}$

    a. $\frac{1}{16}$ **b.** 4   **c.** 8   **d.** 16

101. $12\frac{2}{13} \div 3\frac{7}{8}$

    a. 4   **b.** 9   **c.** 36   **d.** 3

102. In your own words, describe how to divide fractions.

Simplify.

103. $\frac{42}{25} \cdot \frac{125}{36} \div \frac{7}{6}$

104. $\left(\frac{8}{13} \cdot \frac{39}{16} \cdot \frac{8}{9}\right)^2 \div \frac{1}{2}$

105. The FedEx Express air fleet includes 258 Cessnas. These Cessnas make up $\frac{129}{320}$ of the FedEx fleet. How many aircraft make up the entire FedEx Express air fleet? (*Source:* FedEx Corporation)

106. One-third of all native flowering plant species in the United States are at risk of becoming extinct. That translates into 5144 at-risk flowering plant species. Based on this data, how many flowering plant species are native to the United States overall? (*Source:* The Nature Conservancy)

(*Hint:* How many $\frac{1}{3}$s are in 5144?)

THE BIGGER PICTURE Operations on Sets of Numbers

Continue your outline from Sections 1.7 and 1.9. Suggestions are once again written to help you complete this part of your outline, Section I.B. Fractions.

I. Operations on Sets of Numbers

   A. Whole Numbers

     1. Add or Subtract (Sections 1.3, 1.4)

     2. Multiply or Divide (Sections 1.6, 1.7)

     3. Exponent (Section 1.9)

     4. Square Root (Section 1.9)

     5. Order of Operations (Section 1.9)

   B. Fractions

     1. Simplify: Factor the numerator and denominator. Then divide out factors of 1 by dividing out common factors in the numerator and denominator.

$$\text{Simplify: } \frac{20}{28} = \frac{\overset{1}{\cancel{4}} \cdot 5}{\underset{1}{\cancel{4}} \cdot 7} = \frac{5}{7}$$

     2. Multiply: Numerator times numerator over denominator times denominator. $\dfrac{5}{9} \cdot \dfrac{2}{7} = \dfrac{10}{63}$

     3. Divide: First fraction times the reciprocal of the second fraction.

$$\frac{2}{11} \div \frac{3}{4} = \frac{2}{11} \cdot \frac{4}{3} = \frac{8}{33}$$

Perform the indicated operations.

1. $\dfrac{2}{3} \cdot \dfrac{8}{9}$ **2.** $\dfrac{2}{3} \div \dfrac{8}{9}$

3. $12 \cdot \dfrac{1}{9}$ **4.** $4\dfrac{1}{2} \div 1\dfrac{7}{8}$

5. $\sqrt{64}$ **6.** $3^2 \cdot 2^3$

7. $\dfrac{11}{20} \cdot \dfrac{5}{8} \cdot \dfrac{4}{33}$ **8.** $20 \div \dfrac{1}{2}$

9. $3 + 4(18 - 16)^3$ **10.** $100 - 76$

 CHAPTER 2 Group Activity

Blood and Blood Donation (Sections 2.1, 2.2, 2.3)

Blood is the workhorse of the body. It carries to the body's tissues everything they need, from nutrients to antibodies to heat. Blood also carries away waste products like carbon dioxide. Blood contains three types of cells—red blood cells, white blood cells, and platelets—suspended in clear, watery fluid called plasma. Blood is $\dfrac{11}{20}$ plasma, and plasma itself is $\dfrac{9}{10}$ water. In the average healthy adult human, blood accounts for $\dfrac{1}{11}$ of a person's body weight.

Roughly every 2 seconds someone in the United States needs blood. Although only $\dfrac{1}{20}$ of eligible donors donate blood, the American Red Cross is still able to collect nearly 6 million volunteer donations of blood each year. This volume makes Red Cross Biomedical Services the largest blood supplier for blood transfusions in the United States.

Group Activity

Contact your local Red Cross Blood Service office. Find out how many people donated blood in your area in the past two months. Ask whether it is possible to get a breakdown of the blood donations by blood type. (For more on blood type, see Exercises 73 through 77 in Section 2.3.)

1. Research the population of the area served by your local Red Cross Blood Service office. Write the fraction of the local population who gave blood in the past two months.

2. Use the breakdown by blood type to write the fraction of donors giving each type of blood.

Chapter 2 Vocabulary Check

Fill in each blank with one of the words or phrases listed below.

mixed number	equivalent	0	undefined
composite number	improper fraction	simplest form	prime factorization
prime number	proper fraction	numerator	denominator
reciprocals			

1. Two numbers are _____ of each other if their product is 1.

2. A _____ is a natural number greater than 1 that is not prime.

3. Fractions that represent the same portion of a whole are called _____ fractions.

4. An _____ is a fraction whose numerator is greater than or equal to its denominator.

5. A _____ is a natural number greater than 1 whose only factors are 1 and itself.

6. A fraction is in _____ when the numerator and the denominator have no factors in common other than 1.

7. A _____ is one whose numerator is less than its denominator.

8. A _____ contains a whole number part and a fraction part.

9. In the fraction $\frac{7}{9}$, the 7 is called the _____ and the 9 is called the _____.

10. The _____ of a number is the factorization in which all the factors are prime numbers.

11. The fraction $\frac{3}{0}$ is _____.

12. The fraction $\frac{0}{5}$ = _____.

> **Helpful Hint**
>
> Are you preparing for your test? Don't forget to take the Chapter 2 Test on page 173. Then check your answers at the back of the text and use the Chapter Test Prep Video CD to see the fully worked-out solutions to any of the exercises you want to review.

2 Chapter Highlights

DEFINITIONS AND CONCEPTS	**EXAMPLES**
Section 2.1 Introduction to Fractions and Mixed Numbers	
A **fraction** is of the form $\underline{\text{numerator}}$ ← number of parts being considered denominator ← number of equal parts in the whole	Write a fraction to represent the shaded part of the figure. $\frac{3}{8}$ ← number of parts shaded ← number of equal parts

DEFINITIONS AND CONCEPTS	**EXAMPLES**

Section 2.1   Introduction to Fractions and Mixed Numbers (*continued*)

A fraction is called a **proper fraction** if its numerator is less than its denominator.	$\dfrac{1}{3}, \dfrac{2}{5}, \dfrac{7}{8}, \dfrac{100}{101}$
A fraction is called an **improper fraction** if its numerator is greater than or equal to its denominator.	$\dfrac{5}{4}, \dfrac{2}{2}, \dfrac{9}{7}, \dfrac{101}{100}$
A **mixed number** contains a whole number and a fraction.	$1\dfrac{1}{2}, 5\dfrac{7}{8}, 25\dfrac{9}{10}$

TO WRITE A MIXED NUMBER AS AN IMPROPER FRACTION

1. Multiply the denominator of the fraction by the whole number.
2. Add the numerator of the fraction to the product from step 1.
3. Write this sum from step 2 as the numerator of the improper fraction over the original denominator.

$$5\frac{2}{7} = \frac{5 \cdot 7 + 2}{7} = \frac{35 + 2}{7} = \frac{37}{7}$$

TO WRITE AN IMPROPER FRACTION AS A MIXED NUMBER OR A WHOLE NUMBER

1. Divide the denominator into the numerator.
2. The whole number part of the mixed number is the quotient. The fraction is the remainder over the original denominator.

$$\text{quotient}\dfrac{\text{remainder}}{\text{original denominator}}$$

$$\frac{17}{3} = 5\frac{2}{3}$$

$$\begin{array}{r} 5 \\ 3\overline{)17} \\ \underline{15} \\ 2 \end{array}$$

Section 2.2   Factors and Prime Factorization

A **prime number** is a natural number that has exactly two different factors, 1 and itself.	$2, 3, 5, 7, 11, 13, 17, \ldots$
A **composite number** is any natural number other than 1 that is not prime.	$4, 6, 8, 9, 10, 12, 14, 15, 16, \ldots$
The prime factorization of a number is the factorization in which all the factors are prime numbers.	Write the prime factorization of 60. $60 = 6 \cdot 10$ $\quad = 2 \cdot 3 \cdot 2 \cdot 5 \quad \text{or} \quad 2^2 \cdot 3 \cdot 5$

Section 2.3   Simplest Form of a Fraction

Fractions that represent the same portion of a whole are called **equivalent fractions.**	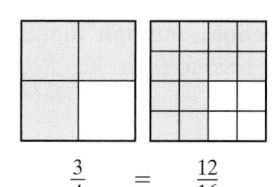 $\dfrac{3}{4} \quad = \quad \dfrac{12}{16}$
A fraction is in **simplest form** or **lowest terms** when the numerator and the denominator have no common factors other than 1.	The fraction $\dfrac{2}{3}$ is in simplest form.

continued

DEFINITIONS AND CONCEPTS	**EXAMPLES**
Section 2.3 Simplest Form of a Fraction (*continued*)	

To write a fraction in simplest form, write the prime factorizations of the numerator and the denominator and then divide both by all common factors.

Write in simplest form: $\dfrac{30}{36}$

$$\frac{30}{36} = \frac{2 \cdot 3 \cdot 5}{2 \cdot 2 \cdot 3 \cdot 3} = \frac{2}{2} \cdot \frac{3}{3} \cdot \frac{5}{2 \cdot 3} = 1 \cdot 1 \cdot 1 \cdot \frac{5}{6} = \frac{5}{6}$$

or $\quad \dfrac{30}{36} = \dfrac{\overset{1}{\cancel{2}} \cdot \overset{1}{\cancel{3}} \cdot 5}{\underset{1}{\cancel{2}} \cdot 2 \cdot \underset{1}{\cancel{3}} \cdot 3} = \dfrac{5}{6}$

Two fractions are equivalent if

Method 1.   They simplify to the same fraction.

Method 2.   Their cross products are equal.

$$\begin{array}{ccc} 24 \cdot 7 & & 8 \cdot 21 \\ = 168 & \dfrac{7}{8} \;\;\;=\;\;\; \dfrac{21}{24} & = 168 \end{array}$$

Since $168 = 168$, $\dfrac{7}{8} = \dfrac{21}{24}$.

Determine whether $\dfrac{7}{8}$ and $\dfrac{21}{24}$ are equivalent.

$\dfrac{7}{8}$ is in simplest form

$$\frac{21}{24} = \frac{\overset{1}{\cancel{3}} \cdot 7}{\underset{1}{\cancel{3}} \cdot 8} = \frac{1 \cdot 7}{1 \cdot 8} = \frac{7}{8}$$

Since both simplify to $\dfrac{7}{8}$, then $\dfrac{7}{8} = \dfrac{21}{24}$.

| **Section 2.4   Multiplying Fractions** ||

To multiply two fractions, multiply the numerators and multiply the denominators.

Multiply.

$$\frac{7}{8} \cdot \frac{3}{5} = \frac{7 \cdot 3}{8 \cdot 5} = \frac{21}{40}$$

$$\frac{3}{4} \cdot \frac{1}{6} = \frac{3 \cdot 1}{4 \cdot 6} = \frac{\overset{1}{\cancel{3}} \cdot 1}{4 \cdot \underset{1}{\cancel{3}} \cdot 2} = \frac{1}{8}$$

To multiply with mixed numbers or whole numbers, first write any mixed or whole numbers as fractions and then multiply as usual.

$$2\frac{1}{3} \cdot \frac{1}{9} = \frac{7}{3} \cdot \frac{1}{9} = \frac{7 \cdot 1}{3 \cdot 9} = \frac{7}{27}$$

| **Section 2.5   Dividing Fractions** ||

To find the **reciprocal** of a fraction, interchange its numerator and denominator.

The reciprocal of $\dfrac{3}{5}$ is $\dfrac{5}{3}$.

To divide two fractions, multiply the first fraction by the reciprocal of the second fraction.

Divide.

$$\frac{3}{10} \div \frac{7}{9} = \frac{3}{10} \cdot \frac{9}{7} = \frac{3 \cdot 9}{10 \cdot 7} = \frac{27}{70}$$

To divide with mixed numbers or whole numbers, first write any mixed or whole numbers as fractions and then divide as usual.

$$2\frac{5}{8} \div 3\frac{7}{16} = \frac{21}{8} \div \frac{55}{16} = \frac{21}{8} \cdot \frac{16}{55} = \frac{21 \cdot 16}{8 \cdot 55}$$

$$= \frac{21 \cdot 2 \cdot \overset{1}{\cancel{8}}}{\underset{1}{\cancel{8}} \cdot 55} = \frac{42}{55}$$

2 CHAPTER REVIEW

(2.1) *Determine whether each number is an improper fraction, a proper fraction, or a mixed number.*

1. $\dfrac{11}{23}$

2. $\dfrac{9}{8}$

3. $\dfrac{1}{2}$

4. $2\dfrac{1}{4}$

Write a fraction to represent the shaded area.

5.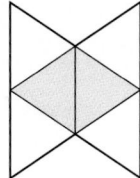

6.

7.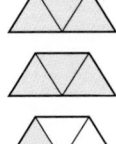

8.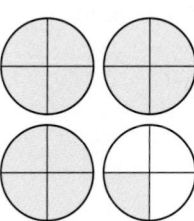

9. A basketball player made 11 free throws out of 12 during a game. What fraction of free throws did the player make?

10. A new car lot contained 23 blue cars out of a total of 131 cars.

    a. How many cars on the lot are not blue?

    b. What fraction of cars on the lot are not blue?

Write each improper fraction as a mixed number or a whole number.

11. $\dfrac{15}{4}$

12. $\dfrac{275}{6}$

13. $\dfrac{39}{13}$

14. $\dfrac{60}{12}$

Write each mixed number as an improper fraction.

15. $1\dfrac{1}{5}$

16. $1\dfrac{1}{21}$

17. $2\dfrac{8}{9}$

18. $3\dfrac{11}{12}$

(2.2) *Identify each number as prime or composite.*

19. 51

20. 17

List all factors of each number.

21. 42

22. 20

Find the prime factorization of each number.

23. 68   **24.** 90   **25.** 785   **26.** 255

(2.3) *Write each fraction in simplest form.*

27. $\dfrac{12}{28}$ **28.** $\dfrac{15}{27}$ **29.** $\dfrac{25}{75}$ **30.** $\dfrac{36}{72}$

31. $\dfrac{29}{32}$ **32.** $\dfrac{18}{23}$ **33.** $\dfrac{48}{6}$ **34.** $\dfrac{54}{9}$

Determine whether each two fractions are equivalent.

35. $\dfrac{10}{34}$ and $\dfrac{4}{14}$ **36.** $\dfrac{8}{12}$ and $\dfrac{12}{16}$ **37.** $\dfrac{20}{36}$ and $\dfrac{15}{18}$ **38.** $\dfrac{30}{50}$ and $\dfrac{9}{15}$

(2.4) *Multiply. Write each answer in simplest form. Estimate where noted.*

39. $\dfrac{3}{5} \cdot \dfrac{1}{2}$ **40.** $\dfrac{6}{7} \cdot \dfrac{5}{12}$ **41.** $\dfrac{24}{5} \cdot \dfrac{15}{8}$ **42.** $\dfrac{27}{21} \cdot \dfrac{7}{18}$

43. $5 \cdot \dfrac{7}{8}$ **44.** $6 \cdot \dfrac{5}{12}$ **45.** $\dfrac{39}{3} \cdot \dfrac{7}{13} \cdot \dfrac{5}{21}$ **46.** $\dfrac{42}{5} \cdot \dfrac{15}{6} \cdot \dfrac{7}{9}$

47. $1\dfrac{5}{8} \cdot 3\dfrac{1}{5}$ **48.** $3\dfrac{6}{11} \cdot 1\dfrac{7}{13}$ **49.** $\dfrac{3}{4} \cdot 8 \cdot 4\dfrac{1}{8}$ **50.** $2\dfrac{1}{9} \cdot 3 \cdot \dfrac{1}{38}$

   Exact: Exact:

   Estimate: Estimate:

51. There are $7\dfrac{1}{3}$ grams of fat in each ounce of hamburger. How many grams of fat are in a 5-ounce hamburger patty?

52. An art teacher needs 45 pieces of PVC piping for an art project. If each piece needs to be $\dfrac{3}{4}$ inch long, find the total length of piping she needs.

△ **53.** Find the area of each rectangle.

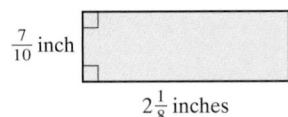

$\frac{7}{10}$ inch

$2\frac{1}{8}$ inches

△ **54.**

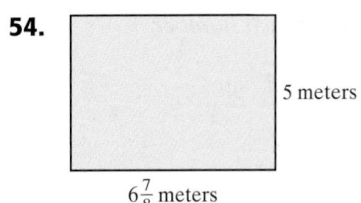

5 meters

$6\frac{7}{8}$ meters

(2.5) *Find the reciprocal of each number.*

55. 7   **56.** $\frac{1}{8}$ **57.** $\frac{14}{23}$ **58.** $\frac{17}{5}$

Divide. Write each answer in simplest form.

59. $\frac{3}{4} \div \frac{3}{8}$ **60.** $\frac{21}{4} \div \frac{7}{5}$ **61.** $\frac{5}{3} \div 2$

62. $5 \div \frac{15}{8}$ **63.** $6\frac{3}{4} \div 1\frac{2}{7}$ **64.** $5\frac{1}{2} \div 2\frac{1}{11}$

65. A truck traveled 341 miles on $15\frac{1}{2}$ gallons of gas. How many miles might we expect the truck to travel on 1 gallon of gas?

66. Herman Heltznutt walks 5 days a week for a total distance of $5\frac{1}{4}$ miles per week. If he walks the same distance each day, find the distance he walks each day.

Mixed Review

Determine whether each number is an improper fraction, a proper fraction, or a mixed number.

67. $\frac{0}{3}$ **68.** $\frac{12}{12}$ **69.** $5\frac{6}{7}$ **70.** $\frac{13}{9}$

Write each improper fraction as a mixed number or a whole number. Write each mixed number as an improper fraction.

71. $\frac{125}{4}$ **72.** $\frac{54}{9}$ **73.** $5\frac{10}{17}$ **74.** $7\frac{5}{6}$

Identify each number as prime or composite.

75. 27   **76.** 23

Find the prime factorization of each number.

77. 180

78. 98

Write each fraction in simplest form.

79. $\dfrac{45}{50}$

80. $\dfrac{30}{42}$

81. $\dfrac{140}{150}$

82. $\dfrac{84}{140}$

Multiply or divide as indicated. Write each answer in simplest form. Estimate where noted.

83. $\dfrac{7}{8} \cdot \dfrac{2}{3}$

84. $\dfrac{6}{15} \cdot \dfrac{5}{8}$

85. $\dfrac{18}{5} \div \dfrac{2}{5}$

86. $\dfrac{9}{2} \div \dfrac{1}{3}$

87. $4\dfrac{1}{6} \cdot 2\dfrac{2}{5}$

Exact:
Estimate:

88. $5\dfrac{2}{3} \cdot 2\dfrac{1}{4}$

Exact:
Estimate:

89. $\dfrac{7}{2} \div 1\dfrac{1}{2}$

90. $1\dfrac{3}{5} \div \dfrac{1}{4}$

△ **91.** A slab of natural granite is purchased and a rectangle with length $5\dfrac{1}{2}$ feet and width $7\dfrac{4}{11}$ feet is cut from it. Find the area of the rectangle.

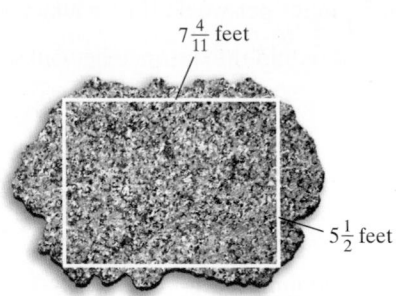

$7\frac{4}{11}$ feet

$5\frac{1}{2}$ feet

92. An area of Mississippi received $23\dfrac{1}{2}$ inches of rain in $30\dfrac{1}{2}$ hours. How many inches per 1 hour is this?

CHAPTER TEST

 Remember to use the Chapter Test Prep Video CD to see the fully worked-out solutions to any of the exercises you want to review.

Write a fraction to represent the shaded area.

1.

2.

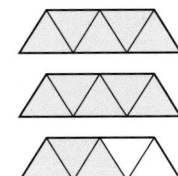

Write each mixed number as an improper fraction.

3. $7\frac{2}{3}$

4. $3\frac{6}{11}$

Write each improper fraction as a mixed number or a whole number.

5. $\frac{23}{5}$

6. $\frac{75}{4}$

Write each fraction in simplest form.

7. $\frac{24}{210}$

8. $\frac{42}{70}$

Determine whether these fractions are equivalent.

9. $\frac{5}{7}$ and $\frac{8}{11}$

10. $\frac{6}{27}$ and $\frac{14}{63}$

Find the prime factorization of each number.

11. 84

12. 495

1. _____

2. _____

3. _____

4. _____

5. _____

6. _____

7. _____

8. _____

9. _____

10. _____

11. _____

12. _____

Perform each indicated operation. Write each answer in simplest form.

13. $\dfrac{4}{4} \div \dfrac{3}{4}$

14. $\dfrac{4}{3} \cdot \dfrac{4}{4}$

15. $2 \cdot \dfrac{1}{8}$

16. $\dfrac{2}{3} \cdot \dfrac{8}{15}$

17. $8 \div \dfrac{1}{2}$

18. $13\dfrac{1}{2} \div 3$

19. $\dfrac{3}{8} \cdot \dfrac{16}{6} \cdot \dfrac{4}{11}$

20. $5\dfrac{1}{4} \div \dfrac{7}{12}$

21. $\dfrac{16}{3} \div \dfrac{3}{12}$

22. $3\dfrac{1}{3} \cdot 6\dfrac{3}{4}$

23. $12 \div 3\dfrac{1}{3}$

24. $\dfrac{14}{5} \cdot \dfrac{25}{21} \cdot 2$

△ **25.** Find the area of the figure.

$\frac{2}{3}$ mile ▭

$1\dfrac{8}{9}$ miles

26. During a 258-mile trip, a car used $10\dfrac{3}{4}$ gallons of gas. How many miles would we expect the car to travel on 1 gallon of gas?

27. How many square yards of artificial turf are necessary to cover a football field, *not* including the end zones and the sidelines? (*Hint:* A football field measures $100 \times 53\dfrac{1}{3}$ yards.)

$53\frac{1}{3}$ yards

100 yards

28. Prior to an oil spill, the stock in an oil company sold for $120 per share. As a result of the liability that the company incurred from the spill, the price per share fell to $\dfrac{3}{4}$ of the price before the spill. What did the stock sell for after the spill?

13. _____

14. _____

15. _____

16. _____

17. _____

18. _____

19. _____

20. _____

21. _____

22. _____

23. _____

24. _____

25. _____

26. _____

27. _____

28. _____

Answers

1. Find the place value of the digit 4 in the whole number 48,761.

2. Write 2036 in words.

3. Write the number, eight hundred five, in standard form.

4. Add: $7 + 6 + 10 + 3 + 5$

5. Add: $34,285 + 149,761$

6. Find the average of 56, 18, and 43.

△ 7. Find the perimeter of the polygon shown.

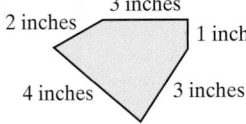

3 inches
2 inches
1 inch
4 inches
3 inches

8. Subtract 8 from 25.

9. The governor's salary in the state of Alabama was recently increased by $1706. If the old salary was $94,655, find the new salary. (*Source: The World Almanac and Book of Facts,* 2003 and 2005)

10. Find $\sqrt{25}$.

11. Subtract: $7826 - 505$
    Check by adding.

12. Find 8^2.

13. The graph below shows the ratings of Best Picture nominees since PG-13 was introduced in 1984. On this graph, each bar represents a different rating, and the height of each bar represents the number of Best Picture nominees for that rating. (*Source:* Academy of Motion Picture Arts and Sciences; Internet Movie Database)

Best Picture Nominee Ratings

Number of Best Picture Nominees

Rating	Number
G	2
PG	15
PG-13	27
R	54
NC-17/X	0
Unrated	2

Source: www.oscar.com, 2001

Rating

a. Which rating did most Best Picture nominees have?
b. Find the total number of Best Picture nominees that were rated G, PG, or PG-13.

Answers

1. _____

2. _____

3. _____

4. _____

5. _____

6. _____

7. _____

8. _____

9. _____

10. _____

11. _____

12. _____

13. a. _____

b. _____

14. _____

15. _____

16. _____

17. _____

18. _____

19. a. _____

    b. _____

    c. _____

    d. _____

20. _____

21. a. _____

    b. _____

    c. _____

22. _____

23. a. _____

    b. _____

    c. _____

    d. _____

24. _____

25. _____

26. _____

27. _____

28. _____

29. _____

30. _____

14. Find $205 \div 8$.

15. Round 568 to the nearest ten.

16. Round 2366 to the nearest hundred.

17. Round each number to the nearest hundred to find an estimated difference.

$$4725$$
$$-2879$$

18. Round each number to the nearest ten to find an estimated sum.
$38 + 43 + 126 + 92$

19. Multiply.

  a. 6×1 **b.** $0(8)$

  c. $1 \cdot 45$ **d.** $(75)(0)$

20. Simplify: $30 \div 3 \cdot 2$

21. Rewrite each using the distributive property.

  a. $3(4 + 5)$ **b.** $10(6 + 8)$

  c. $2(7 + 3)$

22. Multiply: 12×15

23. Find each quotient. Check by multiplying.

  a. $9\overline{)0}$ **b.** $0 \div 12$

  c. $\dfrac{0}{5}$ **d.** $\dfrac{3}{0}$

24. Find the area.

7 miles	Rectangle

22 miles

25. Divide and check: $1872 \div 9$

26. Subtract: $5000 - 986$

27. How many boxes are needed to ship 56 pairs of Nikes to a shoe store in Texarkana if 9 pairs of shoes will fit in each shipping box?

28. Find the product of 9 and 7.

△ **29.** A gardener bought enough plants to fill a rectangular garden with length 30 feet and width 20 feet. Because of shading problems from a nearby tree, the gardener changed the width of the garden to 15 feet. If the area is to remain the same, what is the new length of the garden?

30. Find the sum of 9 and 7.

Write using exponential notation.

31. $4 \cdot 4 \cdot 4$

32. $7 \cdot 7 \cdot 7 \cdot 7$

33. $6 \cdot 6 \cdot 6 \cdot 8 \cdot 8 \cdot 8 \cdot 8 \cdot 8$

34. $2 \cdot 2 \cdot 3 \cdot 3 \cdot 3 \cdot 3$

35. Simplify: $2 \cdot 4 - 3 \div 3$

36. Simplify: $8 \cdot \sqrt{100} - 4^2 \cdot 5$

37. Write a fraction to represent the shaded part of the figure.

38. Write the prime factorization of 156.

39. Write as improper fractions.

  a. $4\dfrac{2}{9}$ **b.** $1\dfrac{8}{11}$

40. Write $7\dfrac{4}{5}$ as an improper fraction.

41. Find all the factors of 20.

42. Determine whether $\dfrac{8}{20}$ and $\dfrac{14}{35}$ are equivalent.

43. Write in simplest form: $\dfrac{42}{66}$

44. Write in simplest form: $\dfrac{70}{105}$

45. Multiply: $3\dfrac{1}{3} \cdot \dfrac{7}{8}$

46. Multiply: $\dfrac{2}{3} \cdot 4$

47. Find the reciprocal of $\dfrac{1}{3}$.

48. Find the reciprocal of 9.

49. Divide and simplify: $\dfrac{5}{16} \div \dfrac{3}{4}$

50. Divide: $1\dfrac{1}{10} \div 5\dfrac{3}{5}$

31. _____

32. _____

33. _____

34. _____

35. _____

36. _____

37. _____

38. _____

39. a. _____

  b. _____

40. _____

41. _____

42. _____

43. _____

44. _____

45. _____

46. _____

47. _____

48. _____

49. _____

50. _____

3

Adding and Subtracting Fractions

Having learned what fractions are and how to multiply and divide them in Chapter 2, we are ready to continue our study of fractions. In this chapter, we learn how to add and subtract fractions and mixed numbers. We then conclude this chapter with solving problems using fractions.

You may have heard before that the surface of the earth is about $\frac{1}{4}$ land and $\frac{3}{4}$ water, but what about the individual continents and oceans?

In Section 3.1, Exercises 45 through 48, and Section 3.3, Exercises 69 and 70, we use fractions to help us see the relative sizes of the continents and oceans.

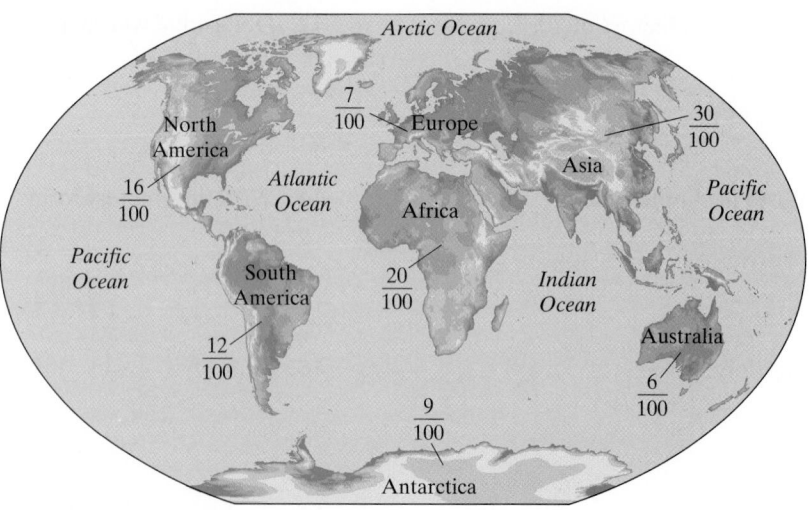

3.1 ADDING AND SUBTRACTING LIKE FRACTIONS

Fractions with the same denominator are called **like fractions.** Fractions that have different denominators are called **unlike fractions.**

Like Fractions

$\frac{2}{5}$ and $\frac{3}{5}$
— same denominator

$\frac{5}{21}, \frac{16}{21},$ and $\frac{7}{21}$
— same denominator

Unlike Fractions

$\frac{2}{5}$ and $\frac{3}{4}$
— different denominator

$\frac{5}{7}$ and $\frac{5}{9}$
— different denominator

Objective **A** Adding Like Fractions

To see how we add like fractions (fractions with the same denominator), study the figures below:

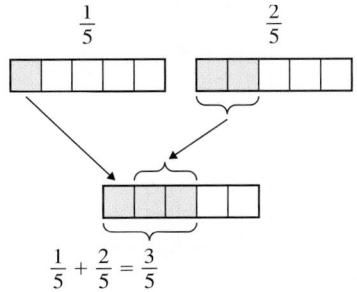

$$\frac{1}{5} + \frac{2}{5} = \frac{3}{5}$$

Adding Like Fractions

To add like fractions, add the numerators and write the sum over the common denominator.

If a, b, and c represent nonzero whole numbers, we have

$$\frac{a}{c} + \frac{b}{c} = \frac{a + b}{c}$$

For example,

$$\frac{1}{4} + \frac{2}{4} = \frac{1 + 2}{4} = \frac{3}{4}$$ ⟵ Add the numerators.
⟵ Keep the denominator.

 **Helpful Hint**

As usual, don't forget to write all answers in simplest form.

PRACTICE PROBLEMS 1–3

Add and simplify.

1. $\dfrac{5}{9} + \dfrac{2}{9}$

2. $\dfrac{5}{8} + \dfrac{1}{8}$

3. $\dfrac{10}{11} + \dfrac{1}{11} + \dfrac{7}{11}$

EXAMPLES Add and simplify.

1. $\dfrac{2}{7} + \dfrac{3}{7} = \dfrac{2 + 3}{7} = \dfrac{5}{7}$ ⟵ Add the numerators.
⟵ Keep the common denominator.

2. $\dfrac{3}{16} + \dfrac{7}{16} = \dfrac{3 + 7}{16} = \dfrac{10}{16} = \dfrac{\cancel{2}^{1} \cdot 5}{\cancel{2} \cdot 8}_{1} = \dfrac{5}{8}$

3. $\dfrac{7}{13} + \dfrac{6}{13} + \dfrac{3}{13} = \dfrac{7 + 6 + 3}{13} = \dfrac{16}{13}$ or $1\dfrac{3}{13}$

⬛ **Work Practice Problems 1–3**

✔ **Concept Check** Find and correct the error in the following:

$$\dfrac{1}{5} + \dfrac{1}{5} = \dfrac{2}{10}$$

Objective 🅱 Subtracting Like Fractions

To see how we subtract like fractions (fractions with the same denominator), study the following figure:

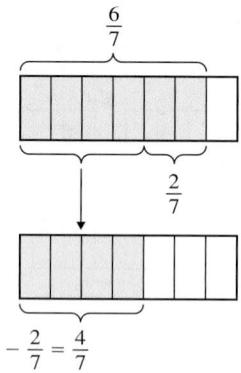

$$\dfrac{6}{7} - \dfrac{2}{7} = \dfrac{4}{7}$$

Subtracting Like Fractions

To subtract like fractions, subtract the numerators and write the difference over the common denominator.

If a, b, and c represent nonzero whole numbers, then

$$\dfrac{a}{c} - \dfrac{b}{c} = \dfrac{a - b}{c}$$

PRACTICE PROBLEMS 4–5

Subtract and simplify.

4. $\dfrac{7}{12} - \dfrac{2}{12}$ **5.** $\dfrac{9}{10} - \dfrac{1}{10}$

For example,

$$\dfrac{4}{5} - \dfrac{2}{5} = \dfrac{4 - 2}{5} = \dfrac{2}{5}$$ ⟵ Subtract the numerators.
⟵ Keep the denominator.

EXAMPLES Subtract and simplify.

4. $\dfrac{8}{9} - \dfrac{1}{9} = \dfrac{8 - 1}{9} = \dfrac{7}{9}$ ⟵ Subtract the numerators.
⟵ Keep the common denominator.

5. $\dfrac{7}{8} - \dfrac{5}{8} = \dfrac{7 - 5}{8} = \dfrac{2}{8} = \dfrac{\cancel{2}^{1}}{\cancel{2} \cdot 4}_{1} = \dfrac{1}{4}$

⬛ **Work Practice Problems 4–5**

Answers

1. $\dfrac{7}{9}$, **2.** $\dfrac{3}{4}$, **3.** $\dfrac{18}{11}$ or $1\dfrac{7}{11}$,

4. $\dfrac{5}{12}$, **5.** $\dfrac{4}{5}$

✔ **Concept Check Answer**

We don't add denominators together; correct solution: $\dfrac{1}{5} + \dfrac{1}{5} = \dfrac{2}{5}$.

Objective C Solving Problems by Adding or Subtracting Like Fractions

Many real-life problems involve finding the perimeters of square or rectangular areas such as pastures, swimming pools, and so on. We can use our knowledge of adding fractions to find perimeters.

EXAMPLE 6 Find the perimeter of the rectangle.

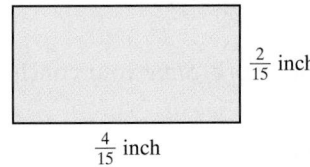

$\frac{2}{15}$ inch

$\frac{4}{15}$ inch

Solution: Recall that perimeter means distance around and that opposite sides of a rectangle are the same length.

$\frac{4}{15}$ inch

$\frac{2}{15}$ inch $\frac{2}{15}$ inch

$\frac{4}{15}$ inch

$$\text{Perimeter} = \frac{2}{15} + \frac{4}{15} + \frac{2}{15} + \frac{4}{15} = \frac{2 + 4 + 2 + 4}{15}$$

$$= \frac{12}{15} = \frac{\overset{1}{\cancel{3}} \cdot 4}{\underset{1}{\cancel{3}} \cdot 5} = \frac{4}{5}$$

The perimeter of the rectangle is $\frac{4}{5}$ inch.

Work Practice Problem 6

We can combine our skills in adding and subtracting fractions with our four problem-solving steps from Chapter 1 to solve many kinds of real-life problems.

EXAMPLE 7 Total Amount of an Ingredient in a Recipe

A recipe calls for $\frac{1}{3}$ of a cup of flour at the beginning and $\frac{2}{3}$ of a cup of flour later. How much total flour is needed to make the recipe?

$\frac{1}{3}$ cup $\frac{2}{3}$ cup

Solution:

1. UNDERSTAND the problem. To do so, read and reread the problem. Since we are finding total flour, we add.   Continued on next page

PRACTICE PROBLEM 6

Find the perimeter of the square.

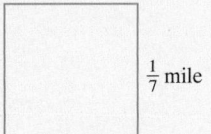

$\frac{1}{7}$ mile

PRACTICE PROBLEM 7

If a piano student practices the piano $\frac{3}{8}$ of an hour in the morning and $\frac{1}{8}$ of an hour in the evening, how long did she practice that day?

Answers

6. $\frac{4}{7}$ mi,   7. $\frac{1}{2}$ hr

2. TRANSLATE.

In words:	total flour	is	flour at the beginning	added to	flour later
	↓	↓	↓	↓	↓
Translate:	total flour	=	$\frac{1}{3}$	+	$\frac{2}{3}$

3. SOLVE: $\frac{1}{3} + \frac{2}{3} = \frac{1+2}{3} = \frac{\cancel{3}^{1}}{\cancel{3}_{1}} = 1$

4. INTERPRET. *Check* your work. *State* your conclusion: The total flour needed for the recipe is 1 cup.

▣ **Work Practice Problem 7**

PRACTICE PROBLEM 8

A jogger ran $\frac{13}{4}$ miles on Monday and $\frac{7}{4}$ miles on Wednesday. How much farther did he run on Monday than on Wednesday?

EXAMPLE 8 **Calculating Distance**

The distance from home to the World Gym is $\frac{7}{8}$ of a mile and from home to the post office is $\frac{3}{8}$ of a mile. How much farther is it from home to the World Gym than from home to the post office?

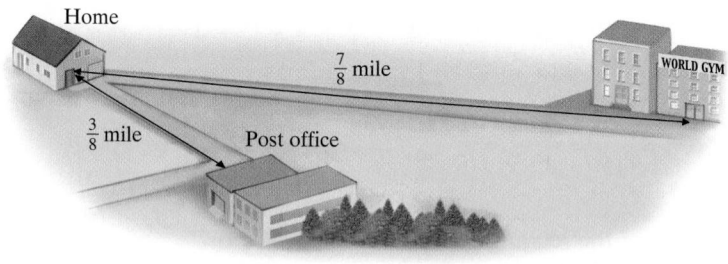

Solution:

1. UNDERSTAND. Read and reread the problem. The phrase "How much farther" tells us to subtract distances.

2. TRANSLATE.

In words:	distance farther	is	home to World Gym distance	minus	home to post office distance
	↓	↓	↓	↓	↓
Translate:	distance farther	=	$\frac{7}{8}$	−	$\frac{3}{8}$

3. SOLVE: $\frac{7}{8} - \frac{3}{8} = \frac{7-3}{8} = \frac{4}{8} = \frac{\cancel{4}^{1}}{2 \cdot \cancel{4}_{1}} = \frac{1}{2}$

4. INTERPRET. *Check* your work. *State* your conclusion: The distance from home to the World Gym is $\frac{1}{2}$ mile farther than from home to the post office.

▣ **Work Practice Problem 8**

Answer

8. $\frac{3}{2}$ or $1\frac{1}{2}$ mi

Mental Math

State whether the fractions in each list are like or unlike fractions.

1. $\dfrac{7}{8}, \dfrac{7}{10}$

2. $\dfrac{2}{3}, \dfrac{4}{9}$

3. $\dfrac{9}{10}, \dfrac{1}{10}$

4. $\dfrac{8}{11}, \dfrac{2}{11}$

5. $\dfrac{2}{31}, \dfrac{30}{31}, \dfrac{19}{31}$

6. $\dfrac{3}{10}, \dfrac{3}{11}, \dfrac{3}{13}$

7. $\dfrac{5}{12}, \dfrac{7}{12}, \dfrac{12}{11}$

8. $\dfrac{1}{5}, \dfrac{2}{5}, \dfrac{4}{5}$

3.1 EXERCISE SET

FOR EXTRA HELP

Student Solutions Manual   PH Math/Tutor Center   CD/Video for Review   Math XL MathXL®   MyMathLab MyMathLab

Objective 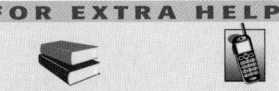 *Add and simplify. See Examples 1 through 3.*

1. $\dfrac{1}{7} + \dfrac{2}{7}$

2. $\dfrac{9}{17} + \dfrac{2}{17}$

3. $\dfrac{1}{10} + \dfrac{1}{10}$

4. $\dfrac{1}{4} + \dfrac{1}{4}$

5. $\dfrac{2}{9} + \dfrac{4}{9}$

6. $\dfrac{3}{10} + \dfrac{2}{10}$

7. $\dfrac{6}{20} + \dfrac{1}{20}$

8. $\dfrac{2}{8} + \dfrac{3}{8}$

9. $\dfrac{3}{14} + \dfrac{4}{14}$

10. $\dfrac{5}{24} + \dfrac{7}{24}$

11. $\dfrac{10}{11} + \dfrac{3}{11}$

12. $\dfrac{13}{17} + \dfrac{9}{17}$

13. $\dfrac{4}{13} + \dfrac{2}{13} + \dfrac{1}{13}$

14. $\dfrac{5}{11} + \dfrac{1}{11} + \dfrac{2}{11}$

15. $\dfrac{7}{18} + \dfrac{3}{18} + \dfrac{2}{18}$

16. $\dfrac{7}{15} + \dfrac{4}{15} + \dfrac{1}{15}$

Objective  *Subtract and simplify. See Examples 4 and 5.*

17. $\dfrac{10}{11} - \dfrac{4}{11}$

18. $\dfrac{9}{13} - \dfrac{5}{13}$

19. $\dfrac{4}{5} - \dfrac{1}{5}$

20. $\dfrac{7}{8} - \dfrac{4}{8}$

21. $\dfrac{7}{4} - \dfrac{3}{4}$

22. $\dfrac{18}{5} - \dfrac{3}{5}$

23. $\dfrac{7}{8} - \dfrac{1}{8}$

24. $\dfrac{5}{6} - \dfrac{1}{6}$

25. $\dfrac{25}{12} - \dfrac{15}{12}$

26. $\dfrac{30}{20} - \dfrac{15}{20}$

27. $\dfrac{11}{10} - \dfrac{3}{10}$

28. $\dfrac{14}{15} - \dfrac{4}{15}$

29. $\dfrac{27}{33} - \dfrac{8}{33}$

30. $\dfrac{37}{45} - \dfrac{18}{45}$

Objectives **A** **B** **Mixed Practice** *Perform the indicated operation. See Examples 1 through 5.*

31. $\dfrac{8}{21} + \dfrac{5}{21}$

32. $\dfrac{7}{37} + \dfrac{9}{37}$

33. $\dfrac{99}{100} - \dfrac{9}{100}$

34. $\dfrac{85}{200} - \dfrac{15}{200}$

35. $\dfrac{13}{28} - \dfrac{13}{28}$

36. $\dfrac{15}{26} - \dfrac{15}{26}$

37. $\dfrac{3}{16} + \dfrac{7}{16} + \dfrac{2}{16}$

38. $\dfrac{5}{18} + \dfrac{1}{18} + \dfrac{6}{18}$

Objective **C** *Find the perimeter of each figure. (Hint: Recall that perimeter means distance around.) See Example 6.*

39.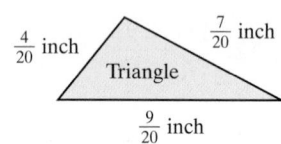

40.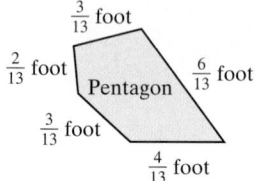

41.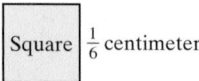

42.

Square $\frac{1}{6}$ centimeter

Solve. Write each answer in simplest form. See Examples 7 and 8.

43. Emil Vasquez, a bodybuilder, worked out $\dfrac{7}{8}$ of an hour one morning before school and $\dfrac{5}{8}$ of an hour that evening. How long did he work out that day?

44. A recipe for Heavenly Hash cake calls for $\dfrac{3}{4}$ cup of sugar and later $\dfrac{1}{4}$ cup of sugar. How much sugar is needed to make the recipe?

The map of the world below shows the fraction of the world's surface land area taken up by each continent. In other words, the continent of Africa makes up $\frac{20}{100}$ of the land in the world. Use this map for Exercises 45 through 48.

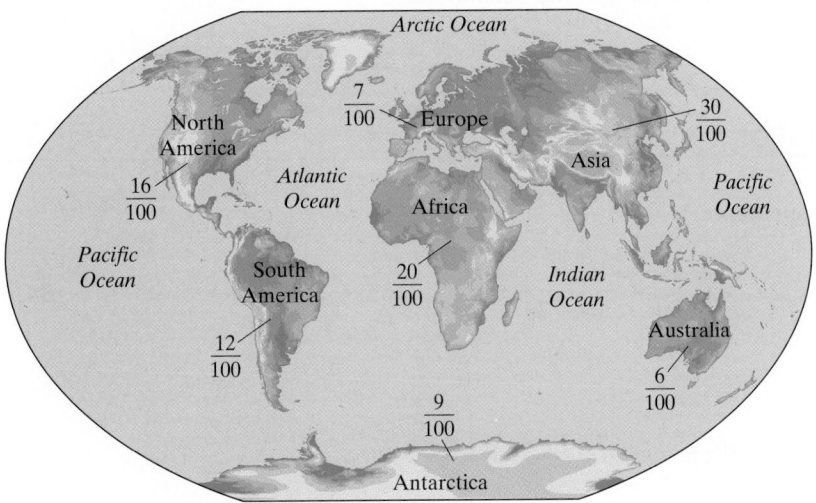

45. Find the fractional part of the world's land area within the continents of North America and South America.

46. Find the fractional part of the world's land area within the continents of Asia and Africa.

47. How much greater is the fractional part of the continent of Antarctica than the fractional part of the continent of Europe?

48. How much greater is the fractional part of the continent of Asia than the continent of Australia?

49. A railroad inspector must inspect $\frac{19}{20}$ of a mile of railroad track. If she has already inspected $\frac{5}{20}$ of a mile, how much more does she need to inspect?

50. Scott Davis has run $\frac{11}{8}$ miles already and plans to complete $\frac{16}{8}$ miles. To do this, how much farther must he run?

51. In the United States, about $\frac{7}{20}$ of all households own two television sets. Approximately $\frac{8}{20}$ of all households own 3 or more television sets. What fraction of U.S. households own 2 or more television sets? (*Source:* Neilsen Media Research)

52. In a recent survey, $\frac{55}{100}$ of people said that visiting family and friends would be their pleasure trip of choice while $\frac{29}{100}$ of people surveyed said that going to a beach resort would be their pleasure trip of choice. What fraction of people surveyed said visiting family and friends or going to a beach resort? (*Source:* American Express)

53. In 2004, the fraction of states in the United States with maximum interstate highway speed limits up to and including 70 mph was $\frac{37}{50}$. The fraction of states with 70 mph speed limits was $\frac{16}{50}$. What fraction of states had speed limits that were less than 70 mph? (*Source:* Insurance Institute for Highway Safety)

54. When people take aspirin, $\frac{31}{50}$ of the time it is used to treat some type of pain. Approximately $\frac{7}{50}$ of all aspirin use is for treating headaches. What fraction of aspirin use is for treating pain other than headaches? (*Source:* Bayer Market Research)

Review

Write the prime factorization of each number. See Section 2.2.

55. 10   **56.** 12   **57.** 8   **58.** 20   **59.** 55   **60.** 28

Concept Extensions

Perform each indicated operation.

61. $\dfrac{3}{8} + \dfrac{7}{8} - \dfrac{5}{8}$

62. $\dfrac{12}{20} - \dfrac{1}{20} - \dfrac{3}{20}$

63. $\dfrac{4}{11} + \dfrac{5}{11} - \dfrac{3}{11} + \dfrac{2}{11}$

64. $\dfrac{9}{12} + \dfrac{1}{12} - \dfrac{3}{12} - \dfrac{5}{12}$

Find and correct the error. See the Concept Check in this section.

65.

$$\dfrac{2}{7} + \dfrac{9}{7} = \dfrac{11}{14}$$

66.

$$\dfrac{3}{4} - \dfrac{1}{4} = \dfrac{2}{8} = \dfrac{1}{4}$$

Solve. Write each answer in simplest form.

67. In your own words, explain how to add like fractions.

68. In your own words, explain how to subtract like fractions.

69. Use the map of the world for Exercises 45 through 48 and find the sum of all the continents' fractions. Explain your answer.

70. Mike Cannon jogged $\dfrac{3}{8}$ of a mile from home and then rested. Then he continued jogging further from home for another $\dfrac{3}{8}$ of a mile until he discovered his watch had fallen off. He walked back along the same path for $\dfrac{4}{8}$ of a mile until he found his watch. Find how far he was from his home.

 STUDY SKILLS BUILDER

How Well Do You Know Your Textbook?

The questions below will determine whether you are familiar with your textbook. For help, see Section 1.1 in this text.

1. What does the ⊚ icon mean?

2. What does the ⟍ icon mean?

3. What does the △ icon mean?

4. Where can you find a review for each chapter? What answers to this review can be found in the back of your text?

5. Each chapter contains an overview of the chapter along with examples. What is this feature called?

6. Each chapter contains a review of vocabulary. What is this feature called?

7. There is a CD in your text. What content is contained on this CD?

8. What is the location of the section that is entirely devoted to study skills?

9. There are Practice Problems that are contained in the margin of the text. What are they and how can they be used?

3.2 LEAST COMMON MULTIPLE

Objective A Finding the Least Common Multiple Using Multiples

A multiple of a number is the product of that number and a natural number. For example,
multiples of 5 are

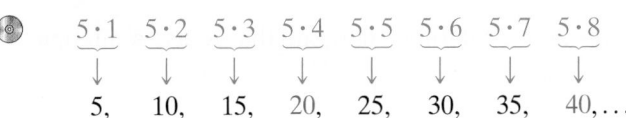

$$5 \cdot 1 \quad 5 \cdot 2 \quad 5 \cdot 3 \quad 5 \cdot 4 \quad 5 \cdot 5 \quad 5 \cdot 6 \quad 5 \cdot 7 \quad 5 \cdot 8$$
$$\downarrow \quad \downarrow \quad \downarrow \quad \downarrow \quad \downarrow \quad \downarrow \quad \downarrow \quad \downarrow$$
$$5, \quad 10, \quad 15, \quad 20, \quad 25, \quad 30, \quad 35, \quad 40, \dots$$

Multiples of 4 are

   4, 8, 12, 16, 20, 24, 28, 32, 36, 40, 44, ...

Common multiples of both 4 and 5 are numbers that are found in both lists above. If we study the lists of multiples and extend them we have

   Common multiples of 4 and 5: 20, 40, 60, 80, ...

We call the smallest number in the list of common multiples the **least common multiple (LCM).** From the list of common multiples of 4 and 5, we see that the LCM of 4 and 5 is 20.

EXAMPLE 1 Find the LCM of 6 and 8.

Solution: Multiples of 6: 6, 12, 18, (24), 30, 36, 42, (48), ...

Multiples of 8: 8, 16, (24), 32, 40, (48), 56, ...

The common multiples are 24, 48, ... The least common multiple (LCM) is 24.

Work Practice Problem 1

PRACTICE PROBLEM 1

Find the LCM of 15 and 50.

Listing all the multiples of every number in a list can be cumbersome and tedious. We can condense the procedure shown in Example 1 with the following steps:

Method 1: Finding the LCM of a List of Numbers Using Multiples of the Largest Number

Step 1: Write the multiples of the largest number (starting with the number itself) until a multiple common to all numbers in the list is found.

Step 2: The multiple found in Step 1 is the LCM.

EXAMPLE 2 Find the LCM of 9 and 12.

Solution: We write the multiples of 12 until we find a number that is also a multiple of 9.

   $12 \cdot 1 = 12$ Not a multiple of 9.
   $12 \cdot 2 = 24$ Not a multiple of 9.
   $12 \cdot 3 = 36$ A multiple of 9.

The LCM of 9 and 12 is 36.

Work Practice Problem 2

PRACTICE PROBLEM 2

Find the LCM of 8 and 10.

Answers
1. 150, **2.** 40

187

PRACTICE PROBLEM 3

Find the LCM of 8 and 16.

EXAMPLE 3 Find the LCM of 7 and 14.

Solution: We write the multiples of 14 until we find one that is also a multiple of 7.

$14 \cdot 1 = 14$ A multiple of 7

The LCM of 7 and 14 is 14.

Work Practice Problem 3

PRACTICE PROBLEM 4

Find the LCM of 25 and 30.

EXAMPLE 4 Find the LCM of 12 and 20.

Solution: We write the multiples of 20 until we find one that is also a multiple of 12.

$20 \cdot 1 = 20$ Not a multiple of 12

$20 \cdot 2 = 40$ Not a multiple of 12

$20 \cdot 3 = 60$ A multiple of 12

The LCM of 12 and 20 is 60.

Work Practice Problem 4

Objective B Finding the LCM Using Prime Factorization

Method 1 for finding multiples works fine for smaller numbers, but may get tedious for larger numbers. A second method that uses prime factorization may be easier to use for larger numbers.

For example, to find the LCM of 270 and 84, let's look at the prime factorization of each.

$270 = 2 \cdot 3 \cdot 3 \cdot 3 \cdot 5$

$84 = 2 \cdot 2 \cdot 3 \cdot 7$

Recall that the LCM must be a multiple of both 270 and 84. Thus, to build the LCM, we will circle the greatest number of factors for each different prime number. The LCM is the product of the circled factors.

Prime Number Factors

$270 =$	$2 \cdot$	$\boxed{(3 \cdot 3 \cdot 3)} \cdot$	$\boxed{(5)}$	
$84 =$	$\boxed{(2 \cdot 2)} \cdot$	$3 \cdot$		$\boxed{(7)}$

$LCM = 2 \cdot 2 \cdot 3 \cdot 3 \cdot 3 \cdot 5 \cdot 7 = 3780$

The number 3780 is the smallest number that both 270 and 84 divide into evenly.

This method 2 is summarized below:

Method 2: Finding the LCM of a List of Numbers Using Prime Factorization

Step 1: Write the prime factorization of each number.

Step 2: For each different prime factor in Step 1, circle the greatest number of times that factor occurs in any one factorization.

Step 3: The LCM is the product of the circled factors.

Answers

3. 16,   **4.** 150

EXAMPLE 5 Find the LCM of 72 and 60.

Solution: First we write the prime factorization of each number.

$72 = 2 \cdot 2 \cdot 2 \cdot 3 \cdot 3$
$60 = 2 \cdot 2 \cdot 3 \cdot 5$

For the prime factors shown, we circle the greatest number of factors found in either factorization.

$72 = \boxed{2 \cdot 2 \cdot 2} \cdot \boxed{3 \cdot 3}$
$60 = 2 \cdot 2 \cdot 3 \cdot \boxed{5}$

The LCM is the product of the circled factors.

$\text{LCM} = 2 \cdot 2 \cdot 2 \cdot 3 \cdot 3 \cdot 5 = 360$

The LCM is 360.

▣ **Work Practice Problem 5**

Helpful Hint

If you prefer working with exponents, circle the factor with the greatest exponent.
  Example 5:

$72 = \boxed{2^3} \cdot \boxed{3^2}$

$60 = 2^2 \cdot 3 \cdot \boxed{5}$

$\text{LCD} = 2^3 \cdot 3^2 \cdot 5 = 360$

Helpful Hint

If the number of factors of a prime number are equal, circle either one, but not both. For example,

$12 = \boxed{2 \cdot 2} \cdot \boxed{3}$
$15 = 3 \cdot \boxed{5}$

Circle either 3 but not both.

The LCM is $2 \cdot 2 \cdot 3 \cdot 5 = 60$.

EXAMPLE 6 Find the LCM of 15, 18, and 54.

Solution: $15 = 3 \cdot \boxed{5}$
$18 = \boxed{2} \cdot 3 \cdot 3$
$54 = 2 \cdot \boxed{3 \cdot 3 \cdot 3}$

The LCM is $2 \cdot 3 \cdot 3 \cdot 3 \cdot 5$ or 270.

▣ **Work Practice Problem 6**

EXAMPLE 7 Find the LCM of 11 and 33.

Solution: $11 = \boxed{11}$
$33 = \boxed{3} \cdot 11$

It makes no difference which 11 is circled.

The LCM is $3 \cdot 11$ or 33.

▣ **Work Practice Problem 7**

PRACTICE PROBLEM 5
Find the LCM of 40 and 108.

PRACTICE PROBLEM 6
Find the LCM of 20, 24, and 45.

PRACTICE PROBLEM 7
Find the LCM of 7 and 21.

Answers
5. 1080, **6.** 360, **7.** 21

Objective C Writing Equivalent Fractions

To add or subtract unlike fractions in the next section, we first write equivalent fractions with the LCM as the denominator. Recall from Section 2.3 that fractions that represent the same portion of a whole are called "equivalent fractions."

$$\frac{1}{3} = \frac{2}{6} = \frac{4}{12}$$

To write $\frac{1}{3}$ as an equivalent fraction with a denominator of 12, we multiply by 1 in the form of $\frac{4}{4}$.

$$\frac{1}{3} = \frac{1}{3} \cdot 1 = \frac{1}{3} \cdot \frac{4}{4} = \frac{1 \cdot 4}{3 \cdot 4} = \frac{4}{12}$$

$$\frac{4}{4} = 1$$

So $\frac{1}{3} = \frac{4}{12}$.

To Write an Equivalent Fraction,

$$\frac{a}{b} = \frac{a}{b} \cdot \frac{c}{c} = \frac{a \cdot c}{b \cdot c}$$

where a, b, and c are nonzero numbers.

✔ **Concept Check** Which of the following is not equivalent to $\frac{3}{4}$?

a. $\frac{6}{8}$ **b.** $\frac{18}{24}$ **c.** $\frac{9}{14}$ **d.** $\frac{30}{40}$

PRACTICE PROBLEM 8

Write an equivalent fraction with the indicated denominator: $\frac{7}{8} = \frac{}{56}$

EXAMPLE 8 Write an equivalent fraction with the indicated denominator.

$$\frac{3}{4} = \frac{}{20}$$

Solution: In the denominators, since $4 \cdot 5 = 20$, we will multiply by 1 in the form of $\frac{5}{5}$.

$$\frac{3}{4} = \frac{3}{4} \cdot \frac{5}{5} = \frac{3 \cdot 5}{4 \cdot 5} = \frac{15}{20}$$

Thus, $\frac{3}{4} = \frac{15}{20}$.

🔲 **Work Practice Problem 8**

Answer

8. $\frac{49}{56}$

✔ **Concept Check Answer**

c

Helpful Hint

To check Example 8, write $\dfrac{15}{20}$ in simplest form.

$$\frac{15}{20} = \frac{3 \cdot \overset{1}{\cancel{5}}}{4 \cdot \underset{1}{\cancel{5}}} = \frac{3}{4}, \text{ the original fraction.}$$

If the original fraction is in lowest terms, we can check our work by writing the new equivalent fraction in simplest form. This form should be the original fraction.

EXAMPLE 9 Write an equivalent fraction with the indicated denominator.

$$\frac{1}{2} = \frac{}{14}$$

Solution: Since $2 \cdot 7 = 14$, we multiply by 1 in the form of $\dfrac{7}{7}$.

$$\frac{1}{2} = \frac{1}{2} \cdot \frac{7}{7} = \frac{1 \cdot 7}{2 \cdot 7} = \frac{7}{14}$$

Thus, $\dfrac{1}{2} = \dfrac{7}{14}$.

▣ **Work Practice Problem 9**

✔ **Concept Check** True or false? When the fraction $\dfrac{2}{9}$ is rewritten as an equivalent fraction with 27 as the denominator, the result is $\dfrac{2}{27}$.

PRACTICE PROBLEM 9

Write an equivalent fraction with the indicated denominator.

$$\frac{3}{5} = \frac{}{15}$$

Answer

9. $\dfrac{9}{15}$

✔ **Concept Check Answer**

false; the correct result would be $\dfrac{6}{27}$

3.2 EXERCISE SET

Objectives **A** **B** **Mixed Practice** *Find the LCM of each list of numbers. See Examples 1 through 7.*

1. 3, 4　　　　**2.** 4, 6　　　　**3.** 9, 15　　　**4.** 15, 20　　　**5.** 12, 18　　　**6.** 10, 15

7. 24, 36　　　**8.** 42, 70　　　**9.** 18, 21　　**10.** 24, 45　　**11.** 15, 25　　**12.** 21, 14

13. 8, 24　　　**14.** 15, 90　　**15.** 6, 7　　　**16.** 13, 8　　　**17.** 8, 6, 27　　**18.** 6, 25, 10

19. 25, 15, 6　　**20.** 4, 14, 20　　**21.** 34, 68　　**22.** 25, 175　　**23.** 84, 294　　**24.** 48, 54

25. 30, 36, 50　**26.** 21, 28, 42　**27.** 50, 72, 120　**28.** 70, 98, 100　**29.** 11, 33, 121　**30.** 10, 15, 100

31. 4, 6, 10, 15　**32.** 25, 3, 15, 10

Objective **C** *Write each fraction as an equivalent fraction with the given denominator. See Examples 8 and 9.*

33. $\dfrac{4}{7} = \dfrac{}{35}$　　**34.** $\dfrac{3}{5} = \dfrac{}{20}$　　**35.** $\dfrac{2}{3} = \dfrac{}{21}$　　**36.** $\dfrac{5}{6} = \dfrac{}{24}$　　**37.** $\dfrac{2}{5} = \dfrac{}{25}$

38. $\dfrac{9}{10} = \dfrac{}{70}$　　**39.** $\dfrac{1}{2} = \dfrac{}{30}$　　**40.** $\dfrac{1}{3} = \dfrac{}{30}$　　**41.** $\dfrac{10}{7} = \dfrac{}{21}$　　**42.** $\dfrac{5}{3} = \dfrac{}{21}$

43. $\dfrac{3}{4} = \dfrac{}{28}$　　**44.** $\dfrac{4}{5} = \dfrac{}{45}$　　**45.** $\dfrac{2}{3} = \dfrac{}{45}$　　**46.** $\dfrac{2}{3} = \dfrac{}{75}$　　**47.** $\dfrac{4}{9} = \dfrac{}{81}$

48. $\dfrac{5}{11} = \dfrac{}{88}$　　**49.** $\dfrac{15}{13} = \dfrac{}{78}$　　**50.** $\dfrac{9}{7} = \dfrac{}{84}$　　**51.** $\dfrac{14}{17} = \dfrac{}{68}$　　**52.** $\dfrac{19}{21} = \dfrac{}{126}$

Review

Add or subtract as indicated. See Section 3.1.

53. $\dfrac{7}{10} - \dfrac{2}{10}$

54. $\dfrac{8}{13} - \dfrac{3}{13}$

55. $\dfrac{1}{5} + \dfrac{1}{5}$

56. $\dfrac{1}{8} + \dfrac{3}{8}$

57. $\dfrac{23}{18} - \dfrac{15}{18}$

58. $\dfrac{36}{30} - \dfrac{12}{30}$

59. $\dfrac{2}{9} + \dfrac{1}{9} + \dfrac{6}{9}$

60. $\dfrac{2}{12} + \dfrac{7}{12} + \dfrac{3}{12}$

Concept Extensions

Write each fraction as an equivalent fraction with the indicated denominator.

61. $\dfrac{37}{165} = \dfrac{}{3630}$

62. $\dfrac{108}{215} = \dfrac{}{4085}$

63. In your own words, explain how to find the LCM of two numbers.

64. In your own words, explain how to write a fraction as an equivalent fraction with a given denominator.

Solve. See the Concept Checks in this section.

65. Which of the following are equivalent to $\dfrac{2}{3}$?

   a. $\dfrac{10}{15}$ **b.** $\dfrac{40}{60}$

   c. $\dfrac{16}{20}$ **d.** $\dfrac{200}{300}$

66. True or False? When the fraction $\dfrac{7}{12}$ is rewritten with a denominator of 48, the result is $\dfrac{11}{48}$. If false, give the correct fraction.

Objectives

A Add Unlike Fractions.

B Subtract Unlike Fractions.

C Solve Problems by Adding or Subtracting Unlike Fractions.

3.3 ADDING AND SUBTRACTING UNLIKE FRACTIONS

Objective **A** Adding Unlike Fractions

In this section we add and subtract fractions with unlike denominators. To add or subtract these unlike fractions, we first write the fractions as equivalent fractions with a common denominator and then add or subtract the like fractions. The common denominator that we use is the least common multiple (LCM) of the denominators. This denominator is called the **least common denominator (LCD).**

To begin, let's add the unlike fractions $\frac{3}{4} + \frac{1}{6}$.

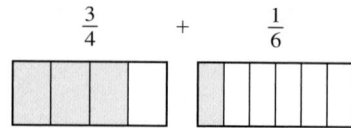

The LCM of denominators 4 and 6 is 12. This means that the number 12 is also the LCD. So we write each fraction as an equivalent fraction with a denominator of 12.

$$\frac{3}{4} = \frac{3}{4} \cdot \frac{3}{3} = \frac{9}{12} \text{ and } \frac{1}{6} = \frac{1}{6} \cdot \frac{2}{2} = \frac{2}{12} \qquad \text{Remember } \frac{3}{3} = 1 \text{ and } \frac{2}{2} = 1.$$

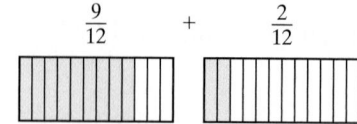

Now we can add, just as in Section 3.1.

$$\frac{3}{4} + \frac{1}{6} = \frac{9}{12} + \frac{2}{12} = \frac{11}{12}$$

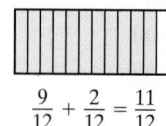

$$\frac{9}{12} + \frac{2}{12} = \frac{11}{12}$$

Adding or Subtracting Unlike Fractions

Step 1: Find the LCM of the denominators of the fractions. This number is the least common denominator (LCD).

Step 2: Write each fraction as an equivalent fraction whose denominator is the LCD.

Step 3: Add or subtract the like fractions.

Step 4: Write the sum or difference in simplest form.

EXAMPLE 1 Add: $\dfrac{2}{5} + \dfrac{4}{15}$

Solution:

Step 1: The LCM of the denominators 5 and 15 is 15. Thus, the LCD is 15. In later examples, we shall simply say, for example, that the LCD of 5 and 15 is 15.

Step 2: $\dfrac{2}{5} = \dfrac{2}{5} \cdot \dfrac{3}{3} = \dfrac{6}{15}, \quad \dfrac{4}{15} = \dfrac{4}{15}$ ← This fraction already has a denominator of 15.

Multiply by 1 in the form $\dfrac{3}{3}$

Step 3: $\dfrac{2}{5} + \dfrac{4}{15} = \dfrac{6}{15} + \dfrac{4}{15} = \dfrac{10}{15}$

Step 4: Write in simplest form.

$$\dfrac{10}{15} = \dfrac{2 \cdot \cancel{5}}{3 \cdot \cancel{5}} = \dfrac{2}{3}$$

🔲 **Work Practice Problem 1**

EXAMPLE 2 Add: $\dfrac{2}{15} + \dfrac{3}{10}$

Solution:

Step 1: The LCD of 15 and 10 is 30.

Step 2: $\dfrac{2}{15} = \dfrac{2}{15} \cdot \dfrac{2}{2} = \dfrac{4}{30} \qquad \dfrac{3}{10} = \dfrac{3}{10} \cdot \dfrac{3}{3} = \dfrac{9}{30}$

Step 3: $\dfrac{2}{15} + \dfrac{3}{10} = \dfrac{4}{30} + \dfrac{9}{30} = \dfrac{13}{30}$

Step 4: $\dfrac{13}{30}$ is in simplest form.

🔲 **Work Practice Problem 2**

EXAMPLE 3 Add: $\dfrac{2}{3} + \dfrac{1}{7}$

Solution: The LCD of 3 and 7 is 21.

$$\dfrac{2}{3} + \dfrac{1}{7} = \dfrac{2}{3} \cdot \dfrac{7}{7} + \dfrac{1}{7} \cdot \dfrac{3}{3}$$

$$= \dfrac{14}{21} + \dfrac{3}{21}$$

$$= \dfrac{17}{21} \qquad \text{Simplest form.}$$

🔲 **Work Practice Problem 3**

PRACTICE PROBLEM 1

Add: $\dfrac{1}{6} + \dfrac{3}{18}$

PRACTICE PROBLEM 2

Add: $\dfrac{5}{6} + \dfrac{2}{9}$

PRACTICE PROBLEM 3

Add: $\dfrac{2}{5} + \dfrac{4}{9}$

Answers

1. $\dfrac{1}{3}$, **2.** $\dfrac{19}{18}$ or $1\dfrac{1}{18}$, **3.** $\dfrac{38}{45}$

PRACTICE PROBLEM 4

Add: $\dfrac{1}{4} + \dfrac{4}{5} + \dfrac{9}{10}$

EXAMPLE 4 Add: $\dfrac{1}{2} + \dfrac{2}{3} + \dfrac{5}{6}$

Solution: The LCD of 2, 3, and 6 is 6.

$$\frac{1}{2} + \frac{2}{3} + \frac{5}{6} = \frac{1}{2}\cdot\frac{3}{3} + \frac{2}{3}\cdot\frac{2}{2} + \frac{5}{6}$$

$$= \frac{3}{6} + \frac{4}{6} + \frac{5}{6}$$

$$= \frac{12}{6} = 2$$

■ Work Practice Problem 4

✔ **Concept Check** Find and correct the error in the following:

$$\frac{2}{9} + \frac{4}{11} = \frac{6}{20} = \frac{3}{10}$$

Objective B Subtracting Unlike Fractions

As indicated in the box on page 194, we follow the same steps when subtracting unlike fractions as when adding them.

PRACTICE PROBLEM 5

Subtract: $\dfrac{7}{12} - \dfrac{5}{24}$

EXAMPLE 5 Subtract: $\dfrac{2}{5} - \dfrac{3}{20}$

Solution:

Step 1: The LCD of 5 and 20 is 20.

Step 2: $\dfrac{2}{5} = \dfrac{2}{5}\cdot\dfrac{4}{4} = \dfrac{8}{20}$ $\dfrac{3}{20} = \dfrac{3}{20}$ ← The fraction already has a denominator of 20.

Step 3: $\dfrac{2}{5} - \dfrac{3}{20} = \dfrac{8}{20} - \dfrac{3}{20} = \dfrac{5}{20}$

Step 4: Write in simplest form.

$$\frac{5}{20} = \frac{\overset{1}{\cancel{5}}}{\cancel{5}\cdot 4} = \frac{1}{4}$$

■ Work Practice Problem 5

PRACTICE PROBLEM 6

Subtract: $\dfrac{9}{10} - \dfrac{3}{7}$

EXAMPLE 6 Subtract: $\dfrac{10}{11} - \dfrac{2}{3}$

Solution:

Step 1: The LCD of 11 and 3 is 33.

Step 2: $\dfrac{10}{11} = \dfrac{10}{11}\cdot\dfrac{3}{3} = \dfrac{30}{33}$ $\dfrac{2}{3} = \dfrac{2}{3}\cdot\dfrac{11}{11} = \dfrac{22}{33}$

Step 3: $\dfrac{10}{11} - \dfrac{2}{3} = \dfrac{30}{33} - \dfrac{22}{33} = \dfrac{8}{33}$

Step 4: $\dfrac{8}{33}$ is in simplest form.

■ Work Practice Problem 6

Answers

4. $\dfrac{39}{20}$ or $1\dfrac{19}{20}$, 5. $\dfrac{3}{8}$, 6. $\dfrac{33}{70}$

✔ **Concept Check Answer**

When adding unlike fractions, we don't add the denominators. Correct solution:
$\dfrac{2}{9} + \dfrac{4}{11} = \dfrac{22}{99} + \dfrac{36}{99} = \dfrac{58}{99}$

EXAMPLE 7 Subtract: $\dfrac{11}{12} - \dfrac{2}{9}$

Solution: The LCD of 12 and 9 is 36.

$$\dfrac{11}{12} - \dfrac{2}{9} = \dfrac{11}{12} \cdot \dfrac{3}{3} - \dfrac{2}{9} \cdot \dfrac{4}{4}$$

$$= \dfrac{33}{36} - \dfrac{8}{36}$$

$$= \dfrac{25}{36}$$

■ **Work Practice Problem 7**

Objective **C** **Solving Problems by Adding or Subtracting Unlike Fractions**

Very often, real-world problems involve adding or subtracting unlike fractions.

EXAMPLE 8 **Finding Total Weight**

A freight truck has $\dfrac{1}{4}$ ton of computers, $\dfrac{1}{3}$ ton of televisions, and $\dfrac{3}{8}$ ton of small appliances. Find the total weight of its load.

Solution:

1. UNDERSTAND. Read and reread the problem. The phrase "total weight" tells us to add.
2. TRANSLATE.

In words:	total weight	is	weight of computers	plus	weight of televisions	plus	weight of appliances
	↓	↓	↓	↓	↓	↓	↓
Translate:	total weight	=	$\dfrac{1}{4}$	+	$\dfrac{1}{3}$	+	$\dfrac{3}{8}$

3. SOLVE: The LCD is 24.

$$\dfrac{1}{4} + \dfrac{1}{3} + \dfrac{3}{8} = \dfrac{1}{4} \cdot \dfrac{6}{6} + \dfrac{1}{3} \cdot \dfrac{8}{8} + \dfrac{3}{8} \cdot \dfrac{3}{3}$$

$$= \dfrac{6}{24} + \dfrac{8}{24} + \dfrac{9}{24}$$

$$= \dfrac{23}{24}$$

4. INTERPRET. *Check* the solution. *State* your conclusion: The total weight of the truck's load is $\dfrac{23}{24}$ ton.

■ **Work Practice Problem 8**

PRACTICE PROBLEM 7

Subtract: $\dfrac{7}{8} - \dfrac{5}{6}$

PRACTICE PROBLEM 8

To repair her sidewalk, a homeowner must pour small amounts of cement in three different locations. She needs $\dfrac{3}{5}$ of a cubic yard, $\dfrac{2}{10}$ of a cubic yard, and $\dfrac{2}{15}$ of a cubic yard for these locations. Find the total amount of cement the homeowner needs.

Answers

7. $\dfrac{1}{24}$, **8.** $\dfrac{14}{15}$ cu yd

PRACTICE PROBLEM 9

Find the difference in length of two boards if one board is $\frac{4}{5}$ of a foot long and the other is $\frac{2}{3}$ of a foot long.

EXAMPLE 9 **Calculating Flight Time**

A flight from Tucson to Phoenix, Arizona, requires $\frac{5}{12}$ of an hour. If the plane has been flying $\frac{1}{4}$ of an hour, find how much time remains before landing.

Solution:

1. UNDERSTAND. Read and reread the problem. The phrase "how much time remains" tells us to subtract.

2. TRANSLATE.

In words:	time remaining	is	flight time from Tucson to Phoenix	minus	flight time already passed
	↓	↓	↓	↓	↓
Translate:	time remaining	=	$\frac{5}{12}$	−	$\frac{1}{4}$

3. SOLVE: The LCD is 12.

$$\frac{5}{12} - \frac{1}{4} = \frac{5}{12} - \frac{1}{4} \cdot \frac{3}{3}$$

$$= \frac{5}{12} - \frac{3}{12}$$

$$= \frac{2}{12} = \frac{\cancel{2}^{1}}{\cancel{2}_{1} \cdot 6} = \frac{1}{6}$$

4. INTERPRET. *Check* the solution. *State* your conclusion: The flight time remaining is $\frac{1}{6}$ of an hour.

⬛ **Work Practice Problem 9**

Answer

9. $\frac{2}{15}$ ft

Scientific Calculator

Many calculators have a fraction key, such as $\boxed{a_{b/c}}$, that allows you to enter fractions, perform operations on fractions, and will give the result as a fraction. If your calculator has a fraction key, use it to calculate

$$\frac{3}{5} + \frac{4}{7}$$

Enter the keystrokes

$\boxed{3}$ $\boxed{a_{b/c}}$ $\boxed{5}$ $\boxed{+}$ $\boxed{4}$ $\boxed{a_{b/c}}$ $\boxed{7}$ $\boxed{=}$

The display should read $\boxed{1\_6 \mid 35}$

which represents the mixed number $1\frac{6}{35}$. Let's write the result as a fraction. To convert from mixed number notation to fractional notation, press

$\boxed{2^{nd}}$ $\boxed{d/c}$

The display now reads $\boxed{41 \mid 35}$

which represents $\frac{41}{35}$, the sum in fractional notation.

Graphing Calculator

Graphing calculators also allow you to perform operations on fractions and will give exact fractional results. The fraction option on a graphing calculator may be found under the $\boxed{\text{MATH}}$ menu. To perform the addition above, try the keystrokes.

$\boxed{3}$ $\boxed{\div}$ $\boxed{5}$ $\boxed{+}$ $\boxed{4}$ $\boxed{\div}$ $\boxed{7}$ $\boxed{\text{MATH}}$ $\boxed{\text{ENTER}}$
$\boxed{\text{ENTER}}$

The display should read

$\boxed{3/5 + 4/7 \blacktriangleright \text{Frac } 41/35}$

Use a calculator to add the following fractions. Give each sum as a fraction.

1. $\frac{1}{16} + \frac{2}{5}$ 2. $\frac{3}{20} + \frac{2}{25}$ 3. $\frac{4}{9} + \frac{7}{8}$

4. $\frac{9}{11} + \frac{5}{12}$ 5. $\frac{10}{17} + \frac{12}{19}$ 6. $\frac{14}{31} + \frac{15}{21}$

3.3 EXERCISE SET

Objective A *Add and simplify. See Examples 1 through 4.*

1. $\frac{2}{3} + \frac{1}{6}$ 2. $\frac{5}{6} + \frac{1}{12}$ 3. $\frac{1}{2} + \frac{1}{3}$ 4. $\frac{2}{3} + \frac{1}{4}$

5. $\frac{2}{11} + \frac{2}{33}$ 6. $\frac{5}{9} + \frac{1}{3}$ 7. $\frac{3}{14} + \frac{3}{7}$ 8. $\frac{2}{5} + \frac{2}{15}$

9. $\frac{11}{35} + \frac{2}{7}$ 10. $\frac{4}{5} + \frac{3}{40}$ 11. $\frac{8}{25} + \frac{7}{35}$ 12. $\frac{5}{14} + \frac{10}{21}$

13. $\frac{7}{15} + \frac{5}{12}$ 14. $\frac{5}{8} + \frac{3}{20}$ 15. $\frac{2}{28} + \frac{2}{21}$ 16. $\frac{6}{25} + \frac{7}{35}$

17. $\dfrac{9}{44} + \dfrac{17}{36}$

18. $\dfrac{2}{33} + \dfrac{2}{21}$

19. $\dfrac{5}{11} + \dfrac{3}{13}$

20. $\dfrac{3}{7} + \dfrac{9}{17}$

21. $\dfrac{1}{3} + \dfrac{1}{9} + \dfrac{1}{27}$

22. $\dfrac{1}{4} + \dfrac{1}{16} + \dfrac{1}{64}$

23. $\dfrac{5}{7} + \dfrac{1}{8} + \dfrac{1}{2}$

24. $\dfrac{10}{13} + \dfrac{7}{10} + \dfrac{1}{5}$

25. $\dfrac{5}{11} + \dfrac{3}{9} + \dfrac{2}{3}$

26. $\dfrac{7}{18} + \dfrac{2}{9} + \dfrac{5}{6}$

27. $\dfrac{13}{20} + \dfrac{3}{5} + \dfrac{1}{3}$

28. $\dfrac{2}{7} + \dfrac{13}{28} + \dfrac{2}{5}$

Objective **B** *Subtract and simplify. See Examples 5 through 7.*

29. $\dfrac{7}{8} - \dfrac{3}{16}$

30. $\dfrac{5}{13} - \dfrac{3}{26}$

31. $\dfrac{5}{6} - \dfrac{3}{7}$

32. $\dfrac{3}{4} - \dfrac{1}{7}$

33. $\dfrac{5}{7} - \dfrac{1}{8}$

34. $\dfrac{10}{13} - \dfrac{7}{10}$

35. $\dfrac{5}{11} - \dfrac{3}{9}$

36. $\dfrac{7}{18} - \dfrac{2}{9}$

37. $\dfrac{11}{35} - \dfrac{2}{7}$

38. $\dfrac{2}{5} - \dfrac{3}{25}$

39. $\dfrac{5}{12} - \dfrac{1}{9}$

40. $\dfrac{7}{12} - \dfrac{5}{18}$

41. $\dfrac{7}{15} - \dfrac{5}{12}$

42. $\dfrac{5}{8} - \dfrac{3}{20}$

43. $\dfrac{3}{28} - \dfrac{2}{21}$

44. $\dfrac{6}{25} - \dfrac{7}{35}$

45. $\dfrac{1}{100} - \dfrac{1}{1000}$

46. $\dfrac{1}{50} - \dfrac{1}{500}$

47. $\dfrac{21}{44} - \dfrac{11}{36}$

48. $\dfrac{7}{18} - \dfrac{2}{45}$

Objectives **A** **B** **Mixed Practice** *Perform the indicated operation. See Examples 1 through 7.*

49. $\dfrac{5}{12} + \dfrac{1}{9}$

50. $\dfrac{7}{12} + \dfrac{5}{18}$

51. $\dfrac{17}{35} - \dfrac{2}{7}$

52. $\dfrac{13}{24} - \dfrac{1}{6}$

53. $\dfrac{9}{28} - \dfrac{3}{40}$

54. $\dfrac{10}{26} - \dfrac{3}{8}$

55. $\dfrac{2}{3} + \dfrac{4}{45} + \dfrac{4}{5}$

56. $\dfrac{3}{16} + \dfrac{1}{4} + \dfrac{1}{16}$

Objective **C** *Find the perimeter of each geometric figure. (Hint: Recall that perimeter means distance around.)*

57.

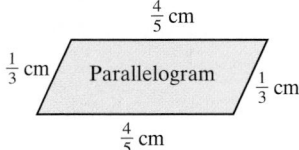

58.

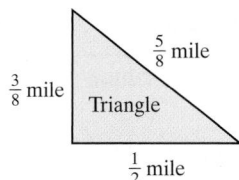

59.

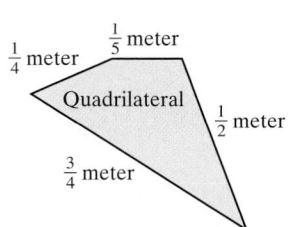

60.

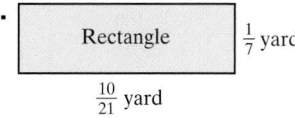

Solve. See Examples 8 and 9.

61. Killer bees have been known to chase people for up to $\frac{1}{4}$ of a mile, while domestic European honeybees will normally chase a person for no more than 100 feet, or $\frac{5}{264}$ of a mile. How much farther will a killer bee chase a person than a domestic honeybee? (*Source:* Coachella Valley Mosquito & Vector Control District)

62. The slowest mammal is the three-toed sloth from South America. The sloth has an average ground speed of $\frac{1}{10}$ mph. In the trees, it can accelerate to $\frac{17}{100}$ mph. How much faster can a sloth travel in the trees? (*Source: The Guiness Book of World Records*)

63. Given the following diagram, find its total length.

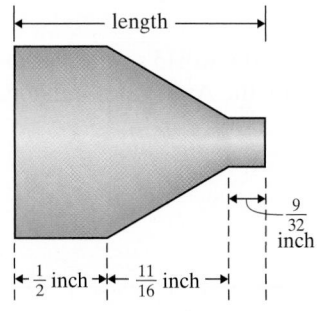

64. Given the following diagram, find its total width.

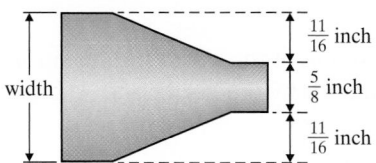

65. About $\frac{13}{20}$ of American students ages 10 to 17 name math, science, or art as their favorite subject in school. Art is the favorite subject for about $\frac{4}{25}$ of the American students ages 10 to 17. For what fraction of students this age is math or science their favorite subject? (*Source:* Peter D. Hart Research Associates for the National Science Foundation)

66. Together, the United States' and Japan's postal services handle $\frac{49}{100}$ of the world's mail volume. Japan's postal service alone handles $\frac{3}{50}$ of the world's mail. What fraction of the world's mail is handled by the postal service of the United States? (*Source:* United States Postal Service)

The table gives the fraction of Americans who eat pasta at various intervals. Use this table to answer Exercises 67 and 68.

How Often Americans Eat Pasta	
Frequency	**Fraction**
3 times per week	$\frac{31}{100}$
1 or 2 times per week	$\frac{23}{50}$
1 or 2 times per month	$\frac{17}{100}$
Less often	$\frac{3}{50}$
(*Source:* Princeton Survey Research)	

67. What fraction of Americans eat pasta 1, 2, or 3 times a week?

68. What fraction of Americans eat pasta 1 or 2 times a month or less often?

The map of the world, first shown in Section 3.1, now shows the fraction of the water's surface area taken up by each ocean. Use this map for Exercises 69 and 70.

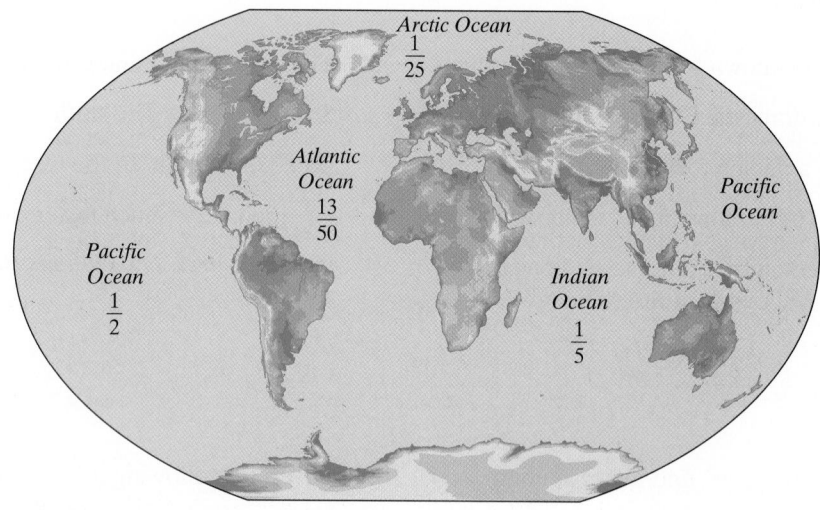

69. What fraction of the world's water surface area is accounted for by the Pacific and Atlantic Oceans?

70. What fraction of the world's water surface area is accounted for by the Arctic and Indian Oceans?

Review

Multiply or divide as indicated. See Sections 2.4 and 2.5.

71. $1\frac{1}{2} \cdot 3\frac{1}{3}$ **72.** $2\frac{5}{6} \div 5$ **73.** $4 \div 7\frac{1}{4}$ **74.** $4\frac{3}{4} \cdot 5\frac{1}{5}$ **75.** $3 \cdot 2\frac{1}{9}$ **76.** $6\frac{2}{7} \cdot 14$

Concept Extensions

For each sum below, do the following:

a. *Draw three rectangles of the same size and represent each fraction in the sum, one fraction per rectangle, by shading.*
b. *Using these rectangles as estimates, determine whether there is an error in the sum.*
c. *If there is an error, correctly calculate the sum.*

See the Concept Check in this section.

77. $\dfrac{3}{5} + \dfrac{4}{5} = \dfrac{7}{10}$

78. $\dfrac{5}{8} + \dfrac{3}{4} = \dfrac{8}{12}$

Subtract from left to right.

79. $\dfrac{2}{3} - \dfrac{1}{4} - \dfrac{2}{5}$

80. $\dfrac{9}{10} - \dfrac{7}{200} - \dfrac{1}{3}$

Perform each indicated operation.

81. $\dfrac{30}{55} + \dfrac{1000}{1760}$

82. $\dfrac{19}{26} - \dfrac{968}{1352}$

 83. In your own words, describe how to add or subtract two fractions with different denominators.

STUDY SKILLS BUILDER

Are You Organized?

Have you ever had trouble finding a completed assignment? When it's time to study for a test, are your notes neat and organized? Have you ever had trouble reading your own mathematics handwriting? (Be honest—I have.)

When any of these things happen, it's time to get organized. Here are a few suggestions:

Write your notes and complete your homework assignment in a notebook with pockets (spiral or ring binder.) Take class notes in this notebook, and then follow the notes with your completed homework assignment. When you receive graded papers or handouts, place them in the notebook pocket so that you will not lose them.

Remember to mark (possibly with an exclamation point) any note(s) that seem extra important to you. Also remember to mark (possibly with a question mark) any notes or homework that you are having trouble with. Don't forget to see your instructor or a math tutor to help you with the concepts or exercises that you are having trouble understanding.

Also, if you are having trouble reading your own handwriting, *slow down* and write your mathematics work clearly!

Exercises

1. Have you been completing your assignments on time?

2. Have you been correcting any exercises you may be having difficulty with?

3. If you are having trouble with a mathematical concept or correcting any homework exercises, have you visited your instructor, a tutor, or your campus math lab?

4. Are you taking lecture notes in your mathematics course? (By the way, these notes should include worked-out examples solved by your instructor.)

5. Is your mathematics course material (handouts, graded papers, lecture notes) organized?

6. If your answer to Exercise 5 is no, take a moment and review your course material. List at least two ways that you might better organize it. Then read the Study Skills Builder on organizing a notebook in Chapter 2.

Operations on Fractions and Mixed Numbers

1. _____

2. _____

3. _____

4. _____

5. _____

6. _____

7. _____

8. _____

9. _____

10. _____

11. _____

12. _____

13. _____

14. _____

15. _____

16. _____

17. _____

18. _____

19. _____

20. _____

21. _____

Find the LCM of each list of numbers.

1. $5, 6$ **2.** $3, 7$ **3.** $2, 14$

4. $5, 25$ **5.** $4, 20, 25$ **6.** $6, 18, 30$

Write each fraction as an equivalent fraction with the indicated denominator.

7. $\dfrac{3}{8} = \dfrac{}{24}$ **8.** $\dfrac{7}{9} = \dfrac{}{36}$ **9.** $\dfrac{1}{4} = \dfrac{}{40}$

10. $\dfrac{2}{5} = \dfrac{}{30}$ **11.** $\dfrac{11}{15} = \dfrac{}{75}$ **12.** $\dfrac{5}{6} = \dfrac{}{48}$

Add or subtract as indicated. Simplify if necessary.

13. $\dfrac{3}{8} + \dfrac{1}{8}$ **14.** $\dfrac{7}{10} - \dfrac{3}{10}$ **15.** $\dfrac{17}{24} - \dfrac{3}{24}$

16. $\dfrac{4}{15} + \dfrac{9}{15}$ **17.** $\dfrac{1}{4} + \dfrac{1}{2}$ **18.** $\dfrac{1}{3} - \dfrac{1}{5}$

19. $\dfrac{7}{9} - \dfrac{2}{5}$ **20.** $\dfrac{3}{10} + \dfrac{2}{25}$ **21.** $\dfrac{7}{8} + \dfrac{1}{20}$

22. $\dfrac{5}{12} - \dfrac{2}{18}$

23. $\dfrac{1}{11} - \dfrac{1}{11}$

24. $\dfrac{3}{17} - \dfrac{2}{17}$

25. $\dfrac{9}{11} - \dfrac{2}{3}$

26. $\dfrac{1}{6} - \dfrac{1}{7}$

27. $\dfrac{2}{9} + \dfrac{1}{18}$

28. $\dfrac{4}{13} + \dfrac{2}{26}$

29. $\dfrac{2}{9} + \dfrac{1}{18} + \dfrac{1}{3}$

30. $\dfrac{3}{10} + \dfrac{1}{5} + \dfrac{6}{25}$

Mixed Practice (*Sections 2.4, 2.5, 3.1, 3.2, 3.3*)   *Perform the indicated operation.*

31. $\dfrac{9}{10} + \dfrac{2}{3}$

32. $\dfrac{9}{10} - \dfrac{2}{3}$

33. $\dfrac{9}{10} \cdot \dfrac{2}{3}$

34. $\dfrac{9}{10} \div \dfrac{2}{3}$

35. $\dfrac{21}{25} - \dfrac{3}{70}$

36. $\dfrac{21}{25} + \dfrac{3}{70}$

37. $\dfrac{21}{25} \div \dfrac{3}{70}$

38. $\dfrac{21}{25} \cdot \dfrac{3}{70}$

39. $3\dfrac{7}{8} \cdot 2\dfrac{2}{3}$

40. $3\dfrac{7}{8} \div 2\dfrac{2}{3}$

41. $\dfrac{2}{9} + \dfrac{5}{27} + \dfrac{1}{2}$

42. $\dfrac{3}{8} + \dfrac{11}{16} + \dfrac{2}{3}$

43. $11\dfrac{7}{10} \div 3\dfrac{3}{100}$

44. $7\dfrac{1}{4} \div 3\dfrac{3}{5}$

45. $\dfrac{14}{15} - \dfrac{4}{27}$

46. $\dfrac{9}{14} - \dfrac{11}{32}$

22. _____

23. _____

24. _____

25. _____

26. _____

27. _____

28. _____

29. _____

30. _____

31. _____

32. _____

33. _____

34. _____

35. _____

36. _____

37. _____

38. _____

39. _____

40. _____

41. _____

42. _____

43. _____

44. _____

45. _____

46. _____

3.4 ADDING AND SUBTRACTING MIXED NUMBERS

Objective A Adding Mixed Numbers

Recall that a mixed number has a whole number part and a fraction part.

$$2\frac{3}{8} \text{ means } 2 + \frac{3}{8}$$

whole number — fraction

✔ **Concept Check** Which of the following are equivalent to 7?

a. $6\frac{5}{5}$ **b.** $6\frac{7}{7}$ **c.** $5\frac{8}{4}$

d. $6\frac{17}{17}$ **e.** all of these

Adding or Subtracting Mixed Numbers

To add or subtract mixed numbers, add or subtract the fractions and then add or subtract the whole numbers.

For example,

$$2\frac{2}{7}$$
$$+ 6\frac{3}{7}$$
$$\overline{8\frac{5}{7}} \leftarrow \text{Add the fractions;}$$
then add the whole numbers

PRACTICE PROBLEM 1

Add: $4\frac{2}{5} + 5\frac{1}{6}$

EXAMPLE 1 Add: $2\frac{1}{3} + 5\frac{3}{8}$. Check by estimating.

Solution: The LCD of 3 and 8 is 24.

$$2\frac{1 \cdot 8}{3 \cdot 8} = 2\frac{8}{24}$$
$$+ 5\frac{3 \cdot 3}{8 \cdot 3} = 5\frac{9}{24}$$
$$\overline{7\frac{17}{24}} \leftarrow \text{Add the fractions}$$
Add the whole numbers

To check by estimating, we round as usual. The fraction $2\frac{1}{3}$ rounds to 2, $5\frac{3}{8}$ rounds to 5, and $2 + 5 = 7$, our estimate.

Our exact answer is close to 7, so our answer is reasonable.

■ **Work Practice Problem 1**

Answer

1. $9\frac{17}{30}$

✔ **Concept Check Answer**

e

Copyright 2007 Pearson Education, Inc.

When adding or subtracting mixed numbers and whole numbers, it is a good idea to estimate to see if your answer is reasonable.

EXAMPLE 2 Add: $3\frac{4}{5} + 1\frac{4}{15}$

Solution: The LCD of 5 and 15 is 15.

$$3\frac{4}{5} = 3\frac{12}{15}$$

$$+1\frac{4}{15} = 1\frac{4}{15}$$ Add the fractions; then add the whole numbers.

$$4\frac{16}{15}$$ Notice that the fraction part is improper.

Since $\frac{16}{15}$ is $1\frac{1}{15}$ we can write the sum as

$$4\frac{16}{15} = 4 + 1\frac{1}{15} = 5\frac{1}{15}$$

■ **Work Practice Problem 2**

PRACTICE PROBLEM 2

Add: $2\frac{5}{14} + 5\frac{6}{7}$

EXAMPLE 3 Add: $1\frac{4}{5} + 4 + 2\frac{1}{2}$

Solution: The LCD of 5 and 2 is 10.

$$1\frac{4}{5} = 1\frac{8}{10}$$

$$4 = 4$$

$$+2\frac{1}{2} = 2\frac{5}{10}$$

$$7\frac{13}{10} = 7 + 1\frac{3}{10} = 8\frac{3}{10}$$

■ **Work Practice Problem 3**

PRACTICE PROBLEM 3

Add: $10 + 2\frac{6}{7} + 3\frac{1}{5}$

Objective **B** **Subtracting Mixed Numbers**

EXAMPLE 4 Subtract: $9\frac{3}{7} - 5\frac{2}{21}$. Check by estimating.

Solution: The LCD of 7 and 21 is 21.

$$9\frac{3}{7} = 9\frac{9}{21}$$ ← The LCD of 7 and 21 is 21.

$$-5\frac{2}{21} = -5\frac{2}{21}$$

$$4\frac{7}{21}$$ ← Subtract the fractions.

Subtract the whole numbers.

PRACTICE PROBLEM 4

Subtract: $29\frac{7}{9} - 13\frac{5}{18}$

Answers

2. $8\frac{3}{14}$, **3.** $16\frac{2}{35}$, **4.** $16\frac{1}{2}$

Continued on next page

Then $4\dfrac{7}{21}$ simplifies to $4\dfrac{1}{3}$. The difference is $4\dfrac{1}{3}$.

To check, $9\dfrac{3}{7}$ rounds to 9, $5\dfrac{2}{21}$ rounds to 5, and $9 - 5 = 4$, our estimate.

Our exact answer is close to 4, so our answer is reasonable.

▣ **Work Practice Problem 4**

When subtracting mixed numbers, borrowing may be needed, as shown in the next example.

PRACTICE PROBLEM 5

Subtract: $9\dfrac{7}{15} - 5\dfrac{3}{5}$

EXAMPLE 5 Subtract: $7\dfrac{3}{14} - 3\dfrac{6}{7}$

Solution: The LCD of 7 and 14 is 14.

$$7\dfrac{3}{14} = 7\dfrac{3}{14}$$
$$-3\dfrac{6}{7} = -3\dfrac{12}{14}$$

Notice that we cannot subtract $\dfrac{12}{14}$ from $\dfrac{3}{14}$, so we borrow from the whole number 7.

borrow 1 from 7

$$7\dfrac{3}{14} = 6 + 1\dfrac{3}{14} = 6 + \dfrac{17}{14} \text{ or } 6\dfrac{17}{14}$$

Now subtract.

$$7\dfrac{3}{14} = 7\dfrac{3}{14} = 6\dfrac{17}{14}$$
$$-3\dfrac{6}{7} = -3\dfrac{12}{14} = -3\dfrac{12}{14}$$
$$3\dfrac{5}{14} \leftarrow \text{Subtract the fractions.}$$
$$\uparrow$$
Subtract the whole numbers.

▣ **Work Practice Problem 5**

✔ **Concept Check** In the subtraction problem $5\dfrac{1}{4} - 3\dfrac{3}{4}$, $5\dfrac{1}{4}$ must be rewritten because $\dfrac{3}{4}$ cannot be subtracted from $\dfrac{1}{4}$. Why is it incorrect to rewrite $5\dfrac{1}{4}$ as $5\dfrac{5}{4}$?

PRACTICE PROBLEM 6

Subtract: $25 - 10\dfrac{2}{9}$

EXAMPLE 6 Subtract: $12 - 8\dfrac{3}{7}$

Solution:

$$12 = 11\dfrac{7}{7} \quad \text{Borrow 1 from 12 and write it as } \dfrac{7}{7}.$$
$$-8\dfrac{3}{7} = -8\dfrac{3}{7}$$
$$3\dfrac{4}{7} \leftarrow \text{Subtract the fractions.}$$
$$\uparrow$$
Subtract the whole numbers.

▣ **Work Practice Problem 6**

Answers

5. $3\dfrac{13}{15}$, **6.** $14\dfrac{7}{9}$

✔ **Concept Check Answer**

Rewrite $5\dfrac{1}{4}$ as $4\dfrac{5}{4}$ by borrowing from the 5.

Objective C Solving Problems by Adding or Subtracting Mixed Numbers

Now that we know how to add and subtract mixed numbers, we can solve real-life problems.

EXAMPLE 7 Calculating Total Weight

Sarah Grahamm purchases two packages of ground round. One package weighs $2\frac{3}{8}$ pounds and the other $1\frac{4}{5}$ pounds. What is the combined weight of the ground round?

Solution:

1. UNDERSTAND. Read and reread the problem. The phrase "combined weight" tells us to add.

2. TRANSLATE.

In words:	combined weight	is	weight of one package	plus	weight of second package
	↓	↓	↓	↓	↓
Translate:	combined weight	=	$2\frac{3}{8}$	+	$1\frac{4}{5}$

3. SOLVE: Before we solve, let's estimate. The fraction $2\frac{3}{8}$ rounds to 2, $1\frac{4}{5}$ rounds to 2, and $2 + 2 = 4$. The combined weight should be close to 4.

$$2\frac{3}{8} = 2\frac{15}{40}$$
$$+1\frac{4}{5} = 1\frac{32}{40}$$
$$\overline{\phantom{+1\frac{4}{5} = }3\frac{47}{40} = 4\frac{7}{40}}$$

4. INTERPRET. *Check* your work. Our estimate of 4 tells us that the exact answer of $4\frac{7}{40}$ is reasonable. *State* your conclusion: The combined weight of the ground round is $4\frac{7}{40}$ pounds.

📖 **Work Practice Problem 7**

EXAMPLE 8 Finding Legal Lobster Size

Lobster fisherman must measure the upper body shells of the lobsters they catch. Lobsters that are too small are thrown back into the ocean. Each state has its own size standard for lobsters to help control the breeding stock. In 1988, Massachusetts increased its legal lobster size from $3\frac{3}{16}$ inches to $3\frac{7}{32}$ inches. How much of an increase was this? (*Source:* Peabody Essex Museum, Salem, Massachusetts)

Continued on next page

Two rainbow trout weigh $2\frac{1}{2}$ pounds and $3\frac{2}{3}$ pounds. What is the total weight of the two trout?

The measurement around the trunk of a tree just below shoulder height is called its girth. The largest known American beech tree in the United States has a girth of $23\frac{1}{4}$ feet. The largest known sugar maple tree in the United States has a girth of $19\frac{5}{12}$ feet. How much larger is the girth of the largest known American beech tree than the girth of the largest known sugar maple tree? (*Source: American Forests*)

Girth

Answers

7. $6\frac{1}{6}$ lb, 8. $3\frac{5}{6}$ ft

Solution:

1. **UNDERSTAND.** Read and reread the problem carefully. The word "increase" found in the problem might make you think that we add to solve the problem. But the phrase "how much of an increase" tells us to subtract to find the increase.

2. **TRANSLATE.**

In words:	increase	is	new lobster size	minus	old lobster size
	↓	↓	↓	↓	↓
Translate:	increase	$=$	$3\dfrac{7}{32}$	$-$	$3\dfrac{3}{16}$

3. **SOLVE:** Before we solve, let's estimate. The fraction $3\dfrac{7}{32}$ rounds to 3, $3\dfrac{3}{16}$ rounds to 3, and $3 - 3 = 0$. The increase is not 0, but will be very small.

$$3\dfrac{7}{32} = 3\dfrac{7}{32}$$
$$-3\dfrac{3}{16} = 3\dfrac{6}{32}$$
$$\rule{2cm}{0.4pt}$$
$$\dfrac{1}{32}$$

4. **INTERPRET.** *Check* your work. Our estimate tells us that the exact increase of $\dfrac{1}{32}$ inch is reasonable. *State* your conclusion: The increase in lobster size is $\dfrac{1}{32}$ of an inch.

◼ **Work Practice Problem 8**

Mental Math

Choose the best estimate for each sum or difference.

1. $3\frac{7}{8} + 2\frac{1}{5}$

   a. 6 **b.** 5 **c.** 1 **d.** 2

2. $3\frac{7}{8} - 2\frac{1}{5}$

   a. 6 **b.** 5 **c.** 1 **d.** 2

3. $8\frac{1}{3} + 1\frac{1}{2}$

   a. 4 **b.** 10 **c.** 6 **d.** 16

4. $8\frac{1}{3} - 1\frac{1}{2}$

   a. 4 **b.** 10 **c.** 6 **d.** 16

3.4 EXERCISE SET

FOR EXTRA HELP

 Student Solutions Manual    PH Math/Tutor Center    CD/Video for Review   *Math XL* MathXL®   *MyMathLab* MyMathLab

Objective A *Add. For those exercises marked, find an exact sum and an estimated sum. See Examples 1 through 3.*

1. $\quad 4\frac{7}{10}$

$\quad +2\frac{1}{10}$

Exact:

Estimate:

2. $\quad 7\frac{4}{9}$

$\quad +3\frac{2}{9}$

Exact:

Estimate:

3. $\quad 10\frac{3}{14}$

$\quad + 3\frac{4}{7}$

Exact:

Estimate:

4. $\quad 12\frac{5}{12}$

$\quad + 4\frac{1}{6}$

Exact:

Estimate:

5. $\quad 9\frac{1}{5}$

$\quad +8\frac{2}{25}$

Exact:

Estimate:

6. $\quad 6\frac{2}{13}$

$\quad +8\frac{7}{26}$

7. $\quad 3\frac{1}{2}$

$\quad +4\frac{1}{8}$

8. $\quad 9\frac{3}{4}$

$\quad +2\frac{1}{8}$

9. $\quad 1\frac{5}{6}$

$\quad +5\frac{3}{8}$

10. $\quad 2\frac{5}{12}$

$\quad +1\frac{5}{8}$

11. $\quad 8\frac{2}{5}$

$\quad +11\frac{2}{3}$

12. $\quad 7\frac{3}{7}$

$\quad +3\frac{3}{5}$

13. $\quad 11\frac{3}{5}$

$\quad +7\frac{2}{5}$

14. $\quad 19\frac{7}{9}$

$\quad + 8\frac{2}{9}$

15. $\quad 40\frac{9}{10}$

$\quad +15\frac{8}{27}$

16. $\quad 102\frac{5}{8}$

$\quad + 96\frac{21}{25}$

17. $\quad 3\frac{5}{8}$

$\quad 2\frac{1}{6}$

$\quad +7\frac{3}{4}$

18. $\quad 4\frac{1}{3}$

$\quad 9\frac{2}{5}$

$\quad +3\frac{1}{6}$

19. $\quad 12\frac{3}{14}$

$\quad 10$

$\quad +25\frac{5}{12}$

20. $\quad 8\frac{2}{9}$

$\quad 32$

$\quad + 9\frac{10}{21}$

Objective B *Subtract. For those exercises marked, find an exact difference and an estimated difference. See Examples 4 through 6.*

21. $\quad 4\dfrac{7}{10}$
$\quad -2\dfrac{1}{10}$

Exact:

Estimate:

22. $\quad 7\dfrac{4}{9}$
$\quad -3\dfrac{2}{9}$

Exact:

Estimate:

23. $\quad 10\dfrac{13}{14}$
$\quad -\ 3\dfrac{4}{7}$

Exact:

Estimate:

24. $\quad 12\dfrac{5}{12}$
$\quad -\ 4\dfrac{1}{6}$

Exact:

Estimate:

25. $\quad 9\dfrac{1}{5}$
$\quad -8\dfrac{6}{25}$

Exact:

Estimate:

26. $\quad 5\dfrac{2}{13}$
$\quad -4\dfrac{7}{26}$

27. $5\dfrac{2}{3} - 3\dfrac{1}{5}$

28. $\quad 23\dfrac{3}{5}$
$\quad -\ 8\dfrac{8}{15}$

29. $\quad 15\dfrac{4}{7}$
$\quad -\ 9\dfrac{11}{14}$

30. $5\dfrac{3}{8} - 2\dfrac{13}{20}$

31. $47\dfrac{4}{18} - 23\dfrac{19}{24}$

32. $6\dfrac{1}{6} - 5\dfrac{11}{14}$

33. $\quad 10$
$\quad -\ 8\dfrac{1}{5}$

34. $\quad 23$
$\quad -17\dfrac{3}{4}$

35. $\quad 11\dfrac{3}{5}$
$\quad -\ 9\dfrac{11}{15}$

36. $\quad 9\dfrac{1}{10}$
$\quad -7\dfrac{2}{5}$

37. $\quad 6$
$\quad -2\dfrac{4}{9}$

38. $\quad 8$
$\quad -1\dfrac{7}{10}$

39. $\quad 63\dfrac{1}{6}$
$\quad -47\dfrac{5}{12}$

40. $\quad 86\dfrac{2}{15}$
$\quad -27\dfrac{3}{10}$

Objectives A B **Mixed Practice** *Perform the indicated operation. See Examples 1 through 6.*

41. $\quad 15\dfrac{1}{6}$
$\quad +13\dfrac{5}{12}$

42. $\quad 21\dfrac{3}{10}$
$\quad +11\dfrac{3}{5}$

43. $\quad 22\dfrac{7}{8}$
$\quad -\ 7$

44. $\quad 27\dfrac{3}{21}$
$\quad -\ 9$

45. $5\dfrac{8}{9} + 2\dfrac{1}{9}$

46. $12\dfrac{13}{16} + 7\dfrac{3}{16}$

47. $33\dfrac{11}{20} - 15\dfrac{19}{30}$

48. $54\dfrac{7}{30} - 38\dfrac{29}{50}$

Objective **C** *Solve. See Examples 7 and 8.*

△ **49.** To prevent intruding birds, birdhouses built for Eastern Bluebirds should have an entrance hole measuring $1\frac{1}{2}$ inches in diameter. Entrance holes in bird houses for Mountain Bluebirds should measure $1\frac{9}{16}$ inches in diameter. How much wider should entrance holes for Mountain Bluebirds be than for Eastern Bluebirds? (*Source:* North American Bluebird Society)

50. If the total weight allowable without overweight charges is 50 pounds and the traveler's luggage weighs $60\frac{5}{8}$ pounds, on how many pounds will the traveler's overweight charges be based?

51. Charlotte Dowlin has $15\frac{2}{3}$ feet of plastic pipe. She cuts off a $2\frac{1}{2}$-foot length and then a $3\frac{1}{4}$-foot length. If she now needs a 10-foot piece of pipe, will the remaining piece do? If not, by how much will the piece be short?

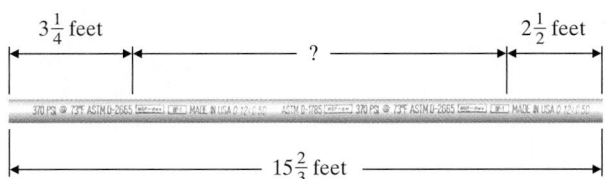
$3\frac{1}{4}$ feet   ? $2\frac{1}{2}$ feet

$15\frac{2}{3}$ feet

52. A trim carpenter cuts a board $3\frac{3}{8}$ feet long from one 6 feet long. How long is the remaining piece?

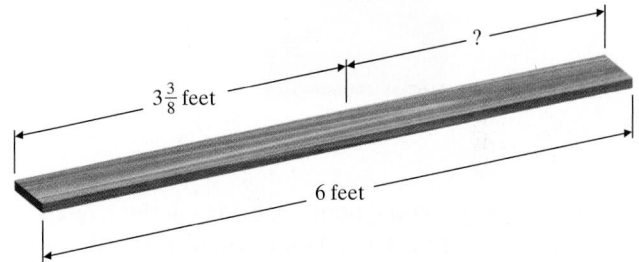
?
$3\frac{3}{8}$ feet
6 feet

⊙ **53.** If Tucson's average annual rainfall is $11\frac{1}{4}$ inches and Yuma's is $3\frac{3}{5}$ inches, how much more rain, on average, does Tucson get than Yuma?

54. A pair of crutches needs adjustment. One crutch is 43 inches and the other is $41\frac{5}{8}$ inches. Find how much the short crutch should be lengthened to make both crutches the same length.

55. On four consecutive days, a concert pianist, practiced for $2\frac{1}{2}$ hours, $1\frac{2}{3}$ hours, $2\frac{1}{4}$ hours, and $3\frac{5}{6}$ hours. Find his total practice time.

56. A tennis coach was preparing her team for a tennis tournament and enforced this practice schedule: Monday, $2\frac{1}{2}$ hours; Tuesday, $2\frac{2}{3}$ hours; Wednesday, $1\frac{3}{4}$ hours; and Thursday, $1\frac{9}{16}$ hours. How long did the team practice that week before Friday's tournament?

57. Jerald Divis, a tax consultant, takes $3\frac{1}{2}$ hours to prepare a personal tax return and $5\frac{7}{8}$ hours to prepare a small business return. How much longer does it take him to prepare the small business return?

58. Jessica Callac takes $2\frac{3}{4}$ hours to clean her room. Her brother Matthew takes $1\frac{1}{3}$ hours to clean his room. If they start at the same time, how long does Matthew have to wait for Jessica to finish?

59. Located on an island in New York City's harbor, the Statue of Liberty is one of the largest statues in the world. The copper figure is $46\frac{1}{20}$ meters tall from feet to tip of torch. The figure stands on a pedestal that is $46\frac{47}{50}$ meters feet tall. What is the overall height of the Statue of Liberty from the base of the pedestal to the tip of the torch? (*Source:* National Park Service)

60. The record for largest rainbow trout ever caught is $42\frac{1}{8}$ pounds and was set in Alaska in 1970. The record for largest tiger trout ever caught is $20\frac{13}{16}$ pounds and was set in Michigan in 1978. How much more did the record-setting rainbow trout weigh than the record-setting tiger trout? (*Source:* International Game Fish Association)

61. The longest floating pontoon bridge in the United States is the Evergreen Point Bridge in Seattle, Washington. It is 2526 yards long. The second-longest pontoon bridge in the United States is the Hood Canal Bridge in Point Gamble, Washington, which is $2173\frac{2}{3}$ yards long. How much longer is the Evergreen Point Bridge than the Hood Canal Bridge? (*Source:* Federal Highway Administration)

62. What is the difference between interest rates of $11\frac{1}{2}\%$ and $9\frac{3}{4}\%$?

The following table lists some upcoming total eclipses of the Sun that will be visible in North America. The duration of each eclipse is listed in the table. Use the table to answer Exercises 63 through 66.

Total Solar Eclipses Visible from North America	
Date of Eclipse	Duration (in Minutes)
August 1, 2008	$2\frac{9}{20}$
August 21, 2017	$2\frac{2}{3}$
April 8, 2024	$4\frac{7}{15}$
(*Source:* NASA/Goddard Space Flight Center)	

63. What is the total duration for the three eclipses?

64. What is the total duration for the two eclipses occuring in even-numbered years?

65. How much longer will the April 8, 2024, eclipse be than the August 21, 2017, eclipse?

66. How much longer will the August 21, 2017, eclipse be than the August 1, 2008, eclipse?

Find the perimeter of each figure.

△ **67.**

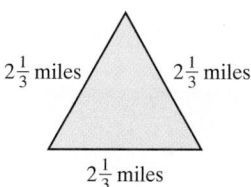

$2\frac{1}{3}$ miles $2\frac{1}{3}$ miles

$2\frac{1}{3}$ miles

△ **68.**

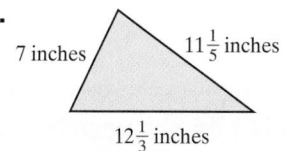

7 inches $11\frac{1}{5}$ inches

$12\frac{1}{3}$ inches

△ **69.**

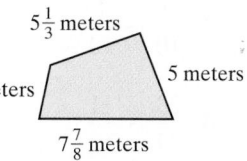

$5\frac{1}{3}$ meters

3 meters   5 meters

$7\frac{7}{8}$ meters

△ **70.**

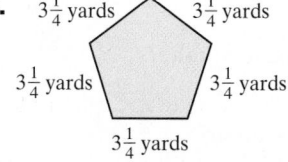

$3\frac{1}{4}$ yards $3\frac{1}{4}$ yards

$3\frac{1}{4}$ yards $3\frac{1}{4}$ yards

$3\frac{1}{4}$ yards

Review

Evaluate each expression. See Section 1.9.

71. 2^3

72. 3^2

73. 5^2

74. 2^5

75. $20 \div 10 \cdot 2$

76. $36 - 5 \cdot 6 + 10$

77. $2 + 3(8 \cdot 7 - 1)$

78. $2(10 - 2 \cdot 5) + 13$

Simplify. Write any mixed number whose fraction part is not a proper fraction in simplest form.

79. $3\frac{5}{5}$

80. $10\frac{8}{7}$

81. $9\frac{10}{16}$

82. $6\frac{7}{14}$

Concept Extensions

Solve. See the Concept Checks in this section.

83. Which of the following are equivalent to 10?

a. $9\frac{5}{5}$ **b.** $9\frac{100}{100}$ **c.** $6\frac{44}{11}$ **d.** $8\frac{13}{13}$

84. Which of the following are equivalent to $7\frac{3}{4}$?

a. $6\frac{7}{4}$ **b.** $5\frac{11}{4}$ **c.** $7\frac{12}{16}$ **d.** all of them

Solve.

85. Explain in your own words why $9\frac{13}{9}$ is equal to $10\frac{4}{9}$.

86. In your own words, explain

  a. when to borrow when subtracting mixed numbers, and

  b. how to borrow when subtracting mixed numbers.

87. Carmen's Candy Clutch is famous for its "Nutstuff," a special blend of nuts and candy. A Supreme box of Nutstuff has $2\frac{1}{4}$ pounds of nuts and $3\frac{1}{2}$ pounds of candy. A Deluxe box has $1\frac{3}{8}$ pounds of nuts and $4\frac{1}{4}$ pounds of candy. Which box is heavier and by how much?

88. Willie Cassidie purchased three Supreme boxes and two Deluxe boxes of Nutstuff from Carmen's Candy Clutch. (See Exercise 87.) What is the total weight of his purchase?

 THE BIGGER PICTURE   **Operations on Sets of Numbers**

Continue your outline from Sections 1.7, 1.9, and 2.5. Suggestions are once again written to help you complete this part of your outline.

I. Some Operations on Sets of Numbers

  A. Whole Numbers

   1. Add or Subtract (Sections 1.3, 1.4)

   2. Multiply or Divide (Sections 1.6, 1.7)

   3. Exponent (Section 1.9)

   4. Square Root (Section 1.9)

   5. Order of Operations (Section 1.9)

  B. Fractions

   1. Simplify (Section 2.3)

   2. Multiply (Section 2.4)

   3. Divide (Section 2.5)

   4. Add or Subtract: Must have same denominators. If not, find the LCD, and write each fraction as an equivalent fraction with the LCD as denominator.

   $$\frac{2}{5}+\frac{1}{15}=\frac{2}{5}\cdot\frac{3}{3}+\frac{1}{15}=\frac{6}{15}+\frac{1}{15}=\frac{7}{15}$$

Perform indicated operations.

1. $\dfrac{3}{17}+\dfrac{2}{17}$

2. $\dfrac{9}{10}-\dfrac{1}{10}$

3. $\dfrac{2}{3}+\dfrac{3}{10}$

4. $\dfrac{23}{24}-\dfrac{11}{12}$

5. $\dfrac{7}{8}+\dfrac{19}{20}$

6. $\dfrac{3^3}{4^3}$

7. $\begin{array}{r} 16 \\ -\ 3\frac{4}{7} \\ \hline \end{array}$

8. $\begin{array}{r} 2\frac{5}{8} \\ 1\frac{1}{6} \\ +5\frac{3}{4} \\ \hline \end{array}$

9. $\dfrac{6}{11}\cdot\dfrac{8}{9}$

10. $2\dfrac{4}{15}\div 1\dfrac{4}{5}$

3.5 ORDER, EXPONENTS, AND THE ORDER OF OPERATIONS

Objectives

A Compare Fractions.

B Evaluate Fractions Raised to Powers.

C Review Operations on Fractions.

D Use the Order of Operations.

Objective **A** Comparing Fractions

Recall that whole numbers can be shown on a number line using equally spaced distances.

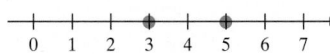

From the number line, we can see the order of numbers. For example, we can see that 3 is less than 5 because 3 is to the left of 5.

For any two numbers on a number line, the number to the left is always the smaller number, and the number to the right is always the larger number.

We use the **inequality symbols** $<$ or $>$ to write the order of numbers.

Inequality Symbols

$<$ means *is less than*.

$>$ means *is greater than*.

For example,

$$3 \text{ is less than } 5 \quad \text{or} \quad 5 \text{ is greater than } 3$$

$$3 < 5 \qquad 5 > 3$$

We can compare fractions the same way. To see fractions on a number line, divide the spaces between whole numbers into equal parts.

For example, let's compare $\frac{2}{5}$ and $\frac{4}{5}$.

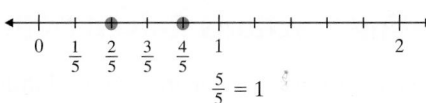

$$\frac{5}{5} = 1$$

Since $\frac{4}{5}$ is to the right of $\frac{2}{5}$,

$$\frac{2}{5} < \frac{4}{5} \qquad \text{Notice that } 2 < 4 \text{ also.}$$

Comparing Fractions

To determine which of two fractions is greater,

Step 1: Write the fractions as like fractions.

Step 2: The fraction with the greater numerator is the greater fraction.

EXAMPLE 1 Insert $<$ or $>$ to form a true statement.

$$\frac{3}{10} \qquad \frac{2}{7}$$

Solution:

Step 1: The LCD of 10 and 7 is 70.

$$\frac{3}{10} = \frac{3}{10} \cdot \frac{7}{7} = \frac{21}{70}; \qquad \frac{2}{7} = \frac{2}{7} \cdot \frac{10}{10} = \frac{20}{70}$$

Continued on next page

PRACTICE PROBLEM 1

Insert $<$ or $>$ to form a true statement.

$$\frac{8}{9} \qquad \frac{10}{11}$$

Answer

1. $<$

217

Step 2: Since $21 > 20$, then $\dfrac{21}{70} > \dfrac{20}{70}$ or

$$\dfrac{3}{10} > \dfrac{2}{7}$$

⬛ **Work Practice Problem 1**

EXAMPLE 2 Insert < or > to form a true statement.

$$\dfrac{9}{10} \qquad \dfrac{11}{12}$$

Solution:

Step 1: The LCD of 10 and 12 is 60.

$$\dfrac{9}{10} = \dfrac{9}{10} \cdot \dfrac{6}{6} = \dfrac{54}{60} \qquad \dfrac{11}{12} = \dfrac{11}{12} \cdot \dfrac{5}{5} = \dfrac{55}{60}$$

Step 2: Since $54 < 55$, then $\dfrac{54}{60} < \dfrac{55}{60}$ or

$$\dfrac{9}{10} < \dfrac{11}{12}$$

⬛ **Work Practice Problem 2**

Helpful Hint

If we think of < and > as arrowheads, a true statement is always formed when the arrow points to the smaller number.

$$\dfrac{2}{3} > \dfrac{1}{3} \qquad\qquad\qquad \dfrac{5}{6} < \dfrac{7}{6}$$

points to smaller number   points to smaller number

Objective B Evaluating Fractions Raised to Powers

Recall from Section 1.9 that exponents indicate repeated multiplication.

$$\underset{\text{base}}{\overset{\text{exponent}}{5^3}} = \underbrace{5 \cdot 5 \cdot 5}_{\text{3 factors of 5}} = 125$$

Exponents mean the same when the base is a fraction. For example,

$$\underset{\text{base}}{\left(\dfrac{1}{3}\right)^4} = \underbrace{\dfrac{1}{3} \cdot \dfrac{1}{3} \cdot \dfrac{1}{3} \cdot \dfrac{1}{3}}_{\text{4 factors of } \frac{1}{3}} = \dfrac{1}{81}$$

EXAMPLES Evaluate each expression.

3. $\left(\dfrac{1}{4}\right)^2 = \dfrac{1}{4} \cdot \dfrac{1}{4} = \dfrac{1}{16}$

4. $\left(\dfrac{3}{5}\right)^3 = \dfrac{3}{5} \cdot \dfrac{3}{5} \cdot \dfrac{3}{5} = \dfrac{27}{125}$

5. $\left(\dfrac{1}{6}\right)^2 \cdot \left(\dfrac{3}{4}\right)^3 = \left(\dfrac{1}{6} \cdot \dfrac{1}{6}\right) \cdot \left(\dfrac{3}{4} \cdot \dfrac{3}{4} \cdot \dfrac{3}{4}\right) = \dfrac{1 \cdot 1 \cdot \overset{1}{\cancel{3}} \cdot \overset{1}{\cancel{3}} \cdot 3}{2 \cdot \underset{1}{\cancel{3}} \cdot 2 \cdot \underset{1}{\cancel{3}} \cdot 4 \cdot 4 \cdot 4} = \dfrac{3}{256}$

⬛ **Work Practice Problems 3-5**

Objective C Reviewing Operations on Fractions

To get ready to use the order of operations with fractions, let's first review the operations on fractions that we have learned.

	Review of Operations on Fractions	
Operation	**Procedure**	**Example**
Multiply	Multiply the numerators and multiply the denominators.	$\frac{5}{9} \cdot \frac{1}{2} = \frac{5 \cdot 1}{9 \cdot 2} = \frac{5}{18}$
Divide	Multiply the first fraction by the reciprocal of the second fraction.	$\frac{2}{3} \div \frac{11}{13} = \frac{2}{3} \cdot \frac{13}{11} = \frac{2 \cdot 13}{3 \cdot 11} = \frac{26}{33}$
Add or Subtract	**1.** Write each fraction as an equivalent fraction whose denominator is the LCD **2.** Add or subtract numerators and write the result over the common denominator.	$\frac{3}{4} + \frac{1}{8} = \frac{3}{4} \cdot \frac{2}{2} + \frac{1}{8} = \frac{6}{8} + \frac{1}{8} = \frac{7}{8}$

EXAMPLES Perform each indicated operation.

6. $\frac{1}{2} \div \frac{8}{7} = \frac{1}{2} \cdot \frac{7}{8} = \frac{1 \cdot 7}{2 \cdot 8} = \frac{7}{16}$

To divide: multiply by the reciprocal.

7. $\frac{6}{35} + \frac{3}{7} = \frac{6}{35} + \frac{3}{7} \cdot \frac{5}{5} = \frac{6}{35} + \frac{15}{35} = \frac{21}{35}$

To add: need the LCD. The LCD is 35.

$$= \frac{\overset{1}{\cancel{7}} \cdot 3}{\underset{1}{\cancel{7}} \cdot 5} = \frac{3}{5}$$

8. $\frac{2}{9} \cdot \frac{3}{11} = \frac{2 \cdot 3}{9 \cdot 11} = \frac{2 \cdot \overset{1}{\cancel{3}}}{\underset{1}{\cancel{3}} \cdot 3 \cdot 11} = \frac{2}{33}$

To multiply: multiply numerators and multiply denominators.

9. $\frac{6}{7} - \frac{1}{3} = \frac{6}{7} \cdot \frac{3}{3} - \frac{1}{3} \cdot \frac{7}{7} = \frac{18}{21} - \frac{7}{21} = \frac{11}{21}$

To subtract: need the LCD. The LCD is 21.

☐ **Work Practice Problems 6–9**

Objective D Using the Order of Operations

The order of operations that we use on whole numbers applies to expressions containing fractions and mixed numbers also.

Order of Operations

1. Perform all operations within parentheses ( ), brackets [ ], or other grouping symbols such as square roots or fraction bars.

2. Evaluate any expressions with exponents.

3. Multiply or divide in order from left to right.

4. Add or subtract in order from left to right.

PRACTICE PROBLEM 10

Simplify: $\dfrac{2}{9} \div \dfrac{4}{7} \cdot \dfrac{3}{10}$

EXAMPLE 10 Simplify: $\dfrac{1}{5} \div \dfrac{2}{3} \cdot \dfrac{4}{5}$

Solution: Multiply or divide *in order* from left to right. We divide first.

$$\dfrac{1}{5} \div \dfrac{2}{3} \cdot \dfrac{4}{5} = \dfrac{1}{5} \cdot \dfrac{3}{2} \cdot \dfrac{4}{5}$$

To divide, multiply by the reciprocal.

$$= \dfrac{3}{10} \cdot \dfrac{4}{5}$$

$$= \dfrac{3 \cdot 4}{10 \cdot 5} \quad \text{Multiply.}$$

$$= \dfrac{3 \cdot 2 \cdot \overset{1}{\cancel{2}}}{\underset{1}{\cancel{2}} \cdot 5 \cdot 5} \quad \text{Simplify.}$$

$$= \dfrac{6}{25} \quad \text{Simplify.}$$

Work Practice Problem 10

PRACTICE PROBLEM 11

Simplify: $\left(\dfrac{2}{5}\right)^2 \div \left(\dfrac{3}{5} - \dfrac{11}{25}\right)$

EXAMPLE 11 Simplify: $\left(\dfrac{2}{3}\right)^2 \div \left(\dfrac{8}{27} + \dfrac{2}{3}\right)$

Solution: Start within the right set of parentheses. We add.

$$\left(\dfrac{2}{3}\right)^2 \div \left(\dfrac{8}{27} + \dfrac{2}{3}\right) = \left(\dfrac{2}{3}\right)^2 \div \left(\dfrac{8}{27} + \dfrac{18}{27}\right) \quad \text{The LCD is 27. Write } \dfrac{2}{3} \text{ as } \dfrac{18}{27}.$$

$$= \left(\dfrac{2}{3}\right)^2 \div \dfrac{26}{27} \quad \text{Simplify inside the parentheses.}$$

$$= \dfrac{4}{9} \div \dfrac{26}{27} \quad \text{Write } \left(\dfrac{2}{3}\right)^2 \text{ as } \dfrac{4}{9}.$$

$$= \dfrac{4}{9} \cdot \dfrac{27}{26}$$

$$= \dfrac{\overset{1}{\cancel{2}} \cdot 2 \cdot 3 \cdot \overset{1}{\cancel{9}}}{\underset{1}{\cancel{9}} \cdot \underset{1}{\cancel{2}} \cdot 13}$$

$$= \dfrac{6}{13}$$

Work Practice Problem 11

✔**Concept Check** What should be done first to simplify

$$3\left[\left(\dfrac{1}{4}\right)^2 + \dfrac{3}{2}\left(\dfrac{6}{7} - \dfrac{1}{3}\right)\right]?$$

Answers

10. $\dfrac{7}{60}$, 11. 1

✔ **Concept Check Answer**

$\dfrac{6}{7} - \dfrac{1}{3}$

Recall from Section 1.7 that the average of a list of numbers is their sum divided by the number of numbers in the list.

EXAMPLE 12 Find the average of $\frac{1}{3}$, $\frac{2}{5}$, and $\frac{2}{9}$.

Solution: The average is their sum, divided by 3.

$$\left(\frac{1}{3} + \frac{2}{5} + \frac{2}{9}\right) \div 3 = \left(\frac{15}{45} + \frac{18}{45} + \frac{10}{45}\right) \div 3 \qquad \text{The LCD is 45.}$$

$$= \frac{43}{45} \div 3 \qquad \text{Add.}$$

$$= \frac{43}{45} \cdot \frac{1}{3}$$

$$= \frac{43}{135} \qquad \text{Multiply.}$$

⬛ **Work Practice Problem 12**

3.5 EXERCISE SET

FOR EXTRA HELP

Student Solutions Manual · PH Math/Tutor Center · CD/Video for Review · MathXL® · MyMathLab

Objective A *Insert < or > to form a true statement. See Examples 1 and 2.*

1. $\frac{7}{9}$ $\frac{6}{9}$

2. $\frac{12}{17}$ $\frac{13}{17}$

3. $\frac{3}{3}$ $\frac{5}{3}$

4. $\frac{3}{23}$ $\frac{4}{23}$

5. $\frac{9}{42}$ $\frac{5}{21}$

6. $\frac{17}{32}$ $\frac{5}{16}$

7. $\frac{9}{8}$ $\frac{17}{16}$

8. $\frac{3}{8}$ $\frac{14}{40}$

9. $\frac{3}{4}$ $\frac{2}{3}$

10. $\frac{2}{5}$ $\frac{1}{3}$

11. $\frac{3}{5}$ $\frac{9}{14}$

12. $\frac{3}{10}$ $\frac{7}{25}$

13. $\frac{1}{10}$ $\frac{1}{11}$

14. $\frac{1}{13}$ $\frac{1}{14}$

15. $\frac{27}{100}$ $\frac{7}{25}$

16. $\frac{37}{120}$ $\frac{9}{30}$

Objective B *Evaluate each expression. See Examples 3 through 5.*

17. $\left(\frac{1}{2}\right)^4$

18. $\left(\frac{1}{7}\right)^2$

19. $\left(\frac{2}{5}\right)^3$

20. $\left(\frac{3}{4}\right)^3$

21. $\left(\frac{4}{7}\right)^3$

22. $\left(\frac{2}{3}\right)^4$

23. $\left(\frac{2}{9}\right)^2$

24. $\left(\frac{7}{11}\right)^2$

25. $\left(\dfrac{3}{4}\right)^2 \cdot \left(\dfrac{2}{3}\right)^3$

26. $\left(\dfrac{1}{6}\right)^2 \cdot \left(\dfrac{9}{10}\right)^2$

27. $\dfrac{9}{10}\left(\dfrac{2}{5}\right)^2$

28. $\dfrac{7}{11}\left(\dfrac{3}{10}\right)^2$

Objective **C** **Mixed Practice** *Perform each indicated operation. See Examples 6 through 9.*

29. $\dfrac{2}{15} + \dfrac{3}{5}$

30. $\dfrac{5}{12} + \dfrac{5}{6}$

31. $\dfrac{3}{7} \cdot \dfrac{1}{5}$

32. $\dfrac{9}{10} \div \dfrac{2}{3}$

33. $1 - \dfrac{4}{9}$

34. $5 - \dfrac{2}{3}$

35. $4\dfrac{2}{9} + 5\dfrac{9}{11}$

36. $7\dfrac{3}{7} + 6\dfrac{3}{5}$

37. $\dfrac{5}{6} - \dfrac{3}{4}$

38. $\dfrac{7}{10} - \dfrac{3}{25}$

39. $\dfrac{6}{11} \div \dfrac{2}{3}$

40. $\dfrac{3}{8} \cdot \dfrac{1}{11}$

41. $0 \cdot \dfrac{9}{10}$

42. $\dfrac{5}{6} \cdot 0$

43. $0 \div \dfrac{9}{10}$

44. $\dfrac{5}{6} \div 0$

45. $\dfrac{20}{35} \cdot \dfrac{7}{10}$

46. $\dfrac{18}{25} \div \dfrac{3}{5}$

47. $\dfrac{4}{7} - \dfrac{6}{11}$

48. $\dfrac{11}{20} + \dfrac{7}{15}$

Objective **D** *Use the order of operations to simplify each expression. See Examples 10 and 11.*

49. $\dfrac{1}{5} + \dfrac{1}{3} \cdot \dfrac{1}{4}$

50. $\dfrac{1}{2} + \dfrac{1}{6} \cdot \dfrac{1}{3}$

51. $\dfrac{5}{6} \div \dfrac{1}{3} \cdot \dfrac{1}{4}$

52. $\dfrac{7}{8} \div \dfrac{1}{4} \cdot \dfrac{1}{7}$

53. $\dfrac{1}{5} \cdot \left(2\dfrac{5}{6} - \dfrac{1}{3}\right)$

54. $\dfrac{4}{7} \cdot \left(6 - 2\dfrac{1}{2}\right)$

55. $2 \cdot \left(\dfrac{1}{4} + \dfrac{1}{5}\right) + 2$

56. $\dfrac{2}{5} \cdot \left(5 - \dfrac{1}{2}\right) - 1$

57. $\left(\dfrac{3}{4}\right)^2 \div \left(\dfrac{3}{4} - \dfrac{1}{12}\right)$

58. $\left(\dfrac{8}{9}\right)^2 \div \left(2 - \dfrac{2}{3}\right)$

59. $\left(\dfrac{2}{3} - \dfrac{5}{9}\right)^2$

60. $\left(1 - \dfrac{2}{5}\right)^3$

61. $\dfrac{5}{9} \cdot \dfrac{1}{2} + \dfrac{2}{3} \cdot \dfrac{5}{6}$

62. $\dfrac{7}{10} \cdot \dfrac{1}{2} + \dfrac{3}{4} \cdot \dfrac{3}{5}$

63. $\dfrac{27}{16} \cdot \left(\dfrac{2}{3}\right)^2 - \dfrac{3}{20}$

64. $\dfrac{64}{27} \cdot \left(\dfrac{3}{4}\right)^2 - \dfrac{7}{10}$

65. $\dfrac{3}{13} \div \dfrac{9}{26} - \dfrac{7}{24} \cdot \dfrac{8}{14}$ **66.** $\dfrac{5}{11} \div \dfrac{15}{77} - \dfrac{7}{10} \cdot \dfrac{5}{14}$ **67.** $\dfrac{3}{14} + \dfrac{10}{21} \div \left(\dfrac{3}{7}\right)\left(\dfrac{9}{4}\right)$ **68.** $\dfrac{11}{15} + \dfrac{7}{9} \div \left(\dfrac{14}{3}\right)\left(\dfrac{2}{3}\right)$

69. $\left(\dfrac{3}{4} + \dfrac{1}{8}\right)^2 - \left(\dfrac{1}{2} + \dfrac{1}{8}\right)$ **70.** $\left(\dfrac{1}{6} + \dfrac{1}{3}\right)^3 + \left(\dfrac{2}{5} \cdot \dfrac{3}{4}\right)^2$

Find the average of each list of numbers. See Example 12.

71. $\dfrac{5}{6}$ and $\dfrac{2}{3}$ **72.** $\dfrac{1}{2}$ and $\dfrac{4}{7}$ **73.** $\dfrac{1}{5}, \dfrac{3}{10},$ and $\dfrac{3}{20}$ **74.** $\dfrac{1}{3}, \dfrac{1}{4},$ and $\dfrac{1}{6}$

Objectives A D Mixed Practice *The table shows the fraction of the population in each country that uses cell phones. Use this table to answer Exercises 75 through 80.*

75. Complete the table by writing each fraction as an equivalent fraction with a denominator of 100.

76. Which of these countries has the largest fraction of cell phone users?

77. Which of these countries has the smallest fraction of cell phone users?

78. In which of these countries do over $\dfrac{3}{4}$ of the population use cell phones? (*Hint*: Write $\dfrac{3}{4}$ as an equivalent fraction with a denominator of 100.)

Country	Fraction of Population Using Cell Phones	Equivalent Fraction with a Denominator of 100
Denmark	$\dfrac{22}{25}$	
Finland	$\dfrac{9}{10}$	
Israel	$\dfrac{24}{25}$	
Spain	$\dfrac{23}{25}$	
Japan	$\dfrac{17}{25}$	
Norway	$\dfrac{91}{100}$	
Singapore	$\dfrac{4}{5}$	
Macao	$\dfrac{41}{50}$	
Sweden	$\dfrac{89}{100}$	
United States	$\dfrac{7}{10}$	

(*Source: International Telecommunication and World Almanac*, 2005)

79. Find the average fraction of all phone users in Denmark, Israel, and Sweden.

80. Find the average fraction of cell phone users in the United States, Japan, and Finland.

Review

Identify each key word with the operation it most likely translates to. After each word, write A for addition, S for subtraction, M for multiplication, and D for division. See Sections 1.3, 1.4, 1.6, and 1.7.

81. increased by   **82.** sum   **83.** triple   **84.** product

85. subtracted from   **86.** decreased by   **87.** quotient   **88.** divided by

89. times   **90.** difference   **91.** total   **92.** more than

Concept Extensions

Solve.

93. Calculate $\dfrac{2^3}{3}$ and $\left(\dfrac{2}{3}\right)^3$. Do both of these expressions simplify to the same number? Explain why or why not.

94. Calculate $\left(\dfrac{1}{2}\right)^2 \cdot \left(\dfrac{3}{4}\right)^2$ and $\left(\dfrac{1}{2} \cdot \dfrac{3}{4}\right)^2$. Do both of these expressions simplify to the same number? Explain why or why not.

Each expression contains one addition, one subtraction, one multiplication, and one division. Write the operations in the order that they should be performed. Do not actually simplify. See the Concept Check in this section.

95. $[9 + 3(4 - 2)] \div \dfrac{10}{21}$ **96.** $[30 - 4(3 + 2)] \div \dfrac{5}{2}$ **97.** $\dfrac{1}{3} \div \left(\dfrac{2}{3}\right)\left(\dfrac{4}{5}\right) - \dfrac{1}{4} + \dfrac{1}{2}$ **98.** $\left(\dfrac{5}{6} - \dfrac{1}{3}\right) \cdot \dfrac{1}{3} + \dfrac{1}{2} \div \dfrac{9}{8}$

Solve.

99. In 2000, about $\dfrac{11}{67}$ of the total weight of mail delivered by the United States Postal Service was first-class mail. That same year, about $\dfrac{75}{134}$ of the total weight of mail delivered by the United States Postal Service was standard mail. Which of these two categories account for a greater portion of the mail handled by weight? (*Source:* U.S. Postal Service)

100. The National Park System (NPS) in the United States includes a wide variety of park types. National military parks account for $\dfrac{3}{128}$ of all NPS parks, and $\dfrac{1}{24}$ of NPS parks are classified as national preserves. Which category, national military park or national preserve, is bigger? (*Source:* National Park Service)

101. Approximately $\dfrac{7}{10}$ of U.S. adults have a savings account. About $\dfrac{11}{25}$ of U.S. adults have a non-interest-bearing checking account. Which type of banking service, savings account or non-interest-bearing checking account, do adults in the United States use more? (*Source:* Scarborough Research/ US Data.com, Inc.)

102. About $\dfrac{127}{500}$ of U.S. adults rent one or two videos per month. Approximately $\dfrac{31}{200}$ of U.S. adults rent three or four videos per month. Which video rental category, 1–2 videos or 3–4 videos per month, is bigger? (*Source:* Telenation/Market Facts, Inc.)

3.6 FRACTIONS AND PROBLEM SOLVING

Objective

A Solve Problems by Performing Operations on Fractions or Mixed Numbers.

Objective **A** Solving Problems Containing Fractions or Mixed Numbers

Now that we know how to add, subtract, multiply, and divide fractions and mixed numbers, we can solve problems containing these numbers.

In the next example, we find the volume of a box. Volume measures the space enclosed by a region and is measured in cubic units. We study volume further in a later chapter.

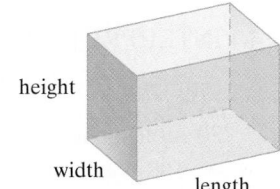

Volume of a box = length · width · height

> **Helpful Hint**
>
> Remember:
>
> **Perimeter** measures the distance around a figure. It is measured in **units**.
>
> ☐ Perimeter
>
> **Area** measures the amount of surface of a figure. It is measured in **square units**.
>
> ▭ Area
>
> **Volume** measures the amount of space enclosed by a region. It is measured in **cubic units**.
>
> ▱ Volume

EXAMPLE 1 Finding Volume of a Camcorder Box

Sony recently produced the smallest camcorder. It measures 5 inches by $2\frac{1}{2}$ inches by $1\frac{3}{4}$ inches and can store 30 minutes of moving images. Find the volume of a box with these dimensions. (*Source: Guinness World Records*)

Solution:

1. UNDERSTAND. Read and reread the problem. The phrase "volume of a box" tells us what to do. The volume of a box is the product of its length, width, and height. Since we are multiplying, it makes no difference which measurement we call length, width, or height.

2. TRANSLATE.

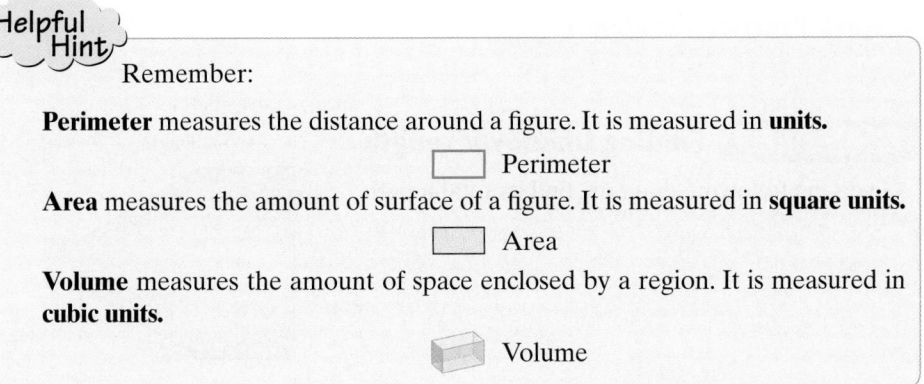

In words: | volume of a box | is | length | · | width | · | height |

Translate: volume of a box $= 5$ in. $\cdot 2\frac{1}{2}$ in. $\cdot 1\frac{3}{4}$ in.

Continued on next page

PRACTICE PROBLEM 1

Find the volume of a box that measures $4\frac{1}{3}$ feet by $1\frac{1}{2}$ feet by $3\frac{1}{3}$ feet.

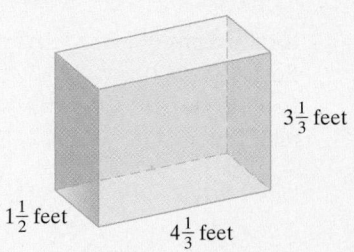

Answer

1. $21\frac{2}{3}$ cu ft

225

3. SOLVE: Before we multiply, let's estimate by rounding each dimension to a whole number. The number 5 rounds to 5, $2\frac{1}{2}$ rounds to 3, and $1\frac{3}{4}$ rounds to 2, so our estimate is $5 \cdot 3 \cdot 2$ or 30 cubic inches.

$$5\,\text{in.} \cdot 2\frac{1}{2}\,\text{in.} \cdot 1\frac{3}{4}\,\text{in.} = \frac{5}{1} \cdot \frac{5}{2} \cdot \frac{7}{4} \quad \text{cubic inches}$$

$$= \frac{5 \cdot 5 \cdot 7}{1 \cdot 2 \cdot 4} \quad \text{cubic inches}$$

$$= \frac{175}{8} \text{ or } 21\frac{7}{8} \quad \text{cubic inches}$$

4. INTERPRET. *Check* your work. The exact answer is somewhat close to our estimate. If you'd like, round $2\frac{1}{2}$ down to 2, and our estimate is $5 \cdot 2 \cdot 2$ or 20 cubic inches. This estimate is also appropriate and closer to our exact answer, so it is reasonable. *State* your conclusion: The volume of a box that measures 5 inches by $2\frac{1}{2}$ inches by $1\frac{3}{4}$ inches is $21\frac{7}{8}$ cubic inches.

🔲 **Work Practice Problem 1**

PRACTICE PROBLEM 2

Given the following diagram, find its total width.

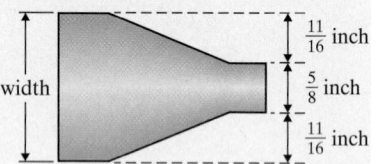

EXAMPLE 2 **Finding Unknown Length**

Given the following diagram, find its total length.

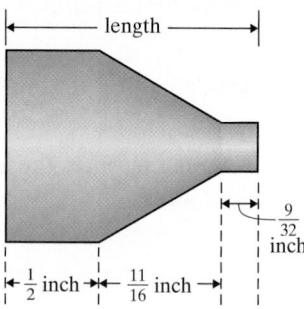

Solution:

1. UNDERSTAND. Read and reread the problem. Then study the diagram. The phrase "total length" tells us to add.

2. TRANSLATE. It makes no difference which length we call first, second, or third length.

In words:	total length	is	first length	+	second length	+	third length
	↓	↓	↓		↓		↓
Translate:	total length	=	$\frac{1}{2}$ in.	+	$\frac{11}{16}$ in.	+	$\frac{9}{32}$ in.

3. SOLVE:

$$\frac{1}{2} + \frac{11}{16} + \frac{9}{32} = \frac{1 \cdot 16}{2 \cdot 16} + \frac{11 \cdot 2}{16 \cdot 2} + \frac{9}{32}$$

$$= \frac{16}{32} + \frac{22}{32} + \frac{9}{32}$$

$$= \frac{47}{32} \text{ or } 1\frac{15}{32}$$

4. INTERPRET. *Check* your work. *State* your conclusion: The total length is $1\frac{15}{32}$ inches.

Many problems require more than one operation to solve as shown in the next application.

🔲 **Work Practice Problem 2**

Answer

2. 2 in.

EXAMPLE 3 **Acreage for Single-Family Home Lots**

A contractor is considering buying land to develop a subdivision for single-family homes. Suppose she buys 44 acres and calculates that $4\frac{1}{4}$ acres of this land will be used for roads and a retention pond. How many $\frac{3}{4}$-acre lots can she sell using the rest of the acreage?

PRACTICE PROBLEM 3

Suppose that 25 acres of land are purchased, but because of roads and wetlands concerns, $6\frac{2}{3}$ acres cannot be developed into lots. How many $\frac{5}{6}$-acre lots can the rest of the land be divided into?

Solution:

1a. UNDERSTAND. Read and reread the problem. The phrase "using the rest of the acreage" tells is that initially we are to subtract.

2a. TRANSLATE. First, let's calculate the amount of acreage that can be used for lots.

In words:	acreage for lots	is	total acreage	minus	acreage for roads and a pond
	↓	↓	↓	↓	↓
Translate:	acreage for lots	=	44	−	$4\frac{1}{4}$

3a. SOLVE:

$$
\begin{array}{r}
44 = 43\frac{4}{4} \\
-\,4\frac{1}{4} = -\,4\frac{1}{4} \\
\hline
39\frac{3}{4}
\end{array}
$$

1b. UNDERSTAND. Now that we know $39\frac{3}{4}$ acres can be used for lots, we calculate how many $\frac{3}{4}$ acres are in $39\frac{3}{4}$. This means that we divide.

2b. TRANSLATE.

In words:	number of $\frac{3}{4}$-acre lots	is	acreage for lots	divided by	size of each lot
	↓	↓	↓	↓	↓
Translate:	number of $\frac{3}{4}$-acre lots	=	$39\frac{3}{4}$	÷	$\frac{3}{4}$

3b. SOLVE:

$$39\frac{3}{4} \div \frac{3}{4} = \frac{159}{4} \cdot \frac{4}{3} = \frac{\overset{53}{\cancel{159}} \cdot \overset{1}{\cancel{4}}}{\underset{1}{\cancel{4}} \cdot \underset{1}{\cancel{3}}} = \frac{53}{1} \text{ or } 53$$

4. INTERPRET. *Check* your work. *State* your conclusion: The contractor can sell $53\frac{3}{4}$-acre lots.

▇ **Work Practice Problem 3**

Answer

3. 22 lots

Translate each to an expression. Then simplify the expression.

1. Find the sum of 11 and 2.

2. Find the product of 11 and 2.

3. Find the quotient of 20 and 6.

4. Find the difference of 20 and 6.

5. Subtract 8 from 35.

6. Find the total of 15 and 18.

7. Find 68 increased by 7.

8. Find 68 decreased by 7.

9. Multiply 21 and 9.

10. Find 37 divided by 9.

Objective **A** *Solve. See Examples 1 through 3.*

11. A recipe for brownies calls for $1\frac{2}{3}$ cups of sugar. If you are doubling the recipe, how much sugar do you need?

12. A nacho recipe calls for $\frac{1}{3}$ cup chedder cheese and $\frac{1}{2}$ cup jalapeño cheese. Find the total amount of cheese in the recipe.

13. A decorative wall in Ben and Joy Lander's garden is to be built using brick that is $2\frac{3}{4}$ inches wide and a mortar joint that is $\frac{1}{2}$ inch wide. Use the diagram to find the height of the wall.

14. Suppose that Ben and Joy Lander (from Exercise 13) decide that they want one more layer of bricks with a mortar joint below and above that layer. Find the new height of the wall.

height   Mortar joint

15. Doug and Claudia Scaggs recently drove $290\frac{1}{4}$ miles on $13\frac{1}{2}$ gallons of gas. Calculate how many miles per gallon they get in their vehicle.

16. A contractor is using 18 acres of his land to sell $\frac{3}{4}$-acre lots. How many lots can he sell?

17. The life expectancy of a circulating coin is 30 years. The life expectancy of a circulating dollar bill is only $\frac{1}{20}$ as long. Find the life expectancy of circulating paper money. (*Source:* The U.S. Mint)

18. The Indian Head one-cent coin of 1859–1864 was made of copper and nickel only. If $\frac{3}{25}$ of the coin was nickel, what part of the whole coin was copper? (*Source:* The U.S. Mint)

19. The Gauge Act of 1846 set the standard gauge for U.S. railroads at $56\frac{1}{2}$ inches. (See figure.) If the standard gauge in Spain is $65\frac{9}{10}$ inches, how much wider is Spain's standard gauge than the U.S. standard gauge? (*Source:* San Diego Railroad Museum)

20. The standard railroad track gauge (see figure) in Spain is $65\frac{9}{10}$ inches, while in neighboring Portugal it is $65\frac{11}{20}$ inches. Which gauge is wider and by how much? (*Source:* San Diego Museum)

Track gauge (U.S. $56\frac{1}{2}$ inches)

$\frac{5}{8}$ inch

Point of measurement of gauge

21. Mark Nguyen is a tailor making costumes for a play. He needs enough material for 1 large shirt that requires $1\frac{1}{2}$ yards of material and 5 small shirts that each require $\frac{3}{4}$ yard of material. He finds a 5-yard remnant of material on sale. Is 5 yards of material enough to make all 6 shirts? If not, how much more material does he need?

22. A beanbag manufacturer makes a large beanbag requiring $4\frac{1}{3}$ yards of vinyl fabric and a smaller size requiring $3\frac{1}{4}$ yards. A 100-yard roll of fabric is to be used to make 12 large beanbags. How many smaller beanbags can be made from the remaining piece?

23. A plumber has a 10-foot piece of PVC pipe. How many $\frac{9}{5}$-foot pieces can be cut from the 10-foot piece?

24. A carpenter has a 12-foot board to be used to make windowsills. If each sill requires $2\frac{5}{16}$ feet, how many sills can be made from the 12-foot board?

25. Suppose that the cross section of a piece of pipe looks like the diagram shown. Find the total outer diameter.

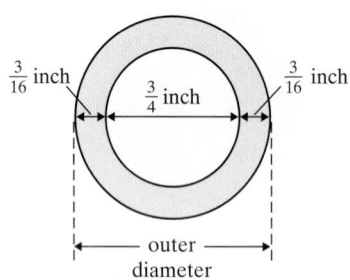

26. Suppose that the cross section of a piece of pipe looks like the diagram shown. Find the total inner diameter.

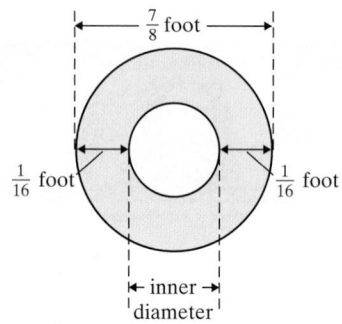

27. A recipe for chocolate chip cookies calls for $2\frac{1}{2}$ cups of flour. If you are making $1\frac{1}{2}$ recipes, how many cups of flour are needed?

28. A recipe for a homemade cleaning solution calls for $1\frac{3}{4}$ cups of vinegar. If you are tripling the recipe, how much vinegar is needed?

29. The Polaroid Pop Shot, the world's first disposable instant camera, can take color photographs measuring $4\frac{1}{2}$ inches by $2\frac{1}{2}$ inches. Find the area of a photograph. (*Source: Guinness World Records*)

30. A model for a proposed computer chip measures $\frac{3}{4}$ inch by $1\frac{1}{4}$ inches. Find its area.

31. A total solar eclipse on March 29, 2006 will last $4\frac{7}{60}$ minutes and can be viewed from Atlantic Ocean, Africa, and Asia. The next total solar eclipse on August 1, 2008, will last $2\frac{9}{20}$ minutes and can be viewed in parts of the Arctic Ocean and Asia. How much longer is the 2006 solar eclipse? (*Source: 2005 World Almanac*)

32. The pole vault record for the 1908 Summer Olympics was $12\frac{1}{6}$ feet. The record for the 2004 Summer Olympics was a little over $19\frac{1}{2}$ feet. Find the difference of these heights. (*Source: 2005 World Almanac*)

△ **33.** A small cell phone measures $3\frac{1}{5}$ inches by $1\frac{7}{10}$ inches by 1 inch. Find the volume of a box with those dimensions. (*Source: Guinness World Records*)

34. Early cell phones were large and heavy. One early model measured approximately 8 inches by $2\frac{1}{2}$ inches by $2\frac{1}{2}$ inches. Find the volume of a box with those dimensions.

35. A stack of $\frac{5}{8}$-inch-wide sheetrock has a height of $41\frac{7}{8}$ inches. How many sheets of sheetrock are in the stack?

36. A stack of $\frac{5}{4}$-inch-wide books has a height of $28\frac{3}{4}$ inches. How many books are in the stack?

37. William Arcencio is remodeling his home. In order to save money, he is upgrading the plumbing himself. He needs 12 pieces of copper tubing, each $\frac{3}{4}$ of a foot long.
  a. If he has a 10-foot piece of tubing, will that be enough?
  b. How much more does he need or how much tubing will he have left over?

38. Trishelle Dallam is building a bookcase. Each shelf will be $2\frac{3}{8}$ feet long, and she needs wood for 7 shelves.
  a. How many shelves can she cut from an 8-foot board?
  b. Based on your answer for part a, how many 8-foot boards will she need?

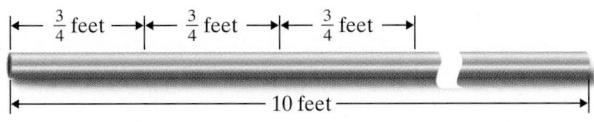

$2\frac{3}{8}$ feet

Recall that the average of a list of numbers is their sum divided by the number of numbers in the list. Use this procedure for Exercises 39 and 40.

39. A female lion had 4 cubs. They weighed $2\frac{1}{8}$, $2\frac{7}{8}$, $3\frac{1}{4}$, and $3\frac{1}{2}$ pounds. What is the average cub weight?

40. Three brook trout were caught, tagged, and then released. They weighed $1\frac{1}{2}$, $1\frac{3}{8}$, and $1\frac{7}{8}$ pounds. Find their average weight.

Find the area and perimeter of each figure.

△ **41.**

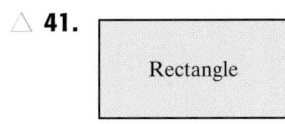

Rectangle $\frac{3}{16}$ inch

$\frac{3}{8}$ inch

△ **42.**

Square $1\frac{7}{10}$ mile

43.

Square | $\frac{5}{9}$ meter

44.

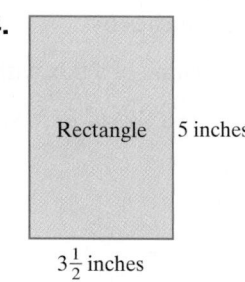

Rectangle | 5 inches

$3\frac{1}{2}$ inches

For Exercises 45 through 48, see the diagram. (Source: www.usflag.org)

45. The length of the U.S. flag is $1\frac{9}{10}$ its width. If a flag is being designed with a width of $2\frac{1}{2}$ feet, find its length.

46. The width of the Union portion the U.S. flag is $\frac{7}{13}$ of the width of the flag. If a flag is being designed with a width of $2\frac{1}{2}$ feet, find the width of the Union portion.

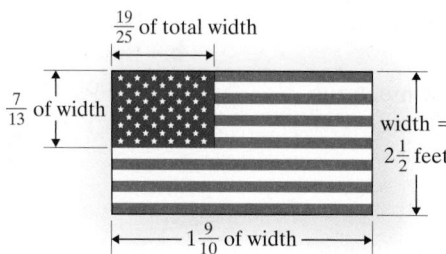

$\frac{19}{25}$ of total width

$\frac{7}{13}$ of width

width = $2\frac{1}{2}$ feet

$1\frac{9}{10}$ of width

47. There are 13 stripes of equal width in the flag. If the width of a flag is $2\frac{1}{2}$ feet, find the width of each stripe.

48. The length of the Union portion of the flag is $\frac{19}{25}$ of the total width. If the width of a flag is $2\frac{1}{2}$ feet, find the length of the Union portion.

Review

Simplify. See Section 1.9.

49. $\sqrt{9}$

50. $\sqrt{4}$

51. 9^2

52. 4^2

53. $8 \div 4 \cdot 2$

54. $20 \div 5 \cdot 2$

55. $3^2 - 2^2 + 5^2$

56. $8^2 - 6^2 + 7^2$

57. $5 + 3[14 - (12 \div 3)]$

58. $7 + 2[20 - (35 \div 5)]$

Copyright 2007 Pearson Education, Inc.

Concept Extensions

59. Suppose that you are finding the average of $1\frac{3}{4}$, $1\frac{1}{8}$, and $1\frac{9}{10}$. Can the average be $2\frac{1}{4}$? Can the average be $\frac{15}{16}$? Why or why not?

The figure shown is for Exercises 60 and 61.

△ **60.** Find the area of the figure. (*Hint:* The area of the figure can be found by finding the sum of the areas of the rectangles shown in the figure.)

△ **61.** Find the perimeter of the figure.

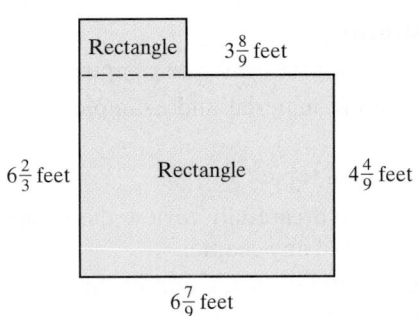

62. On a particular day, 240 customers ate lunch at a local restaurant. If $\frac{3}{10}$ of them ordered a $7 lunch, $\frac{5}{12}$ of them ordered a $5 lunch, and the remaining customers ordered a $9 lunch, how many customers ordered a $9 lunch?

63. Scott purchased a case of 24 apples. He used $\frac{1}{3}$ of them to make an apple pie, $\frac{1}{4}$ of them to make apple crisp, and kept the rest for after-school snacks for his children. How many apples did Chris keep for snacks?

64. Coins were practically made by hand in the late 1700s. Back then, it took 3 years to produce our nation's first million coins. Today, it takes only $\frac{11}{13,140}$ as long to produce the same amount. Calculate how long it takes today in hours to produce one million coins. (*Hint:* First convert 3 years to equivalent hours.) (*Source:* The U.S. Mint)

65. The largest suitcase measures $13\frac{1}{3}$ feet by $8\frac{3}{4}$ feet by $4\frac{4}{25}$ feet. Find its volume. (*Source: Guinness World Records*)

STUDY SKILLS BUILDER

Tips for Studying for an Exam

To prepare for an exam, try the following study techniques:

- Start the study process days before your exam.
- Make sure that you are up-to-date on your assignments.
- If there is a topic that you are unsure of, use one of the many resources that are available to you. For example,

    See your instructor.

    Visit a learning resource center on campus.

    Read the textbook material and examples on the topic.

    View a video on the topic.

- Reread your notes and carefully review the Chapter Highlights at the end of any chapter.
- Work the review exercises at the end of the chapter. Check your answers and correct any mistakes. If you have trouble, use a resource listed above.
- Find a quiet place to take the Chapter Test found at the end of the chapter. Do not use any resources when taking this sample test. This way, you will have a clear indication of how prepared you are for your exam. Check your answers and make sure that you correct any missed exercises.
- Get lots of rest the night before the exam. It's hard to show how well you know the material if your brain is foggy from lack of sleep.

Good luck and keep a positive attitude.

Let's see how you did on your last exam.

1. How many days before your last exam did you start studying for that exam?

2. Were you up-to-date on your assignments at that time or did you need to catch up on assignments?

3. List the most helpful text supplement (if you used one).

4. List the most helpful campus supplement (if you used one).

5. List your process for preparing for a mathematics test.

6. Was this process helpful? In other words, were you satisfied with your performance on your exam?

7. If not, what changes can you make in your process that will make it more helpful to you?

Are You Prepared for a Test on Chapter 3?

Below I have listed some *common trouble areas* for students in Chapter 3. After studying for your test—but before taking your test—read these.

Make sure you remember how to perform different operations on fractions!!! Try to add, subtract, multiply, then divide $\frac{3}{5}$ and $\frac{7}{15}$. Check your results below.

$$\frac{3}{5} + \frac{7}{15} = \frac{3}{5} \cdot \frac{3}{3} + \frac{7}{15} = \frac{9}{15} + \frac{7}{15} = \frac{16}{15} \text{ or } 1\frac{1}{15}$$

To add or subtract, the fractions must have a common denominator.

$$\frac{3}{5} - \frac{7}{15} = \frac{3}{5} \cdot \frac{3}{3} - \frac{7}{15} = \frac{9}{15} - \frac{7}{15} = \frac{2}{15}$$

$$\frac{3}{5} \cdot \frac{7}{15} = \frac{3 \cdot 7}{5 \cdot 15} = \frac{\cancel{3} \cdot 7}{5 \cdot \cancel{3} \cdot 5} = \frac{7}{25}$$

To multiply, multiply numerators and multiply denominators.

$$\frac{3}{5} \div \frac{7}{15} = \frac{3}{5} \cdot \frac{15}{7} = \frac{3 \cdot 15}{5 \cdot 7} = \frac{3 \cdot 3 \cdot \cancel{5}}{\cancel{5} \cdot 7} = \frac{9}{7} \text{ or } 1\frac{2}{7}$$

To divide, multiply by the reciprocal.

CHAPTER 3   Group Activity

Sections 3.1–3.6

This activity may be completed by working in groups or individually.

Lobsters are normally classified by weight. Use the weight classification table to answer the questions in this activity.

Classification of Lobsters	
Class	**Weight (in Pounds)**
Chicken	1 to $1\frac{1}{8}$
Quarter	$1\frac{1}{4}$
Half	$1\frac{1}{2}$ to $1\frac{3}{4}$
Select	$1\frac{3}{4}$ to $2\frac{1}{2}$
Large select	$2\frac{1}{2}$ to $3\frac{1}{2}$
Jumbo	Over $3\frac{1}{2}$

(*Source:* The Maine Lobster Promotion Council)

1. A lobster fisher has kept four lobsters from a lobster trap. Classify each lobster if they have the following weights:

   a. $1\frac{7}{8}$ pounds

   b. $1\frac{9}{16}$ pounds

   c. $2\frac{3}{4}$ pounds

   d. $2\frac{3}{8}$ pounds

2. A recipe requires 5 pounds of lobster. Using the minimum weight for each class, decide whether a chicken, half, and select lobster will be enough for the recipe, and explain your reasoning. If not, suggest a better choice of lobsters to meet the recipe requirements.

3. A lobster market customer has selected two chickens, a select, and a large select. What is the most that these four lobsters could weigh? What is the least that these four lobsters could weigh?

4. A lobster market customer wishes to buy three quarters. If lobsters sell for $7 per pound, how much will the customer owe for her purchase?

5. Why do you think there is no classification for lobsters weighing under 1 pound?

Chapter 3 Vocabulary Check

Fill in each blank with one of the words or phrases listed below.

equivalent	least common multiple	like
mixed number	< >	least common denominator

1. Fractions that have the same denominator are called _____ fractions.
2. The _____ is the smallest number that is a multiple of all numbers in a list of numbers.
3. _____ fractions represent the same portion of a whole.
4. A _____ has a whole number part and a fraction part.
5. The symbol _____ means is greater than.
6. The symbol _____ means is less than.
7. The LCM of the denominators in a list of fractions is called the _____.

> **Helpful Hint**
>
> Are you preparing for your test? Don't forget to take the Chapter 3 Test on page 244. Then check your answers at the back of the text and use the Chapter Test Prep Video CD to see the fully worked-out solutions to any of the exercises you want to review.

3 Chapter Highlights

DEFINITIONS AND CONCEPTS	**EXAMPLES**
Section 3.1 Adding and Subtracting Like Fractions	
Fractions that have the same denominator are called **like fractions.**	$\dfrac{1}{3}$ and $\dfrac{2}{3}$; $\dfrac{5}{7}$ and $\dfrac{6}{7}$
To add or subtract like fractions, combine the numerators and place the sum or difference over the common denominator.	$\dfrac{2}{7} + \dfrac{3}{7} = \dfrac{5}{7} \leftarrow$ Add the numerators. $\quad\leftarrow$ Keep the common denominator.
	$\dfrac{7}{8} - \dfrac{4}{8} = \dfrac{3}{8} \leftarrow$ Subtract the numerators. $\quad\leftarrow$ Keep the common denominator.
Section 3.2 Least Common Multiple	
The **least common multiple (LCM)** is the smallest number that is a multiple of all numbers in a list of numbers.	The LCM of 2 and 6 is 6 because 6 is the smallest number that is a multiple of both 2 and 6.
METHOD 1 FOR FINDING THE LCM OF A LIST OF NUMBERS USING MULTIPLES	Find the LCM of 4 and 6 using Method 1.
Step 1. Write the multiples of the largest number (starting with the number itself) until a multiple common to all numbers in the list is found.	$6 \cdot 1 = 6$ Not a multiple of 4 $6 \cdot 2 = 12$ A multiple of 4
Step 2. The multiple found in step 1 is the LCM.	The LCM is 12.

DEFINITIONS AND CONCEPTS	**EXAMPLES**

Section 3.2   Least Common Multiple (*continued*)

METHOD 2 FOR FINDING THE LCM OF A LIST OF NUMBERS USING PRIME FACTORIZATION

Step 1. Write the prime factorization of each number.

Step 2. For each different prime factor in step 1, circle the greatest number of times that factor occurs in any one factorization.

Step 3. The LCM is the product of the circle factors.

Equivalent fractions represent the same portion of a whole.

Find the LCM of 6 and 20 using Method 2.

$$6 = 2 \cdot \enclose{circle}{3}$$
$$20 = \enclose{circle}{2 \cdot 2} \cdot \enclose{circle}{5}$$

The LCM is

$$2 \cdot 2 \cdot 3 \cdot 5 = 60$$

Write an equivalent fraction with the indicated denominator.

$$\frac{2}{8} = \frac{}{16}$$
$$\frac{2 \cdot 2}{8 \cdot 2} = \frac{4}{16}$$

Section 3.3   Adding and Subtracting Unlike Fractions

TO ADD OR SUBTRACT FRACTIONS WITH UNLIKE DENOMINATORS

Step 1. Find the LCD.

Step 2. Write each fraction as an equivalent fraction whose denominator is the LCD.

Step 3. Add or subtract the like fractions.

Step 4. Write the sum or difference in simplest form.

Add: $\dfrac{3}{20} + \dfrac{2}{5}$

Step 1. The LCD of 20 and 5 is 20.

Step 2. $\dfrac{3}{20} = \dfrac{3}{20}$; $\dfrac{2}{5} = \dfrac{2}{5} \cdot \dfrac{4}{4} = \dfrac{8}{20}$

Step 3. $\dfrac{3}{20} + \dfrac{2}{5} = \dfrac{3}{20} + \dfrac{8}{20} = \dfrac{11}{20}$

Step 4. $\dfrac{11}{20}$ is in simplest form.

Section 3.4   Adding and Subtracting Mixed Numbers

To add or subtract with mixed numbers, add or subtract the fractions and then add or subtract the whole numbers.

Add: $2\dfrac{1}{2} + 5\dfrac{7}{8}$

$$2\dfrac{1}{2} = 2\dfrac{4}{8}$$
$$+5\dfrac{7}{8} = 5\dfrac{7}{8}$$
$$\overline{\phantom{+5\dfrac{7}{8}} \; 7\dfrac{11}{8} = 7 + 1\dfrac{3}{8} = 8\dfrac{3}{8}}$$

Section 3.5   Order, Exponents, and the Order of Operations

To compare like fractions, compare the numerators. The order of the fractions is the same as the order of the numerators.

Compare $\dfrac{3}{10}$ and $\dfrac{4}{10}$.

$$\dfrac{3}{10} < \dfrac{4}{10} \text{ since } 3 < 4$$

continued

DEFINITIONS AND CONCEPTS	EXAMPLES

Section 3.5 Order, Exponents, and the Order of Operations (*continued*)

To compare unlike fractions, first write the fractions as like fractions. Then the fraction with the greater numerator is the greater fraction.

Compare $\frac{2}{5}$ and $\frac{3}{7}$.

$$\frac{2}{5} = \frac{2}{5} \cdot \frac{7}{7} = \frac{14}{35} \qquad \frac{3}{7} = \frac{3}{7} \cdot \frac{5}{5} = \frac{15}{35}$$

Since $14 < 15$, then

$$\frac{14}{35} < \frac{15}{35} \quad \text{or} \quad \frac{2}{5} < \frac{3}{7}$$

Exponents mean repeated multiplication when the base is a whole number or a fraction.

$$\left(\frac{1}{2}\right)^3 = \frac{1}{2} \cdot \frac{1}{2} \cdot \frac{1}{2} = \frac{1}{8}$$

ORDER OF OPERATIONS

1. Perform all operations within parentheses ( ), brackets [ ], or other grouping symbols such as square roots or fraction bars.

2. Evaluate any expressions with exponents.

3. Multiply or divide in order from left to right.

4. Add or subtract in order from left to right.

Perform each indicated operation.

$$\frac{1}{2} + \frac{2}{3} \cdot \frac{1}{5} = \frac{1}{2} + \frac{2}{15} \qquad \text{Multiply.}$$

$$= \frac{1}{2} \cdot \frac{15}{15} + \frac{2}{15} \cdot \frac{2}{2} \qquad \text{The LCD is 30.}$$

$$= \frac{15}{30} + \frac{4}{30}$$

$$= \frac{19}{30} \qquad \text{Add.}$$

Section 3.6 Fractions and Problem Solving

PROBLEM-SOLVING STEPS

A stack of $\frac{3}{4}$-inch plywood has a height of $50\frac{1}{4}$ inches. How many sheets of plywood are in the stack?

1. UNDERSTAND the problem.

1. UNDERSTAND. Read and reread the problem. We want to know how many $\frac{3}{4}$'s are in $50\frac{1}{4}$, so we divide.

2. TRANSLATE the problem.

2. TRANSLATE.

number of sheets in stack	is	height of stack	÷	height of a sheet

$$\begin{array}{c}\text{number of} \\ \text{sheets} \\ \text{in} \\ \text{stack}\end{array} = 50\frac{1}{4} \div \frac{3}{4}$$

3. SOLVE the problem.

3. SOLVE. $50\frac{1}{4} \div \frac{3}{4} = \frac{201}{4} \cdot \frac{4}{3}$

$$= \frac{\overset{67}{\cancel{201}} \cdot \overset{1}{\cancel{4}}}{\underset{1}{\cancel{4}} \cdot \underset{1}{\cancel{3}}}$$

$$= 67$$

4. INTERPRET the results.

4. INTERPRET. *Check* your work and *state* your conclusion. There are 67 sheets of plywood in the stack.

3 CHAPTER REVIEW

(3.1) *Add or subtract as indicated. Simplify your answers.*

1. $\dfrac{7}{11} + \dfrac{3}{11}$
    2. $\dfrac{4}{50} + \dfrac{2}{50}$
    3. $\dfrac{11}{15} - \dfrac{1}{15}$
    4. $\dfrac{4}{21} - \dfrac{1}{21}$
    5. $\dfrac{4}{15} + \dfrac{3}{15} + \dfrac{2}{15}$

6. $\dfrac{3}{20} + \dfrac{7}{20} + \dfrac{2}{20}$
    7. $\dfrac{1}{12} + \dfrac{11}{12}$
    8. $\dfrac{3}{4} + \dfrac{1}{4}$
    9. $\dfrac{11}{25} + \dfrac{6}{25} + \dfrac{2}{25}$
    10. $\dfrac{4}{21} + \dfrac{1}{21} + \dfrac{11}{21}$

Solve.

11. One evening Mark Alorenzo did $\dfrac{3}{8}$ of his homework before supper, another $\dfrac{2}{8}$ of it while his children did their homework, and $\dfrac{1}{8}$ after his children went to bed. What part of his homework did he do that evening?

△ **12.** The Simpson's will be fencing in their land, which is in the shape of a rectangle. In order to do this, they need to find its perimeter. Find the perimeter of their land.

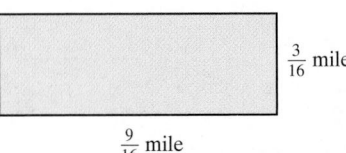

$\frac{3}{16}$ mile

$\frac{9}{16}$ mile

(3.2) *Find the LCM of each list of numbers.*

13. $5, 11$
    14. $20, 30$
    15. $20, 24$
    16. $16, 5$
    17. $12, 21, 63$
    18. $6, 8, 18$

Write each fraction as an equivalent fraction with the given denominator.

19. $\dfrac{7}{8} = \dfrac{}{64}$
    20. $\dfrac{2}{3} = \dfrac{}{30}$
    21. $\dfrac{7}{11} = \dfrac{}{33}$
    22. $\dfrac{10}{13} = \dfrac{}{26}$
    23. $\dfrac{4}{15} = \dfrac{}{60}$
    24. $\dfrac{5}{12} = \dfrac{}{60}$

(3.3) *Add or subtract as indicated. Simplify your answers.*

25. $\dfrac{7}{18} + \dfrac{2}{9}$
    26. $\dfrac{4}{15} + \dfrac{1}{5}$
    27. $\dfrac{4}{13} - \dfrac{1}{26}$
    28. $\dfrac{7}{12} - \dfrac{1}{9}$

29. $\dfrac{1}{3} + \dfrac{9}{14}$
    30. $\dfrac{7}{18} + \dfrac{5}{24}$
    31. $\dfrac{11}{15} - \dfrac{4}{9}$
    32. $\dfrac{9}{14} - \dfrac{3}{35}$

Find the perimeter of each figure.

△ **33.**

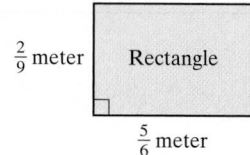

$\frac{2}{9}$ meter | Rectangle

$\frac{5}{6}$ meter

△ **34.**

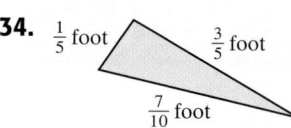

$\frac{1}{5}$ foot $\frac{3}{5}$ foot

$\frac{7}{10}$ foot

35. Find the difference in length of two scarves if one scarf is $\frac{5}{12}$ of a yard long and the other is $\frac{2}{3}$ of a yard long.

36. Truman Kalzote cleaned $\frac{3}{5}$ of his house yesterday and $\frac{1}{10}$ of it today. How much of the house has been cleaned?

(3.4) *Add or subtract as indicated. Simplify your answers.*

37. $31\frac{2}{7} + 14\frac{10}{21}$

38. $24\frac{4}{5} + 35\frac{1}{5}$

39. $69\frac{5}{22} - 36\frac{7}{11}$

40. $36\frac{3}{20} - 32\frac{5}{6}$

41. $\begin{array}{r} 29\frac{2}{9} \\ 27\frac{7}{18} \\ + 54\frac{2}{3} \\ \hline \end{array}$

42. $\begin{array}{r} 7\frac{3}{8} \\ 9\frac{5}{6} \\ + 3\frac{1}{12} \\ \hline \end{array}$

43. $\begin{array}{r} 9\frac{3}{5} \\ - 4\frac{1}{7} \\ \hline \end{array}$

44. $\begin{array}{r} 8\frac{3}{11} \\ - 5\frac{1}{5} \\ \hline \end{array}$

Solve.

45. The average annual snowfall at a certain ski resort is $62\frac{3}{10}$ inches. Last year it had $54\frac{1}{2}$ inches. How many inches below average was last year's snowfall?

△ **46.** Find the perimeter of a rectangular sheet of gift wrap that is $2\frac{1}{4}$ feet by $3\frac{1}{3}$ feet.

$2\frac{1}{4}$ feet

$3\frac{1}{3}$ feet

△ **47.** Find the perimeter of a sheet of shelf paper needed to fit exactly a square drawer $1\frac{1}{4}$ feet long on each side.

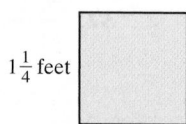

$1\frac{1}{4}$ feet

48. Dinah's homemade canned peaches contain $15\frac{3}{5}$ ounces per can. A can of Amy's brand contains $15\frac{5}{8}$ ounces per can. Amy's brand weighs how much more than Dinah's?

(3.5) *Insert < or > to form a true statement.*

49. $\dfrac{5}{11}$ $\dfrac{6}{11}$

50. $\dfrac{4}{35}$ $\dfrac{3}{35}$

51. $\dfrac{5}{14}$ $\dfrac{16}{42}$

52. $\dfrac{6}{35}$ $\dfrac{17}{105}$

53. $\dfrac{7}{8}$ $\dfrac{6}{7}$

54. $\dfrac{7}{10}$ $\dfrac{2}{3}$

Evaluate each expression. Use the order of operations to simplify.

55. $\left(\dfrac{3}{7}\right)^2$

56. $\left(\dfrac{4}{5}\right)^3$

57. $\left(\dfrac{1}{2}\right)^4 \cdot \left(\dfrac{3}{5}\right)^2$

58. $\left(\dfrac{1}{3}\right)^2 \cdot \left(\dfrac{9}{10}\right)^2$

59. $\dfrac{5}{13} \div \dfrac{1}{2} \cdot \dfrac{4}{5}$

60. $\dfrac{8}{11} \div \dfrac{1}{3} \cdot \dfrac{11}{12}$

61. $\left(\dfrac{6}{7} - \dfrac{3}{14}\right)^2$

62. $\dfrac{2}{7} \cdot \left(\dfrac{1}{5} + \dfrac{3}{10}\right)$

63. $\dfrac{8}{9} - \dfrac{1}{8} \div \dfrac{3}{4}$

64. $\dfrac{9}{10} - \dfrac{1}{9} \div \dfrac{2}{3}$

65. $\left(\dfrac{1}{3}\right)^2 - \dfrac{2}{27}$

66. $\dfrac{9}{10} \div \left(\dfrac{1}{5} + \dfrac{1}{20}\right)$

67. $\left(\dfrac{3}{4} + \dfrac{1}{2}\right) \div \left(\dfrac{4}{9} + \dfrac{1}{3}\right)$

68. $\left(\dfrac{3}{8} - \dfrac{1}{16}\right) \div \left(\dfrac{1}{2} - \dfrac{1}{8}\right)$

69. $\dfrac{6}{7} \cdot \dfrac{5}{2} - \dfrac{3}{4} \cdot \dfrac{1}{2}$

70. $\dfrac{9}{10} \cdot \dfrac{1}{3} - \dfrac{2}{5} \cdot \dfrac{1}{11}$

Find the average of each list of fractions.

71. $\dfrac{2}{3}, \dfrac{5}{6}, \dfrac{1}{9}$

72. $\dfrac{4}{5}, \dfrac{9}{10}, \dfrac{3}{20}$

(3.6)

73. Saturn has 28 moons. The planet Uranus has only $\frac{3}{4}$ as many. Find the number of moons for Uranus. (*Source:* NASA)

74. James Hardaway just bought $5\frac{7}{8}$ acres of land adjacent to the $9\frac{3}{4}$ acres he already owned. How much land does he now own?

Find the unknown measurements.

△ **75.**
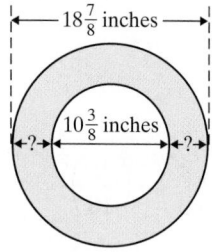

△ **76.**
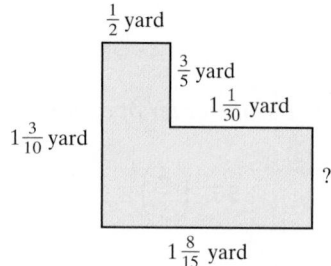

Find the perimeter and area of each rectangle. Attach the proper units to each. Remember that perimeter is measured in units and area is measured in square units.

△ **77.**
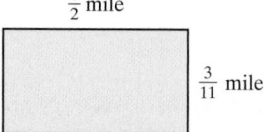

△ **78.**
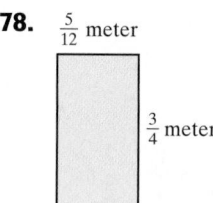

Mixed Review

Find the LCM of each list of numbers.

79. 15, 30, 45

80. 6, 15, 20

Write each fraction as an equivalent fraction with the given denominator.

81. $\frac{5}{6} = \frac{}{48}$

82. $\frac{7}{8} = \frac{}{72}$

Add or subtract as indicated. Simplify your answers.

83. $\frac{5}{12} - \frac{3}{12}$

84. $\frac{3}{10} - \frac{1}{10}$

85. $\frac{2}{3} + \frac{1}{4}$

86. $\frac{5}{11} + \frac{2}{55}$

87. $7\dfrac{3}{4}$

$+5\dfrac{2}{3}$

88. $2\dfrac{7}{8}$

$+9\dfrac{1}{2}$

89. $12\dfrac{3}{5}$

$-9\dfrac{1}{7}$

90. $32\dfrac{10}{21}$

$-24\dfrac{3}{7}$

Evaluate each expression. Use the order of operations to simplify.

91. $\dfrac{2}{5} + \left(\dfrac{2}{5}\right)^2 - \dfrac{3}{25}$

92. $\dfrac{1}{4} + \left(\dfrac{1}{2}\right)^2 - \dfrac{3}{8}$

93. $\left(\dfrac{5}{6} - \dfrac{3}{4}\right)^2$

94. $\left(2 - \dfrac{2}{3}\right)^3$

95. $\dfrac{2}{3} \div \left(\dfrac{3}{5} + \dfrac{5}{3}\right)$

96. $\dfrac{3}{8} \cdot \left(\dfrac{2}{3} - \dfrac{4}{9}\right)$

Insert $<$ or $>$ to form a true statement.

97. $\dfrac{3}{14}$ $\dfrac{2}{3}$

98. $\dfrac{7}{23}$ $\dfrac{3}{16}$

Solve.

99. Gregor Krowsky studied math for $\dfrac{3}{8}$ of an hour and geography for $\dfrac{1}{8}$ of an hour. How long did he study?

100. Two packages to be mailed weigh $3\dfrac{3}{4}$ pounds and $2\dfrac{3}{5}$ pounds. Find their combined weight.

101. A ribbon $5\dfrac{1}{2}$ yards long is cut from a reel of ribbon with 50 yards on it. Find the length of the piece remaining on the reel.

102. Linda Taneff has a board that is $10\dfrac{2}{3}$ feet in length. She plans to cut it into 5 equal lengths to use for a bookshelf. Find the length of each piece.

103. A recipe for pico de gallo calls for $1\dfrac{1}{2}$ tablespoons of cilantro. Five recipes will be made for a charity event. How much cilantro is needed?

104. Beryl Goldstein mixed $\dfrac{5}{8}$ of a gallon of water with $\dfrac{1}{8}$ of a gallon of punch concentrate. Then she and her friends drank $\dfrac{3}{8}$ of a gallon of the punch. How much of the punch was left?

3 CHAPTER TEST

 Remember to use the Chapter Test Prep Video CD to see the fully worked-out solutions to any of the exercises you want to review.

1. Find the LCM of 4 and 15.

2. Find the LCM of 8, 9, and 12.

Insert < or > to form a true statement.

3. $\dfrac{5}{6} \quad \dfrac{26}{30}$

4. $\dfrac{7}{8} \quad \dfrac{8}{9}$

Perform each indicated operation. Simplify your answers.

5. $\dfrac{7}{9} + \dfrac{1}{9}$

6. $\dfrac{8}{15} - \dfrac{2}{15}$

7. $\dfrac{9}{10} + \dfrac{2}{5}$

8. $\dfrac{1}{6} + \dfrac{3}{14}$

9. $\dfrac{7}{8} - \dfrac{1}{3}$

10. $\dfrac{6}{21} - \dfrac{1}{7}$

11. $\dfrac{9}{20} + \dfrac{2}{3}$

12. $\dfrac{16}{25} - \dfrac{1}{2}$

13. $\dfrac{11}{12} + \dfrac{3}{8} + \dfrac{5}{24}$

14. $\begin{aligned} 3\tfrac{7}{8} \\ 7\tfrac{2}{5} \\ +2\tfrac{3}{4} \\ \hline \end{aligned}$

15. $\begin{aligned} 8\tfrac{2}{9} \\ 12 \\ +10\tfrac{1}{15} \\ \hline \end{aligned}$

16. $\begin{aligned} 5\tfrac{1}{6} \\ -3\tfrac{7}{8} \\ \hline \end{aligned}$

17. $\begin{aligned} 19 \\ -2\tfrac{3}{11} \\ \hline \end{aligned}$

18. $\dfrac{2}{7} \cdot \left(6 - \dfrac{1}{6}\right)$

19. $\left(\dfrac{2}{3}\right)^4$

Answers

1. _____

2. _____

3. _____

4. _____

5. _____

6. _____

7. _____

8. _____

9. _____

10. _____

11. _____

12. _____

13. _____

14. _____

15. _____

16. _____

17. _____

18. _____

19. _____

20. $\dfrac{1}{2} \div \dfrac{2}{3} \cdot \dfrac{3}{4}$

21. $\left(\dfrac{4}{5}\right)^2 + \left(\dfrac{1}{2}\right)^3$

22. $\left(\dfrac{3}{4}\right)^2 \div \left(\dfrac{2}{3} + \dfrac{5}{6}\right)$

23. Find the average of $\dfrac{5}{6}, \dfrac{4}{3}$, and $\dfrac{7}{12}$.

Solve.

24. A carpenter cuts a piece $2\dfrac{3}{4}$ feet long from a cedar plank that is $6\dfrac{1}{2}$ feet long. How long is the remaining piece?

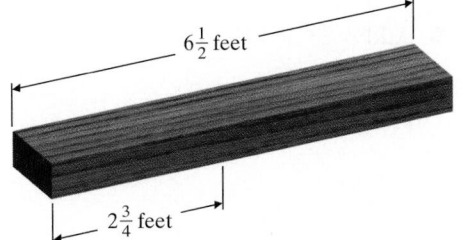

25. A small airplane used $58\dfrac{3}{4}$ gallons of fuel on a $7\dfrac{1}{2}$ hour trip. How many gallons of fuel were used for each hour?

The circle graph below shows us how the average consumer spends money. For example, $\dfrac{7}{50}$ of your spending goes for food. Use this information for Exercises 26 through 28.

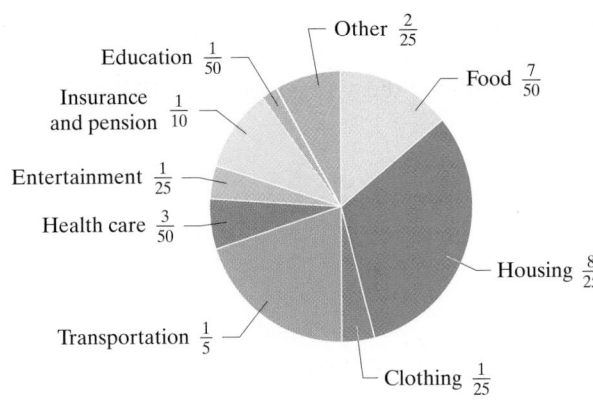

Consumer Spending

Other $\frac{2}{25}$
Education $\frac{1}{50}$
Insurance and pension $\frac{1}{10}$
Entertainment $\frac{1}{25}$
Health care $\frac{3}{50}$
Transportation $\frac{1}{5}$
Clothing $\frac{1}{25}$
Food $\frac{7}{50}$
Housing $\frac{8}{25}$

(*Source:* U.S. Bureau of Labor Statistics; based on survey)

26. What fraction of spending goes for housing and food combined?

27. What fraction of spending goes for education, transportation, and clothing?

28. Suppose your family spent $47,000 on the items in the graph above. How much might we expect was spent on health care?

Find the perimeter of each figure. For Exercise 29, find the area also.

△ **29.**

Rectangle — $\frac{2}{3}$ foot
1 foot

△ **30.**

$\frac{2}{15}$ inch $\frac{4}{15}$ inch
$\frac{6}{15}$ inch
Pentagon
$\frac{8}{15}$ inch
$\frac{1}{3}$ inch

20. _____

21. _____

22. _____

23. _____

24. _____

25. _____

26. _____

27. _____

28. _____

29. _____

30. _____

Write each number in words.

Answers

1. 85

2. 107

3. 126

4. 5026

5. Add: 23 + 136

6. Find the perimeter.

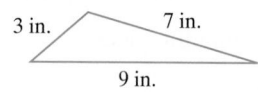

3 in.   7 in.

9 in.

7. Subtract: 543 − 29. Then check by adding.

8. Divide: 3268 ÷ 27

9. Round 278,362 to the nearest thousand.

10. Find all the factors of 30.

11. Multiply: 236 × 86

12. Multiply: 236 × 86 × 0

13. Find each quotient and then check the answer by multiplying.

a. $1\overline{)8}$

b. 11 ÷ 1

c. $\dfrac{9}{9}$

d. 7 ÷ 7

e. $\dfrac{10}{1}$

f. $6\overline{)6}$

14. Find the average of 25, 17, 19, and 39.

15. The Hudson River in New York State is 306 miles long. The Snake River, in the northwestern United States, is 732 miles longer than the Hudson River. How long is the Snake River? (*Source:* U.S. Department of the Interior)

16. Evaluate: $\sqrt{121}$

Answers

1. _____

2. _____

3. _____

4. _____

5. _____

6. _____

7. _____

8. _____

9. _____

10. _____

11. _____

12. _____

13. a. _____

b. _____

c. _____

d. _____

e. _____

f. _____

14. _____

15. _____

16. _____

246

Evaluate.

17. 8^2 **18.** 5^3 **19.** 2^5 **20.** 10^3

Write the shaded part as an improper fraction and a mixed number.

21.

22.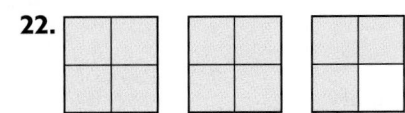

23.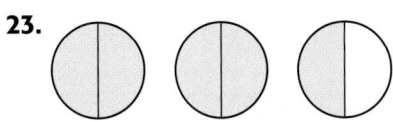

24.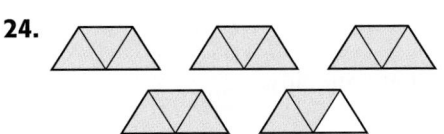

25. Of the numbers $3, 9, 11, 17, 26$, which are prime and which are composite?

26. Simplify: $\dfrac{6^2 + 4 \cdot 4 + 2^3}{37 - 5^2}$

27. Find the prime factorization of 180.

28. Find the difference of 87 and 25.

29. Write $\dfrac{72}{26}$ in simplest form.

30. Write $9\dfrac{7}{8}$ as an improper fraction.

31. Determine whether $\dfrac{16}{40}$ and $\dfrac{10}{25}$ are equivalent.

32. Insert $<$ or $>$ to form a true statement. $\dfrac{4}{7}$ $\dfrac{5}{9}$

Multiply.

33. $\dfrac{2}{3} \cdot \dfrac{5}{11}$ **34.** $2\dfrac{5}{8} \cdot \dfrac{4}{7}$

35. $\dfrac{1}{4} \cdot \dfrac{1}{2}$ **36.** $7 \cdot 5\dfrac{2}{7}$

17. _____

18. _____

19. _____

20. _____

21. _____

22. _____

23. _____

24. _____

25. _____

26. _____

27. _____

28. _____

29. _____

30. _____

31. _____

32. _____

33. _____

34. _____

35. _____

36. _____

37. _____

38. _____

39. _____

40. _____

41. _____

42. _____

43. _____

44. _____

45. _____

46. _____

47. _____

48. _____

49. _____

50. _____

Divide.

37. $\dfrac{11}{18} \div 2\dfrac{5}{6}$ **38.** $\dfrac{15}{19} \div \dfrac{3}{5}$

39. $5\dfrac{2}{3} \div 2\dfrac{5}{9}$ **40.** $\dfrac{8}{11} \div \dfrac{1}{22}$

41. Add and simplify: $\dfrac{3}{16} + \dfrac{7}{16}$

42. Subtract and simplify: $\dfrac{11}{20} - \dfrac{7}{20}$

43. Find the LCM of 6 and 8.

44. Find the LCM of 7 and 5.

45. Add: $\dfrac{1}{2} + \dfrac{2}{3} + \dfrac{5}{6}$

46. Evaluate: $\left(\dfrac{5}{9}\right)^2$

47. Subtract: $9\dfrac{3}{7} - 5\dfrac{2}{21}$

48. Subtract: $\dfrac{31}{100} - \dfrac{5}{25}$

49. Simplify: $\left(\dfrac{2}{3}\right)^2 \div \left(\dfrac{8}{27} + \dfrac{2}{3}\right)$

50. $\dfrac{1}{10} \div \dfrac{7}{8} \cdot \dfrac{2}{5}$

4

Decimals

Decimal numbers represent parts of a whole, just like fractions. In this chapter, we learn to perform arithmetic operations using decimals and to analyze the relationship between factions and decimals. We also learn how decimals are used in the real world.

V ideo rental chains are suffering losses in revenue and this trend is predicted to continue. With many discount chains offering cheap DVDs, consumers are choosing to purchase rather than rent. There are also more rent-by-mail and video-on-demand companies competing for your business.

In Section 4.3, Exercise 65, we calculate the predicted loss of revenue for video rental stores.

Video Rental Revenues

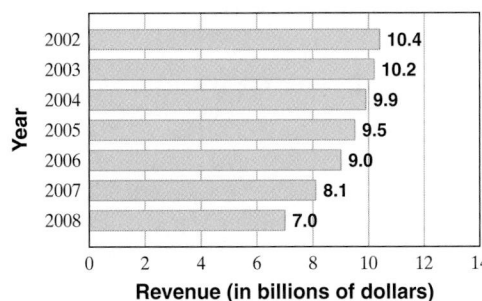

Source: Forrester Research; Note: Many of these years are projections.

Objectives

A Know the Meaning of Place Value for a Decimal Number, and Write Decimals in Words.

B Write Decimals in Standard Form.

C Write Decimals as Fractions.

D Write Fractions as Decimals.

4.1 INTRODUCTION TO DECIMALS

Objective **A** Decimal Notation and Writing Decimals in Words

Like fractional notation, decimal notation is used to denote a part of a whole. Numbers written in decimal notation are called **decimal numbers,** or simply **decimals.** The decimal 17.758 has three parts.

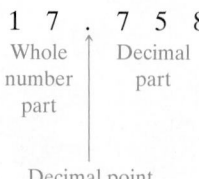

In Section 1.2, we introduced place value for whole numbers. Place names and place values for the whole number part of a decimal number are exactly the same, as shown next. Place names and place values for the decimal part are also shown.

> **Helpful Hint**
>
> Notice that place values to the left of the decimal point end in "s." Place values to the right of the decimal point end in "ths."

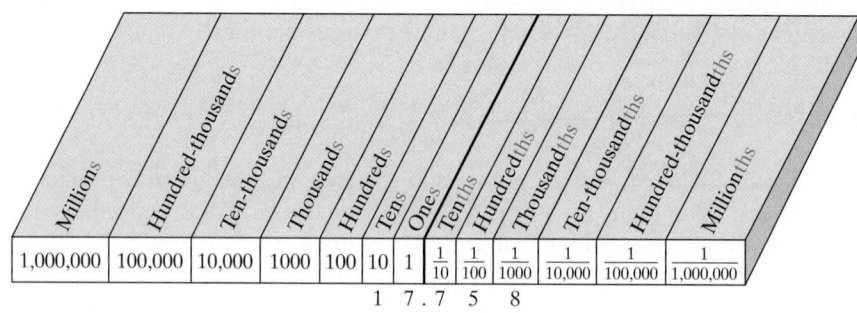

Notice that the value of each place is $\frac{1}{10}$ of the value of the place to its left. For example,

$$1 \cdot \frac{1}{10} = \frac{1}{10}$$
$$\underset{\text{ones}}{\uparrow} \qquad \underset{\text{tenths}}{\uparrow}$$

$$\frac{1}{10} \cdot \frac{1}{10} = \frac{1}{100}$$
$$\underset{\text{tenths}}{\uparrow} \qquad \underset{\text{hundredths}}{\uparrow}$$

The decimal number 17.758 means

1 ten	+	7 ones	+	7 tenths	+	5 hundredths	+	8 thousandths
↓	↓	↓	↓	↓	↓	↓	↓	↓
or $1 \cdot 10$ +		$7 \cdot 1$ +		$7 \cdot \frac{1}{10}$ +		$5 \cdot \frac{1}{100}$ +		$8 \cdot \frac{1}{1000}$
or 10 +		7 +		$\frac{7}{10}$ +		$\frac{5}{100}$ +		$\frac{8}{1000}$

250

Writing (or Reading) a Decimal in Words

Step 1: Write the whole number part in words.

Step 2: Write "and" for the decimal point.

Step 3: Write the decimal part in words as though it were a whole number, followed by the place value of the last digit.

EXAMPLE 1 Write the decimal 1.3 in words.

Solution: one and three tenths

◻ **Work Practice Problem 1**

EXAMPLE 2

Write the decimal in the following sentence in words: The Golden Jubilee Diamond is a 545.67 carat cut diamond. (*Source: The Guinness Book of Records*)

Solution: five hundred forty-five and sixty-seven hundredths

◻ **Work Practice Problem 2**

EXAMPLE 3 Write the decimal 19.5023 in words.

Solution: nineteen and five thousand, twenty-three ten-thousandths

◻ **Work Practice Problem 3**

EXAMPLE 4

Write the decimal in the following sentence in words: The oldest known fragments of the Earth's crust are Zircon crystals; they were discovered in Australia and are thought to be 4.276 billion years old. (*Source: The Guinness Book of Records*)

Darwin

Australia

Perth

Brisbane

Canberra   Sydney

Melbourne

Solution: four and two hundred seventy-six thousandths

◻ **Work Practice Problem 4**

Suppose that you are paying for a purchase of $368.42 at Circuit City by writing a check. Checks are usually written using the following format.

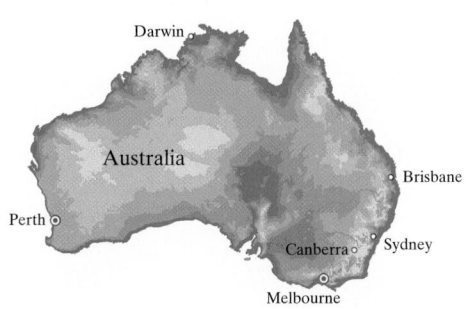

Elayn Martin-Gay

60-8124/7233
1000613331   1403

DATE *(Current date)*

PAY TO THE ORDER OF *Circuit City* $ *368.42*

Three hundred sixty-eight and $\frac{42}{100}$ ———— DOLLARS

FIRST STATE BANK
OF FARTHINGTON
FARTHINGTON, IL 64422

MEMO   *Elayn Martin-Gay*

⑆621497260⑆ ⑈0006⑈333⑈⑆ ⑆1403

PRACTICE PROBLEM 1

Write the decimal 8.7 in words.

PRACTICE PROBLEM 2

Write the decimal 97.28 in words.

PRACTICE PROBLEM 3

Write the decimal 302.1056 in words.

PRACTICE PROBLEM 4

Write the decimal 72.1085 in words.

Answers

1. eight and seven tenths,
2. ninety-seven and twenty-eight hundredths,   **3.** three hundred two and one thousand fifty-six ten-thousandths,   **4.** seventy-two and one thousand eighty-five ten-thousandths

PRACTICE PROBLEM 5

Fill in the check to CLECO (Central Louisiana Electric Company) to pay for your monthly electric bill of $207.40.

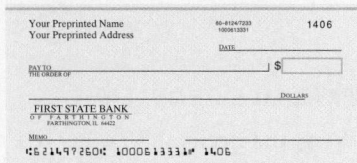

PRACTICE PROBLEMS 6–7

Write each decimal in standard form.

6. Three hundred and ninety-six hundredths

7. Thirty-nine and forty-two thousandths

EXAMPLE 5 Fill in the check to Camelot Music to pay for your purchase of $92.98.

Solution:

☐ **Work Practice Problem 5**

Objective B Writing Decimals in Standard Form

A decimal written in words can be written in standard form by reversing the preceding procedure.

EXAMPLES Write each decimal in standard form.

6. Forty-eight and twenty-six hundredths is

48.26

└── hundredths place

7. Six and ninety-five thousandths is

6.095

└── thousandths place

☐ **Work Practice Problems 6–7**

Helpful Hint

When converting a decimal from words to decimal notation, make sure the last digit is in the correct place by inserting 0s if necessary. For example,

Two and thirty-eight thousandths is 2.038

└── thousandths place

Objective C Writing Decimals as Fractions

Once you master reading and writing decimals, writing a decimal as a fraction follows naturally.

Decimal	In Words	Fraction
0.7	seven tenths	$\dfrac{7}{10}$
0.51	fifty-one hundredths	$\dfrac{51}{100}$
0.009	nine thousandths	$\dfrac{9}{1000}$
0.05	five hundredths	$\dfrac{5}{100} = \dfrac{1}{20}$

Answers

5. CLECO; 207.40; Two hundred seven and $\dfrac{40}{100}$, **6.** 300.96, **7.** 39.042

Notice that the number of decimal places in a decimal number is the same as the number of zeros in the denominator of the equivalent fraction. We can use this fact to write decimals as fractions.

$$0.51 = \frac{51}{100} \qquad 0.009 = \frac{9}{1000}$$

2 decimal places   2 zeros   3 decimal places   3 zeros

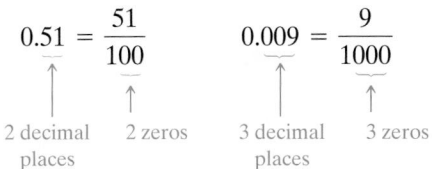 **Write 0.43 as a fraction.**

Solution: $0.43 = \frac{43}{100}$

2 decimal places   2 zeros

▣ **Work Practice Problem 8**

EXAMPLE 9 Write 5.7 as a mixed number.

Solution: $5.7 = 5\frac{7}{10}$

1 decimal place   1 zero

▣ **Work Practice Problem 9**

EXAMPLES Write each decimal as a fraction or a mixed number. Write your answer in simplest form.

10. $0.125 = \frac{125}{1000} = \frac{1}{8}$

11. $23.5 = 23\frac{5}{10} = 23\frac{\overset{1}{\cancel{5}}}{2 \cdot \cancel{5}} = 23\frac{1}{2 \cdot 1} = 23\frac{1}{2}$

12. $105.083 = 105\frac{83}{1000}$

▣ **Work Practice Problems 10–12**

Objective ⓓ Writing Fractions as Decimals

If the denominator of a fraction is a power of 10, we can write it as a decimal by reversing the procedure above.

EXAMPLES Write each fraction as a decimal.

13. $\frac{8}{10} = 0.8$

1 zero   1 decimal place

14. $\frac{87}{10} = 8.7$

1 zero   1 decimal place

15. $\frac{18}{1000} = 0.018$

3 zeros   3 decimal places

16. $\frac{507}{100} = 5.07$

2 zeros   2 decimal places

▣ **Work Practice Problems 13–16**

Mental Math

Determine the place value for the digit 7 in each number.

1. 70   **2.** 700   **3.** 0.7   **4.** 0.07

4.1 EXERCISE SET

FOR EXTRA HELP

Student Solutions Manual   PH Math/Tutor Center   CD/Video for Review   Math XL MathXL®   MyMathLab MyMathLab

Objective A *Write each decimal number in words. See Examples 1 through 4.*

1. 6.52   **2.** 7.59   **3.** 16.23   **4.** 47.65

5. 0.205   **6.** 0.495   **7.** 167.009   **8.** 233.056

9. 200.005   **10.** 5000.02   **11.** 105.6   **12.** 410.30

13. The English Channel Tunnel is 31.04 miles long. (*Source: Railway Directory & Year Book*)

14. The Lake Pontchartrain Causeway bridge over Lake Pontchartrain in Louisiana is approximately 23.87 miles long.

15. The recommended daily allowance of riboflavin for teenage boys between the ages of 15 and 18 is 1.8 milligrams. (*Source:* Food and Nutrition Board of the Institute of Medicine, National Academy of Sciences)

16. Saturn makes a complete orbit of the Sun every 29.48 years. (*Source:* National Space Science Data Center)

17. The 2005 series finale of Everybody Loves Raymond received a Nielsen rating of 32.9. (*Source:* Nielsen Media Research)

18. The top-rated television series for the 2003–2004 viewing season was *CSI: Crime Scene Investigators,* which received a rating of 15.9. (*Source:* Nielsen Media Research)

Fill in each check for the described purchase. See Example 5.

19. Your monthly car loan of $321.42 to R. W. Financial.

```
Your Preprinted Name          60–8124/7233        1407
Your Preprinted Address        1000613331
                                        DATE _____
PAY TO                                          $ [        ]
THE ORDER OF _____
                                                   DOLLARS
FIRST STATE BANK
O F  F A R T H I N G T O N
FARTHINGTON, IL 64422
MEMO _____     _____
⑆621497260⑆ 1000613331⑈ 1407
```

20. Your part of the monthly apartment rent, which is $213.70. You pay this to Amanda Dupre.

```
Your Preprinted Name          60–8124/7233        1408
Your Preprinted Address        1000613331
                                        DATE _____
PAY TO                                          $ [        ]
THE ORDER OF _____
                                                   DOLLARS
FIRST STATE BANK
O F  F A R T H I N G T O N
FARTHINGTON, IL 64422
MEMO _____     _____
⑆621497260⑆ 1000613331⑈ 1408
```

21. Your cell phone bill of $59.68 to Bell South.

```
Your Preprinted Name          60–8124/7233        1409
Your Preprinted Address        1000613331
                                        DATE _____
PAY TO                                          $ [        ]
THE ORDER OF _____
                                                   DOLLARS
FIRST STATE BANK
O F  F A R T H I N G T O N
FARTHINGTON, IL 64422
MEMO _____     _____
⑆621497260⑆ 1000613331⑈ 1409
```

22. Your grocery bill of $87.49 to Albertsons.

```
Your Preprinted Name          60–8124/7233        1410
Your Preprinted Address        1000613331
                                        DATE _____
PAY TO                                          $ [        ]
THE ORDER OF _____
                                                   DOLLARS
FIRST STATE BANK
O F  F A R T H I N G T O N
FARTHINGTON, IL 64422
MEMO _____     _____
⑆621497260⑆ 1000613331⑈ 1410
```

Objective **B** *Write each decimal number in standard form. See Examples 6 and 7.*

23. Six and five tenths

24. Three and nine tenths

25. Nine and eight hundredths

26. Twelve and six hundredths

27. Seven hundred five and six hundred twenty-five thousandths

28. Eight hundred four and three hundred ninety-nine thousandths

29. Sixty-four ten-thousandths

30. Thirty-eight ten-thousandths

31. The record rainfall amount for a 24-hour period in Alabama is thirty-two and fifty-two hundredths inches. This record was set at Dauphin Island Sea Lab in 1997. (*Source:* National Climatic Data Center)

32. The United States Postal Service vehicle fleet averages nine and sixty-two hundredths miles per gallon of fuel. (*Source:* United States Postal Service)

33. Americans consume an average of fifteen and eight-tenths pounds of watermelon annually. (*Source:* Agricultural Marketing Service, U.S. Department of Agriculture)

34. Shaquille O'Neal of the NBA's Los Angeles Lakers scored an average of twenty-one and five tenths points per basketball game during the 2003–2004 regular season. (*Source:* National Basketball Association)

Objective C *Write each decimal as a fraction or a mixed number. Write your answer in simplest form. See Examples 8 through 12.*

35. 0.3   **36.** 0.9   **37.** 0.27   **38.** 0.39   **39.** 0.8

40. 0.4   **41.** 0.15   **42.** 0.64   **43.** 5.47   **44.** 6.3

45. 0.048   **46.** 0.082   **47.** 7.008   **48.** 9.005   **49.** 15.802

50. 11.406   **51.** 0.3005   **52.** 0.2006   **53.** 487.32   **54.** 298.62

Objective D *Write each fraction as a decimal. See Examples 13 through 16.*

55. $\frac{6}{10}$ **56.** $\frac{3}{10}$ **57.** $\frac{45}{100}$ **58.** $\frac{75}{100}$

59. $\frac{37}{10}$ **60.** $\frac{28}{10}$ **61.** $\frac{268}{1000}$ **62.** $\frac{709}{1000}$

63. $\frac{9}{100}$ **64.** $\frac{7}{100}$ **65.** $\frac{4026}{1000}$ **66.** $\frac{3601}{1000}$

67. $\frac{28}{1000}$ **68.** $\frac{63}{1000}$ **69.** $\frac{563}{10}$ **70.** $\frac{206}{10}$

Objectives A B C D **Mixed Practice** *Fill in the chart. The first row is completed for you.*

	Decimal Number in Standard Form	In Words	Fraction
	0.37	thirty-seven hundredths	$\frac{37}{100}$
71.			$\frac{43}{100}$
72.			$\frac{89}{100}$
73.		eight tenths	
74.		five tenths	
75.	0.077		
76.	0.019		

Review

Round 47,261 to the indicated place value. See Section 1.5.

77. tens   **78.** hundreds   **79.** thousands   **80.** ten-thousands

Concept Extensions

81. In your own words, describe how to write a decimal as a fraction or a mixed number.

82. In your own words, describe how to write a fraction as a decimal.

83. Write 0.00026849576 in words.

84. Write $7\frac{12}{100}$ as a decimal.

85. Write $17\frac{268}{1000}$ as a decimal.

86. Write 0.00026849576 as a fraction.

![Study Skills Builder icon] **STUDY SKILLS BUILDER**

Are You Getting All the Mathematics Help That You Need?

Remember that, in addition to your instructor, there are many places to get help with your mathematics course. For example,

- This text has an accompanying video lesson for every section and worked out solutions to every Chapter Test exercise on video.
- The back of the book contains answers to odd-numbered exercises and selected solutions.
- A student *Solutions Manual* is available that contains worked-out solutions to odd-numbered exercises as well as solutions to every exercise in the Integrated Reviews, Chapter Reviews, Chapter Tests, and Cumulative Reviews.

- Don't forget to check with your instructor for other local resources available to you, such as a tutor center.

Exercises

1. List items you find helpful in the text and all student supplements to this text.

2. List all the campus help that is available to you for this course.

3. List any help (besides the textbook) from Exercises 1 and 2 above that you are using.

4. List any help (besides the textbook) that you feel you should try.

5. Write a goal for yourself that includes trying anything you listed in Exercise 4 during the next week.

4.2 ORDER AND ROUNDING

Objective **A** Comparing Decimals

One way to compare decimals is to compare their graphs on a number line. Recall that for any two numbers on a number line, the number to the left is smaller and the number to the right is larger. The decimals 0.5 and 0.8 are graphed as follows:

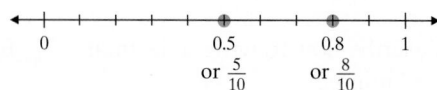

Comparing decimals by comparing their graphs on a number line can be time consuming. Another way to compare the size of decimals is to compare digits in corresponding places.

Comparing Two Decimals

Compare digits in the same places from left to right. When two digits are not equal, the number with the larger digit is the larger decimal. If necessary, insert 0s after the last digit to the right of the decimal point to continue comparing.

Compare hundredths-place digits

$$28.2\underset{\uparrow}{5}3 \qquad 28.2\underset{\uparrow}{6}3$$

$$5 \quad < \quad 6$$

so $28.253 \quad < \quad 28.263$

Before we continue, let's take a moment and convince ourselves that inserting a zero after the last digit to the right of a decimal point does not change the value of the number.

For example, let's show that

$$0.7 = 0.70$$

If we write 0.7 as a fraction, we have

$$0.7 = \frac{7}{10}$$

Let's now multiply by 1. Recall that multiplying a number by 1 does not change the value of the number.

$$0.7 = \frac{7}{10} = \frac{7}{10} \cdot 1 = \frac{7}{10} \cdot \frac{10}{10} = \frac{7 \cdot 10}{10 \cdot 10} = \frac{70}{100} = 0.70$$

Thus $0.7 = 0.70$ and so on.

> **Helpful Hint**
>
> For any decimal, inserting 0s after the last digit to the right of the decimal point does not change the value of the number.
>
> $$7.6 = 7.60 = 7.600, \text{ and so on}$$
>
> When a whole number is written as a decimal, the decimal point is placed to the right of the ones digit.
>
> $$25 = 25.0 = 25.00, \text{ and so on}$$

EXAMPLE 1 Insert <, >, or = to form a true statement.

0.378   0.368

Solution:

0. 3 78   0. 3 68   The tenths places are the same.

0.3 7 8   0.3 6 8   The hundredths places are different.

Since 7 > 6, then 0.378 > 0.368.

▣ **Work Practice Problem 1**

EXAMPLE 2 Insert <, >, or = to form a true statement.

0.052   0.236

Solution: 0. 0 52 < 0. 2 36   0 is smaller than 2 in the tenths place.
                    ↑   ↑

▣ **Work Practice Problem 2**

EXAMPLE 3 Insert <, >, or = to form a true statement.

0.52   0.063

Solution: 0. 5 2 > 0. 0 63   0 is smaller than 5 in the tenths place.
                  ↑   ↑

▣ **Work Practice Problem 3**

EXAMPLE 4 Write the decimals in order from smallest to largest.

7.035, 8.12, 7.03, 7.1

Solution: By comparing the ones digits, the decimal 8.12 is the largest number. To write the rest of the decimals in order, we compare digits to the right of the decimal point. We will insert zeros to help us compare.

7.035   7.030   7.100

Helpful Hint
You may also immediately notice that 7.1 is larger than both 7.035 and 7.03.

By comparing digits to the right of the decimal point, we can now arrange the decimals from smallest to largest.

7.030, 7.035, 7.100, 8.12   or

7.03, 7.035, 7.1, 8.12

▣ **Work Practice Problem 4**

Objective B Rounding Decimals

We **round the decimal part** of a decimal number in nearly the same way as we round whole numbers. The only difference is that we delete digits to the right of the rounding place, instead of replacing these digits by 0s. For example,

24.954   rounded to the nearest hundredth is   24.95
   ↑
hundredths place

Rounding Decimals to a Place Value to the Right of the Decimal Point

Step 1: Locate the digit to the right of the given place value.

Step 2: If this digit is 5 or greater, add 1 to the digit in the given place value and delete all digits to its right. If this digit is less than 5, delete all digits to the right of the given place value.

PRACTICE PROBLEM 5

Round 123.7814 to the nearest thousandth.

EXAMPLE 5 Round 736.2359 to the nearest tenth.

Solution:

Step 1: We locate the digit to the right of the tenths place.

```
                 ┌──── tenths place
                 ↓
        736.2③59
              └──→ digit to the right
```

Step 2: Since the digit to the right is less than 5, we delete it and all digits to its right.

Thus, 736.2359 rounded to the nearest tenth is 736.2.

Work Practice Problem 5

PRACTICE PROBLEM 6

Round 123.7817 to the nearest tenth.

EXAMPLE 6 Round 736.2359 to the nearest hundredth.

Solution:

Step 1: We locate the digit to the right of the hundredths place.

```
                  ┌──── hundredths place
                  ↓
        736.23⑤9
               └──→ digit to the right
```

Step 2: Since the digit to the right is 5, we add 1 to the digit in the hundredths place and delete all digits to the right of the hundredths place.

```
        736.23⑤9
             ↑ └─ Delete these digits.
           Add 1.
```

Thus, 736.2359 rounded to the nearest hundredth is 736.24.

Work Practice Problem 6

Rounding often occurs with money amounts. Since there are 100 cents in a dollar, each cent is $\frac{1}{100}$ of a dollar. This means that if we want to round to the nearest cent, we round to the nearest hundredth of a dollar.

PRACTICE PROBLEM 7

In Cititown, the price of a gallon of gasoline is $2.1589. Round this to the nearest cent.

EXAMPLE 7 The price of a gallon of gasoline in Aimsville is currently $2.1779. Round this to the nearest cent.

Solution:

```
  hundredths place ──┐   ┌── 7 is greater than 5
                     ↓   ↓
            $2.17⑦9
                  ↑  └─── Delete these digits.
                Add 1.
```

Since the digit to the right is greater than 5, we add 1 to the hundredths digit and delete all digits to the right of the hundredths digit.

Thus, $2.1779 rounded to the nearest cent is $2.18.

Work Practice Problem 7

Answers

5. 123.781, **6.** 123.8, **7.** $2.16

EXAMPLE 8 Round $0.098 to the nearest cent.

Solution:

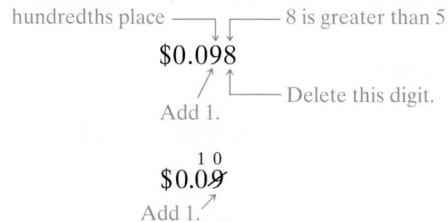

hundredths place ⎤ ⎡ 8 is greater than 5

$0.09̂8

Add 1. ⎦ ⎣ Delete this digit.

$0.09̸ (1 0)

Add 1.

$9 + 1 = 10$, so replace the digit 9 by 0 and carry the 1 to the place value to the left. Thus, $0.098 rounded to the nearest cent is $0.10.

🖥 **Work Practice Problem 8**

✔**Concept Check** 1756.0894 rounded to the nearest ten is

a. 1756.1   **b.** 1760.0894

c. 1760   **d.** 1750

EXAMPLE 9 Determining State Taxable Income

A high school teacher's taxable income is $41,567.72. The tax tables in the teacher's state use amounts to the nearest dollar. Round the teacher's income to the nearest whole dollar.

Solution: Rounding to the nearest whole dollar means rounding to the ones place.

ones place ⎤ ⎡ 7 is greater than 5

$41,567.72

Add 1. ⎦ ⎣ Delete these digits.

Thus, the teacher's income rounded to the nearest dollar is $41,568.

🖥 **Work Practice Problem 9**

PRACTICE PROBLEM 8

Round $1.095 to the nearest cent.

PRACTICE PROBLEM 9

Water bills in Gotham City are always rounded to the nearest dollar. Lois's water bill was $24.62. Round her bill to the nearest dollar.

Answers

8. $1.10,   **9.** $25

✔ **Concept Check Answer**

c

4.2 EXERCISE SET

 Student Solutions Manual  PH Math/Tutor Center  CD/Video for Review MathXL® MathXL  MyMathLab MyMathLab

Objective **A** *Insert <, >, or = to form a true statement. See Examples 1 through 3.*

1. 0.15   0.16

2. 0.12   0.15

3. 0.57   0.54

4. 0.59   0.52

5. 0.098   0.1

6. 0.0756   0.2

7. 0.54900   0.549

8. 0.98400   0.984

9. 167.908   167.980

10. 519.3405   519.3054

11. 420,000   0.000042

12. 0.000987   987,000

Write the decimals in order from smallest to largest. See Example 4.

13. 0.006, 0.06, 0.0061

14. 0.082, 0.008, 0.080

15. 0.042, 0.36, 0.03

16. 0.21, 0.056, 0.065

17. 1.1, 1.16, 1.01, 1.09

18. 3.6, 3.069, 3.09, 3.06

19. 21.001, 20.905, 21.03, 21.12

20. 36.050, 35.72, 35.702, 35.072

Objective **B** *Round each decimal to the given place value. See Examples 5 and 6.*

21. 0.57, to the nearest tenth

22. 0.54, to the nearest tenth

23. 0.234, to the nearest hundredth

24. 0.452, to the nearest hundredth

25. 0.5942, to the nearest thousandth

26. 63.4523, to the nearest thousandth

27. 98,207.23, to the nearest ten

28. 68,934.543, to the nearest ten

29. 12.342, to the nearest tenth

30. 42.9878, to the nearest thousandth

31. 17.667, to the nearest hundredth

32. 0.766, to the nearest hundredth

33. 0.501, to the nearest tenth

34. 0.602, to the nearest tenth

35. 0.1295, to the nearest thousandth

36. 0.8295, to the nearest thousandth

37. 3829.34, to the nearest ten

38. 4520.876, to the nearest hundred

Round each monetary amount to the nearest cent or dollar as indicated. See Examples 7 through 9.

39. $0.067, to the nearest cent

40. $0.025, to the nearest cent

41. $42,650.14, to the nearest dollar

42. $768.45, to the nearest dollar

43. $26.95, to the nearest dollar

44. $14,769.52, to the nearest dollar

45. $0.1992, to the nearest cent

46. $0.7633, to the nearest cent

Round each number to the given place value.

47. At this writing, the disc of the smallest hard drive was created by Toshiba and measures 2.16 centimeters across. Round this number to the nearest tenth.

2.16 cm or 0.85 in.

48. A large tropical cockroach of the family Dictyoptera is the fastest-moving insect. This insect was clocked at a speed of 3.36 miles per hour. Round this number to the nearest tenth. (*Source:* University of California, Berkeley)

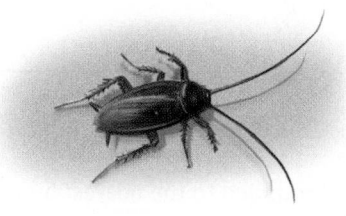

49. During the 2004 Boston Marathon, Catherine Ndereba of Kenya was the first woman to cross the finish line. Her time was 2.4075 hours. Round this time to the nearest hundredth. (*Source:* Boston Athletic Association)

50. The population density of the state of Louisiana is 102.5794 people per square mile. Round this population density to the nearest tenth. (*Source:* U.S. Census Bureau)

51. A used biology textbook is priced at $47.89. Round this price to the nearest dollar.

52. A used office desk is advertised at $19.95 by Drawley's Office Furniture. Round this price to the nearest dollar.

53. The length of a day on Mars is 24.6229 hours. Round this figure to the nearest thousandth. (*Source:* National Space Science Data Center)

54. Venus makes a complete orbit around the Sun every 224.695 days. Round this figure to the nearest whole day. (*Source:* National Space Science Data Center)

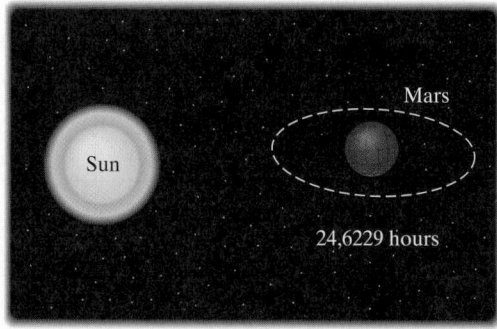

Sun   Mars

24,6229 hours

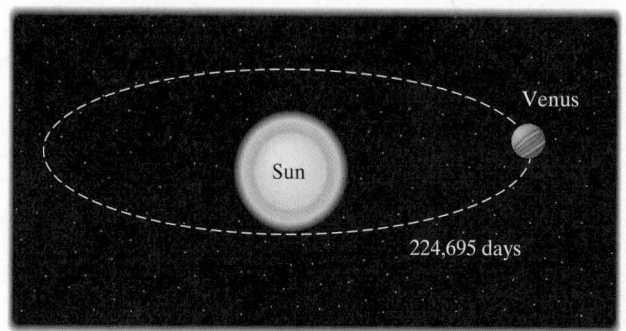

Sun   Venus

224,695 days

55. Millennium Force is a roller coaster at Cedar Point, an amusement park in Sandusky, Ohio. At the time of its debut, Millennium Force was the world's tallest and fastest roller coaster. A ride on the Millennium Force lasts about 2.75 minutes. Round this figure to the nearest tenth. (*Source:* Cedar Fair, L.P.)

56. During the 2003 NFL season, the average length of an Oakland Raiders' punt was 46.9 yards. Round this figure to the nearest whole yard. (*Source:* National Football League)

Review

Perform each indicated operation. See Sections 1.3 and 1.4.

57. $3452 + 2314$

58. $8945 + 4536$

59. $94 - 23$

60. $82 - 47$

61. $482 - 239$

62. $4002 - 3897$

Concept Extensions

Solve. See the Concept Check in this section.

63. 2849.1738 rounded to the nearest hundred is
   a. 2849.17
   b. 2800
   c. 2850
   d. 2849.174

64. 146.059 rounded to the nearest ten is
   a. 146.0
   b. 146.1
   c. 140
   d. 150

65. 2849.1738 rounded to the nearest hundredth is
   a. 2849.17
   b. 2800
   c. 2850
   d. 2849.174

66. 146.059 rounded to the nearest tenth is
   a. 146.0
   b. 146.1
   c. 140
   d. 150

Mixed Practice (*Sections 4.1, 4.2*) *The table gives the leading bowling averages for the Professional Bowlers Association for each of the years listed. Use the table to answer Exercises 67 through 69.*

67. What is the highest average score on the list? Write this score as a mixed number. Which bowler achieved that average?

Year	Bowler	Average Score
1996	Walter Ray Williams, Jr.	225.370
1997	Walter Ray Williams, Jr.	222.008
1998	Walter Ray Williams, Jr.	226.130
1999	Parker Bohn III	228.040
2000	Chris Barnes	220.930
2002	Parker Bohn III	221.546
2003	Walter Ray Williams, Jr	224.940
2004	Mike Koivuniemi	222.730
(*Source:* Professional Bowlers Association)		

68. What is the lowest average score on the list? Write this score as a mixed number. Which bowler had that average?

69. Make a list of the leading averages in order from greatest to least for the years shown in the table.

70. Write a 4-digit number that rounds to 26.3.

71. Write a 5-digit number that rounds to 1.7.

 72. Explain how to identify the value of the 9 in the decimal 486.3297.

73. Write a decimal number that is greater than 48.1, but less than 48.2.

74. Which number(s) rounds to 0.26?

0.26559   0.26499   0.25786   0.25186

75. Which number(s) rounds to 0.06?

0.0612   0.066   0.0586   0.0506

STUDY SKILLS BUILDER

Are You Satisfied with Your Performance on a Particular Quiz or Exam?

If not, don't forget to analyze your quiz or exam and look for common errors. Were most of your errors a result of:

- *Carelessness?* Did you turn in your quiz or exam before the allotted time expired? If so, resolve next time to use the entire time allotted. Any extra time can be spent checking your work.
- *Running out of time?* If so, make a point to better manage your time on your next quiz or exam. Try completing any questions that you are unsure of last and delay checking your work until all questions have been answered.
- *Not understanding a concept?* If so, review that concept and correct your work. Try to understand how this happened so that you make sure it doesn't happen before the next quiz or exam.
- *Test conditions?* When studying for a quiz or exam, make sure you place yourself in conditions similar to test conditions. For example, before your next quiz or exam, use a few sheets of blank paper and take a sample test without the aid of your notes or text.

(See your instructor or use the Chapter Test at the end of each chapter.)

Exercises

1. Have you corrected all your previous quizzes and exams?

2. List any errors you have found common to two or more of your graded papers.

3. Is one of your common errors not understanding a concept? If so, are you making sure you understand all the concepts for the next quiz or exam?

4. Is one of your common errors making careless mistakes? If so, are you now taking all the time allotted to check over your work so that you can minimize the number of careless mistakes?

5. Are you satisfied with your grades thus far on quizzes and tests?

6. If your answer to Exercise 5 is no, are there any more suggestions you can make to your instructor or yourself to help? If so, list them here and share these with your instructor.

4.3 ADDING AND SUBTRACTING DECIMALS

Objective **A** Adding Decimals

Adding decimals is similar to adding whole numbers. We add digits in corresponding place values from right to left, carrying if necessary. To make sure that digits in corresponding place values are added, we line up the decimal points vertically.

Adding or Subtracting Decimals

Step 1: Write the decimals so that the decimal points line up vertically.

Step 2: Add or subtract as with whole numbers.

Step 3: Place the decimal point in the sum or difference so that it lines up vertically with the decimal points in the problem.

In this section, we will insert zeros in decimals numbers so that place value digits line up neatly. For instance, see Example 1.

PRACTICE PROBLEM 1

Add.

a. $15.52 + 2.371$

b. $20.06 + 17.612$

c. $0.125 + 122.8$

EXAMPLE 1 Add: $23.85 + 1.604$

Solution: First we line up the decimal points vertically.

$$
\begin{array}{r}
23.85\underline{0} \quad \text{Insert one 0 so that digits line up neatly.}\\
+\ 1.604 \\
\hline
\uparrow \\
\end{array}
$$
line up decimal points

Then we add the digits from right to left as for whole numbers.

$$
\begin{array}{r}
\overset{1}{2}3.850 \\
+\ 1.604 \\
\hline
25.454
\end{array}
$$
Place the decimal point in the sum so that all decimal points line up.

■ **Work Practice Problem 1**

Helpful Hint

Recall that 0's may be placed after the last digit to the right of the decimal point without changing the value of the decimal. This may be used to help line up place values when adding decimals.

$$
\begin{array}{r}
3.2 \\
15.567 \\
+\ 0.11 \\
\end{array}
\qquad \text{becomes} \qquad
\begin{array}{r}
3.2\underline{00} \quad \text{Insert two 0s.}\\
15.567 \\
+\ 0.11\underline{0} \quad \text{Insert one 0.}\\
\hline
18.877 \quad \text{Add.}
\end{array}
$$

Answers

1. a. 17.891, **b.** 37.672, **c.** 122.925

EXAMPLE 2 Add: 763.7651 + 22.001 + 43.89

Solution: First we line up the decimal points.

$$
\begin{array}{r}
\overset{1}{7}6\overset{1}{3}.\overset{1}{7}651 \\
22.0010 \quad \text{Insert one 0.} \\
+\ \ 43.8900 \quad \text{Insert two 0s.} \\
\hline
829.6561 \quad \text{Add.}
\end{array}
$$

 **Work Practice Problem 2**

> **Helpful Hint** Don't forget that the decimal point in a whole number is after the last digit.

EXAMPLE 3 Add: 45 + 2.06

Solution:

$$
\begin{array}{r}
45.00 \quad \text{Insert a decimal point and two 0s.} \\
+\ \ 2.06 \quad \text{Line up decimal points.} \\
\hline
47.06 \quad \text{Add.}
\end{array}
$$

Work Practice Problem 3

✔**Concept Check** What is wrong with the following calculation of the sum of 7.03, 2.008, 19.16, and 3.1415?

$$
\begin{array}{r}
7.03 \\
2.008 \\
19.16 \\
+3.1415 \\
\hline
3.6042
\end{array}
$$

Objective B Subtracting Decimals

Subtracting decimals is similar to subtracting whole numbers. We line up digits and subtract from right to left, borrowing when needed.

EXAMPLE 4 Subtract: 35.218 − 23.65. Check your answer.

Solution: First we line up the decimal points.

$$
\begin{array}{r}
\overset{4}{3}\cancel{5}.\overset{11}{2}\overset{1}{1}\cancel{1}8 \\
-\ 23.650 \quad \text{Insert one 0.} \\
\hline
11.568 \quad \text{Subtract.}
\end{array}
$$

Recall that we can check a subtraction problem by adding.

$$
\begin{array}{r}
\overset{1}{1}1.\overset{1}{5}68 \quad \text{Difference} \\
+\ 23.650 \quad \text{Subtrahend} \\
\hline
35.218 \quad \text{Minuend}
\end{array}
$$

Work Practice Problem 4

PRACTICE PROBLEM 5

Subtract. Check your answers.

a. $5.8 - 3.92$

b. $9.72 - 4.068$

EXAMPLE 5   Subtract: $3.5 - 0.068$. Check your answer.

Solution:
$$
\begin{array}{r}
\overset{\overset{9}{4}\,\overset{}{\cancel{10}}\,10}{3.\cancel{5}\,0\,0} \quad \text{Insert two 0s.}\\
-\,0.0\,6\,8 \quad \text{Line up decimal points.}\\
\hline
3.4\,3\,2 \quad \text{Subtract.}
\end{array}
$$

Check:
$$
\begin{array}{r}
3.432 \quad \text{Difference}\\
+\,0.068 \quad \text{Subtrahend}\\
\hline
3.500 \quad \text{Minuend}
\end{array}
$$

⬛ **Work Practice Problem 5**

PRACTICE PROBLEM 6

Subtract. Check your answers.

a. $53 - 29.31$

b. $120 - 68.22$

EXAMPLE 6   Subtract: $85 - 17.31$. Check your answer.

Solution:
$$
\begin{array}{r}
\overset{7\ 14\ \overset{9}{\cancel{10}}\ 10}{8\,\cancel{5}.\cancel{0}\,\cancel{0}}\\
-\,1\,7.3\,1\\
\hline
6\,7.6\,9
\end{array}
$$

Check:
$$
\begin{array}{r}
67.69 \quad \text{Difference}\\
+\,17.31 \quad \text{Subtrahend}\\
\hline
85.00 \quad \text{Minuend}
\end{array}
$$

⬛ **Work Practice Problem 6**

Objective **C** Estimating When Adding or Subtracting Decimals

To help avoid errors, we can also estimate to see if our answer is reasonable when adding or subtracting decimals. Although only one estimate is needed per operation, we show two to show variety.

PRACTICE PROBLEM 7

Add or subtract as indicated. Then estimate to see if the answer is reasonable by rounding the given numbers and adding or subtracting the rounded numbers.

a. $48.1 + 326.97$

b. $18.09 - 0.746$

EXAMPLE 7   Add or subtract as indicated. Then estimate to see if the answer is reasonable by rounding the given numbers and adding or subtracting the rounded numbers.

a. $27.6 + 519.25$

Exact		Estimate 1		Estimate 2
$\overset{1}{}27.60$	rounds to	30		30
$+\,519.25$	rounds to	$+\,500$	or	$+\,520$
546.85		530		550

Since the exact answer is close to either estimate, it is reasonable. (In the first estimate, each number is rounded to the place value of the leftmost digit. In the second estimate, each number is rounded to the nearest ten.)

b. $11.01 - 0.862$

Exact		Estimate 1		Estimate 2
$\overset{0\ \ 9\ 10\,10}{1\cancel{1}.\cancel{0}\cancel{1}\cancel{0}}$	rounds to	10		11
$-\,0.862$	rounds to	$-\,1$	or	$-\,1$
10.148		9		10

In the first estimate, we rounded the first number to the nearest ten and the second number to the nearest one. In the second estimate, we rounded both numbers to the nearest one. Both estimates show us that our answer is reasonable.

Remember: Estimates are for our convenience to quickly check the reasonableness of an answer.

⬛ **Work Practice Problem 7**

✔**Concept Check** Why shouldn't the sum 21.98 + 42.36 be estimated as 30 + 50 = 80?

Objective D Solving Problems by Adding or Subtracting Decimals

Decimals are very common in real-life problems.

EXAMPLE 8 **Calculating the Cost of Owning an Automobile**

Find the total monthly cost of owning and operating a certain automobile given the expenses shown.

Monthly car payment:	$256.63
Monthly insurance cost:	$47.52
Average gasoline bill per month:	$95.33

Solution:

1. UNDERSTAND. Read and reread the problem. The phrase "total monthly cost" tells us to add.

2. TRANSLATE.

In words:	total monthly cost	is	car payment	plus	insurance cost	plus	gasoline bill
	↓	↓	↓	↓	↓	↓	↓
Translate:	total monthly cost	=	$256.63	+	$47.52	+	$95.33

3. SOLVE: Let's also estimate by rounding each number to the nearest ten.

$$
\begin{array}{l}
\overset{1\,1\,1}{256.63} \quad \text{rounds to} \quad 260 \\
47.52 \quad \text{rounds to} \quad 50 \\
\underline{+\ 95.33} \quad \text{rounds to} \quad \underline{100} \\
\$399.48 \quad \text{Exact.} \qquad 410 \quad \text{Estimate.}
\end{array}
$$

4. INTERPRET. *Check* your work. Since our estimate is close to our exact answer, our answer is reasonable. *State* your conclusion: The total monthly cost is $399.48.

⬛ **Work Practice Problem 8**

The next bar graph has horizontal bars. To visualize the value represented by a bar, see how far it extends to the right. The value of each bar is labeled and we will study bar graphs further in a later chapter.

EXAMPLE 9 **Comparing Average Heights**

The bar graph shows the current average heights for adults in various countries. How much greater is the average height in Denmark than the average height in the United States?

Continued on next page

PRACTICE PROBLEM 8

Find the total monthly cost of owning and operating a certain automobile given the expenses shown.

Monthly car payment:	$536.52
Monthly insurance cost:	$52.68
Average gasoline bill per month:	$87.50

Answer
8. $676.70

✔ **Concept Check Answer**

Each number is rounded incorrectly. The estimate is too high.

PRACTICE PROBLEM 9

Use the bar graph in Example 9. How much greater is the average height in the Netherlands than the average height in Czechoslovakia?

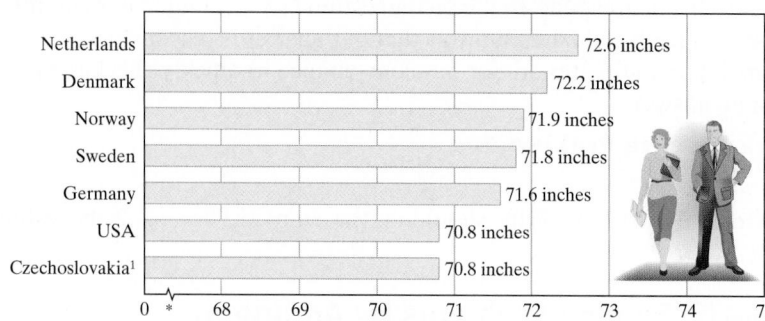

Average Adult Height

Netherlands	72.6 inches
Denmark	72.2 inches
Norway	71.9 inches
Sweden	71.8 inches
Germany	71.6 inches
USA	70.8 inches
Czechoslovakia[1]	70.8 inches

0 * 68 69 70 71 72 73 74 75

[1]Average for Czech Republic, Slovakia
Source: USA Today, 8/28/97

* The ⟿ means that some numbers are purposefully missing on the axis.

Solution:

1. UNDERSTAND. Read and reread the problem. Since we want to know "how much greater," we subtract.

2. TRANSLATE.

In words:	How much greater	is	Denmark's average height	minus	U.S. average height
	↓	↓	↓	↓	↓
Translate:	How much greater	=	72.2	−	70.8

3. SOLVE: We estimate by rounding each number to the nearest whole.

$$\begin{array}{r} \overset{1\ \ 12}{7\cancel{2}.\cancel{2}} \\ -\ 70.8 \\ \hline 1.4 \end{array}$$ rounds to $\quad\begin{array}{r}72 \\ -71 \\ \hline 1\end{array}$ Estimate.

4. INTERPRET. *Check* your work. Since our estimate is close to our exact answer, 1.4 inches is reasonable. *State* your conclusion: The average height in Denmark is 1.4 inches greater than the average U.S. height.

▪ **Work Practice Problem 9**

Answer

9. 1.8 in.

🖩 **CALCULATOR EXPLORATIONS**

Entering Decimal Numbers

To enter a decimal number, find the key marked ⟨ · ⟩. To enter the number 2.56, for example, press the keys ⟨ 2 ⟩ ⟨ · ⟩ ⟨ 5 ⟩ ⟨ 6 ⟩.

The display will read | 2.56 |.

Operations on Decimal Numbers

Operations on decimal numbers are performed in the same way as operations on whole or signed numbers. For example, to find 8.625 − 4.29, press the keys ⟨ 8.625 ⟩ ⟨ − ⟩ ⟨ 4.29 ⟩ ⟨ = ⟩ or ⟨ ENTER ⟩.

The display will read | 4.335 |. (Although entering 8.625, for example, requires pressing more than one key, we group numbers together here for easier reading.)

Use a calculator to perform each indicated operation.

1. 315.782 + 12.96
2. 29.68 + 85.902
3. 6.249 − 1.0076
4. 5.238 − 0.682
5.
```
   12.555
  224.987
    5.2
+ 622.65
```
6.
```
   47.006
    0.17
  313.259
+ 139.088
```

Mental Math

Find the sum or difference.

1.	0.3 + 0.2	2.	0.4 + 0.5	3.	1.00 + 0.26	4.	3.00 + 0.19

5.	7.6 + 1.3	6.	4.5 + 3.2	7.	0.9 − 0.3	8.	0.6 − 0.2

4.3 EXERCISE SET

FOR EXTRA HELP

Student Solutions Manual · PH Math/Tutor Center · CD/Video for Review · MathXL · MyMathLab

Objectives A C Mixed Practice *Add. See Examples 1 through 3, and 7. For those exercises marked, also estimate to see if the answer is reasonable.*

1. $1.3 + 2.2$

2. $2.5 + 4.1$

3. $5.7 + 1.13$

4. $2.31 + 6.4$

5. $0.003 + 0.091$

6. $0.004 + 0.085$

7. $19.23 + 602.782$

8. $47.14 + 409.567$

9. $490 + 93.09$

10. $600 + 83.0062$

11. 234.89
　+ 230.67
　Exact:　　　Estimate:

12. 734.89
　+ 640.56
　Exact:　　　Estimate:

13. 100.009
　　6.08
　+　9.034
　Exact:　　　Estimate:

14. 200.89
　　7.49
　+　62.83
　Exact:　　Estimate:

15. $24.6 + 2.39 + 0.0678$

16. $32.4 + 1.58 + 0.0934$

17. Find the sum of 45.023, 3.006, and 8.403

18. Find the sum of 65.0028, 5.0903, and 6.9003

Objectives B C Mixed Practice *Subtract and check. See Examples 4 through 7. For those exercises marked, also estimate to see if the answer is reasonable.*

19. $8.8 - 2.3$

20. $7.6 - 2.1$

21. $18 - 2.7$

22. $28 - 3.3$

23.   654.9
   − 56.67

24.   863.23
   − 39.453

25. 5.9 − 4.07
   Exact:
   Estimate:

26. 6.4 − 3.04
   Exact:
   Estimate:

27. 923.5 − 61.9

28. 845.93 − 45.8

29. 500.34 − 123.45

30. 600.74 − 463.98

31.   1000
   − 123.4
 Exact:

 Estimate:

32.   2000
   − 327.47
 Exact:

 Estimate:

33. 200 − 5.6

34. 800 − 8.9

35. 3 − 0.0012

36. 7 − 0.097

37. Subtract 6.7 from 23.

38. Subtract 9.2 from 45.

Objectives **A** **B** **Mixed Practice** *Perform the indicated operation. See Examples 1 through 6.*

39. 86.05 + 1.978

40. 95.07 + 4.216

41. 86.05 − 1.978

42. 95.07 − 4.216

43. Add 150 and 93.17.

44. Add 250 and 86.07.

45. 150 − 93.17

46. 250 − 86.07

47. Subtract 8.94 from 12.1.

48. Subtract 6.73 from 20.2.

Objective **D** *Solve. See Examples 8 and 9.*

49. Find the total monthly cost of owning and maintaining a car given the information shown.

Monthly car payment:	$275.36
Monthly insurance cost:	$ 83.00
Average cost of gasoline per month:	$ 81.60
Average maintenance cost per month:	$ 14.75

50. Find the total monthly cost of owning and maintaining a car given the information shown.

Monthly car payment:	$306.42
Monthly insurance cost:	$ 53.50
Average cost of gasoline per month:	$123.00
Average maintenance cost per month:	$ 23.50

51. Gasoline was $1.739 per gallon on one day and $1.879 per gallon the next day. By how much did the price change?

52. A pair of eyeglasses costs a total of $347.89. The frames of the glasses are $97.23. How much do the lenses of the eyeglasses cost?

53. Find the perimeter.

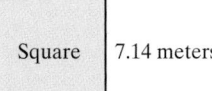

Square | 7.14 meters

54. Find the perimeter.

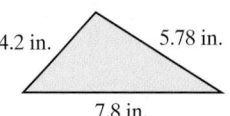

4.2 in.   5.78 in.

7.8 in.

The iPod mini is a minuture version of Apple Computer's popular iPod portable audio player. This mini was introduced in January 2004 with a storage capacity of 4 gigabytes. (This is about 1000 3-minute or 3-megabyte songs.)

55. The top face of the iPod mini shown measures 3.6 inches by 2.0 inches. Find the perimeter of the rectangular face.

56. The face of the larger Apple iPod measures 4.1 inches by 2.4 inches. Find the perimeter of this rectangular face.

57. Ann-Margaret Tober bought a book for $32.48. If she paid with two $20 bills, what was her change?

58. Phillip Guillot bought a car part for $18.26. If he paid with two $10 bills, what was his change?

59. Americans' consumption of sugar is on the decline. During 2000, Americans consumed an average of 150.1 pounds of sugar in its various forms such as refined white sugar, honey, and corn sweeteners. By 2002, the average American was consuming 146 pounds of sugar products per year. How much less sugar was the average American consuming annually in 2002 than in 2000? (*Source:* Economic Research Service, U.S. Department of Agriculture)

60. In 2001, the average wage for U.S. production workers was $14.29 per hour. One year later in 2002, this average wage had climbed to $14.95 per hour. How much of an increase was this? (*Source:* Bureau of Labor Statistics)

61. The average wind speed at the weather station on Mt. Washington in New Hampshire is 35.2 miles per hour. The highest speed ever recorded at the station is 321.0 miles per hour. How much faster is the highest speed than the average wind speed? (*Source:* National Climatic Data Center)

62. The average annual rainfall in Omaha, Nebraska, is 30.22 inches. The average annual rainfall in New Orleans, Louisiana, is 61.88 inches. On average, how much more rain does New Orleans receive annually than Omaha? (*Source:* National Climatic Data Center)

63. In October 1997, Andy Green set a new one-mile land speed record. This record was 129.567 miles per hour faster than a previous record of 633.468 set in 1983. What was Green's record-setting speed? (*Source:* United States Auto Club)

64. It costs $3.13 to send a 2-pound package locally via parcel post at a U.S. Post Office. To send the same package as Priority Mail, it costs $3.95. How much more does it cost to send a package as Priority Mail? (*Source:* USPS)

This bar graph shows the predicted decrease in home video rental revenue for chains such as Blockbuster and Hollywood Video. Use this graph for Exercise 65.

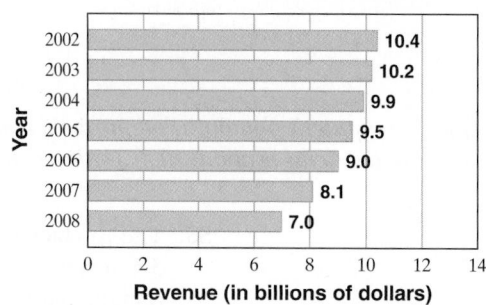

Video Rental Revenues

Source: Forrester Research; Note: Many of these years are projections.

65. Find the decrease in video rental revenue from the year 2002 to 2008.

66. It is predicted that home video *sales* (not shown on the bar graph) will increase from $15.3 billion in 2002 to $24.6 billion in 2008. Find the amount of increase.

67. The snowiest city in the United States is Blue Canyon, California, which receives an average of 111.6 more inches of snow than the second-snowiest city. The second-snowiest city in the United States is Marquette, Michigan. Marquette receives an average of 129.2 inches of snow annually. How much snow does Blue Canyon receive on average each year? (*Source:* National Climatic Data Center)

68. The driest city in the world is Aswan, Egypt, which receives an average of only 0.02 inches of rain per year. Yuma, Arizona, is the driest city in the United States. Yuma receives an average of 2.63 more inches of rain each year than Aswan. What is the average annual rainfall in Yuma? (*Source:* National Climatic Data Center)

△ **69.** A landscape architect is planning a border for a flower garden that's shaped like a triangle. The sides of the garden measure 12.4 feet, 29.34 feet, and 25.7 feet. Find the amount of border material needed.

△ **70.** A contractor needs to buy railing to completely enclose a newly built rectangular deck. If the deck has a length of 15.7 feet and a width of 10.6 feet, find the amount of railing needed.

The table shows the average retail price of a gallon of gasoline (all grades and formulations) in the United States in May of each of the years shown. Use this table to answer Exercises 71 and 72.

Year	Gasoline Price (dollars per gallon)
2000	1.563
2001	1.531
2002	1.441
2003	1.638
2004	1.861

(*Source:* Energy Information Administration)

71. How much more was the average cost of a gallon of gasoline in 2000 than in 2002?

72. How much more was the average cost of a gallon of gasoline in 2004 than in 2001?

The following table shows spaceflight information for astronaut James A. Lovell. Use this table to answer Exercises 73 and 74.

Spaceflights of James A. Lovell		
Year	Mission	Duration (in hours)
1965	Gemini 6	330.583
1966	Gemini 12	94.567
1968	Apollo 8	147.0
1970	Apollo 13	142.9

(*Source:* NASA)

73. Find the total time spent in spaceflight by astronaut James A. Lovell.

74. Find the total time James A. Lovell spent in spaceflight on all Apollo missions.

The bar graph shows the top five chocolate-consuming nations in the world. Use this table to answer Exercises 75 through 79.

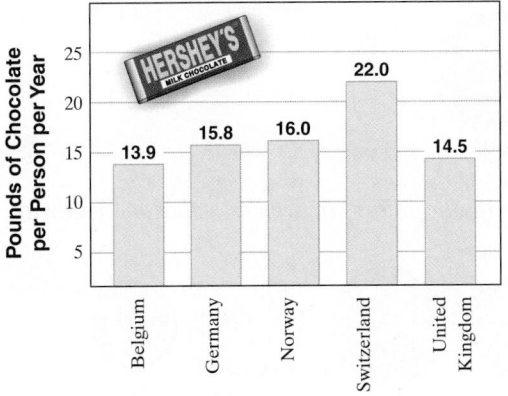

The World's Top Chocolate-Consuming Countries

Source: Hershey Foods Corporation

75. Which country in the table has the greatest chocolate consumption per person?

76. Which country in the table has the least chocolate consumption per person?

77. How much more is the greatest chocolate consumption than the least chocolate consumption shown in the table?

78. How much more chocolate does the average German consume than the average citizen of the United Kingdom?

79. Make a new chart listing the countries and their corresponding chocolate consumptions in order from greatest to least.

Review

Multiply. See Sections 1.6 and 2.4.

80. $23 \cdot 2$

81. $46 \cdot 3$

82. $43 \cdot 90$

83. $30 \cdot 32$

84. $\left(\dfrac{2}{3}\right)^2$

85. $\left(\dfrac{1}{5}\right)^3$

86. $\dfrac{12}{7} \cdot \dfrac{14}{3}$

87. $\dfrac{25}{36} \cdot \dfrac{24}{40}$

Concept Extensions

Solve. See the first Concept Check in this section.

88. A friend asks you to check his calculation to the right. Is it correct? If not, explain your friends' error and correct the calculation.

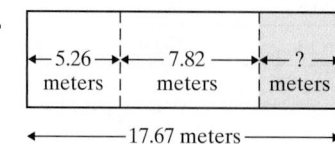

$$\begin{array}{r} \overset{1}{9}.2 \\ \overset{1}{8}.63 \\ +\,4.005 \\ \hline 4.960 \end{array}$$

Find the unknown length in each figure.

△ **89.**

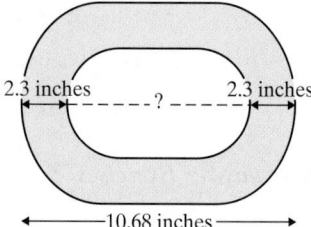

2.3 inches   ?   2.3 inches

10.68 inches

△ **90.**

←5.26→ meters   ←7.82→ meters   ←?→ meters

←17.67 meters→

Let's review the values of these common U.S. coins in order to answer the following exercises.

Penny	Nickel	Dime	Quarter
$0.01	$0.05	$0.10	$0.25

Write the value of each group of coins. To do so, it is usually easiest to start with the coin(s) of greatest value and end with the coin(s) of least value.

91.

92.

93. Name the different ways that coins can have a value of $0.17 given that you may use no more than 10 coins.

94. Name the different ways that coin(s) can have a value of $0.25 given that there are no pennies.

95. Why shouldn't the sum

    $82.95 + 51.26$

be estimated as $90 + 60 = 150$?
See the Concept Check in this section.

96. Explain how adding or subtracting decimals is similar to adding or subtracting whole numbers.

97. Laser beams can be used to measure the distance to the moon. One measurement showed the distance to the moon to be 256,435.235 miles. A later measurement showed that the distance is 256,436.012 miles. Find how much farther away the moon is in the second measurement as compared to the first.

4.4 MULTIPLYING DECIMALS AND CIRCUMFERENCE OF A CIRCLE

Objective **A** Multiplying Decimals

Multiplying decimals is similar to multiplying whole numbers. The only difference is that we place a decimal point in the product. To discover where a decimal point is placed in the product, let's multiply 0.6×0.03. We first write each decimal as an equivalent fraction and then multiply.

$$0.6 \times 0.03 = \frac{6}{10} \times \frac{3}{100} = \frac{18}{1000} = 0.018$$

1 decimal place   2 decimal places   3 decimal places

Notice that $1 + 2 = 3$, the number of decimal places in the product. Now let's multiply 0.03×0.002.

$$0.03 \times 0.002 = \frac{3}{100} \times \frac{2}{1000} = \frac{6}{100,000} = 0.00006$$

2 decimal places   3 decimal places   5 decimal places

Again, we see that $2 + 3 = 5$, the number of decimal places in the product.

Instead of writing decimals as fractions each time we want to multiply, we notice a pattern from these examples and state a rule that we can use:

> **Multiplying Decimals**
>
> **Step 1:** Multiply the decimals as though they are whole numbers.
>
> **Step 2:** The decimal point in the product is placed so that the number of decimal places in the product is equal to the *sum* of the number of decimal places in the factors.

EXAMPLE 1 Multiply: 23.6×0.78

Solution:

$$
\begin{array}{r}
23.6 \quad \text{1 decimal place} \\
\times\, 0.78 \quad \text{2 decimal places} \\
\hline
1888 \\
16520 \\
\hline
18.408
\end{array}
$$

Since $1 + 2 = 3$, insert the decimal point in the product so that there are 3 decimal places.

▣ Work Practice Problem 1

EXAMPLE 2 Multiply: 0.283×0.3

Solution:

$$
\begin{array}{r}
0.283 \quad \text{3 decimal places} \\
\times\quad 0.3 \quad \text{1 decimal place} \\
\hline
0.0849
\end{array}
$$

Since $3 + 1 = 4$, insert the decimal point in the product so that there are 4 decimal places.

Insert one 0 since the product must have 4 decimal places.

▣ Work Practice Problem 2

PRACTICE PROBLEM 1

Multiply: 45.9×0.42

PRACTICE PROBLEM 2

Multiply: 0.112×0.6

Answers

1. 19.278, **2.** 0.0672

277

PRACTICE PROBLEM 3

Multiply: 0.0721×48

EXAMPLE 3 Multiply: 0.0531×16

Solution:

$$
\begin{array}{r}
0.0531 \quad \text{4 decimal places} \\
\times \quad 16 \quad \text{0 decimal places} \\
\hline
3186 \\
5310 \\
\hline
0.8496 \\
\end{array}
$$

4 decimal places $(4 + 0 = 4)$

◾ **Work Practice Problem 3**

✔ Concept Check True or false? The number of decimal places in the product of 0.261 and 0.78 is 6. Explain.

Objective **B** Estimating When Multiplying Decimals

Just as for addition and subtraction, we can estimate when multiplying decimals to check the reasonableness of our answer.

PRACTICE PROBLEM 4

Multiply: 30.26×2.98. Then estimate to see whether the answer is reasonable.

EXAMPLE 4 Multiply: 28.06×1.95. Then estimate to see whether the answer is reasonable by rounding each factor, then multiplying the rounded numbers.

Solution:

Exact:	**Estimate 1**	**Estimate 2**
28.06	28 Rounded to ones or	30 Rounded to tens
$\times\ 1.95$	$\times\ 2$	$\times\ 2$
14030	56	60
252540		
280600		
54.7170		

The answer 54.7170 is reasonable.

◾ **Work Practice Problem 4**

As shown in Example 4, estimated results will vary depending on what estimates are used. Notice that estimating results is a good way to see whether the decimal point has been correctly placed.

Objective **C** Multiplying by Powers of 10

There are some patterns that occur when we multiply a number by a power of 10 such as 10, 100, 1000, 10,000, and so on.

$23.6951 \times 10 = 236.951$ Move the decimal point *1 place* to the *right*.
1 zero

$23.6951 \times 100 = 2369.51$ Move the decimal point *2 places* to the *right*.
2 zeros

$23.6951 \times 100,000 = 2,369,510.$ Move the decimal point *5 places* to the *right* (insert a 0).
5 zeros

Answers

3. 3.4608, **4.** 90.1748

✔ **Concept Check Answer**

false: 3 decimal places and 2 decimal places means 5 decimal places in the product

Notice that we move the decimal point the same number of places as there are zeros in the power of 10.

Multiplying Decimals by Powers of 10 such as 10, 100, 1000, 10,000 . . .

Move the decimal point to the *right* the same number of places as there are *zeros* in the power of 10.

EXAMPLES Multiply.

5. $7.68 \times 10 = 76.8$ 7.68

6. $23.702 \times 100 = 2370.2$ 23.702

7. $76.3 \times 1000 = 76,300$ 76.300

Work Practice Problems 5–7

PRACTICE PROBLEMS 5–7

Multiply.

5. 23.7×10

6. 203.004×100

7. 1.15×1000

There are also powers of 10 that are less than 1. The decimals 0.1, 0.01, 0.001, 0.0001, and so on are examples of powers of 10 less than 1. Notice the pattern when we multiply by these powers of 10:

$569.2 \times 0.1 = 56.92$ Move the decimal point *1 place* to the *left*.

1 decimal place

$569.2 \times 0.01 = 5.692$ Move the decimal point *2 places* to the *left*.

2 decimal places

$569.2 \times 0.0001 = 0.05692$ Move the decimal point *4 places* to the *left* (insert one 0).

4 decimal places

Multiplying Decimals by Powers of 10 such as 0.1, 0.01, 0.001, 0.0001 . . .

Move the decimal point to the *left* the same number of places as there are *decimal places* in the power of 10.

EXAMPLES Multiply.

8. $42.1 \times 0.1 = 4.21$ 42.1

9. $76,805 \times 0.01 = 768.05$ 76,805.

10. $9.2 \times 0.001 = 0.0092$ 0009.2

Work Practice Problems 8–10

PRACTICE PROBLEMS 8–10

Multiply.

8. 7.62×0.1

9. 1.9×0.01

10. 7682×0.001

Many times we see large numbers written, for example, in the form 295.3 million rather than in the longer standard notation. The next example shows us how to interpret these numbers.

Answers

5. 237,   **6.** 20,300.4,   **7.** 1150,
8. 0.762,   **9.** 0.019,   **10.** 7.682.

PRACTICE PROBLEM 11

According to the 2000 Census, there were 115.9 million households in the United States. Write this number in standard notation. (*Source:* U.S. Census Bureau)

EXAMPLE 11 At the beginning of 2005, the population of the United States was projected to be 295.3 million. Write this number in standard notation. (*Source:* U.S. Census Bureau)

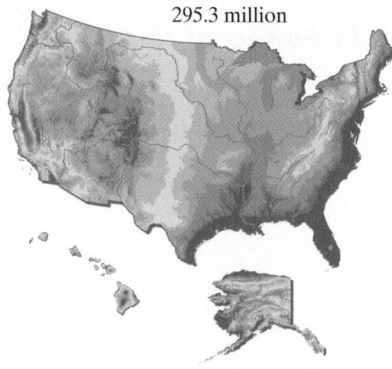

295.3 million

Solution: 295.3 million = 295.3 × 1 million

= 295.3 × 1,000,000 = 295,300,000

☐ **Work Practice Problem 11**

Objective D Finding the Circumference of a Circle

Recall that the distance around a polygon is called its **perimeter.** The distance around a circle is given a special name called the **circumference,** and this distance depends on the radius or the diameter of the circle.

Circumference of a Circle

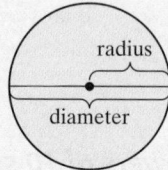

radius

diameter

Circumference = 2 · π · radius   or   Circumference = π · diameter

---

The symbol π is the Greek letter pi, pronounced "pie." It is a number between 3 and 4. The number π rounded to two decimal places is 3.14, and a fraction approximation for π is $\frac{22}{7}$.

EXAMPLE 12 Find the circumference of a circle whose radius is 5 inches. Then use the approximation 3.14 for π to approximate the circumference.

Solution: Circumference = $2 \cdot \pi \cdot$ radius
                            = $2 \cdot \pi \cdot 5$ inches
                            = 10π inches

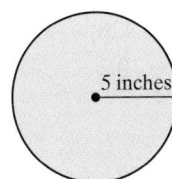

5 inches

Next, we replace π with the approximation 3.14.

      Circumference = 10π inches

("is approximately") $\rightarrow$ $\approx 10(3.14)$ inches

             = 31.4 inches

The *exact* circumference or distance around the circle is 10π inches, which is *approximately* 31.4 inches.

🔲 **Work Practice Problem 12**

PRACTICE PROBLEM 12

Find the circumference of a circle whose radius is 11 meters. Then use the approximation 3.14 for π to approximate this circumference.

Objective **E** Solving Problems by Multiplying Decimals

The solutions to many real-life problems are found by multiplying decimals. We continue using our four problem-solving steps to solve such problems.

EXAMPLE 13 Finding the Total Cost of Materials for a Job

A college student is hired to paint a billboard with paint costing $2.49 per quart. If the job requires 3 quarts of paint, what is the total cost of the paint?

Solution:

1. **UNDERSTAND.** Read and reread the problem. The phrase "total cost" might make us think addition, but since this problem requires repeated addition, let's multiply.
2. **TRANSLATE.**

In words:	Total cost	is	cost per quart of paint	times	number of quarts
	↓	↓	↓	↓	↓
Translate:	Total cost	=	2.49	×	3

3. **SOLVE.** We can estimate to check our calculations. The number 2.49 rounds to 2 and $2 \times 3 = 6$.

$$\begin{array}{r} \overset{1\ 2}{2.49} \\ \times\quad 3 \\ \hline 7.47 \end{array}$$

4. **INTERPRET.** *Check* your work. Since 7.47 is close to our estimate of 6, our answer is reasonable. *State* your conclusion: The total cost of the paint is $7.47.

🔲 **Work Practice Problem 13**

PRACTICE PROBLEM 13

Elaine Rehmann is fertilizing her garden. She uses 5.6 ounces of fertilizer per square yard. The garden measures 60.5 square yards. How much fertilizer does she need?

Answers
12. 22π m; 69.08 m, **13.** 338.8 oz

Mental Math

Do not multiply. Just give the number of decimal places in the product. See the Concept Check in this section.

1. 0.46 $\times$ 0.81	**2.** 57.9 $\times$ 0.36	**3.** 0.428 $\times$ 0.2	**4.** 0.0073 $\times$ 21	**5.** 0.028 $\times$ 1.36	**6.** 5.1296 $\times$7.3987

4.4 EXERCISE SET

FOR EXTRA HELP

Student Solutions Manual · PH Math/Tutor Center · CD/Video for Review · MathXL® · MyMathLab

Objectives **A** **B** **Mixed Practice** *Multiply. See Examples 1 through 4. For those exercises marked, also estimate to see if the answer is reasonable.*

1.   0.2
    $\times$0.6

2.   0.7
    $\times$0.9

 **3.**   1.2
    $\times$0.5

4.   6.8
    $\times$0.3

5. 0.26×5

6. 0.19×6

7. 5.3×4.2
    Exact:
    Estimate:

8. 6.2×3.8
    Exact:
    Estimate:

9.   0.576
   $\times$ 0.7

10.   0.971
    $\times$ 0.5

 **11.**   1.0047
    $\times$ 8.2
  Exact: Estimate:

12.   2.0005
    $\times$ 5.5
  Exact: Estimate:

13.   490.2
   $\times$0.023

14.   300.9
   $\times$0.032

15. Multiply 16.003 and 5.31

16. Multiply 31.006 and 3.71

Objective **C** *Multiply. See Examples 5 through 10.*

17. 6.5×10

18. 7.2×100

19. 6.5×0.1

20. 4.7×0.1

21. 7.2×0.01

 **22.** 0.06×0.01

23. 7.093×100

24. 0.5×100

25. 6.046×1000

26. 9.1×1000

27. 37.62×0.001

28. 14.3×0.001

Objectives **A** **B** **C** **Mixed Practice** *Multiply. See Examples 1 through 10.*

29. 0.123×0.4

30. 0.216×0.3

31. 0.123×100

32. 0.216×100

33. 8.6×0.15

34. 0.42×5.7

35. 9.6×0.01

36. 5.7×0.01

37. 562.3×0.001

38. 993.5×0.001

39. 5.62
$\underline{\times\ 7.7}$

40. 8.03
$\underline{\times\ 5.5}$

Write each number in standard notation. See Example 11.

41. The storage silos at the main Hershey chocolate factory in Hershey, Pennsylvania, can hold enough cocoa beans to make 5.5 billion Hershey's milk chocolate bars. (*Source:* Hershey Foods Corporation)

42. The total value of works from Pablo Picasso (if sold) is $1.5 billion. (*Source: Top 10 of Everything,* 2005)

43. The Blue Streak is the oldest roller coaster at Cedar Point, an amusement park in Sandusky, Ohio. Since 1964, it has given more than 49.8 million rides. (*Source:* Cedar Fair, L.P.)

44. About 36.4 million American households own at least one dog. (*Source:* American Pet Products Manufacturers Association)

45. The most-visited national park in the United States is the Blue Ridge Parkway in Virginia and North Carolina. An estimated 353 thousand people visited the park each week in 2003. (*Source:* National Park Service)

46. There are 844 thousand places to eat out in the United States. (*Source:* National Restaurant Association)

Objective **D** *Find the circumference of each circle. Then use the approximation 3.14 for π and approximate each circumference. See Example 12.*

47.
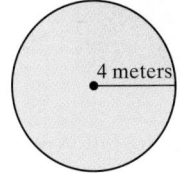
4 meters

48.
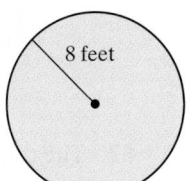
8 feet

49.
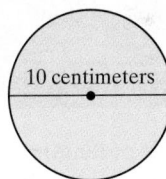
10 centimeters

50.
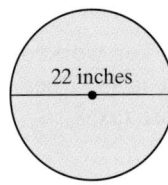
22 inches

51.
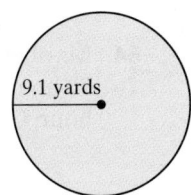
9.1 yards

52.
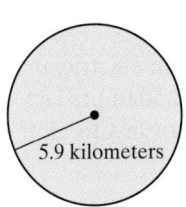
5.9 kilometers

Objectives **D** **E** **Mixed Practice** *Solve. See Examples 12 and 13. For circumference applications find the exact circumference and then use 3.14 for π to approximate the circumference.*

53. A 1-ounce serving of cream cheese contains 6.2 grams of saturated fat. How much saturated fat is in 4 ounces of cream cheese? (*Source: Home and Garden Bulletin No. 72;* U.S. Department of Agriculture)

54. A 3.5-ounce serving of lobster meat contains 0.1 gram of saturated fat. How much saturated fat do 3 servings of lobster meat contain? (*Source:* The National Institute of Health)

55. The average cost of driving a car in 2003 was $0.52 per mile. How much would it have cost to drive a car 8750 miles in 2003? (*Source:* American Automobile Association)

56. In 2003, a U.S. airline passenger paid $0.1174, on average, to fly 1 mile. How much would it have cost to fly from Atlanta, Georgia, to Minneapolis, Minnesota, a distance of 905 miles? Round to the nearest cent. (*Source:* Air Transport Association of America, Inc.)

△ **57.** In 1893, the first ride called a Ferris wheel was constructed by Washington Gale Ferris. Its diameter was 250 feet. Find its circumference. Give an exact answer and an approximation using 3.14 for π. (*Source: The Handy Science Answer Book*, Visible Ink Press, 1994)

△ **58.** The radius of Earth is approximately 3950 miles. Find the distance around Earth at the equator. Give an exact answer and an approximation using 3.14 for π. (*Hint:* Find the circumference of a circle with radius 3950 miles.)

△ **59.** The London Eye, built for the Millennium celebration in London, resembles a gigantic ferris wheel with a diameter of 135 meters. If Adam Hawn rides the Eye for one revolution, find how far he travels. (Give an exact answer and an approximation using 3.14 for π. (*Source:* Londoneye.com)

△ **60.** The world's longest suspension bridge is the Akashi Kaikyo Bridge in Japan. This bridge has two circular caissons, which are underwater foundations. If the diameter of a caisson is 80 meters, find its circumference. Give an exact answer and an approximation using 3.14 for π. (*Source: Scientific American;* How Things Work Today)

61. A meter is a unit of length in the metric system that is approximately equal to 39.37 inches. Sophia Wagner is 1.65 meters tall. Find her approximate height in inches.

62. The doorway to a room is 2.15 meters tall. Approximate this height in inches. (*Hint:* See Exercise 61.)

63. Jose Severos, an electrician for Central Power and Light, worked 40 hours last week. Calculate his pay before taxes for last week if his hourly wage is $13.88.

64. Maribel Chin, an assembly line worker, worked 20 hours last week. Her hourly rate is $8.52 per hour. Calculate Maribel's pay before taxes.

△ **65. a.** Approximate the circumference of each circle.

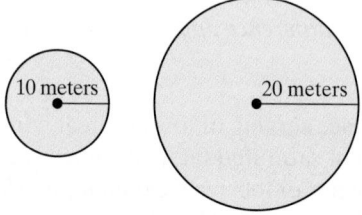

b. If the radius of a circle is doubled, is its corresponding circumference doubled?

△ **66. a.** Approximate the circumference of each circle.

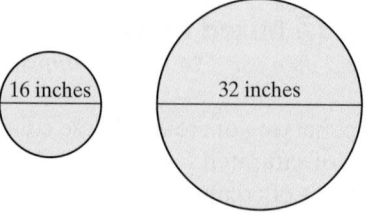

b. If the diameter of a circle is doubled, is its corresponding circumference doubled?

67. Recall that the top face of the Apple iPod mini (see Section 4.3) measures 3.6 inches by 2.0 inches. Find the area of the face of the iPod mini.

68. Recall that the face of the regular Apple iPod measures 4.1 inches by 2.4 inches. Find the area of the face of this iPod.

Review

Divide. See Sections 1.7 and 2.5.

69. $130 \div 5$

70. $495 \div 27$

71. $2016 \div 56$

72. $1863 \div 69$

73. $2920 \div 365$

74. $2916 \div 6$

75. $\dfrac{24}{7} \div \dfrac{8}{21}$

76. $\dfrac{162}{25} \div \dfrac{9}{75}$

Concept Extensions

Mixed Practice (Sections 4.3, 4.4) *Perform the indicated operations.*

77. $3.6 + 0.04$

78. 3.6×0.04

79. $3.6 - 0.04$

80. $100 - 48.6$

81. 0.221×0.5

82. $7.2 + 0.14 + 98.6$

83. Find how far radio waves travel in 20.6 seconds. (Radio waves travel at a speed of $1.86 \times 100,000$ miles per second.)

84. If it takes radio waves approximately 8.3 minutes to travel from the Sun to the Earth, find approximately how far it is from the Sun to the Earth. (*Hint:* See Exercise 83.)

85. In your own words, explain how to find the number of decimal places in a product of decimal numbers.

86. In your own words, explain how to multiply by a power of 10.

87. Write down two decimal numbers whose product will contain 5 decimal places. Without multiplying, explain how you know your answer is correct.

Operations on Decimals

Perform the indicated operations.

Answers

1. _____

2. _____

3. _____

4. _____

5. _____

6. _____

7. _____

8. _____

9. _____

10. _____

11. _____

12. _____

13. _____

14. _____

15. _____

16. _____

17. _____

18. _____

19. _____

20. _____

21. _____

22. _____

23. _____

24. _____

25. _____

26. _____

1. $1.6 + 0.97$

2. $3.2 + 0.85$

3. $9.8 - 0.9$

4. $10.2 - 6.7$

5. $\begin{array}{r} 0.8 \\ \times\, 0.2 \\ \hline \end{array}$

6. $\begin{array}{r} 0.6 \\ \times\, 0.4 \\ \hline \end{array}$

7. $8 + 2.16 + 0.9$

8. $6 + 3.12 + 0.6$

9. $\begin{array}{r} 9.6 \\ \times\, 0.5 \\ \hline \end{array}$

10. $\begin{array}{r} 8.7 \\ \times\, 0.7 \\ \hline \end{array}$

11. $\begin{array}{r} 123.6 \\ -\ 48.04 \\ \hline \end{array}$

12. $\begin{array}{r} 325.2 \\ -\ 36.08 \\ \hline \end{array}$

13. $25 + 0.026$

14. $0.125 + 44$

15. $100 - 17.3$

16. $300 - 26.1$

17. 2.8×100

18. 1.6×1000

19. $\begin{array}{r} 96.21 \\ 7.028 \\ +\ 121.7 \\ \hline \end{array}$

20. $\begin{array}{r} 0.268 \\ 1.93 \\ +\ 142.881 \\ \hline \end{array}$

21. Find the product of 1.2 and 5.

22. Find the sum of 1.2 and 5.

23. $\begin{array}{r} 12.004 \\ \times\ \ \ \ 2.3 \\ \hline \end{array}$

24. $\begin{array}{r} 28.006 \\ \times\ \ \ \ 5.2 \\ \hline \end{array}$

25. Subtract 4.6 from 10.

26. Subtract 0.26 from 18.

27.   268.19
          + 146.25

28.   860.18
          + 434.85

29. 160 − 43.19

30. 120 − 101.21

31. 15.62 × 10

32. 15.62 + 10

33. 15.62 − 10

34. 117.26 × 2.6

35. 117.26 − 2.6

36. 117.26 + 2.6

37. 0.0072 × 0.06

38. 0.0025 × 0.03

39. 0.0072 + 0.06

40. 0.03 − 0.0025

41. 0.862 × 1000

42. 2.93 × 0.01

43. Estimate the distance in miles between Garden City, Kansas, and Wichita, Kansas, by rounding each given distance to the nearest ten.

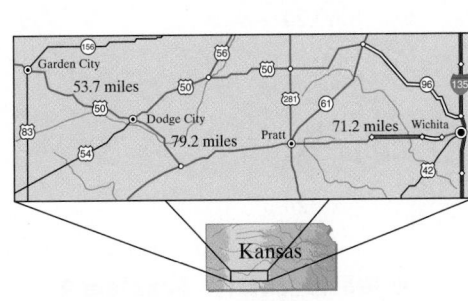

27. _____

28. _____

29. _____

30. _____

31. _____

32. _____

33. _____

34. _____

35. _____

36. _____

37. _____

38. _____

39. _____

40. _____

41. _____

42. _____

43. _____

A Divide Decimals.

B Estimate When Dividing Decimals.

C Divide Decimals by Powers of 10.

D Solve Problems by Dividing Decimals.

E Review Order of Operations to Simplify Expressions Containing Decimals.

4.5 DIVIDING DECIMALS AND ORDER OF OPERATIONS

Objective A Dividing Decimals

Dividing decimal numbers is similar to dividing whole numbers. The only difference is that we place a decimal point in the quotient. If the divisor is a whole number, we place the decimal point in the quotient directly above the decimal point in the dividend, and then divide as with whole numbers. Recall that division can be checked by multiplication.

$$
\begin{array}{r}
0.26 \quad \leftarrow \text{quotient} \\
\text{divisor} \rightarrow 32{\overline{)8.32}} \quad \leftarrow \text{dividend} \\
-6\,4 \\
\hline
1\,92 \\
-1\,92 \\
\hline
0
\end{array}
$$

Check:
$$
\begin{array}{r}
0.26 \quad \text{Quotient} \\
\times\ 32 \quad \text{Divisor} \\
\hline
52 \\
7\,80 \\
\hline
8.32 \quad \text{Dividend}
\end{array}
$$

Dividing by a Whole Number

Step 1: Place the decimal point in the quotient directly above the decimal point in the dividend.

Step 2: Divide as with whole numbers.

PRACTICE PROBLEM 1

Divide: 517.2 ÷ 6. Check your answer.

EXAMPLE 1 Divide: 270.2 ÷ 7. Check your answer.

Solution:

Write the decimal point.
$$
\begin{array}{r}
38.6 \\
7{\overline{)270.2}} \\
-21 \\
\hline
60 \\
-56 \\
\hline
4\,2 \\
-4\,2 \\
\hline
0
\end{array}
$$

Check:
$$
\begin{array}{r}
^{6\,4} \\
38.6 \\
\times\ 7 \\
\hline
270.2
\end{array}
$$

The quotient is 38.6.

■ **Work Practice Problem 1**

PRACTICE PROBLEM 2

Divide: 26.19 ÷ 9. Check your answer.

EXAMPLE 2 Divide: 60.24 ÷ 8. Check your answer.

Solution:

Write the decimal point.
$$
\begin{array}{r}
7.53 \\
8{\overline{)60.24}} \\
-56 \\
\hline
4\,2 \\
-4\,0 \\
\hline
24 \\
-24 \\
\hline
0
\end{array}
$$

Check:
$$
\begin{array}{r}
^{4\,2} \\
7.53 \\
\times\ 8 \\
\hline
60.24
\end{array}
$$

■ **Work Practice Problem 2**

Sometimes to continue dividing we need to insert zeros after the last digit in the dividend.

EXAMPLE 3 Divide and Check: $0.5 \div 4$.

Solution:

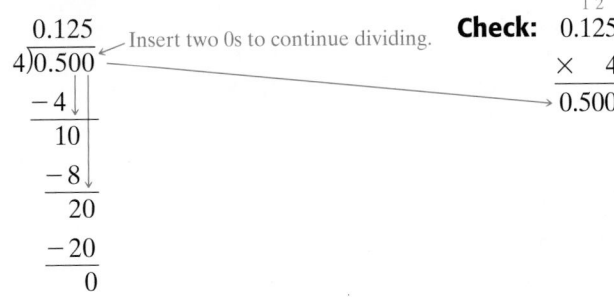

Check: $\begin{array}{r} \overset{1\;2}{0.125} \\ \times \quad 4 \\ \hline 0.500 \end{array}$

◻ **Work Practice Problem 3**

PRACTICE PROBLEM 3

Divide and check.
a. $0.4 \div 8$
b. $13.62 \div 12$

If the divisor is not a whole number, before we divide we need to move the decimal point to the right until the divisor is a whole number.

$$1.5\overline{)64.85}$$

divisor ⌐   ⌐ dividend

To understand how this works, let's rewrite

$$1.5\overline{)64.85} \quad \text{as} \quad \frac{64.85}{1.5}$$

and then multiply by 1 in the form of $\frac{10}{10}$. We use the form $\frac{10}{10}$ so that the denominator (divisor) becomes a whole number.

$$\frac{64.85}{1.5} = \frac{64.85}{1.5} \cdot 1 = \frac{64.85}{1.5} \cdot \frac{10}{10} = \frac{64.85 \cdot 10}{1.5 \cdot 10} = \frac{648.5}{15}$$

which can be written as $15.\overline{)648.5}$. Notice that

$$1.5\overline{)64.85} \text{ is equivalent to } 15.\overline{)648.5}$$

The decimal points in the dividend and the divisor were both moved one place to the right, and the divisor is now a whole number. This procedure is summarized next:

Dividing by a Decimal

Step 1: Move the decimal point in the divisor to the right until the divisor is a whole number.

Step 2: Move the decimal point in the dividend to the right the *same number of places* as the decimal point was moved in Step 1.

Step 3: Divide. Place the decimal point in the quotient directly over the moved decimal point in the dividend.

Answers

3. a. 0.05,   **b.** 1.135

PRACTICE PROBLEM 4

Divide: 166.88 ÷ 5.6

EXAMPLE 4 Divide: 10.764 ÷ 2.3

Solution: We move the decimal points in the divisor and the dividend one place to the right so that the divisor is a whole number.

$$2.3\overline{)10.764}$$ becomes

$$
\begin{array}{r}
4.68 \\
23.\overline{)107.64} \\
-92 \\
\hline
15\,6 \\
-13\,8 \\
\hline
1\,84 \\
-1\,84 \\
\hline
0
\end{array}
$$

■ **Work Practice Problem 4**

PRACTICE PROBLEM 5

Divide: 1.976 ÷ 0.16

EXAMPLE 5 Divide: 5.264 ÷ 0.32

Solution:

$$0.32\overline{)5.264}$$ becomes

$$
\begin{array}{r}
16.45 \\
32\overline{)526.40} \quad \text{Insert one 0.} \\
-32 \\
\hline
206 \\
-192 \\
\hline
14\,4 \\
-12\,8 \\
\hline
1\,60 \\
-1\,60 \\
\hline
0
\end{array}
$$

■ **Work Practice Problem 5**

✔ **Concept Check** Is it always true that the number of decimal places in a quotient equals the sum of the decimal places in the dividend and divisor?

PRACTICE PROBLEM 6

Divide 23.4 ÷ 0.57. Round the quotient to the nearest hundredth.

EXAMPLE 6 Divide: 17.5 ÷ 0.48. Round the quotient to the nearest hundredth.

Solution: First we move the decimal points in the divisor and the dividend two places. Then we divide and round the quotient to the nearest hundredth.

hundredths place

$$
\begin{array}{r}
36.458 \approx 36.46 \\
48.\overline{)1750.000} \\
-144 \\
\hline
310 \\
-288 \\
\hline
22\,0 \\
-19\,2 \\
\hline
2\,80 \\
-2\,40 \\
\hline
400 \\
-384 \\
\hline
16
\end{array}
$$

"is approximately"

When rounding to the nearest hundredth, carry the division process out to one more decimal place, the thousandths place.

■ **Work Practice Problem 6**

Answers

4. 29.8, **5.** 12.35, **6.** 41.05

✔ **Concept Check Answer**

no

Objective B Estimating When Dividing Decimals

Just as for addition, subtraction, and multiplication of decimals, we can estimate when dividing decimals to check the reasonableness of our answer.

EXAMPLE 7 Divide: $272.356 \div 28.4$. Then estimate to see whether the proposed result is reasonable.

Solution:

Exact:	Estimate 1		Estimate 2

$$
\begin{array}{r}
9.59 \\
284.\overline{)2723.56} \\
-2556 \\
\hline
1675 \\
-1420 \\
\hline
2556 \\
-2556 \\
\hline
0
\end{array}
$$

$$
\begin{array}{r}
9 \\
30\overline{)270}
\end{array}
\quad \text{or} \quad
\begin{array}{r}
10 \\
30\overline{)300}
\end{array}
$$

The estimate is 9 or 10, so 9.59 is reasonable.

Work Practice Problem 7

✔ **Concept Check** If a quotient is to be rounded to the nearest thousandth, to what place should the division be carried out? (Assume that the division carries out to your answer.)

Objective C Dividing Decimals by Powers of 10

As with multiplication, there are patterns that occur when we divide decimals by powers of 10 such as 10, 100, 1000, and so on.

$$\frac{569.2}{10} = 56.92 \qquad \text{Move the decimal point } 1 \text{ place to the } left.$$
— 1 zero

$$\frac{569.2}{10,000} = 0.05692 \qquad \text{Move the decimal point } 4 \text{ places to the } left.$$
— 4 zeros

This pattern suggests the following rule:

> ### Dividing Decimals by Powers of 10 such as 10, 100, or 1000
>
> Move the decimal point of the dividend to the *left* the same number of places as there are *zeros* in the power of 10.

EXAMPLES Divide.

8. $\dfrac{786.1}{1000} = 0.7861$ Move the decimal point *3 places* to the *left.*
— 3 zeros

9. $\dfrac{0.12}{10} = 0.012$ Move the decimal point *1 place* to the *left.*
— 1 zero

Work Practice Problems 8–9

PRACTICE PROBLEM 7

Divide: $713.7 \div 91.5$. Then estimate to see whether the proposed answer is reasonable.

PRACTICE PROBLEMS 8–9

Divide.

8. $\dfrac{128.3}{1000}$ **9.** $\dfrac{0.56}{10}$

Answers
7. 7.8, **8.** 0.1283, **9.** 0.056

✔ **Concept Check Answer**
ten-thousandths place

Objective D Solving Problems by Dividing Decimals

Many real-life problems involve dividing decimals.

EXAMPLE 10 Calculating Materials Needed for a Job

A gallon of paint covers a 250-square-foot area. If Betty Adkins wishes to paint a wall that measures 1450 square feet, how many gallons of paint does she need? If she can buy only gallon containers of paint, how many gallon containers does she need?

Solution:

1. UNDERSTAND. Read and reread the problem. We need to know how many 250s are in 1450, so we divide.

2. TRANSLATE.

In words:	number of gallons	is	square feet	divided by	square feet per gallon
	↓	↓	↓	↓	↓
Translate:	number of gallons	=	1450	÷	250

3. SOLVE. Let's see if our answer is reasonable by estimating. The dividend 1450 rounds to 1500 and divisor 250 rounds to 300. Then $1500 \div 300 = 5$.

$$
\begin{array}{r}
5.8 \\
250\overline{)1450.0} \\
-1250 \\
\hline
200\ 0 \\
-200\ 0 \\
\hline
0
\end{array}
$$

4. INTERPRET. *Check* your work. Since our estimate is close to our answer of 5, our answer is reasonable. *State* your conclusion: Betty needs 5.8 gallons of paint. If she can buy only gallon containers of paint, she needs 6 gallon containers of paint to complete the job.

■ **Work Practice Problem 10**

Objective E Simplifying Expressions with Decimals

In the remaining examples, we will review the order of operations by simplifying expressions that contain decimals.

Order of Operations

1. Perform all operations within parentheses ( ), brackets [ ], or other grouping symbols such as square roots or fraction bars.
2. Evaluate any expressions with exponents.
3. Multiply or divide in order from left to right.
4. Add or subtract in order from left to right.

EXAMPLE 11 Simplify: $723.6 \div 1000 \times 10$

Solution: Multiply or divide in order from left to right.

$$723.6 \div 1000 \times 10 = 0.7236 \times 10 \qquad \text{Divide.}$$
$$= 7.236 \qquad \text{Multiply.}$$

▣ **Work Practice Problem 11**

PRACTICE PROBLEM 11

Simplify: $897.8 \div 100 \times 10$

EXAMPLE 12 Simplify: $0.5(8.6 - 1.2)$

Solution: According to the order of operations, we simplify inside the parentheses first.

$$0.5(8.6 - 1.2) = 0.5(7.4) \qquad \text{Subtract.}$$
$$= 3.7 \qquad \text{Multiply.}$$

▣ **Work Practice Problem 12**

PRACTICE PROBLEM 12

Simplify: $8.69(3.2 - 1.8)$

EXAMPLE 13 Simplify: $\dfrac{5.68 + (0.9)^2 \div 100}{0.2}$

Solution: First we simplify the numerator of the fraction. Then we divide.

$$\frac{5.68 + (0.9)^2 \div 100}{0.2} = \frac{5.68 + 0.81 \div 100}{0.2} \qquad \text{Simplify } (0.9)^2.$$
$$= \frac{5.68 + 0.0081}{0.2} \qquad \text{Divide.}$$
$$= \frac{5.6881}{0.2} \qquad \text{Add.}$$
$$= 28.4405 \qquad \text{Divide.}$$

▣ **Work Practice Problem 13**

PRACTICE PROBLEM 13

Simplify: $\dfrac{20.06 - (1.2)^2 \div 10}{0.02}$

Answers
11. 89.78,   **12.** 12.166,   **13.** 995.8

▦ **CALCULATOR EXPLORATIONS**

Calculator errors can easily be made by pressing an incorrect key or by not pressing a correct key hard enough. Estimation is a valuable tool that can be used to check calculator results.

EXAMPLE Use estimation to determine whether the calculator result is reasonable or not. (For example, a result that is not reasonable can occur if proper keys are not pressed.)

Simplify: $82.064 \div 23$
Calculator display: ⬚ 35.68 ⬚

Solution: Round each number to the nearest 10. Since $80 \div 20 = 4$, the calculator display 35.68 is not reasonable.

Use estimation to determine whether each result is reasonable or not.

1. 102.62×41.8 Result: 428.9516

2. $174.835 \div 47.9$ Result: 3.65

3. $1025.68 - 125.42$ Result: 900.26

4. $562.781 + 2.96$ Result: 858.781

Mental Math

Recall properties of division and simplify.

1. $\dfrac{5.9}{1}$

2. $\dfrac{0.7}{0.7}$

3. $\dfrac{0}{9.86}$

4. $\dfrac{2.36}{0}$

5. $\dfrac{7.261}{7.261}$

6. $\dfrac{8.25}{1}$

7. $\dfrac{11.1}{0}$

8. $\dfrac{0}{89.96}$

4.5 EXERCISE SET

FOR EXTRA HELP

Student Solutions Manual · PH Math/Tutor Center · CD/Video for Review · Math XL · MathXL® · MyMathLab

Objectives A B Mixed Practice *Divide. See Examples 1 through 5 and 7. For those exercises marked, also estimate to see if the answer is reasonable.*

1. $3\overline{)13.8}$

2. $2\overline{)11.8}$

 3. $5\overline{)0.47}$

4. $6\overline{)0.51}$

5. $0.06\overline{)18}$

6. $0.04\overline{)20}$

 7. $0.82\overline{)4.756}$

8. $0.92\overline{)3.312}$

9. $5.5\overline{)36.3}$
   Exact:
   Estimate:

10. $2.2\overline{)21.78}$
    Exact:
    Estimate:

11. $6.195 \div 15$

12. $8.823 \div 17$

13. $0.54 \div 12$

14. $1.35 \div 18$

15. Divide 4.2 by 0.6.

16. Divide 3.6 by 0.9.

17. $0.27\overline{)1.296}$

18. $0.34\overline{)2.176}$

19. $0.02\overline{)42}$

20. $0.03\overline{)24}$

21. $0.6\overline{)18}$

22. $0.4\overline{)20}$

23. $0.005\overline{)35}$

24. $0.0007\overline{)35}$

25. $7.2\overline{)70.56}$
    Exact:
    Estimate:

26. $6.3\overline{)54.18}$
    Exact:
    Estimate:

27. $5.4\overline{)51.84}$

28. $7.7\overline{)33.88}$

29. $\dfrac{1.215}{0.027}$

30. $\dfrac{3.213}{0.051}$

31. $0.25\overline{)13.648}$

32. $0.75\overline{)49.866}$

33. $3.78\overline{)0.02079}$

34. $2.96\overline{)0.01332}$

Divide. Round the quotients as indicated. See Example 6.

35. Divide 429.34 by 2.4 and round the quotient to the nearest whole number.

36. Divide 54.8 by 2.6 and round the quotient to the nearest whole number.

37. Divide 0.549 by 0.023 and round the quotient to the nearest hundredth.

38. Divide 0.0453 by 0.98 and round the quotient to the nearest thousandth.

39. Divide 45.23 by 0.4 and round the quotient to the nearest tenth.

40. Divide 83.32 by 0.063 and round the quotient to the nearest tenth.

Objective C *Divide. See Examples 8 and 9.*

41. $\dfrac{54.982}{100}$ **42.** $\dfrac{342.54}{100}$ **43.** $\dfrac{26.87}{10}$ **44.** $\dfrac{13.49}{10}$ **45.** $\dfrac{12.9}{1000}$ **46.** $\dfrac{0.27}{1000}$

Objectives A C Mixed Practice *Divide. See Examples 1 through 6.*

47. $7\overline{)88.2}$ **48.** $9\overline{)130.5}$ **49.** $\dfrac{13.1}{10}$ **50.** $\dfrac{17.7}{10}$

51. $6.8\overline{)83.13}$ **52.** $4.8\overline{)123.72}$ **53.** $\dfrac{456.25}{10,000}$ **54.** $\dfrac{986.11}{10,000}$

Objective D *Solve. See Example 10.*

55. Dorren Schmidt pays $73.86 per month to pay back a loan of $1772.64. In how many months will the loan be paid off?

56. Josef Jones is painting the walls of a room. The walls have a total area of 546 square feet. A quart of paint covers 52 square feet. If he must buy paint in whole quarts, how many quarts does he need?

57. The leading monetary winner in men's professional golf in 2003 was Vijay Singh. He earned $7,573,907. Suppose he had earned this working 40 hours per week for a year. Determine his hourly wage to the nearest cent. (*Note:* There are 52 weeks in a year.) (*Source:* 2005 *World Almanac*)

58. Juanita Gomez bought unleaded gasoline for her car at $1.169 per gallon. She wanted to keep a record of how many gallons her car is using but forgot to write down how many gallons she purchased. She wrote a check for $27.71 to pay for it. How many gallons, to the nearest tenth of a gallon, did she buy?

59. A pound of fertilizer covers 39 square feet of lawn. Vivian Bulgakov's lawn measures 7883.5 square feet. How much fertilizer, to the nearest tenth of a pound, does she need to buy?

60. A page of a book contains about 1.5 kilobytes of information. If a computer disk can hold 740 kilobytes of information, how many pages of a book can be stored on one computer disk? Round to the nearest tenth of a page.

61. There are approximately 39.37 inches in 1 meter. How many meters, to the nearest tenth of a meter, are there in 200 inches?

$$\xleftarrow{\hspace{0.5cm}} 1 \text{ meter} \xrightarrow{\hspace{0.5cm}}$$
$$\xleftarrow{\hspace{0.3cm}} \approx 39.37 \text{ inches} \xrightarrow{\hspace{0.3cm}}$$

62. There are 2.54 centimeters in 1 inch. How many inches are there in 50 centimeters? Round to the nearest tenth.

$$\xleftarrow{\hspace{0.5cm}} 1 \text{ inch} \xrightarrow{\hspace{0.5cm}}$$
$$\xleftarrow{\hspace{0.3cm}} 2.54 \text{ cm} \xrightarrow{\hspace{0.3cm}}$$

63. In the United States, an average child will wear down 730 crayons by his or her tenth birthday. Find the number of boxes of 64 crayons this is equivalent to. Round to the nearest tenth. (*Source:* Binney & Smith Inc.)

64. American farmers receive an average of $238 per 100 chickens. What is the average price per chicken? (*Source:* National Agricultural Statistics Service)

A child is to receive a dose of 0.5 teaspoon of cough medicine every 4 hours. If the bottle contains 4 fluid ounces, answer Exercises 65 through 68.

65. A fluid ounce equals 6 teaspoons. How many teaspoons are in 4 fluid ounces?

66. The bottle of medicine contains how many doses for the child?

67. If the child takes a dose every four hours, how many days will the medicine last?

68. If the child takes a dose every six hours, how many days will the medicine last?

69. During the 24 Hours of the Le Mans endurance auto race in 2004, the winning team of Seiji Ara, Tom Kristensen, and Rinaldo Capello drove a total of 3211.2 miles in 24 hours. What was their average speed in miles per hour? (*Source:* Automobile Club de l'Ouest)

70. In 2000, Kenyan runner Tegla Loroupe set a new world record for the women's 20,000-meter event. Her time for the event was 3926.6 seconds. What was her average speed in meters per second? Round to the nearest tenth. (*Source:* 2005 *Guinness World Record.*)

71. Lauren Jackson of the WNBA's Seattle Storm scored a total of 634 points during the 31 basketball games she played in the 2004 regular season. What was the average number of points she scored per game? Round to the nearest hundredth. (*Source:* Women's National Basketball Association)

72. During the 2004 Major League Soccer season, the Metro Stars was the top-scoring team with a total of 47 goals throughout the season. The Metro Stars played 30 games. What was the average number of goals the team scored per game? Round to the nearest hundredth. (*Source:* Major League Soccer)

Objective **E** *Simplify each expression. See Examples 11 through 13.*

73. $0.7(6 - 2.5)$

74. $1.4(2 - 1.8)$

75. $\dfrac{0.29 + 1.69}{3}$

76. $\dfrac{1.697 - 0.29}{0.7}$

77. $30.03 + 5.1 \times 9.9$

78. $60 - 6.02 \times 8.97$

79. $7.8 - 4.83 \div 2.1 + 9.2$

80. $90 - 62.1 \div 2.7 + 8.6$

81. $93.07 \div 10 \times 100$

82. $35.04 \div 100 \times 10$

83. $\dfrac{7.8 + 1.1 \times 100 - 3.6}{0.2}$

84. $\dfrac{9.6 - 7.8 \div 10 + 1.2}{0.02}$

85. $5(20.6 - 2.06) - (0.8)^2$

86. $(10.6 - 9.8)^2 \div 0.01 + 8.6$

87. $6 \div 0.1 + 8.9 \times 10 - 4.6$

88. $8 \div 10 + 7.6 \times 0.1 - (0.1)^2$

Review

Write each decimal as a fraction.

89. 0.9

90. 0.7

91. 0.05

92. 0.08

Concept Extensions

Mixed Practice (Sections 4.3, 4.4, 4.5) *Perform the indicated operation.*

93. $1.278 \div 0.3$

94. 1.278×0.3

95. $1.278 + 0.3$

96. $1.278 - 0.3$

97.
$$\begin{array}{r} 8.6 \\ \times\ 3.1 \\ \hline \end{array}$$

98. $7.2 + 0.05 + 49.1$

99.
$$\begin{array}{r} 1000 \\ -\ 95.71 \\ \hline \end{array}$$

100. $\dfrac{87.2}{10,000}$

Choose the best estimate.

101. 8.62×41.7
 a. 36
 b. 32
 c. 360
 d. 3.6

102. $1.437 + 20.69$
 a. 34
 b. 22
 c. 3.4
 d. 2.2

103. $78.6 \div 97$
 a. 7.86
 b. 0.786
 c. 786
 d. 7860

104. $302.729 - 28.697$
 a. 270
 b. 20
 c. 27
 d. 300

Recall from Section 1.7 that the average of a list of numbers is their total divided by how many numbers there are in the list. Use this procedure to find the average of the test scores listed in Exercises 105 and 106. If necessary, round to the nearest tenth.

105. 86, 78, 91, 87

106. 56, 75, 80

107. In 2003, American manufacturers shipped approximately 745.94 million music CDs to retailers. How many music CDs were shipped per week on average? (*Source:* Recording Industry Association of America)

△ **108.** The area of a rectangle is 38.7 square feet. If its width is 4.5 feet, find its length.

△ **109.** The perimeter of a square is 180.8 centimeters. Find the length of a side.

△ **110.** Don Larson is building a horse corral that's shaped like a rectangle with dimensions of 24.28 meters by 15.675 meters. He plans to make a four-wire fence; that is, he will string four wires around the corral. How much wire will he need?

✎ **111.** When dividing decimals, describe the process you use to place the decimal point in the quotient.

✎ **112.** In your own words, describe how to quickly divide a number by a power of 10 such as 10, 100, 1000, etc.

To convert wind speeds in miles per hour to knots, divide by 1.15. Use this information and the Saffir-Simpson Hurricane Intensity chart below to answer Exercises 113 through 114. Round to the nearest tenth.

113. The chart gives wind speeds in miles per hour. What is the range of wind speeds for a Category 1 hurricane in knots?

114. What is the range of wind speeds for a Category 4 hurricane in knots?

Saffir-Simpson Hurricane Intensity Scale				
Category	Wind Speed	Barometric Pressure [inches of mercury (Hg)]	Storm Surge	Damage Potential
1 (Weak)	75–95 mph	≥28.94 in.	4–5 ft	Minimal damage to vegetation
2 (Moderate)	96–110 mph	28.50–28.93 in.	6–8 ft	Moderate damage to houses
3 (Strong)	111–130 mph	27.91–28.49 in.	9–12 ft	Extensive damage to small buildings
4 (Very Strong)	131–155 mph	27.17–27.90 in.	13–18 ft	Extreme structural damage
5 (Devastating)	>155 mph	<27.17 in.	>18 ft	Catastrophic building failures possible

---

THE BIGGER PICTURE   Operations on Sets of Numbers

Continue your outline from Sections 1.7, 1.9, 2.5, and 3.4. Suggestions are once again written to help you complete this part of your outline.

I. Some Operations on Sets of Numbers

  A. Whole Numbers

    1. Add or Subtract (Sections 1.3, 1.4)

    2. Multiply or Divide (Sections 1.6, 1.7)

    3. Exponent (Section 1.9)

    4. Square Root (Section 1.9)

    5. Order of Operations (Section 1.9)

  B. Fractions

    1. Simplify (Section 2.3)

    2. Multiply (Section 2.4)

    3. Divide (Section 2.5)

    4. Add or Subtract (Section 3.4)

  C. Decimals

    1. Add or Subtract: Line up decimal points.

$$\begin{array}{r} 1.27 \\ +0.6 \\ \hline 1.87 \end{array}$$

    2. Multiply:

$$\begin{array}{r} 2.56 \\ \times\ 3.2 \\ \hline 512 \\ 7680 \\ \hline 8.192 \end{array}$$

    2 decimal places
    1 decimal place
    2 + 1 = 3
    3 decimal places

3. Divide:

$$8)\overline{5.6} \quad\to\quad 0.7 \qquad 0.6)\overline{0.786} \quad\to\quad 1.31$$

Perform indicated operations.

1. $3.6 + 8.092 + 10.48$

2. $7 - 3.049$

3. 91.332×100

4. $\dfrac{68}{10}$

5. $\begin{array}{r} 5.2 \\ \times\ 0.27 \end{array}$

6. $9)\overline{77.94}$

7. $0.35)\overline{0.01785}$

8. $2.3 - (0.4)^2$

9. $\dfrac{8}{15} - \dfrac{2}{5}$

10. $\dfrac{8}{15} \cdot \dfrac{2}{5}$

4.6 FRACTIONS AND DECIMALS

Objectives

A Write Fractions as Decimals.

B Compare Fractions and Decimals.

C Solve Area Problems Containing Fractions and Decimals.

Objective **A** Writing Fractions as Decimals

To write a fraction as a decimal, we interpret the fraction bar to mean division and find the quotient.

Writing Fractions as Decimals

To write a fraction as a decimal, divide the numerator by the denominator.

EXAMPLE 1 Write $\frac{1}{4}$ as a decimal.

Solution: $\frac{1}{4} = 1 \div 4$

$$
\begin{array}{r}
0.25 \\
4\overline{)1.00} \\
-8 \\
\hline
20 \\
-20 \\
\hline
0
\end{array}
$$

Thus, $\frac{1}{4}$ written as a decimal is 0.25.

▣ **Work Practice Problem 1**

PRACTICE PROBLEM 1

a. Write $\frac{2}{5}$ as a decimal.

b. Write $\frac{9}{40}$ as a decimal.

EXAMPLE 2 Write $\frac{2}{3}$ as a decimal.

Solution:

$$
\begin{array}{r}
0.666\ldots \\
3\overline{)2.000} \\
-18 \\
\hline
20 \\
-18 \\
\hline
20 \\
-18 \\
\hline
2
\end{array}
$$

This pattern will continue because $\frac{2}{3} = 0.6666\ldots$

Remainder is 2, then 0 is brought down.

Remainder is 2, then 0 is brought down.

Remainder is 2.

Notice the digit 2 keeps occurring as the remainder. This will continue so that the digit 6 will keep repeating in the quotient. We place a bar over the digit 6 to indicate that it repeats.

$$\frac{2}{3} = 0.666\ldots = 0.\overline{6}$$

We can also write a decimal approximation for $\frac{2}{3}$. For example, $\frac{2}{3}$ rounded to the nearest hundredth is 0.67. This can be written as $\frac{2}{3} \approx 0.67$.

▣ **Work Practice Problem 2**

PRACTICE PROBLEM 2

a. Write $\frac{5}{6}$ as a decimal.

b. Write $\frac{2}{9}$ as a decimal.

Answers
1. a. 0.4, **b.** 0.225,
2. a. 0.8$\overline{3}$, **b.** 0.$\overline{2}$

Copyright 2007 Pearson Education, Inc.

PRACTICE PROBLEM 3

Write $\dfrac{28}{13}$ as a decimal. Round to the nearest thousandth.

EXAMPLE 3 Write $\dfrac{22}{7}$ as a decimal. (The fraction $\dfrac{22}{7}$ is an approximation for π.) Round to the nearest hundredth.

Solution:

$$3.142 \approx 3.14 \qquad \text{Carry the division out to the thousandths place.}$$

$$
\begin{array}{r}
3.142 \\
7\overline{)22.000} \\
-21 \\
\hline
1\,0 \\
-\ 7 \\
\hline
30 \\
-28 \\
\hline
20 \\
-14 \\
\hline
6
\end{array}
$$

The fraction $\dfrac{22}{7}$ in decimal form is approximately 3.14.

■ **Work Practice Problem 3**

PRACTICE PROBLEM 4

Write $3\dfrac{5}{16}$ as a decimal.

EXAMPLE 4 Write $2\dfrac{3}{16}$ as a decimal.

Solution:

Option 1. Write the fractional part only as a decimal.

$$\frac{3}{16} \longrightarrow
\begin{array}{r}
0.1875 \\
16\overline{)3.0000} \\
-1\,6 \\
\hline
1\,40 \\
-1\,28 \\
\hline
120 \\
-112 \\
\hline
80 \\
-80 \\
\hline
0
\end{array}$$

Thus $2\dfrac{3}{16} = 2.1875$

Option 2. Write $2\dfrac{3}{16}$ as an improper fraction, and divide.

$$2\frac{3}{16} = \frac{35}{16} \longrightarrow
\begin{array}{r}
2.1875 \\
16\overline{)35.0000} \\
-32 \\
\hline
3\,0 \\
-1\,6 \\
\hline
1\,40 \\
-1\,28 \\
\hline
120 \\
-112 \\
\hline
80 \\
-80 \\
\hline
0
\end{array}$$

Thus $2\dfrac{3}{16} = 2.1875$

■ **Work Practice Problem 4**

Some fractions may be written as decimals using our knowledge of decimals. From Section 4.1, we know that if the denominator of a fraction is 10, 100, 1000, or so on, we can immediately write the fraction as a decimal. For example,

$$\frac{4}{10} = 0.4, \qquad \frac{12}{100} = 0.12, \text{ and so on.}$$

Answers

3. 2.154, **4.** 3.3125

EXAMPLE 5 Write $\frac{4}{5}$ as a decimal.

Solution: Let's write $\frac{4}{5}$ as an equivalent fraction with a denominator of 10.

$$\frac{4}{5} = \frac{4}{5} \cdot \frac{2}{2} = \frac{8}{10} = 0.8$$

Work Practice Problem 5

EXAMPLE 6 Write $\frac{1}{25}$ as a decimal.

Solution: $\frac{1}{25} = \frac{1}{25} \cdot \frac{4}{4} = \frac{4}{100} = 0.04$

Work Practice Problem 6

✔**Concept Check** Suppose you are writing the fraction $\frac{9}{16}$ as a decimal. How do you know you have made a mistake if your answer is 1.735?

Objective B Comparing Decimals and Fractions

Now we can compare decimals and fractions by writing fractions as equivalent decimals.

EXAMPLE 7 Insert $<$, $>$, or $=$ to form a true statement.

$$\frac{1}{8} \qquad 0.12$$

Solution: First we write $\frac{1}{8}$ as an equivalent decimal. Then we compare decimal places.

$$\begin{array}{r} 0.125 \\ 8\overline{)1.000} \\ -8 \\ \hline 20 \\ -16 \\ \hline 40 \\ -40 \\ \hline 0 \end{array}$$

Original numbers	$\frac{1}{8}$	0.12
Decimals	0.125	0.120
Compare	0.125 > 0.12	

Thus, $\frac{1}{8} > 0.12$

Work Practice Problem 7

EXAMPLE 8 Insert $<$, $>$, or $=$ to form a true statement.

$$0.\overline{7} \qquad \frac{7}{9}$$

Solution: We write $\frac{7}{9}$ as a decimal and then compare.

$$\begin{array}{r} 0.77\ldots = 0.\overline{7} \\ 9\overline{)7.00} \\ -6\,3 \\ \hline 70 \\ -63 \\ \hline 7 \end{array}$$

Original numbers	$0.\overline{7}$	$\frac{7}{9}$
Decimals	$0.\overline{7}$	$0.\overline{7}$
Compare	$0.\overline{7} = 0.\overline{7}$	

Thus, $0.\overline{7} = \frac{7}{9}$

Work Practice Problem 8

PRACTICE PROBLEM 5
Write $\frac{3}{5}$ as a decimal.

PRACTICE PROBLEM 6
Write $\frac{3}{50}$ as a decimal.

PRACTICE PROBLEM 7
Insert $<$, $>$, or $=$ to form a true statement.
$$\frac{1}{5} \qquad 0.25$$

PRACTICE PROBLEM 8
Insert $<$, $>$, or $=$ to form a true statement.
a. $\frac{1}{2}$ 0.54 **b.** $0.\overline{4}$ $\frac{4}{9}$

c. $\frac{5}{7}$ 0.72

Answers
5. 0.6, **6.** 0.06, **7.** <,
8. a. <, **b.** =, **c.** <

✔ **Concept Check Answer**
$\frac{9}{16}$ is less than 1 while 1.735 is greater than 1.

PRACTICE PROBLEM 9

Write the numbers in order from smallest to largest.

a. $\frac{1}{3}, 0.302, \frac{3}{8}$ **b.** $1.26, 1\frac{1}{4}, 1\frac{2}{5}$

c. $0.4, 0.41, \frac{5}{7}$

EXAMPLE 9 Write the numbers in order from smallest to largest.

$$\frac{9}{20}, \frac{4}{9}, 0.456$$

Solution:

Original numbers	$\frac{9}{20}$	$\frac{4}{9}$	0.456
Decimals	0.450	0.444...	0.456
Compare in order	2nd	1st	3rd

Written in order, we have

1st 2nd 3rd
↓ ↓ ↓

$$\frac{4}{9}, \frac{9}{20}, 0.456$$

🖥 **Work Practice Problem 9**

Objective ⓒ Solving Area Problems Containing Fractions and Decimals

Sometimes real-life problems contain both fractions and decimals. In this section, we solve such problems concerning area. In the next example, we review the area of a triangle. This concept will be studied more in depth in a later chapter.

PRACTICE PROBLEM 10

Find the area of the triangle.

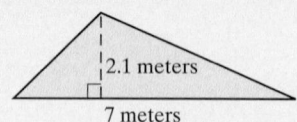

2.1 meters

7 meters

EXAMPLE 10 The area of a triangle is Area $= \frac{1}{2} \cdot$ base $\cdot$ height. Find the area of the triangle shown.

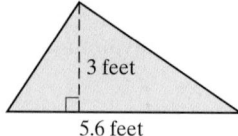

3 feet

5.6 feet

Solution:

$$\text{Area} = \frac{1}{2} \cdot \text{base} \cdot \text{height}$$

$$= \frac{1}{2} \cdot 5.6 \cdot 3$$

$$= 0.5 \cdot 5.6 \cdot 3 \qquad \text{Write } \frac{1}{2} \text{ as the decimal 0.5.}$$

$$= 8.4$$

The area of the triangle is 8.4 square feet.

🖥 **Work Practice Problem 10**

Answers
9. a. $0.302, \frac{1}{3}, \frac{3}{8}$,   **b.** $1\frac{1}{4}, 1.26, 1\frac{2}{5}$,

c. $0.4, 0.41, \frac{5}{7}$,   **10.** 7.35 sq m

Objective **A** *Write each number as a decimal. See Examples 1 through 6.*

1. $\dfrac{1}{5}$ **2.** $\dfrac{1}{20}$ **3.** $\dfrac{17}{25}$ **4.** $\dfrac{13}{25}$ **5.** $\dfrac{3}{4}$ **6.** $\dfrac{3}{8}$

7. $\dfrac{2}{25}$ **8.** $\dfrac{3}{25}$ **9.** $\dfrac{6}{5}$ **10.** $\dfrac{5}{4}$ **11.** $\dfrac{11}{12}$ **12.** $\dfrac{5}{12}$

13. $\dfrac{17}{40}$ **14.** $\dfrac{19}{25}$ **15.** $\dfrac{9}{20}$ **16.** $\dfrac{31}{40}$ **17.** $\dfrac{1}{3}$ **18.** $\dfrac{7}{9}$

19. $\dfrac{7}{16}$ **20.** $\dfrac{9}{16}$ **21.** $\dfrac{7}{11}$ **22.** $\dfrac{9}{11}$ **23.** $5\dfrac{17}{20}$ **24.** $4\dfrac{7}{8}$

25. $\dfrac{78}{125}$ **26.** $\dfrac{159}{375}$

Round each number as indicated.

27. Round your decimal answer to Exercise 17 to the nearest hundredth.

28. Round your decimal answer to Exercise 18 to the nearest hundredth.

29. Round your decimal answer to Exercise 19 to the nearest hundredth.

30. Round your decimal answer to Exercise 20 to the nearest hundredth.

31. Round your decimal answer to Exercise 21 to the nearest tenth.

32. Round your decimal answer to Exercise 22 to the nearest tenth.

Write each fraction as a decimal. If necessary, round to the nearest hundredth.

33. During a recent Boston Marathon, $\dfrac{17}{25}$ of the starting runners over the age of 70 finished the race. (*Source:* Boston Athletic Association)

34. About $\dfrac{21}{50}$ of all blood donors have type A blood. (*Source:* American Red Cross Biomedical Services)

35. Of the U.S. mountains that are over 14,000 feet in elevation, $\dfrac{56}{91}$ are located in Colorado. (*Source:* U.S. Geological Survey)

36. By October 2000, $\dfrac{29}{46}$ of all individuals who had flown in space were citizens of the United States. (*Source:* Congressional Research Service)

37. The United States contains the greatest fraction of people who use the internet, with about $\dfrac{67}{94}$ people using it. (*Source:* UCLA Center for Communication Policy)

38. Hungary has the lowest fraction of people using the Internet, with only $\dfrac{7}{40}$ people using it. (*Source:* UCLA Center for Communication Policy)

Objective **B** *Insert* $<$, $>$, *or* $=$ *to form a true statement. See Examples 7 and 8.*

39. 0.562   0.569

40. 0.983   0.988

41. 0.215 $\dfrac{43}{200}$

42. $\dfrac{29}{40}$ 0.725

43. $\dfrac{9}{100}$ 0.0932

44. $\dfrac{1}{200}$ 0.00563

45. $0.\overline{6}$ $\dfrac{5}{6}$

46. $0.\overline{1}$ $\dfrac{2}{17}$

47. $\dfrac{51}{91}$ $0.56\overline{4}$

48. $0.58\overline{3}$ $\dfrac{6}{11}$

49. $\dfrac{4}{7}$ 0.14

50. $\dfrac{5}{9}$ 0.557

51. 1.38 $\dfrac{18}{13}$

52. 0.372 $\dfrac{22}{59}$

53. 7.123 $\dfrac{456}{64}$

54. 12.713 $\dfrac{89}{7}$

Write the numbers in order from smallest to largest. See Example 9.

55. 0.34, 0.35, 0.32

56. 0.47, 0.42, 0.40

57. 0.49, 0.491, 0.498

58. 0.72, 0.727, 0.728

59. $\dfrac{3}{4}$, 0.78, 0.73

60. $\dfrac{2}{5}$, 0.49, 0.42

61. $\dfrac{4}{7}$, 0.453, 0.412

62. $\dfrac{6}{9}$, 0.663, 0.668

63. $5.23, \dfrac{42}{8}, 5.34$ **64.** $7.56, \dfrac{67}{9}, 7.562$ **65.** $\dfrac{12}{5}, 2.37, \dfrac{17}{8}$ **66.** $\dfrac{29}{16}, 1.75, \dfrac{59}{32}$

Objective Ⓒ *Find the area of each triangle or rectangle. See Example 10.*

△ **67.**

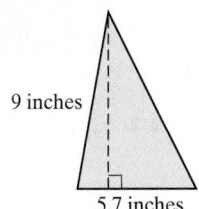

9 inches

5.7 inches

△ **68.**

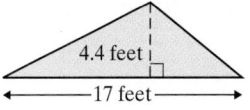

4.4 feet

17 feet

△ **69.**

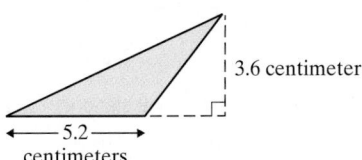

3.6 centimeters

5.2 centimeters

△ **70.**

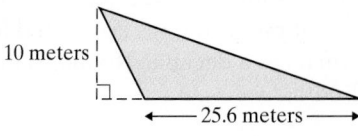

10 meters

25.6 meters

△ **71.**

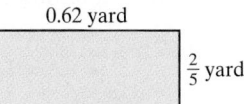

0.62 yard

$\dfrac{2}{5}$ yard

△ **72.**

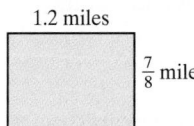

1.2 miles

$\dfrac{7}{8}$ mile

Review

Simplify. See Sections 1.9 and 3.5.

73. 2^3 **74.** 5^4 **75.** $6^2 \cdot 2$ **76.** $4 \cdot 3^4$ **77.** $\left(\dfrac{1}{3}\right)^4$

78. $\left(\dfrac{4}{5}\right)^3$ **79.** $\left(\dfrac{3}{5}\right)^2$ **80.** $\left(\dfrac{7}{2}\right)^2$ **81.** $\left(\dfrac{2}{5}\right)\left(\dfrac{5}{2}\right)^2$ **82.** $\left(\dfrac{2}{3}\right)^2\left(\dfrac{3}{2}\right)^3$

Concept Extensions

Without calculating, describe each number as < 1, $= 1$, or > 1. See the Concept Check in this section.

83. 1.0 **84.** 1.0000 **85.** 1.00001 **86.** $\dfrac{101}{99}$ **87.** $\dfrac{99}{100}$ **88.** $\dfrac{99}{99}$

In 2004, there were 10,649 commercial radio stations in the United States. The most popular formats are listed in the table along with their counts. Use this graph to answer Exercises 89 through 92.

89. Write the fraction of radio stations with a country music format as a decimal. Round to the nearest thousandth.

90. Write the fraction of radio stations with a news/talk format as a decimal. Round to the nearest hundredth.

91. Estimate, by rounding each number in the table to the nearest hundred, the total number of stations with the top six formats in 2004.

92. Use your estimate from Exercise 91 to write the fraction of radio stations accounted for by the top six formats as a decimal. Round to the nearest hundredth.

Top Commercial Radio Station Formats in 2004

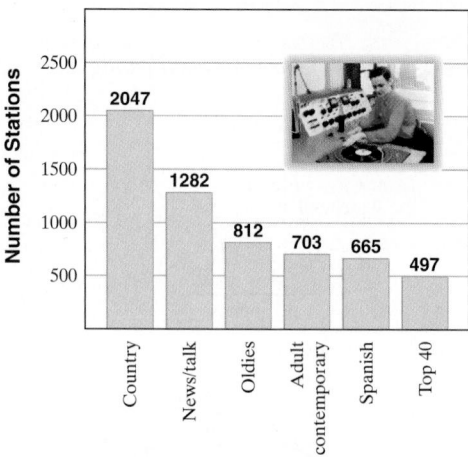

Format (Total stations: 10,649)

93. Describe 2 ways to determine the larger of two fractions.

94. Describe two ways to write fractions as decimals.

95. Describe two ways to write mixed numbers as decimals.

Find the value of each expression. Give the result as a decimal.

96. $2(7.8) - \dfrac{1}{5}$

97. $(9.6)(5) - \dfrac{3}{4}$

98. $8.25 - \left(\dfrac{1}{2}\right)^2$

99. $\left(\dfrac{1}{10}\right)^2 + (1.6)(2.1)$

100. $\dfrac{1}{4}(9.6 + 5.2)$

101. $\dfrac{3}{8}(5.9 - 4.7)$

CHAPTER 4   Group Activity

Maintaining a Checking Account
(Sections 4.1, 4.2, 4.3, 4.4)

This activity may be completed by working in groups or individually.

A checking account is a convenient way of handling money and paying bills. To open a checking account, the bank or savings and loan association requires a customer to make a deposit. Then the customer receives a checkbook that contains checks, deposit slips, and a register for recording checks written and deposits made. It is important to record all payments and deposits that affect the account. It is also important to keep the checkbook balance current by subtracting checks written and adding deposits made.

About once a month checking customers receive a statement from the bank listing all activity that the account has had in the last month. The statement lists a beginning balance, all checks and deposits, any service charges made against the account, and an ending balance. Because it may take several days for checks that a customer has written to clear the banking system, the check register may list checks that do not appear on the monthly bank statement. These checks are called **outstanding checks.** Deposits that are recorded in the check register but do not appear on the statement are called **deposits in transit.** Because of these differences, it is important to balance, or reconcile, the checkbook against the monthly statement. The steps for doing so are listed below.

Balancing or Reconciling a Checkbook

Step 1: Place a check mark in the checkbook register next to each check and deposit listed on the monthly bank statement. Any entries in the register without a check mark are outstanding checks or deposits in transit.

Step 2: Find the ending checkbook register balance and add to it any outstanding checks and any interest paid on the account.

Step 3: From the total in Step 2, subtract any deposits in transit and any service charges.

Step 4: Compare the amount found in Step 3 with the ending balance listed on the bank statement. If they are the same, the checkbook balances with the bank statement. Be sure to update the check register with service charges and interest.

Step 5: If the checkbook does not balance, recheck the balancing process. Next, make sure that the running checkbook register balance was calculated correctly. Finally, compare the checkbook register with the statement to make sure that each check was recorded for the correct amount.

For the checkbook register and monthly bank statement given:

a. *update the checkbook register*   **b.** *list the outstanding checks and deposits in transit*

c. *balance the checkbook—be sure to update the register with any interest or service fees*

#	Date	Description	Payment	✔	Deposit	Balance
						425.86
114	4/1	Market Basket	30.27			
115	4/3	May's Texaco	8.50			
	4/4	Cash at ATM	50.00			
116	4/6	UNO Bookstore	121.38			
	4/7	Deposit			100.00	
117	4/9	MasterCard	84.16			
118	4/10	Blockbuster	6.12			
119	4/12	Kroger	18.72			
120	4/14	Parking sticker	18.50			
	4/15	Direct deposit			294.36	
121	4/20	Rent	395.00			
122	4/25	Student fees	20.00			
	4/28	Deposit			75.00	

Checkbook Register

First National Bank Monthly Statement 4/30		
BEGINNING BALANCE:		425.86
Date	Number	Amount
CHECKS AND ATM WITHDRAWALS		
4/3	114	30.27
4/4	ATM	50.00
4/11	117	84.16
4/13	115	8.50
4/15	119	18.72
4/22	121	395.00
DEPOSITS		
4/7		100.00
4/15	Direct deposit	294.36
SERVICE CHARGES		
Low balance fee		7.50
INTEREST		
Credited 4/30		1.15
ENDING BALANCE:		227.22

Chapter 4 Vocabulary Check

Fill in each blank with one of the words listed below.

vertically	decimal	and
sum	denominator	numerator

1. Like fractional notation, _____ notation is used to denote a part of a whole.

2. To write fractions as decimals, divide the _____ by the _____.

3. To add or subtract decimals, write the decimals so that the decimal points line up _____.

4. When writing decimals in words, write "_____" for the decimal point.

5. When multiplying decimals, the decimal point in the product is placed so that the number of decimal places in the product is equal to the _____ of the number of decimal places in the factors.

Helpful Hint Are you preparing for your test? Don't forget to take the Chapter 4 Test on page 315. Then check your answers at the back of the text and use the Chapter Test Prep Video CD to see the fully worked-out solutions to any of the exercises you want to review.

4 Chapter Highlights

DEFINITIONS AND CONCEPTS	**EXAMPLES**
Section 4.1 Introduction to Decimals	

PLACE-VALUE CHART

hundreds	tens	ones	decimal point	tenths	hundredths	thousandths	ten-thousandths	hundred-thousandths
4				2	6	5		
100	10	1		$\frac{1}{10}$	$\frac{1}{100}$	$\frac{1}{1000}$	$\frac{1}{10,000}$	$\frac{1}{100,000}$

4.265 means

$$4 \cdot 1 + 2 \cdot \frac{1}{10} + 6 \cdot \frac{1}{100} + 5 \cdot \frac{1}{1000}$$

or

$$4 + \frac{2}{10} + \frac{6}{100} + \frac{5}{1000}$$

WRITING (OR READING) A DECIMAL IN WORDS

Step 1. Write the whole number part in words.

Step 2. Write "and" for the decimal point.

Step 3. Write the decimal part in words as though it were a whole number, followed by the place value of the last digit.

Write 3.08 in words.
Three and eight hundredths

A decimal written in words can be written in standard form by reversing the above procedure.

Write "four and twenty-one thousandths" in standard form.

4.021

DEFINITIONS AND CONCEPTS	**EXAMPLES**

Section 4.2   Order and Rounding

To **compare decimals,** compare digits in the same place from left to right. When two digits are not equal, the number with the larger digit is the larger decimal.

$$3.0261 > 3.0186 \text{ because}$$

$$\begin{array}{ccc} \uparrow & & \uparrow \\ 2 & > & 1 \end{array}$$

TO ROUND DECIMALS TO A PLACE VALUE TO THE RIGHT OF THE DECIMAL POINT

Step 1. Locate the digit to the right of the given place value.

Step 2. If this digit is 5 or greater, add 1 to the digit in the given place value and delete all digits to its right. If this digit is less than 5, delete all digits to the right of the given place value.

Round 86.1256 to the nearest hundredth.

hundredths place

Step 1. 86.12⑤6

digit to the right

Step 2. Since the digit to the right is 5 or greater, we add 1 to the digit in the hundredths place and delete all digits to its right.

86.1256 rounded to the nearest hundredth is 86.13.

Section 4.3   Adding and Subtracting Decimals

TO ADD OR SUBTRACT DECIMALS

Step 1. Write the decimals so that the decimal points line up vertically.

Step 2. Add or subtract as with whole numbers.

Step 3. Place the decimal point in the sum or difference so that it lines up vertically with the decimal points in the problem.

Add: 4.6 + 0.28   Subtract: 2.8 − 1.04

$$\begin{array}{r} 4.60 \\ +0.28 \\ \hline 4.88 \end{array} \qquad \begin{array}{r} {}^{7\,10} \\ 2.8\cancel{0} \\ -1.04 \\ \hline 1.76 \end{array}$$

Section 4.4   Multiplying Decimals and Circumference of a Circle

TO MULTIPLY DECIMALS

Step 1. Multiply the decimals as though they are whole numbers.

Step 2. The decimal point in the product is placed so that the number of decimal places in the product is equal to the *sum* of the number of decimal places in the factors.

Multiply: 1.48 × 5.9

$$\begin{array}{r} 1.4\,8 \leftarrow 2 \text{ decimal places} \\ \times\ \ 5.9 \leftarrow 1 \text{ decimal place} \\ \hline 1\,3\,3\,2 \\ 7\,4\,0\,0 \\ \hline 8.7\,3\,2 \leftarrow 3 \text{ decimal places} \end{array}$$

The **circumference** of a circle is the distance around the circle.

$C = 2 \cdot \pi \cdot \text{radius or}$
$C = \pi \cdot \text{diameter},$

where $\pi \approx 3.14$ or $\dfrac{22}{7}$.

Find the exact circumference of a circle with radius 5 miles and an approximation by using 3.14 for π.

$$\begin{aligned} C &= 2 \cdot \pi \cdot \text{radius} \\ &= 2 \cdot \pi \cdot 5 \\ &= 10\pi \\ &\approx 10(3.14) \\ &= 31.4 \end{aligned}$$

The circumference is exactly 10π miles and *approximately* 31.4 miles.

continued

DEFINITIONS AND CONCEPTS	EXAMPLES
Section 4.5 Dividing Decimals and Order of Operations	

TO DIVIDE DECIMALS

Step 1. If the divisor is not a whole number, move the decimal point in the divisor to the right until the divisor is a whole number.

Step 2. Move the decimal point in the dividend to the right the *same number of places* as the decimal point was moved in Step 1.

Step 3. Divide. The decimal point in the quotient is directly over the moved decimal point in the dividend.

ORDER OF OPERATIONS

1. Perform all operations within parentheses ( ), brackets [ ], or grouping symbols such as square roots or fraction bars.
2. Evaluate any expressions with exponents.
3. Multiply or divide in order from left to right.
4. Add or subtract in order from left to right.

Divide: $1.118 \div 2.6$

$$
\begin{array}{r}
0.43 \\
2.6\overline{)1.118} \\
-1\,04 \\
\hline
78 \\
-78 \\
\hline
0
\end{array}
$$

Simplify.

$$1.9(12.8 - 4.1) = 1.9(8.7) \quad \text{Subtract.}$$
$$= 16.53 \quad \text{Multiply.}$$

Section 4.6 Fractions and Decimals	

To **write fractions as decimals,** divide the numerator by the denominator.

Write $\dfrac{3}{8}$ as a decimal.

$$
\begin{array}{r}
0.375 \\
8\overline{)3.000} \\
-2\,4 \\
\hline
60 \\
-56 \\
\hline
40 \\
-40 \\
\hline
0
\end{array}
$$

 STUDY SKILLS BUILDER

Are You Prepared for a Test on Chapter 4?

Below I have listed some *common trouble areas* for students in Chapter 4. After studying for your test—but before taking your test—read these.

- Don't forget the order of operations. To simplify $0.7 + 1.3(5 - 0.1)$, should you add, subtract, or multiply first? First, perform the subtraction within parentheses, then multiply, and finally add.

$$0.7 + 1.3(5 - 0.1) = 0.7 + 1.3(4.9) \quad \text{Subtract.}$$
$$= 0.7 + 6.37 \quad \text{Multiply.}$$
$$= 7.07 \quad \text{Add.}$$

- If you are having trouble with ordering or operations on decimals, don't forget that you can insert 0s after

the last digit to the right of the decimal point as needed.

Addition	Addition with zeros inserted	Subtraction	Subtraction with zeros inserted
8.1	8.100	7	$\overset{\overset{9}{6}\,\cancel{10}\,10}{\cancel{7}.\cancel{0}\cancel{0}}$
0.6	0.600	-0.28	-0.28
$+23.003$	$+23.003$		6.72
	31.703		

Place in order from smallest to largest: 0.108, 0.18, 0.0092
If we insert zeros, we have: 0.1080, 0.1800, 0.0092
The decimals in order are: 0.0092, 0.1080, 0.1800 or 0.0092, 0.108, 0.18

4 CHAPTER REVIEW

(4.1) *Determine the place value of the digit 4 in each decimal.*

1. 23.45

2. 0.000345

Write each decimal in words.

3. 0.45

4. 0.00345

5. 109.23

6. 46.007

Write each decimal in standard form.

7. Two and fifteen hundredths

8. Five hundred three and one hundred two thousandths

Write the decimal as a fraction or a mixed number. Write your answer in simplest form.

9. 0.16

10. 12.023

11. 1.0045

12. 25.25

Write each fraction as a decimal.

13. $\dfrac{9}{10}$

14. $\dfrac{25}{100}$

15. $\dfrac{45}{1000}$

16. $\dfrac{261}{10}$

(4.2) *Insert* $<$, $>$, *or* $=$ *to make a true statement.*

17. 0.49   0.43

18. 0.973   0.9730

Write the decimals in order from smallest to largest.

19. 8.6, 8.09, 0.92

20. 0.09, 0.1, 0.091

Round each decimal to the given place value.

21. 0.623, nearest tenth

22. 0.9384, nearest hundredth

Round each money amount to the nearest cent.

23. $0.259

24. $12.461

Solve.

25. Every day in America an average of 13,490.5 people get married. Round this number to the nearest whole.

26. A certain kind of chocolate candy bar contains 10.75 teaspoons of sugar. Write this number as a mixed number.

(4.3) *Add or subtract as indicated.*

27. 2.4 + 7.12

28. 3.9 − 1.2

29. 6.4 + 0.88

30. 19.02 + 6.98 + 0.007

31. 892.1 − 432.4

32. 100.342 − 0.064

33. Subtract 34.98 from 100.

34. Subtract 10.02 from 200.

35. Find the total distance between Grove City and Jerome.

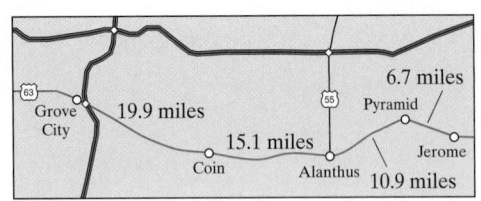

36. The price of oil was $49.02 per barrel on October 23. It was $51.46 on October 24. Find by how much the price of oil increased from the 23rd to the 24th.

△ **37.** Find the perimeter.

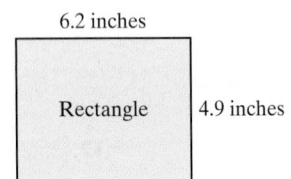

38. Find the perimeter.

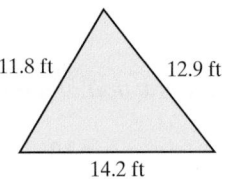

(4.4) *Multiply.*

39. 3.7
     × 5

40. 9.1
     × 6

41. 7.2 × 10

42. 9.345 × 1000

43. 4.02
     × 2.3

44. 39.02
     × 87.3

Solve.

△ **45.** Find the exact circumference of the circle. Then use the approximation 3.14 for π and approximate the circumference.

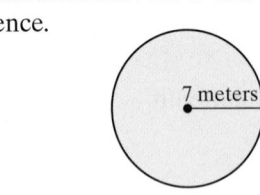

46. A kilometer is approximately 0.625 mile. It is 102 kilometers from Hays to Colby. Write 102 kilometers in miles to the nearest tenth of a mile.

Write each number in standard notation.

47. Saturn is a distance of about 887 million miles from the Sun.

48. The tail of a comet can be over 600 thousand miles long.

(4.5) *Divide. Round the quotient to the nearest thousandth if necessary.*

49. 3)$\overline{0.2631}$

50. 20)$\overline{316.5}$

51. 21 ÷ 0.3

52. 0.0063 ÷ 0.03

53. $0.34\overline{)2.74}$ **54.** $19.8\overline{)601.92}$ **55.** $\dfrac{2.67}{100}$ **56.** $\dfrac{93}{10}$

57. There are approximately 3.28 feet in 1 meter. Find how many meters are in 24 feet to the nearest tenth of a meter.

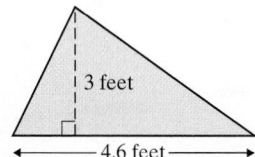
≈3.28 feet

58. George Strait pays $69.71 per month to pay back a loan of $3136.95. In how many months will the loan be paid off?

Simplify each expression.

59. $7.6 \times 1.9 + 2.5$ **60.** $(2.3)^2 - 1.4$ **61.** $\dfrac{7 + 0.74}{0.06}$

62. $0.9(6.5 - 5.6)$ **63.** $\dfrac{(1.5)^2 + 0.5}{0.05}$ **64.** $0.0726 \div 10 \times 1000$

(4.6) *Write each fraction as a decimal. Round to the nearest thousandth if necessary.*

65. $\dfrac{4}{5}$ **66.** $\dfrac{12}{13}$ **67.** $2\dfrac{1}{3}$ **68.** $\dfrac{13}{60}$

Insert $<$, $>$, or $=$ to make a true statement.

69. $0.392 \quad 0.392$ **70.** $\dfrac{4}{7} \quad 0.625$ **71.** $0.293 \quad \dfrac{5}{17}$

Write the numbers in order from smallest to largest.

72. $0.837, 0.839, \dfrac{17}{20}$ **73.** $\dfrac{3}{7}, 0.42, 0.43$ **74.** $\dfrac{18}{11}, 1.63, \dfrac{19}{12}$

Find each area.

△ **75.**

3 feet

4.6 feet

△ **76.**

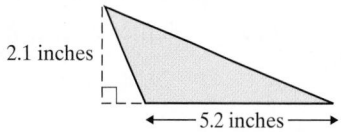
2.1 inches

5.2 inches

Mixed Review

77. Write 200.0032 in words.

78. Write sixteen thousand twenty-five and fourteen thousandths in standard form.

79. Write 0.00231 as a fraction or a mixed number.

80. Write the numbers $\dfrac{6}{7}, \dfrac{8}{9}, 0.75$ in order from smallest to largest.

Write each fraction as a decimal. Round to the nearest thousandth, if necessary.

81. $\dfrac{7}{100}$ **82.** $\dfrac{9}{80}$ (Do not round.)   **83.** $\dfrac{8935}{175}$

Insert $<, >,$ or $=$ to make a true statement.

84. 402.00032   402.000032   **85.** 0.230505   0.23505   **86.** $\dfrac{6}{11}$ 0.55

Round each decimal to the given place value.

87. 42.895, nearest hundredth   **88.** 16.34925, nearest thousandth

Round each money amount to the nearest dollar.

89. $123.46, nearest dollar   **90.** $3645.52, nearest dollar

Add or subtract as indicated.

91. $4.9 - 3.2$ **92.** $5.23 - 2.74$

93. $200.49 + 16.82 + 103.002$ **94.** $0.00236 + 100.45 + 48.29$

Multiply or divide as indicated. Round to the nearest thousandth, if necessary.

95. $\begin{array}{r} 2.54 \\ \times\ 3.2 \\ \hline \end{array}$ **96.** $\begin{array}{r} 3.45 \\ \times\ 2.1 \\ \hline \end{array}$ **97.** $0.005\overline{)24.5}$ **98.** $2.3\overline{)54.98}$

Solve.

△ **99.** Tomaso is going to fertilize his lawn, a rectangle that measures 77.3 feet by 115.9 feet. Approximate the area of the lawn by rounding each measurement to the nearest ten feet.

100. Estimate the cost of the items to see whether the groceries can be purchased with a $5 bill.

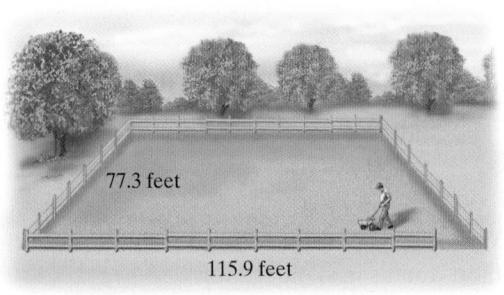

Simplify each expression.

101. $\dfrac{(3.2)^2}{100}$ **102.** $(2.6 + 1.4)(4.5 - 3.6)$

4 CHAPTER TEST

 Use the Chapter Test Prep Video CD to see the fully worked-out solutions to any of the exercises you want to review.

Write the decimal as indicated.

1. 45.092, in words

2. Three thousand and fifty-nine thousandths, in standard form

Round the decimal to the indicated place value.

3. 34.8923, nearest tenth

4. 0.8623, nearest thousandth

5. Insert $<$, $>$, or $=$ to make a true statement. 25.0909   25.9090

6. Write the numbers in order from smallest to largest. $\dfrac{4}{9}$ 0.454   0.445

Write the decimal as a fraction or a mixed number in simplest form.

7. 0.345

8. 24.73

Write the fraction or mixed number as a decimal. If necessary, round to the nearest thousandth.

9. $\dfrac{13}{20}$

10. $5\dfrac{8}{9}$

11. $\dfrac{16}{17}$

Perform the indicated operations. Round the result to the nearest thousandth if necessary.

12. $2.893 + 4.2 + 10.49$

13. Subtract 8.6 from 20.

14. $\begin{array}{r} 10.2 \\ \times\ \ 4.3 \\ \hline \end{array}$

15. $0.23\overline{)12.88}$

16. $\begin{array}{r} 0.165 \\ \times\ 0.47 \\ \hline \end{array}$

17. $7\overline{)46.71}$

1. _____

2. _____

3. _____

4. _____

5. _____

6. _____

7. _____

8. _____

9. _____

10. _____

11. _____

12. _____

13. _____

14. _____

15. _____

16. _____

17. _____

18. _____

18. 126.9×100

19. $\dfrac{47.3}{10}$

19. _____

20. $0.3[1.57 - (0.6)^2]$

21. $\dfrac{0.23 + 1.63}{0.3}$

20. _____

22. At its farthest, Pluto is 4,583 million miles from the Sun. Write this number using standard notation.

21. _____

△ **23.** Find the area.

△ **24.** Find the exact circumference of the circle. Then use the approximation 3.14 for π and approximate the circumference.

22. _____

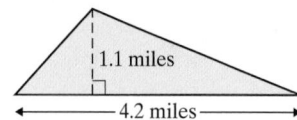

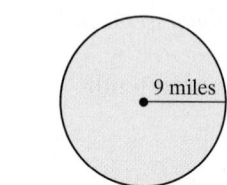

23. _____

24. _____

25. Vivian Thomas is going to put insecticide on her lawn to control grubworms. The lawn is a rectangle that measures 123.8 feet by 80 feet. The amount of insecticide required is 0.02 ounces per square foot.

   a. Find the area of her lawn.

25. a. _____

   b. Find how much insecticide Vivian needs to purchase.

b. _____

26. Find the total distance from Bayette to Center City.

26. _____

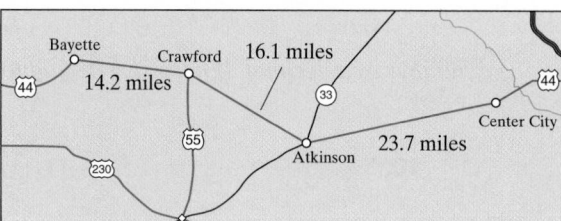

Answers

1. Write 106,052,447 in words.

2. Write two hundred seventy-six thousand, four in standard form.

3. The governor's salary in the state of Alabama was recently increased by $1706. If the old salary was $94,655, find the new salary. (*Source: The World Almanac and Book of Facts,* 2003 and 2005)

4. There are 12 fluid ounces of soda in a can. How many fluid ounces of soda are in a case (24 cans) of soda?

5. Subtract: $900 - 174$. Then check by adding.

6. Simplify: $5^2 \cdot 2^3$

7. Round each number to the nearest hundred to find an estimated sum.

$$
\begin{array}{r}
294 \\
625 \\
1071 \\
+\ 349 \\
\end{array}
$$

8. Simplify: $7 \cdot \sqrt{144}$

9. A digital video disc (DVD) can hold about 4800 megabytes (MB) of information. How many megabytes can 12 DVDs hold?

10. Find the perimeter and area of the square.

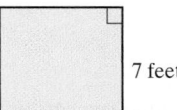

7 feet

11. Divide: $6819 \div 17$

12. Write $2\dfrac{5}{8}$ as an improper fraction.

13. Simplify: $4^3 + [3^2 - (10 \div 2)] - 7 \cdot 3$

14. Write $\dfrac{64}{5}$ as a mixed number.

15. Identify the numerator and the denominator: $\dfrac{3}{7}$

16. Simplify: $24 \div 8 \cdot 3$

17. Write $\dfrac{6}{60}$ in simplest form.

18. Simplify: $(8 - 5)^2 + (10 - 8)^3$

1. _____

2. _____

3. _____

4. _____

5. _____

6. _____

7. _____

8. _____

9. _____

10. _____

11. _____

12. _____

13. _____

14. _____

15. _____

16. _____

17. _____

18. _____

19. Multiply: $\dfrac{3}{4} \cdot 20$

20. Simplify: $1 + 2[30 \div (7 - 2)]$

21. Divide: $\dfrac{7}{8} \div \dfrac{2}{9}$

22. Find the average of 117, 125, and 142.

23. Multiply: $1\dfrac{2}{3} \cdot 2\dfrac{1}{4}$

24. A total of $324 is paid for 36 tickets to the Audubon Zoo. How much did each ticket cost?

25. Divide: $\dfrac{3}{4} \div 5$

26. Simplify: $\left(\dfrac{3}{4} \div \dfrac{1}{2}\right) \cdot \dfrac{9}{10}$

Simplify.

27. $\dfrac{8}{9} - \dfrac{1}{9}$

28. $\dfrac{4}{15} + \dfrac{2}{15}$

29. $\dfrac{7}{8} - \dfrac{5}{8}$

30. $\dfrac{1}{20} + \dfrac{3}{20} + \dfrac{4}{20}$

Write an equivalent fraction with the indicated denominator.

31. $\dfrac{3}{4} = \dfrac{}{20}$

32. $\dfrac{7}{9} = \dfrac{}{45}$

Perform the indicated operations.

33. $\dfrac{2}{15} + \dfrac{3}{10}$

34. $\dfrac{7}{30} - \dfrac{2}{9}$

35. Sarah Grahamm purchases two packages of ground round. One package weighs $2\dfrac{3}{8}$ pounds and the other $1\dfrac{4}{5}$ pounds. What is the combined weight of the ground round?

36. A color cartridge for a business printer weights $2\dfrac{5}{16}$ pounds. How much do 12 cartridges weigh?

Evaluate each expression.

37. $\left(\dfrac{1}{4}\right)^2$

38. $\left(\dfrac{7}{11}\right)^2$

19. _____

20. _____

21. _____

22. _____

23. _____

24. _____

25. _____

26. _____

27. _____

28. _____

29. _____

30. _____

31. _____

32. _____

33. _____

34. _____

35. _____

36. _____

37. _____

38. _____

39. $\left(\dfrac{1}{6}\right)^2 \cdot \left(\dfrac{3}{4}\right)^3$

40. $\left(\dfrac{1}{2}\right)^3 \cdot \left(\dfrac{4}{9}\right)^2$

41. Write 0.43 as a fraction.

42. Write $\dfrac{3}{4}$ as a decimal.

43. Insert $<$, $>$, or $=$ to form a true statement.
0.378   0.368

44. Write "five and six hundredths" in standard form.

45. Subtract: $35.218 - 23.65$
Check your answer.

46. Add: $75.1 + 0.229$

Multiply.

47. 23.702×100

48. 1.7×0.07

49. $76,805 \times 0.01$

50. Divide: $0.1157 \div 0.013$

39. _____

40. _____

41. _____

42. _____

43. _____

44. _____

45. _____

46. _____

47. _____

48. _____

49. _____

50. _____

5

Percent

This chapter is mainly devoted to percent, a concept used virtually every day in ordinary and business life. Understanding percent and using it efficiently depends on understanding ratios because a percent is a ratio whose denominator is 100. We present techniques to write percents as fractions and as decimals and then solve problems relating to sales tax, commission, discounts, interest, and other real-life situations that use percents.

The Nutrition Labeling and Education Act (NLEA) was signed into law on November 8, 1990. It requires food manufacturers to include nutrition information on their product labels. The NLEA provides specific guidelines concerning the use of terms such as "low fat," or "high fiber." Labels contain information about portion sizes, vitamins and minerals, and sodium, fat, and cholesterol content of foods. The result of this important legislation is to help consumers make more informed and healthier food choices. In Exercises 13 and 14 of Section 5.6, we will determine what percent of some foods' total calories is from fat.

Nutrition Facts		
Serving Size 18 crackers (29g)		
Servings Per Container About 9		
Amount Per Serving		
Calories 120 Calories from Fat 35		
		% Daily Value*
Total Fat 4g		**6%**
Saturated Fat 0.5g		**3%**
Polyunsaturated Fat 0g		
Monounsaturated Fat 1.5g		
Cholesterol 0mg		**0%**
Sodium 220mg		**9%**
Total Carbohydrate 21g		**7%**
Dietary Fiber 2g		**7%**
Sugars 3g		
Protein 2g		
Vitamin A 0% • Vitamin C 0%		
Calcium 2% • Iron 4%		
Phosphorus 10%		

5.1 RATIO AND PROPORTION

Objectives

A Write Ratios as Fractions.

B Write Rates as Fractions.

C Determine Whether Proportions Are True.

D Find an Unknown Number in a Proportion.

E Solve Problems by Writing Proportions.

Objective **A** Writing Ratios as Fractions

A **ratio** is the quotient of two quantities. A ratio, in fact, is no different from a fraction, except that a ratio is sometimes written using notation other than fractional notation. For example, the ratio of 1 to 2 can be written as

$$1 \text{ to } 2 \quad \text{or} \quad \frac{1}{2} \quad \text{or} \quad 1 : 2$$

fractional notation   *colon notation*

Writing a Ratio as a Fraction

The order of the quantities is important when writing ratios. To write a ratio as a fraction, write the *first number* of the ratio as the *numerator* of the fraction and the *second number* as the *denominator*.

For example, the ratio of 6 to 11 is $\frac{6}{11}$, *not* $\frac{11}{6}$.

EXAMPLE 1 Write the ratio of 12 to 17 using fractional notation.

Solution: The ratio is $\frac{12}{17}$.

> **Helpful Hint**
> Don't forget that order is important when writing ratios. The ratio $\frac{17}{12}$ is *not* the same as the ratio $\frac{12}{17}$.

Work Practice Problem 1

PRACTICE PROBLEM 1

Write the ratio of 20 to 23 using fractional notation.

To simplify a ratio, we just write the fraction in simplest form. Common factors as well as common units can be divided out.

EXAMPLE 2 Write the ratio of $15 to $10 as a fraction in simplest form.

Solution:

$$\frac{\$15}{\$10} = \frac{15}{10} = \frac{3 \cdot \cancel{5}}{2 \cdot \cancel{5}} = \frac{3}{2}$$

> **Helpful Hint**
> In this example, although $\frac{3}{2} = 1\frac{1}{2}$, a ratio is a quotient of *two* quantities. For that reason, ratios are not written as mixed numbers.

Work Practice Problem 2

PRACTICE PROBLEM 2

Write the ratio of $8 to $6 as a fraction in simplest form.

If a ratio contains decimal numbers or mixed numbers, we simplify by writing the ratio as a ratio of whole numbers.

Answers

1. $\frac{20}{23}$,   2. $\frac{4}{3}$

PRACTICE PROBLEM 3

Write the ratio of 1.71 to 4.56 as a fraction in simplest form.

EXAMPLE 3 Write the ratio of 2.6 to 3.1 as a fraction in simplest form.

Solution: The ratio in fraction form is

$$\frac{2.6}{3.1}$$

Now let's clear the ratio of decimals.

$$\frac{2.6}{3.1} = \frac{2.6}{3.1} \cdot 1 = \frac{2.6}{3.1} \cdot \frac{10}{10} = \frac{2.6 \cdot 10}{3.1 \cdot 10} = \frac{26}{31} \text{ Simplest form}$$

Work Practice Problem 3

PRACTICE PROBLEM 4

Use the circle graph below to write the ratio of work miles to total miles as a fraction in simplest form.

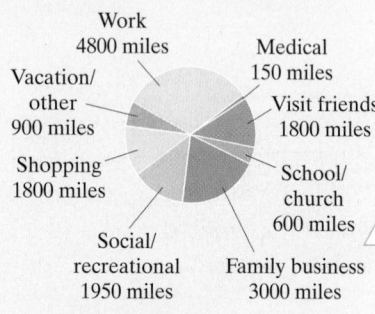

Work
4800 miles
Medical
150 miles
Vacation/
other
900 miles
Visit friends
1800 miles
Shopping
1800 miles
School/
church
600 miles
Social/
recreational
1950 miles
Family business
3000 miles

Total yearly mileage: 15,000

Sources: The American Automobile Manufacturers Association and The National Automobile Dealers Association.

EXAMPLE 4 **Writing a Ratio from a Circle Graph**

The circle graph in the margin shows the part of a car's total mileage that falls into a particular category. Write the ratio of medical miles to total miles as a fraction in simplest form.

Solution:

$$\frac{\text{medical miles}}{\text{total miles}} = \frac{150 \text{ miles}}{15,000 \text{ miles}} = \frac{150}{15,000} = \frac{\overset{1}{\cancel{150}}}{\underset{1}{\cancel{150} \cdot 100}} = \frac{1}{100}$$

Work Practice Problem 4

△ **PRACTICE PROBLEM 5**

Given the triangle shown:

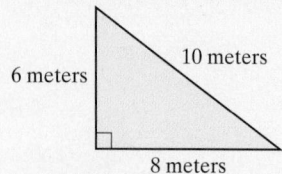

6 meters
10 meters
8 meters

a. Find the ratio of the length of the shortest side to the length of the longest side.

b. Find the ratio of the length of the longest side to the perimeter of the triangle.

△ **EXAMPLE 5** Given the rectangle shown:

a. Find the ratio of its width to its length.

b. Find the ratio of its length to its perimeter.

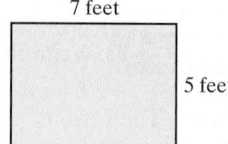

7 feet
5 feet

Solution:

a. The ratio of its width to its length is

$$\frac{\text{width}}{\text{length}} = \frac{5 \text{ feet}}{7 \text{ feet}} = \frac{5}{7}$$

b. Recall that the perimeter of the rectangle is the distance around the rectangle: $7 + 5 + 7 + 5 = 24$ feet. The ratio of its length to its perimeter is

$$\frac{\text{length}}{\text{perimeter}} = \frac{7 \text{ feet}}{24 \text{ feet}} = \frac{7}{24}$$

Work Practice Problem 5

✔ **Concept Check** Explain why the answer $\frac{7}{5}$ would be incorrect for part (a) of Example 5.

Objective B **Writing Rates as Fractions**

A special type of ratio is a rate. **Rates** are used to compare *different* kinds of quantities. For example, suppose that a recreational runner can run 3 miles in 33 minutes. If we write this rate as a fraction, we have

$$\frac{3 \text{ miles}}{33 \text{ minutes}} = \frac{1 \text{ mile}}{11 \text{ minutes}} \text{ In simplest form}$$

Answers

3. $\frac{3}{8}$, 4. $\frac{8}{25}$, 5. a. $\frac{3}{5}$, b. $\frac{5}{12}$

✔ **Concept Check Answer**

$\frac{7}{5}$ would be the ratio of the rectangle's length to its width.

Helpful Hint

When comparing quantities with different units, write the units as part of the comparison. They do not divide out.

Same Units: $\dfrac{3 \text{ inches}}{12 \text{ inches}} = \dfrac{1}{4}$

Different Units: $\dfrac{2 \text{ miles}}{20 \text{ minutes}} = \dfrac{1 \text{ mile}}{10 \text{ minutes}}$ Units are still written.

EXAMPLE 6 Write the rate as a fraction in simplest form: 10 nails every 6 feet

Solution:

$$\frac{10 \text{ nails}}{6 \text{ feet}} = \frac{5 \text{ nails}}{3 \text{ feet}}$$

■ **Work Practice Problem 6**

EXAMPLES Write each rate as a fraction in simplest form.

7. $2160 for 12 weeks is $\dfrac{2160 \text{ dollars}}{12 \text{ weeks}} = \dfrac{180 \text{ dollars}}{1 \text{ week}}$

8. 360 miles on 16 gallons of gasoline is $\dfrac{360 \text{ miles}}{16 \text{ gallons}} = \dfrac{45 \text{ miles}}{2 \text{ gallons}}$

■ **Work Practice Problems 7–8**

Note: A **unit rate** is a rate with a denominator of 1. A familiar example of a unit rate is mph, read as **"miles per hour."** For example, 55 mph means 55 miles per 1 hour or $\dfrac{55 \text{ miles}}{1 \text{ hour}}$.

If we write the rate in Example 8 as a unit rate, we have

Helpful Hint In this context, the word "per" translates to division.

$$\frac{45 \text{ miles}}{2 \text{ gallons}} = \frac{22.5 \text{ miles}}{1 \text{ gallon}} \text{ or } 22.5 \text{ miles/gallon}$$

Objective C Determining Whether Proportions Are True

A **proportion** is a statement that 2 ratios or rates are equal. For example,

$$\frac{5}{6} = \frac{10}{12}$$

is a proportion. We can read this as, "5 is to 6 as 10 is to 12."

Let's write each sentence as a proportion.

"12 diamonds is to 15 rubies as 4 diamonds is to 5 rubies" translates to

$$\begin{array}{ccc} \text{diamonds} & \rightarrow & \dfrac{12}{15} = \dfrac{4}{5} \leftarrow \text{diamonds} \\ \text{rubies} & \rightarrow & \leftarrow \text{rubies} \end{array}$$

"5 hits is to 9 at bats as 20 hits is to 36 at bats" translates to

$$\begin{array}{ccc} \text{hits} & \rightarrow & \dfrac{5}{9} = \dfrac{20}{36} \leftarrow \text{hits} \\ \text{at bats} & \rightarrow & \leftarrow \text{at bats} \end{array}$$

PRACTICE PROBLEM 6

Write the rate as a fraction in simplest form: 12 commercials every 45 minutes

PRACTICE PROBLEMS 7–8

Write each rate as a fraction in simplest form.

7. $1680 for 8 weeks

8. 236 miles on 12 gallons of gasoline

Answers

6. $\dfrac{4 \text{ commercials}}{15 \text{ min}}$, **7.** $\dfrac{\$210}{1 \text{ wk}}$,

8. $\dfrac{59 \text{ mi}}{3 \text{ gal}}$

Helpful Hint

Notice in the previous proportions that the numerators contain the same units and the denominators contain the same units. In this text, proportions will be written so that this is the case.

Like other mathematical statements, a proportion may be either true or false. A proportion is true if its ratios are equal. Since ratios are fractions, one way to determine whether a proportion is true is to write both fractions in simplest form and compare them.

Another way is to compare cross products as we did in Section 2.3.

Using Cross Products to Determine Whether Proportions Are True or False

Cross products

$a \cdot d$ $b \cdot c$

$$\frac{a}{b} = \frac{c}{d}$$

If cross products are *equal*, the proportion is *true*.

If $ad = bc$, then the proportion is true.

If cross products are *not equal*, the proportion is *false*.

If $ad \neq bc$, then the proportion is false.

PRACTICE PROBLEM 9

Is $\dfrac{3}{6} = \dfrac{4}{8}$ a true proportion?

EXAMPLE 9 Is $\dfrac{2}{3} = \dfrac{4}{6}$ a true proportion?

Solution:

Cross products

$2 \cdot 6$ $3 \cdot 4$

$$\frac{2}{3} = \frac{4}{6}$$

$2 \cdot 6 \stackrel{?}{=} 3 \cdot 4$ Are cross products equal?

$12 = 12$ Equal, so proportion is true.

Since the cross products are equal, the proportion is true.

Work Practice Problem 9

PRACTICE PROBLEM 10

Is $\dfrac{3.6}{6} = \dfrac{5.4}{8}$ a true proportion?

EXAMPLE 10 Is $\dfrac{4.1}{7} = \dfrac{2.9}{5}$ a true proportion?

Solution:

Cross products

$4.1 \cdot 5$ $7 \cdot 2.9$

$$\frac{4.1}{7} = \frac{2.9}{5}$$

$4.1 \cdot 5 \stackrel{?}{=} 7 \cdot 2.9$ Are cross products equal?

$20.5 \neq 20.3$ Not equal, so proportion is false.

Since the cross products are not equal, $\dfrac{4.1}{7} \neq \dfrac{2.9}{5}$. The proportion is false.

Work Practice Problem 10

Answers

9. yes,   **10.** no

Objective D Finding Unknown Numbers in Proportions

When one number of a proportion is unknown, we can use cross products to find the unknown number. For example, to find the unknown number n in the proportion $\dfrac{n}{30} = \dfrac{2}{3}$, we first find the cross products.

$n \cdot 3$ $30 \cdot 2$ Find the cross products.

$$\frac{n}{30} = \frac{2}{3}$$

If the proportion is true, then cross products are equal.

$n \cdot 3 = 30 \cdot 2$ Set the cross products equal to each other.

$n \cdot 3 = 60$ Write $2 \cdot 30$ as 60.

To find the unknown number n, we ask ourselves, "What number times 3 is 60?" The number is 20 and can be found by dividing 60 by 3.

$n = \dfrac{60}{3}$ Divide 60 by the number multiplied by n.

$n = 20$ Simplify.

Thus, the unknown number is 20.

To *check,* replace n with this value, 20, and verify that a true proportion results.

Finding an Unknown Value n in a Proportion

Step 1: Set the cross products equal to each other.

Step 2: Divide the number not multiplied by n by the number multiplied by n.

EXAMPLE 11 Find the value of the unknown number n.

$$\frac{51}{34} = \frac{3}{n}$$

Solution:

Step 1:

$$\frac{51}{34} = \frac{3}{n}$$

$51 \cdot n = 34 \cdot 3$ Set cross products equal.

$51 \cdot n = 102$ Multiply.

Step 2:

$n = \dfrac{102}{51}$ Divide 102 by 51, the number multiplied by n.

$n = 2$ Simplify.

Check to see that 2 is the unknown number n.

■ **Work Practice Problem 11**

PRACTICE PROBLEM 11

Find the value of the unknown number n.

$$\frac{15}{2} = \frac{60}{n}$$

Answer

11. $n = 8$

PRACTICE PROBLEM 12

Find the unknown number n.

$$\frac{8}{n} = \frac{5}{9}$$

EXAMPLE 12 Find the unknown number n.

$$\frac{7}{n} = \frac{6}{5}$$

Solution:

Step 1:

$$\frac{7}{n} = \frac{6}{5}$$

$7 \cdot 5 = n \cdot 6$ Set the cross products equal to each other.
$35 = n \cdot 6$ Multiply.

Step 2:

$$\frac{35}{6} = n$$ Divide 35 by 6, the number multiplied by n.

$$5\frac{5}{6} = n$$

Check to see that $5\frac{5}{6}$ is the unknown number.

⬛ **Work Practice Problem 12**

PRACTICE PROBLEM 13

Find the unknown number n.

$$\frac{n}{6} = \frac{0.7}{1.2}$$

EXAMPLE 13 Find the unknown number n.

$$\frac{n}{3} = \frac{0.8}{1.5}$$

Solution:

Step 1:

$$\frac{n}{3} = \frac{0.8}{1.5}$$

$n \cdot 1.5 = 3 \cdot 0.8$ Set the cross products equal to each other.
$n \cdot 1.5 = 2.4$ Multiply.

Step 2:

$$n = \frac{2.4}{1.5}$$ Divide 2.4 by 1.5, the number multiplied by n.

$$n = 1.6$$ Simplify.

Check to see that 1.6 is the unknown number.

⬛ **Work Practice Problem 13**

Answers

12. $n = 14\frac{2}{5}$, **13.** $n = 3.5$

Objective E Solving Problems by Writing Proportions

EXAMPLE 14 Finding Medicine Dosage

The standard dose of an antibiotic is 4 cc (cubic centimeters) for every 25 pounds (lb) of body weight. At this rate, find the standard dose for a 140-lb woman.

Solution:

1. UNDERSTAND. Read and reread the problem. You may want to draw a diagram such as the one below to estimate a reasonable solution. From the diagram, we can see that a reasonable solution is a little over 20 cc.

140–pound woman

25 pounds $\longrightarrow$ 4 cc

25 pounds $\longrightarrow$ 4 cc

25 pounds $\longrightarrow$ 4 cc

25 pounds $\longrightarrow$ 4 cc

25 pounds $\longrightarrow$ 4 cc

15 pounds $\longrightarrow$?

$\overline{140 \text{ pounds}}$ over $\overline{20 \text{ cc}}$

2. TRANSLATE. We will let n represent the unknown number. From the problem, we know that 4 cc is to 25 pounds as n cc is to 140 pounds, or

cubic centimeters $\rightarrow$ $\dfrac{4}{25} = \dfrac{n}{140}$ $\leftarrow$ cubic centimeters
pounds $\rightarrow$ $\phantom{\dfrac{4}{25} = \dfrac{n}{140}}$ $\leftarrow$ pounds

3. SOLVE:

$$\dfrac{4}{25} = \dfrac{n}{140}$$

$4 \cdot 140 = 25 \cdot n$ Set the cross products equal to each other.

$560 = 25 \cdot n$ Multiply.

$\dfrac{560}{25} = n$ Divide 560 by 25, the number multiplied by n.

$n = 22\dfrac{2}{5}$ or 22.4 Simplify.

4. INTERPRET. *Check* your work. This result is reasonable since it is a little over 20 cc. *State* your conclusion: The standard dose for a 140-lb woman is 22.4 cc.

🔲 **Work Practice Problem 14**

PRACTICE PROBLEM 14

An auto mechanic recommends that 3 ounces of isopropyl alcohol be mixed with a tankful of gas (14 gallons) to increase the octane of the gasoline for better engine performance. At this rate, how many gallons of gas can be treated with a 16-ounce bottle of alcohol?

Answer

14. $74\dfrac{2}{3}$ or $74.\overline{6}$ gal

5.1 EXERCISE SET

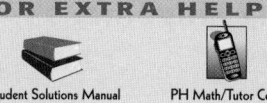

Objective A *Write each ratio using fractional notation. Do not simplify. See Examples 1 through 3.*

1. 23 to 10

2. 14 to 5

3. $3\frac{3}{4}$ to $1\frac{2}{3}$

4. $2\frac{2}{5}$ to $6\frac{1}{2}$

Write each ratio as a ratio of whole numbers using fractional notation. Write the fraction in simplest form. See Examples 1 through 3.

5. 16 to 24

6. 25 to 150

7. 7.7 to 10

8. 8.1 to 10

9. 10 hours to 24 hours

10. 18 quarts to 30 quarts

11. $32 to $100

12. $46 to $102

13. 24 days to 14 days

14. 80 miles to 120 miles

15. 32,000 bytes to 46,000 bytes

16. 600 copies to 150 copies

17. 8 inches to 20 inches

18. 9 yards to 2 yards

Find the ratio described in each exercise as a fraction in simplest form. See Examples 4 and 5.

19. Find the ratio of the longest side to the perimeter of the right-triangular-shaped billboard.

20. Find the ratio of the width to the perimeter of the rectangular vegetable garden.

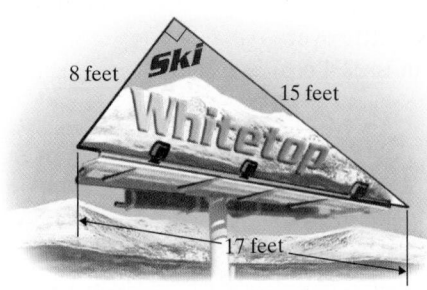

8 feet   SKI   15 feet   Whitetop   17 feet

4.5 meters   2 meters

At the Honey Island Parent Teacher Organization meeting one night, there were 125 women and 100 men present.

21. Find the ratio of women to men.

22. Find the ratio of men to the total number of people present.

328

23. Of the U.S. mountains that are over 14,000 feet in elevation, 57 are located in Colorado and 19 are located in Alaska. Find the ratio of the number of mountains over 14,000 feet found in Alaska to the number of mountains over 14,000 feet found in Colorado. (*Source:* U.S. Geological Survey)

24. Citizens of the United States eat an average of 25 pints of ice cream per year. Residents of the New England states eat an average of 39 pints of ice cream per year. Find the ratio of the amount of ice cream eaten by New Englanders to the amount eaten by the average U.S. citizen. (*Source:* International Dairy Foods Association)

Objective B *Write each rate as a fraction in simplest form. See Examples 6 through 8.*

25. 5 shrubs every 15 feet

26. 14 lab tables for 28 students

27. 15 returns for 100 sales

28. 150 graduate students for 8 advisors

29. 8 phone lines for 36 employees

30. 6 laser printers for 28 computers

31. 18 gallons of pesticide for 4 acres of crops

32. 4 inches of rain in 18 hours

33. 6 flight attendants for 200 passengers

34. 240 pounds of grass seed for 9 lawns

35. 355 calories in a 10-fluid-ounce chocolate milkshake (*Source: Home and Garden Bulletin No. 72,* U.S. Department of Agriculture)

36. 160 calories in an 8-fluid-ounce serving of cream of tomato soup (*Source: Home and Garden Bulletin No. 72,* U.S. Department of Agriculture)

Write each rate as a unit rate.

37. 330 calories in a 3-ounce serving

38. 275 miles in 11 hours

39. A hummingbird moves its wings at a rate of 5400 wingbeats a minute write this rate in wingbeats per second.

40. A bat moves its wings at a rate of 1200 wingbeats a minute. Write this rate in wingbeats per second.

Objective **C** *Determine whether each proportion is a true proportion. See Examples 9 and 10.*

41. $\dfrac{8}{6} = \dfrac{9}{7}$ **42.** $\dfrac{7}{12} = \dfrac{4}{7}$ **43.** $\dfrac{9}{36} = \dfrac{2}{8}$ **44.** $\dfrac{8}{24} = \dfrac{3}{9}$

Write each sentence as a proportion. Then determine whether the proportion is a true proportion. See Examples 9 and 10.

45. one and eight tenths is to two as four and five tenths is to five

46. fifteen hundredths is to three as thirty-five hundredths is to seven

47. two thirds is to one fifth as two fifths is to one ninth

48. ten elevenths is to three fourths as one fourth is to one half

Objective **D** *For each proportion, find the unknown number n. See Examples 11 through 13.*

49. $\dfrac{n}{5} = \dfrac{6}{10}$ **50.** $\dfrac{n}{3} = \dfrac{12}{9}$ **51.** $\dfrac{18}{54} = \dfrac{3}{n}$ **52.** $\dfrac{25}{100} = \dfrac{7}{n}$

53. $\dfrac{n}{8} = \dfrac{50}{100}$ **54.** $\dfrac{n}{21} = \dfrac{12}{18}$ **55.** $\dfrac{8}{15} = \dfrac{n}{6}$ **56.** $\dfrac{12}{10} = \dfrac{n}{16}$

57. $\dfrac{0.05}{12} = \dfrac{n}{0.6}$ **58.** $\dfrac{7.8}{13} = \dfrac{n}{2.6}$ **59.** $\dfrac{8}{1\frac{1}{3}} = \dfrac{24}{n}$ **60.** $\dfrac{12}{\frac{3}{4}} = \dfrac{48}{n}$

61. $\dfrac{n}{1\frac{1}{5}} = \dfrac{4\frac{1}{6}}{6\frac{2}{3}}$ **62.** $\dfrac{n}{3\frac{1}{8}} = \dfrac{7\frac{3}{5}}{2\frac{3}{8}}$ **63.** $\dfrac{25}{n} = \dfrac{3}{\frac{7}{30}}$ **64.** $\dfrac{9}{n} = \dfrac{5}{\frac{11}{15}}$

Objective **E** *Solve. See Example 14.*

It takes Sandra Hallahan 30 minutes to word process and spell check 4 pages.

65. Find how long it takes her to word process and spell check 22 pages.

66. Find how many pages she can word process and spell check in 4.5 hours.

On an architect's blueprint, 1 inch corresponds to 8 feet.

67. Find the length of a wall represented by a line $2\frac{7}{8}$ inches long on the blueprint.

68. Find the length of a wall represented by a line $5\frac{1}{4}$ inches on the blueprint.

The scale on an Italian map states that 1 centimeter corresponds to 30 kilometers.

69. Find how far apart Milan and Rome are if their corresponding points on the map are 15 centimeters apart.

70. On the map, a small Italian village is located 0.4 centimeter from the Mediterranean Sea. Find the actual distance.

A Honda Civic averages 450 miles on a 12-gallon tank of gas.

71. If Dave Smythe runs out of gas in a Honda Civic and AAA comes to his rescue with $1\frac{1}{2}$ gallons of gas, determine how far he can go. Round to the nearest mile.

72. Find how many gallons of gas Denise Wolcott can expect to burn on a 2000-mile vacation trip in a Honda Civic. Round to the nearest gallon.

73. A student would like to estimate the height of the Statue of Liberty in New York City's harbor. The length of the Statue of Liberty's right arm is 42 feet. The student's right arm is 2 feet long and her height is $5\frac{1}{3}$ feet. Use this information to estimate the height of the Statue of Liberty. How close is your estimate to the statue's actual height of 111 feet, 1 inch from heel to top of head? (*Source:* National Park Service)

74. The length of the Statue of Liberty's index finger is 8 feet while the height to the top of the head is about 111 feet. Suppose your measurements are proportionaly the same as this statue and your height is 5 feet.

  a. Use this information to find the proposed length of your index finger. Give an exact measurement and then a decimal rounded to the nearest hundredth.

  b. Measure your index finger and write it as decimal in feet rounded to the nearest hundredth. How close is the length of your index finger to the answer to **a**? Explain why.

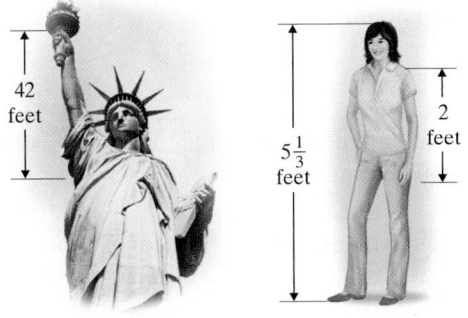

75. The daily supply of oxygen for one person is provided by 625 square feet of lawn. A total of 3750 square feet of lawn would provide the daily supply of oxygen for how many people? (*Source:* Professional Lawn Care Association of America)

76. In the United States, approximately 71 million of the 200 million cars and light trucks in service have driver-side air bags. In a parking lot containing 800 cars and light trucks, how many would be expected to have driver-side air bags? (*Source:* Insurance Institute for Highway Safety)

77. The adult daily dosage for a certain medicine is 150 mg (milligrams) of medicine for every 20 pounds of body weight.

    a. At this rate, find the daily dose for a man who weighs 275 pounds.

    b. If the man is to receive 500 mg of this medicine every 8 hours, is he receiving the proper dosage?

78. The adult daily dosage for a certain medicine is 80 mg (milligrams) for every 25 pounds of body weight.

    a. At this rate, find the daily dose for a woman who weighs 190 pounds.

    b. If she is to receive this medicine every 6 hours, find the amount to be given every 6 hours.

79. The gas/oil ratio for a certain chainsaw is 50 to 1.

    a. How much oil (in gallons) should be mixed with 5 gallons of gasoline?

    b. If 1 gallon equals 128 fluid ounces, write the answer to part **a** in fluid ounces. Round to the nearest whole ounce.

80. The gas/oil ratio for a certain tractor mower is 20 to 1.

    a. How much oil (in gallons) should be mixed with 10 gallons of gas?

    b. If 1 gallon equals 4 quarts, write the answer to part **a** in quarts.

Review

Find the prime factorization of each number. See Section 2.2.

81. 20   **82.** 24   **83.** 200   **84.** 300   **85.** 32   **86.** 81

Concept Extensions

As we have seen earlier, proportions are often used in medicine dosage calculations. The exercises below have to do with liquid drug preparations, where the weight of the drug is contained in a volume of solution. The description of mg and ml below will help.

mg means milligrams (A paper clip weighs about a gram. A milligram is about the weight of $\frac{1}{1000}$ of a paper clip.)

ml means milliliter (A liter is about a quart, A milliliter is about the amount of liquid in $\frac{1}{1000}$ of a quart.)

One way to solve the applications below is to set up the proportion $\frac{mg}{ml} = \frac{mg}{ml}$.

A solution strength of 15 mg of medicine in 1 ml of solution is available.

87. If a patient needs 12 mg of medicine, how many ml do you administer?

88. If a patient need 33 mg of medicine, how many ml do you administer?

A solution strength of 8 mg of medicine in 1 ml of solution is available.

89. If a patient needs 10 mg of medicine, how many ml do you administer?

90. If a patient needs 6 mg of medicine, how many ml do you administer?

91. Is the ratio $\frac{11}{15}$ the same as the ratio of $\frac{15}{11}$? Explain your answer.

92. Explain why the ratio $\frac{40}{17}$ is incorrect for Exercise 39.

93. Explain the difference between a ratio and a proportion.

94. Explain how to find the unknown number in a proportion such as $\frac{n}{18} = \frac{12}{8}$.

For each proportion, find the unknown number n.

95. $\dfrac{n}{1150} = \dfrac{588}{483}$

96. $\dfrac{222}{1515} = \dfrac{37}{n}$

THE BIGGER PICTURE Operations on Sets of Numbers and Solving Equations

Continue your outline from Sections 1.7, 1.9, 2.5, 3.4, and 4.5. Suggestions are once again written to help you complete this part of your outline. Notice that this part of the outline has to do with solving a certain type of equation, proportions.

I. Some Operations on Sets of Numbers
A. Whole Numbers
  1. **Add or Subtract** (Sections 1.3, 1.4)
  2. **Multiply or Divide** (Sections 1.6, 1.7)
  3. **Exponent** (Section 1.9)
  4. **Square Root** (Section 1.9)
  5. **Order of Operations** (Section 1.9)
B. Fractions
  1. **Simplify** (Section 2.3)
  2. **Multiply** (Section 2.4)
  3. **Divide** (Section 2.5)
  4. **Add or Subtract** (Section 3.4)
C. Decimals
  1. **Add or Subtract** (Section 4.3)
  2. **Multiply** (Section 4.4)
  3. **Divide** (Section 4.5)

II. Solving Equations
A. Proportions: Set cross products equal to each other. Then solve.

$$\frac{14}{3} = \frac{2}{n}, \text{ or } 14 \cdot n = 3 \cdot 2, \text{ or } 14 \cdot n = 6, \text{ or } n = \frac{6}{14} = \frac{3}{7}$$

Perform indicated operations.

1. $\frac{7}{20} - \frac{1}{10}$
2. $\frac{7}{20} \cdot \frac{1}{10}$
3. $\frac{7}{20} \div \frac{1}{10}$
4. $\frac{7}{20} + \frac{1}{10}$
5. $7.6 + 0.02$
6. $7.6(0.02)$

For each proportion, find the unknown number, n.

7. $\frac{4}{n} = \frac{50}{100}$
8. $\frac{60}{10} = \frac{15}{n}$
9. $\frac{n}{0.8} = \frac{0.06}{12}$
10. $\dfrac{\frac{7}{8}}{\frac{1}{4}} = \dfrac{n}{\frac{5}{6}}$

5.2 INTRODUCTION TO PERCENT

Objective **A** Understanding Percent

The word **percent** comes from the Latin phrase *per centum*, which means **"per 100."** For example, 53% (percent) means 53 per 100. In the square below, 53 of the 100 squares are shaded. Thus, 53% of the figure is shaded.

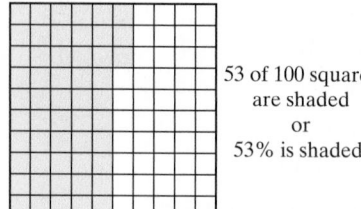

53 of 100 squares
are shaded
or
53% is shaded.

Since 53% means 53 per 100, 53% is the ratio of 53 to 100, or $\frac{53}{100}$.

$$53\% = \frac{53}{100}$$

Also,

$$7\% = \frac{7}{100} \qquad \text{7 parts per 100 parts}$$

$$73\% = \frac{73}{100} \qquad \text{73 parts per 100 parts}$$

$$109\% = \frac{109}{100} \qquad \text{109 parts per 100 parts}$$

Percent

Percent means **per one hundred.** The "%" symbol is used to denote percent.

Percent is used in a variety of everyday situations. For example:

- The interest rate is 5.7%.
- 50.5% of U.S. homes have Internet access.
- The store is having a 25%-off sale.
- 78% of us trust our local fire department.
- The enrollment in community colleges has increased 141% in the last 30 years.

EXAMPLE 1

In a survey of 100 people, 17 people drive blue cars. What percent of people drive blue cars?

Solution: Since 17 people out of 100 drive blue cars, the fraction is $\frac{17}{100}$. Then

$$\frac{17}{100} = 17\%$$

■ **Work Practice Problem 1**

 **EXAMPLE 2** 46 out of every 100 college students live at home. What percent of students live at home? (*Source:* Independent Insurance Agents of America)

Solution:

$$\frac{46}{100} = 46\%$$

Work Practice Problem 2

PRACTICE PROBLEM 2

29 out of 100 executives are in their forties. What percent of executives are in their forties?

Objective B Writing Percents as Decimals

Since percent means "per hundred," we have that

$$1\% = \frac{1}{100} = 0.01$$

In other words, the percent symbol means "per hundred" or, equivalently, "$\frac{1}{100}$" or "0.01." Thus

$$87\% = 87 \times \frac{1}{100} = \frac{87}{100}$$

or

$$87\% = 87 \times (0.01) = 0.87$$

Of course, we know that the end results are the same, that is,

$$\frac{87}{100} = 0.87$$

The above gives us two options for converting percents. We can replace the percent symbol, %, by $\frac{1}{100}$ or 0.01 and then multiply.

For consistency, when we

- convert from a percent to a *decimal,* we will drop the % symbol and multiply by 0.01. (this section)
- convert from a percent to a *fraction,* we will drop the % symbol and multiply by $\frac{1}{100}$. (next section)

Thus, to write 53.% as a decimal,

$$53\% = 53(0.01) = 0.53 \quad \text{Replace the percent symbol with 0.01. Then multiply.}$$

Writing a Percent as a Decimal

Replace the percent symbol with its decimal equivalent, 0.01; then multiply.

$$43\% = 43(0.01) = 0.43$$

 **Helpful Hint**

If it helps, think of writing a percent as a decimal by

Percent → | Remove the % symbol and move decimal point 2 places to the left | → Decimal

Answer

2. 29%

PRACTICE PROBLEM 3

Write 89% as a decimal.

EXAMPLE 3 Write 23% as a decimal.

Solution:

$23\% = 23(0.01)$ Replace the percent symbol with 0.01.

$= 0.\underset{\smile}{23}$ Multiply.

☐ **Work Practice Problem 3**

PRACTICE PROBLEMS 4–7

Write each percent as a decimal.

4. 2.7%   **5.** 150%

6. 0.69%   **7.** 500%

EXAMPLES Write each percent as a decimal.

4. $4.6\% = 4.6(0.01) = 0.\underset{\smile}{046}$ Replace the percent symbol with 0.01. Then multiply.

5. $190\% = 190(0.01) = 1.\underset{\smile}{90}$ or 1.9

6. $0.74\% = 0.74(0.01) = 0.\underset{\smile}{0074}$

7. $100\% = 100(0.01) = 1.\underset{\smile}{00}$ or 1

☐ **Work Practice Problems 4–7**

Helpful Hint
We just learned that
$100\% = 1$

✔ **Concept Check**   Why is it incorrect to write the percent 0.033% as 3.3 in decimal form?

Objective C Writing Decimals as Percents

To write a decimal as a percent, we use the result of Example 7 above. In this example, we found that $1 = 100\%$.

$$0.38 = 0.38(1) = 0.38(100\%) = 38\%$$

Notice that the result is

$$0.38 = 0.38(100\%) = \underset{\smile}{38}.\%$$ Multiply by 1 in the form of 100%.

Writing a Decimal as a Percent

Multiply by 1 in the form of 100%.

$$0.27 = 0.27(100\%) = \underset{\smile}{27}.\%$$

Helpful Hint

If it helps, think of writing a decimal as a percent by reversing the steps in the Helpful Hint on the previous page.

Percent ← | Move the decimal point 2 places to the right and attach a % symbol. | ← Decimal

---

Answers

3. 0.89, **4.** 0.027, **5.** 1.5, **6.** 0.0069, **7.** 5

✔ Concept Check Answer

To write a percent as a decimal, the decimal point should be moved two places to the left, not to the right. So the correct answer is 0.00033.

EXAMPLE 8 Write 0.65 as a percent.

Solution:

$0.65 = 0.65(100\%) = \underset{\curvearrowright}{65.}\%$ Multiply by 100%.

$= 65\%$

▣ **Work Practice Problem 8**

EXAMPLES Write each decimal as a percent.

9. $1.25 = 1.25(100\%) = \underset{\curvearrowright}{125.}\%$ or 125%

10. $0.012 = 0.012(100\%) = \underset{\curvearrowright}{001.2}\%$ or 1.2%

11. $0.6 = 0.6(100\%) = \underset{\curvearrowright}{060.}\%$ or 60%

Helpful Hint

A zero was inserted as a placeholder.

▣ **Work Practice Problems 9–11**

✔ **Concept Check** Why is it incorrect to write the decimal 0.0345 as 34.5% in percent form?

PRACTICE PROBLEM 8

Write 0.19 as a percent.

PRACTICE PROBLEMS 9–11

Write each decimal as a percent.

9. 1.75   **10.** 0.044   **11.** 0.7

Answers
8. 19%, **9.** 175%, **10.** 4.4%,
11. 70%

✔ **Concept Check Answer**

To change a decimal to a percent, multiply by 100%, or move the decimal point *only* two places to the right. So the correct answer is 3.45%.

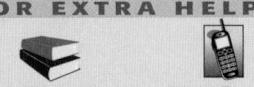 
Objective A *Solve. See Examples 1 and 2.*

1. A basketball player makes 81 out of 100 attempted free throws. What percent of free throws was made?

2. In a survey of 100 people, 54 preferred chocolate syrup on their ice cream. What percent preferred chocolate syrup?

3. Michigan leads the United States in tart cherry production, producing 75 out of every 100 tart cherries each year.
  a. What percent of tart cherries are produced in Michigan?
  b. What percent of tart cherries are *not* produced in Michigan? (*Source:* Cherry Marketing Institute)

4. 51 out of 100 adults ages 30 to 49 say the best way to meet a potential date is through volunteer activities.
  a. What percent of adults ages 30 to 49 say the best way to meet a potential date is through volunteer activities?
  b. What percent of adults ages 30 to 49 say the best way to meet a potential date is *not* through volunteer activities? (*Source:* NFO Research for Combe)

Adults were asked what type of cookie was their favorite. The circle graph below shows the average results for every 100 people. Use this graph to answer Exercises 5 through 8. See Examples 1 and 2.

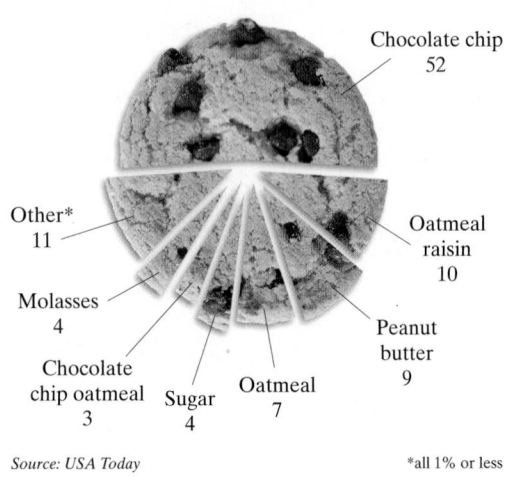

Chocolate chip 52

Other* 11

Oatmeal raisin 10

Molasses 4

Peanut butter 9

Chocolate chip oatmeal 3

Sugar 4

Oatmeal 7

Source: USA Today

*all 1% or less

5. What percent preferred peanut butter cookies?

6. What percent preferred oatmeal raisin cookies?

7. What type of cookie was preferred by most adults? What percent preferred this type of cookie?

8. What two types of cookies were preferred by the same number of adults? What percent preferred each type?

Objective B *Write each percent as a decimal. See Examples 3 through 7.*

9. 48%

10. 64%

11. 6%

12. 9%

13. 100%

14. 136%

15. 61.3%

16. 52.7%

17. 2.8%   **18.** 1.7%   **19.** 0.6%   **20.** 0.9%

21. 300%   **22.** 700%   **23.** 32.58%   **24.** 72.18%

Write each percent as a decimal. See Examples 3 through 7.

25. 67% of American men are happy with their current weight. (*Source:* Gallup for Wheat Foods Council)

26. About 95% of tableservice restaurants in the United States include appetizers on their menus. (*Source:* National Restaurant Association)

27. Video games made up 21.2% of the total toy market in the United States in 2000. (*Source:* The NPD Group Worldwide)

28. In 2003, 50.3% of all paper used was recycled. (*Source:* American Forest & Paper Association)

29. At the beginning of 2005, the U.S. unemployment rate was 5.7%. (*Source:* NH Economic and Labor Market Unemployment Bureau)

30. In 2003, rock music accounted for 25.2% of recorded music sales in the United States. (*Source:* Recording Industry Association of America)

Objective **C** *Write each decimal as a percent. See Examples 8 through 11.*

31. 0.98   **32.** 0.75   **33.** 3.1   **34.** 4.8   **35.** 29.00

36. 56.00   **37.** 0.003   **38.** 0.006   **39.** 0.22   **40.** 0.45

41. 5.3   **42.** 1.6   **43.** 0.056   **44.** 0.027   **45.** 0.3328

46. 0.1115   **47.** 3.00   **48.** 5.00   **49.** 0.7   **50.** 0.8

Write each decimal as a percent. See Examples 8 through 11.

51. The Munoz family saves 0.10 of their take-home pay.

52. The cost of an item for sale is 0.7 of the sale price.

53. People take aspirin for a variety of reasons. The most common use of aspirin is to prevent heart disease, accounting for 0.38 of all aspirin use. (*Source:* Bayer Market Research)

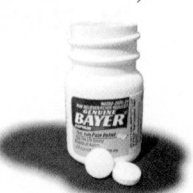

54. About 0.25 of the world's automobiles are produced in North America. (*Source:* Automotive Intelligence)

55. Nearly 0.093 of people in the United States are affected by pollen allergies. (*Source:* National Institute of Allergy and Infectious Diseases)

56. According to the 2000 census, 0.509 of the American population is female. (*Source:* U.S. Census Bureau)

Review

Write each fraction as a decimal. See Section 4.6.

57. $\dfrac{1}{4}$ **58.** $\dfrac{3}{5}$ **59.** $\dfrac{13}{20}$ **60.** $\dfrac{11}{40}$ **61.** $\dfrac{9}{10}$ **62.** $\dfrac{7}{10}$

Concept Extensions

Solve. See the Concept Checks in this section.

63. Which of the following are correct?
   a. $6.5\% = 0.65$ **b.** $7.8\% = 0.078$
   c. $120\% = 0.12$ **d.** $0.35\% = 0.0035$

64. Which of the following are correct?
   a. $0.231 = 23.1\%$ **b.** $5.12 = 0.0512\%$
   c. $3.2 = 320\%$ **d.** $0.0175 = 0.175\%$

Recall that $1 = 100\%$. This means that 1 whole is 100%. Use this for Exercises 65 and 66. (Source: Some Body by Dr. Pete Rowen)

65. The four blood types are A, B, O, and AB. (Each blood type can also be further classified as Rh-positive or Rh-negative depending upon whether your blood contains protein or not.) Given the percent blood types for the U.S. below, calculate the percent of U.S. population with AB blood type.

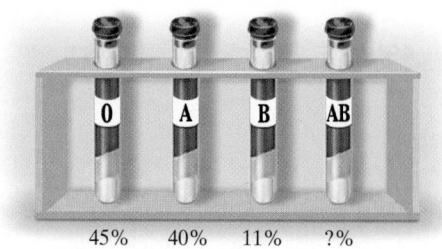

   45%   40%   11%   ?%

66. The top four components of bone are below. Find the missing percent.
   1. Minerals—45%
   2. Living tissue—30%
   3. Water—20%
   4. Other—?

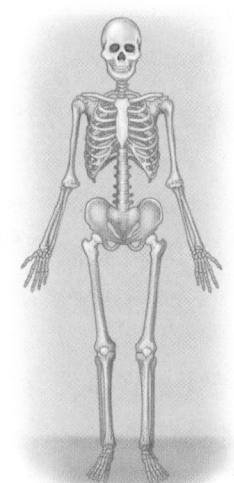

The bar graph shows the predicted fastest-growing occupations. Use this graph for Exercises 67 through 70.

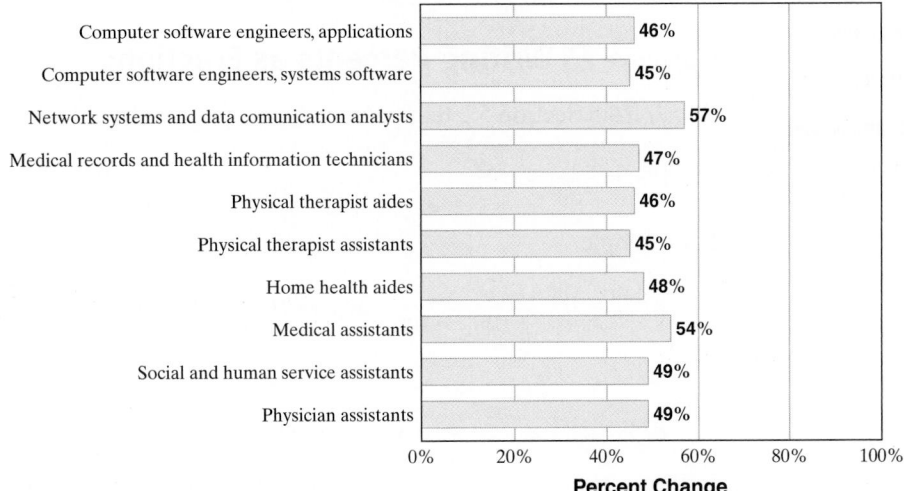

Fastest-Growing Occupations 2002–2012

Source: Bureau of Labor Statistics

67. What occupation is predicted to be the fastest growing?

68. What occupation is predicted to be the second fastest growing?

69. Write the percent change for physician assistants as a decimal.

70. Write the percent change for medical assistants as a decimal.

 71. In your own words, explain how to write a percent as a decimal.

 72. In your own words, explain how to write a decimal as a percent.

📖 STUDY SKILLS BUILDER

Are You Satisfied with Your Performance in this Course thus Far?

To see if there is room for improvement, answer these questions:

1. Am I attending all classes and arriving on time?

2. Am I working and checking my homework assignments on time?

3. Am I getting help (from my instructor or a campus learning resource lab) when I need it?

4. In addition to my instructor, am I using the text supplements that might help me?

5. Am I satisfied with my performance on quizzes and exams?

If you answered no to any of these questions, read or reread Section 1.1 for suggestions in these areas. Also, you might want to contact your instructor for additional feedback.

5.3 PERCENTS AND FRACTIONS

Objective **A** Writing Percents as Fractions

Recall from Section 5.2 that percent means per hundred. Thus

$$1\% = \frac{1}{100} = 0.01$$

For example,

$$87\% = 87 \times \frac{1}{100} = \frac{87}{100} \quad \text{Writing 87\% as a fraction.}$$

or

$$87\% = 87 \times 0.01 = 0.87 \quad \text{Writing 87\% as a decimal.}$$

In this section we are writing percents as fractions, so we do the following.

Writing a Percent as a Fraction

Replace the percent symbol with its fraction equivalent, $\frac{1}{100}$; then multiply. Don't forget to simplify the fraction if possible.

$$7\% = 7 \cdot \frac{1}{100} = \frac{7}{100}$$

PRACTICE PROBLEMS 1–5

Write each percent as a fraction or mixed number in simplest form.

1. 25%

2. 2.3%

3. 175%

4. $66\frac{2}{3}\%$

5. 8%

EXAMPLES Write each percent as a fraction or mixed number in simplest form.

1. $40\% = 40 \cdot \dfrac{1}{100} = \dfrac{40}{100} = \dfrac{2 \cdot \overset{1}{\cancel{20}}}{5 \cdot \underset{1}{\cancel{20}}} = \dfrac{2}{5}$

2. $1.9\% = 1.9 \cdot \dfrac{1}{100} = \dfrac{1.9}{100}$. We don't want the numerator of the fraction to contain a decimal, so we multiply by 1 in the form of $\dfrac{10}{10}$.

$$= \frac{1.9}{100} \cdot \frac{10}{10} = \frac{1.9 \cdot 10}{100 \cdot 10} = \frac{19}{1000}$$

3. $125\% = 125 \cdot \dfrac{1}{100} = \dfrac{125}{100} = \dfrac{5 \cdot \overset{1}{\cancel{25}}}{4 \cdot \underset{1}{\cancel{25}}} = \dfrac{5}{4} \text{ or } 1\frac{1}{4}$

4. $33\frac{1}{3}\% = 33\frac{1}{3} \cdot \dfrac{1}{100} = \dfrac{100}{3} \cdot \dfrac{1}{100} = \dfrac{\overset{1}{\cancel{100}} \cdot 1}{3 \cdot \underset{1}{\cancel{100}}} = \dfrac{1}{3}$

        ⌣→ Write as ⌣
        an improper fraction.

5. $100\% = 100 \cdot \dfrac{1}{100} = \dfrac{100}{100} = 1$

Helpful Hint

Just as in the previous section, we confirm that $100\% = 1$

■ Work Practice Problems 1–5

Answers

1. $\dfrac{1}{4}$, **2.** $\dfrac{23}{1000}$, **3.** $\dfrac{7}{4}$ or $1\dfrac{3}{4}$,

4. $\dfrac{2}{3}$, **5.** $\dfrac{2}{25}$

Objective B Writing Fractions as Percents

Recall that to write a percent as a fraction, we replace the percent symbol by its fraction equivalent, $\frac{1}{100}$. We reverse these steps to write a fraction as a percent.

Writing a Fraction as a Percent

Multiply by 1 in the form of 100%.

$$\frac{1}{8} = \frac{1}{8} \cdot 100\% = \frac{1}{8} \cdot \frac{100}{1}\% = \frac{100}{8}\% = 12\frac{1}{2}\% \quad \text{or} \quad 12.5\%$$

Helpful Hint

From Example 5, we know that

$$100\% = 1$$

Recall that when we multiply a number by 1, we are not changing the value of that number. This means that when we multiply a number by 100%, we are not changing its value but rather writing the number as an equivalent percent.

EXAMPLES Write each fraction or mixed number as a percent.

6. $\frac{9}{20} = \frac{9}{20} \cdot 100\% = \frac{9}{20} \cdot \frac{100}{1}\% = \frac{900}{20}\% = 45\%$

7. $\frac{2}{3} = \frac{2}{3} \cdot 100\% = \frac{2}{3} \cdot \frac{100}{1}\% = \frac{200}{3}\% = 66\frac{2}{3}\%$

8. $1\frac{1}{2} = \frac{3}{2} \cdot 100\% = \frac{3}{2} \cdot \frac{100}{1}\% = \frac{300}{2}\% = 150\%$

Helpful Hint

$\frac{200}{3} = 66.\overline{6}$. Thus, another way to write $\frac{200}{3}\%$ is $66.\overline{6}\%$.

 **Work Practice Problems 6–8**

✔ Concept Check Which digit in the percent 76.4582% represents

a. A tenth percent?

b. A thousandth percent?

c. A hundredth percent?

d. A whole percent?

PRACTICE PROBLEMS 6–8

Write each fraction or mixed number as a percent.

6. $\frac{1}{2}$ **7.** $\frac{7}{40}$ **8.** $2\frac{1}{4}$

Answers

6. 50%,   **7.** $17\frac{1}{2}\%$,   **8.** 225%

✔ Concept Check Answers

a. 4,   **b.** 8,   **c.** 5,   **d.** 6

PRACTICE PROBLEM 9

Write $\frac{3}{17}$ as a percent. Round to the nearest hundredth percent.

EXAMPLE 9 Write $\frac{1}{12}$ as a percent. Round to the nearest hundredth percent.

Solution:

$$\frac{1}{12} = \frac{1}{12} \cdot 100\% = \frac{1}{12} \cdot \frac{100\%}{1} = \frac{100}{12}\% \approx 8.33\%$$

"approximately"

$$\begin{array}{r} 8.333 \approx 8.33 \\ 12\overline{)100.000} \\ -96 \\ \hline 4\,0 \\ -3\,6 \\ \hline 40 \\ -36 \\ \hline 40 \\ -36 \\ \hline 4 \end{array}$$

Thus, $\frac{1}{12}$ is approximately 8.33%.

🔲 **Work Practice Problem 9**

Objective C Converting Percents, Decimals, and Fractions

Let's summarize what we have learned so far about percents, decimals, and fractions:

Summary of Converting Percents, Decimals, and Fractions

- *To write a percent as a decimal,* replace the % symbol with its decimal equivalent, 0.01; then multiply.
- *To write a percent as a fraction,* replace the % symbol with its fraction equivalent, $\frac{1}{100}$; then multiply.
- *To write a decimal or fraction as a percent,* multiply by 100%.

If we let p represent a number, below we summarize using symbols.

Write a percent as a decimal:	Write a percent as a fraction:	Write a number as a percent:
$p\% = p(0.01)$	$p\% = p \cdot \dfrac{1}{100}$	$p = p \cdot 100\%$

Answer

9. 17.65%

EXAMPLE 10 17.8% of automobile thefts in the continental United States occur in the Midwest. Write this percent as a decimal and as a fraction. (*Source:* The American Automobile Manufacturers Association)

Solution:

As a decimal: $17.8\% = 17.8(0.01) = 0.178$.

As a fraction: $17.8\% = 17.8 \cdot \dfrac{1}{100} = \dfrac{17.8}{100} = \dfrac{17.8}{100} \cdot \dfrac{10}{10} = \dfrac{178}{1000} = \dfrac{\overset{1}{\cancel{2}} \cdot 89}{\underset{1}{\cancel{2}} \cdot 500} = \dfrac{89}{500}$.

Thus, 17.8% written as a decimal is 0.178, and written as a fraction is $\dfrac{89}{500}$.

▣ **Work Practice Problem 10**

EXAMPLE 11 An advertisement for a stereo system reads "$\dfrac{1}{4}$ off." What percent off is this?

Solution: Write $\dfrac{1}{4}$ as a percent.

$$\dfrac{1}{4} = \dfrac{1}{4} \cdot 100\% = \dfrac{1}{4} \cdot \dfrac{100\%}{1} = \dfrac{100}{4}\% = 25\%$$

Thus, "$\dfrac{1}{4}$ off" is the same as "25% off."

▣ **Work Practice Problem 11**

Note: It is helpful to know a few basic percent conversions. Appendix B.2 contains a handy reference of percent, decimal, and fraction equivalencies.

PRACTICE PROBLEM 10

A family decides to spend no more than 22.5% of its monthly income on rent. Write 22.5% as a decimal and as a fraction.

PRACTICE PROBLEM 11

Provincetown's budget for waste disposal increased by $1\dfrac{1}{4}$ times over the budget from last year. What percent increase is this?

Answers

10. $0.225, \dfrac{9}{40}$, **11.** 125%

Mental Math

Write each fraction as a percent.

1. $\dfrac{13}{100}$

2. $\dfrac{92}{100}$

3. $\dfrac{87}{100}$

4. $\dfrac{71}{100}$

5. $\dfrac{1}{100}$

6. $\dfrac{2}{100}$

5.3 EXERCISE SET

FOR EXTRA HELP

Student Solutions Manual   PH Math/Tutor Center   CD/Video for Review   Math XL MathXL®   MyMathLab MyMathLab

Objective **A** *Write each percent as a fraction or mixed number in simplest form. See Examples 1 through 5.*

1. 12%

2. 24%

3. 4%

4. 2%

5. 4.5%

6. 7.5%

7. 175%

8. 250%

9. 73%

10. 86%

11. 12.5%

12. 62.5%

13. 6.25%

14. 3.75%

15. 6%

16. 16%

17. $10\dfrac{1}{3}\%$

18. $7\dfrac{3}{4}\%$

19. $22\dfrac{3}{8}\%$

20. $15\dfrac{5}{8}\%$

Objective **B** *Write each fraction or mixed number as a percent. See Examples 6 through 8.*

21. $\dfrac{3}{4}$

22. $\dfrac{5}{8}$

23. $\dfrac{7}{10}$

24. $\dfrac{3}{10}$

25. $\dfrac{2}{5}$

26. $\dfrac{4}{5}$

27. $\dfrac{59}{100}$

28. $\dfrac{73}{100}$

29. $\dfrac{17}{50}$

30. $\dfrac{47}{50}$

31. $\dfrac{3}{8}$

32. $\dfrac{5}{16}$

346

33. $\dfrac{5}{16}$ **34.** $\dfrac{7}{16}$ **35.** $1\dfrac{3}{5}$ **36.** $1\dfrac{3}{4}$ **37.** $\dfrac{7}{9}$ **38.** $\dfrac{1}{3}$

39. $\dfrac{13}{20}$ **40.** $\dfrac{3}{20}$ **41.** $2\dfrac{1}{2}$ **42.** $2\dfrac{1}{5}$ **43.** $1\dfrac{9}{10}$ **44.** $2\dfrac{7}{10}$

Write each fraction as a percent. Round to the nearest hundredth percent. See Example 9.

45. $\dfrac{7}{11}$ **46.** $\dfrac{5}{12}$ **47.** $\dfrac{4}{15}$ **48.** $\dfrac{10}{11}$

49. $\dfrac{1}{7}$ **50.** $\dfrac{1}{9}$ **51.** $\dfrac{11}{12}$ **52.** $\dfrac{5}{6}$

Objective C *Complete each table. See Examples 10 and 11.*

53.

Percent	Decimal	Fraction
35%		
		$\dfrac{1}{5}$
	0.5	
70%		
		$\dfrac{3}{8}$

54.

Percent	Decimal	Fraction
50%		
		$\dfrac{2}{5}$
	0.25	
12.5%		
		$\dfrac{5}{8}$
		$\dfrac{7}{50}$

55.

Percent	Decimal	Fraction
40%		
	0.235	
		$\dfrac{4}{5}$
$33\dfrac{1}{3}\%$		
		$\dfrac{7}{8}$
7.5%		

56.

Percent	Decimal	Fraction
	0.525	
		$\dfrac{3}{4}$
$66\dfrac{2}{3}\%$		
		$\dfrac{5}{6}$
100%		

57.

Percent	Decimal	Fraction
200%		
	2.8	
705%		
		$4\frac{27}{50}$

58.

Percent	Decimal	Fraction
800%		
	3.2	
608%		
		$9\frac{13}{50}$

Solve. See Examples 10 and 11.

59. Approximately 14.8% of new luxury cars are silver, making silver the most popular new vehicle color for that class. Write this percent as a decimal and a fraction. (*Source:* Ward's Communications)

60. In 1950, the United States produced 75.7% of all motor vehicles made worldwide. Write this percent as a decimal and a fraction. (*Source:* American Automobile Manufacturers Association)

61. At this writing, 23% of Americans surveyed are in favor of abolishing the penny. Write this percent as a decimal and a fraction.

62. 52% of Americans say that their ideal family size is fewer than three children. Write this percent as a decimal and a fraction. (*Source:* Gallup)

63. In 2003, $\frac{137}{500}$ of all new cars sold in the United States were imports. Write this fraction as a percent. (*Source:* Ward's AutoInfoBank)

64. In 1997, $\frac{41}{250}$ of all new cars sold in the United States were imports. Write this fraction as a percent. (*Source:* Ward's Communications)

65. The sales tax in Slidell, Louisiana, is 8.75%. Write this percent as a decimal.

66. A real estate agent receives a commission of 3% of the sale price of a house. Write this percent as a decimal.

67. In the 2003/2004 television season, the top-rated show was *CSI: Crime Scene Investigation,* which had an average audience share of $\frac{6}{25}$ of all those watching television during that time slot. Write this fraction as a percent. (*Source:* Nielsen Media Research)

68. The 2003 National Assessment of Educational Progress showed that $\frac{8}{25}$ of U.S. fourth-graders were proficient in math. Write this fraction as a percent. (*Source:* National Center for Education Statistics)

In Exercises 69 through 74, you are asked to write each percent in this circle graph as a decimal and a fraction.

World Population by Continent

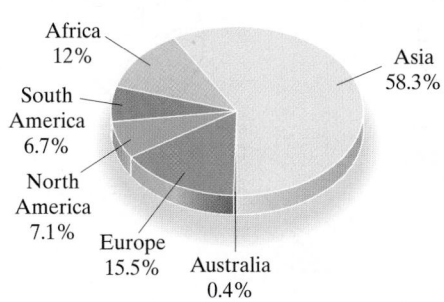

69. 0.4%   **70.** 58.3%   **71.** 12%

72. 6.7%   **73.** 7.1%   **74.** 15.5%

Review

Find the value of n. See Section 5.1.

75. $3 \cdot n = 45$ **76.** $7 \cdot n = 48$ **77.** $8 \cdot n = 80$

78. $2 \cdot n = 16$ **79.** $6 \cdot n = 72$ **80.** $5 \cdot n = 35$

Concept Extensions

Solve. See the Concept Check in this section.

81. Given the percent 52.8647%, round as indicated.

    a. Round to a tenth of a percent.
    b. Round to a hundredth of a percent.

82. Given the percent 0.5269%, round as indicated.

    a. Round to a tenth of a percent.
    b. Round to a hundredth of a percent.

83. Write 1.07835 as a percent rounded to the nearest tenth of a percent.

84. Write 1.25348 as a percent rounded to the nearest tenth of a percent.

85. Write 0.65794 as a percent rounded to the nearest hundredth of a percent.

86. Write 0.92571 as a percent rounded to the nearest hundredth of a percent.

87. Write 0.7682 as a percent rounded to the nearest percent.

88. Write 0.2371 as a percent rounded to the nearest percent.

What percent of the figure is shaded?

89.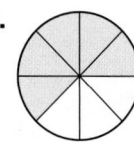

90.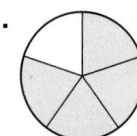

91.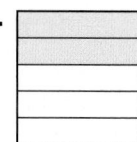

92.

Fill in the blanks.

93. A fraction written as a percent is greater than 100% when the numerator is _____ than the denominator. (greater/less)

94. A decimal written as a percent is less than 100% when the decimal is _____ than 1. (greater/less)

95. In your own words, explain how to write a percent as a fraction.

96. In your own words, explain how to write a fraction as a decimal.

Write each fraction as a decimal and then write each decimal as a percent. Round the decimal to three decimal places (nearest thousandth) and the percent to the nearest tenth of a percent.

97. $\dfrac{21}{79}$

98. $\dfrac{56}{102}$

99. $\dfrac{850}{736}$

100. $\dfrac{506}{248}$

STUDY SKILLS BUILDER

What to Do the Day of an Exam?

On the day of an exam, don't forget to try the following:

- Allow yourself plenty of time to arrive.
- Read the directions on the test carefully.
- Read each problem carefully as you take your test. Make sure that you answer the question asked.
- Watch your time and pace yourself so that you may attempt each problem on your test.
- Check your work and answers.
- ***Do not turn your test in early.*** If you have extra time, spend it double-checking your work.

Good luck!

Answer the following questions based on your most recent mathematics exam, whenever that was.

1. How soon before class did you arrive?

2. Did you read the directions on the test carefully?

3. Did you make sure you answered the question asked for each problem on the exam?

4. Were you able to attempt each problem on your exam?

5. If your answer to Question 4 is no, list reasons why.

6. Did you have extra time on your exam?

7. If your answer to Question 6 is yes, describe how you spent that extra time.

5.4 SOLVING PERCENT PROBLEMS USING EQUATIONS

Objectives

Ⓐ Write Percent Problems as Equations.

Ⓑ Solve Percent Problems

Note: Sections 5.4 and 5.5 introduce two methods for solving percent problems. It is not necessary that you study both sections. You may want to check with your instructor for further advice.

Throughout this text, we have written mathematical statements such as $3 + 10 = 13$, or area = length · width. These statements are called "equations." An **equation** is a mathematical statement that contains an equal sign. To solve percent problems in this section, we translate the problems into such mathematical statements, or equations.

Objective Ⓐ Writing Percent Problems as Equations

Recognizing key words in a percent problem is helpful in writing the problem as an equation. Three key words in the statement of a percent problem and their meanings are as follows:

> **of** means **multiplication** (·)
>
> **is** means **equals** (=)
>
> **what** (or some equivalent) means **the unknown number**

In our examples, we let the letter n stand for the unknown number.

> **Helpful Hint**
>
> Any letter of the alphabet can be used to represent the unknown number. In this section, we use the letter n.

EXAMPLE 1 Translate to an equation.

5 is what percent of 20?

Solution: 5 is what percent of 20?

$$5 = n \cdot 20$$

⬛ **Work Practice Problem 1**

> **Helpful Hint**
>
> Remember that an equation is simply a mathematical statement that contains an equal sign (=).
>
> $$5 = n \cdot 20$$
>
> ↑
> equal sign

EXAMPLE 2 Translate to an equation.

1.2 is 30% of what number?

Solution: 1.2 is 30% of what number?

$$1.2 = 30\% \cdot n$$

⬛ **Work Practice Problem 2**

PRACTICE PROBLEM 1

Translate: 6 is what percent of 24?

PRACTICE PROBLEM 2

Translate: 1.8 is 20% of what number?

Answers

1. $6 = n \cdot 24$, **2.** $1.8 = 20\% \cdot n$

PRACTICE PROBLEM 3

Translate: What number is 40% of 3.6?

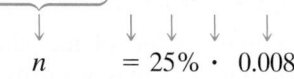 Translate to an equation.

What number is 25% of 0.008?

Solution: What number is 25% of 0.008?

$$n = 25\% \cdot 0.008$$

▢ **Work Practice Problem 3**

PRACTICE PROBLEMS 4–6

Translate each to an equation.

4. 42% of 50 is what number?

5. 15% of what number is 9?

6. What percent of 150 is 90?

EXAMPLES Translate each of the following to an equation:

4. 38% of 200 is what number?

$$38\% \cdot 200 = n$$

5. 40% of what number is 80?

$$40\% \cdot n = 80$$

6. What percent of 85 is 34?

$$n \cdot 85 = 34$$

▢ **Work Practice Problems 4–6**

✔ **Concept Check** In the equation $2 \cdot n = 10$, what step should be taken to solve the equation for n?

Objective **B** **Solving Percent Problems**

You may have noticed by now that each percent problem has contained three numbers—in our examples, two are known and one is unknown. Each of these numbers is given a special name.

15% of 60 is 9

| 15% percent | · | 60 base | = | 9 amount |

We call this equation the **percent equation.**

Percent Equation

percent · base = amount

Helpful Hint

Notice that the percent equation given above is a true statement. To see this, simplify the left side as shown:

$$15\% \cdot 60 = 9$$
$$0.15 \cdot 60 = 9 \quad \text{Write 15\% as 0.15.}$$
$$9 = 9 \quad \text{Multiply.}$$

The statement $9 = 9$ is true.

Answers

3. $n = 40\% \cdot 3.6$,　**4.** $42\% \cdot 50 = n$,
5. $15\% \cdot n = 9$,　**6.** $n \cdot 150 = 90$

✔ **Concept Check Answer**

If $2 \cdot n = 10$, then $n = \dfrac{10}{2}$, or $n = 5$.

After a percent problem has been written as a percent equation, we can use the equation to find the unknown number. This is called **solving** the equation.

Solving Percent Equations for the Amount

EXAMPLE 7

What number is 35% of 40?

$\downarrow \quad\quad \downarrow \quad \downarrow \quad \downarrow \quad \downarrow$

Solution: $n \quad\quad = 35\% \quad\cdot\quad 40$ Translate to an equation.

$\quad\quad\quad\quad\quad n \quad\quad = 0.35 \quad\cdot\quad 40$ Write 35% as 0.35.

$\quad\quad\quad\quad\quad n \quad\quad = 14$ Multiply $0.35 \cdot 40 = 14$.

Thus, 14 is 35% of 40.

 **Work Practice Problem 7**

> **Helpful Hint**
> When solving a percent equation, write the percent as a decimal (or fraction).

EXAMPLE 8

85% of 300 is $\underbrace{\text{what number?}}$

$\downarrow \quad \downarrow \quad \downarrow \quad \downarrow \quad\quad \downarrow$

Solution: $85\% \quad\cdot\quad 300 = \quad\quad n$ Translate to an equation.

$\quad\quad\quad\quad 0.85 \quad\cdot\quad 300 = \quad\quad n$ Write 85% as 0.85.

$\quad\quad\quad\quad\quad\quad\quad\quad 255 = \quad\quad n$ Multiply $0.85 \cdot 300 = 255$.

Thus, 85% of 300 is 255.

 **Work Practice Problem 8**

Solving Percent Equations for the Base

EXAMPLE 9

12% of $\underbrace{\text{what number}}$ is 0.6?

$\downarrow \quad \downarrow \quad\quad \downarrow \quad\quad \downarrow \quad \downarrow$

Solution: $12\% \quad\cdot \quad\quad n \quad\quad = 0.6$ Translate to an equation.

$\quad\quad\quad\quad 0.12 \quad\cdot \quad\quad n \quad\quad = 0.6$ Write 12% as 0.12.

Recall from Section 5.1 that if "0.12 times some number is 0.6," then the number is 0.6 divided by 0.12.

$n = \dfrac{0.6}{0.12}$ Divide 0.6 by 0.12, the number multiplied by n.

$n = 5$

Thus, 12% of 5 is 0.6.

 **Work Practice Problem 9**

PRACTICE PROBLEM 7
What number is 20% of 85?

PRACTICE PROBLEM 8
90% of 150 is what number?

PRACTICE PROBLEM 9
15% of what number is 1.2?

Answers
7. 17,　**8.** 135,　**9.** 8

PRACTICE PROBLEM 10

27 is $4\frac{1}{2}$% of what number?

EXAMPLE 10

$$13 \quad \text{is} \quad 6\frac{1}{2}\% \quad \text{of} \quad \underbrace{\text{what number?}}$$

$$\downarrow \quad \downarrow \quad \downarrow \quad \downarrow \quad \downarrow$$

Solution:

13	$=$	$6\frac{1}{2}\%$	$\cdot$	n	Translate to an equation.
13	$=$	0.065	$\cdot$	n	$6\frac{1}{2}\% = 6.5\% = 0.065$.
$\dfrac{13}{0.065}$	$=$			n	Divide 13 by 0.065, the number multiplied by n.
200	$=$			n	

Thus, 13 is $6\frac{1}{2}$% of 200.

☐ **Work Practice Problem 10**

Solving Percent Equations for Percent

EXAMPLE 11

$$\underbrace{\text{What percent}} \quad \text{of} \quad 12 \quad \text{is} \quad 9?$$

$$\downarrow \qquad\qquad \downarrow \quad\ \ \downarrow \quad \downarrow$$

PRACTICE PROBLEM 11

What percent of 80 is 8?

Solution:

n	$\cdot$	12	$=$	9	Translate to an equation.
		n	$=$	$\dfrac{9}{12}$	Divide 9 by 12, the number multiplied by n.
		n	$=$	0.75	

Next, since we are looking for percent, we write 0.75 as a percent.

$n = 75\%$

So, 75% of 12 is 9.

☐ **Work Practice Problem 11**

> **Helpful Hint**
>
> If your unknown in the percent equation is the percent, don't forget to convert your answer to a percent.

PRACTICE PROBLEM 12

35 is what percent of 25?

EXAMPLE 12

$$78 \quad \text{is} \quad \underbrace{\text{What percent}} \quad \text{of} \quad 65?$$

$$\downarrow \quad \downarrow \qquad\qquad \downarrow \qquad\quad \downarrow$$

Solution:

78	$=$	n	$\cdot$	65	Translate to an equation.
$\dfrac{78}{65}$	$=$	n			Divide 78 by 65, the number multiplied by n.
1.2	$=$	n			
120%	$=$	n			Write 1.2 as a percent.

So, 78 is 120% of 65.

☐ **Work Practice Problem 12**

Answers

10. 600, **11.** 10%, **12.** 140%

**Concept Check** Consider these problems

1. 75% of 50 =

   a. 50
   b. a number greater than 50
   c. a number less than 50

2. 40% of a number is 10. Is the number

   a. 10
   b. less than 10
   c. greater than 10?

3. 800 is 120% of what number? Is the number

   a. 800
   b. less than 800
   c. greater than 800?

Helpful Hint

Use the following to see if your answers are reasonable.

(100%) of a number = the number

$\left(\begin{array}{c}\text{a percent} \\ \text{greater than} \\ 100\%\end{array}\right)$ of a number = a number larger than the original number

$\left(\begin{array}{c}\text{a percent} \\ \text{less than } 100\%\end{array}\right)$ of a number = a number less than the original number

Mental Math

Identify the percent, the base, and the amount in each equation. Recall that percent · base = amount.

1. $42\% \cdot 50 = 21$

2. $30\% \cdot 65 = 19.5$

3. $107.5 = 125\% \cdot 86$

4. $99 = 110\% \cdot 90$

5.4 EXERCISE SET

FOR EXTRA HELP

Student Solutions Manual | PH Math/Tutor Center | CD/Video for Review | Math XL MathXL® | MyMathLab MyMathLab

Objective 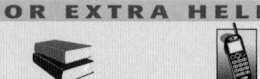 *Translate each to an equation. Do not solve. See Examples 1 through 6.*

1. 15% of 72 is what number?

2. 72% of 63 is what number?

3. 30% of what number is 80?

4. 50% of what number is 8?

5. 1.9 is 40% of what number?

6. 0.5 is 20% of what number?

7. What percent of 90 is 20?

8. 4.5 is what percent of 45?

9. What number is 9% of 43?

10. What number is 25% of 55?

Objective  *Solve. See Examples 7 and 8.*

11. 10% of 35 is what number?

12. 25% of 60 is what number?

13. What number is 14% of 52?

14. What number is 30% of 17?

Solve. See Examples 9 and 10.

15. 5% of what number is 30?

16. 25% of what number is 25?

17. 1.2 is 12% of what number?

18. 0.22 is 44% of what number?

Solve. See Examples 11 and 12.

19. What percent of 60 is 66?

20. What percent of 20 is 30?

21. 16 is what percent of 50?

22. 27 is what percent of 50?

Objectives A B Mixed Review *Solve. See Examples 1 through 12.*

23. 0.1 is 10% of what number?

24. 0.5 is 5% of what number?

25. 125% of 36 is what number?

26. 200% of 13.5 is what number?

27. 82.5 is $16\frac{1}{2}\%$ of what number?

28. 7.2 is $6\frac{1}{4}\%$ of what number?

356

29. 126 is what percent of 31.5?

30. 264 is what percent of 33?

31. What number is 42% of 60?

32. What number is 36% of 80?

33. What percent of 150 is 67.5?

34. What percent of 105 is 88.2?

35. 120% of what number is 42?

36. 160% of what number is 40?

37. 2.4% of 26 is what number?

38. 4.8% of 32 is what number?

39. What percent of 600 is 3?

40. What percent of 500 is 2?

41. 6.67 is 4.6% of what number?

42. 9.75 is 7.5% of what number?

43. 1575 is what percent of 2500?

44. 2520 is what percent of 3500?

Review

Find the value of n in each proportion. See Section 5.1.

45. $\dfrac{27}{n} = \dfrac{9}{10}$

46. $\dfrac{35}{n} = \dfrac{7}{5}$

47. $\dfrac{n}{5} = \dfrac{8}{11}$

48. $\dfrac{n}{3} = \dfrac{6}{13}$

Write each phrase as a proportion.

49. 17 is to 12 as n is to 20

50. 20 is to 25 as n is to 10

51. 8 is to 9 as 14 is to n

52. 5 is to 6 as 15 is to n

Concept Extensions

For each equation, determine the next step taken to find the value of n. See the first Concept Check in this section.

53. $5 \cdot n = 32$

    a. $n = 5 \cdot 32$
    b. $n = \dfrac{5}{32}$
    c. $n = \dfrac{32}{5}$
    d. none of these

54. $n = 0.7 \cdot 12$

    a. $n = 8.4$
    b. $n = \dfrac{12}{0.7}$
    c. $n = \dfrac{0.7}{12}$
    d. none of these

55. $0.06 = n \cdot 7$

    a. $n = 0.06 \cdot 7$
    b. $n = \dfrac{0.06}{7}$
    c. $n = \dfrac{7}{0.06}$
    d. none of these

56. Write a word statement for the equation $20\% \cdot n = 18.6$. Use the phrase "some number" for "n".

57. Write a word statement for the equation $n = 33\frac{1}{3}\% \cdot 24$. Use the phrase "some number" for "n".

PRACTICE PROBLEM 1

Translate to a proportion.
15% of what number is 55?

EXAMPLE 1 Translate to a proportion.

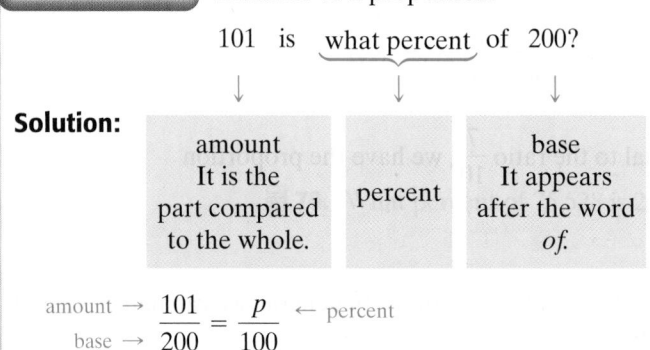

12% of what number is 47?

Solution:

| percent | base It appears after the word *of*. | amount It is the part compared to the whole. |

amount → $\dfrac{47}{b} = \dfrac{12}{100}$ ← percent
base →

◻ **Work Practice Problem 1**

PRACTICE PROBLEM 2

Translate to a proportion.
35 is what percent of 70?

EXAMPLE 2 Translate to a proportion.

101 is what percent of 200?

Solution:

| amount It is the part compared to the whole. | percent | base It appears after the word *of*. |

amount → $\dfrac{101}{200} = \dfrac{p}{100}$ ← percent
base →

◻ **Work Practice Problem 2**

PRACTICE PROBLEM 3

Translate to a proportion.
What number is 25% of 68?

EXAMPLE 3 Translate to a proportion.

What number is 90% of 45?

Solution:

| amount It is the part compared to the whole. | percent | base It appears after the word *of*. |

amount → $\dfrac{a}{45} = \dfrac{90}{100}$ ← percent
base →

◻ **Work Practice Problem 3**

PRACTICE PROBLEM 4

Translate to a proportion.
520 is 65% of what number?

EXAMPLE 4 Translate to a proportion.

238 is 40% of what number?

Solution: amount percent base

$\dfrac{238}{b} = \dfrac{40}{100}$

◻ **Work Practice Problem 4**

Answers

1. $\dfrac{55}{b} = \dfrac{15}{100}$, **2.** $\dfrac{35}{70} = \dfrac{p}{100}$,

3. $\dfrac{a}{68} = \dfrac{25}{100}$, **4.** $\dfrac{520}{b} = \dfrac{65}{100}$

29. 126 is what percent of 31.5?

30. 264 is what percent of 33?

31. What number is 42% of 60?

32. What number is 36% of 80?

33. What percent of 150 is 67.5?

34. What percent of 105 is 88.2?

35. 120% of what number is 42?

36. 160% of what number is 40?

37. 2.4% of 26 is what number?

38. 4.8% of 32 is what number?

39. What percent of 600 is 3?

40. What percent of 500 is 2?

41. 6.67 is 4.6% of what number?

42. 9.75 is 7.5% of what number?

43. 1575 is what percent of 2500?

44. 2520 is what percent of 3500?

Review

Find the value of n in each proportion. See Section 5.1.

45. $\dfrac{27}{n} = \dfrac{9}{10}$

46. $\dfrac{35}{n} = \dfrac{7}{5}$

47. $\dfrac{n}{5} = \dfrac{8}{11}$

48. $\dfrac{n}{3} = \dfrac{6}{13}$

Write each phrase as a proportion.

49. 17 is to 12 as n is to 20

50. 20 is to 25 as n is to 10

51. 8 is to 9 as 14 is to n

52. 5 is to 6 as 15 is to n

Concept Extensions

For each equation, determine the next step taken to find the value of n. See the first Concept Check in this section.

53. $5 \cdot n = 32$

    a. $n = 5 \cdot 32$ **b.** $n = \dfrac{5}{32}$ **c.** $n = \dfrac{32}{5}$ **d.** none of these

54. $n = 0.7 \cdot 12$

    a. $n = 8.4$ **b.** $n = \dfrac{12}{0.7}$ **c.** $n = \dfrac{0.7}{12}$ **d.** none of these

55. $0.06 = n \cdot 7$

    a. $n = 0.06 \cdot 7$ **b.** $n = \dfrac{0.06}{7}$ **c.** $n = \dfrac{7}{0.06}$ **d.** none of these

56. Write a word statement for the equation $20\% \cdot n = 18.6$. Use the phrase "some number" for "n".

57. Write a word statement for the equation $n = 33\dfrac{1}{3}\% \cdot 24$. Use the phrase "some number" for "n".

For each exercise, determine whether the percent, n, is (a) 100%, (b) greater than 100%, or (c) less than 100%. See the last Concept Check in this section.

58. n% of 20 is 30

59. n% of 98 is 98

60. n% of 120 is 85

For each exercise, determine whether the number, n, is (a) equal to 45, (b) greater than 45, or (c) less than 45.

61. 55% of 45 is n

62. 230% of 45 is n

63. 100% of 45 is n

64. 30% of n is 45

65. 100% of n is 45

66. 180% of n is 45

Solve.

67. In your own words, explain how to solve a percent equation.

68. Write a percent problem that uses the percent 50%.

69. 1.5% of 45,775 is what number?

70. What percent of 75,528 is 27,945.36?

71. 22,113 is 180% of what number?

THE BIGGER PICTURE Operations on Sets of Numbers and Solving Equations

Continue your outline from Sections 1.7, 1.9, 2.5, 3.4, 4.5, and 5.1. Suggestions are once again written to help you complete this part of your outline. Notice that this part of the outline has to do with solving equations.

I. Some Operations on Sets of Numbers

  A. Whole Numbers

    1. Add or Subtract (Sections 1.3, 1.4)

    2. Multiply or Divide (Sections 1.6, 1.7)

    3. Exponent (Section 1.9)

    4. Square Root (Section 1.9)

    5. Order of Operations (Section 1.9)

  B. Fractions

    1. Simplify (Section 2.3)

    2. Multiply (Section 2.4)

    3. Divide (Section 2.5)

    4. Add or Subtract (Section 3.4)

  C. Decimals

    1. Add or Subtract (Section 4.3)

    2. Multiply (Section 4.4)

    3. Divide (Section 4.5)

II. Solving Equations

  A. Proportions (Section 5.1)

  B. Percent Problems

    1. Solved by Equations: Remember that "of" means multiplication and "is" means equals.

    12% of some number is 6 translates to

$$12\% \cdot n = 6 \text{ or } 0.12 \cdot n = 6 \text{ or } n = \frac{6}{0.12} \text{ or } n = 50$$

Perform the indicated operations.

1. $\dfrac{2}{9} + \dfrac{1}{5}$

2. $42 \div 2 \cdot 3$

3. $0.03(0.7)$

4. $\sqrt{49} + \sqrt{1}$

Solve.

5. $\dfrac{3}{8} = \dfrac{n}{128}$

6. $\dfrac{7.2}{n} = \dfrac{36}{8}$

7. 215 is what percent of 86?

8. 95% of 48 is what number?

9. 4.2 is what percent of 15?

10. 93.6 is 52% of what number?

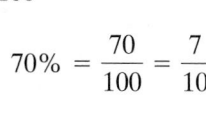

5.5 SOLVING PERCENT PROBLEMS USING PROPORTIONS

Objectives

Ⓐ Write Percent Problems as Proportions.

Ⓑ Solve Percent Problems.

There is more than one method that can be used to solve percent problems. (See the note at the beginning of Section 5.4.) In the last section, we used the percent equation. In this section, we will use proportions.

Objective Ⓐ Writing Percent Problems as Proportions

To understand the proportion method, recall that 70% means the ratio of 70 to 100, or $\frac{70}{100}$.

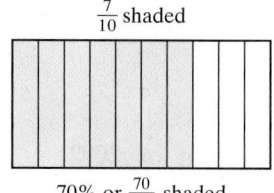

$$70\% = \frac{70}{100} = \frac{7}{10}$$

$\frac{7}{10}$ shaded

70% or $\frac{70}{100}$ shaded

Since the ratio $\frac{70}{100}$ is equal to the ratio $\frac{7}{10}$, we have the proportion

$$\frac{7}{10} = \frac{70}{100}.$$

We call this proportion the "percent proportion." In general, we can name the parts of this proportion as follows:

Percent Proportion

$$\frac{\text{amount}}{\text{base}} = \frac{\text{percent}}{100} \quad \leftarrow \text{always 100}$$

or

$$\begin{array}{l}\text{amount} \rightarrow \\ \text{base} \rightarrow\end{array} \frac{a}{b} = \frac{p}{100} \quad \leftarrow \text{percent}$$

When we translate percent problems to proportions, the **percent,** p, can be identified by looking for the symbol % or the word *percent*. The **base,** b, usually follows the word *of*. The **amount,** a, is the part compared to the whole.

Helpful Hint

Part of Proportion	How It's Identified
Percent	% or percent
Base	Appears after *of*
Amount	Part compared to whole

PRACTICE PROBLEM 1

Translate to a proportion.
15% of what number is 55?

EXAMPLE 1 Translate to a proportion.

12% of what number is 47?

Solution:

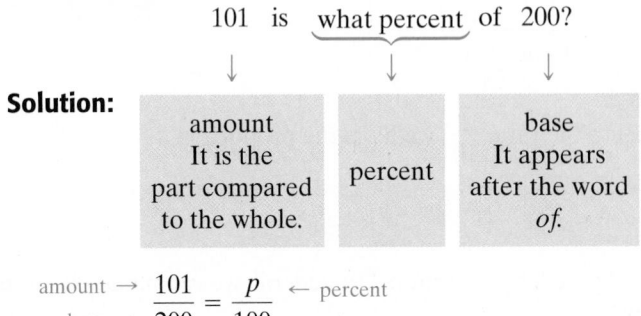

$$\text{amount} \rightarrow \frac{47}{b} = \frac{12}{100} \leftarrow \text{percent}$$

base

🖥 **Work Practice Problem 1**

PRACTICE PROBLEM 2

Translate to a proportion.
35 is what percent of 70?

EXAMPLE 2 Translate to a proportion.

101 is what percent of 200?

Solution:

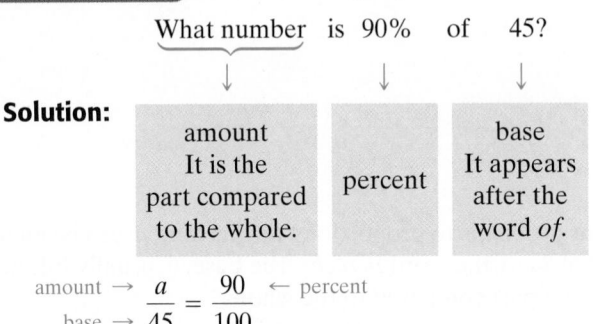

$$\text{amount} \rightarrow \frac{101}{200} = \frac{p}{100} \leftarrow \text{percent}$$

base

🖥 **Work Practice Problem 2**

PRACTICE PROBLEM 3

Translate to a proportion.
What number is 25% of 68?

EXAMPLE 3 Translate to a proportion.

What number is 90% of 45?

Solution:

amount
It is the
part compared
to the whole.   percent   base
It appears
after the
word *of.*

$$\text{amount} \rightarrow \frac{a}{45} = \frac{90}{100} \leftarrow \text{percent}$$

base

🖥 **Work Practice Problem 3**

PRACTICE PROBLEM 4

Translate to a proportion.
520 is 65% of what number?

EXAMPLE 4 Translate to a proportion.

238 is 40% of what number?

Solution: 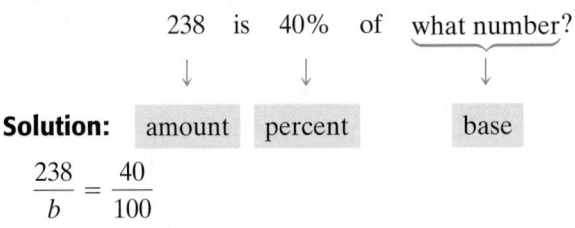 amount   percent   base

$$\frac{238}{b} = \frac{40}{100}$$

🖥 **Work Practice Problem 4**

Answers

1. $\dfrac{55}{b} = \dfrac{15}{100}$, **2.** $\dfrac{35}{70} = \dfrac{p}{100}$,

3. $\dfrac{a}{68} = \dfrac{25}{100}$, **4.** $\dfrac{520}{b} = \dfrac{65}{100}$

EXAMPLE 5 Translate to a proportion.

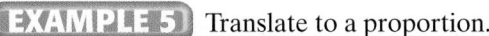

What percent of 30 is 75?

Solution: percent   base   amount

$$\frac{75}{30} = \frac{p}{100}$$

◻ **Work Practice Problem 5**

EXAMPLE 6 Translate to a proportion.

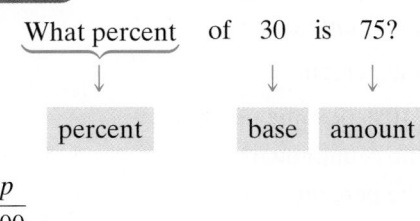

45% of 105 is what number?

Solution: percent   base   amount

$$\frac{a}{105} = \frac{45}{100}$$

◻ **Work Practice Problem 6**

Objective B Solving Percent Problems

The proportions that we have written in this section contain three values that can change: The percent, the base, and the amount. If any two of these values are known, we can find the third (the unknown value). To do this, we write a percent proportion and find the unknown value as we did in Section 5.1.

EXAMPLE 7 Solving Percent Proportion for the Amount

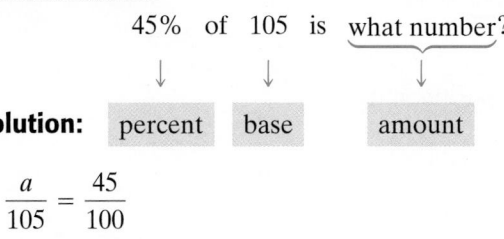

What number is 30% of 9?

Solution: amount   percent   base

$$\frac{a}{9} = \frac{30}{100}$$

To solve, we set cross products equal to each other.

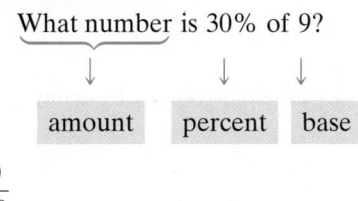

$$\frac{a}{9} = \frac{30}{100}$$

$a \cdot 100 = 9 \cdot 30$ Set cross products equal.

$a \cdot 100 = 270$ Multiply.

Recall from Section 5.1 that if "some number times 100 is 270," then the number is 270 divided by 100.

$$a = \frac{270}{100}$$ Divide 270 by 100, the number multiplied by a.

$a = 2.7$ Simplify.

Thus, 2.7 is 30% of 9.

◻ **Work Practice Problem 7**

PRACTICE PROBLEM 5

Translate to a proportion.
What percent of 50 is 65?

PRACTICE PROBLEM 6

Translate to a proportion.
36% of 80 is what number?

PRACTICE PROBLEM 7

What number is 8% of 120?

Helpful Hint
The proportion in Example 7 contains the ratio $\frac{30}{100}$. A ratio in a proportion may be simplified before solving the proportion. The unknown number in both

$$\frac{a}{9} = \frac{30}{100} \text{ and } \frac{a}{9} = \frac{3}{10} \text{ is 2.7}$$

Answers

5. $\frac{65}{50} = \frac{p}{100}$,   6. $\frac{a}{80} = \frac{36}{100}$,

7. 9.6

✔ **Concept Check** Consider the statement 78 is what percent of 350?

Which part of the percent proportion is unknown?

  a. the amount **b.** the base **c.** the percent

Consider another statement: "14 is 10% of some number."

Which part of the percent proportion is unknown?

  a. the amount **b.** the base **c.** the percent

PRACTICE PROBLEM 8

75% of what number is 60?

EXAMPLE 8 **Solving Percent Problems for the Base**

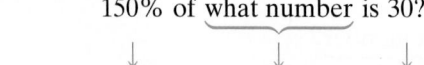

150% of what number is 30?

Solution: percent   base   amount

$\dfrac{30}{b} = \dfrac{150}{100}$ Write the proportion.

$\dfrac{30}{b} = \dfrac{3}{2}$ Write $\dfrac{150}{100}$ as $\dfrac{3}{2}$.

$30 \cdot 2 = b \cdot 3$ Set cross products equal.

$60 = b \cdot 3$ Multiply.

$\dfrac{60}{3} = b$ Divide 60 by 3, the number multiplied by b.

$20 = b$ Simplify.

Thus, 150% of 20 is 30.

▣ **Work Practice Problem 8**

✔ **Concept Check** When solving a percent problem by using a proportion, describe how you can check the result.

PRACTICE PROBLEM 9

15.2 is 5% of what number?

EXAMPLE 9

20.8 is 40% of what number?

Solution: amount percent   base

$\dfrac{20.8}{b} = \dfrac{40}{100}$ or $\dfrac{20.8}{b} = \dfrac{2}{5}$ Write the proportion and simplify $\dfrac{40}{100}$.

$20.8 \cdot 5 = b \cdot 2$ Set cross products equal.

$104 = b \cdot 2$ Multiply.

$\dfrac{104}{2} = b$ Divide 104 by 2, the number multiplied by b.

$52 = b$ Simplify.

So, 20.8 is 40% of 52.

▣ **Work Practice Problem 9**

Answers

8. 80, **9.** 304

✔ **Concept Check Answers**

c, b;

By putting the result into the proportion and checking that the proportion is true

EXAMPLE 10 **Solving Percent Problems for the Percent**

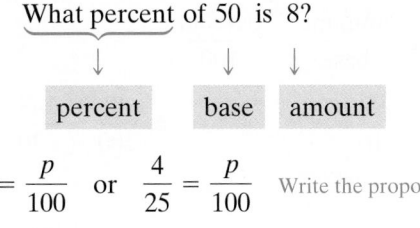

What percent of 50 is 8?

Solution: percent   base   amount

$$\frac{8}{50} = \frac{p}{100} \quad \text{or} \quad \frac{4}{25} = \frac{p}{100} \qquad \text{Write the proportion and simplify } \frac{8}{50}.$$

$$4 \cdot 100 = 25 \cdot p \qquad \text{Set cross products equal.}$$

$$400 = 25 \cdot p \qquad \text{Multiply.}$$

$$\frac{400}{25} = p \qquad \text{Divide 400 by 25, the number multiplied by } p.$$

$$16 = p \qquad \text{Simplify.}$$

So, 16% of 50 is 8.

🔲 **Work Practice Problem 10**

> **Helpful Hint**
>
> Recall from our percent proportion that this number already is a percent. Just keep the number as is and attach a % symbol.

EXAMPLE 11

504 is what percent of 360?

Solution: amount   percent   base

$$\frac{504}{360} = \frac{p}{100}$$

Let's choose not to simplify the ratio $\frac{504}{360}$.

$$504 \cdot 100 = 360 \cdot p \qquad \text{Set cross products equal.}$$

$$50,400 = 360 \cdot p \qquad \text{Multiply.}$$

$$\frac{50,400}{360} = p \qquad \text{Divide 50,400 by 360, the number multiplied by } p.$$

$$140 = p \qquad \text{Simplify.}$$

Notice that by choosing not to simplify $\frac{504}{360}$, we had larger numbers in our equation. Either way, we find that 504 is 140% of 360.

🔲 **Work Practice Problem 11**

You may have noticed the following while working examples.

> **Helpful Hint**
>
> Use the following to see whether your answers are reasonable.
>
> 100% of a number = the number
>
> $\left(\begin{array}{c}\text{a percent} \\ \text{greater than} \\ 100\%\end{array}\right)$ of a number = $\begin{array}{c}\text{a number larger} \\ \text{than the original number}\end{array}$
>
> $\left(\begin{array}{c}\text{a percent} \\ \text{less than } 100\%\end{array}\right)$ of a number = $\begin{array}{c}\text{a number less} \\ \text{than the original number}\end{array}$

PRACTICE PROBLEM 10

What percent of 40 is 6?

PRACTICE PROBLEM 11

336 is what percent of 160?

Answers

10. 15%, **11.** 210%

Mental Math

Identify the amount, the base, and the percent in each equation. Recall that $\dfrac{\text{amount}}{\text{base}} = \dfrac{\text{percent}}{100}$.

1. $\dfrac{12.6}{42} = \dfrac{30}{100}$

2. $\dfrac{201}{300} = \dfrac{67}{100}$

3. $\dfrac{20}{100} = \dfrac{102}{510}$

4. $\dfrac{40}{100} = \dfrac{248}{620}$

5.5 EXERCISE SET

FOR EXTRA HELP

Student Solutions Manual   PH Math/Tutor Center   CD/Video for Review    MathXL®    MyMathLab

Objective A *Translate each to a proportion. Do not solve. See Examples 1 through 6.*

1. 32% of 65 is what number?

2. 92% of 30 is what number?

3. What number is 19% of 130?

4. What number is 5% of 125?

5. 2.3 is 58% of what number?

6. 1.2 is 47% of what number?

7. 40% of what number is 75?

8. 520 is 85% of what number?

9. What percent of 200 is 70?

10. 8.2 is what percent of 82?

Objective B *Solve. See Example 7.*

11. 10% of 55 is what number?

12. 25% of 84 is what number?

13. What number is 18% of 105?

14. What number is 40% of 29?

Solve. See Examples 8 and 9.

15. 15% of what number is 60?

16. 75% of what number is 75?

17. 7.8 is 78% of what number?

18. 1.1 is 44% of what number?

Solve. See Examples 10 and 11.

19. 105 is what percent of 84?

20. 77 is what percent of 44?

21. 14 is what percent of 50?

22. 37 is what percent of 50?

Objectives **A** **B** **Mixed Practice** *Solve. See Examples 1 through 11.*

23. 2.9 is 10% of what number?

24. 6.2 is 5% of what number?

25. 2.4% of 80 is what number?

26. 6.5% of 120 is what number?

27. 160 is 16% of what number?

28. 30 is 6% of what number?

29. 348.6 is what percent of 166?

30. 262.4 is what percent of 82?

31. What number is 89% of 62?

32. What number is 53% of 130?

33. What percent of 8 is 3.6?

34. What percent of 5 is 1.6?

35. 140% of what number is 119?

36. 170% of what number is 221?

37. 1.8% of 48 is what number?

38. 7.8% of 24 is what number?

39. What percent of 500 is 3?

40. What percent of 800 is 4?

41. 3.5 is 2.5% of what number?

42. 9.18 is 6.8% of what number?

43. 2486 is what percent of 2200?

44. 9310 is what percent of 3800?

Review

Add or subtract the fractions. See Sections 3.1, 3.3, and 3.4.

45. $\dfrac{11}{16} + \dfrac{3}{16}$

46. $\dfrac{5}{8} - \dfrac{7}{12}$

47. $3\dfrac{1}{2} - \dfrac{11}{30}$

48. $2\dfrac{2}{3} + 4\dfrac{1}{2}$

Add or subtract the decimals. See Section 4.3.

49.
$$\begin{array}{r} 0.41 \\ +\,0.29 \\ \hline \end{array}$$

50.
$$\begin{array}{r} 10.78 \\ 4.3 \\ +\,\,0.21 \\ \hline \end{array}$$

51.
$$\begin{array}{r} 2.38 \\ -\,0.19 \\ \hline \end{array}$$

52.
$$\begin{array}{r} 16.37 \\ -\,2.61 \\ \hline \end{array}$$

Concept Extensions

53. Write a word statement for the proportion $\dfrac{n}{28} = \dfrac{25}{100}$. Use the phrase "the number" for "n."

Solve. See the Concept Checks in this section.

Suppose you have finished solving three percent problems using proportions that you set up correctly. Check each answer to see if each makes the proportion a true proportion. If any proportion is not true, solve it to find the correct solution.

54. $\dfrac{a}{64} = \dfrac{25}{100}$
Is the amount equal to 17?

55. $\dfrac{520}{b} = \dfrac{65}{100}$
Is the base equal to 800?

56. $\dfrac{36}{12} = \dfrac{P}{100}$
Is the percent equal to 50 (50%)?

57. Write a percent statement that translates to
$\dfrac{16}{80} = \dfrac{20}{100}$

58. In your own words, explain how to use a proportion to solve a percent problem.

Solve. Round to the nearest tenth, if necessary.

59. What number is 22.3% of 53,862?

60. What percent of 110,736 is 88,542?

61. 8652 is 119% of what number?

 THE BIGGER PICTURE   Operations on Sets of Numbers and Solving Equations

Continue your outline from Sections 1.7, 1.9, 2.5, 3.4, 4.5, and 5.1. (If you did not cover Section 5.4, pay no attention to the part of the outline numbered II.B.1.) Suggestions are once again written to help you complete this part of your outline. Notice that this part of the outline has to do with solving equations.

I. Some Operations on Sets of Numbers

  A. Whole Numbers

    1. **Add or Subtract** (Sections 1.3, 1.4)

    2. **Multiply or Divide** (Sections 1.6, 1.7)

    3. **Exponent** (Section 1.9)

    4. **Square Root** (Section 1.9)

    5. **Order of Operations** (Section 1.9)

  B. Fractions

    1. **Simplify** (Section 2.3)

    2. **Multiply** (Section 2.4)

    3. **Divide** (Section 2.5)

    4. **Add or Subtract** (Section 3.4)

  C. Decimals

    1. **Add or Subtract** (Section 4.3)

    2. **Multiply** (Section 4.4)

    3. **Divide** (Section 4.5)

II. Solving Equations

  A. Proportions (Section 5.1)

B. Percent Problems

  1. **Solved by Equations** (Section 5.4—you may not have covered this section)

  2. **Solved by Proportions:** Remember that percent, p, is identified by % or percent,

    base, b, usually appears after "of" and

    amount, a, is the part compared to the whole.

    12% of some number is 6 translates to

$$\frac{6}{b} = \frac{12}{100} \text{ or } 6 \cdot 100 = b \cdot 12 \text{ or } \frac{600}{12} = b \text{ or } 50 = b$$

Perform the indicated operations.

1. $\dfrac{2}{9} + \dfrac{1}{5}$ **2.** $42 \div 2 \cdot 3$

3. $0.03\,(0.7)$ **4.** $\sqrt{49} + \sqrt{1}$

Solve.

5. $\dfrac{3}{8} = \dfrac{n}{128}$ **6.** $\dfrac{7.2}{n} = \dfrac{36}{8}$

7. 215 is what percent of 86?

8. 95% of 48 is what number?

9. 4.2 is what percent of 15?

10. 93.6 is 52% of what number?

Percent and Percent Problems

Write each number as a percent.

1. 0.12   **2.** 0.68   **3.** $\dfrac{1}{8}$ **4.** $\dfrac{5}{2}$

5. 5.2   **6.** 8   **7.** $\dfrac{3}{50}$ **8.** $\dfrac{11}{25}$

9. $7\dfrac{1}{2}$ **10.** $3\dfrac{1}{4}$ **11.** 0.03   **12.** 0.05

Write each percent as a decimal.

13. 65%   **14.** 31%   **15.** 8%   **16.** 7%

17. 142%   **18.** 400%   **19.** 2.9%   **20.** 6.6%

Write each percent as a decimal and as a fraction or mixed number in simplest form.
(If necessary when writing as a decimal, round to the nearest thousandth.)

21. 3%   **22.** 5%   **23.** 5.25%   **24.** 12.75%

Answers

1. _____
2. _____
3. _____
4. _____
5. _____
6. _____
7. _____
8. _____
9. _____
10. _____
11. _____
12. _____
13. _____
14. _____
15. _____
16. _____
17. _____
18. _____
19. _____
20. _____
21. _____
22. _____
23. _____
24. _____

25. _____

26. _____

27. _____

28. _____

29. _____

30. _____

31. _____

32. _____

33. _____

34. _____

35. _____

36. _____

37. _____

38. _____

39. _____

40. _____

25. 38%   **26.** 45%   **27.** $12\frac{1}{3}\%$ **28.** $16\frac{2}{3}\%$

Solve each percent problem.

29. 12% of 70 is what number?   **30.** 36 is 36% of what number?

31. 212.5 is 85% of what number?   **32.** 66 is what percent of 55?

33. 23.8 is what percent of 85?   **34.** 38% of 200 is what number?

35. What number is 25% of 44?   **36.** What percent of 99 is 128.7?

37. What percent of 250 is 215?   **38.** What number is 45% of 84?

39. 42% of what number is 63?   **40.** 95% of what number is 58.9?

5.6 APPLICATIONS OF PERCENT

Objectives

A Solve Applications Involving Percent.

B Find Percent Increase and Percent Decrease.

Objective **A** Solving Applications Involving Percent

Percent is used in a variety of everyday situations. The next examples show just a few ways that percent occurs in real-life settings. (Each of these examples shows two ways of solving these problems. If you studied Section 5.4 only, see *Method 1*. If you studied Section 5.5 only, see *Method 2*.)

EXAMPLE 1 Finding Percent of Nursing Schools with Increases in Enrollment

There is a world wide shortage of nurses that is projected to be 20% below requirements by 2020. Until 2001, there has also been a continual decline in enrollment in nursing schools. That has recently changed.

In 2003, 2178 of the total 2593 nursing schools in the U.S. had an increase in applications or enrollment. What percent of nursing schools had an increase? Round to the nearest whole percent. (*Source:* CNN and *Nurse Week*)

Solution: *Method 1.* First, we state the problem in words.

In words: 2178 is what percent of 2593?

Translate: $2178 = n \cdot 2593$

Next, solve for n.

$\dfrac{2178}{2593} = n$ Divide 2178 by 2593, the number multiplied by n.

$0.84 \approx n$ Divide and round to the nearest hundredth.

$84\% \approx n$ Write as a percent.

In 2003, about 84% of nursing schools had an increase in applications or enrollment.

Method 2.

In words: 2178 is what percent of 2593?

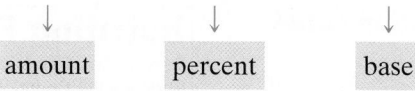

amount   percent   base

Translate: $\begin{array}{l}\text{amount} \to \\ \text{base} \to\end{array} \dfrac{2178}{2593} = \dfrac{p}{100} \leftarrow \text{percent}$

Next, solve for p.

$2178 \cdot 100 = 2593 \cdot p$ Set cross products equal.

$217{,}800 = 2593 \cdot p$ Multiply.

$\dfrac{217{,}800}{2593} = p$ Divide 217,800 by 2593, the number multiplied by p.

$84 \approx p$

In 2003, about 84% of nursing schools had an increase in applications or enrollment.

🔲 **Work Practice Problem 1**

PRACTICE PROBLEM 1

There are 106 nursing schools in Ohio. Of these schools, 61 offer RN (registered nurse) degrees. What percent of nursing schools in Ohio offer RN degrees? Round to the nearest whole percent.

Answer

1. 58%

PRACTICE PROBLEM 2

The freshmen class of 775 students is 31% of all students at Euclid University. How many students go to Euclid University?

EXAMPLE 2 Finding the Base Number of Absences

Mr. Buccaran, the principal at Slidell High School, counted 31 freshmen absent during a particular day. If this is 4% of the total number of freshmen, how many freshmen are there at Slidell High School?

Solution: *Method 1.* First we state the problem in words; then we translate.

In words: 31   is   4%   of   what number?
            ↓   ↓   ↓   ↓   ↓
Translate: 31   =   4%   · n

Next, we solve for n.

$31 = 0.04 \cdot n$ Write 4% as a decimal.

$\dfrac{31}{0.04} = n$ Divide 31 by 0.04, the number multiplied by n.

$775 = n$ Simplify.

There are 775 freshmen at Slidell High School.

Method 2. First we state the problem in words; then we translate.

In words: 31   is   4%   of   what number?

            amount   percent   base

Translate: $\text{amount} \rightarrow \dfrac{31}{b} = \dfrac{4}{100} \leftarrow \text{percent}$

Next, we solve for b.

$31 \cdot 100 = b \cdot 4$ Set cross products equal.

$3100 = b \cdot 4$ Multiply.

$\dfrac{3100}{4} = b$ Divide 3100 by 4, the number multiplied by b.

$775 = b$ Simplify.

There are 775 freshmen at Slidell High School.

■ **Work Practice Problem 2**

PRACTICE PROBLEM 3

The nutrition label below is from a can of cashews. Find what percent of total calories are from fat. Round to the nearest tenth of a percent.

Nutrition Facts

Serving Size ¼ cup (33g)
Servings Per Container About 9

Amount Per Serving

Calories 190 **Calories from Fat** 130

	% Daily Value
Total Fat 16g	**24%**
Saturated Fat 3g	**16%**
Cholesterol 0mg	**0%**
Sodium 135mg	**6%**
Total Carbohydrate 9g	**3%**
Dietary Fiber 1g	**5%**
Sugars 2g	
Protein 5g	

Vitamin A 0% • Vitamin C 0%
Calcium 0% • Iron 8%

Answers

2. 2500, **3.** 68.4%

EXAMPLE 3 Finding Nutrition Label Percents

Standardized nutrition labels like the one shown at the right have been on foods since 1994. It is recommended that no more than 30% of your calorie intake be from fat. Find what percent of the total calories shown are fat.

Solution: *Method 1.*

In words: 10   is   what percent   of   80?
            ↓   ↓   ↓   ↓   ↓
Translate: 10   = n ·   80

Nutrition Facts

Serving Size 1 pouch (20g)
Servings Per Container 6

Amount Per Serving

Calories	80
Calories from fat	10

	% Daily Value*
Total Fat 1g	**2%**
Sodium 45mg	**2%**
Total Carbohydrate 17g	**6%**
Sugars 9g	
Protein 0g	
Vitamin C	25%

Not a significant source of saturated fat, cholesterol, dietary fiber, vitamin A, calcium and iron.

*Percent Daily Values are based on a 2,000 calorie diet.

Fruit snacks nutrition label

Next, we solve for n.

$\dfrac{10}{80} = n$ Divide 10 by 80, the number multiplied by n.

$0.125 = n$ Simplify.

$12.5\% = n$ Write 0.125 as a percent.

12.5% of this food's total calories are from fat.

Method 2.

In words: 10 is what percent of 80?

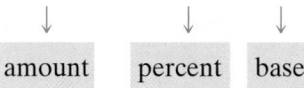

amount percent base

Translate: amount → $\dfrac{10}{80} = \dfrac{p}{100}$ ← percent
base →

Next, we solve for p.

$10 \cdot 100 = 80 \cdot p$ Set cross products equal.

$1000 = 80 \cdot p$ Multiply.

$\dfrac{1000}{80} = p$ Divide 1000 by 80, the number multiplied by p.

$12.5 = p$ Simplify.

12.5% of this food's total calories are from fat.

■ **Work Practice Problem 3**

EXAMPLE 4 **Finding the Base Increase in Population**

The state of Nevada had the largest percent increase in population, about 66%, from the 1990 census to the 2000 census. In 1990, the population of Nevada was about 1202 thousand.

a. Find the increase in population from 1990 to 2000.
b. Find the population of Nevada in 2000.

(*Source:* U.S. Census Bureau)

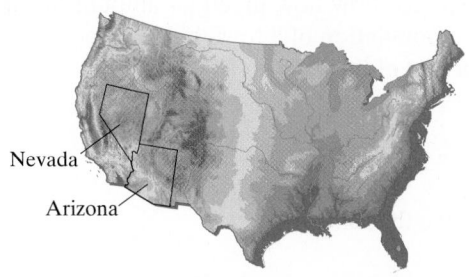

Nevada
Arizona

Solution: *Method 1.* First we find the increase in population.

In words: What number is 66% of 1202?

Translate: n $= 66\% \cdot 1202$
Next, we solve for n.

$n = 0.66 \cdot 1202$ Write 66% as a decimal.

$n = 793.32$ Multiply.

Continued on next page

PRACTICE PROBLEM 4

The state of Arizona had the second-largest percent increase in population, 40%, from the 1990 census to the 2000 census. In 1990, the population of Arizona was about 3665 thousand. (*Source:* U.S. Census Bureau)

a. Find the increase in population from 1990 to 2000.

b. Find the population of Arizona in 2000.

Answers
4. a. 1466 thousand, **b.** 5131 thousand

The increase in population is 793.32 thousand. This means that the

$$\begin{array}{c} \text{Nevada} \\ \text{population} \\ \text{in 2000} \end{array} = \begin{array}{c} \text{Population} \\ \text{in 1990} \end{array} + \begin{array}{c} \text{Increase} \\ \text{in population} \end{array}$$

$$= 1202 \text{ thousand} + 793.32 \text{ thousand}$$

$$= 1995.32 \text{ thousand}$$

Method 2. First we find the increase in population.

In words: What number is 66% of 1202?

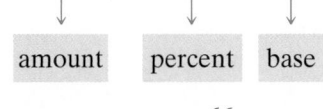

amount   percent   base

Translate: $\text{amount} \rightarrow \dfrac{a}{1202} = \dfrac{66}{100} \leftarrow \text{percent}$

Next, we solve for a.

$a \cdot 100 = 1202 \cdot 66$ Set cross products equal.

$a \cdot 100 = 79{,}332$ Multiply.

$a = \dfrac{79{,}332}{100}$ Divide 79,332 by 100, the number multiplied by a.

$a = 793.32$ Simplify.

The increase in population is 793.32 thousand. This means that the population of Nevada in 2000 was

$$\begin{array}{c} \text{Nevada} \\ \text{population} \\ \text{in 2000} \end{array} = \begin{array}{c} \text{Population} \\ \text{in 1990} \end{array} + \begin{array}{c} \text{Increase} \\ \text{in population} \end{array}$$

$$= 1202 \text{ thousand} + 793.32 \text{ thousand}$$

$$= 1995.32 \text{ thousand}$$

Work Practice Problem 4

Objective B Finding Percent Increase and Percent Decrease

We often use percents to show how much an amount has increased or decreased.
Suppose that the population of a town is 10,000 people and then it increases by 2000 people. The **percent of increase** is

$$\text{amount of increase} \rightarrow \dfrac{2000}{10{,}000} = 0.2 = 20\% \quad \text{original amount} \rightarrow$$

In general, we have the following.

Percent of Increase

$$\text{percent of increase} = \dfrac{\text{amount of increase}}{\text{original amount}}$$

Then write the quotient as a percent.

EXAMPLE 5 Finding Percent Increase

The number of applications for a mathematics scholarship at Yale increased from 34 to 45 in one year. What is the percent increase? Round to the nearest whole percent.

Solution: First we find the amount of increase by subtracting the original number of applicants from the new number of applicants.

$$\text{amount of increase} = 45 - 34 = 11$$

The amount of increase is 11 applicants. To find the percent of increase,

$$\text{percent of increase} = \frac{\text{amount of increase}}{\text{original amount}} = \frac{11}{34} \approx 0.32 = 32\%$$

The number of applications increased by about 32%.

📗 **Work Practice Problem 5**

✔ **Concept Check** A student is calculating the percent increase in enrollment from 180 students one year to 200 students the next year. Explain what is wrong with the following calculations:

$$\frac{\text{Amount}}{\text{of increase}} = 200 - 180 = 20$$

$$\frac{\text{Percent of}}{\text{increase}} = \frac{20}{200} = 0.1 = 10\%$$

Suppose that your income was $300 a week and then it decreased by $30. The **percent of decrease** is

$$\text{amount of decrease} \rightarrow \frac{\$30}{\$300} = 0.1 = 10\%$$
$$\text{original amount} \rightarrow$$

Percent of Decrease

$$\text{percent of decrease} = \frac{\text{amount of decrease}}{\text{original amount}}$$

Then write the quotient as a percent.

EXAMPLE 6 Finding Percent Decrease

In response to a decrease in sales, a company with 1500 employees reduces the number of employees to 1230. What is the percent decrease?

Solution: First we find the amount of decrease by subtracting 1230 from 1500.

$$\text{amount of decrease} = 1500 - 1230 = 270$$

The amount of decrease is 270. To find the percent of decrease,

$$\frac{\text{percent of}}{\text{decrease}} = \frac{\text{amount of decrease}}{\text{original amount}} = \frac{270}{1500} = 0.18 = 18\%$$

The number of employees decreased by 18%.

📗 **Work Practice Problem 6**

PRACTICE PROBLEM 5

The number of people attending the local play, *Peter Pan*, increased from 285 on Friday to 333 on Saturday. Find the percent increase in attendance? Round to the nearest tenth of a percent.

Helpful Hint Make sure that this number is the original number and not the new number.

PRACTICE PROBLEM 6

A town with a population of 20,200 in 1995 decreased to 18,483 in 2005. What was the percent decrease?

Answers
5. 16.8%, **6.** 8.5%

✔ **Concept Check Answer**
To find the percent of increase, you have to divide the amount of increase (20) by the original amount (180).

5.6 EXERCISE SET

Student Solutions Manual   PH Math/Tutor Center   CD/Video for Review   MathXL®   MyMathLab

Objective A *Solve. See Examples 1 and 2.*

1. An inspector found 24 defective bolts during an inspection. If this is 1.5% of the total number of bolts inspected, how many bolts were inspected?

2. A day care worker found 28 children absent one day during an epidemic of chicken pox. If this was 35% of the total number of children attending the day care center, how many children attend this day care center?

3. 18% of Frank's wages are withheld for income tax. Find the amount withheld from Frank's wages of $3680 per month.

4. The Hodder family paid 20% of the purchase price of a $75,000 home as a down payment. Determine the amount of the down payment.

5. Vera Faciane earns $2000 per month and budgets $300 per month for food. What percent of her monthly income is spent on food?

6. Last year, Mai Toberlan bought a share of stock for $83. She was paid a dividend of $4.15. Determine what percent of the stock price is the dividend.

7. A manufacturer of electronic components expects 1.04% of its products to be defective. Determine the number of defective components expected in a batch of 28,350 components. Round to the nearest whole component.

8. An owner of a repair service company estimates that for every 40 hours a repairperson is on the job, he can bill for only 78% of the hours. The remaining hours, the repairperson is idle or driving to or from a job. Determine the number of hours per 40-hour week the owner can bill for a repairperson.

9. Of the 535 members of the 108th U.S. Congress, 73 have attended a community college. What percent of the members of the 108th Congress is this? Round to the nearest tenth of a percent. (*Source:* American Association of Community Colleges)

10. The Los Angeles County courts excused 775,130 prospective jurors from jury duty in a recent year. This represented 28% of all juror qualification affidavits sent out that year. How many juror qualification affidavits were sent out that year? Round to the nearest whole affidavit. (*Source:* Los Angeles Superior Court)

11. There are about 98,400 female dental hygienists registered in the United States. If this represents about 98.3% of the nation's dental hygienists, find the approximate number of dental hygienists in the United States. (*Source:* The American Dental Hygienists' Association)

12. 31.6% of all households in the United States own at least one pet dog. There are 11,250 households in Anytown. How many of these households would you expect own a dog? (*Source:* American Veterinary Medical Association)

For each food described, find what percent of total calories is from fat. If necessary, round to the nearest tenth of a percent. See Example 3.

13. Ranch dressing serving size of 2 tablespoons

	Calories
Total	40
From fat	20

14. Unsweetened cocoa powder serving size of 1 tablespoon

	Calories
Total	20
From fat	5

15.

Nutrition Facts
Serving Size 18 crackers (29g)
Servings Per Container About 9

Amount Per Serving

Calories 120 Calories from Fat 35

	% Daily Value*
Total Fat 4g	**6%**
Saturated Fat 0.5g	**3%**
Polyunsaturated Fat 0g	
Monounsaturated Fat 1.5g	
Cholesterol 0mg	**0%**
Sodium 220mg	**9%**
Total Carbohydrate 21g	**7%**
Dietary Fiber 2g	**7%**
Sugars 3g	
Protein 2g	

Vitamin A 0% • Vitamin C 0%
Calcium 2% • Iron 4%
Phosphorus 10%

Snack Crackers

16.

Nutrition Facts
Serving Size 28 crackers (31g)
Servings Per Container About 6

Amount Per Serving

Calories 130 Calories from Fat 35

	% Daily Value*
Total Fat 4g	**6%**
Saturated Fat 2g	**10%**
Polyunsaturated Fat 1g	
Monounsaturated Fat 1g	
Cholesterol 0mg	**0%**
Sodium 470mg	**20%**
Total Carbohydrate 23g	**8%**
Dietary Fiber 1g	**4%**
Sugars 4g	
Protein 2g	

Vitamin A 0% • Vitamin C 0%
Calcium 0% • Iron 2%

Snack Crackers

Solve. Round money amounts to the nearest cent and all other amounts to the nearest tenth. See Example 4.

17. Ace Furniture Company currently produces 6200 chairs per month. If production decreases by 8%, find the decrease and the new number of chairs produced each month.

18. The enrollment at a local college decreased by 5% over last year's enrollment of 7640. Find the decrease in enrollment and the current enrollment.

19. By carefully planning their meals, a family was able to decrease their weekly grocery bill by 20%. Their weekly grocery bill used to be $170. What is their new weekly grocery bill?

20. The profit of Ramone Company last year was $175,000. This year's profit decreased by 11%. Find this year's profit.

21. A car manufacturer announced that next year the price of a certain model of car would increase by 4.5%. This year the price is $19,286. Find the increase in price and the new price.

22. A union contract calls for a 6.5% salary increase for all employees. Determine the increase and the new salary that a worker currently making $38,500 under this contract can expect.

23. From 2002 to 2012, the number of people employed as physician assistants in the United States is expected to increase by 49%. The number of people employed as physician assistants in 2002 was 63,000. Find the predicted number of physician assistants in 2012. (*Source:* Bureau of Labor Statistics)

24. The state of North Dakota had the smallest percent increase in population, 0.5%, from the 1990 census to the 2000 census. In 1990, the population of North Dakota was 638,800. What was the population of North Dakota in 2000? (*Source:* U.S. Census Bureau)

North Dakota

25. The population of Americans aged 65 and older was 35 million in 2000. That population is projected to increase by 80% by 2025. Find the increase and the projected 2025 population. (*Source:* Bureau of the Census)

26. The from 2000 to 2010, the number of masters degrees awarded to women is projected to increase by 8.3%. The number of women who received masters degrees in 2000 was 265,000. Find the predicted number of women to be awarded masters degrees in 2010. (*Source:* U.S. National Center for Education Statistics)

Objective **B** *Find the amount of increase and the percent increase. See Example 5.*

	Original Amount	New Amount	Amount of Increase	Percent Increase
27.	40	50		
28.	10	15		
29.	85	187		
30.	78	351		

Find the amount of decrease and the percent decrease. See Example 6.

	Original Amount	New Amount	Amount of Decrease	Percent Decrease
31.	8	6		
32.	25	20		
33.	160	40		
34.	200	162		

Solve. Round percents to the nearest tenth, if necessary. See Examples 5 and 6.

35. There are 150 calories in a cup of whole milk and only 84 in a cup of skim milk. In switching to skim milk, find the percent decrease in number of calories per cup.

36. In reaction to a slow economy, the number of employees at a soup company decreased from 530 to 477. What was the percent decrease in the number of employees?

37. By changing his driving routines, Alan Miller increased his car's rate of miles per gallon from 19.5 to 23.7. Find the percent increase.

38. John Smith decided to decrease the number of calories in his diet from 3250 to 2100. Find the percent decrease.

39. The number of cable TV systems recently decreased from 10,845 to 10,700. Find the percent decrease.

40. Before taking a typing course, Geoffry Landers could type 32 words per minute. By the end of the course, he was able to type 76 words per minute. Find the percent increase.

41. In 1940, the average size of a U.S. farm was 174 acres. By 2003, the average size of a U.S. farm had increased to 441 acres. What was the percent increase? (*Source:* National Agricultural Statistics Service)

42. In 1995, 272.6 million recorded music cassettes were shipped to retailers in the United States. By 2000, this number had decreased to 76.0 million cassettes. What was the percent decrease? (*Source:* Recording Industry Association of America)

43. In 1994, approximately 16,000,000 Americans subscribed to cellular phone service. By 2003, this number had increased to about 159,000,000 American subscribers. What was the percent increase? (*Source:* Network World, Inc.)

44. In 1970, there were 1754 deaths from boating accidents in the United States. By 2003, the number of deaths from boating accidents had decreased to 703. What was the percent decrease? (*Source:* U.S. Coast Guard)

45. In 1994, approximately 16,000 occupational therapy assistants and aides were employed in the United States. According to one survey, by 2005, this number is expected to increase to 29,000 assistants and aides. What is the percent increase? (*Source:* Bureau of Labor Statistics)

46. In 1994, approximately 206,000 medical assistants were employed in the United States. By 2005, this number is expected to increase to 327,000 medical assistants. What is the percent increase? (*Source:* Bureau of Labor Statistics)

47. In 1999, discarded electronics, including obsolete computer equipment, accounted for 75,000 tons of solid waste per year in Massachusetts. By 2006, discarded electronic waste is expected to increase to 300,000 tons of waste per year in the state. Find the percent increase. (*Source:* Massachusetts Department of Environmental Protection)

48. The average soft-drink size has increased from 13.1 oz to 19.9 oz over the past two decades. Find the percent increase. (*Source:* University of North Carolina at Chapel Hill, *Journal for American Medicine*)

19.9 oz

13.1 oz

49. The population of Tokyo is expected to decrease from 127,333 thousand in 2004 to 99,887 thousand in 2050. Find the percent decrease. (*Source:* International Programs Center, Bureau of the Census, U.S. Dept. of Commerce)

Japan

Tokyo

50. In 2002, approximately 394,000 computer application software engineers were employed in the United States. By 2012, this number is expected to increase to 573,000. What is the percent increase? (*Source:* Bureau of Labor Statistics)

Review

Perform each indicated operation. See Sections 4.3 and 4.4.

51. 0.12
  $\times$ 38

52. 42
  $\times 0.7$

53. $9.20 + 1.98$

54. $46 + 7.89$

55. $78 - 19.46$

56. $64.80 - 10.72$

Concept Extensions

57. If a number is increased by 100%, how does the increased number compare with the original number? Explain your answer.

58. In your own words, explain what is wrong with the following statement. "Last year we had 80 students attend. This year we have a 50% increase or a total of 160 students attend."

59. Explain what errors were made by each student when solving percent of increase or decrease problems and then correct the errors. *"The population of a certain rural town was 150 in 1980, 180 in 1990, and 150 in 2000."*

    a. Find the percent of increase in population from 1980 to 1990.

        Miranda's solution: Percent of increase $= \dfrac{30}{180} = 0.1\overline{6} \approx 16.7\%$

    b. Find the percent of decrease in population from 1990 to 2000.

        Jeremy's solution: Percent of decrease $= \dfrac{30}{150} = 0.20 = 20\%$

    c. The percent of increase from 1980 to 1990 is the same as the percent of decrease from 1990 to 2000. True or false.

        Chris's answer: True because they had the same amount of increase as the amount of decrease.

5.7 PERCENT AND PROBLEM SOLVING: SALES TAX, COMMISSION, AND DISCOUNT

Objectives

A Calculate Sales Tax and Total Price.

B Calculate Commissions.

C Calculate Discount and Sale Price.

Objective **A** Calculating Sales Tax and Total Price

Percents are frequently used in the retail trade. For example, most states charge a tax on certain items when purchased. This tax is called a **sales tax,** and retail stores collect it for the state. Sales tax is almost always stated as a percent of the purchase price.

A 6% sales tax rate on a purchase of a $10 item gives a sales tax of

sales tax = 6% of $10 = 0.06 · $10.00 = $0.60

The total price to the customer would be

purchase price plus sales tax

$10.00 + $0.60 = $10.60

This example suggests the following equations:

Sales Tax and Total Price

sales tax = tax rate · purchase price

total price = purchase price + sales tax

In this section we round dollar amounts to the nearest cent.

EXAMPLE 1 Finding Sales Tax and Purchase Price

Find the sales tax and the total price on the purchase of an $85.50 trench coat in a city where the sales tax rate is 7.5%.

Solution: The purchase price is $85.50 and the tax rate is 7.5%.

sales tax = tax rate · purchase price

sales tax = 7.5% · $85.50
          = 0.075 · $85.5   Write 7.5% as a decimal.
          ≈ $6.41   Rounded to the nearest cent.

Thus, the sales tax is $6.41. Next find the total price.

total price = purchase price + sales tax

total price = $85.50 + $6.41
           = $91.91

The sales tax on $85.50 is $6.41, and the total price is $91.91.

📖 **Work Practice Problem 1**

PRACTICE PROBLEM 1

If the sales tax rate is 6%, what is the sales tax and the total amount due on a $29.90 Goodgrip tire?

Answer
1. tax: $1.79; total: $31.69

PRACTICE PROBLEM 2

The sales tax on a $13,500 automobile is $1080. Find the sales tax rate.

PRACTICE PROBLEM 3

Mr. Olsen is a sales representative for Miko Copiers. Last month he sold $37,632 worth of copy equipment and supplies. What is his commission for the month if he is paid a commission of 6.6% of his total sales for the month?

Answers

2. 8%, **3.** $2483.71

✔ **Concept Check Answer**

Since $10\% = \frac{1}{10}$, the sales tax is $\frac{\$50}{10} = \$5$. The total price should have been $55.

✔**Concept Check** The purchase price of a textbook is $50 and sales tax is 10%. If you are told by the cashier that the total price is $75, how can you tell that a mistake has been made?

EXAMPLE 2 Finding a Sales Tax Rate

The sales tax on a $300 printer is $22.50. Find the sales tax rate.

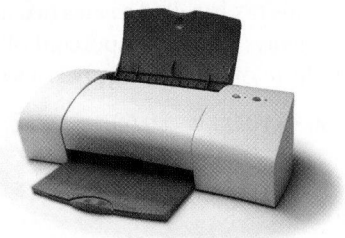

Solution: Let r represent the unknown sales tax rate. Then

sales tax	=	tax rate	·	purchase price

$$\$22.50 = r \cdot \$300$$
$$\frac{22.50}{300} = r \quad \text{Divide 22.50 by 300, the number multiplied by } r.$$
$$0.075 = r \quad \text{Simplify.}$$
$$7.5\% = r \quad \text{Write 0.075 as a percent.}$$

The sales tax rate is 7.5%.

▪ **Work Practice Problem 2**

Objective **B** **Calculating Commissions**

A **wage** is payment for performing work. Hourly wage, commissions, and salary are some of the ways wages can be paid. Many people who work in sales are paid a commission. An employee who is paid a **commission** is paid a percent of his or her total sales.

Commission

$$\text{commission} = \text{commission rate} \cdot \text{sales}$$

EXAMPLE 3 Finding the Amount of Commission

Sherry Souter, a real estate broker for Wealth Investments, sold a house for $114,000 last week. If her commission is 1.5% of the selling price of the home, find the amount of her commission.

Solution:

commission	=	commission rate	·	sales
commission	=	1.5%	·	$114,000
	=	0.015	·	$114,000 Write 1.5% as 0.015.
	=	$1710		Multiply.

Her commission on the house is $1710.

◼ **Work Practice Problem 3**

EXAMPLE 4 **Finding a Commission Rate**

A salesperson earned $1560 for selling $13,000 worth of television and stereo systems. Find the commission rate.

Solution: Let r stand for the unknown commission rate. Then

$$\underbrace{\text{commission}}_{\downarrow} = \underbrace{\text{commission rate}}_{\downarrow} \cdot \underbrace{\text{sales}}_{\downarrow}$$

$$\$1560 = r \cdot \$13,000$$

$$\frac{1560}{13,000} = r \quad \text{Divide 1560 by 13,000, the number multiplied by } r.$$

$$0.12 = r \quad \text{Simplify.}$$

$$12\% = r \quad \text{Write 0.12 as a percent.}$$

The commission rate is 12%.

◼ **Work Practice Problem 4**

Objective C Calculating Discount and Sale Price

Suppose that an item that normally sells for $40 is on sale for 25% off. This means that the **original price** of $40 is reduced, or **discounted**, by 25% of $40, or $10. The **discount rate** is 25%, the **amount of discount** is $10, and the **sale price** is $40 − $10, or $30. Study the diagram below to visualize these terms.

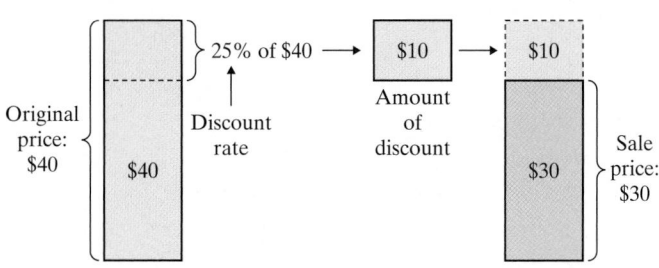

To calculate discounts and sale prices, we can use the following equations:

Discount and Sale Price

amount of discount = discount rate · original price

sale price = original price − amount of discount

A Panasonic TV is advertised on sale for 15% off the regular price of $700. Find the discount and the sale price.

EXAMPLE 5 Finding a Discount and a Sale Price

A speaker that normally sells for $65 is on sale for 25% off. What is the discount and what is the sale price?

Solution: First we find the discount.

$$\text{amount of discount} = \text{discount rate} \cdot \text{original price}$$

$$\text{amount of discount} = 25\% \cdot \$65$$
$$= 0.25 \cdot \$65 \quad \text{Write 25\% as 0.25.}$$
$$= \$16.25 \quad \text{Multiply.}$$

The discount is $16.25. Next, find the sale price.

$$\text{sale price} = \text{original price} - \text{discount}$$

$$\text{sale price} = \$65 - \$16.25$$
$$= \$48.75 \quad \text{Subtract.}$$

The sale price is $48.75.

▣ **Work Practice Problem 5**

Answer
5. $105; $595

Objective A *Solve. See Examples 1 and 2.*

1. What is the sales tax on a suit priced at $150 if the sales tax rate is 5%?

2. If the sales tax rate is 6%, find the sales tax on a microwave oven priced at $188.

3. The purchase price of a camcorder is $799. What is the total price if the sales tax rate is 7.5%?

4. A stereo system has a purchase price of $426. What is the total price if the sales tax rate is 8%?

5. A chair and ottoman have a purchase price of $600. If the sales tax on this purchase is $57, find the sales tax rate.

6. The sales tax on the purchase of a $2500 computer is $162.50. Find the sales tax rate.

7. The sales tax on a table saw is $10.20.

   a. What is the purchase price of the table saw (before tax) if the sales tax rate is 8.5%?

   b. Find the total price of the table saw.

8. The sales tax on a one-half-carat diamond ring is $76.

   a. Find the purchase price of the ring (before tax) if the sales tax rate is 9.5%.

   b. Find the total price of the ring.

9. A gold and diamond bracelet sells for $1800. Find the total price if the sales tax rate is 6.5%.

10. The purchase price of a personal computer is $1890. If the sales tax rate is 8%, what is the total price?

11. The sales tax on the purchase of a truck is $920. If the tax rate is 8%, find the purchase price of the truck.

12. The sales tax on the purchase of a desk is $27.50. If the tax rate is 5%, find the purchase price of the desk.

13. The sales tax is $98.70 on a stereo sound system purchase of $1645. Find the sales tax rate.

14. The sales tax is $103.50 on a necklace purchase of $1150. Find the sales tax rate.

15. A cell phone costs $90 and a battery recharger costs $15. What is the total price for purchasing these items if the sales tax rate is 7%?

16. Ms. Warner bought a blouse for $35, a skirt for $55, and a blazer for $95. Find the total price she paid, given a sales tax rate of 6.5%.

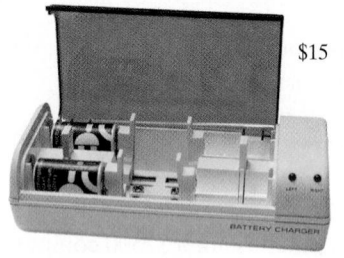
$15

$90

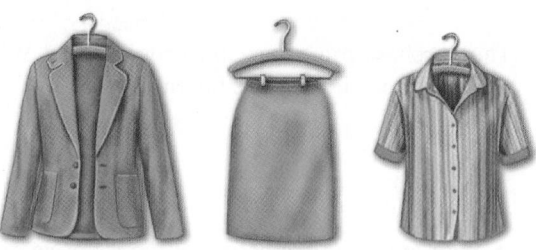

Objective **B** *Solve. See Examples 3 and 4.*

17. Jane Moreschi, a sales representative for a large furniture warehouse, is paid a commission rate of 4%. Find her commission if she sold $1,236,856 worth of furniture last year.

18. Rosie Davis-Smith is a beauty consultant for a home cosmetic business. She is paid a commission rate of 4.8%. Find her commission if she sold $1638 in cosmetics last month.

19. A salesperson earned a commission of $1380.40 for selling $9860 worth of paper products. Find the commission rate.

20. A salesperson earned a commission of $3575 for selling $32,500 worth of books to various bookstores. Find the commission rate.

21. How much commission will Jack Pruet make on the sale of a $125,900 house if he receives 1.5% of the selling price?

22. Frankie Lopez sold $9638 of jewelry this week. Find her commission for the week if she receives a commission rate of 5.6%.

23. A real estate agent earned a commission of $2565 for selling a house. If his rate is 3%, find the selling price of the house.

24. A salesperson earned $1750 for selling fertilizer. If her commission rate is 7%, find the selling price of the fertilizer.

Objective **C** *Find the amount of discount and the sale price. See Example 5.*

	Original Price	Discount Rate	Amount of Discount	Sale Price
25.	$68	10%		
26.	$47	20%		
27.	$96.50	50%		
28.	$110.60	40%		
29.	$215	35%		
30.	$370	25%		
31.	$21,700	15%		
32.	$17,800	12%		

33. A $300 fax machine is on sale for 15% off. Find the discount and the sale price.

34. A $2000 designer dress is on sale for 30% off. Find the discount and the sale price.

Objectives **A** **B** **Mixed Practice** Complete each table.

	Purchase Price	Tax Rate	Sales Tax	Total Price
35.	$586	9%		
36.	$243	8%		
37.	$82	5.5%		
38.	$65	8.4%		

	Sale	Commission Rate	Commission
39.	$235,800	3%	
40.	$195,450	5%	
41.	$17,900		$1432
42.	$25,600		$2304

Review

Multiply. See Sections 4.4 and 4.6.

43. $2000 \cdot 0.3 \cdot 2$

44. $500 \cdot 0.08 \cdot 3$

45. $400 \cdot 0.03 \cdot 11$

46. $1000 \cdot 0.05 \cdot 5$

47. $600 \cdot 0.04 \cdot \dfrac{2}{3}$

48. $6000 \cdot 0.06 \cdot \dfrac{3}{4}$

Concept Extensions

Solve. See the Concept Check in this section.

49. Your purchase price is $68 and the sales tax rate is 9.5%. Round each amount and use the rounded amounts to estimate the total price. Choose the best estimate.

    a. $105   **b.** $58   **c.** $93   **d.** $77

50. Your purchase price is $200 and the tax rate is 10%. Choose the best estimate.

    a. $190   **b.** $210   **c.** $220   **d.** $300

One very useful application of percent is mentally calculating a tip. Recall that to find 10% of a number, simply move the decimal point one place to the left. To find 20% of a number, just double 10% of the number. To find 15% of a number, find 10% and then add to that number half of the 10% amount. Mentally fill in the chart below. To do so, start by rounding the bill amount to the nearest dollar.

	Tipping Chart			
	Bill Amount	10%	15%	20%
51.	$40.21			
52.	$15.89			
53.	$72.17			
54.	$9.33			

55. Suppose that the original price of a shirt is $50. Which is better, a 60% discount or a discount of 30% followed by a discount of 35% of the reduced price. Explain your answer.

56. Which is better, a 30% discount followed by an additional 25% off or a 20% discount followed by an additional 40% off? To see, suppose an item costs $100 and calculate each discounted price. Explain your answer.

57. A diamond necklace sells for $24,966. If the tax rate is 7.5%, find the total price.

58. A house recently sold for $562,560. The commission rate on the sale is 5.5%. If the real estate agent is to receive 60% of the commission, find the amount received by the agent.

STUDY SKILLS BUILDER

Are You Familiar with Your Textbook Supplements?

Below is a review of some of the student supplements available for additional study. Check to see if you are using the ones most helpful to you.

- Chapter Test Prep Videos on CD. This material is found with your textbook and is fully explained there. The CD contains video clip solutions to the Chapter Test exercises in this text and are excellent help when studying for chapter tests.

- Lecture Videos on CD-ROM. These video segments are keyed to each section of the text. The material is presented by me, Elayn Martin-Gay, and I have placed a (⊙) by the exercises in the text that I have worked on the video.

- The *Student Solutions Manual*. This contains worked out solutions to odd-numbered exercises as well as every exercise in the Integrated Reviews, Chapter Reviews, Chapter Tests, and Cumulative Reviews.

- Prentice Hall Tutor Center. Mathematic questions may be phoned, faxed, or emailed to this center.

- MyMathLab, MathXL, and Interact Math. These are computer and Internet tutorials. This supplement may already be available to you somewhere on campus, for example at your local learning resource lab. Take a moment and find the name and location of any such lab on campus.

  As usual, your instructor is your best source of information.

Let's see how you are doing with textbook supplements.

1. Name one way the Lecture Videos can be helpful to you.

2. Name one way the Chapter Test Prep Video can help you prepare for a chapter test.

3. List any textbook supplements that you have found useful.

4. Have you located and visited a learning resource lab located on your campus?

5. List the textbook supplements that are currently housed in your campus' learning resource lab.

5.8 PERCENT AND PROBLEM SOLVING: INTEREST

Objectives

A Calculate Simple Interest.

B Calculate Compound Interest.

C Calculate Monthly Payments.

Objective **A** Calculating Simple Interest

Interest is money charged for using other people's money. When you borrow money, you pay interest. When you loan or invest money, you earn interest. The money borrowed, loaned, or invested is called the **principal amount,** or simply **principal.** Interest is normally stated in terms of a percent of the principal for a given period of time. The **interest rate** is the percent used in computing the interest. Unless stated otherwise, *the rate is understood to be per year.* When the interest is computed on the original principal, it is called **simple interest.** Simple interest is calculated using the following equation:

Simple Interest

$$\text{simple interest} = \text{principal} \cdot \text{rate} \cdot \text{time}$$

where the rate is understood to be per year and time is in years.

EXAMPLE 1 Finding Simple Interest

Find the simple interest after 2 years on $500 at an interest rate of 12%.

Solution: In this example, the principal is $500, the rate is 12%, and the time is 2 years.

$$
\begin{aligned}
\text{simple interest} &= \text{principal} \cdot \text{rate} \cdot \text{time} \\
\text{simple interest} &= \$500 \cdot 12\% \cdot 2 \\
&= \$500 \cdot 0.12 \cdot 2 \quad \text{Write 12\% as 0.12.} \\
&= \$120 \quad \text{Multiply.}
\end{aligned}
$$

The simple interest is $120.

■ **Work Practice Problem 1**

If time is not given in years, we need to convert the given time to years.

EXAMPLE 2 Finding Simple Interest

Ivan Borski borrowed $2400 at 10% simple interest for 8 months to buy a used Chevy S-10. Find the simple interest he paid.

Solution: Since there are 12 months in a year, we first find what part of a year 8 months is.

$$8 \text{ months} = \frac{8}{12} \text{ year} = \frac{2}{3} \text{ year}$$

Now we find the simple interest.

$$
\begin{aligned}
\text{simple interest} &= \text{principal} \cdot \text{rate} \cdot \text{time} \\
\text{simple interest} &= \$2400 \cdot 10\% \cdot \frac{2}{3} \\
&= \$2400 \cdot 0.10 \cdot \frac{2}{3} \\
&= \$160
\end{aligned}
$$

The interest on Ivan's loan is $160.

■ **Work Practice Problem 2**

PRACTICE PROBLEM 1

Find the simple interest after 3 years on $750 at an interest rate of 8%.

PRACTICE PROBLEM 2

Juanita Lopez borrowed $800 for 9 months at a simple interest rate of 20%. How much interest did she pay?

Answers
1. $180, **2.** $120

When money is borrowed, the borrower pays the original amount borrowed, or the principal, as well as the interest. When money is invested, the investor receives the original amount invested, or the principal, as well as the interest. In either case, the **total amount** is the sum of the principal and the interest.

Finding the Total Amount of a Loan or Investment

total amount (paid or received) = principal + interest

PRACTICE PROBLEM 3

If $500 is borrowed at a simple interest rate of 12% for 6 months, find the total amount paid.

EXAMPLE 3 Finding the Total Amount of an Investment

An accountant invested $2000 at a simple interest rate of 10% for 2 years. What total amount of money will she have from her investment in 2 years?

Solution: First we find her interest.

simple interest	=	principal	·	rate	·	time

simple interest = $2000 · 10% · 2

= $2000 · 0.10 · 2

= $400

The interest is $400.

Next, we add the interest to the principal.

total amount	=	principal	+	interest

total amount = $2000 + $400

= $2400

After 2 years, she will have a total amount of $2400.

▣ **Work Practice Problem 3**

✔ **Concept Check**   Which investment would earn more interest: An amount of money invested at 8% interest for 2 years, or the same amount of money invested at 8% for 3 years? Explain.

Objective **B** Calculating Compound Interest

Recall that simple interest depends on the original principal only. Another type of interest is compound interest. **Compound interest** is computed on not only the principal, but also on the interest already earned in previous compounding periods. Compound interest is used more often than simple interest.

Let's see how compound interest differs from simple interest. Suppose that $2000 is invested at 7% interest **compounded annually** for 3 years. This means that interest is added to the principal at the end of each year and that next year's interest is computed on this new amount. In this section, we round dollar amounts to the nearest cent.

Answer

3. $530

✔ Concept Check Answer

8% for 3 years. Since the interest rate is the same, the longer you keep the money invested, the more interest you earn.

	Amount at Beginning of Year	Principal	·	Rate	·	Time	= Interest	Amount at End of Year
1st year	$2000	$2000	·	0.07	·	1	= $140	$2000 + 140 = $2140
2nd year	$2140	$2140	·	0.07	·	1	= $149.80	$2140 + 149.80 = $2289.80
3rd year	$2289.80	$2289.80	·	0.07	·	1	= $160.29	$2289.80 + 160.29 = $2450.09

The compound interest earned can be found by

total amount	−	original principal	=	compound interest
↓		↓		↓
$2450.09	−	$2000	=	$450.09

The simple interest earned would have been

principal	·	rate	·	time	=	interest
↓		↓		↓		↓
$2000	·	0.07	·	3	=	$420

Since compound interest earns "interest on interest," compound interest earns more than simple interest.

Computing compound interest using the method above can be tedious. We can use a **compound interest table** to compute interest more quickly. The compound interest table in this textbook is found in Appendix B.3. This table gives the total compound interest and principal paid on $1 for given rates and numbers of years. Then we can use the following equation to find the total amount of interest and principal:

Finding Total Amounts with Compound Interest

total amount = original principal · compound interest factor (from table)

EXAMPLE 4 Finding Total Amount Received on an Investment

$4000 is invested at 8% compounded semiannually for 10 years. Find the total amount at the end of 10 years.

Solution: Look in Appendix B.3. The compound interest factor for 10 years at 8% in the Compounded Semiannually section is 2.19112.

total amount	=	original principal	·	compound interest factor
↓		↓		↓
total amount	=	$4000	·	2.19112
	=	$8764.48		

Therefore, the total amount at the end of 10 years is $8764.48.

◻ **Work Practice Problem 4**

PRACTICE PROBLEM 4

$5500 is invested at 7% compounded daily for 5 years. Find the total amount at the end of 5 years. Use 1 year = 365 days.

EXAMPLE 5 Finding Compound Interest Earned

In Example 4 we found that the total amount for $4000 invested at 8% compounded semiannually for 10 years is $8764.48. Find the compound interest earned.

Solution:

interest earned	=	total amount	−	original principal
↓		↓		↓
interest earned	=	$8764.48	−	$4000
	=	$4764.48		

The compound interest earned is $4764.48.

◻ **Work Practice Problem 5**

PRACTICE PROBLEM 5

If the total amount is $9933.14 when $5500 is invested, find the compound interest earned.

Answers
4. $7804.61, **5.** $4433.14

Objective ⓒ Calculating a Monthly Payment

We conclude this section with a method to find the monthly payment on a loan.

Finding the Monthly Payment of a Loan

$$\text{monthly payment} = \frac{\text{principal} + \text{interest}}{\text{total number of payments}}$$

PRACTICE PROBLEM 6

Find the monthly payment on a $3000 3-year loan if the interest on the loan is $1123.58.

EXAMPLE 6 Finding a Monthly Payment

Find the monthly payment on a $2000 loan for 2 years. The interest on the 2-year loan is $435.88.

Solution: First we determine the total number of monthly payments. The loan is for 2 years. Since there are 12 months per year, the number of payments is 2 · 12, or 24. Now we calculate the monthly payment.

$$\text{monthly payment} = \frac{\text{principal} + \text{interest}}{\text{total number of payments}}$$

$$\text{monthly payment} = \frac{\$2000 + \$435.88}{24}$$

$$\approx \$101.50$$

The monthly payment is about $101.50.

Answer

6. $114.54

▣ **Work Practice Problem 6**

🖩 CALCULATOR EXPLORATIONS   Compound Interest Factor

A compound interest factor may be found by using your calculator and evaluating the formula

$$\textbf{compound interest factor} = \left(1 + \frac{r}{n}\right)^{nt}$$

where r is the interest rate, t is the time in years, and n is the number of times compounded per year. For example, we stated earlier that the compound interest factor for 10 years at 8% compounded semiannually is 2.19112. Let's find this factor by evaluating the compound interest factor formula when $r = 8\%$ or 0.08, $t = 10$, and $n = 2$ (compounded semiannually means 2 times per year). Thus,

$$\text{compound interest factor} = \left(1 + \frac{0.08}{2}\right)^{2 \cdot 10}$$

$$\text{or } \left(1 + \frac{0.08}{2}\right)^{20}$$

To evaluate, press the keys

| (| 1 | + | 0.08 | ÷ | 2 |) | y^x | or | ∧ | 20 | = |

or **ENTER**. The display will read $\boxed{2.1911231}$. Rounded to 5 decimal places, this is 2.19112.

Find the compound interest factors. Use the table in the Appendix B.3 to check your answers.

1. 5 years, 9%, compounded quarterly
2. 15 years, 14%, compounded daily
3. 20 years, 11%, compounded annually
4. 1 year, 7%, compounded semiannually
5. Find the total amount after 4 years when $500 is invested at 6% compounded quarterly.
6. Find the total amount for 19 years when $2500 is invested at 5% compounded daily.

5.8 EXERCISE SET

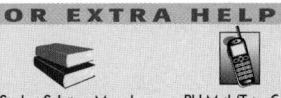 
Objective A *Find the simple interest. See Examples 1 and 2.*

	Principal	Rate	Time
1.	$200	8%	2 years
3.	$160	11.5%	4 years
5.	$5000	10%	$1\frac{1}{2}$ years
7.	$375	18%	6 months
9.	$2500	16%	21 months

	Principal	Rate	Time
2.	$800	9%	3 years
4.	$950	12.5%	5 years
6.	$1500	14%	$2\frac{1}{4}$ years
8.	$775	15%	8 months
10.	$1000	10%	18 months

Solve. See Examples 1 through 3.

11. A company borrows $62,500 for 2 years at a simple interest of 12.5% to buy an airplane. Find the total amount paid on the loan.

12. $65,000 is borrowed to buy a house. If the simple interest rate on the 30-year loan is 10.25%, find the total amount paid on the loan.

13. A money market fund advertises a simple interest rate of 9%. Find the total amount received on an investment of $5000 for 15 months.

14. The Real Service Company takes out a 270-day (9-month) short-term, simple interest loan of $4500 to finance the purchase of some new equipment. If the interest rate is 14%, find the total amount that the company pays back.

15. Marsha Waide borrows $8500 and agrees to pay it back in 4 years. If the simple interest rate is 12%, find the total amount she pays back.

16. Ms. Lapchinski gives her 18-year-old daughter a graduation gift of $2000. If this money is invested at 8% simple interest for 5 years, find the total amount.

Objective B *Find the total amount in each compound interest account. See Example 4.*

17. $6150 is compounded semiannually at a rate of 14% for 15 years.

18. $2060 is compounded annually at a rate of 15% for 10 years.

19. $1560 is compounded daily at a rate of 8% for 5 years.

20. $1450 is compounded quarterly at a rate of 10% for 15 years.

21. $10,000 is compounded semiannually at a rate of 9% for 20 years.

22. $3500 is compounded daily at a rate of 8% for 10 years.

Find the total amount of compound interest earned. See Example 5.

23. $2675 is compounded annually at a rate of 9% for 1 year.

24. $6375 is compounded semiannually at a rate of 10% for 1 year.

25. $2000 is compounded annually at a rate of 8% for 5 years.

26. $2000 is compounded semiannually at a rate of 8% for 5 years.

27. $2000 is compounded quarterly at a rate of 8% for 5 years.

28. $2000 is compounded daily at a rate of 8% for 5 years.

Objective **C** *Solve. See Example 6.*

29. A college student borrows $1500 for 6 months to pay for a semester of school. If the interest is $61.88, find the monthly payment.

30. Jim Tillman borrows $1800 for 9 months. If the interest is $148.90, find his monthly payment.

31. $20,000 is borrowed for 4 years. If the interest on the loan is $10,588.70, find the monthly payment.

32. $105,000 is borrowed for 15 years. If the interest on the loan is $181,125, find the monthly payment.

Review

Find the perimeter of each figure. See Section 1.3.

△ **33.**

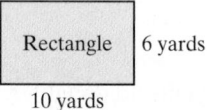

Rectangle   6 yards

10 yards

△ **34.**

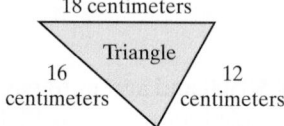

18 centimeters

Triangle

16 centimeters   12 centimeters

△ **35.**

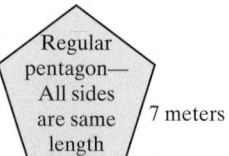

Regular pentagon— All sides are same length   7 meters

△ **36.**

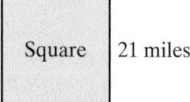

Square   21 miles

Concept Extensions

37. Explain how to look up a compound interest factor in the compound interest table.

38. Explain how to find the amount of interest in a compounded account.

39. Compare the following accounts: Account 1: $1000 is invested for 10 years at a simple interest rate of 6%. Account 2: $1000 is compounded semiannually at a rate of 6% for 10 years. Discuss how the interest is computed for each account. Determine which account earns more interest. Why?

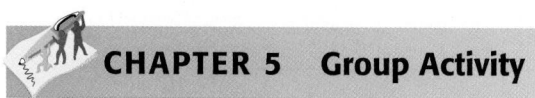

CHAPTER 5   Group Activity

Sections 5.2, 5.3, 5.8

How Much Can You Afford for a House?

When a home buyer takes out a mortgage to buy a house, the loan is generally repaid on a monthly basis with a monthly mortgage payment. (Some banks also offer bi-weekly payment programs.) An important consideration in choosing a house is the amount of the monthly payment. Usually, the amount that a home buyer can afford to make as a monthly payment will dictate the house purchase price that can be afforded.

The first step in deciding how much can be afforded for a house is finding out how much income the household has each month before taxes. The Mortgage Bankers Association of American (MBAA) suggests that the monthly mortgage payment be between 25% and 28% of the total monthly income. If other long-term debts exist (such as car or education loans and long-term credit card debt repayment), the MBAA further recommends that the total of housing costs and other monthly debt payments not exceed 36% of the total monthly income.

Once the size of the monthly payment that can be afforded has been found, a mortgage payment calculator can be used to work backward to estimate the mortgage amount that will give that desired monthly payment. For example, the Interest.com Web site includes a mortgage payment calculator at http://www.interest.com/calculators/monthlypayment.shtml. (Alternatively, visit www.interest.com and navigate to "Use our mortgage calculators.") Look for the calculator to calculate the monthly payment for a particular mortgage loan. With this mortgage payment calculator, the user can input the interest rate (as a percent), the term of the loan (in years), and total home loan amount (in dollars). This information is then used to calculate the associated monthly payment. To work backward with this mortgage payment calculator to find the total loan amount that can be afforded:

- Enter the interest rate that is likely for your loan and the term of the loan in which you are interested.

- Then make a guess (perhaps $100,000?) for the total home loan amount that can be afforded.
- Have the mortgage calculator calculate the monthly payment.
- If the monthly payment that is calculated is higher than the range that can be afforded, repeat the calculation using the same interest rate and loan term but a lower value for the total home loan amount.
- If the monthly payment that is calculated is lower than the range that can be afforded, repeat the calculation using the same interest rate and loan term but a higher value for the total home loan amount.
- Repeat these calculations methodically until a monthly payment is obtained that is in the range that can be afforded. The initial principal value that gave this monthly payment amount is an estimate of the mortgage amount that can be afforded to buy a home.

Group Activity

1. Research current interest rates on 30-year mortgages.
2. Use the method described above to find the size of mortgages that can be afforded by households with the following total monthly incomes before taxes. (Assume in each case that the household has no other debts.) Use a loan term of 30 years and a current interest rate on a 30-year mortgage.

   a. $3000   **b.** $3500   **c.** $4000
   d. $4500   **e.** $5000   **f.** $5500

3. Create a table of your results.

Chapter 5 Vocabulary Check

Fill in each blank with one of the words or phrases listed below.

percent	of	amount	100%	compound interest
base	is	0.01	$\frac{1}{100}$	not equal
equal	cross products	rate	ratio	proportion

1. A _____ is the quotient of two numbers. It can be written as a fraction, using a colon, or using the word *to*.

2. $\frac{x}{2} = \frac{7}{16}$ is an example of a _____.

3. A _____ is used to compare different kinds of quantities.

4. In the proportion $\frac{x}{2} = \frac{7}{16}$, $x \cdot 16$ and $2 \cdot 7$ are called _____.

5. If cross products are _____ the proportion is true.

6. If cross products are _____ the proportion is false.

7. In a mathematical statement, _____ usually means "multiplication."

8. In a mathematical statement, _____ means "equals."

9. _____ means "per hundred."

10. _____ is computed not only on the principal, but also on interest already earned in previous compounding periods.

11. In the percent proportion $\frac{\rule{2cm}{0.4pt}}{\rule{2cm}{0.4pt}} = \frac{percent}{100}$

12. To write a decimal or fraction as a percent, multiply by _____.

13. The decimal equivalent of the % symbol is _____.

14. The fraction equivalent of the % symbol is

_____.

Helpful Hint

Are you preparing for your test? Don't forget to take the Chapter 5 Test on page 402. Then check your answers at the back of the text and use the Chapter Test Prep Video CD to see the fully worked-out solutions to any of the exercises you want to review.

5 Chapter Highlights

DEFINITIONS AND CONCEPTS	EXAMPLES
Section 5.1 Ratio and Proportion	

A **ratio** is the quotient of two quantities.	The ratio of 3 to 4 can be written as $$\frac{3}{4} \quad \text{or} \quad 3:4$$ fraction notation colon notation
Rates are used to compare different kinds of quantities.	Write the rate 12 spikes every 8 inches as a fraction in simplest form. $$\frac{12 \text{ spikes}}{8 \text{ inches}} = \frac{3 \text{ spikes}}{2 \text{ inches}}$$
A **proportion** is a statement that two ratios or rates are equal.	$\frac{1}{2} = \frac{4}{8}$ is a proportion.

DEFINITIONS AND CONCEPTS	**EXAMPLES**

Section 5.1 Ratio and Proportion (*continued*)

USING CROSS PRODUCTS TO DETERMINE WHETHER PROPORTIONS ARE TRUE OR FALSE

Cross products

$$a \cdot d \qquad \frac{a}{b} = \frac{c}{d} \qquad b \cdot c$$

If cross products are equal, the proportion is true.
If $ad = bc$, then the proportion is true.
If cross products are not equal, the proportion is false.
If $ad \neq bc$, then the proportion is false.

FINDING AN UNKNOWN VALUE *N* IN A PROPORTION

Step 1. Set the cross products equal to each other.

Step 2. Divide the number not multiplied by n by the number multiplied by n.

Is $\dfrac{6}{10} = \dfrac{9}{15}$ a true proportion?

Cross products

$$6 \cdot 15 \qquad \frac{6}{10} = \frac{9}{15} \qquad 10 \cdot 9$$

$6 \cdot 15 \overset{?}{=} 10 \cdot 9$ Are cross products equal?
$90 = 90$

Since cross products are equal, the proportion is a true proportion.

Find n: $\dfrac{n}{7} = \dfrac{5}{8}$

Step 1.

$$\frac{n}{7} = \frac{5}{8}$$

$n \cdot 8 = 7 \cdot 5$ Set the cross products equal to each other.
$n \cdot 8 = 35$ Multiply.

Step 2.

$n = \dfrac{35}{8}$ Divide 35 by 8, the number multiplied by n.

$n = 4\dfrac{3}{8}$

Section 5.2 Introduction to Percent

Percent means "per hundred." The % symbol denotes percent.

To write a percent as a decimal, replace the % symbol with its decimal equivalent, 0.01, and multiply.
To write a decimal as a percent, multiply by 100%.

$51\% = \dfrac{51}{100}$ 51 per 100

$7\% = \dfrac{7}{100}$ 7 per 100

$32\% = 32(0.01) = 0.32$

$0.08 = 0.08(100\%) = 08.\% = 8\%$

Section 5.3 Percents and Fractions

To write a percent as a fraction, replace the % symbol with its fraction equivalent, $\dfrac{1}{100}$, and multiply.

To write a fraction as a percent, multiply by 100%.

$25\% = \dfrac{25}{100} = \dfrac{\overset{1}{\cancel{25}}}{4 \cdot \cancel{25}} = \dfrac{1}{4}$

$\dfrac{1}{6} = \dfrac{1}{6} \cdot 100\% = \dfrac{1}{6} \cdot \dfrac{100}{1}\% = \dfrac{100}{6}\% = 16\dfrac{2}{3}\%$

DEFINITIONS AND CONCEPTS	**EXAMPLES**

Section 5.4 Solving Percent Problems Using Equations

Three key words in the statement of a percent problem are

  of, which means **multiplication** (·)
  is, which means **equals** (=)
  what (or some equivalent word or phrase), which stands for **the unknown number**

Solve:

$$6 \quad \text{is} \quad 12\% \quad \text{of} \quad \text{what number?}$$

$$6 = 12\% \cdot n$$
$$6 = 0.12 \cdot n \qquad \text{Write 12\% as a decimal.}$$
$$\frac{6}{0.12} = n \qquad \text{Divide 6 by 0.12, the number multiplied by } n.$$
$$50 = n$$

Thus, 6 is 12% of 50.

Section 5.5 Solving Percent Problems Using Proportions

PERCENT PROPORTION

$$\frac{\text{amount}}{\text{base}} = \frac{\text{percent}}{100} \quad \leftarrow \text{always 100}$$

or

$$\text{amount} \rightarrow \frac{a}{b} = \frac{p}{100} \quad \leftarrow \text{percent}$$
$$\text{base} \rightarrow$$

Solve:

$$20.4 \text{ is what percent of 85?}$$

amount   percent   base

$$\text{amount} \rightarrow \frac{20.4}{85} = \frac{p}{100} \quad \leftarrow \text{percent}$$
$$\text{base} \rightarrow$$

$$20.4 \cdot 100 = 85 \cdot p \qquad \text{Set cross products equal.}$$
$$2040 = 85 \cdot p \qquad \text{Multiply.}$$
$$\frac{2040}{85} = p \qquad \text{Divide 2040 by 85, the number multiplied by } p.$$
$$24 = p \qquad \text{Simplify.}$$

Thus, 20.4 is 24% of 85.

Section 5.6 Applications of Percent

PERCENT OF INCREASE

$$\text{percent of increase} = \frac{\text{amount of increase}}{\text{original amount}}$$

PERCENT OF DECREASE

$$\text{percent of decrease} = \frac{\text{amount of decrease}}{\text{original amount}}$$

A town with a population of 16,480 decreased to 13,870 over a 12-year period. Find the percent decrease. Round to the nearest whole percent.

$$\text{amount of decrease} = 16,480 - 13,870$$
$$= 2610$$

$$\text{percent of decrease} = \frac{\text{amount of decrease}}{\text{original amount}}$$
$$= \frac{2610}{16,480} \approx 0.16$$
$$= 16\%$$

The town's population decreased by 16%.

Section 5.7 Percent and Problem Solving: Sales Tax, Commission, and Discount

SALES TAX AND TOTAL PRICE

$$\text{sales tax} = \text{sales tax rate} \cdot \text{purchase price}$$
$$\text{total price} = \text{purchase price} + \text{sales tax}$$

Find the sales tax and the total price of a purchase of $42 if the sales tax rate is 9%.

sales tax = sales tax rate · purchase price

$$\text{sales tax} = 9\% \cdot \$42$$
$$= 0.09 \cdot \$42$$
$$= \$3.78$$

DEFINITIONS AND CONCEPTS	**EXAMPLES**

Section 5.7   Percent and Problem Solving: Sales Tax, Commission, and Discount (*continued*)

	The total price is
	$$\text{total price} = \text{purchase price} + \text{sales tax}$$ $$\text{total price} = \$42 + \$3.78$$ $$= \$45.78$$
COMMISSION $$\text{commission} = \text{commission rate} \cdot \text{total sales}$$	A salesperson earns a commission of 3%. Find the commission from sales of $12,500 worth of appliances. $$\text{commission} = \text{commission rate} \cdot \text{sales}$$ $$\text{commission} = 3\% \cdot \$12,500$$ $$= 0.03 \cdot 12,500$$ $$= \$375$$
DISCOUNT AND SALE PRICE $$\text{amount of discount} = \text{discount rate} \cdot \text{original price}$$ $$\text{sale price} = \text{original price} - \text{amount of discount}$$	A suit is priced at $320 and is on sale today for 25% off. What is the sale price? $$\text{amount of discount} = \text{discount rate} \cdot \text{original price}$$ $$\text{amount of discount} = 25\% \cdot \$320$$ $$= 0.25 \cdot 320$$ $$= \$80$$ $$\text{sale price} = \text{original price} - \text{amount of discount}$$ $$\text{sale price} = \$320 - \$80$$ $$= \$240$$ The sale price is $240.

Section 5.8   Percent and Problem Solving: Interest

SIMPLE INTEREST $$\text{interest} = \text{principal} \cdot \text{rate} \cdot \text{time}$$ where the rate is understood to be per year.	Find the simple interest after 3 years on $800 at an interest rate of 5%. $$\text{interest} = \text{principal} \cdot \text{rate} \cdot \text{time}$$ $$\text{interest} = \$800 \cdot 5\% \cdot 3$$ $$= \$800 \cdot 0.05 \cdot 3 \quad \text{Write 5\% as 0.05.}$$ $$= \$120 \quad \text{Multiply.}$$ The interest is $120.
Compound interest is computed not only on the principal, but also on interest already earned in previous compounding periods. (See Appendix B.3.) $$\text{total amount} = \text{original principal} \cdot \text{compound interest factor}$$	$800 is invested at 5% compounded quarterly for 10 years. Find the total amount at the end of 10 years. $$\text{total amount} = \text{original principal} \cdot \text{compound interest factor}$$ $$\text{total amount} = \$800 \cdot 1.64362$$ $$\approx \$1314.90$$

STUDY SKILLS BUILDER

Are You Prepared for a Test on Chapter 5?

Below I have listed some *common trouble areas* for students in Chapter 5. After studying for your test—but before taking your test—read these.

- Can you convert from percents to fractions or decimals and from fractions or decimals to percents?

    Percent to decimal: $7.5\% = 7.5(0.01) = 0.075$

    Percent to fraction: $11\% = 11 \cdot \dfrac{1}{100} = \dfrac{11}{100}$

    Decimal to percent: $0.36 = 0.36(100\%) = 36\%$

Fraction to percent: $\dfrac{6}{7} = \dfrac{6}{7} \cdot 100\% = \dfrac{6}{7} \cdot \dfrac{100}{1}\%$
$$= \dfrac{600}{7}\% = 85\dfrac{5}{7}\%$$

- Do you remember how to find percent increase or percent decrease? The number of CDs increased from 40 to 48. Find the percent increase.

$$\dfrac{\text{percent}}{\text{increase}} = \dfrac{\text{increase}}{\text{original number}} = \dfrac{8}{40} = 0.20 = 20\%$$

---

5 CHAPTER REVIEW

(5.1) *Write each ratio as a fraction in simplest form.*

1. 23 to 37

2. 6000 people to 4800 people

3. $121 to $143

4. 4.25 yards to 8.75 yards

The circle graph below shows how the top 20 movies (or films) of 2004 were rated, use this graph to answer the questions.

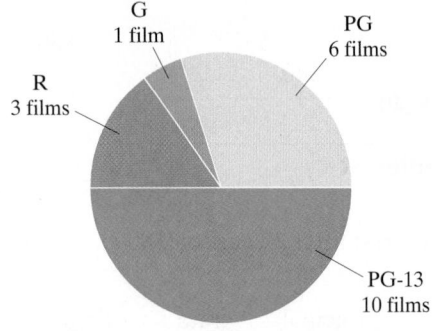

Top 20 Movies of 2004

G
1 film

PG
6 films

R
3 films

PG-13
10 films

Source: Internet search and Bryan Gay

5. a. How many top 20 movies were rated PG?

  b. Find the ratio of top 20 PG-rated movies to total movies for that year.

6. a. How many top 20 movies were rated R?

  b. Find the ratio of top 20 R-rated movies to total movies for that year.

Write each rate as a fraction in simplest form.

7. 6 professors for 20 graduate research assistants

8. 15 word processing pages printed in 6 minutes

Write each rate as a unit rate.

9. 468 miles in 9 hours

10. 180 feet in 12 seconds

Determine whether each proportion is true.

11. $\dfrac{21}{8} = \dfrac{14}{6}$

12. $\dfrac{3.75}{3} = \dfrac{7.5}{6}$

Find the unknown number n in each proportion.

13. $\dfrac{n}{9} = \dfrac{5}{3}$

14. $\dfrac{4}{13} = \dfrac{10}{n}$

15. $\dfrac{27}{\frac{9}{4}} = \dfrac{n}{5}$

16. $\dfrac{0.4}{n} = \dfrac{2}{4.7}$

Solve. An owner of a Ford Escort can drive 420 miles on 11 gallons of gas.

17. If Tom Aloiso runs out of gas in an Escort and AAA comes to his rescue with $1\dfrac{1}{2}$ gallons of gas, determine whether Tom can then drive to a gas station 65 miles away.

18. Find how many gallons of gas Tom can expect to burn on a 3000-mile trip. Round to the nearest gallon.

Yearly homeowner property taxes are figured at a rate of $1.15 tax for every $100 of house value.

19. If a homeowner pays $627.90 in property taxes, find the value of his home.

20. Find the property taxes on a town house valued at $89,000.

(5.2) *Solve.*

21. In a survey of 100 adults, 37 preferred pepperoni on their pizzas. What percent preferred pepperoni?

22. A basketball player made 77 out 100 attempted free throws. What percent of free throws was made?

Write each percent as a decimal.

23. 83%

24. 75%

25. 0.5%

26. 0.7%

27. 200%

28. 400%

29. 26.25%

30. 85.34%

Write each decimal as a percent.

31. 2.6

32. 0.055

33. 0.35

34. 1.02

35. 0.71

36. 0.65

37. 4

38. 9

(5.3) *Write each percent as a fraction or mixed number in simplest form.*

39. 1%

40. 10%

41. 25%

42. 8.5%

43. 10.2%

44. $16\dfrac{2}{3}\%$

45. $33\dfrac{1}{3}\%$

46. 110%

Write each fraction or mixed number as a percent.

47. $\dfrac{1}{5}$

48. $\dfrac{7}{10}$

49. $\dfrac{5}{6}$

50. $1\dfrac{2}{3}$

51. $1\dfrac{1}{4}$

52. $\dfrac{3}{5}$

53. $\dfrac{1}{16}$

54. $\dfrac{5}{8}$

(5.4) *Translate each to an equation and solve.*

55. 1250 is 1.25% of what number?

56. What number is $33\dfrac{1}{3}\%$ of 24,000?

57. 124.2 is what percent of 540?

58. 22.9 is 20% of what number?

59. What number is 40% of 7500?

60. 693 is what percent of 462?

(5.5) *Translate each to a proportion and solve.*

61. 104.5 is 25% of what number?

62. 16.5 is 5.5% of what number?

63. What number is 36% of 180?

64. 63 is what percent of 35?

65. 93.5 is what percent of 85?

66. What number is 33% of 500?

(5.6) *Solve.*

67. In a survey of 2000 people, it was found that 1320 have a microwave oven. Find the percent of people who own microwaves.

68. Of the 12,360 freshmen entering County College, 2000 are enrolled in basic college mathematics. Find the percent of entering freshmen who are enrolled in basic college mathematics. Round to the nearest whole percent.

69. The number of violent crimes in a city decreased from 675 to 534. Find the percent decrease. Round to the nearest tenth of a percent.

70. The current charge for dumping waste in a local landfill is $16 per cubic foot. To cover new environmental costs, the charge will increase to $33 per cubic foot. Find the percent increase.

71. This year the fund drive for a charity collected $215,000. Next year, a 4% decrease is expected. Find how much is expected to be collected in next year's drive.

72. A local union negotiated a new contract that increases the hourly pay 15% over last year's pay. The old hourly rate was $11.50. Find the new hourly rate rounded to the nearest cent.

(5.7) *Solve.*

73. If the sales tax rate is 5.5%, what is the total amount charged for a $250 coat?

74. Find the sales tax paid on a $25.50 purchase if the sales tax rate is 4.5%.

75. Russ James is a sales representative for a chemical company and is paid a commission rate of 5% on all sales. Find his commission if he sold $100,000 worth of chemicals last month.

76. Carol Sell is a sales clerk in a clothing store. She receives a commission of 7.5% on all sales. Find her commission for the week if her sales for the week were $4005. Round to the nearest cent.

77. A $3000 mink coat is on sale for 30% off. Find the discount and the sale price.

78. A $90 calculator is on sale for 10% off. Find the discount and the sale price.

(5.8) *Solve.*

79. Find the simple interest due on $4000 loaned for 4 months at 12% interest.

80. Find the simple interest due on $6500 loaned for 3 months at 20%.

81. Find the total amount in an account if $5500 is compounded annually at 12% for 15 years.

82. Find the total amount in an account if $6000 is compounded semiannually at 11% for 10 years.

83. Find the compound interest earned if $100 is compounded quarterly at 12% for 5 years.

84. Find the compound interest earned if $1000 is compounded quarterly at 18% for 20 years.

Mixed Review

Find the unknown number n in each proportion.

85. $\dfrac{3}{n} = \dfrac{15}{8}$

86. $\dfrac{42}{5} = \dfrac{n}{10}$

Write each percent as a decimal.

87. 3.8%

88. 24.5%

89. 0.9%

Write each decimal as a percent.

90. 0.54

91. 95.2

92. 0.3

Write each percent as a fraction or mixed number in simplest form.

93. 47%

94. $6\dfrac{2}{5}\%$

95. 5.6%

Write each fraction or mixed number as a percent.

96. $\dfrac{3}{8}$

97. $\dfrac{2}{13}$

98. $\dfrac{6}{5}$

Translate each into an equation and solve.

99. 43 is 16% of what number?

100. 27.5 is what percent of 25?

101. What number is 36% of 1968?

102. 67 is what percent of 50?

Translate each into a proportion and solve.

103. 75 is what percent of 25?

104. What number is 16% of 240?

105. 28 is 5% of what number?

106. 52 is what percent of 16?

Solve.

107. The total number of cans in a soft drink machine is 300. If 78 soft drinks have been sold, find the percent of soft drink cans that have been sold.

108. A home valued at $96,950 last year has lost 7% of its value this year. Find the loss in value.

109. A dinette set sells for $568.00. If the sales tax rate is 8.75%, find the purchase price of the dinette set.

110. The original price of a video game is $23.00. It is on sale for 15% off. What is the amount of the discount?

111. A candy salesman makes a commission of $1.60 from each case of candy he sells. If a case of candy costs $12.80, what is his rate of commission?

112. Find the total amount due on a 6 month loan of $1400 at a simple interest rate of 13%.

113. Find the total amount due on a loan of $5,500 for 9 years at 12.5% simple interest.

5 CHAPTER TEST

 Use the Chapter Test Prep Video CD to see the fully worked-out solutions to any of the exercises you want to review.

Answers

Write each ratio or rate as a fraction in simplest form.

1. $75 to $10

2. 8.6 to 10

Find each unit rate.

3. 8 inches of rain in 12 hours

4. QR10 (Quest for Curiosity) is the world's first bipedal robot capable of running (moving with both legs off the ground at the same time) at a rate of 108 inches each 12 seconds. (*Source: Guinness World Records*)

Find the unknown number n in each proportion.

5. $\dfrac{8}{n} = \dfrac{11}{6}$

6. $\dfrac{1.5}{5} = \dfrac{2.4}{n}$

Solve.

7. The standard dose of medicine for a dog is 10 grams for every 15 pounds of body weight. What is the standard dose for a dog that weighs 80 pounds?

8. Currently 27 out of every 50 American adults drink coffee every day. In a town with a population of 7900 adults, how many of these adults would you expect to drink coffee every day? (*Source: National Coffee Association*)

Write each percent as a decimal.

9. 85%

10. 500%

11. 0.8%

Write each decimal as a percent.

12. 0.056

13. 6.1

14. 0.39

1. _____

2. _____

3. _____

4. _____

5. _____

6. _____

7. _____

8. _____

9. _____

10. _____

11. _____

12. _____

13. _____

14. _____

402

Write each percent as a fraction or mixed number in simplest form.

15. 120%   **16.** 38.5%   **17.** 0.2%

Write each fraction or mixed number as a percent.

18. $\frac{11}{20}$ **19.** $\frac{3}{8}$ **20.** $1\frac{5}{9}$

Solve.

21. What number is 42% of 80?   **22.** 0.6% of what number is 7.5?

23. 567 is what percent of 756?

Solve. Round all dollar amounts to the nearest cent.

24. An alloy is 12% copper. How much copper is contained in 320 pounds of this alloy?

25. A farmer in Nebraska estimates that 20% of his potential crop, or $11,350, has been lost to a hard freeze. Find the total value of his potential crop.

26. If the local sales tax rate is 1.25%, find the total amount charged for a stereo system priced at $354.

27. A town's population increased from 25,200 to 26,460. Find the percent increase.

28. A $120 framed picture is on sale for 15% off. Find the discount and the sale price.

29. Randy Nguyen is paid a commission rate of 4% on all sales. Find Randy's commission if his sales were $9875.

30. A sales tax of $1.53 is added to an item's price of $152.99. Find the sales tax rate. Round to the nearest whole percent.

31. Find the simple interest earned on $2000 saved for $3\frac{1}{2}$ years at an interest rate of 9.25%.

32. $1365 is compounded annually at 8%. Find the total amount in the account after 5 years.

33. A couple borrowed $400 from a bank at 13.5% for 6 months for car repairs. Find the total amount due the bank at the end of the 6-month period.

15. _____

16. _____

17. _____

18. _____

19. _____

20. _____

21. _____

22. _____

23. _____

24. _____

25. _____

26. _____

27. _____

28. _____

29. _____

30. _____

31. _____

32. _____

33. _____

Answers

1. _____

2. _____

3. a. _____

   b. _____

   c. _____

4. a. _____

   b. _____

   c. _____

5. _____

6. _____

7. _____

8. _____

9. _____

10. _____

11. _____

12. _____

13. _____

14. _____

15. _____

16. _____

17. _____

18. _____

19. _____

20. _____

21. _____

22. _____

1. How many cases can be filled with 9900 cans of jalapeños if each case holds 48 cans? How many cans will be left over? Will there be enough cases to fill an order for 200 cases?

2. Multiply: 409×76

3. Write each fraction as a mixed number or a whole number.

  a. $\dfrac{30}{7}$ **b.** $\dfrac{16}{15}$ **c.** $\dfrac{84}{6}$

4. Write each mixed number as an improper fraction.

  a. $2\dfrac{5}{7}$ **b.** $10\dfrac{1}{10}$ **c.** $5\dfrac{3}{8}$

5. Use a factor tree to find the prime factorization of 24.

6. Find the area of the rectangle.

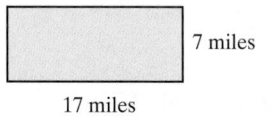

7 miles

17 miles

7. Write $\dfrac{10}{27}$ in simplest form.

8. Find the average of 28, 34, and 70.

9. Multiply and simplify: $\dfrac{23}{32} \cdot \dfrac{4}{7}$

10. Round 76,498 to the nearest ten.

11. Find the reciprocal of $\dfrac{11}{8}$.

12. Write the shaded part of the figure as an improper fraction and as a mixed number.

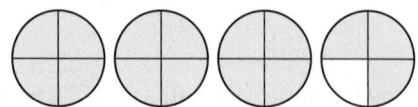

△ **13.** Find the perimeter of the rectangle.

$\frac{2}{15}$ inch

$\frac{4}{15}$ inch

14. Find $2 \cdot 5^2$

15. Find the LCM of 12 and 20.

16. Subtract $\dfrac{7}{9}$ from $\dfrac{10}{9}$.

17. Add: $\dfrac{2}{5} + \dfrac{4}{15}$

18. Find $\dfrac{2}{3}$ of 510.

19. Subtract: $7\dfrac{3}{14} - 3\dfrac{6}{7}$

20. Simplify: $9 \cdot \sqrt{25} - 6 \cdot \sqrt{4}$

Perform each indicated operation.

21. $\dfrac{1}{2} \div \dfrac{8}{7}$

22. $20\dfrac{4}{5} + 12\dfrac{7}{8}$

23. $\dfrac{2}{9} \cdot \dfrac{3}{11}$

24. $1\dfrac{7}{8} \cdot 3\dfrac{2}{5}$

Write each fraction as a decimal.

25. $\dfrac{8}{10}$

26. $\dfrac{9}{100}$

27. $\dfrac{87}{10}$

28. $\dfrac{48}{10,000}$

29. The price of a gallon of gasoline in Aimsville is currently \$2.1779. Round this to the nearest cent.

30. Subtract: $38 - 10.06$

31. Add: $763.7651 + 22.001 + 43.89$

32. 12.483×100

33. Multiply: 23.6×0.78

34. 76.3×1000

Divide.

35. $\dfrac{786.1}{1000}$

36. $0.5\overline{)0.638}$

37. $\dfrac{0.12}{10}$

38. $0.23\overline{)11.6495}$

39. Simplify: $723.6 \div 1000 \times 10$

40. Simplify: $\dfrac{3.19 - 0.707}{13}$

41. Write $\dfrac{1}{4}$ as a decimal.

42. Write $\dfrac{5}{9}$ as a decimal. Give an exact answer and a three-decimal-place approximation.

43. Translate to an equation: What number is 25% of 0.008?

44. Write $\dfrac{3}{8}$ as a percent.

23. _____

24. _____

25. _____

26. _____

27. _____

28. _____

29. _____

30. _____

31. _____

32. _____

33. _____

34. _____

35. _____

36. _____

37. _____

38. _____

39. _____

40. _____

41. _____

42. _____

43. _____

44. _____

6

Geometry

The word *geometry* is formed from the Greek words *geo*, meaning Earth, and *metron*, meaning measure. Geometry literally means to measure the Earth. In this chapter we learn about various geometric figures and their properties such as perimeter, area, and volume. Knowledge of geometry can help us solve practical problems in real-life situations. For instance, knowing certain measures of a circular swimming pool allows us to calculate how much water it can hold.

Modern soccer may have its origins as far back as 3000 years. Although soccer (called football in England) was originally banned in England for its vulgarity, perhaps Eton College had the earliest known rules of the game in 1815. Today soccer is undisputed as the most watched and played sport. This past World Cup was watched by 33 billion people around the world.

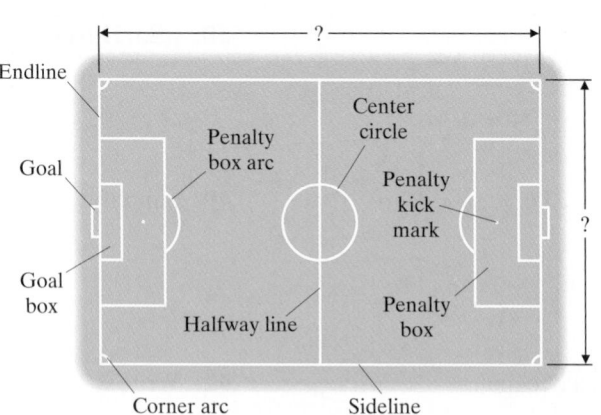

Dimensions of soccer playing fields are determined by many factors, including the ages of the players. In Exercises 69, 70, Section 6.3, and 37, 38, Section 6.5, we calculate the perimeter and area of various-sized fields.

△ # 6.1 LINES AND ANGLES

Objective Ⓐ Identify Lines, Line Segments, Rays, and Angles

Let's begin with a review of two important concepts—space and plane.

Space extends in all directions indefinitely. Examples of objects in space are houses, grains of salt, bushes, your *Developmental Mathematics* textbook, and you.

A **plane** is a flat surface that extends indefinitely. Surfaces like a plane are a classroom floor or a blackboard or whiteboard.

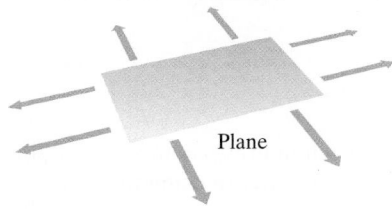

Plane

The most basic concept of geometry is the idea of a point in space. A **point** has no length, no width, and no height, but it does have location. We represent a point by a dot, and we usually label points with capital letters.

Point *P*

A **line** is a set of points extending indefinitely in two directions. A line has no width or height, but it does have length. We can name a line by any two of its points or by a single lowercase letter. A **line segment** is a piece of a line with two endpoints.

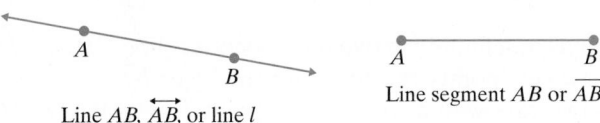

Line *AB*, $\overleftrightarrow{AB}$, or line *l*   Line segment *AB* or $\overline{AB}$

A **ray** is a part of a line with one endpoint. A ray extends indefinitely in one direction. An **angle** is made up of two rays that share the same endpoint. The common endpoint is called the **vertex.**

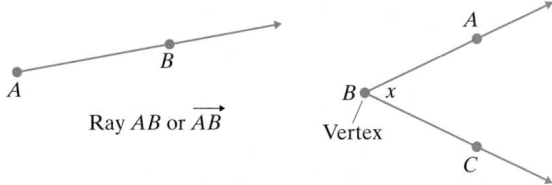

Ray *AB* or $\overrightarrow{AB}$ Vertex

The angle in the figure above can be named

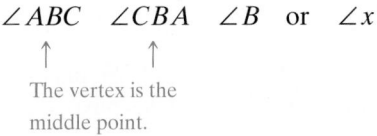

$\angle ABC$ $\angle CBA$ $\angle B$ or $\angle x$

The vertex is the middle point.

Rays *BA* and *BC* are **sides** of the angle.

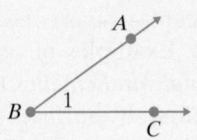
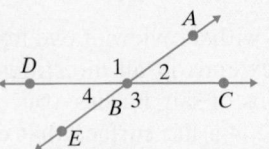

Helpful Hint

Naming an Angle

When there is no confusion as to what angle is being named, you may use the vertex alone.

Name of ∠B is all right.   Name of ∠B is *not* all right.
There is no confusion. ∠B means ∠1.   There is confusion. Does ∠B mean ∠1, ∠2, ∠3, or ∠4?

PRACTICE PROBLEM 1

Identify each figure as a line, a ray, a line segment, or an angle. Then name the figure using the given points.

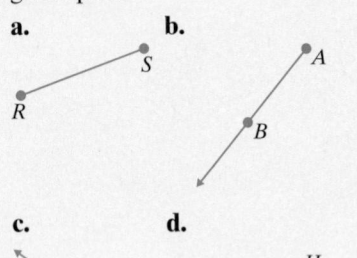

a.   **b.**

c.   **d.**

EXAMPLE 1 Identify each figure as a line, a ray, a line segment, or an angle. Then name the figure using the given points.

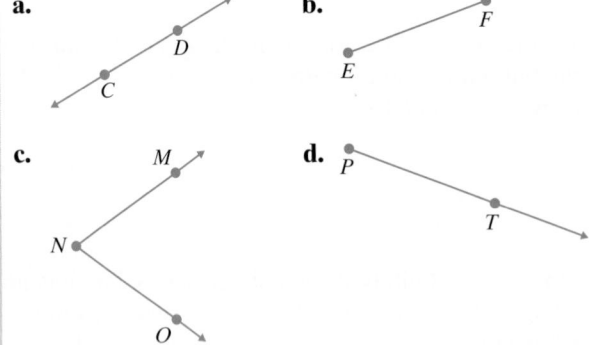

a.   **b.**

c.   **d.**

Solution:

Figure (a) extends indefinitely in two directions. It is line CD or $\overleftrightarrow{CD}$.
Figure (b) has two endpoints. It is line segment EF or $\overline{EF}$.
Figure (c) has two rays with a common endpoint. It is $\angle MNO$, $\angle ONM$, or $\angle N$.
Figure (d) is part of a line with one endpoint. It is ray PT or $\overrightarrow{PT}$.

Work Practice Problem 1

PRACTICE PROBLEM 2

Use the figure in Example 2 to list other ways to name ∠z.

EXAMPLE 2 List other ways to name ∠y.

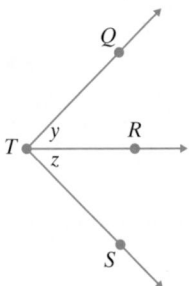

Solution: Two other ways to name ∠y are ∠QTR and ∠RTQ. We may *not* use the vertex alone to name this angle because three different angles have T as their vertex.

Work Practice Problem 2

Answers

1. a. line segment; line segment RS or $\overline{RS}$, **b.** ray; ray AB or $\overrightarrow{AB}$, **c.** line; line EF or $\overleftrightarrow{EF}$, **d.** angle; ∠TVH, or ∠HVT or ∠V,
2. ∠RTS, ∠STR

Objective B Classifying Angles as Acute, Right, Obtuse, or Straight

An angle can be measured in **degrees.** The symbol for degrees is a small, raised circle,°. There are 360° in a full revolution, or a full circle.

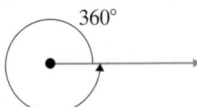

$\frac{1}{2}$ of a revolution measures $\frac{1}{2}(360°) = 180°$. An angle that measures 180° is called a **straight angle.**

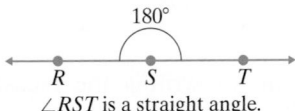

∠RST is a straight angle.

$\frac{1}{4}$ of a revolution measures $\frac{1}{4}(360°) = 90°$. An angle that measures 90° is called a **right angle.** The symbol ∟ is used to denote a right angle.

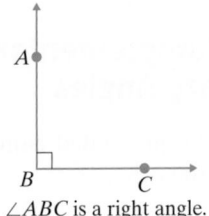

∠ABC is a right angle.

An angle whose measure is between 0° and 90° is called an **acute angle.**

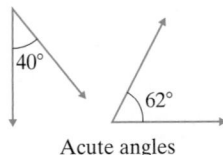

Acute angles

An angle whose measure is between 90° and 180° is called an **obtuse angle.**

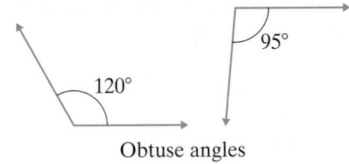

Obtuse angles

EXAMPLE 3 Classify each angle as acute, right, obtuse, or straight.

a.   **b.**

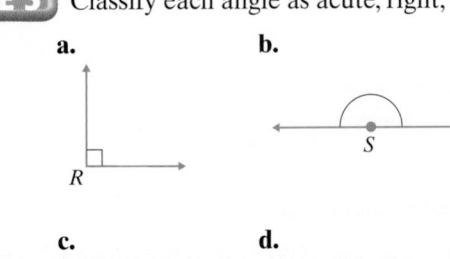

c.   **d.**

Continued on next page

PRACTICE PROBLEM 3

Classify each angle as acute, right, obtuse, or straight.

a.   **b.**

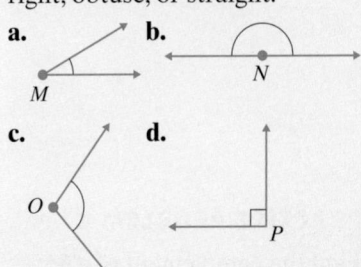

c.   **d.**

Answers

3. a. acute, **b.** straight, **c.** obtuse, **d.** right

Solution:

a. $\angle R$ is a right angle, denoted by ⌐.

b. $\angle S$ is a straight angle.

c. $\angle T$ is an acute angle. It measures between 0° and 90°.

d. $\angle Q$ is an obtuse angle. It measures between 90° and 180°.

▣ **Work Practice Problem 3**

Let's look at $\angle B$ below, whose measure is 62°.

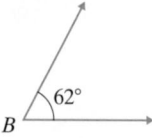

There is a shorthand notation for writing the measure of this angle. To write "The measure of $\angle B$ is 62°," we can write,

$$m\angle B = 62°.$$

By the way, note that $\angle B$ is an acute angle because $m\angle B$ is between 0° and 90°.

Objective ◉ Identifying Complementary and Supplementary Angles

Two angles that have a sum of 90° are called **complementary angles.** We say that each angle is the **complement** of the other.

$\angle R$ and $\angle S$ are complementary angles because

$$m\angle R + m\angle S = 60° + 30° = 90°$$

Complementary angles
60° + 30° = 90°

Two angles that have a sum of 180° are called **supplementary angles.** We say that each angle is the **supplement** of the other.

$\angle M$ and $\angle N$ are supplementary angles because

$$m\angle M + m\angle N = 125° + 55° = 180°$$

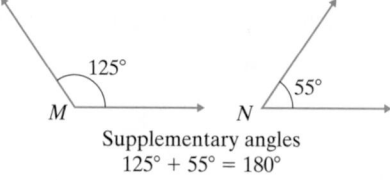

Supplementary angles
125° + 55° = 180°

PRACTICE PROBLEM 4

Find the complement of a 36° angle.

Answer

4. 54°

EXAMPLE 4 Find the complement of a 48° angle.

Solution: Two angles that have a sum of 90° are complementary. This means that the complement of an angle that measures 48° is an angle that measures 90° − 48° = 42°.

▣ **Work Practice Problem 4**

EXAMPLE 5 Find the supplement of a 107° angle.

Solution: Two angles that have a sum of 180° are supplementary. This means that the supplement of an angle that measures 107° is an angle that measures 180° − 107° = 73°.

■ **Work Practice Problem 5**

✔ **Concept Check** True or false? The supplement of a 38° angle is 52°. Explain.

Objective **D** Finding Measures of Angles

Measures of angles can be added or subtracted to find measures of related angles.

EXAMPLE 6 Find the measure of ∠x.

Solution: $m\angle x = m\angle QTS - m\angle RTS$
$= 87° - 52°$
$= 35°$

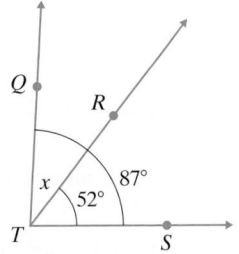

■ **Work Practice Problem 6**

Two lines in a plane can be either parallel or intersecting. **Parallel lines** never meet. **Intersecting lines** meet at a point. The symbol ∥ is used to indicate "is parallel to." For example, in the figure $p\|q$.

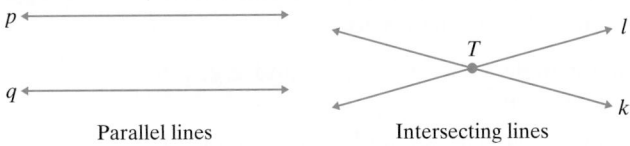

Parallel lines   Intersecting lines

Some intersecting lines are perpendicular. Two lines are **perpendicular** if they form right angles when they intersect. The symbol ⊥ is used to denote "is perpendicular to." For example, in the figure below, $n \perp m$.

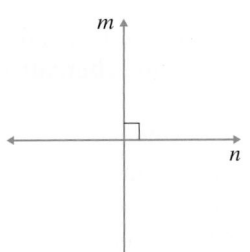

Perpendicular lines

When two lines intersect, four angles are formed. Two angles that are opposite each other are called **vertical angles.** Vertical angles have the same measure. Two angles that share a common side are called **adjacent angles.** Adjacent angles formed by intersecting lines are supplementary. That is, they have a sum of 180°.

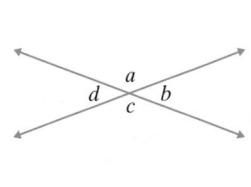

Vertical angles:
∠a and ∠c
∠d and ∠b

Adjacent angles:
∠a and ∠b
∠b and ∠c
∠c and ∠d
∠d and ∠a

PRACTICE PROBLEM 5

Find the supplement of an 88° angle.

PRACTICE PROBLEM 6

a. Find the measure of ∠y.

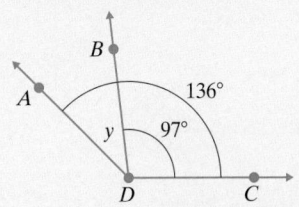

b. Find the measure of ∠x.

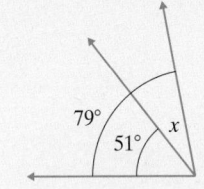

Answers
5. 92°, **6. a.** 39°, **b.** 28°

✔ **Concept Check Answer**

false; the complement of a 38° angle is 52°; the supplement of a 38° angle is 142°

Here are a few real-life examples of the lines we just discussed.

Parallel lines

Vertical angles

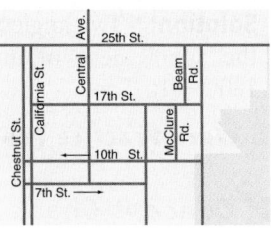

Perpendicular lines

PRACTICE PROBLEM 7

Find the measure of $\angle a$, $\angle b$, and $\angle c$.

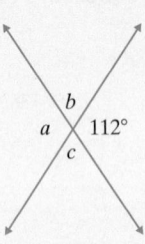

EXAMPLE 7 Find the measure of $\angle x$, $\angle y$, and $\angle z$ if the measure of $\angle t$ is 42°.

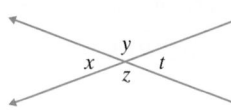

Solution: Since $\angle t$ and $\angle x$ are vertical angles, they have the same measure, so $\angle x$ measures 42°.

Since $\angle t$ and $\angle y$ are adjacent angles, their measures have a sum of 180°. So $\angle y$ measures $180° - 42° = 138°$.

Since $\angle y$ and $\angle z$ are vertical angles, they have the same measure. So $\angle z$ measures 138°.

◻ **Work Practice Problem 7**

A line that intersects two or more lines at different points is called a **transversal.** Line l is a transversal that intersects lines m and n. The eight angles formed have special names. Some of these names are:

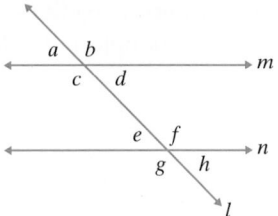

Corresponding angles: $\angle a$ and $\angle e$, $\angle c$ and $\angle g$, $\angle b$ and $\angle f$, $\angle d$ and $\angle h$

Alternate interior angles: $\angle c$ and $\angle f$, $\angle d$ and $\angle e$

When two lines cut by a transversal are *parallel,* the following are true:

Parallel Lines Cut by a Transversal

If two parallel lines are cut by a transversal, then the measures of **corresponding angles are equal** and the measures of the **alternate interior angles are equal.**

PRACTICE PROBLEM 8

Given that $m \parallel n$ and that the measure of $\angle w = 40°$, find the measures of all the angles shown.

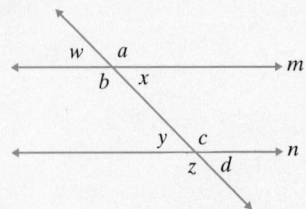

EXAMPLE 8 Given that $m \parallel n$ and that the measure of $\angle w$ is 100°, find the measures of $\angle x$, $\angle y$, and $\angle z$.

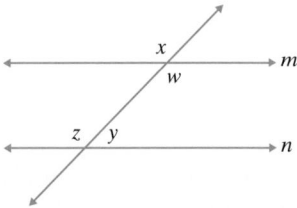

Solution:

$m\angle x = 100°$. $\angle x$ and $\angle w$ are vertical angles.

$m\angle z = 100°$. $\angle x$ and $\angle z$ are corresponding angles.

$m\angle y = 180° - 100° = 80°$. $\angle z$ and $\angle y$ are supplementary angles.

◻ **Work Practice Problem 8**

Answers

7. $m\angle a = 112°; m\angle b = 68°;$
$m\angle c = 68°,$
8. $m\angle x = 40°; m\angle y = 40°;$
$m\angle z = 140°; m\angle a = 140°;$
$m\angle b = 140°; m\angle c = 140°;$
$m\angle d = 40°$

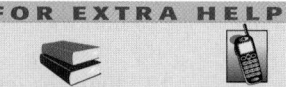

6.1 EXERCISE SET

Objective **A** *Identify each figure as a line, a ray, a line segment, or an angle. Then name the figure using the given points. See Example 1.*

1.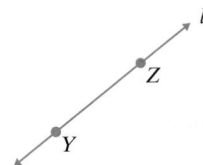

2.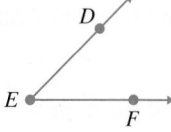

3.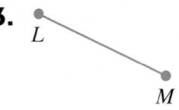

4.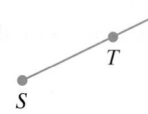

5.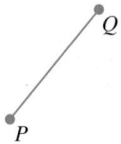

6.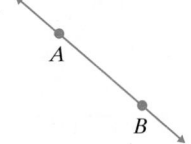

7.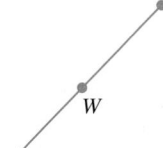

8.

Objective **B** *Fill in each blank. See Example 3.*

9. A right angle has a measure of _____.

10. A straight angle has a measure of _____.

11. An acute angle measures between _____ and _____.

12. An obtuse angle measures between _____ and _____.

Classify each angle as acute, right, obtuse, or straight. See Example 3.

13.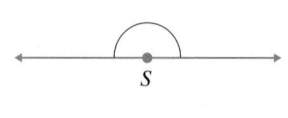

14.

15.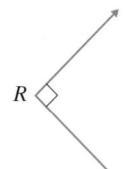

16.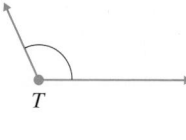

17.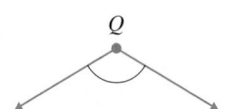

18.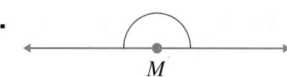

19.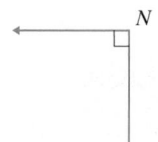

20.

Objective **C** *Find each complementary or supplementary angle as indicated. See Examples 4 and 5.*

21. Find the complement of a 17° angle.

22. Find the complement of an 87° angle.

23. Find the supplement of a 17° angle.

24. Find the supplement of an 87° angle.

25. Find the complement of a 58° angle.

26. Find the complement of a 22° angle.

27. Find the supplement of a 105° angle.

28. Find the supplement of a 155° angle.

29. Identify the pairs of complementary angles.

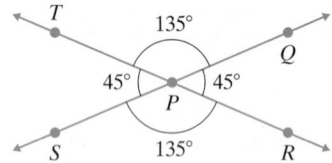

30. Identify the pairs of complementary angles.

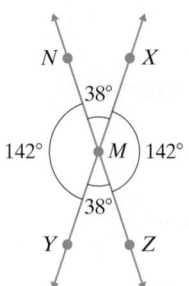

31. Identify the pairs of supplementary angles.

32. Identify the pairs of supplementary angles.

Objective **D** *Find the measure of ∠x in each figure. See Example 6.*

33.

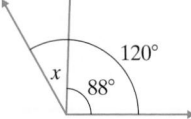

34.

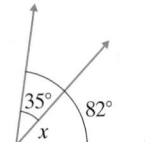

35.

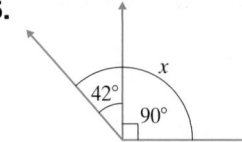

36.

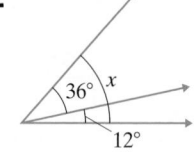

Find the measures of angles x, y, and z in each figure. See Examples 7 and 8.

37.

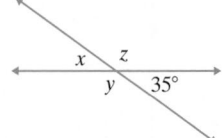

38.

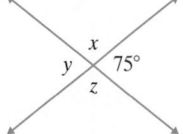

39.

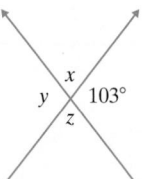

40.

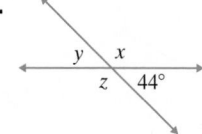

41. $m \parallel n$

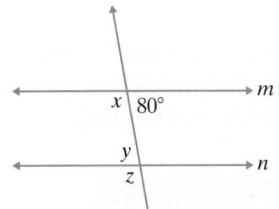

42. $m \parallel n$

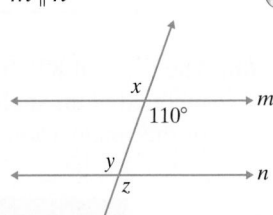

43. $m \parallel n$

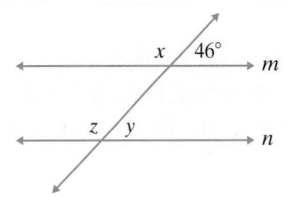

44. $m \parallel n$

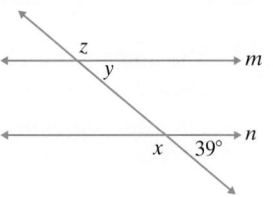

Objectives Ⓐ Ⓓ **Mixed Practice** *Find two other ways of naming each angle. See Example 2.*

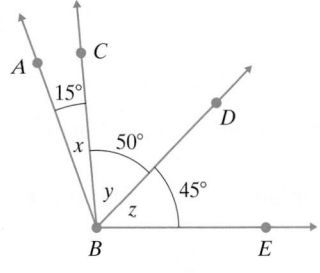

45. $\angle x$

46. $\angle y$

47. $\angle z$

48. $\angle ABE$ (just name one other way)

Find the measure of each angle in the figure above.

49. $\angle ABC$

50. $\angle EBD$

51. $\angle CBD$

52. $\angle CBA$

53. $\angle DBA$

54. $\angle EBC$

55. $\angle CBE$

56. $\angle ABE$

Review

Perform each indicated operation. See Sections 2.4, 2.5, 3.3, and 3.4.

57. $\dfrac{7}{8} + \dfrac{1}{4}$

58. $\dfrac{7}{8} - \dfrac{1}{4}$

59. $\dfrac{7}{8} \cdot \dfrac{1}{4}$

60. $\dfrac{7}{8} \div \dfrac{1}{4}$

61. $3\dfrac{1}{3} - 2\dfrac{1}{2}$

62. $3\dfrac{1}{3} + 2\dfrac{1}{2}$

63. $3\dfrac{1}{3} \div 2\dfrac{1}{2}$

64. $3\dfrac{1}{3} \cdot 2\dfrac{1}{2}$

Concept Extensions

65. The angle between the two walls of the Vietnam Veterans Memorial in Washington, D.C., is 125.2°. Find the supplement of this angle. (*Source:* National Park Service)

66. The faces of Khafre's Pyramid at Giza, Egypt, are inclined at an angle of 53.13°. Find the complement of this angle. (*Source:* PBS *NOVA* Online)

Answer true or false for Exercises 67 through 70. See the Concept Check in this section.

67. The complement of a 100° angle is an 80° angle.

68. It is possible to find the complement of a 120° angle.

69. It is possible to find the supplement of a 120° angle.

70. The supplement of a 5° angle is a 175° angle.

71. If lines m and n are parallel, find the measures of angles a through e.

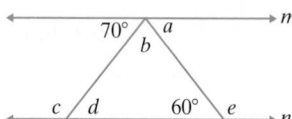

72. In your own words, describe how to find the complement and the supplement of a given angle.

73. Find two complementary angles with the same measure.

74. Can two supplementary angles both be acute? Explain why or why not.

△ 6.2 PLANE FIGURES AND SOLIDS

Objectives

A Identify Plane Figures.

B Identify Solids.

In order to prepare for the sections ahead in this chapter, we first review plane figures and solids.

Objective A Identifying Plane Figures

Recall from Section 6.1 that a **plane** is a flat surface that extends indefinitely.

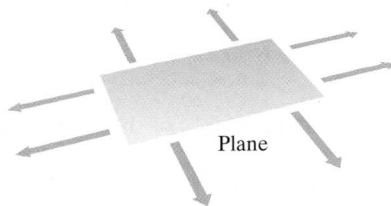

Plane

A **plane figure** is a figure that lies on a plane. Plane figures, like planes, have length and width but no thickness or depth.

A **polygon** is a closed plane figure that basically consists of three or more line segments that meet at their end points.

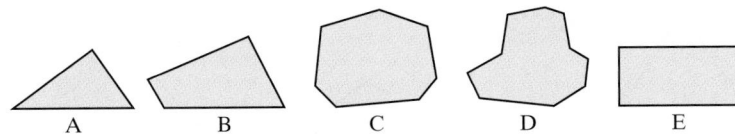

A **regular polygon** is one whose sides are all the same length and whose angles are the same measure.

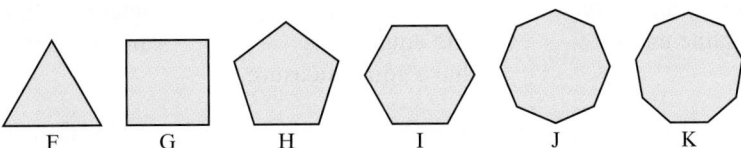

A polygon is named according to the number of its sides.

Polygons		
Number of Sides	**Name**	**Figure Examples**
3	Triangle	A, F
4	Quadrilateral	B, E, G
5	Pentagon	H
6	Hexagon	I
7	Heptagon	C
8	Octagon	J
9	Nonagon	K
10	Decagon	D

Some triangles and quadrilaterals are given special names, so let's study these polygons further. We begin with triangles.

The sum of the measures of the angles of a triangle is 180°.

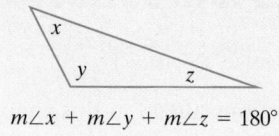

$$m\angle x + m\angle y + m\angle z = 180°$$

PRACTICE PROBLEM 1

Find the measure of $\angle x$.

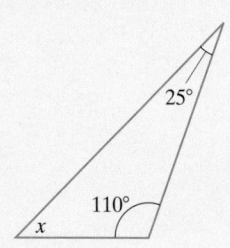

EXAMPLE 1 Find the measure of $\angle a$.

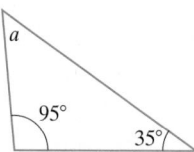

Solution: Since the sum of the measures of the three angles is 180°, we have measure of $\angle a$, or $m\angle a = 180° - 95° - 35° = 50°$

To check, see that $95° + 35° + 50° = 180°$.

◻ **Work Practice Problem 1**

We can classify triangles according to the lengths of their sides. (We will use tick marks to denote the sides and angles of a figure that are equal.)

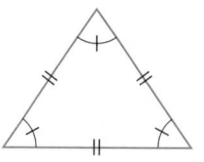
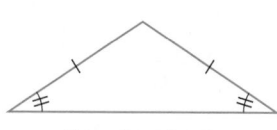
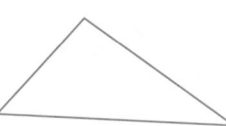

Equilateral triangle
All three sides are the same length. Also, all three angles have the same measure.

Isosceles triangle
Two sides are the same length. Also, the angles opposite the equal sides have equal measure.

Scalene triangle
No sides are the same length. No angles have the same measure.

One other important type of triangle is a right triangle. A **right triangle** is a triangle with a right angle. The side opposite the right angle is called the **hypotenuse,** and the other two sides are called **legs.**

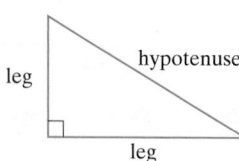

PRACTICE PROBLEM 2

Find the measure of $\angle y$.

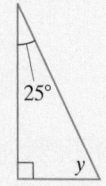

EXAMPLE 2 Find the measure of $\angle b$.

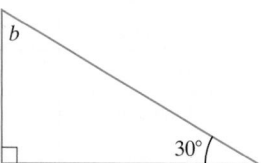

Solution: We know that the measure of the right angle, ⌐, is 90°. Since the sum of the measures of the angles is 180°, we have

measure of $\angle b$, or $m\angle b = 180° - 90° - 30° = 60°$

◻ **Work Practice Problem 2**

Answers

1. 45°, **2.** 65°

> **Helpful Hint**
>
> From the previous example, can you see that in a right triangle, the sum of the other two acute angles is 90°? This is because
>
> $$90° + 90° = 180°$$
>
> ↑   ↑   ↑
> right angle's measure   sum of other two angles' measures   sum of angles' measures

Now we review some special quadrilaterals. A **parallelogram** is a special quadrilateral with opposite sides parallel and equal in length.

A **rectangle** is a special **parallelogram** that has four right angles.

A **square** is a special **rectangle** that has all four sides equal in length.

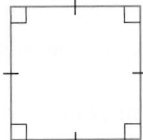

A **rhombus** is a special **parallelogram** that has all four sides equal in length.

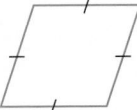

A **trapezoid** is a quadrilateral with exactly one pair of opposite sides parallel.

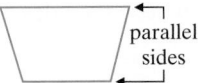

parallel sides

✔ **Concept Check** True or false? All quadrilaterals are parallelograms. Explain.

In addition to triangles, quadrilaterals, and other polygons, circles are also plane figures. A **circle** is a plane figure that consists of all points that are the same fixed distance from a point c. The point c is called the **center** of the circle. A **radius** of a circle is the distance from the center of the circle to any point on the circle. A **diameter** of a circle is the distance across the circle passing through the center. Notice that the diameter is twice the radius, and the radius is half the diameter.

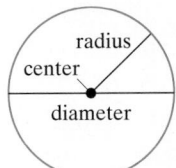

radius
center
diameter

✔ **Concept Check Answer**
false

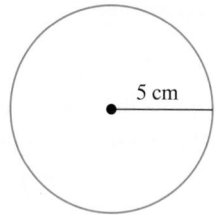

$$\boxed{\text{diameter}} = \boxed{2} \cdot \boxed{\text{radius}} \qquad \boxed{\text{radius}} = \boxed{\dfrac{\text{diameter}}{2}}$$

$$d = 2 \cdot r \qquad r = \dfrac{d}{2}$$

PRACTICE PROBLEM 3

Find the radius of the circle.

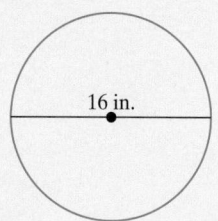

EXAMPLE 3 Find the diameter of the circle.

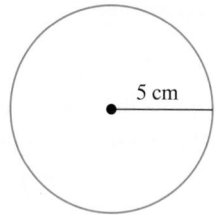

Solution: The diameter is twice the radius.

$d = 2 \cdot r$

$d = 2 \cdot 5 \text{ cm} = 10 \text{ cm}$

The diameter is 10 centimeters.

■ **Work Practice Problem 3**

Objective **B** Identifying Solid Figures

Recall from Section 6.1 that space extends in all directions indefinitely.

A **solid** is a figure that lies in space. Solids have length, width, and height or depth.

A **rectangular solid** is a solid that consists of six sides, or faces, all of which are rectangles.

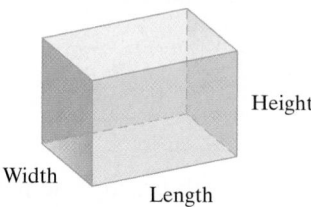

A **cube** is a rectangular solid whose six sides are squares.

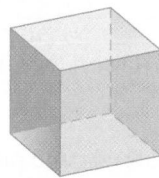

A **pyramid** is shown below. The pyramids we will study have square bases and heights that are perpendicular to their base.

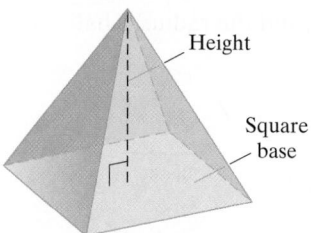

Answer

3. 8 in.

A **sphere** consists of all points in space that are the same distance from a point c. The point c is called the **center** of the sphere. A **radius** of a sphere is the distance from the center to any point on the sphere. A **diameter** of a sphere is the distance across the sphere passing through the center.

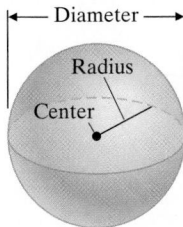

The radius and diameter of a sphere are related in the same way as the radius and diameter of a circle.

$$d = 2 \cdot r \quad \text{or} \quad r = \frac{d}{2}$$

EXAMPLE 4 Find the radius of the sphere.

Solution: The radius is half the diameter.

$$r = \frac{d}{2}$$

$$r = \frac{36 \text{ feet}}{2} = 18 \text{ feet}$$

The radius is 18 feet.

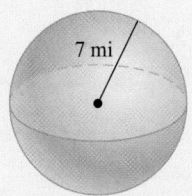

Work Practice Problem 4

The **cylinders** we will study have bases that are in the shape of circles and heights that are perpendicular to their base.

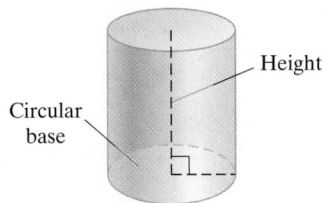

The **cones** we will study have bases that are circles and heights that are perpendicular to their base.

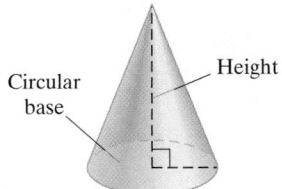

PRACTICE PROBLEM 4

Find the diameter of the sphere.

Answer

4. 14 mi

FOR EXTRA HELP

| Student Solutions Manual | PH Math/Tutor Center | CD/Video for Review | Math XL MathXL® | MyMathLab MyMathLab |

Identify each polygon. See the table at the beginning of this section.

1.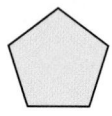

2.

3.

4.

5.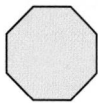

6.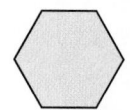

7.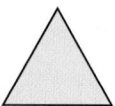

8.

Objective A *Classify each triangle as equilateral, isosceles, or scalene. Also identify any triangles that are also right triangles.*

9.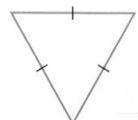

10.

11.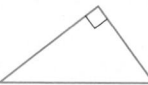

12.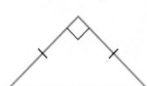

13.

14.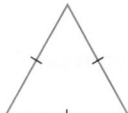

Find the measure of ∠x in each figure. See Examples 1 and 2.

15.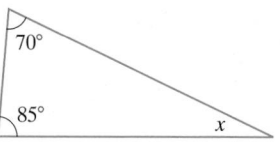

16.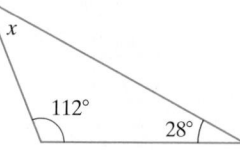

17.

18.

19.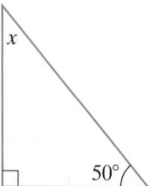

20.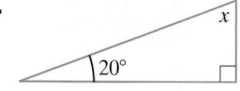

Fill in each blank.

21. Twice the radius of a circle is its _____.

22. A rectangle with all four sides equal is a _____.

23. A parallelogram with four right angles is a _____.

24. Half the diameter of a circle is its _____.

25. A quadrilateral with opposite sides parallel is a _____.

26. A quadrilateral with exactly one pair of opposite sides parallel is a _____.

27. The side opposite the right angle of a right triangle is called the _____.

28. A triangle with no equal sides is a _____.

Find the unknown diameter or radius in each figure. See Example 3.

29.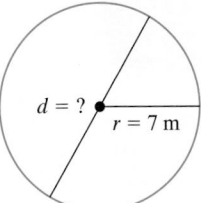
$d = ?$ $r = 7$ m

30.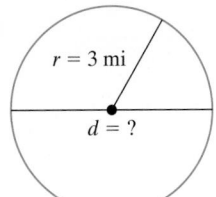
$r = 3$ mi $d = ?$

31.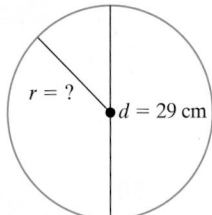
$r = ?$ $d = 29$ cm

32.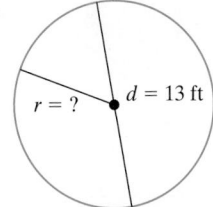
$r = ?$ $d = 13$ ft

33.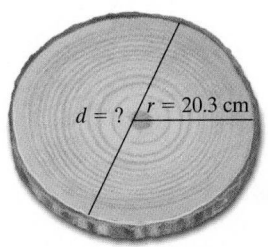
$d = ?$ $r = 20.3$ cm

34.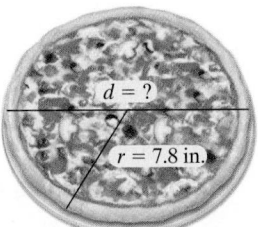
$d = ?$ $r = 7.8$ in.

35.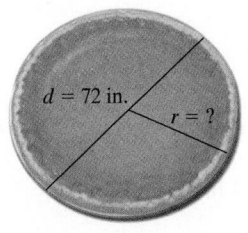
$d = 72$ in. $r = ?$

Largest pumpkin pie (*Source: Guinness World Records*)

36.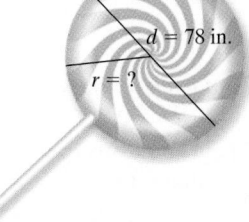
$d = 78$ in. $r = ?$

Largest lollipop (*Source: Guinness World Records*)

Objective **B** *Identify each solid.*

37.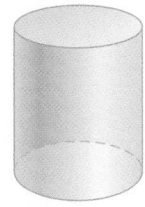

38.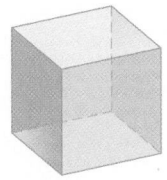

39.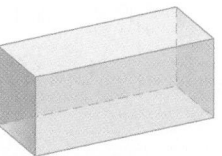

40.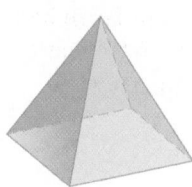

41.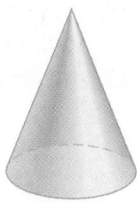

42.

Identify the shape of each item.

43.

44.

45.

46.

47.

48.

49.

50.

Find each unknown radius or diameter. See Example 4.

51. The radius of a sphere is 7.4 inches. Find its diameter.

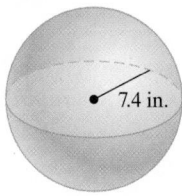

52. The radius of a sphere is 5.8 meters. Find its diameter.

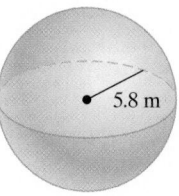

53. Find the radius of the sphere.

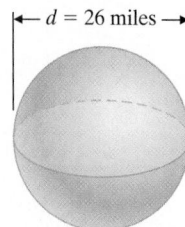

54. Find the radius of the sphere.

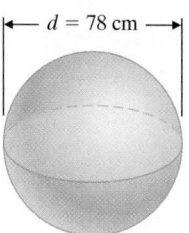

55. Saturn has a radius of approximately 36,184 miles. What is its diameter?

56. A sphere-shaped wasp nest found in Japan had a radius of approximately 15 inches. What was its diameter? (*Source: Guinness World Records*)

Review

Perform each indicated operation. See Sections 1.3, 1.6, 4.3, and 4.4.

57. 2(18) + 2(36)

58. 4(87)

59. 4(3.14)

60. 2(7.8) + 2(9.6)

Concept Extensions

Determine whether each statement is true or false. See the Concept Check in this section.

61. A square is also a rhombus.

62. A square is also a regular polygon.

63. A rectangle is also a parallelogram.

64. A trapezoid is also a parallelogram.

65. A pentagon is also a quadrilateral.

66. A rhombus is also a parallelogram.

67. Is an isosceles right triangle possible? If so, draw one.

68. The following demonstration is credited to the mathematician Pascal, who is said to have developed it as a young boy.

Cut a triangle from a piece of paper. The length of the sides and the size of the angles is unimportant. Tear the points off the triangle as shown.

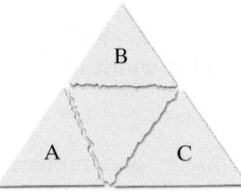

Place the points of the triangle together. Notice that a straight line is formed. What was Pascal trying to show?

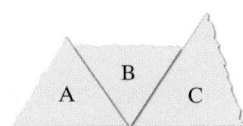

69. In your own words, explain whether a square is also a rhombus.

PRACTICE PROBLEM 1

a. Find the perimeter of the rectangle.

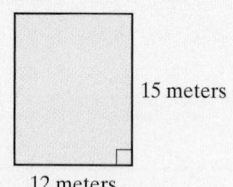

15 meters

12 meters

b. Find the perimeter of the rectangular lot shown below:

60 feet

80 feet

PRACTICE PROBLEM 2

Find the perimeter of a rectangle with a length of 22 centimeters and a width of 10 centimeters.

Answers

1. a. 54 m, **b.** 280 ft, **2.** 64 cm

426

6.3 PERIMETER

Objective **A** Using Formulas to Find Perimeters

Recall from Section 1.3 that the perimeter of a polygon is the distance around the polygon. This means that the perimeter of a polygon is the sum of the lengths of its sides.

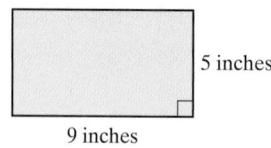 Find the perimeter of the rectangle below.

5 inches

9 inches

Solution:

perimeter = 9 inches + 9 inches + 5 inches + 5 inches

= 28 inches

Work Practice Problem 1

Notice that the perimeter of the rectangle in Example 1 can be written as $2 \cdot (9 \text{ inches}) + 2 \cdot (5 \text{ inches})$.

↑ length   ↑ width

In general, we can say that the perimeter of a rectangle is always

$2 \cdot \text{length} + 2 \cdot \text{width}$

As we have just seen, the perimeter of some special figures such as rectangles form patterns. These patterns are given as **formulas.** The formula for the perimeter of a rectangle is shown next:

Perimeter of a Rectangle

perimeter = $2 \cdot \text{length} + 2 \cdot \text{width}$

In symbols, this can be written as

$P = 2 \cdot l + 2 \cdot w$

length

width   width

length

EXAMPLE 2 Find the perimeter of a rectangle with a length of 11 inches and a width of 3 inches.

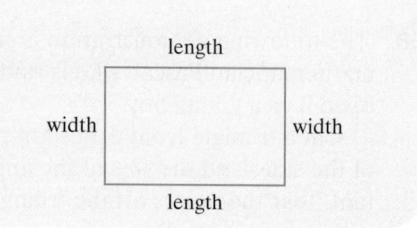

11 in.

3 in.

Solution: We use the formula for perimeter and replace the letters by their known lengths.

$P = 2 \cdot l + 2 \cdot w$

$= 2 \cdot 11 \text{ in.} + 2 \cdot 3 \text{ in.}$ Replace l with 11 in. and w with 3 in.

$= 22 \text{ in.} + 6 \text{ in.}$

$= 28 \text{ in.}$

The perimeter is 28 inches.

Work Practice Problem 2

Recall that a square is a special rectangle with all four sides the same length. The formula for the perimeter of a square is shown next:

Perimeter of a Square

Perimeter = side + side + side + side
         = 4 · side

In symbols,

$P = 4 \cdot s$

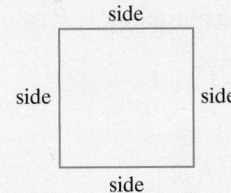

<EXAMPLE 3> **Finding the Perimeter of a Field**

How much fencing is needed to enclose a square field 50 yards on a side?

Solution: To find the amount of fencing needed, we find the distance around, or perimeter. The formula for the perimeter of a square is $P = 4 \cdot s$. We use this formula and replace s by 50 yards.

$P = 4 \cdot s$
  $= 4 \cdot 50$ yd
  $= 200$ yd

The amount of fencing needed is 200 yards.

▣ **Work Practice Problem 3**

The formula for the perimeter of a triangle with sides of lengths a, b, and c is given next:

Perimeter of a Triangle

Perimeter = side a + side b + side c

In symbols,

$P = a + b + c$

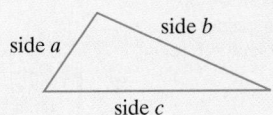

PRACTICE PROBLEM 3

Find the perimeter of a square tabletop if each side is 5 feet long.

Answer

3. 20 ft

PRACTICE PROBLEM 4

Find the perimeter of a triangle if the sides are 5 centimeters, 9 centimeters, and 7 centimeters in length.

EXAMPLE 4 Find the perimeter of a triangle if the sides are 3 inches, 7 inches, and 6 inches.

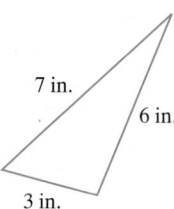

Solution: The formula for the perimeter is $P = a + b + c$, where a, b, and c are the lengths of the sides. Thus,

$$P = a + b + c$$
$$= 3 \text{ in.} + 7 \text{ in.} + 6 \text{ in.}$$
$$= 16 \text{ in.}$$

The perimeter of the triangle is 16 inches.

■ **Work Practice Problem 4**

Recall that to find the perimeter of other polygons, we find the sum of the lengths of their sides.

PRACTICE PROBLEM 5

Find the perimeter of the trapezoid shown.

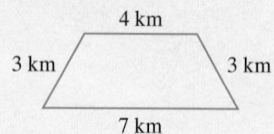

EXAMPLE 5 Find the perimeter of the trapezoid shown below:

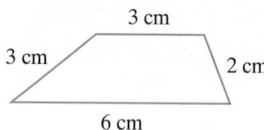

Solution: To find the perimeter, we find the sum of the lengths of its sides.

perimeter = 3 cm + 2 cm + 6 cm + 3 cm = 14 cm

The perimeter is 12 centimeters.

■ **Work Practice Problem 5**

PRACTICE PROBLEM 6

Find the perimeter of the room shown.

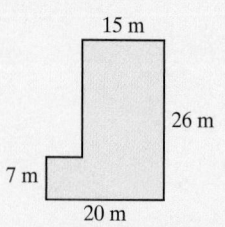

EXAMPLE 6 Finding the Perimeter of a Room

Find the perimeter of the room shown below:

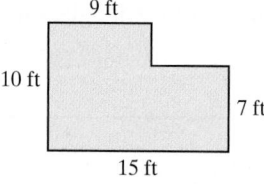

Solution: To find the perimeter of the room, we first need to find the lengths of all sides of the room.

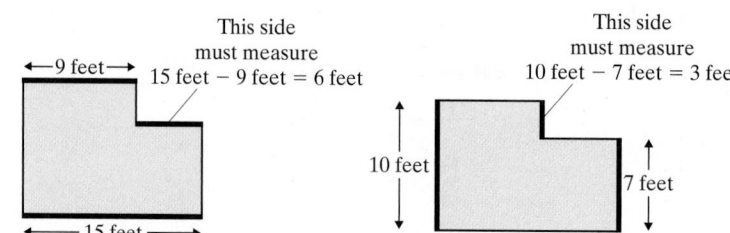

This side must measure 15 feet − 9 feet = 6 feet

This side must measure 10 feet − 7 feet = 3 feet

Answers

4. 21 cm, **5.** 17 km, **6.** 92 m

Now that we know the measures of all sides of the room, we can add the measures to find the perimeter.

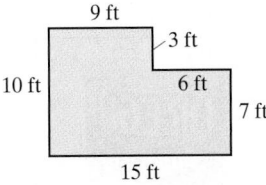

perimeter = 10 ft + 9 ft + 3 ft + 6 ft + 7 ft + 15 ft

= 50 ft

The perimeter of the room is 50 feet.

⬛ **Work Practice Problem 6**

EXAMPLE 7 **Calculating the Cost of Baseboard**

A rectangular room measures 10 feet by 12 feet. Find the cost to install new baseboard around the room if the cost of the baseboard is $0.66 per foot.

Solution: First we find the perimeter of the room.

$P = 2 \cdot l + 2 \cdot w$

$\quad = 2 \cdot 12 \text{ ft} + 2 \cdot 10 \text{ ft}$ Replace *l* with 12 feet and *w* with 10 feet.

$\quad = 24 \text{ ft} + 20 \text{ ft}$

$\quad = 44 \text{ ft}$

The cost of the baseboard is

cost = $0.66 \cdot 44$ ft = 29.04

The cost of the baseboard is $29.04.

⬛ **Work Practice Problem 7**

Objective **B** **Using Formulas to Find Circumferences**

Recall from Section 4.4 that the distance around a circle is called the **circumference.** This distance depends on the radius or the diameter of the circle.

The formulas for circumference are shown next:

Circumference of a Circle

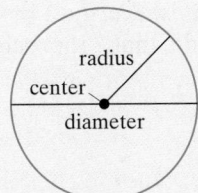

Circumference = $2 \cdot \pi \cdot$ radius or Circumference = $\pi \cdot$ diameter

In symbols,

$\quad C = 2 \cdot \pi \cdot r$ or $C = \pi \cdot d$,

where $\pi \approx 3.14$ or $\pi \approx \dfrac{22}{7}$.

PRACTICE PROBLEM 7

A rectangular lot measures 60 feet by 120 feet. Find the cost to install fencing around the lot if the cost of fencing is $1.90 per foot.

Answer

7. $684

To better understand circumference and π(pi), try the following experiment. Take any can and measure its circumference and its diameter.

The can in the figure above has a circumference of 23.5 centimeters and a diameter of 7.5 centimeters. Now divide the circumference by the diameter.

$$\frac{\text{circumference}}{\text{diameter}} = \frac{23.5 \text{ cm}}{7.5 \text{ cm}} \approx 3.13$$

Try this with other sizes of cylinders and circles—you should always get a number close to 3.1. The exact ratio of circumference to diameter is π. (Recall that $\pi \approx 3.14$ or $\approx \frac{22}{7}$.)

PRACTICE PROBLEM 8

a. An irrigation device waters a circular region with a diameter of 20 yards. Find the exact circumference of the watered region, then use $\pi \approx 3.14$ to give an approximation.

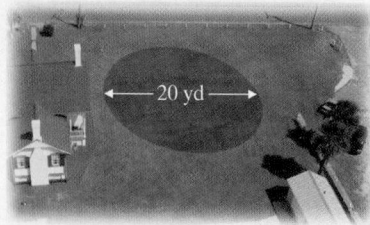

b. A manufacturer of clocks is designing a new model. To help the designer calculate the cost of materials to make the new clock, calculate the circumference of a clock with a face diameter of 12 inches. Give an exact circumference; then use $\pi \approx 3.14$ to approximate.

Answers

8. a. exactly 20π yd ≈ 62.8 yd,
b. exactly 12π in. ≈ 37.68 in.

✔ Concept Check Answer

a square with side length 5 in.

EXAMPLE 8 Finding Circumference of Spa

Mary Catherine Dooley plans to install a border of new tiling around the circumference of her circular spa. If her spa has a diameter of 14 feet, find its exact circumference. Then use the approximation 3.14 for π to approximate the circumference.

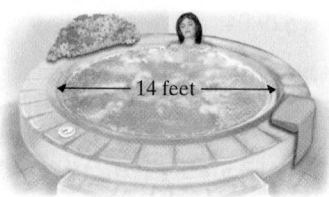

14 feet

Solution: Because we are given the diameter, we use the formula $C = \pi \cdot d$.

$C = \pi \cdot d$
    $= \pi \cdot 14 \text{ ft}$ Replace d with 14 feet.
    $= 14\pi \text{ ft}$

The circumference of the spa is *exactly* 14π feet. By replacing π with the *approximation* 3.14, we find that the circumference is *approximately* 14 feet $\cdot 3.14 = 43.96$ feet.

Work Practice Problem 8

✔ Concept Check The distance around which figure is greater: a square with side length 5 inches or a circle with radius 3 inches?

Objective Ⓐ *Find the perimeter of each figure. See Examples 1 through 6.*

1.
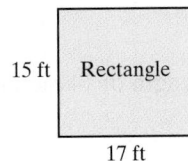
15 ft   Rectangle
17 ft

2.
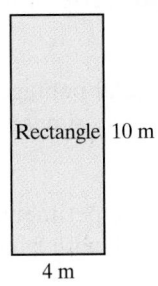
Rectangle 10 m
4 m

3.
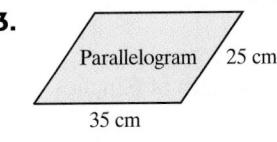
Parallelogram   25 cm
35 cm

4.
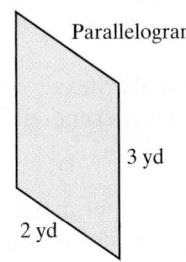
Parallelogram
3 yd
2 yd

5.
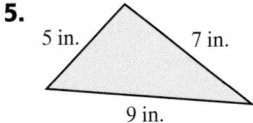
5 in.   7 in.
9 in.

6.
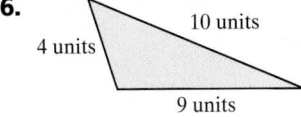
10 units
4 units
9 units

7.
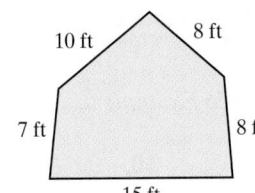
10 ft   8 ft
7 ft   8 ft
15 ft

8.
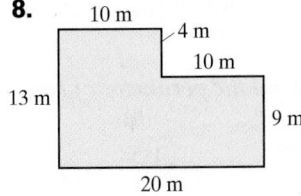
10 m   4 m
10 m
13 m   9 m
20 m

Find the perimeter of each regular polygon.

9.
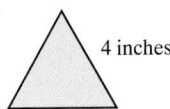
4 inches

10.

8 m

11.

21 cm

12.
 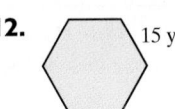
15 yd

Solve. See Examples 1 through 7.

13. A polygon has sides of length 5 feet, 3 feet, 2 feet, 7 feet, and 4 feet. Find its perimeter.

14. A triangle has sides of length 8 inches, 12 inches, and 10 inches. Find its perimeter.

15. Baseboard is to be installed in a square room that measures 15 feet on one side. Find how much baseboard is needed.

16. Find how much fencing is needed to enclose a rectangular rose garden 85 feet by 15 feet.

17. If a football field is 53 yards wide and 120 yards long, what is the perimeter?

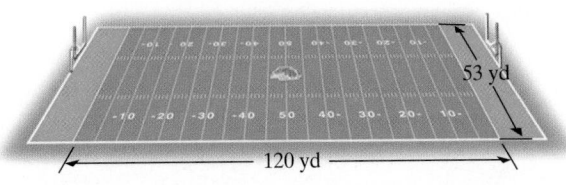
53 yd
120 yd

18. A stop sign has eight equal sides of length 12 inches. Find its perimeter.

19. A metal strip is being installed around a workbench that is 8 feet long and 3 feet wide. Find how much stripping is needed.

20. Find how much fencing is needed to enclose a rectangular garden 70 feet by 21 feet.

21. If the stripping in Exercise 19 costs $3 per foot, find the total cost of the stripping.

22. If the fencing in Exercise 20 costs $2 per foot, find the total cost of the fencing.

23. A regular hexagon has a side length of 6 inches. Find its perimeter.

24. A regular pentagon has a side length of 14 meters. Find its perimeter.

25. Find the perimeter of the top of a square compact disc case if the length of one side is 7 inches.

26. Find the perimeter of a square ceramic tile with a side of length 5 inches.

27. A rectangular room measures 6 feet by 8 feet. Find the cost of installing a strip of wallpaper around the room if the wallpaper costs $0.86 per foot.

28. A rectangular house measures 75 feet by 60 feet. Find the cost of installing gutters around the house if the cost is $2.36 per foot.

Find the perimeter of each figure. See Example 6.

29.

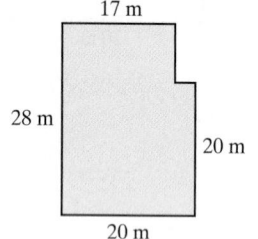

30.

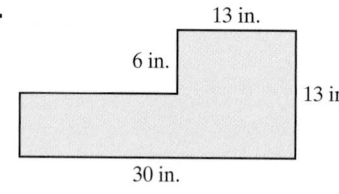

31.

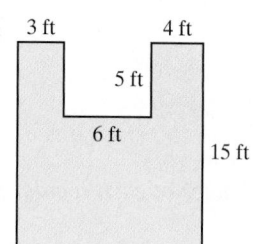

32.

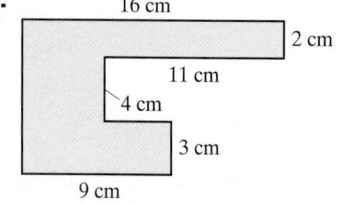

33.

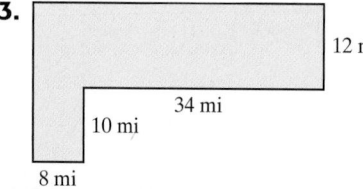

34.

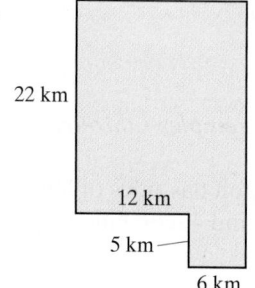

Objective [B] *Find the circumference of each circle. Give the exact circumference and then an approximation. Use* $\pi \approx 3.14$. *See Example 8.*

35.

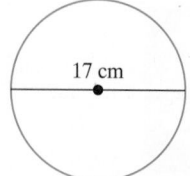

36.

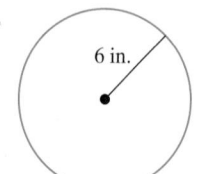

37.

38.

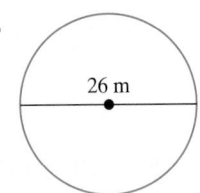

50 ft

39.

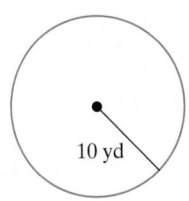

26 m

40.

10 yd

41. A circular fountain has a radius of 5 feet. Approximate the distance around the fountain. Use $\frac{22}{7}$ for π.

42. A circular walkway has a radius of 40 meters. Approximate the distance around the walkway. Use 3.14 for π.

43. Meteor Crater, near Winslow, Arizona, is 4000 feet in diameter. Approximate the distance around the crater. Use 3.14 for π. (*Source: The Handy Science Answer Book*)

44. The largest pearl, the *Pearl of Lao-tze*, has a diameter of $5\frac{1}{2}$ inches. Approximate the distance around the pearl. Use $\frac{22}{7}$ for π. (*Source: The Guinness Book of Records*)

Objectives Ⓐ Ⓑ **Mixed Practice** *Find the distance around each figure. For circles, give the exact circumference and then an approximation. Use $\pi \approx 3.14$.*

45.

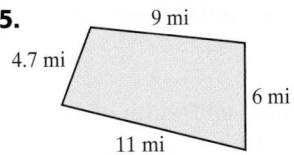

9 mi
4.7 mi
6 mi
11 mi

46.

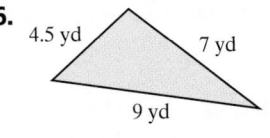

4.5 yd   7 yd
9 yd

47.

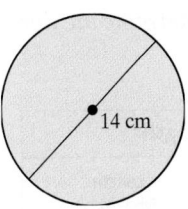

14 cm

48.

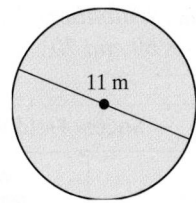

11 m

49.

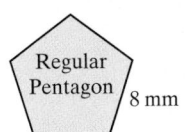

Regular Pentagon   8 mm

50.

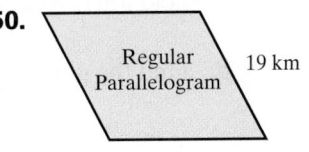

Regular Parallelogram   19 km

51.

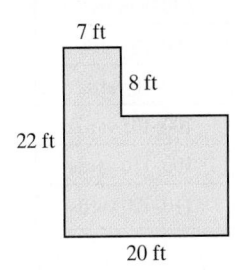

7 ft
8 ft
22 ft
20 ft

52.

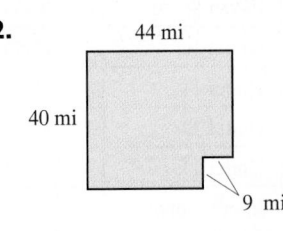

44 mi
40 mi
9 mi

Review

Simplify. See Section 1.9.

53. $5 + 6 \cdot 3$

54. $25 - 3 \cdot 7$

55. $(20 - 16) \div 4$

56. $6 \cdot (8 + 2)$

57. $(18 + 8) - (12 + 4)$

58. $72 \div (2 \cdot 6)$

59. $(72 \div 2) \cdot 6$

60. $4^1 \cdot (2^3 - 8)$

Concept Extensions

Recall from Section 1.6 that area measures the amount of surface of a region. Given the following situations, tell whether you are more likely to be concerned with area or perimeter.

61. ordering fencing to fence a yard

62. ordering grass seed to plant in a yard

63. buying carpet to install in a room

64. buying gutters to install on a house

65. ordering paint to paint a wall

66. ordering baseboards to install in a room

67. buying a wallpaper border to go on the walls around a room

68. buying fertilizer for your yard

There are a number of factors that determine the dimensions of a rectangular soccer field. Use the table below to answer Exercises 69 and 70.

Soccer Field Width and Length		
Age	Width Min–Max	Length Min–Max
Under 6/7:	15–20 yards	25–30 yards
Under 8:	20–25 yards	30–40 yards
Under 9:	30–35 yards	40–50 yards
Under 10:	40–50 yards	60–70 yards
Under 11:	40–50 yards	70–80 yards
Under 12:	40–55 yards	100–105 yards
Under 13:	50–60 yards	100–110 yards
International:	70–80 yards	110–120 yards

69. a. Find the minimum length and width of a soccer field for 8-year-old children. (Carefully consider the age.)

b. Find the perimeter of this field.

70. a. Find the maximum length and width of a soccer field for 12-year-old children.

b. Find the perimeter of this field.

Solve. See the Concept Check in this section. Choose the figure that has greater distance around.

71. a. A square with side length 3 inches
b. A circle with diameter 4 inches

72. a. A circle with diameter 7 inches
b. A square with side length 7 inches

73. a. Find the circumference of each circle. Approximate the circumference by using 3.14 for π.

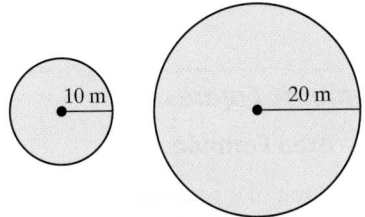

b. If the radius of a circle is doubled, is its corresponding circumference doubled?

74. a. Find the circumference of each circle. Approximate the circumference by using 3.14 for π.

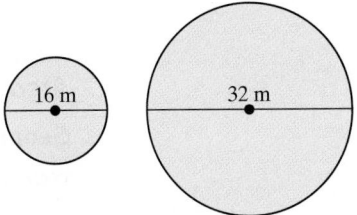

b. If the diameter of a circle is doubled, is its corresponding circumference doubled?

75. Find the perimeter of the skating rink.

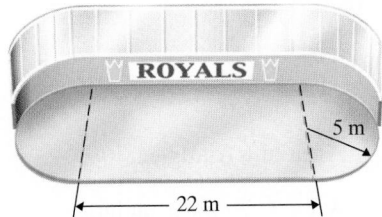

76. In your own words, explain how to find the perimeter of any polygon.

77. The perimeter of this rectangle is 30 feet. Find its width.

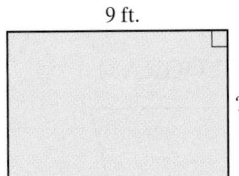

9 ft.

?

Find the perimeter. Round your results to the nearest tenth.

78.

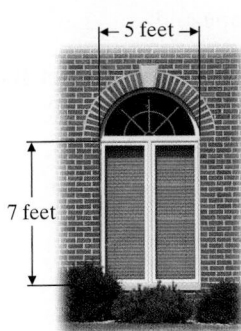

← 5 feet →

7 feet

79.

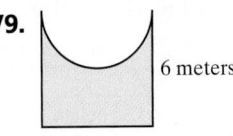

6 meters

6 meters

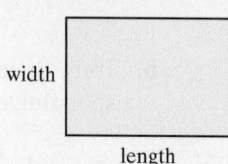

6.4 AREA

Objective A Finding Area of Geometric Figures

Recall that area measures the amount of surface of a region. Thus far, we know how to find the area of a rectangle and a square. These formulas, as well as formulas for finding the areas of other common geometric figures, are given next:

Area Formulas of Common Geometric Figures

Geometric Figure	Area Formula
RECTANGLE	Area of a rectangle: **Area = length · width** $A = lw$
SQUARE 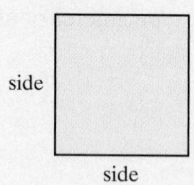	Area of a square: **Area = side · side** $A = s \cdot s = s^2$
TRIANGLE 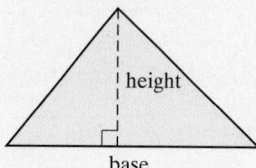	Area of a triangle: **Area $= \dfrac{1}{2} \cdot$ base · height** $A = \dfrac{1}{2} \cdot b \cdot h$
PARALLELOGRAM 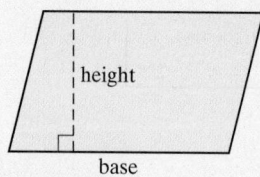	Area of a parallelogram: **Area = base · height** $A = b \cdot h$
TRAPEZOID 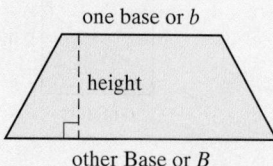	Area of a trapezoid: **Area $= \dfrac{1}{2} \cdot$ (one base + other Base) · height** $A = \dfrac{1}{2} \cdot (b + B) \cdot h$

Use these formulas for the following examples.

Helpful Hint

Area is always measured in square units.

EXAMPLE 1 Find the area of the triangle.

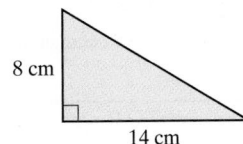

8 cm

14 cm

Solution: $A = \dfrac{1}{2} \cdot b \cdot h$

$= \dfrac{1}{2} \cdot 14 \text{ cm} \cdot 8 \text{ cm}$

$= \dfrac{\overset{1}{\cancel{2}} \cdot 7 \cdot 8}{\underset{1}{\cancel{2}}} \text{ sq cm}$

$= 56 \text{ square cm}$

The area is 56 square centimeters.

Helpful Hint

You may see 56 sq cm, for example, written with the notation 56 cm². Both of these notations mean the same quantity.

■ **Work Practice Problem 1**

EXAMPLE 2 Find the area of the parallelogram.

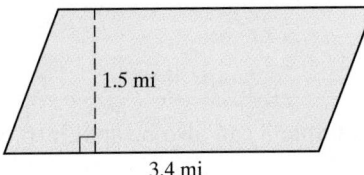

1.5 mi

3.4 mi

Solution:

$A = b \cdot h$

$= 3.4 \text{ miles} \cdot 1.5 \text{ miles}$

$= 5.1 \text{ square miles}$

The area is 5.1 square miles.

■ **Work Practice Problem 2**

Helpful Hint

When finding the area of figures, be sure all measurements are changed to the same unit before calculations are made.

EXAMPLE 3 Find the area of the figure.

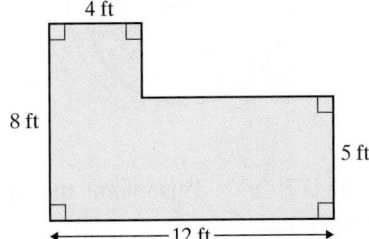

4 ft

8 ft

5 ft

12 ft

Continued on next page

PRACTICE PROBLEM 1

Find the area of the triangle.

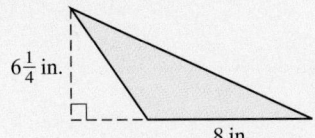

$6\frac{1}{4}$ in.

8 in.

PRACTICE PROBLEM 2

Find the area of the square.

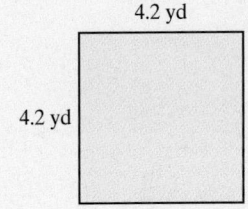

4.2 yd

4.2 yd

PRACTICE PROBLEM 3

Find the area of the figure.

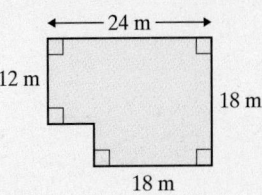

24 m

12 m

18 m

18 m

Answers

1. 25 sq in., **2.** 17.64 sq yd,
3. 396 sq m

Solution: Split the figure into two rectangles. To find the area of the figure, we find the sum of the areas of the two rectangles.

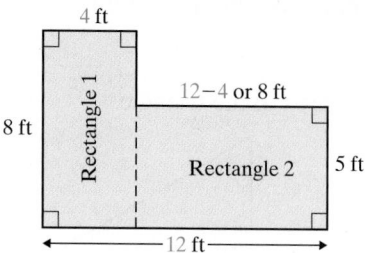

Area of Rectangle 1 $= l \cdot w$

$\qquad\qquad\qquad = 8 \text{ feet} \cdot 4 \text{ feet}$

$\qquad\qquad\qquad = 32 \text{ square feet}$

Notice that the length of Rectangle 2 is 12 feet $-$ 4 feet, or 8 feet.

Area of Rectangle 2 $= l \cdot w$

$\qquad\qquad\qquad = 8 \text{ feet} \cdot 5 \text{ feet}$

$\qquad\qquad\qquad = 40 \text{ square feet}$

Area of the Figure $=$ Area of Rectangle 1 $+$ Area of Rectangle 2

$\qquad\qquad\qquad = 32 \text{ square feet} + 40 \text{ square feet}$

$\qquad\qquad\qquad = 72 \text{ square feet}$

▣ **Work Practice Problem 3**

Helpful Hint

The figure in Example 3 can also be split into two rectangles as shown:

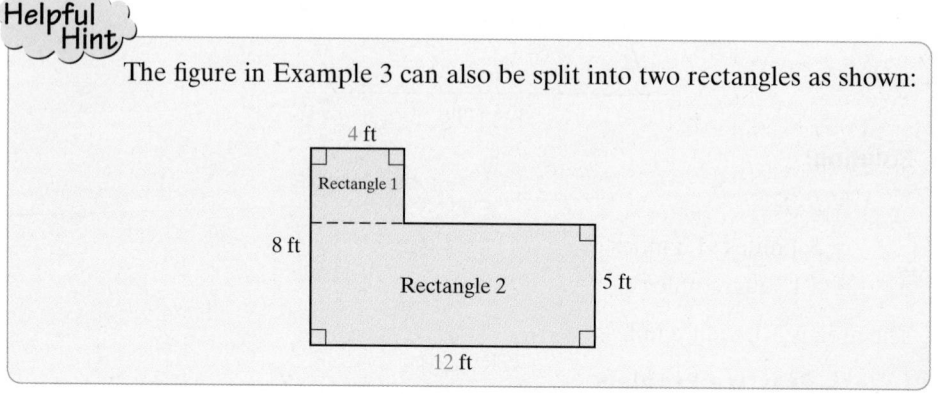

To better understand the formula for area of a circle, try the following. Cut a circle into many pieces as shown:

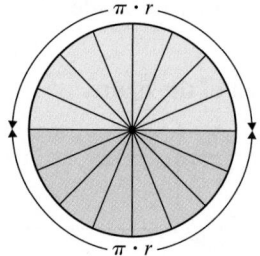

The circumference of a circle is $2 \cdot \pi \cdot r$. This means that the circumference of half a circle is half of $2 \cdot \pi \cdot r$, or $\pi \cdot r$.

Then unfold the two halves of the circle and place them together as shown:

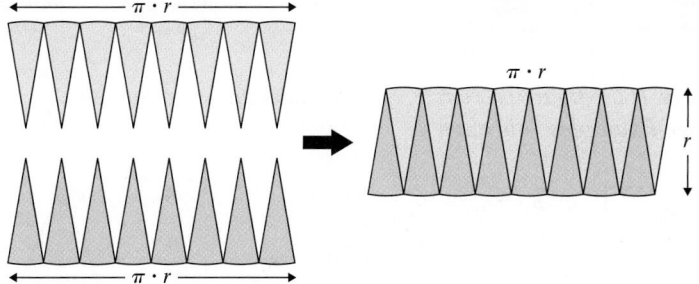

The figure on the right is almost a parallelogram with a base of $\pi \cdot r$ and a height of r. The area is

$$A = \boxed{\text{base}} \cdot \boxed{\text{height}}$$

$$= (\pi \cdot r) \cdot r$$
$$= \pi \cdot r^2$$

This is the formula for area of a circle.

Area Formula of a Circle

CIRCLE

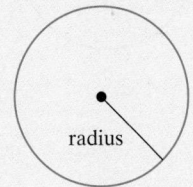

radius

Area of a circle:

Area $= \pi \cdot (\textbf{radius})^2$

$A = \pi \cdot r^2$

(A fraction approximation for π is $\dfrac{22}{7}$.)

(A decimal approximation for π is 3.14.)

EXAMPLE 4 Find the area of a circle with a radius of 3 feet. Find the exact area and an approximation. Use 3.14 as an approximation for π.

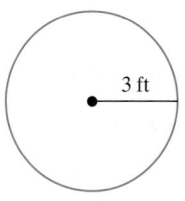

3 ft

Solution: We let $r = 3$ ft and use the formula.

$A = \pi \cdot r^2$

$\quad = \pi \cdot (3 \text{ ft})^2$

$\quad = \pi \cdot 9$ square ft, or $9 \cdot \pi$ square ft

To approximate this area, we substitute 3.14 for π.

$9 \cdot \pi$ square feet $\approx 9 \cdot 3.14$ square feet

$\qquad\qquad\qquad = 28.26$ square feet

The *exact* area of the circle is 9π square feet, which is *approximately* 28.26 square feet.

📖 **Work Practice Problem 4**

✔ Concept Check Use diagrams to decide which figure would have a larger area: a circle of diameter 10 inches or a square 10 inches long on each side.

PRACTICE PROBLEM 4

Find the area of the given circle. Find the exact area and an approximation. Use 3.14 as an approximation for π.

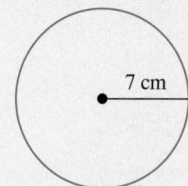

7 cm

Answer

4. 49π sq cm ≈ 153.86 sq cm

✔ **Concept Check Answer**

a square 10 in. long on each side

Objective **A** *Find the area of the geometric figure. If the figure is a circle, give an exact area and then use the given* **approximation** *for π to approximate the area. See Examples 1 through 4.*

1.
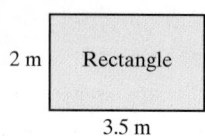
2 m · Rectangle · 3.5 m

2.
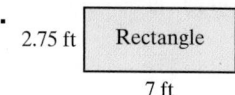
2.75 ft · Rectangle · 7 ft

3.
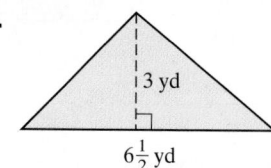
3 yd · $6\frac{1}{2}$ yd

4.
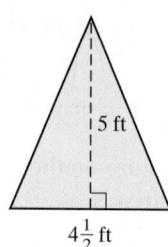
5 ft · $4\frac{1}{2}$ ft

5.
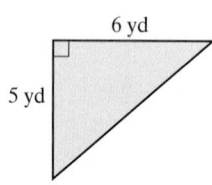
6 yd · 5 yd

6.
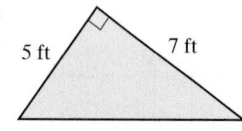
5 ft · 7 ft

7. Use 3.14 for π.
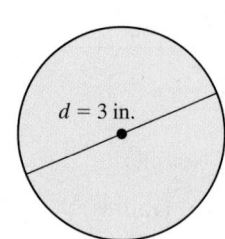
d = 3 in.

8. Use $\frac{22}{7}$ for π.
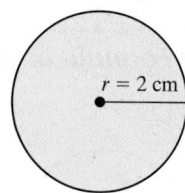
r = 2 cm

9.
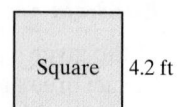
Square · 4.2 ft

10.
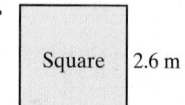
Square · 2.6 m

11.
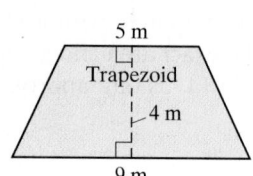
5 m · Trapezoid · 4 m · 9 m

12.
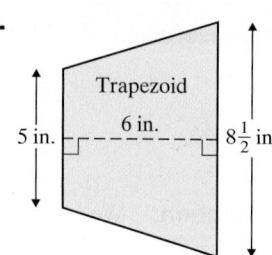
Trapezoid · 5 in. · 6 in. · $8\frac{1}{2}$ in.

13.
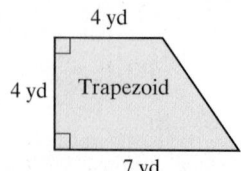
4 yd · 4 yd · Trapezoid · 7 yd

14.
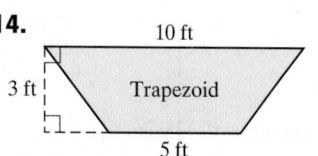
10 ft · 3 ft · Trapezoid · 5 ft

15.
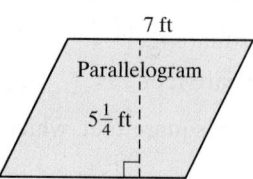
7 ft · Parallelogram · $5\frac{1}{4}$ ft

16.
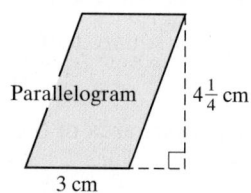
Parallelogram · $4\frac{1}{4}$ cm · 3 cm

440

17.

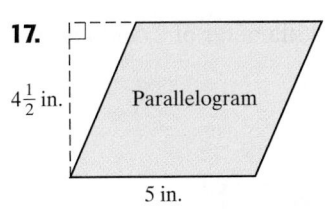

$4\frac{1}{2}$ in.

Parallelogram

5 in.

18.

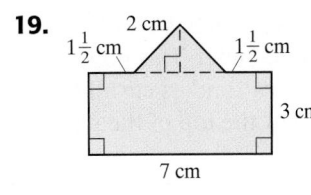

4 m

6 m

Parallelogram

19.

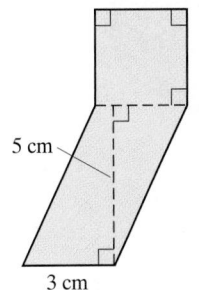

2 cm

$1\frac{1}{2}$ cm $1\frac{1}{2}$ cm

3 cm

7 cm

20.

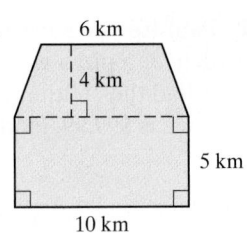

6 km

4 km

5 km

10 km

21.

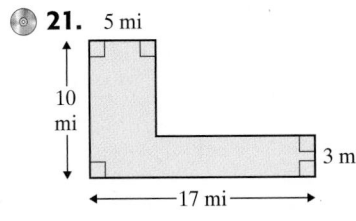

5 mi

10 mi

3 mi

17 mi

22.

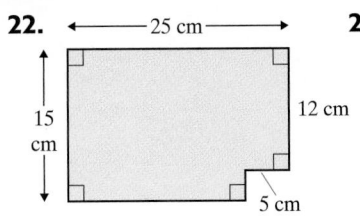

25 cm

15 cm

12 cm

5 cm

23.

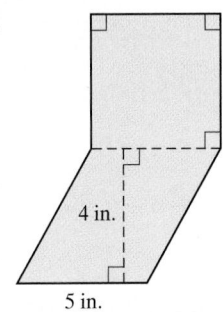

5 cm

3 cm

24.

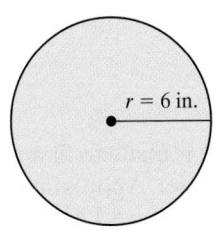

4 in.

5 in.

25. Use $\frac{22}{7}$ for π.

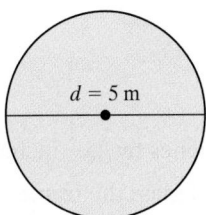

$r = 6$ in.

26. Use 3.14 for π.

$d = 5$ m

Solve. See Examples 1 through 4.

27. A $10\frac{1}{2}$-foot by 16-foot concrete wall is to be built using concrete blocks. Find the area of the wall.

28. The floor of Terry's attic is 24 feet by 35 feet. Find how many square feet of insulation are needed to cover the attic floor.

29. The world's largest flag measures 505 feet by 225 feet. It's the U.S. "Super flag" owned by "Ski" Demski of Long Beach, California. Find its area. (*Source: Guinness World Records,* 2005)

30. The longest illuminated sign is in Ramat Gan, Israel, and measures 197 feet by 66 feet. Find its area. (*Source: The Guinness Book of Records*)

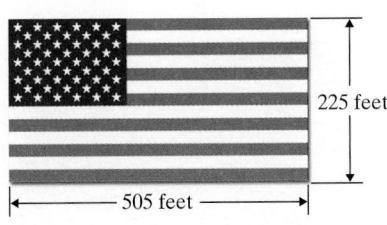

225 feet

505 feet

31. Paul Revere's Pizza in the USA will bake and deliver a pizza with a 4-foot diameter. This pizza is called the "Ultimate Party Pizza" and its current price is $99.99. Find the area of the top of the pizza.

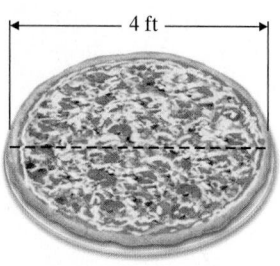

4 ft

32. The face of a watch has a diameter of 2 centimeters. What is its area?

2 cm

33. One side of a concrete block measures 8 inches by 16 inches. Find the area of the side in square inches. Find the area in square feet (144 sq in. = 1 sq ft).

34. A standard *double* roll of wallpaper is $6\frac{5}{6}$ feet wide and 33 feet long. Find the area of the *double* roll.

35. A picture frame measures 20 inches by $25\frac{1}{2}$ inches. Find how many square inches of glass the frame requires.

36. A mat to go under a tablecloth is made to fit a round dining table with a 4-foot diameter. Approximate how many square feet of mat there are. Use 3.14 as an approximation for π.

37. A drapery panel measures 6 feet by 7 feet. Find how many square feet of material are needed for *four* panels.

38. A page in this book measures 27.5 centimeters by 20.5 centimeters. Find its area.

39. Find how many square feet of land are in the plot shown:

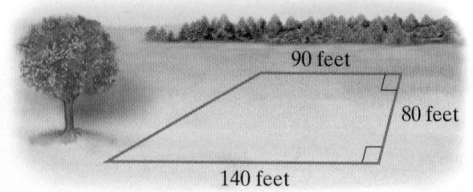

90 feet

80 feet

140 feet

40. For Gerald Gomez to determine how much grass seed he needs to buy, he must know the size of his yard. Use the drawing to determine how many square feet are in his yard.

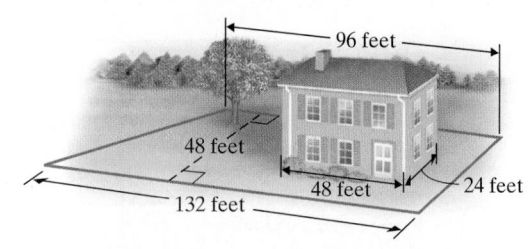

96 feet

48 feet

48 feet   24 feet

132 feet

41. The shaded part of the roof shown is in the shape of a trapezoid and needs to be shingled. The number of packages of shingles to buy depends on the area. Use the dimensions given to find the area of the shaded part of the roof to the nearest whole square foot.

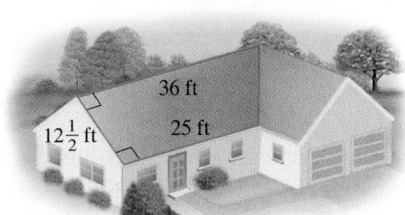

42. The end of the building shaded in the drawing is to be bricked. The number of bricks to buy depends on the area.

a. Find the area.

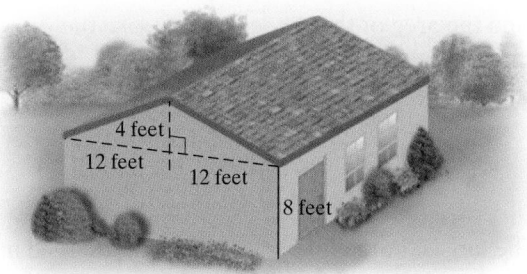

b. If the side area of each brick (including mortar room) is $\frac{1}{6}$ square feet, find the number of bricks needed to buy.

Review

Find the perimeter or circumference of each geometric figure. See Section 6.3.

43. Give an exact circumference and an approximation. Use 3.14 for π.

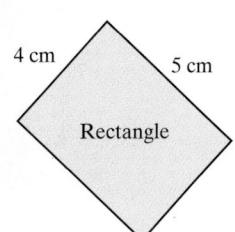

14 in.

44.

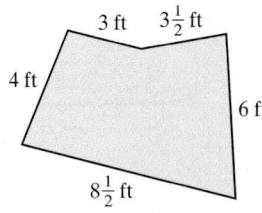

4 cm   5 cm

Rectangle

45.

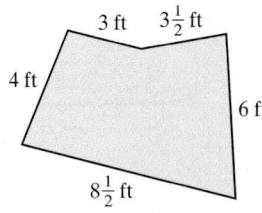

3 ft $3\frac{1}{2}$ ft

4 ft

6 ft

$8\frac{1}{2}$ ft

46.

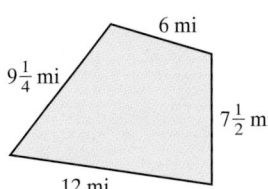

6 mi

$9\frac{1}{4}$ mi

$7\frac{1}{2}$ mi

12 mi

47.

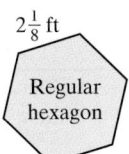

$2\frac{1}{8}$ ft

Regular hexagon

48.

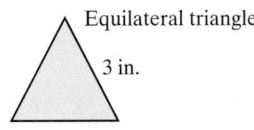

Equilateral triangle

3 in.

Concept Extensions

49. A pizza restaurant recently advertised two specials. The first special was a 12-inch diameter pizza for $10. The second special was two 8-inch diameter pizzas for $9. Determine the better buy. (*Hint:* First compare the areas of the pizzas in the two specials and then find a price per square inch for the pizzas in both specials.)

50. Find the approximate area of the state of Utah.

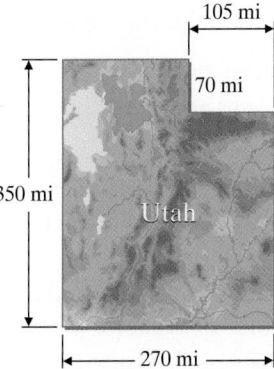

105 mi

70 mi

350 mi

Utah

270 mi

51. Find the area of a rectangle that measures 2 *feet* by 8 *inches*. Give the area in square feet and in square inches.

52. In your own words, explain why perimeter is measured in units and area is measured in square units. (*Hint:* See Section 1.6 for an introduction on the meaning of area.)

53. Find the area of the shaded region. Use the approximation 3.14 for π.

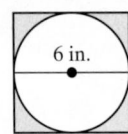

54. Estimate the cost of a piece of carpet for a rectangular room 10 feet by 15 feet. The cost of the carpet is $6.50 per yard.

55. The largest pumpkin pie was made and served in Windsor, California. The pie had a diameter of 72 inches. Find the area of the top of the pie. (*Source: Guinness World Records*)

56. The largest lollipop was made in Gränna, Sweden. It had a diameter of 78 inches. Find the area of a face of the lollipop. (*Source: Guinness World Records*)

Find the area of each figure. If needed, use $\pi \approx 3.14$ and round results to the nearest tenth.

57. Find the skating area.

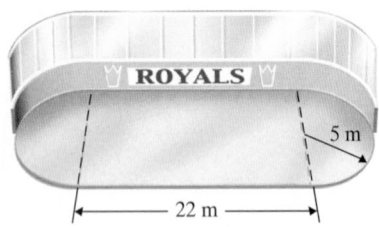

58.

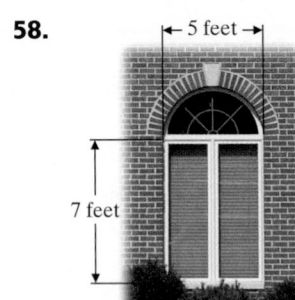

59. Do two rectangles with the same perimeter have the same area? To see, find the perimeter and the area of each rectangle.

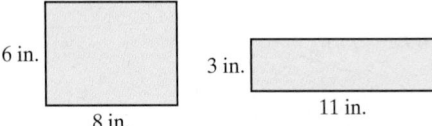

  STUDY SKILLS BUILDER

How Well Do You Know Your Textbook?

Let's check to see whether you are familiar with your textbook yet. Remember, for help, see Section 1.1 in this text.

1. What does the 💿 icon mean?

2. What does the ✐ icon mean?

3. What does the △ icon mean?

4. Where can you find a review for each chapter? What answers to this review can be found in the back of your text?

5. Each chapter contains an overview of the chapter along with examples. What is this feature called?

6. Each chapter contains a review of vocabulary. What is this feature called?

7. There are free CDs in your text. What content is contained on these CDs?

8. What is the location of the section that is entirely devoted to study skills?

9. There are Practice Problems that are contained in the margin of the text. What are they and how can they be used?

△ 6.5 VOLUME

Objective A Finding Volume of Solids

Volume is a measure of the space of a region. The volume of a box or can, for example, is the amount of space inside. Volume can be used to describe the amount of juice in a pitcher or the amount of concrete needed to pour a foundation for a house.

The volume of a solid is the number of **cubic units** in the solid. A cubic centimeter and a cubic inch are illustrated.

Actual size

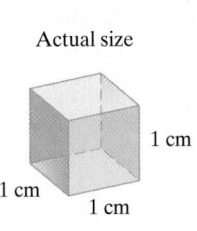

1 cm

1 cm

1 cm

1 cubic centimeter

Actual size

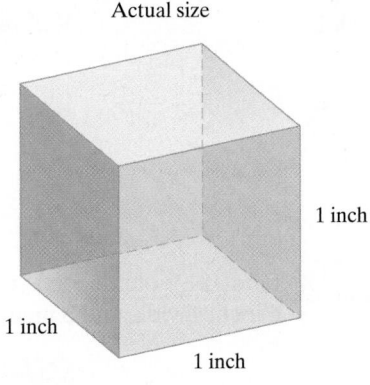

1 inch

1 inch

1 inch

1 cubic inch

Formulas for finding the volumes of some common solids are given next:

Volume Formulas of Common Solids

Solid	**Volume Formulas**
RECTANGULAR SOLID 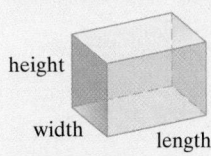 height width length	Volume of a rectangular solid: **Volume** = **length** · **width** · **height** $V = l \cdot w \cdot h$
CUBE 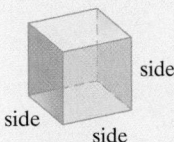 side side side side	Volume of a cube: **Volume** = **side** · **side** · **side** $V = s^3$
SPHERE 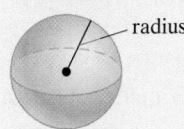 radius	Volume of a sphere: **Volume** = $\frac{4}{3} \cdot \pi \cdot ($**radius**$)^3$ $V = \frac{4}{3} \cdot \pi \cdot r^3$
CIRCULAR CYLINDER 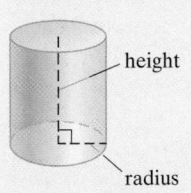 height radius	Volume of a circular cylinder: **Volume** = $\pi \cdot ($**radius**$)^2 \cdot$ **height** $V = \pi \cdot r^2 \cdot h$

(continued)

445

Volume Formulas of Common Solids (continued)

Solid	Volume Formulas
CONE 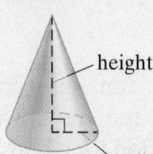	Volume of a cone: $$\textbf{Volume} = \frac{1}{3} \cdot \pi \cdot (\textbf{radius})^2 \cdot \textbf{height}$$ $$V = \frac{1}{3} \cdot \pi \cdot r^2 \cdot h$$
SQUARE-BASED PYRAMID 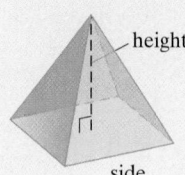	Volume of a square-based pyramid: $$\textbf{Volume} = \frac{1}{3} \cdot (\textbf{side})^2 \cdot \textbf{height}$$ $$V = \frac{1}{3} \cdot s^2 \cdot h$$

> **Helpful Hint**
> Volume is always measured in cubic units.

PRACTICE PROBLEM 1

Find the volume of a rectangular box that is 5 feet long, 2 feet wide, and 4 feet deep.

EXAMPLE 1 Find the volume of a rectangular box that is 12 inches long, 6 inches wide, and 3 inches high.

3 in.

6 in.   12 in.

Solution:

$$V = l \cdot w \cdot h$$
$$V = 12 \text{ in.} \cdot 6 \text{ in.} \cdot 3 \text{ in.} = 216 \text{ cubic in.}$$

The volume of the rectangular box is 216 cubic inches.

🔲 **Work Practice Problem 1**

✔ **Concept Check** Juan is calculating the volume of the following rectangular solid. Find the error in his calculation.

Volume = $l + w + h$

= 14 cm + 8 cm + 5 cm

= 27 cu cm

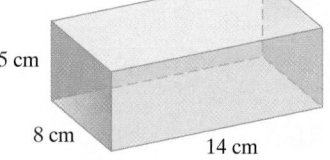

5 cm

8 cm   14 cm

PRACTICE PROBLEM 2

Approximate the volume of a ball of radius $\frac{1}{2}$ centimeter. Use $\frac{22}{7}$ for π. Give an exact answer and an approximate answer.

EXAMPLE 2 Approximate the volume of a ball of radius 3 inches. Use the approximation $\frac{22}{7}$ for π. Give an exact answer and an approximate answer.

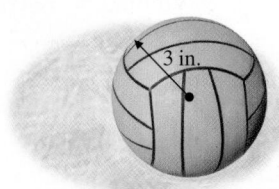

3 in.

Answers

1. 40 cu ft,   **2.** $\frac{1}{6}\pi$ cu cm $\approx \frac{11}{21}$ cu cm

✔ **Concept Check Answer**

Volume = $l \cdot w \cdot h$

= 14 · 8 · 5

= 560 cu cm

Solution:

$$V = \frac{4}{3} \cdot \pi \cdot r^3$$

$$\approx \frac{4}{3} \cdot \pi (3 \text{ in.})^3$$

$$= \frac{4}{3} \cdot \pi \cdot 27 \text{ cu in.}$$

$$= \frac{4 \cdot \pi \cdot \overset{1}{\cancel{3}} \cdot 9}{\underset{1}{\cancel{3}}} \text{ cu in.}$$

$$= 36\pi \text{ cu in.}$$

This is the exact volume. To approximate the volume, use the approximation $\frac{22}{7}$ for π.

$$V = 36\pi \text{ cu in.}$$

$$= 36 \cdot \frac{22}{7} \text{ cu in.} \quad \text{Replace } \pi \text{ with } \frac{22}{7}.$$

$$= \frac{36 \cdot 22}{7} \text{ cu in.}$$

$$= \frac{792}{7} \quad \text{or} \quad 113\frac{1}{7} \text{ cubic inches}$$

The volume is *approximately* $113\frac{1}{7}$ cubic inches.

🔲 **Work Practice Problem 2**

EXAMPLE 3 Approximate the volume of a can that has a $3\frac{1}{2}$-inch radius and a height of 6 inches. Use $\frac{22}{7}$ for π. Give an exact volume and an approximate volume.

$3\frac{1}{2}$ in.

6 in.

Solution: Using the formula for a circular cylinder, we have

$$V = \pi \cdot r^2 \cdot h \qquad 3\frac{1}{2} = \frac{7}{2}$$

$$= \pi \cdot \left(\frac{7}{2} \text{ in.}\right)^2 \cdot 6 \text{ in.}$$

$$= \pi \cdot \frac{49}{4} \text{ sq in.} \cdot 6 \text{ in.}$$

$$= \frac{\pi \cdot 49 \cdot \overset{1}{\cancel{2}} \cdot 3}{\underset{1}{\cancel{2} \cdot 2}} \text{ cu in.}$$

$$= 73\frac{1}{2}\pi \text{ cu in. or } 73.5\pi \text{ cu in.}$$

Continued on next page

PRACTICE PROBLEM 3

Approximate the volume of a cylinder of radius 5 inches and height 7 inches. Use 3.14 for π. Give an exact answer and an approximate answer.

Answer
3. 175π cu in. ≈ 549.5 cu in.

This is the exact volume. To approximate the volume, use the approximation $\frac{22}{7}$ for π.

$$V = 73\frac{1}{2}\pi \text{ or } \frac{147}{2} \cdot \frac{22}{7} \text{ cu in.} \quad \text{\small Replace } \pi \text{ with } \frac{22}{7}.$$

$$= \frac{21 \cdot \overset{1}{\cancel{7}} \cdot \overset{1}{\cancel{2}} \cdot 11}{\underset{1}{\cancel{2}} \cdot \underset{1}{\cancel{7}}} \text{ cu in.}$$

$$= 231 \text{ cubic in.}$$

The volume is approximately 231 cubic inches.

◾ **Work Practice Problem 3**

PRACTICE PROBLEM 4

Find the volume of a square-based pyramid that has a 3-meter side and a height of 5.1 meters.

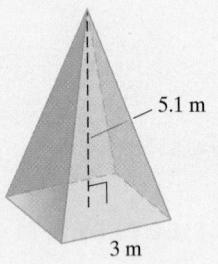

5.1 m

3 m

EXAMPLE 4 Approximate the volume of a cone that has a height of 14 centimeters and a radius of 3 centimeters. Use 3.14 for π. Give an exact answer and an approximate answer.

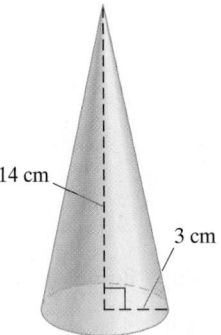

14 cm

3 cm

Solution: Using the formula for volume of a cone, we have

$$V = \frac{1}{3} \cdot \pi \cdot r^2 \cdot h$$

$$= \frac{1}{3} \cdot \pi \cdot (3 \text{ cm})^2 \cdot 14 \text{ cm} \quad \text{\small Replace } r \text{ with 3 cm and } h \text{ with 14 cm.}$$

$$= 42\pi \text{ cu cm}$$

Thus, 42π cubic centimeters is the exact volume. To approximate the volume, use the approximation 3.14 for π.

$$V \approx 42 \cdot 3.14 \text{ cu cm} \quad \text{\small Replace } \pi \text{ with 3.14.}$$

$$= 131.88 \text{ cu cm}$$

The volume is approximately 131.88 cubic centimeters.

◾ **Work Practice Problem 4**

Answer

4. 15.3 cu m

6.5 EXERCISE SET

 Student Solutions Manual  PH Math/Tutor Center  CD/Video for Review Math XL MathXL® MyMathLab MyMathLab

Objective Ⓐ *Find the volume of each solid. See Examples 1 through 4. Use $\frac{22}{7}$ for π.*

1.

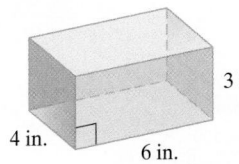

3 in.
4 in.
6 in.

2.

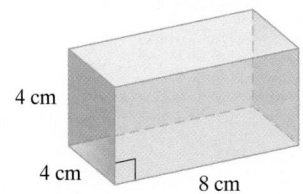

4 cm
4 cm
8 cm

3.

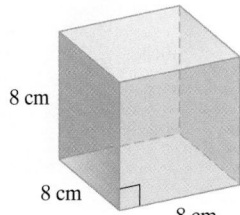

8 cm
8 cm
8 cm

4.

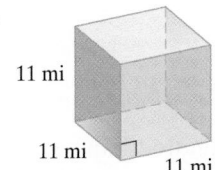

11 mi
11 mi
11 mi

5.

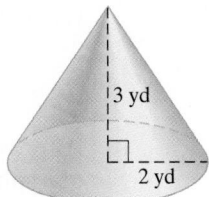

3 yd
2 yd

6.

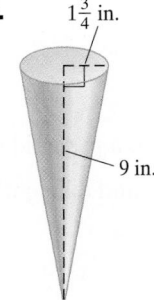

$1\frac{3}{4}$ in.
9 in.

7.

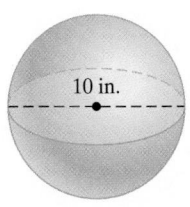

10 in.

8.

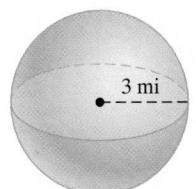

3 mi

9.

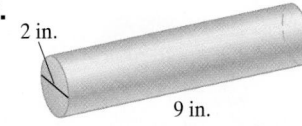

2 in.
9 in.

10.

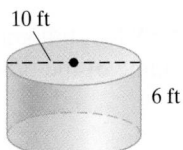

10 ft
6 ft

11.

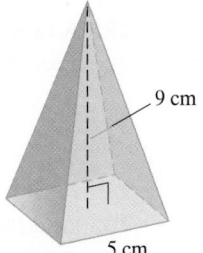

9 cm
5 cm

12.

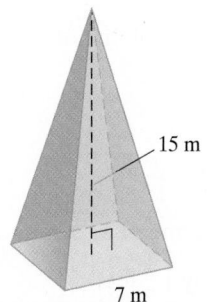

15 m
7 m

449

Solve.

13. Find the volume of a cube with edges of $1\frac{1}{3}$ inches.

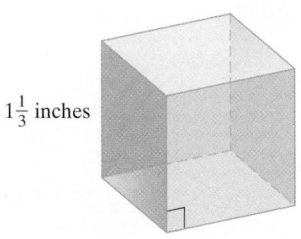

$1\frac{1}{3}$ inches

14. A water storage tank is in the shape of a cone with the pointed end down. If the radius is 14 feet and the depth of the tank is 15 feet, approximate the volume of the tank in cubic feet. Use $\frac{22}{7}$ for π.

14 ft

15 ft

15. Find the volume of a rectangular box 2 feet by 1.4 feet by 3 feet.

16. Find the volume of a box in the shape of a cube that is 5 feet on each side.

17. Find the volume of a pyramid with a square base 5 inches on a side and a height of $1\frac{3}{10}$ inches.

18. Approximate to the nearest hundredth the volume of a sphere with a radius of 2 centimeters. Use 3.14 for π.

19. A paperweight is in the shape of a square-based pyramid 20 centimeters tall. If an edge of the base is 12 centimeters, find the volume of the paperweight.

20. A birdbath is made in the shape of a hemisphere (half-sphere). If its radius is 10 inches, approximate the volume. Use $\frac{22}{7}$ for π.

10 in.

21. Find the exact volume of a sphere with a radius of 7 inches.

22. A tank is in the shape of a cylinder 8 feet tall and 3 feet in radius. Find the exact volume of the tank.

23. Find the volume of a rectangular block of ice 2 feet by $2\frac{1}{2}$ feet by $1\frac{1}{2}$ feet.

24. Find the capacity (volume in cubic feet) of a rectangular ice chest with inside measurements of 3 feet by $1\frac{1}{2}$ feet by $1\frac{3}{4}$ feet.

25. An ice cream cone with a 4-centimeter diameter and 3-centimeter depth is filled exactly level with the top of the cone. Approximate how much ice cream (in cubic centimeters) is in the cone. Use $\dfrac{22}{7}$ for π.

26. A child's toy is in the shape of a square-based pyramid 10 inches tall. If an edge of the base is 7 inches, find the volume of the toy.

27. Ball lightning is a rare form of lightning in which a moving white or colored luminous sphere is seen. It can last from a few seconds to a few minutes and travels at about walking pace. An average sphere size is 6 inches in diameter. Find the exact volume of a sphere with this diameter and then approximate the volume using 3.14 for π.

28. A monkey ball tree produces large green fruit in the shape of spheres. These fruits are approximately 4 inches (or 10 centimeters) in diameter and have a coarse surface. Find the exact volume of a sphere with diameter 4 inches and then approximate the volume using 3.14 for π. (Round to the nearest tenth.)

Review

Evaluate. See Section 1.9.

29. 5^2

30. 7^2

31. 3^2

32. 20^2

33. $1^2 + 2^2$

34. $5^2 + 3^2$

35. $4^2 + 2^2$

36. $1^2 + 6^2$

There are a number of factors that determine the dimensions of a rectangular soccer field. Use the table below to answer Exercises 37 and 38. See Section 6.4.

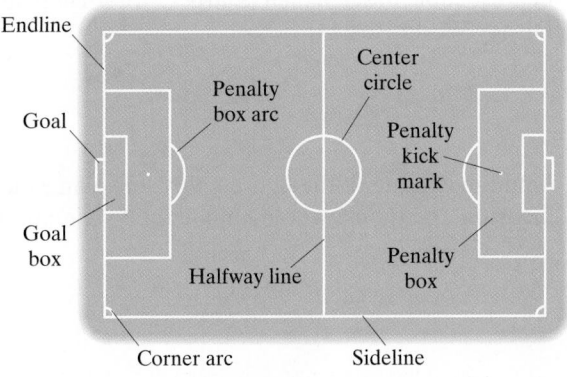

	Soccer Field Width and Length	
Age	**Width Min–Max**	**Length Min–Max**
Under 6/7:	15–20 yards	25–30 yards
Under 8:	20–25 yards	30–40 yards
Under 9:	30–35 yards	40–50 yards
Under 10:	40–50 yards	60–70 yards
Under 11:	40–50 yards	70–80 yards
Under 12:	40–55 yards	100–105 yards
Under 13:	50–60 yards	100–110 yards
International:	70–80 yards	110–120 yards

37. a. Find the minimum length and width of a soccer field for 9-year-old children. (Carefully consider the age.)

   b. Find the area of this field.

38. a. Find the maximum length and width of a soccer field for 11-year-old children.

   b. Find the area of this field.

Concept Extensions

39. The Great Pyramid of Khufu at Giza is the tallest of the ancient Egyptian pyramids. Its original height was 146.5 meters. The length of each side of its square base was originally 230 meters. Find the volume of the Great Pyramid of Khufu as it was originally built. Round to the nearest whole cubic meter. (*Source:* PBS *NOVA* Online)

40. The second-tallest pyramid at Giza is Khafre's Pyramid. Its original height was 471 feet. The length of each side of its square base was originally 704 feet. Find the volume of Khafre's Pyramid as it was originally built. (*Source:* PBS *NOVA* Online)

41. Menkaure's Pyramid, the shortest of the three Great Pyramids at Giza, was originally 65.5 meters tall. Each of the sides of its square base was originally 344 meters long. What was the volume of Menkaure's Pyramid as it was originally built? Round to the nearest whole cubic meter. (*Source:* PBS *NOVA* Online)

42. Due to factors such as weathering and loss of outer stones, the Great Pyramid of Khufu now stands only 137 meters tall. Its square base is now only 227 meters on a side. Find the current volume of the Great Pyramid of Khufu to the nearest whole cubic meter. How much has its volume decreased since it was built? See Exercise 39 for comparison. (*Source:* PBS *NOVA* Online)

43. The centerpiece of the New England Aquarium in Boston is its Giant Ocean Tank. This exhibit is a four-story cylindrical saltwater tank containing sharks, sea turtles, stingrays, and tropical fish. The radius of the tank is 16.3 feet and its height is 32 feet (assuming that a story is 8 feet). What is the volume of the Giant Ocean Tank? Use $\pi \approx 3.14$ and round to the nearest tenth of a cubic foot. (*Source:* New England Aquarium)

44. Except for service dogs for guests with disabilities, Walt Disney World does not allow pets in its parks or hotels. However, the resort does make pet-boarding services available to guests. The pet-care kennels at Walt Disney World offer three different sizes of indoor kennels. Of these, the smaller two kennels measure

a. 2′1″ by 1′8″ by 1′7″ and
b. 1′1″ by 2′ by 8″

What is the volume of each kennel rounded to the nearest cubic foot? Which is larger? (*Source:* Walt Disney World Resort)

45. Can you compute the volume of a rectangle? Why or why not?

46. Find the volume of the figure below. Give an exact measure and then a whole number approximation.

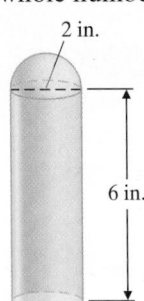

2 in.

6 in.

Geometry Concepts

△ **1.** Find the supplement and the complement of a 27° angle.

Find the measures of angles x, y, and z in each figure.

2.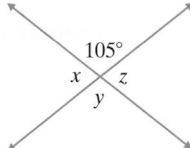
105°
x   z
y

3. *m∥n*

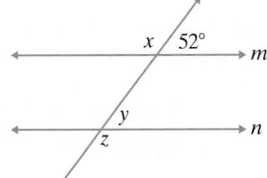
x / 52° m
y
z   n

4. Find the measure of ∠x.   **5.** Find the diameter.   **6.** Find the radius.

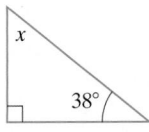
x
38°

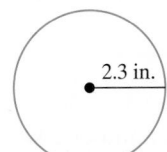
2.3 in.

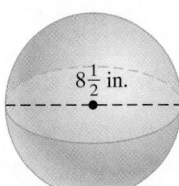
$8\frac{1}{2}$ in.

For Exercises 7 through 11, find the perimeter (or circumference) and area of each figure. For the circle give an exact circumference and area. Then use π ≈ 3.14 to approximate each. Don't forget to attach correct units.

7.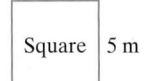
Square | 5 m

8.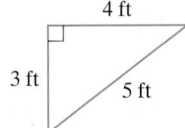
4 ft
3 ft
5 ft

9.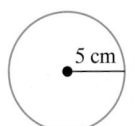
5 cm

10. 11 mi
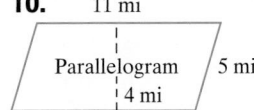
Parallelogram 5 mi
4 mi

11.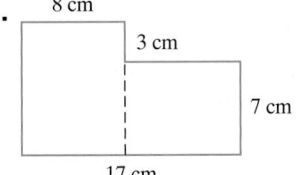
8 cm
3 cm
7 cm
17 cm

12. The smallest cathedral is in Highlandville, Missouri. The rectangular floor of the cathedral measures 14 feet by 17 feet. Find its perimeter and its area. (*Source: The Guinness Book of Records*)

Find the volume of each solid. Don't forget to attach correct units.

13. A cube with edges of 4 inches each.

14. A rectangular box 2 feet by 3 feet by 5.1 feet.

15. A pyramid with a square base 10 centimeters on a side and a height of 12 centimeters.

16. A sphere with a diameter of 3 miles. Give the exact volume and then use $\pi \approx \frac{22}{7}$ to approximate.

Answers

1. _____

2. _____

3. _____

4. _____

5. _____

6. _____

7. _____

8. _____

9. _____

10. _____

11. _____

12. _____

13. _____

14. _____

15. _____

16. _____

6.6 SQUARE ROOTS AND THE PYTHAGOREAN THEOREM

Objective **A** Finding Square Roots

The square of a number is the number times itself. For example:

The square of 5 is 25 because 5^2 or $5 \cdot 5 = 25$.
The square of 4 is 16 because 4^2 or $4 \cdot 4 = 16$.
The square of 10 is 100 because 10^2 or $10 \cdot 10 = 100$.

Recall from Chapter 1 that the reverse process of squaring is finding a **square root.** For example:

A square root of 16 is 4 because $4^2 = 16$.
A square root of 25 is 5 because $5^2 = 25$.
A square root of 100 is 10 because $10^2 = 100$.

We use the symbol $\sqrt{}$, called a **radical sign,** to name square roots. For example:

$\sqrt{16} = 4$ because $4^2 = 16$
$\sqrt{25} = 5$ because $5^2 = 25$

Square Root of a Number

A square root of a number a is a number b whose square is a. We use the radical sign $\sqrt{}$ to name square roots.

PRACTICE PROBLEM 1

Find each square root.

a. $\sqrt{100}$ **b.** $\sqrt{64}$
c. $\sqrt{121}$ **d.** $\sqrt{0}$

EXAMPLE 1 Find each square root.

a. $\sqrt{49}$ **b.** $\sqrt{1}$ **c.** $\sqrt{81}$

Solution:

a. $\sqrt{49} = 7$ because $7^2 = 49$
b. $\sqrt{1} = 1$ because $1^2 = 1$
c. $\sqrt{81} = 9$ because $9^2 = 81$

◻ **Work Practice Problem 1**

PRACTICE PROBLEM 2

Find: $\sqrt{\dfrac{1}{4}}$

EXAMPLE 2 Find: $\sqrt{\dfrac{1}{36}}$

Solution: $\sqrt{\dfrac{1}{36}} = \dfrac{1}{6}$ because $\dfrac{1}{6} \cdot \dfrac{1}{6} = \dfrac{1}{36}$

◻ **Work Practice Problem 2**

PRACTICE PROBLEM 3

Find: $\sqrt{\dfrac{9}{16}}$

Answers
1. a. 10, **b.** 8, **c.** 11, **d.** 0,
2. $\dfrac{1}{2}$, **3.** $\dfrac{3}{4}$

EXAMPLE 3 Find: $\sqrt{\dfrac{4}{25}}$

Solution: $\sqrt{\dfrac{4}{25}} = \dfrac{2}{5}$ because $\dfrac{2}{5} \cdot \dfrac{2}{5} = \dfrac{4}{25}$

◻ **Work Practice Problem 3**

Objective B Approximating Square Roots

Thus far, we have found square roots of perfect squares. Numbers like $\frac{1}{4}$, 36, $\frac{4}{25}$, and 1 are called **perfect squares** because their square root is a whole number or a fraction. A square root such as $\sqrt{5}$ cannot be written as a whole number or a fraction since 5 is not a perfect square.

Although $\sqrt{5}$ cannot be written as a whole number or a fraction, it can be approximated by estimating, by using a table (as in Appendix B.1), or by using a calculator.

EXAMPLE 4 Use Appendix B.1 or a calculator to approximate the square root of 43 to the nearest thousandth.

Solution: $\sqrt{43} \approx 6.557$

Work Practice Problem 4

PRACTICE PROBLEM 4

Use Appendix B.1 or a calculator to approximate the square root of 11 to the nearest thousandth.

Helpful Hint

$\sqrt{43}$ is *approximately* 6.557. This means that if we multiply 6.557 by 6.557, the product is *close* to 43.

$6.557 \times 6.557 = 42.994249$

EXAMPLE 5 Approximate $\sqrt{32}$ to the nearest thousandth.

Solution: $\sqrt{32} \approx 5.657$

Work Practice Problem 5

PRACTICE PROBLEM 5

Approximate $\sqrt{29}$ to the nearest thousandth.

Objective C Using the Pythagorean Theorem

One important application of square roots has to do with right triangles. Recall that a **right triangle** is a triangle in which one of the angles is a right angle, or measures 90°. The **hypotenuse** of a right triangle is the side opposite the right angle. The **legs** of a right triangle are the other two sides. These are shown in the following figure. The right angle in the triangle is indicated by the small square drawn in that angle.

The following theorem is true for all right triangles:

Pythagorean Theorem

In any **right triangle,**

$$(\text{leg})^2 + (\text{other leg})^2 = (\text{hypotenuse})^2$$

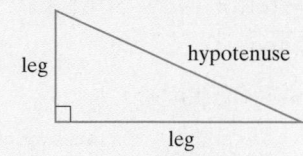

Answers
4. 3.317, **5.** 5.385

Using the Pythagorean theorem, we can use one of the following formulas to find an unknown length of a right triangle:

Finding an Unknown Length of a Right Triangle

$$\text{hypotenuse} = \sqrt{(\text{leg})^2 + (\text{other leg})^2}$$

or

$$\text{leg} = \sqrt{(\text{hypotenuse})^2 - (\text{other leg})^2}$$

PRACTICE PROBLEM 6

Find the length of the hypotenuse of the given right triangle.

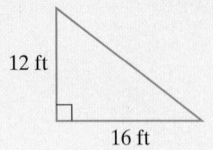

12 ft
16 ft

EXAMPLE 6 Find the length of the hypotenuse of the given right triangle.

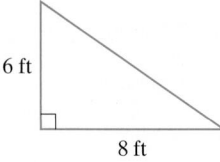

6 ft
8 ft

Solution: Since we are finding the hypotenuse, we use the formula

$$\text{hypotenuse} = \sqrt{(\text{leg})^2 + (\text{other leg})^2}$$

Putting the known values into the formula, we have

$$\begin{aligned}
\text{hypotenuse} &= \sqrt{(6)^2 + (8)^2} \quad \text{The legs are 6 feet and 8 feet.} \\
&= \sqrt{36 + 64} \\
&= \sqrt{100} \\
&= 10
\end{aligned}$$

The hypotenuse is 10 feet long.

▣ **Work Practice Problem 6**

PRACTICE PROBLEM 7

Approximate the length of the hypotenuse of the given right triangle. Round to the nearest whole unit.

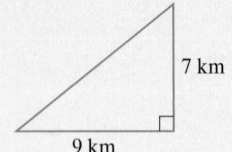

7 km
9 km

EXAMPLE 7 Approximate the length of the hypotenuse of the given right triangle. Round the length to the nearest whole unit.

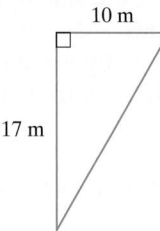

10 m
17 m

Solution:

$$\begin{aligned}
\text{hypotenuse} &= \sqrt{(\text{leg})^2 + (\text{other leg})^2} \\
&= \sqrt{(17)^2 + (10)^2} \quad \text{The legs are 10 meters and 17 meters.} \\
&= \sqrt{289 + 100} \\
&= \sqrt{389} \\
&\approx 20 \quad \text{From Appendix B.1 or a calculator}
\end{aligned}$$

The hypotenuse is exactly $\sqrt{389}$ meters, which is approximately 20 meters.

▣ **Work Practice Problem 7**

Answers

6. 20 ft,   **7.** 11 km

EXAMPLE 8 Find the length of the leg in the given right triangle. Give the exact length and a two-decimal-place approximation.

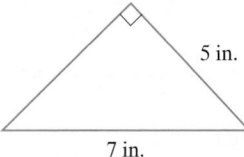

Solution: Notice that the hypotenuse measures 7 inches and the length of one leg measures 5 inches. Since we are looking for the length of the other leg, we use the formula

$$\text{leg} = \sqrt{(\text{hypotenuse})^2 - (\text{other leg})^2}$$

Putting the known values into the formula, we have

$$\text{leg} = \sqrt{(7)^2 - (5)^2} \quad \text{The hypotenuse is 7 inches, and the other leg is 5 inches.}$$
$$= \sqrt{49 - 25}$$
$$= \sqrt{24} \quad \text{Exact answer}$$
$$\approx 4.90 \quad \text{From Appendix B.1 or a calculator}$$

The length of the leg is exactly $\sqrt{24}$ inches, which is approximately 4.90 inches.

▣ **Work Practice Problem 8**

✔**Concept Check** The following lists are the lengths of the sides of two triangles. Which set forms a right triangle? Explain.

a. 8, 15, 17   **b.** 24, 30, 40

EXAMPLE 9 **Finding the Diagonal Length of a City Block**

A standard city block is a square that measures 300 feet on a side. Find the length of the diagonal of a city block rounded to the nearest whole foot.

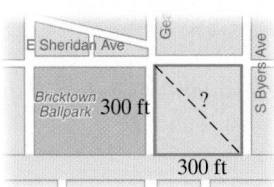

Solution: The diagonal is the hypotenuse of a right triangle, so we use the formula

$$\text{hypotenuse} = \sqrt{(\text{leg})^2 + (\text{other leg})^2}$$

Putting the known values into the formula we have

$$\text{hypotenuse} = \sqrt{(300)^2 + (300)^2} \quad \text{The legs are both 300 feet.}$$
$$= \sqrt{90,000 + 90,000}$$
$$= \sqrt{180,000}$$
$$\approx 424 \quad \text{From Appendix B.1 or a calculator}$$

The length of the diagonal is approximately 424 feet.

▣ **Work Practice Problem 9**

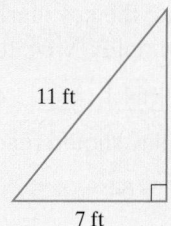

Finding Square Roots

To simplify or approximate square roots using a calculator, locate the key marked $\boxed{\sqrt{}}$.

To simplify $\sqrt{64}$, for example, press the keys

$$\boxed{64}\ \boxed{\sqrt{}}\quad \text{or}\quad \boxed{\sqrt{}}\ \boxed{64}$$

The display should read $\boxed{8}$. Then

$$\sqrt{64} = 8$$

To *approximate* $\sqrt{10}$, press the keys

$$\boxed{10}\ \boxed{\sqrt{}}\quad \text{or}\quad \boxed{\sqrt{}}\ \boxed{10}$$

The display should read $\boxed{3.16227766}$. This is an *approximation* for $\sqrt{10}$. A three-decimal-place approximation is

$$\sqrt{10} \approx 3.162$$

Is this answer reasonable? Since 10 is between perfect squares 9 and 16, $\sqrt{10}$ is between $\sqrt{9} = 3$ and $\sqrt{16} = 4$. Our answer is reasonable since 3.162 is between 3 and 4.

Simplify.

1. $\sqrt{1024}$ **2.** $\sqrt{676}$

Approximate each square root. Round each answer to the nearest thousandth.

3. $\sqrt{15}$ **4.** $\sqrt{19}$

5. $\sqrt{97}$ **6.** $\sqrt{56}$

6.6 EXERCISE SET

Objective A *Find each square root. See Examples 1 through 3.*

1. $\sqrt{4}$

2. $\sqrt{9}$

3. $\sqrt{64}$

4. $\sqrt{144}$

5. $\sqrt{\dfrac{1}{81}}$

6. $\sqrt{\dfrac{1}{64}}$

7. $\sqrt{\dfrac{16}{64}}$

8. $\sqrt{\dfrac{36}{81}}$

Objective B *Use Appendix B.1 or a calculator to approximate each square root. Round the square root to the nearest thousandth. See Examples 4 and 5.*

9. $\sqrt{3}$

10. $\sqrt{5}$

11. $\sqrt{15}$

12. $\sqrt{17}$

13. $\sqrt{47}$

14. $\sqrt{85}$

15. $\sqrt{26}$

16. $\sqrt{35}$

Objectives A B Mixed Practice *Find each square root. If necessary, round the square root to the nearest thousandth.*

17. $\sqrt{256}$

18. $\sqrt{625}$

19. $\sqrt{14}$

20. $\sqrt{18}$

21. $\sqrt{\dfrac{49}{144}}$

22. $\sqrt{\dfrac{121}{169}}$

23. $\sqrt{71}$

24. $\sqrt{62}$

Objective **C** *Find the unknown length in each right triangle. If necessary, approximate the length to the nearest thousandth. See Examples 6 through 8.*

25.
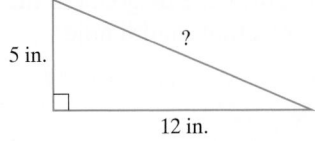

26.
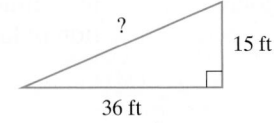

27.
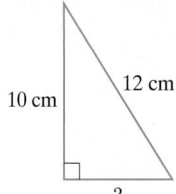

28.
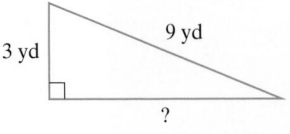

29.
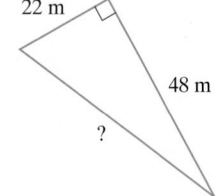

30.
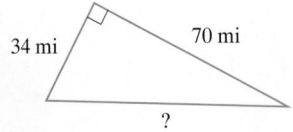

31.
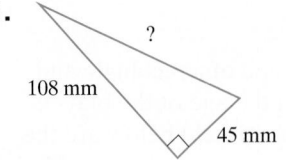

32.
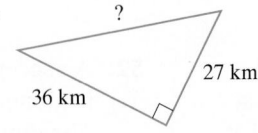

Sketch each right triangle and find the length of the side not given. If necessary, approximate the length to the nearest thousandth. (Each length is in units.) See Examples 6 through 8.

33. leg = 3, leg = 4

34. leg = 9, leg = 12

35. leg = 5, hypotenuse = 13

36. leg = 6, hypotenuse = 10

37. leg = 10, leg = 14

38. leg = 2, leg = 16

39. leg = 35, leg = 28

40. leg = 30, leg = 15

41. leg = 30, leg = 30

42. leg = 21, leg = 21

43. hypotenuse = 2, leg = 1

44. hypotenuse = 7, leg = 6

45. leg = 7.5, leg = 4

46. leg = 12, leg = 22.5

Solve. See Example 9.

47. A standard city block is a square with each side measuring 100 yards. Find the length of the diagonal of a city block to the nearest hundredth yard.

48. A section of land is a square with each side measuring 1 mile. Find the length of the diagonal of the section of land to the nearest thousandth mile.

49. Find the height of the tree. Round the height to one decimal place.

50. Find the height of the antenna. Round the height to one decimal place.

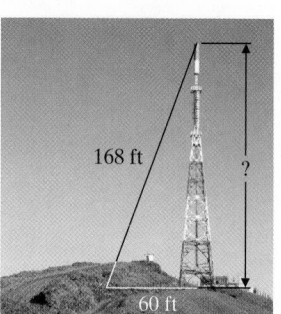

51. The playing field for football is a rectangle that is 300 feet long by 160 feet wide. Find, to the nearest foot, the length of a straight-line run that started at one corner and went diagonally to end at the opposite corner.

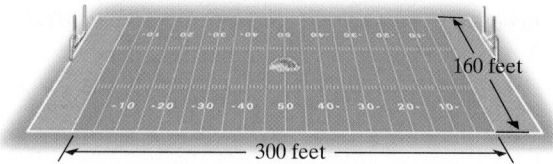

52. A soccer field is in the shape of a rectangle and its dimensions depend on the age of the players. The dimensions of the soccer field below are the minimum dimensions for international play. Find the length of the diagonal of this rectangle. Round answer to the nearest tenth of a yard.

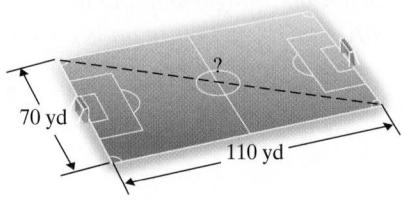

Review

Find the value of n in each proportion. See Section 5.1.

53. $\dfrac{n}{6} = \dfrac{2}{3}$

54. $\dfrac{8}{n} = \dfrac{4}{8}$

55. $\dfrac{9}{11} = \dfrac{n}{55}$

56. $\dfrac{5}{6} = \dfrac{35}{n}$

57. $\dfrac{3}{n} = \dfrac{7}{14}$

58. $\dfrac{n}{9} = \dfrac{4}{6}$

Concept Extensions

Determine what two whole numbers each square root is between without using a calculator or table. Then use a calculator or table to check.

59. $\sqrt{38}$ **60.** $\sqrt{27}$ **61.** $\sqrt{101}$ **62.** $\sqrt{85}$

63. Without using a calculator, explain how you know that $\sqrt{105}$ is *not* approximately 9.875.

Does the set form the lengths of the sides of a right triangle? See the Concept Check in this section.

64. 25, 60, 65   **65.** 20, 45, 50

STUDY SKILLS BUILDER

Learning New Terms?

By now, you have encountered many new terms. It's never too late to make a list of new terms and review them frequently. Remember that placing these new terms (including page references) on 3 × 5 index cards might help you later when you're preparing for a quiz.

Answer the following.

1. How do new terms stand out in this text so that they can be found?

2. Name one way placing a word and its definition on a 3 × 5 card might be helpful.

A Decide Whether Two Triangles are Congruent.

B Find the Ratio of Corresponding Sides in Similar Triangles.

C Find Unknown Lengths of Sides in Similar Triangles.

6.7 CONGRUENT AND SIMILAR TRIANGLES

Objective **A** Deciding Whether Two Triangles Are Congruent

Two triangles are **congruent** when they have the same shape and the same size. In congruent triangles, the measures of corresponding angles are equal and the lengths of corresponding sides are equal. The following triangles are congruent:

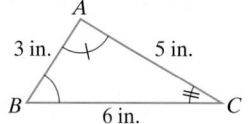 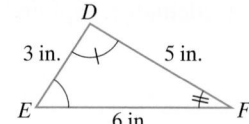

Since these triangles are congruent, the measures of corresponding angles are equal.

Angles with equal measure: $\angle A$ and $\angle D$, $\angle B$ and $\angle E$, $\angle C$ and $\angle F$ Also, the lengths of corresponding sides are equal.

Equal corresponding sides: $\overline{AB}$ and $\overline{DE}$, $\overline{BC}$ and $\overline{EF}$, $\overline{CA}$ and $\overline{FD}$

Any one of the following may be used to determine whether two triangles are congruent:

Congruent Triangles

Angle-Side-Angle (ASA)

If the measures of two angles of a triangle equal the measures of two angles of another triangle, and the lengths of the sides between each pair of angles are equal, the triangles are congruent.

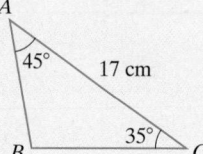 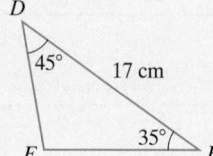

For example, these two triangles are congruent by Angle-Side-Angle.

Side-Side-Side (SSS)

If the lengths of the three sides of a triangle equal the lengths of the corresponding sides of another triangle, the triangles are congruent.

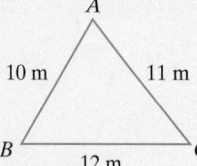 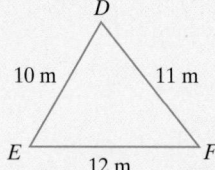

For example, these two triangles are congruent by Side-Side-Side.

(continued)

Congruent Triangles (continued)

Side-Angle-Side (SAS)

If the lengths of two sides of a triangle equal the lengths of corresponding sides of another triangle, and the measures of the angles between each pair of sides are equal, the triangles are congruent.

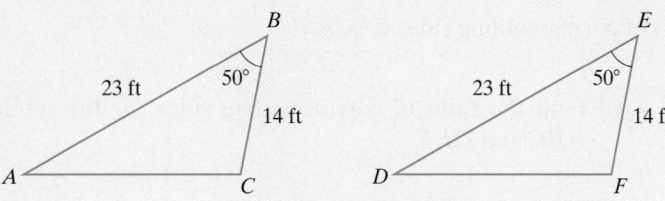

For example, these two triangles are congruent by Side-Angle-Side.

EXAMPLE 1 Determine whether triangle *ABC* is congruent to triangle *DEF*.

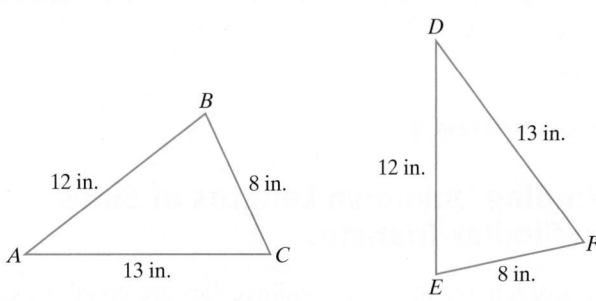

Solution: Since the lengths of all three sides of triangle *ABC* equal the lengths of all three sides of triangle *DEF*, the triangles are congruent.

▣ **Work Practice Problem 1**

In Example 1, notice that as soon as we know that the two triangles are congruent, we know that all three corresponding angles are congruent.

Objective ⓑ Finding the Ratios of Corresponding Sides in Similar Triangles

Two triangles are **similar** when they have the same shape but not necessarily the same size. In similar triangles, the measures of corresponding angles are equal and corresponding sides are in proportion. The following triangles are similar:

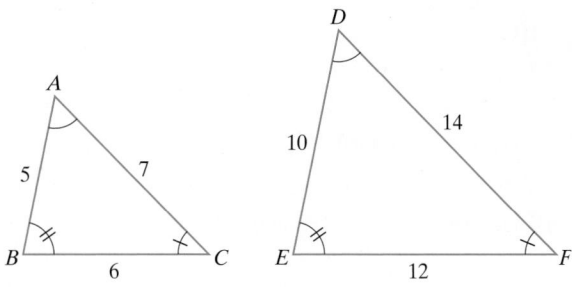

Since these triangles are similar, the measures of corresponding angles are equal.

PRACTICE PROBLEM 1

a. Determine whether triangle *MNO* is congruent to triangle *RQS*.

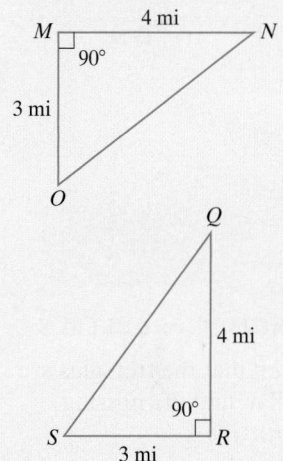

b. Determine whether triangle *GHI* is congruent to triangle *JKL*.

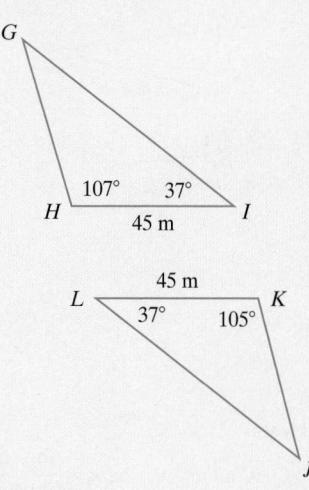

Answers

1. a. congruent, **b.** not congruent

Angles with equal measure: $\angle A$ and $\angle D$, $\angle B$ and $\angle E$, $\angle C$ and $\angle F$. Also, the lengths of corresponding sides are in proportion.

Sides in proportion: $\dfrac{AB}{DE} = \dfrac{BC}{EF} = \dfrac{CA}{FD}$ or, in this particular case,

$$\frac{AB}{DE} = \frac{5}{10} = \frac{1}{2}, \frac{BC}{EF} = \frac{6}{12} = \frac{1}{2}, \frac{CA}{FD} = \frac{7}{14} = \frac{1}{2}$$

The ratio of corresponding sides is $\dfrac{1}{2}$.

PRACTICE PROBLEM 2

Find the ratio of corresponding sides for the similar triangles QRS and XYZ.

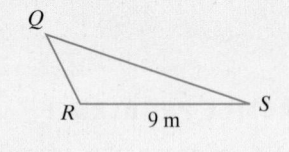

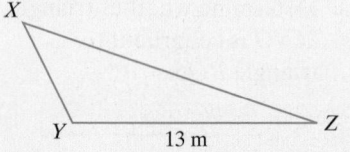

EXAMPLE 2 Find the ratio of corresponding sides for the similar triangles ABC and DEF.

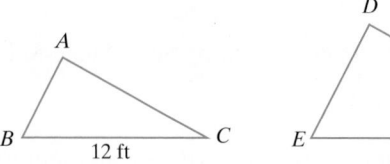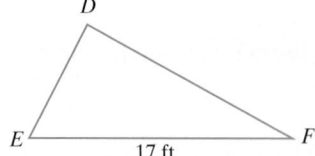

Solution: We are given the lengths of two corresponding sides. Their ratio is

$$\frac{12 \ \cancel{\text{feet}}}{17 \ \cancel{\text{feet}}} = \frac{12}{17}$$

▣ **Work Practice Problem 2**

Objective C Finding Unknown Lengths of Sides in Similar Triangles

Because the ratios of lengths of corresponding sides are equal, we can use proportions to find unknown lengths in similar triangles.

PRACTICE PROBLEM 3

Given that the triangles are similar, find the missing length n.

a.

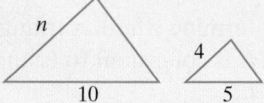

b.

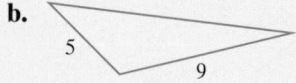

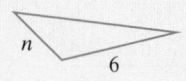

EXAMPLE 3 Given that the triangles are similar, find the missing length n.

Solution: Since the triangles are similar, corresponding sides are in proportion. Thus, the ratio of 2 to 3 is the same as the ratio of 10 to n, or

$$\frac{2}{3} = \frac{10}{n}$$

To find the unknown length n, we set cross products equal.

$$\frac{2}{3} = \frac{10}{n}$$

$3 \cdot 10 = 2 \cdot n$ Set cross products equal.

$2 \cdot n = 30$ Multiply.

$n = \dfrac{30}{2}$ Divide 30 by 2, the number multiplied by n.

$n = 15$

The missing length is 15 units.

▣ **Work Practice Problem 3**

Answers

2. $\dfrac{9}{13}$, **3. a.** $n = 8$, **b.** $n = \dfrac{10}{3}$ or $3\dfrac{1}{3}$

✔**Concept Check**   The following two triangles are similar. Which vertices of the first triangle appear to correspond to which vertices of the second triangle?

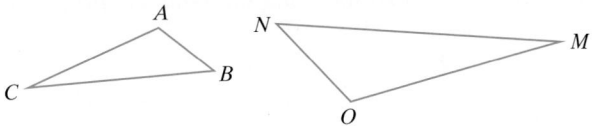

Many applications involve a diagram containing similar triangles. Surveyors, astronomers, and many other professionals continually use similar triangles in their work.

EXAMPLE 4   **Finding the Height of a Tree**

Mel Rose is a 6-foot-tall park ranger who needs to know the height of a particular tree. He measures the shadow of the tree to be 69 feet long when his own shadow is 9 feet long. Find the height of the tree.

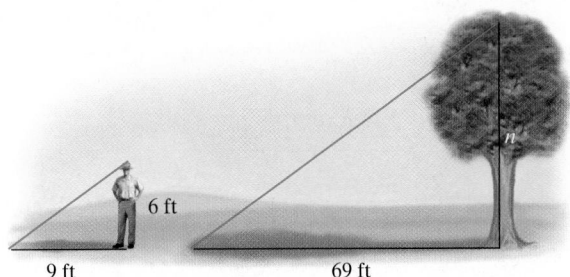

6 ft

9 ft   69 ft

Solution:

1. UNDERSTAND. Read and reread the problem. Notice that the triangle formed by the Sun's rays, Mel, and his shadow is similar to the triangle formed by the Sun's rays, the tree, and its shadow.

2. TRANSLATE. Write a proportion from the similar triangles formed.

$$\dfrac{\text{Mel's height}}{\text{height of tree}} \rightarrow \dfrac{6}{n} = \dfrac{9}{69} \leftarrow \dfrac{\text{length of Mel's shadow}}{\text{length of tree's shadow}}$$

or $\dfrac{6}{n} = \dfrac{3}{23}$ Simplify $\dfrac{9}{69}$. (ratio in lowest terms)

3. SOLVE for n:

$$\dfrac{6}{n} \diagdown\!\!\!\!\diagup \dfrac{3}{23}$$

$6 \cdot 23 = n \cdot 3$ Set cross products equal.

$138 = n \cdot 3$ Multiply.

$\dfrac{138}{3} = n$ Divide 138 by 3, the number multiplied by n.

$46 = n$

4. INTERPRET. *Check* to see that replacing n with 46 in the proportion makes the proportion true. *State* your conclusion: The height of the tree is 46 feet.

🔲 **Work Practice Problem 4**

PRACTICE PROBLEM 4

Tammy Shultz, a firefighter, needs to estimate the height of a burning building. She estimates the length of her shadow to be 8 feet long and the length of the building's shadow to be 60 feet long. Find the approximate height of the building if she is 5 feet tall.

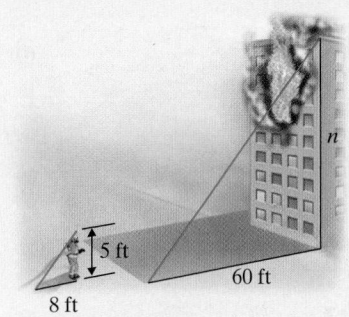

5 ft

60 ft

8 ft

Answer

4. approximately 37.5 ft

✔ **Concept Check Answer**

A corresponds to O; B corresponds to N; C corresponds to M

Mental Math

Each pair of triangles is similar. Name the congruent angles and the corresponding sides that are proportional.

1.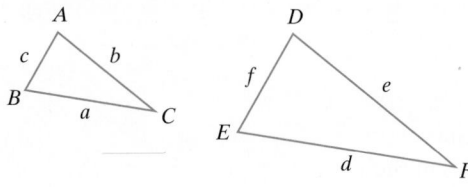

2.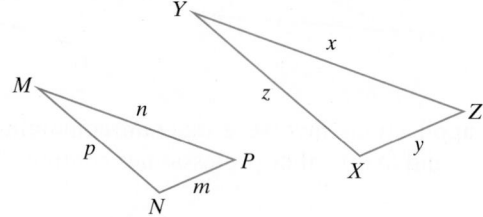

 **6.7** EXERCISE SET

FOR EXTRA HELP

Student Solutions Manual   PH Math/Tutor Center   CD/Video for Review   MathXL®   MyMathLab

Objective **A** *Determine whether each pair of triangles is congruent. See Example 1.*

1.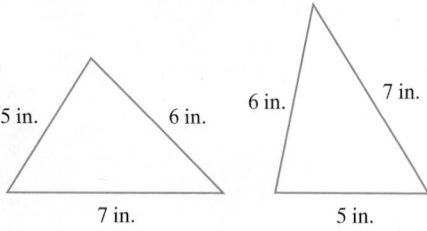

2.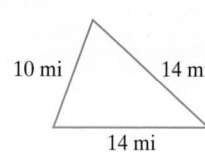

3.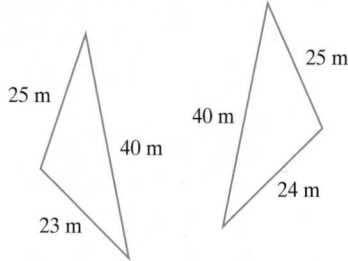

4.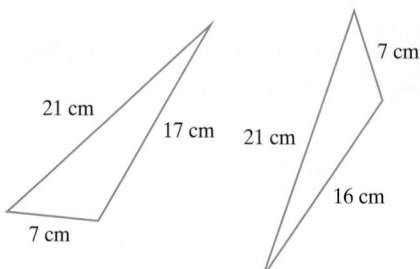

5.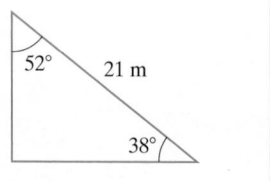

6.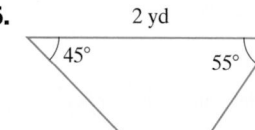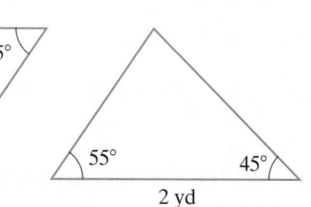

7.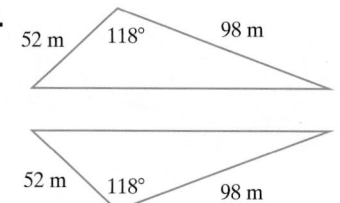

8.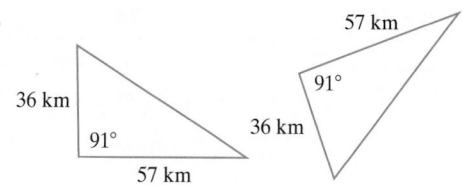

Objective **B** *Find each ratio of the corresponding sides of the given similar triangles. See Example 2.*

9.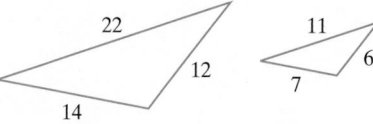

10.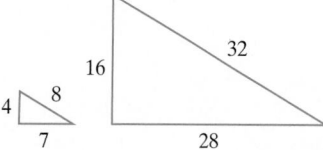

11.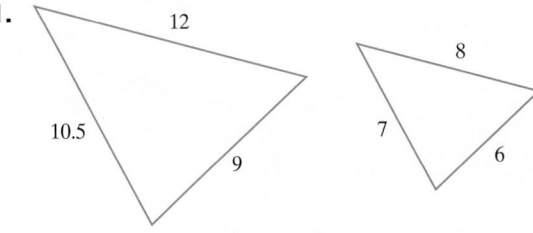

12.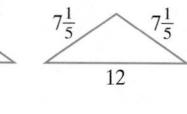

Objective **C** *Given that the pairs of triangles are similar, find the length of the side labeled n. See Example 3.*

13.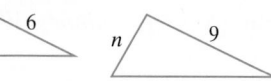

14.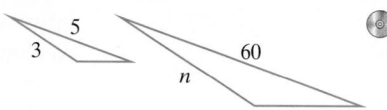

15.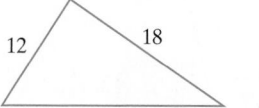

16.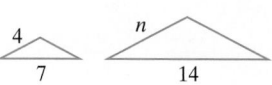

17.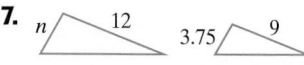

18.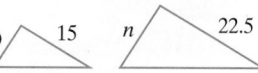

19.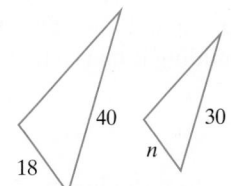

20.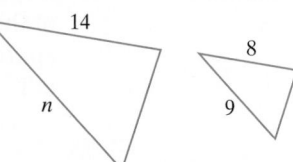

21.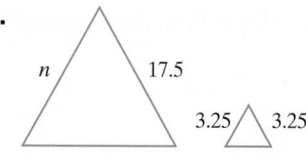

22.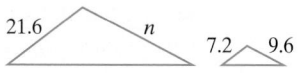

23.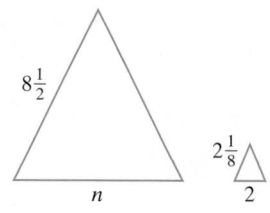

24.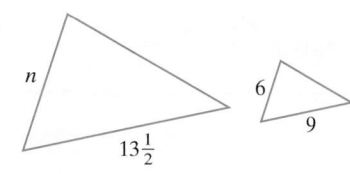

25.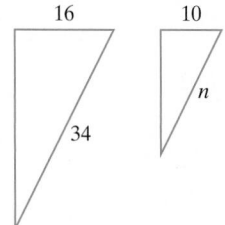

26.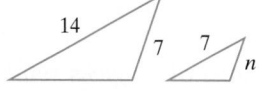

27.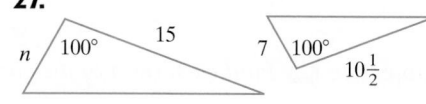

28.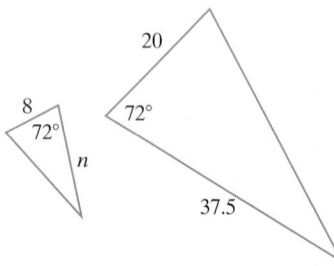

Solve. See Example 4.

29. Given the following diagram, approximate the height of the Bank One Tower in Oklahoma City, OK. (*Source: The World Almanac*, 2005)

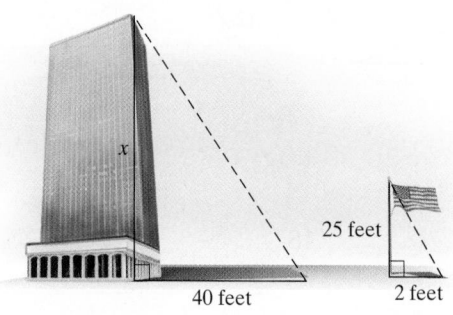

30. The tallest tree standing today is a redwood located in the Humboldt Redwoods State Park near Ukiah, California. Given the following diagram, approximate its height. (*Source: Guinness World Records*, 2005)

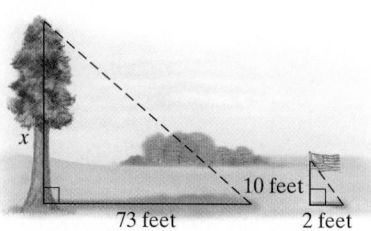

31. Samantha Black, a 5-foot-tall park ranger, needs to know the height of a tree. She notices that when the shadow of the tree is 48 feet long, her shadow is 4 feet long. Find the height of the tree.

32. Lloyd White, a firefighter, needs to estimate the height of a burning building. He estimates the length of his shadow to be 9 feet long and the length of the building's shadow to be 75 feet long. Find the approximate height of the building if he is 6 feet tall.

33. If a 30-foot tree casts an 18-foot shadow, find the length of the shadow cast by a 24-foot tree.

34. If a 24-foot flagpole casts a 32-foot shadow, find the length of the shadow cast by a 44-foot antenna. Round to the nearest tenth.

35. A triangular park is planned and waiting to be approved by the city zoning commission. A drawing of the park shows sides of length 5 inches, $7\frac{1}{2}$ inches and $10\frac{5}{8}$ inches. If the scale on the drawing is $\frac{1}{4}$ in. = 10 ft, find the actual proposed dimensions of the park.

36. Ben and Joyce Lander draw a triangular deck on their house plans. Joyce measures sides of the deck drawing on the plans to be 3 inches, $4\frac{1}{2}$ inches, and 6 inches. If the scale on the drawing is $\frac{1}{4}$ in. = 1 foot, find the lengths of the sides of the deck they want built.

Review

Find the average of each list of numbers. See Section 1.7.

37. 14, 17, 21, 18

38. 87, 84, 93

39. 76, 79, 88

40. 7, 8, 4, 6, 3, 8

Concept Extensions

41. The print area on a particular page measures 7 inches by 9 inches. A printing shop is to copy the page and reduce the print area so that its length is 5 inches. What will its width be? Will the print now fit on a 3-by-5-inch index card?

Given that the pairs of triangles are similar, find the length of the side labeled n. Round your results to 1 decimal place.

 42.

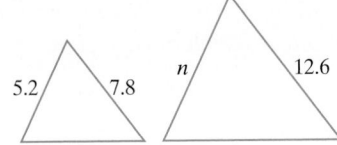

 43.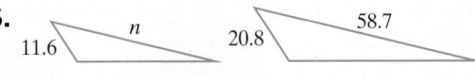

44. In your own words, describe any differences in similar triangles and congruent triangles.

CHAPTER 6   Group Activity

The Cost of Road Signs
Sections 6.1, 6.2, 6.4

There are nearly 4 million miles of streets and roads in the United States. With streets, roads, and highways come the need for traffic control, guidance, warning, and regulation. Road signs perform many of these tasks. Just in our routine travels, we see a wide variety of road signs every day. Think how many road signs must exist on the 4 million miles of roads in the United States. Have you ever wondered how much signs like these cost?

The cost of a road sign generally depends on the type of sign. Costs for several types of signs and signposts are listed in the table. Examples of various types of signs are shown below.

Road Sign Costs	
Type of Sign	**Cost**
Regulatory, warning, marker	$15–$18 per square foot
Large guide	$20–$25 per square foot
Type of Post	**Cost**
U-channel	$125–$200 each
Square tube	$10–$15 per foot
Steel breakaway posts	$15–$25 per foot

The cost of a sign is based on its area. For diamond, square, or rectangular signs, the area is found by multiplying the length (in feet) times the width (in feet). Then the area is multiplied by the cost per square foot. For signs with irregular shapes, costs are generally figured *as if* the sign were a rectangle, multiplying the height and width at the tallest and widest parts of the sign.

Group Activity

Locate four different kinds of road signs on or near your campus. Measure the dimensions of each sign, including the height of the post on which it is mounted. Using the cost data given in the table, find the minimum and maximum costs of each sign, including its post. Summarize your results in a table, and include a sketch of each sign.

Regulatory	Warning	Marker	Large Guide	Posts

STOP

SPEED LIMIT 75

NO PARKING ANY TIME

INTERSTATE 95

20

MARICOPA 85 COUNTY

93 Kingman EXIT 1 MILE

REST AREA

3rd St RIGHT LANE

ALBANY 32
ROCHESTER 248
BUFFALO 315

U-channel

Square tube

Steel breakaway posts

Chapter 6 Vocabulary Check

Fill in each blank with one of the words or phrases listed below.

transversal	line segment	obtuse	straight	adjacent
right	volume	area	legs	acute
right triangle	perimeter	hypotenuse	vertical	supplementary
similar	congruent	square root	ray	angle
line	complementary	vertex		

1. A _____ is a triangle with a right angle. The side opposite the right angle is called the _____, and the other two sides are called _____.
2. A _____ is a piece of a line with two endpoints.
3. Two angles that have a sum of 90° are called _____ angles.
4. A _____ is a set of points extending indefinitely in two directions.
5. The _____ of a polygon is the distance around the polygon.
6. An _____ is made up of two rays that share the same endpoint. The common endpoint is called the _____.
7. _____ triangles have the same shape and the same size.
8. _____ measures the amount of surface of a region.
9. A _____ is a part of a line with one endpoint. A ray extends indefinitely in one direction.
10. A _____ of a number a is a number b whose square is a.
11. A line that intersects two or more lines at different points is called a _____.
12. An angle that measures 180° is called a _____ angle.
13. The measure of the space of a solid is called its _____.
14. When two lines intersect, four angles are formed. Two of these angles that are opposite each other are called _____ angles.
15. Two of these angles from Exercise 14 that share a common side are called _____ angles.
16. An angle whose measure is between 90° and 180° is called an _____ angle.
17. An angle that measures 90° is called a _____ angle.
18. An angle whose measure is between 0° and 90° is called an _____ angle.
19. Two angles that have a sum of 180° are called _____ angles.
20. _____ triangles have exactly the same shape but not necessarily the same size.

> **Helpful Hint**
>
> Are you preparing for your test? Don't forget to take the Chapter 6 Test on page 483. Then check your answers at the back of the text and use the Chapter Test Prep Video CD to see the fully worked-out solutions to any of the exercises you want to review.

6 Chapter Highlights

DEFINITIONS AND CONCEPTS	EXAMPLES
Section 6.1 Lines and Angles	
A **line** is a set of points extending indefinitely in two directions. A line has no width or height, but it does have length. We name a line by any two of its points.	Line AB or $\overleftrightarrow{AB}$

continued

DEFINITIONS AND CONCEPTS	**EXAMPLES**

Section 6.1   Lines and Angles (*continued*)

A **line segment** is a piece of a line with two endpoints.	Line segment AB or $\overline{AB}$
A **ray** is a part of a line with one endpoint. A ray extends indefinitely in one direction.	Ray AB or $\overrightarrow{AB}$
An **angle** is made up of two rays that share the same endpoint. The common endpoint is called the **vertex.**	
An angle that measures 180° is called a **straight angle.**	$\angle RST$ is a straight angle.
An angle that measures 90° is called a **right angle.** The symbol ∟ is used to denote a right angle.	$\angle ABC$ is a right angle.
An angle whose measure is between 0° and 90° is called an **acute angle.**	Acute angles
An angle whose measure is between 90° and 180° is called an **obtuse angle.**	Obtuse angles
Two angles that have a sum of 90° are called **complementary angles.** We say that each angle is the **complement** of the other.	Complementary angles 60° + 30° = 90°
Two angles that have a sum of 180° are called **supplementary angles.** We say that each angle is the **supplement** of the other.	Supplementary angles 125° + 55° = 180°

DEFINITIONS AND CONCEPTS	**EXAMPLES**

Section 6.1 Lines and Angles (*continued*)

When two lines intersect, four angles are formed. Two of these angles that are opposite each other are called **vertical angles.** Vertical angles have the same measure.

Two of these angles that share a common side are called **adjacent angles.** Adjacent angles formed by intersecting lines are supplementary.

A line that intersects two or more lines at different points is called a **transversal.** Line l is a transversal that intersects lines m and n. The eight angles formed have special names. Some of these names are:

Corresponding angles: $\angle a$ and $\angle e$, $\angle c$ and $\angle g$, $\angle b$ and $\angle f$, $\angle d$ and $\angle h$

Alternate interior angles: $\angle c$ and $\angle f$, $\angle d$ and $\angle e$

PARALLEL LINES CUT BY A TRANSVERSAL

If two parallel lines are cut by a transversal, then the measures of **corresponding angles are equal** and the measures of **alternate interior angles are equal.**

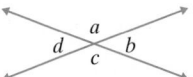

Vertical angles:
$\angle a$ and $\angle c$
$\angle d$ and $\angle b$
Adjacent angles:
$\angle a$ and $\angle b$
$\angle b$ and $\angle c$
$\angle c$ and $\angle d$
$\angle d$ and $\angle a$

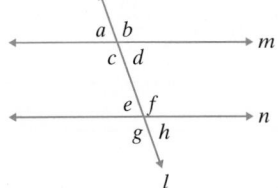

Section 6.2 Plane Figures and Solids

The **sum of the measures** of the angles of a triangle is $180°$.

Find the measure of $\angle x$.

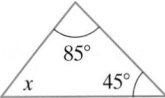

The measure of $\angle x = 180° - 85° - 45° = 50°$

A **right triangle** is a triangle with a right angle. The side opposite the right angle is called the **hypotenuse,** and the other two sides are called **legs.**

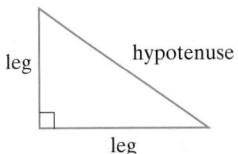

For a circle or a sphere:

diameter $=$ 2 $\cdot$ radius
$$d = 2 \cdot r$$

radius $= \dfrac{\text{diameter}}{2}$

$$r = \dfrac{d}{2}$$

Find the diameter of the circle.

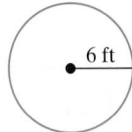

$d = 2 \cdot r$
$\quad = 2 \cdot 6 \text{ feet} = 12 \text{ feet}$

DEFINITIONS AND CONCEPTS	EXAMPLES

Section 6.3   Perimeter

PERIMETER FORMULAS
Rectangle:

$$P = 2 \cdot l + 2 \cdot w$$

Square:

$$P = 4 \cdot s$$

Triangle:

$$P = a + b + c$$

Circumference of a Circle:

$$C = 2 \cdot \pi \cdot r \quad \text{or} \quad C = \pi \cdot d,$$

where $\pi \approx 3.14$ or $\pi \approx \dfrac{22}{7}$

Find the perimeter of the rectangle with length 28 meters and width 15 meters.

$$\begin{aligned} P &= 2 \cdot l + 2 \cdot w \\ &= 2 \cdot 28 \text{ m} + 2 \cdot 15 \text{ m} \\ &= 56 \text{ m} + 30 \text{ m} \\ &= 86 \text{ m} \end{aligned}$$

The perimeter is 86 meters.

Section 6.4   Area

AREA FORMULAS
Rectangle:

$$A = l \cdot w$$

Square:

$$A = s^2$$

Triangle:

$$A = \frac{1}{2} \cdot b \cdot h$$

Parallelogram:

$$A = b \cdot h$$

Trapezoid:

$$A = \frac{1}{2} \cdot (b + B) \cdot h$$

Circle:

$$A = \pi \cdot r^2$$

Find the area of the square with side length 8 centimeters.

$$\begin{aligned} A &= s^2 \\ &= (8 \text{ cm})^2 \\ &= 64 \text{ square centimeters} \end{aligned}$$

The area of the square is 64 square centimeters.

Section 6.5   Volume

VOLUME FORMULAS
Rectangular Solid:

$$V = l \cdot w \cdot h$$

Cube:

$$V = s^3$$

Sphere:

$$V = \frac{4}{3} \cdot \pi \cdot r^3$$

Find the volume of the sphere. Use $\dfrac{22}{7}$ for π.

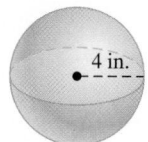
4 in.

DEFINITIONS AND CONCEPTS	**EXAMPLES**

Section 6.5   Volume *(continued)*

Right Circular Cylinder:

$$V = \pi \cdot r^2 \cdot h$$

Cone:

$$V = \frac{1}{3} \cdot \pi \cdot r^2 \cdot h$$

Square-Based Pyramid:

$$V = \frac{1}{3} \cdot s^2 \cdot h$$

$$V = \frac{4}{3} \cdot \pi \cdot r^3$$

$$\approx \frac{4}{3} \cdot \frac{22}{7} \cdot (4 \text{ inches})^3$$

$$= \frac{4 \cdot 22 \cdot 64}{3 \cdot 7} \text{ cubic inches}$$

$$= \frac{5632}{21} \quad \text{or} \quad 268\frac{4}{21} \text{ cubic inches}$$

Section 6.6   Square Roots and the Pythagorean Theorem

SQUARE ROOT OF A NUMBER

A **square root** of a number a is a number b whose square is a. We use the radical sign $\sqrt{}$ to name square roots.

PYTHAGOREAN THEOREM

$$(\text{leg})^2 + (\text{other leg})^2 = (\text{hypotenuse})^2$$

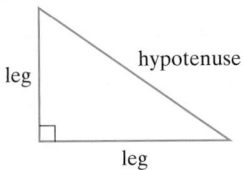

TO FIND AN UNKNOWN LENGTH OF A RIGHT TRIANGLE

$$\text{hypotenuse} = \sqrt{(\text{leg})^2 + (\text{other leg})^2}$$
$$\text{leg} = \sqrt{(\text{hypotenuse})^2 - (\text{other leg})^2}$$

$$\sqrt{9} = 3, \ \sqrt{100} = 10, \ \sqrt{1} = 1$$

Find the hypotenuse of the given triangle.

3 in.   hypotenuse   8 in.

$$\text{hypotenuse} = \sqrt{(\text{leg})^2 + (\text{other leg})^2}$$
$$= \sqrt{(3)^2 + (8)^2} \quad \text{The legs are 3 and 8 inches.}$$
$$= \sqrt{9 + 64}$$
$$= \sqrt{73} \text{ inches}$$
$$\approx 8.5 \text{ inches}$$

Section 6.7   Congruent and Similar Triangles

Congruent triangles have the same shape and the same size. Corresponding angles are equal, and corresponding sides are equal.

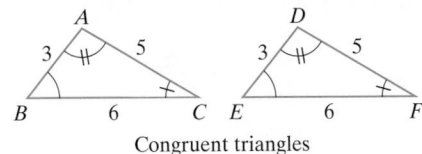

Congruent triangles

Similar triangles have exactly the same shape but not necessarily the same size. Corresponding angles are equal, and the ratios of the lengths of corresponding sides are equal.

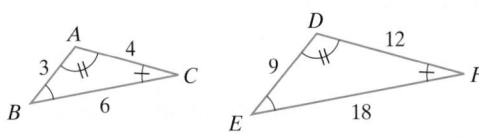

$$\frac{AB}{DE} = \frac{3}{9} = \frac{1}{3}, \frac{BC}{EF} = \frac{6}{18} = \frac{1}{3},$$
$$\frac{CA}{FD} = \frac{4}{12} = \frac{1}{3}$$

6 CHAPTER REVIEW

(6.1) *Classify each angle as acute, right, obtuse, or straight.*

1.

2.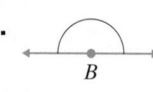

3.

4.

5. Find the complement of a 25° angle.

6. Find the supplement of a 105° angle.

Find the measure of angle x in each figure.

7.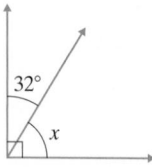

8.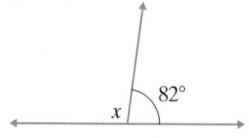

9.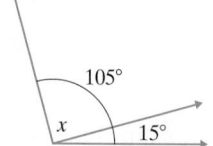

10.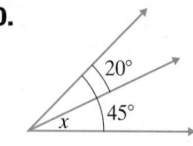

11. Identify the pairs of supplementary angles.

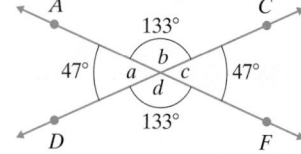

12. Identify the pairs of complementary angles.

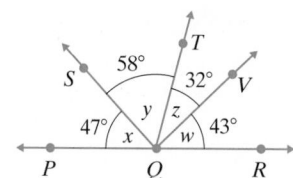

476

Find the measures of angles x, y, and z in each figure.

13.

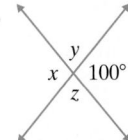

14.

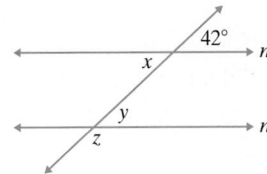

15. Given that $m \parallel n$.

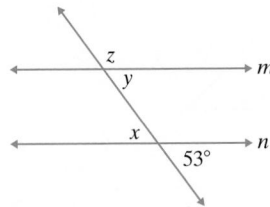

16. Given that $m \parallel n$.

(6.2) *Find the measure of ∠x in each figure.*

17.

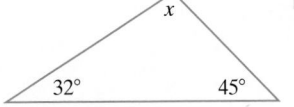

18.

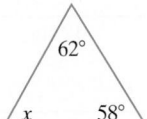

19.

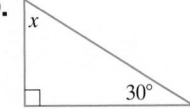

20.

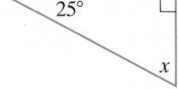

Find the unknown diameter or radius as indicated.

21.

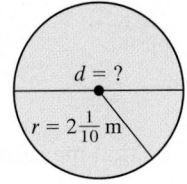

22.

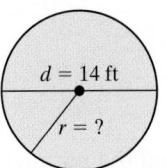

23.

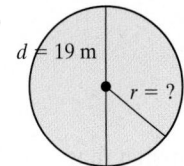

24.

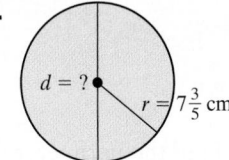

Identify each solid.

25.

26.

27.

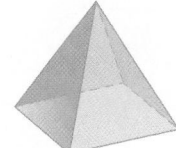

28.

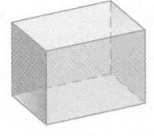

Find the unknown radius or diameter as indicated.

29. The radius of a sphere is 9 inches. Find its diameter.

30. The diameter of a sphere is 4.7 meters. Find its radius.

Identify each regular polygon.

31.

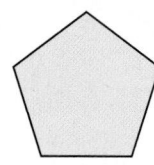

32.

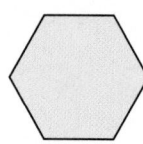

Identify each triangle as equilateral, isosceles, or scalene. Also identify any triangle that is a right triangle.

33.

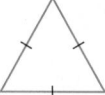

34.

(6.3) *Find the perimeter of each figure.*

35.

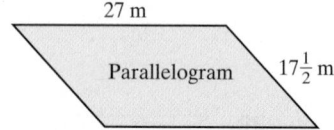

27 m

Parallelogram $17\frac{1}{2}$ m

36.

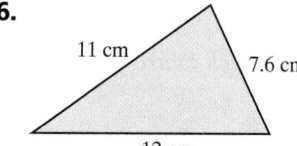

11 cm   7.6 cm

12 cm

37.

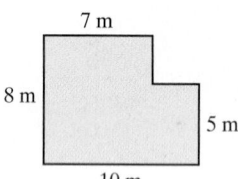

7 m

8 m

5 m

10 m

38.

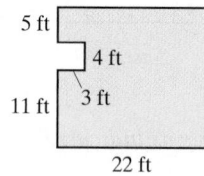

5 ft

4 ft

11 ft   3 ft

22 ft

Solve.

39. Find the perimeter of a rectangular sign that measures 6 feet by 10 feet.

40. Find the perimeter of a town square that measures 110 feet on a side.

Find the circumference of each circle. Use $\pi \approx 3.14$.

41.

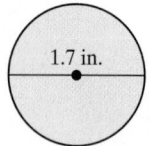

1.7 in.

42.

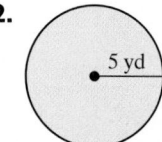

5 yd

(6.4) *Find the area of each figure. For the circles, find the exact area and then use $\pi \approx 3.14$ to approximate the area.*

43.

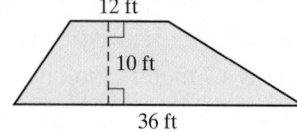

12 ft

10 ft

36 ft

44.

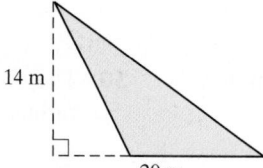

14 m

20 m

45.

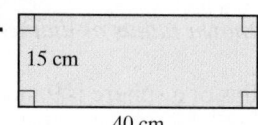

15 cm

40 cm

46.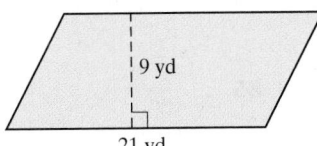
9 yd
21 yd

47.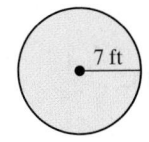
7 ft

48.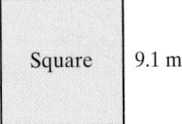
Square 9.1 m

49.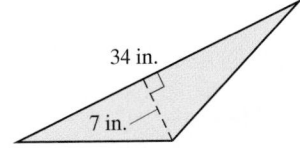
34 in.
7 in.

50.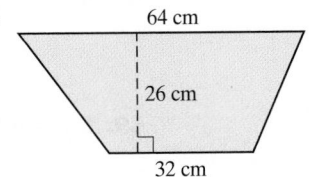
64 cm
26 cm
32 cm

51.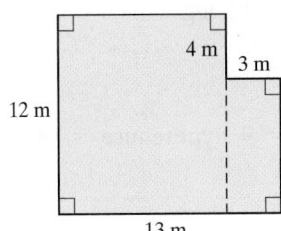
4 m
3 m
12 m
13 m

52. The amount of sealer necessary to seal a driveway depends on the area. Find the area of a rectangular driveway 36 feet by 12 feet.

53. Find how much carpet is necessary to cover the floor of the room shown.

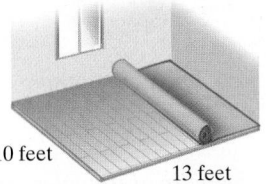
10 feet
13 feet

(6.5) *Find the volume of each solid. For Exercises 56 and 57, give an exact volume and an approximation.*

54.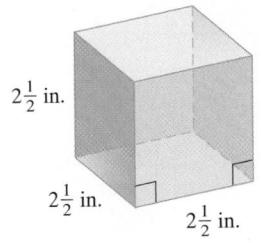
$2\frac{1}{2}$ in.
$2\frac{1}{2}$ in.
$2\frac{1}{2}$ in.

55.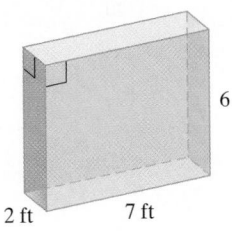
6 ft
2 ft
7 ft

56. Use $\pi \approx 3.14$.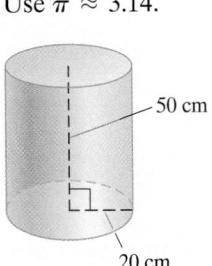
50 cm
20 cm

57. Use $\pi \approx \dfrac{22}{7}$.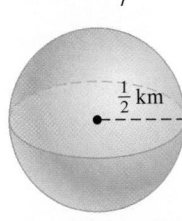
$\frac{1}{2}$ km

58. Find the volume of a pyramid with a square base 2 feet on a side and a height of 2 feet.

59. Approximate the volume of a tin can 8 inches high and 3.5 inches in radius. Use 3.14 for π.

60. A chest has 3 drawers. If each drawer has inside measurements of $2\frac{1}{2}$ feet by $1\frac{1}{2}$ feet by $\frac{2}{3}$ foot, find the total volume of the 3 drawers.

61. A cylindrical canister for a shop vacuum is 2 feet tall and 1 foot in *diameter*. Find its exact volume.

(6.6) *Simplify.*

62. $\sqrt{64}$

63. $\sqrt{144}$

64. $\sqrt{\dfrac{4}{25}}$

65. $\sqrt{\dfrac{1}{100}}$

Find the unknown length of each given right triangle. If necessary, round to the nearest tenth.

66. leg = 12, leg = 5

67. leg = 20, leg = 21

68. leg = 9, hypotenuse = 14

69. leg = 124, hypotenuse = 155

70. A baseball diamond is in the shape of a square and has sides of length 90 feet. Find the distance across the diamond from third base to first base, to the nearest tenth of a foot.

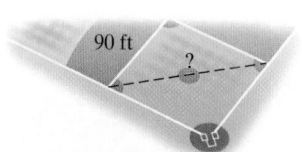

71. Find the height of the building rounded to the nearest tenth.

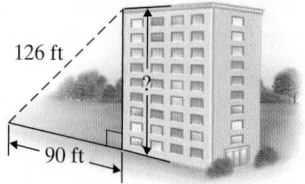

(6.7) *Given that the pairs of triangles are similar, find the unknown length n.*

72.

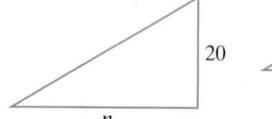

73.

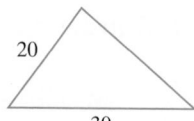

74.

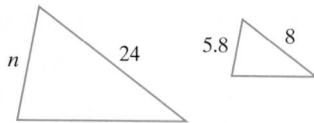

Solve.

75. A housepainter needs to estimate the height of a condominium. He estimates the length of his shadow to be 7 feet long and the length of the building's shadow to be 42 feet long. Find the approximate height of the building if the housepainter is $5\dfrac{1}{2}$ feet tall.

76. Santa's elves are making a triangular sail for a toy sailboat. The toy sail is to be the same shape as a real sailboat's sail. Use the following diagram to find the unknown lengths x and y.

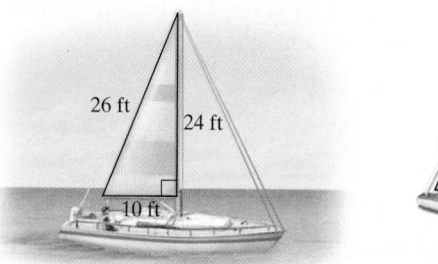

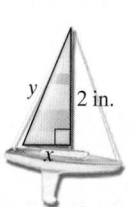

Mixed Review

Find the following.

77. Find the supplement of a 72° angle.

78. Find the complement of a 1° angle.

Find the measure of angle x in each figure.

79.

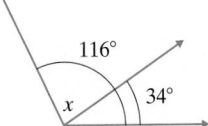

80.

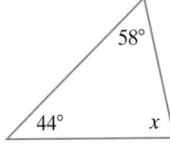

81.

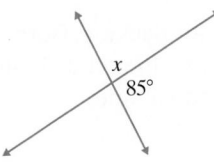

82.

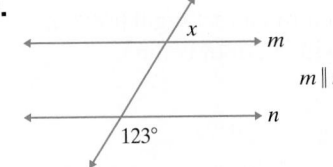

Find the unknown diameter or radius as indicated.

83.

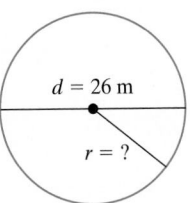

84.

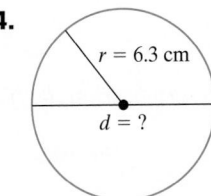

Find the perimeter (or circumference) of each figure. Use $\pi \approx 3.14$.

85.

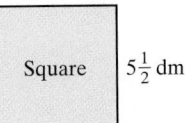

86.

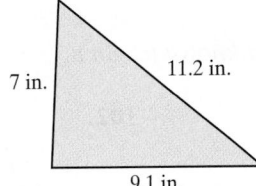

87.

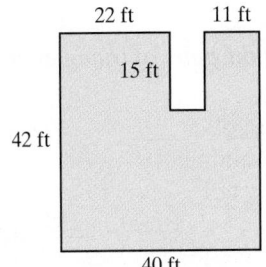

Find the area of each figure. For the circles, find the exact area and then use $\pi = 3.14$ to approximate the area.

88.

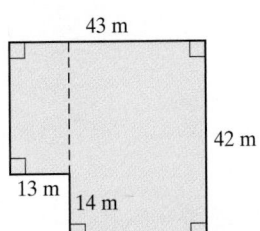

89.

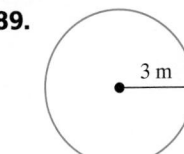

Find the volume of each solid.

90. Give an approximation using $\frac{22}{7}$ for π.

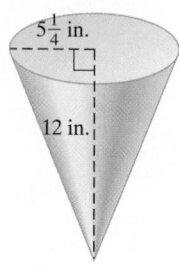

91.

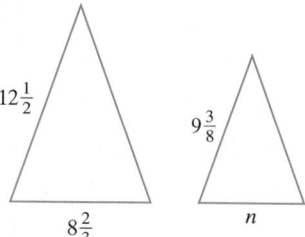

Solve.

92. Find the volume of air in a rectangular room 15 feet by 12 feet with a 7-foot ceiling.

93. A mover has two boxes left for packing. Both are cubical, one 3 feet on a side and the other 1.2 feet on a side. Find their combined volume.

Simplify.

94. $\sqrt{1}$

95. $\sqrt{36}$

96. $\sqrt{\dfrac{16}{81}}$

Find the unknown length of each given right triangle. If necessary, round to the nearest tenth.

97. leg = 66, leg = 56

98. leg = 12, hypotenuse = 24

99. leg = 17, hypotenuse = 51

100. leg = 10, leg = 17

Given that the pairs of triangles are similar, find the unknown length n.

101.

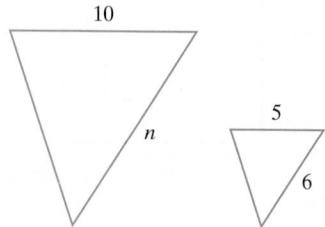

102.

6 CHAPTER TEST

Answers

1. Find the complement of a 78° angle.

2. Find the supplement of a 124° angle.

3. Find the measure of ∠x.

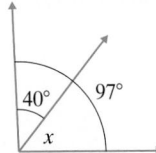

Find the measure of x, y, and z in each figure.

4.

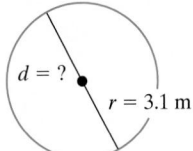

5. Given: m ∥ n.

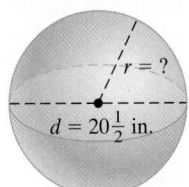

Find the unknown diameter or radius as indicated.

6.

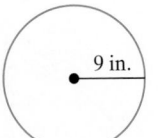

d = ?
r = 3.1 m

7.

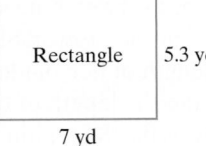

r = ?
d = 20½ in.

8. Find the measure of ∠x.

92°
62°   x

Find the perimeter (or circumference) and area of each figure. For the circle, give the exact value and then use π ≈ 3.14 for an approximation.

9.

9 in.

10.

Rectangle   5.3 yd
7 yd

11.

6 in.
11 in.
7 in.
23 in.

1. _____

2. _____

3. _____

4. _____

5. _____

6. _____

7. _____

8. _____

9. _____

10. _____

11. _____

483

12. _____

13. _____

14. _____

Find the volume of each solid. For the cylinder, use $\pi \approx \dfrac{22}{7}$.

12.

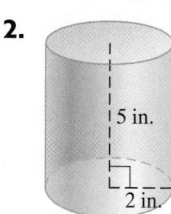

5 in.

2 in.

13.

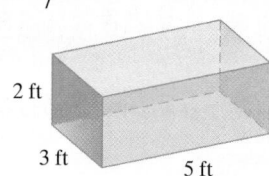

2 ft

3 ft   5 ft

Find each square root and simplify. Round the square root to the nearest thousandth if necessary.

14. $\sqrt{49}$ **15.** $\sqrt{79}$ **16.** $\sqrt{\dfrac{64}{100}}$

15. _____

16. _____

Solve.

17. Find the perimeter of a square photo with a side length of 4 inches.

18. How much soil is needed to fill a rectangular hole 3 feet by 3 feet by 2 feet?

17. _____

19. Find how much baseboard is needed to go around a rectangular room that measures 18 feet by 13 feet. If baseboard costs $1.87 per foot, also calculate the total cost needed for materials.

20. Approximate to the nearest hundredth of a centimeter the length of the hypotenuse of a right triangle with legs of 4 centimeters each.

18. _____

19. _____

21. Vivian Thomas is going to put insecticide on her lawn to control grubworms. The lawn is a rectangle measuring 123.8 feet by 80 feet. The amount of insecticide required is 0.02 ounces per square foot. Find how much insecticide Vivian needs to purchase.

22. Given that the following triangles are similar, find the missing length n.

20. _____

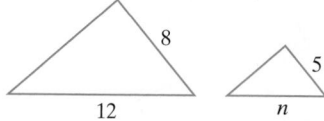

8

12

5

n

21. _____

23. Tamara Watford, a surveyor, needs to estimate the height of a tower. She estimates the length of her shadow to be 4 feet long and the length of the tower's shadow to be 48 feet long. Find the height of the approximate tower if she is $5\dfrac{3}{4}$ feet tall.

22. _____

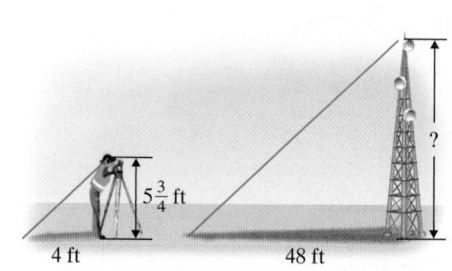

$5\dfrac{3}{4}$ ft

?

4 ft   48 ft

23. _____

1. Write the decimal 19.5023 in words.

2. Add: $\dfrac{7}{11} + \dfrac{1}{6}$

3. Round 736.2359 to the nearest tenth.

4. Round 736.2359 to the nearest hundred.

5. Add: $45 + 2.06$

6. Divide: $3\dfrac{1}{3} \div 1\dfrac{5}{6}$

Multiply.

7. 7.68×10

8. $\dfrac{7}{11} \cdot \dfrac{1}{6}$

9. 76.3×1000

10. $5\dfrac{1}{2} \cdot 2\dfrac{1}{11}$

11. Divide: $270.2 \div 7$. Check your answer.

12. Divide: $\dfrac{56.7}{100}$

13. Simplify: $0.5(8.6 - 1.2)$

14. Simplify: $\dfrac{5 + 2(8 - 3)}{30 \div 6 \cdot 5}$

15. Insert $<$, $>$, or $=$ to form a true statement. $\dfrac{1}{8}$ ____ 0.12

16. Insert $<$, $>$, or $=$ to form a true statement. $\dfrac{3}{4}$ ____ $\dfrac{13}{16}$

17. Multiply: $25 \cdot 9000$

18. Find: $\dfrac{2}{9} + \dfrac{7}{15} - \dfrac{1}{3}$

19. Multiply: $20 \cdot 7000$

20. Solve for n: $\dfrac{7}{8} = \dfrac{n}{20}$

21. In a survey of 100 people, 17 people drive blue cars. What percent drive blue cars?

22. In a survey of 50 people, 34 people prefer taking pictures with digital cameras. What percent is this?

Answers

1. _____
2. _____
3. _____
4. _____
5. _____
6. _____
7. _____
8. _____
9. _____
10. _____
11. _____
12. _____
13. _____
14. _____
15. _____
16. _____
17. _____
18. _____
19. _____
20. _____
21. _____
22. _____

23. _____

24. _____

25. _____

26. _____

27. _____

28. _____

29. _____

30. _____

31. _____

32. _____

33. _____

34. _____

35. _____

36. _____

37. _____

38. _____

39. _____

40. _____

41. _____

42. _____

43. _____

44. _____

45. _____

46. _____

Write each percent as a fraction or mixed number in simplest form.

23. 1.9% **24.** 26% **25.** 125% **26.** 560%

27. 85% of 300 is what number?

28. What percent of 16 is 2.4?

29. 20.8 is 40% of what number?

30. Find: $\sqrt{\dfrac{25}{81}}$

31. Mr. Buccaran, the principal at Slidell High School, counted 31 freshmen absent during a particular day. If this is 4% of the total number of freshmen, how many freshmen are there at Slidell High School?

32. Flooring tiles cost $90 for a box with 40 tiles. Each tile is 1 square foot. Find the unit price in dollars per square foot.

33. Sherry Souter, a real estate broker for Wealth Investments, sold a house for $114,000 last week. If her commission is 1.5% of the selling price of the home, find the amount of her commission.

34. A student can complete 7 exercises in 6 minutes. At this rate, how many exercises can be completed in 30 minutes?

35. Simplify: $2 \cdot 4 - 3 \div 3$

36. Write seventy thousand, fifty-two in standard form.

37. Write $\dfrac{1}{12}$ as a percent. Round to the nearest hundredth percent.

38. Write $\dfrac{1}{8}$ as a percent.

39. Find the measure of $\angle a$.

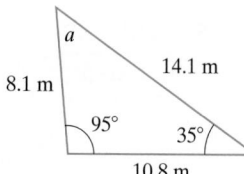

40. Find the perimeter of the triangle in Exercise 43.

41. Find the perimeter of the rectangle below:

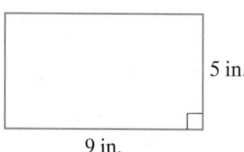

42. Find the area of the rectangle in Exercise 45.

43. Find $\sqrt{\dfrac{4}{25}}$.

44. Find $\sqrt{\dfrac{9}{16}}$.

45. Find the ratio of corresponding sides for triangles ABC and DEF.

46. Use the result of Exercise 49 to find the value of x.

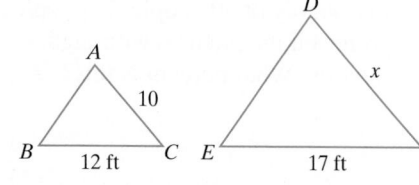

7

Statistics and Probability

We often need to make decisions based on known statistics or the probability of an event occurring. For example, we decide whether or not to bring an umbrella to work based on the probability of rain. We choose an investment based on its mean, or average, return. We can predict which football team will win based on the trend in its previous wins and losses. This chapter reviews presenting data in a usable form on a graph and the basic ideas of statistics and probability.

A tornado is a violent, whirling column of air that is often spawned by the unstable weather conditions that occur during thunderstorms. Although tornadoes are capable of sustaining wind speeds of 250 to more than 300 mph, most tornadoes have wind speeds under 110 mph. The average forward speed of a tornado is 30 mph, but some tornadoes have been known to travel over land at speeds up to 70 mph. The path of a tornado can extend anywhere from a few feet to 100 miles long. Each year in the United States, an average of 800 tornadoes occur, causing an average of 80 deaths. The deadliest tornado in the United States was the Tri-State Tornado Outbreak on March 18, 1925, which killed 689 people and injured over 2000 more in Missouri, Illinois, and Indiana. In Exercises 19 through 24 on page 495 and the Chapter Highlights on page 522, we will see how graphs can be used to summarize data about tornadoes.

7.1 READING PICTOGRAPHS, BAR GRAPHS, HISTOGRAMS, AND LINE GRAPHS

Often data is presented visually in a graph. In this section, we practice reading several kinds of graphs including pictographs, bar graphs, and line graphs.

Objective **A** Reading Pictographs

A **pictograph** such as the one below is a graph in which pictures or symbols are used. This type of graph contains a key that explains the meaning of the symbol used. An advantage of using a pictograph to display information is that comparisons can easily be made. A disadvantage of using a pictograph is that it is often hard to tell what fractional part of a symbol is shown. For example, in the pictograph below, Sweden shows a part of a symbol, but it's hard to read with any accuracy what fractional part of a symbol is shown.

PRACTICE PROBLEM 1

Use the pictograph shown in Example 1 to answer the following questions:

a. Approximate the amount of nuclear energy that was generated in Japan.

b. Approximate the total nuclear energy generated in Japan and Russia.

EXAMPLE 1 Calculating Nuclear Energy Generated

The following pictograph shows the approximate amount of nuclear energy generated by selected countries in the year 2002. Use this pictograph to answer the questions.

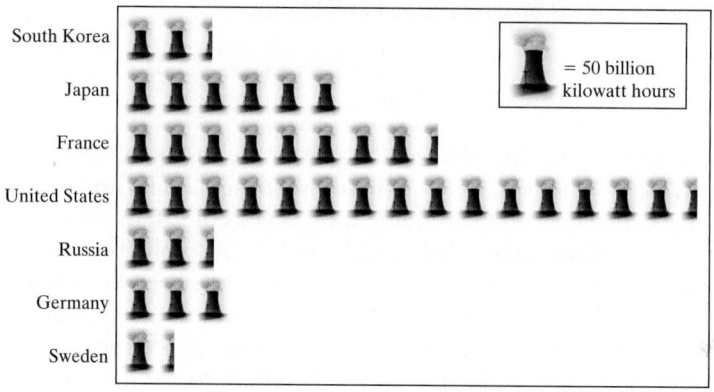

Nuclear Energy Generated by Selected Countries (2002)

= 50 billion kilowatt hours

Source: Energy Information Administration

a. Approximate the amount of nuclear energy that was generated in Germany.

b. Approximate how much more nuclear energy was generated in France than in Germany.

Solution:

a. Germany corresponds to 3 symbols, and each symbol represents 50 billion kilowatt hours of energy. This means that Germany generated approximately $3 \cdot (50 \text{ billion})$ or 150 billion kilowatt hours of energy.

b. France shows $5\frac{1}{2}$ more symbols than Germany. This means that France generated $5\frac{1}{2} \cdot (50 \text{ billion})$ or 275 billion more kilowatt hours of nuclear energy than Germany.

Work Practice Problem 1

Answers

1. a. 300 billion kilowatt hours,
b. 425 billion kilowatt hours

Objective B Reading Bar Graphs

Another way to visually present data is with a **bar graph.** Bar graphs can appear with vertical bars or horizontal bars. Although we have studied bar graphs in previous sections, we now practice reading the height of the bars contained in a bar graph. An advantage to using bar graphs is that a scale is usually included for greater accuracy. Care must be taken when reading bar graphs, as well as other types of graphs—they may be misleading, as shown later in this section.

EXAMPLE 2 Finding Number of Endangered Species

The following bar graph shows the number of endangered species in the U.S. in 2001. Use this graph to answer the questions.

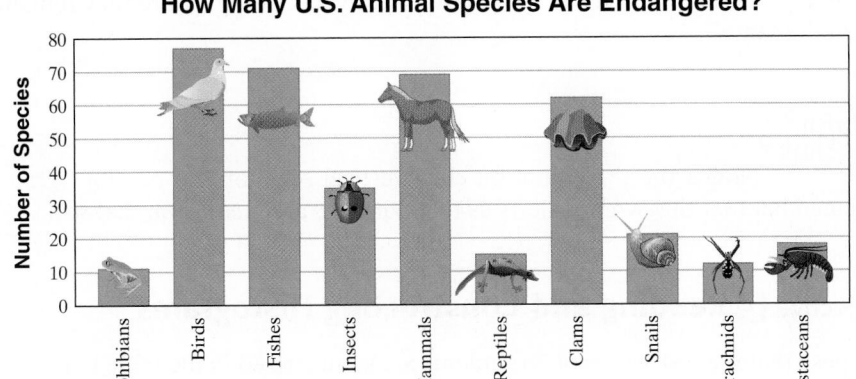

How Many U.S. Animal Species Are Endangered?

Source: U.S. Fish and Wildlife Service

a. Approximate the number of endangered species that are reptiles.

b. Which category has the most endangered species?

Solution:

a. To approximate the number of endangered species that are reptiles, we go to the top of the bar that represents reptiles. From the top of this bar, we move horizontally to the left until the scale is reached. We read the height of the bar on the scale as approximately 15. There are approximately 15 reptile species that are endangered, as shown.

b. The most endangered species is represented by the tallest (longest) bar. The tallest bar corresponds to birds.

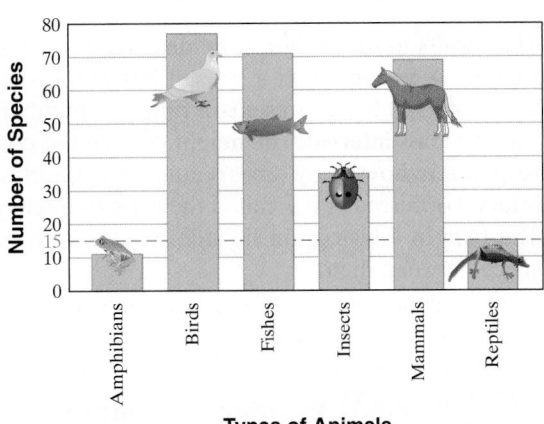

How Many Species Are Endangered?

Source: U.S. Fish and Wildlife Service

■ **Work Practice Problem 2**

PRACTICE PROBLEM 2

Use the bar graph in Example 2 to answer the following questions:

a. Approximate the number of endangered species that are insects.

b. Which category shows the fewest endangered species?

Answers

2. a. 35, **b.** amphibians

As mentioned previously, graphs can be misleading. Both graphs below show the same information, but with different scales. Special care should be taken when forming conclusions from the appearance of a graph.

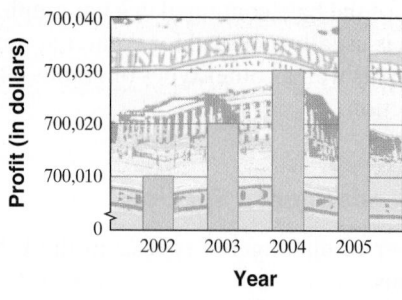

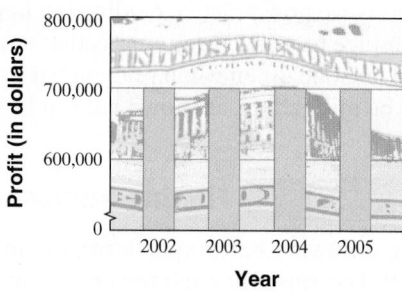

Are profits shown in the graphs above greatly increasing, or are they remaining about the same?

Helpful Hint

Notice the ⟩ symbol on each vertical scale on the previous graphs. Remember that this symbol alerts us that numbers are missing on that scale.

Objective C Reading and Constructing Histograms

Suppose that the test scores of 36 students are summarized in the table below:

Student Scores	Frequency (Number of Students)
40–49	1
50–59	3
60–69	2
70–79	10
80–89	12
90–99	8

The results in the table can be displayed in a histogram. A **histogram** is a special bar graph. The width of each bar represents a range of numbers called a **class interval.** The height of each bar corresponds to how many times a number in the class interval occurred and is called the **class frequency.** The bars in a histogram lie side by side with no space between them.

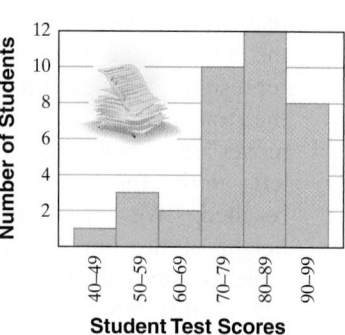

Student Test Scores

PRACTICE PROBLEM 3

Use the histogram on the right to determine how many students scored 70–79 on the test.

Answer

3. 10

EXAMPLE 3 **Reading a Histogram on Student Test Scores**

Use the preceding histogram to determine how many students scored 50–59 on the test.

Solution: We find the bar representing 50–59. The height of this bar is 3, which means 3 students scored 50–59 on the test.

■ **Work Practice Problem 3**

EXAMPLE 4 Reading a Histogram on Student Test Scores

Use the preceding histogram to determine how many students scored 80 or above on the test.

Solution: We see that two different bars fit this description. There are 12 students who scored 80–89 and 8 students who scored 90–99. The sum of these two categories is 12 + 8 or 20 students. Thus, 20 students scored 80 or above on the test.

🔲 **Work Practice Problem 4**

Now we will look at a way to construct histograms.

The daily high temperatures for 1 month in New Orleans, Louisiana, are recorded in the following list:

85°	90°	95°	89°	88°	94°
87°	90°	95°	92°	95°	94°
82°	92°	96°	91°	94°	92°
89°	89°	90°	93°	95°	91°
88°	90°	88°	86°	93°	89°

The data in this list have not been organized and can be hard to interpret. One way to organize the data is to place it in a **frequency distribution table.** We will do this in Example 5.

EXAMPLE 5 Completing a Frequency Distribution on Temperature

Complete the frequency distribution table for the preceding temperature data.

Solution: Go through the data and place a tally mark in the second column of the table next to the class interval. Then count the tally marks and write each total in the third column of the table.

Class Intervals (Temperatures)	Tally	Class Frequency (Number of Days)
82°–84°	I	1
85°–87°	III	3
88°–90°	﷿HL ﷿HL I	11
91°–93°	﷿HL II	7
94°–96°	﷿HL III	8

🔲 **Work Practice Problem 5**

EXAMPLE 6 Constructing a Histogram

Construct a histogram from the frequency distribution table in Example 5.

Solution:

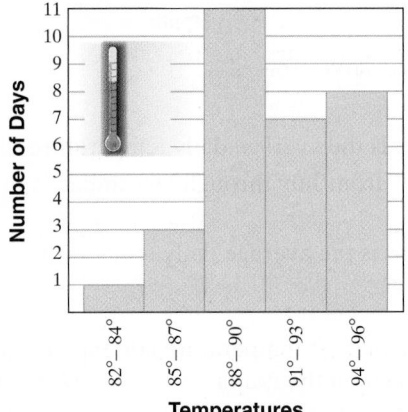

🔲 **Work Practice Problem 6**

PRACTICE PROBLEM 4

Use the histogram for Example 3 to determine how many students scored less than 60 on the test.

PRACTICE PROBLEM 5

Complete the frequency distribution table for the data below. Each number represents a credit card owner's unpaid balance for one month.

0	53	89	125
265	161	37	76
62	201	136	42

Class Intervals (Credit Card Balances)	Tally	Class Frequency (Number of Months)
$0–$49	___	___
$50–$99	___	___
$100–$149	___	___
$150–$199	___	___
$200–$249	___	___
$250–$299	___	___

PRACTICE PROBLEM 6

Construct a histogram from the frequency distribution table above.

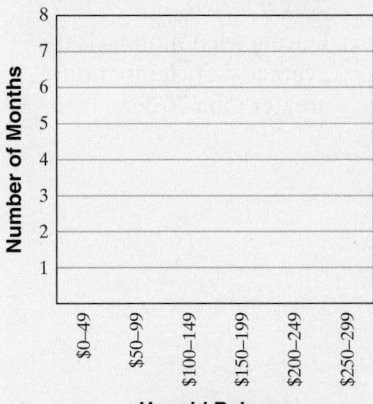

Answers

4. 4,

5.

Tally	Class Frequency (Number of Months)
III	3
IIII	4
II	2
I	1
I	1
I	1

6.

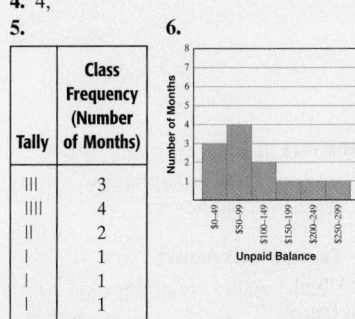

✔ **Concept Check** Which of the following sets of data is better suited to representation by a histogram? Explain.

Set 1		Set 2	
Grade on Final	# of Students	Section Number	Avg. Grade on Final
51–60	12	150	78
61–70	18	151	83
71–80	29	152	87
81–90	23	153	73
91–100	25		

Objective D Reading Line Graphs

Another common way to display information with a graph is by using a **line graph.** An advantage of a line graph is that it can be used to visualize relationships between two quantities. A line graph can also be very useful in showing a change over time.

PRACTICE PROBLEM 7

Use the temperature graph in Example 7 to answer the following questions:

a. During what month is the average daily temperature the lowest?

b. During what month is the average daily temperature 25°F?

c. During what months is the average daily temperature greater than 70°F?

EXAMPLE 7 **Reading Temperatures from Line Graph**

The following line graph shows the average daily temperature for each month for Omaha, Nebraska. Use this graph to answer the questions.

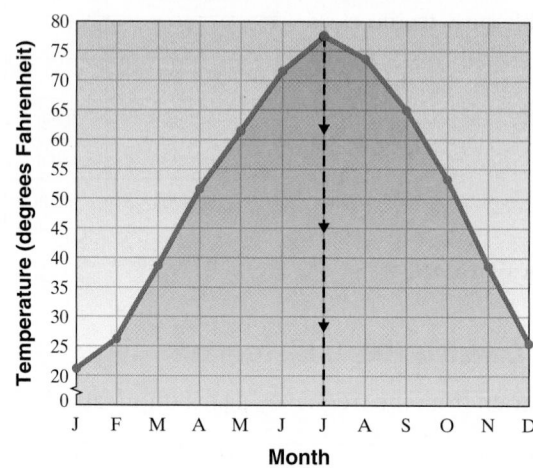

Average Daily Temperature for Omaha, Nebraska

Source: National Climatic Data Center

a. During what month is the average daily temperature the highest?

b. During what month, from July through December, is the average daily temperature 65°F?

c. During what months is the average daily temperature less than 30°F?

Solution:

a. The month with the highest temperature corresponds to the highest point. This is the red point shown on the graph above. We follow this highest point downward to the horizontal month scale and see that this point corresponds to July.

b. The months July through December correspond to the right side of the graph. We find the 65°F mark on the vertical temperature scale and move to the right until a point on the right side of the graph is reached. From that point, we move downward to the horizontal month scale and read the corresponding month. During the month of September, the average daily temperature was 65°F.

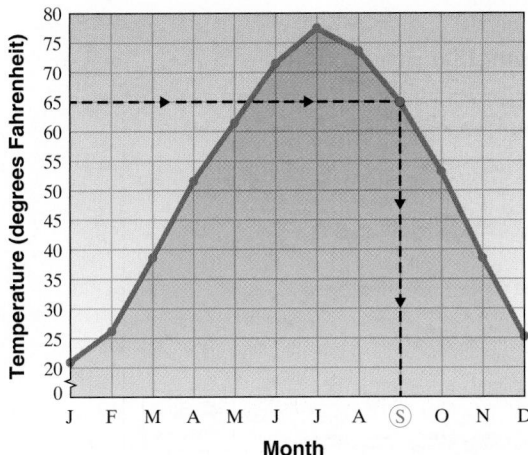

Source: National Climatic Data Center

c. To see what months the temperature is less than 30°F, we find what months correspond to points that fall below the 30°F mark on the vertical scale. These months are January, February, and December.

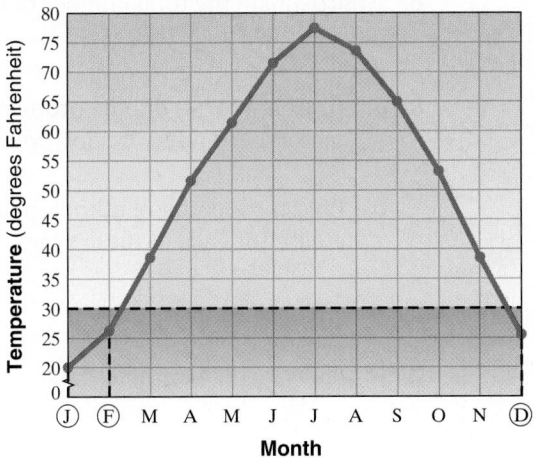

Source: National Climatic Data Center

🔲 **Work Practice Problem 7**

Objective **A** *The following pictograph shows the annual automobile production by one plant for the years 1999–2005. Use this graph to answer Exercises 1 through 10. See Example 1.*

Automobile Production

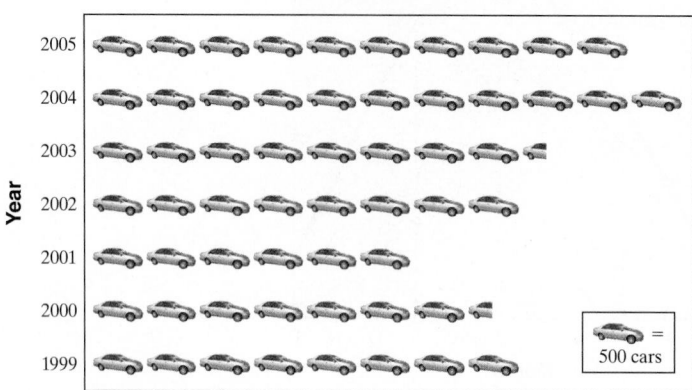

1. In what year was the greatest number of cars manufactured?

2. In what year was the least number of cars manufactured?

3. Approximate the number of cars manufactured in 2002.

4. Approximate the number of cars manufactured in 2003.

5. Approximate the total number of cars manufactured in 2004 and 2005.

6. Approximate the total number of cars manufactured in 2002 and 2003.

7. a. In what year(s) did the production of cars decrease from the previous year?

b. Find the amount of automobile production decrease for each of these years.

8. a. In what year(s) did the production of cars increase from the previous year?

b. Find the amount of automobile production increase for each of these years.

9. In what year(s) were 4000 cars manufactured?

10. In what year(s) were 5500 cars manufactured?

The following pictograph shows the average number of ounces of chicken consumed per person per week in the United States. Use this graph to answer Exercises 11 through 18. See Example 1.

Chicken Consumption

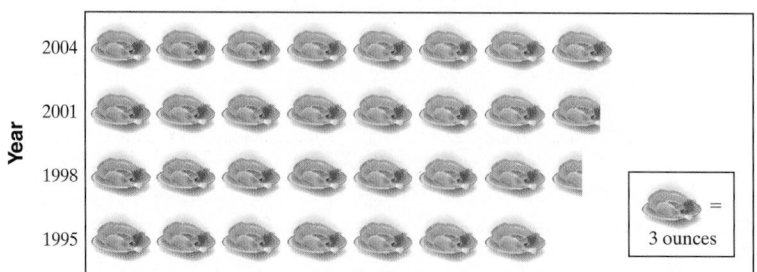

Source: National Agricultural Statistics Service

11. Approximate the number of ounces of chicken consumed per week in 1998.

12. Approximate the number of ounces of chicken consumed per week in 2004.

13. In what year(s) was the number of ounces of chicken consumed per week greater than 21 ounces?

14. In what year(s) was the number of ounces of chicken consumed per week 21 ounces or less?

15. What was the increase in average chicken consumption from 1995 to 2004?

16. What was the increase in average chicken consumption from 1998 to 2004?

17. Suppose that you need to represent 17 ounces on this pictograph. How many symbols represent 17 ounces?

18. Describe a trend in eating habits shown by this graph.

Objective **B** *The following bar graph shows the average number of people killed by tornadoes during the months of the year. Use this graph to answer Exercises 19 through 24. See Example 2.*

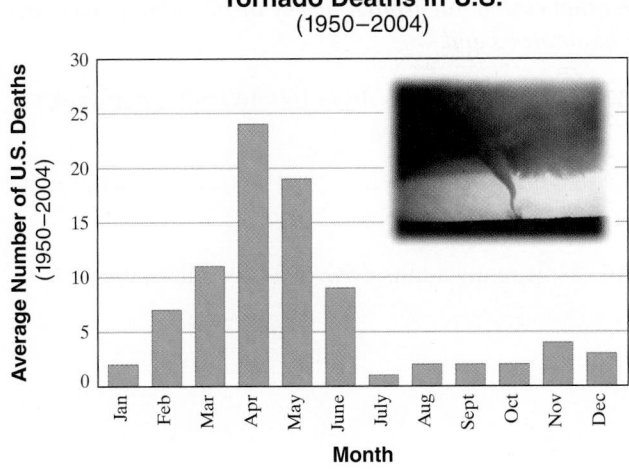

Tornado Deaths in U.S.
(1950–2004)

Source: Storm Prediction Center

19. In which month(s) did the most tornado-related deaths occur?

20. In which month(s) did the fewest tornado-related deaths occur?

21. Approximate the average number of tornado-related deaths that occurred in May.

22. Approximate the average number of tornado-related deaths that occurred in April.

23. In which month(s) did more than 5 deaths occur?

24. In which month(s) did more than 15 deaths occur?

The following horizontal bar graph shows the 2004 population of the world's largest agglomerations (cities plus their suburbs). Use this graph to answer Exercises 25 through 32. See Example 2.

World's Largest Agglomerations

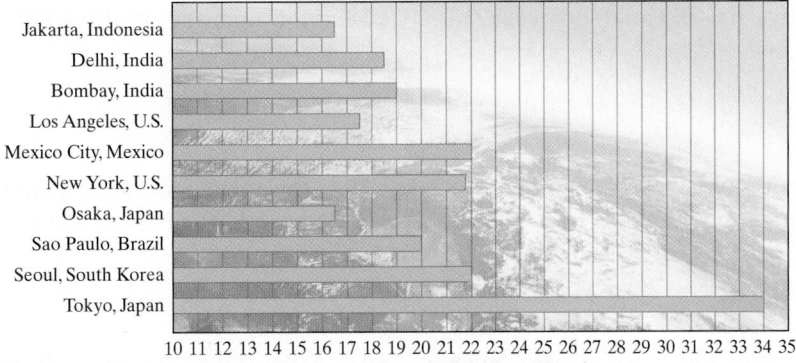

Source: Thomas Brinkhoff: *The Principal Agglomerations of the World,*
http://www.citypopulation.de, 8/17/2004

25. Estimate the population of Delhi, India.

26. Estimate the population of Seoul, South Korea.

27. Name the city with the largest population and estimate its population.

28. Name the city whose population is between 17 and 18 million and estimate its population.

29. Name the city in the United States with the largest population and estimate its population.

30. Name the city in the graph with the smallest population and estimate its population.

31. How much larger is the population of Tokyo than the population of Sao Paulo?

32. How much larger is the population of Mexico City than the population of Bombay?

Objective **C** *The following histogram shows the number of miles that each adult, from a survey of 100 adults, drives per week. Use this histogram to answer Exercises 33 through 42. See Examples 3 and 4.*

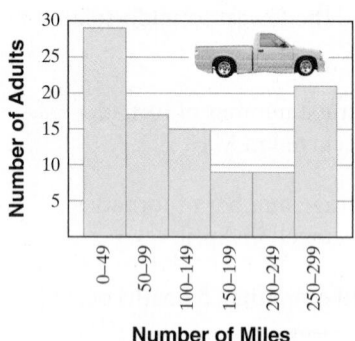

33. How many adults drive 100–149 miles per week?

34. How many adults drive 200–249 miles per week?

35. How many adults drive fewer than 150 miles per week?

36. How many adults drive 200 miles or more per week?

37. How many adults drive 100–199 miles per week?

38. How many adults drive 150–249 miles per week?

39. How many more adults drive 250–299 miles per week than 200–249 miles per week?

40. How many more adults drive 0–49 miles per week than 50–99 miles per week?

41. What is the ratio of adults who drive 150–199 miles per week to the total number of adults surveyed?

42. What is the ratio of adults who drive 50–99 miles per week to the total number of adults surveyed?

The following histogram shows the projected ages of householders for the year 2010. Use this histogram to answer Exercises 43 through 50. For Exercises 45 through 48, estimate to the nearest whole million. See Examples 3 and 4.

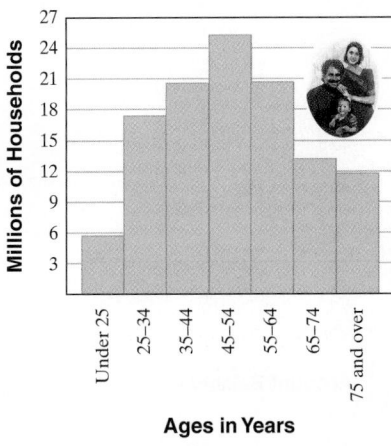

Ages in Years

Source: U.S. Bureau of the Census, *Current Population Reports*

43. The most householders will be in what age range?

44. The least number of householders will be in what age range?

45. How many householders will be 55–64 years old?

46. How many householders will be 35–44 years old?

47. How many householders will be 44 years old or younger?

48. How many householders will be 55 years old or older?

49. Which bar represents the household you expect to be in during the year 2010?

50. How many more householders will be 45–54 years old than 55–64 years old?

The following list shows the golf scores for an amateur golfer. Use this list to complete the frequency distribution table to the right. See Example 5.

78	84	91	93	97
97	95	85	95	96
101	89	92	89	100

	Class Intervals (Scores)	Tally	Class Frequency (Number of Games)
51.	70–79		
52.	80–89		
53.	90–99		
54.	100–109		

Twenty-five people in a survey were asked to give their current checking account balances. Use the balances shown in the following list to complete the frequency distribution table to the right. See Example 5.

$53	$105	$162	$443	$109
$468	$47	$259	$316	$228
$207	$357	$15	$301	$75
$86	$77	$512	$219	$100
$192	$288	$352	$166	$292

	Class Intervals (Account Balances)	Tally	Class Frequency (Number of People)
55.	$0–$99		
56.	$100–$199		
57.	$200–$299		
58.	$300–$399		
59.	$400–$499		
60.	$500–$599		

61. Use the frequency distribution table from Exercises 51 through 54 to construct a histogram. See Example 6.

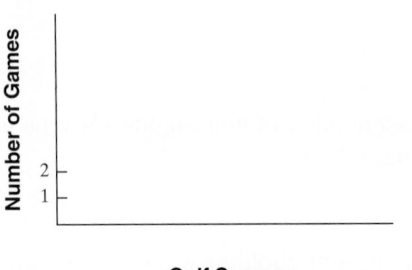

62. Use the frequency distribution table from Exercises 55 through 60 to construct a histogram. See Example 6.

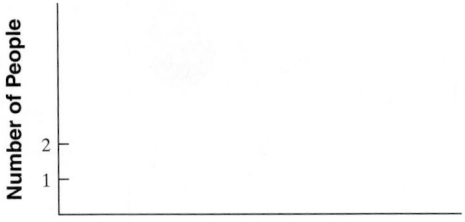

Objective D *The following line graph shows the World Cup goals per game average during the years shown. Use this graph to answer Exercises 63 through 70. See Example 7.*

63. Find the average number of goals per game in 1994.

64. Find the average number of goals per game in 2002.

65. During what year shown was the average number of goals per game the highest?

66. During what year shown was the average number of goals per game the lowest?

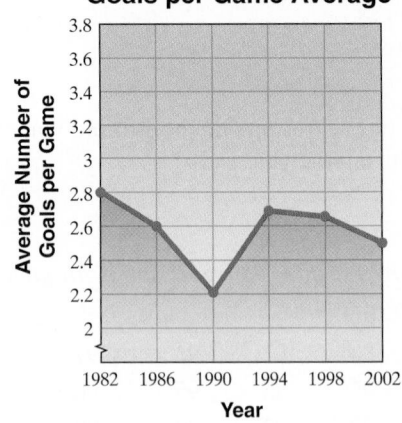

Source: Soccer America Magazine

67. Between 1998 and 2002, did the average number of goals per game increase or decrease?

68. Between 1990 and 1994, did the average number of goals per game increase or decrease?

69. During what year(s) was the average goals per game less than 2.5?

70. During what year(s) was the average goals per game greater than 2.6?

Review

Find each percent. See Sections 5.4 and 5.5.

71. 30% of 12

72. 45% of 120

73. 10% of 62

74. 95% of 50

Write each fraction as a percent. See Section 5.3.

75. $\frac{1}{4}$

76. $\frac{2}{5}$

77. $\frac{17}{50}$

78. $\frac{9}{10}$

Concept Extensions

The following double-line graph shows temperature highs and lows for a week. Use this graph to answer Exercises 79 through 84.

79. What was the high temperature reading on Thursday?

80. What was the low temperature reading on Thursday?

81. What day was the temperature the lowest? What was this low temperature?

82. What day of the week was the temperature the highest? What was this high temperature?

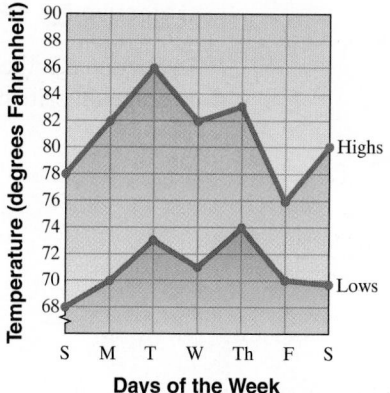

83. On what day of the week was the difference between the high temperature and the low temperature the greatest? What was this difference in temperature?

84. On what day of the week was the difference between the high temperature and the low temperature the least? What was this difference in temperature?

85. True or false? With a bar graph, the width of the bar is just as important as the height of the bar. Explain your answer.

7.2 READING CIRCLE GRAPHS

Objective **A** Reading Circle Graphs

In Section 5.2, the following **circle graph** was shown. This particular graph shows the average favorite cookie for every 100 people.

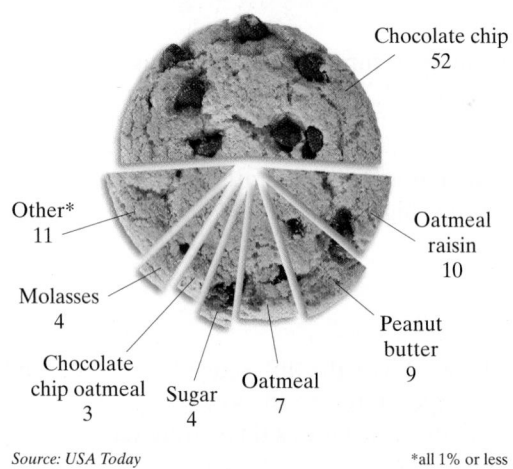

Chocolate chip
52

Other*
11

Oatmeal
raisin
10

Molasses
4

Peanut
butter
9

Chocolate
chip oatmeal
3

Sugar
4

Oatmeal
7

Source: USA Today   *all 1% or less

Each sector of the graph (shaped like a piece of pie) shows a category and the relative size of the category. In other words, the most popular cookie is the chocolate chip cookie, and it is represented by the largest sector.

EXAMPLE 1 Find the ratio of people preferring chocolate chip cookies to total people. Write the ratio as a fraction in simplest form.

Solution: The ratio is

$$\frac{\text{people preferring chocolate chip}}{\text{total people}} = \frac{52}{100} = \frac{13}{25}$$

Work Practice Problem 1

A circle graph is often used to show percents in different categories, with the whole circle representing 100%.

EXAMPLE 2 Using a Circle Graph

The following circle graph shows the percent of Americans with various numbers of working computers at home. Using the circle graph shown, determine the percent of Americans that have one or more working computers at home.

Number of Working Computers at Home

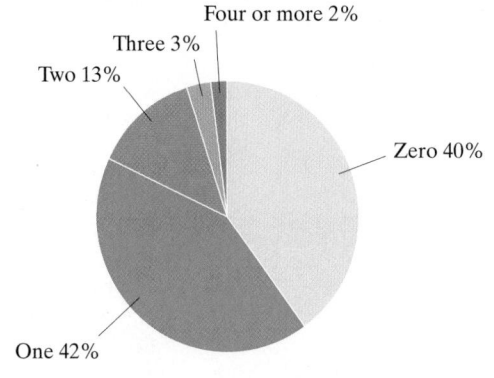

Four or more 2%

Three 3%

Two 13%

Zero 40%

One 42%

Source: UCLA Center for Communication Policy

PRACTICE PROBLEM 1

Find the ratio of people preferring oatmeal raisin cookies to total people. Write the ratio as a fraction in simplest form.

PRACTICE PROBLEM 2

Using the circle graph shown in Example 2, determine the percent of Americans that have two or more working computers at home.

Answers

1. $\frac{1}{10}$, **2.** 18%

500

Solution: To find this percent, we add the percents corresponding to one, two, three, and four or more working computers at home. The percent of Americans that have one or more working computers at home is

$$42\% + 13\% + 3\% + 2\% = 60\%$$

■ **Work Practice Problem 2**

> **Helpful Hint**
>
> Since a circle graph represents a whole, the percents should add to 100% or 1. Notice this is true for Example 2.

EXAMPLE 3 **Finding Percent of Population**

In 2005, the population of the United States is approximately 295,500,000. Using the circle graph from Example 2, find the number of Americans that have no working computers at home.

Solution: We use the percent equation.

amount	=	percent	·	base

$$\text{amount} = 0.40 \cdot 295{,}500{,}000$$
$$= 0.40(295{,}500{,}000) = 118{,}200{,}000$$

Thus, 118,200,000 Americans have no working computer at home.

■ **Work Practice Problem 3**

✔ **Concept Check** Can the following data be represented by a circle graph? Why or why not?

Responses to the Question, "In Which Activities Are You Involved?"	
Intramural sports	60%
On-campus job	42%
Fraternity/sorority	27%
Academic clubs	21%
Music programs	14%

Objective B Drawing Circle Graphs

To draw a circle graph, we use the fact that a whole circle contains 360° (degrees).

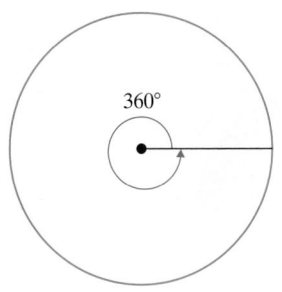

360°

PRACTICE PROBLEM 3

Using the circle graph from Example 2, find the number of Americans that have four or more working computers at home.

Answer
3. 5,910,000 Americans

✔ **Concept Check Answer**

no; the percents add up to more than 100%

PRACTICE PROBLEM 4

Use the data shown to draw a circle graph.

Freshmen	30%
Sophomores	27%
Juniors	25%
Seniors	18%

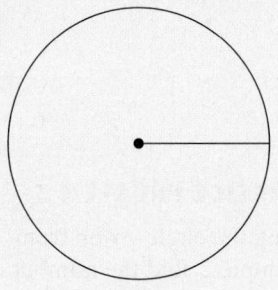

EXAMPLE 4 **Drawing Circle Graph for U.S. Armed Forces Personnel**

The following table shows the percent of U.S. armed forces personnel that are in each branch of service. (*Source:* U.S. Department of Defense)

Branch of Service	Percent
Army	33
Navy	27
Marine Corps	12
Air Force	25
Coast Guard	3

Draw a circle graph showing this data.

Solution: First we find the number of degrees in each sector representing each branch of service. Remember that the whole circle contains 360°. (We will round degrees to the nearest whole.)

Sector	Degrees in Each Sector
Army	33% × 360° = 0.33 × 360° = 118.8° ≈ 119°
Navy	27% × 360° = 0.27 × 360° = 97.2° ≈ 97°
Marine Corps	12% × 360° = 0.12 × 360° = 43.2° ≈ 43°
Air Force	25% × 360° = 0.25 × 360° = 90° = 90°
Coast Guard	3% × 360° = 0.03 × 360° = 10.8° ≈ 11°

Next we draw a circle and mark its center. Then we draw a line from the center of the circle to the circle itself.

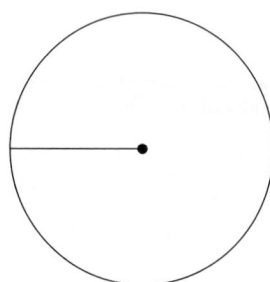

To construct the sectors, we will use a **protractor.** We place the hole in the protractor over the center of the circle. Then we adjust the protractor so that 0° on the protractor is aligned with the line that we drew.

It makes no difference which sector we draw first. To construct the "Army" sector, we find 119° on the protractor and mark our circle. Then we remove the protractor and use this mark to draw a second line from the center to the circle itself.

Answer

4.

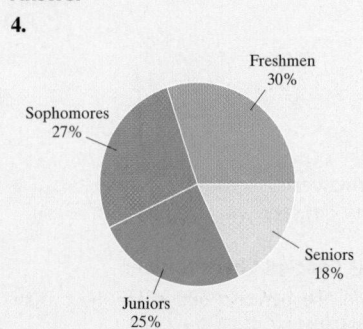

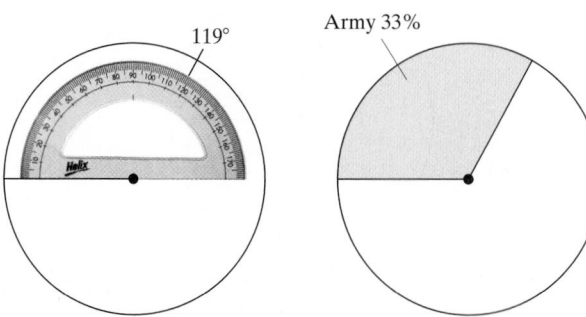

To construct the "Navy" sector, we follow the same procedure as above, except that we line up 0° with the second line we drew and mark the protractor at 97°.

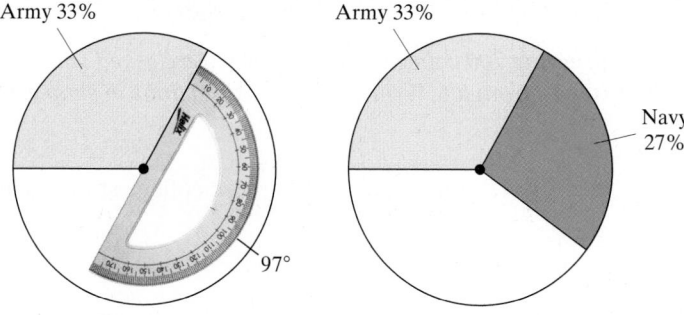

We continue in this manner until the circle graph is complete.

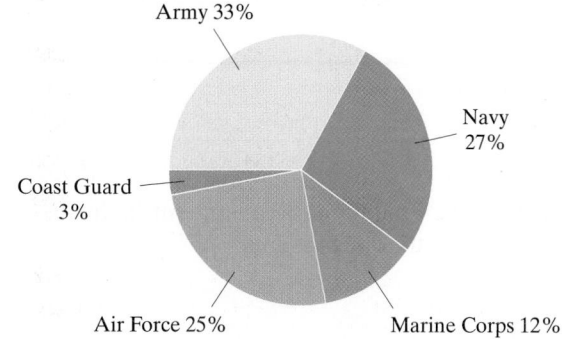

🔲 **Work Practice Problem 4**

✔Concept Check True or false? The larger a sector in a circle graph, the larger the percent of the total it represents. Explain your answer.

FOR EXTRA HELP

Student Solutions Manual

PH Math/Tutor Center

CD/Video for Review

Math XL
MathXL®

MyMathLab
MyMathLab

Objective 🅐 *The following circle graph is a result of surveying 700 college students. They were asked where they live while attending college. Use this graph to answer Exercises 1 through 6. Write all ratios as fractions in simplest form. See Example 1.*

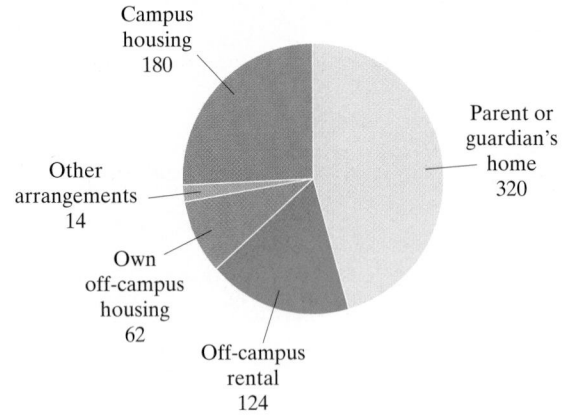

Campus housing 180

Parent or guardian's home 320

Other arrangements 14

Own off-campus housing 62

Off-campus rental 124

1. Where do most of these college students live?

2. Besides the category "Other Arrangements," where do least of these college students live?

3. Find the ratio of students living in campus housing to total students.

4. Find the ratio of students living in off-campus rentals to total students.

5. Find the ratio of students living in campus housing to students living in a parent or guardian's home.

6. Find the ratio of students living in off-campus rentals to students living in a parent or guardian's home.

The following circle graph shows the percent of the land area of the continents of Earth. Use this graph for Exercises 7 through 14. See Examples 2 and 3.

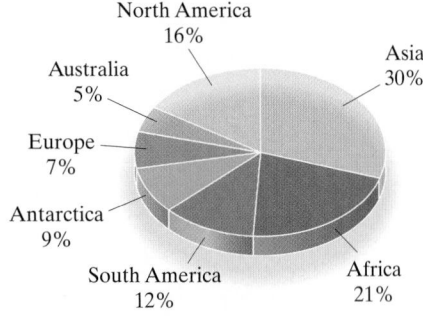

North America 16%

Australia 5%

Europe 7%

Antarctica 9%

South America 12%

Africa 21%

Asia 30%

Source: National Geographic Society

7. Which continent is the largest?

8. Which continent is the smallest?

9. What percent of the land on Earth is accounted for by Asia and Europe together?

10. What percent of the land on Earth is accounted for by North and South America?

The total amount of land on Earth is approximately 57,000,000 square miles. Use the graph to find the area of the continents given in Exercises 11 through 14.

11. Asia

12. South America

13. Australia

14. Europe

The following circle graph shows the percent of the types of books available at Midway Memorial Library. Use this graph for Exercises 15 through 24. See Examples 2 and 3.

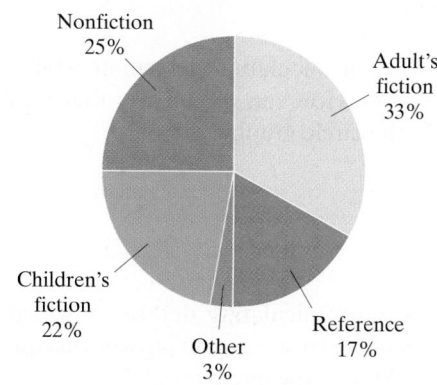

Nonfiction 25%

Adult's fiction 33%

Children's fiction 22%

Other 3%

Reference 17%

15. What percent of books are classified as some type of fiction?

16. What percent of books are nonfiction or reference?

17. What is the second-largest category of books?

18. What is the third-largest category of books?

If this library has 125,600 books, find how many books are in each category given in Exercises 19 through 24.

19. Nonfiction

20. Reference

21. Children's fiction

22. Adult's fiction

23. Reference or other

24. Nonfiction or other

Objective B *Draw a circle graph to represent the information given in each table. See Example 4.*

25.

2004 Light Vehicle Sales by Vehicle Origin	
Country of Origin	**Percent**
United States	58
Asia	36
Europe	6
(*Source:* Ward's AutoInfoBank)	

26.

Number of Times the "Are We There Yet?" Question Is Asked to Parents During Road Trips:	
Never	20%
Once	11%
2–5 times	36%
6–10 times	14%
More than 10 times	19%
(*Source:* KRC Research for Goodyear Tire & Rubber Co.)	

Review

Write the prime factorization of each number. See Section 2.2.

27. 20   **28.** 25   **29.** 40   **30.** 16   **31.** 85   **32.** 105

Concept Extensions

The following circle graph shows the relative sizes of the great oceans.

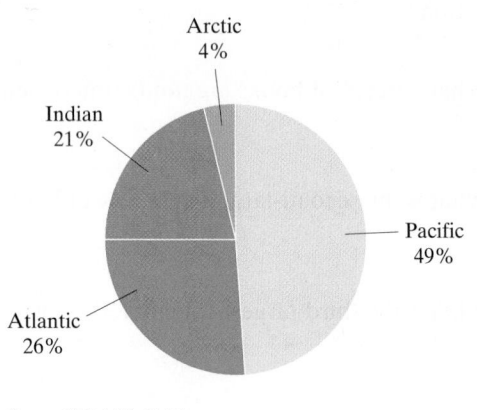

Arctic 4%

Indian 21%

Pacific 49%

Atlantic 26%

Source: Philip's World Atlas

33. Without calculating, determine which ocean is the largest. How can you answer this question by looking at the circle graph?

34. Without calculating, determine which ocean is the smallest. How can you answer this question by looking at the circle graph?

These oceans together make up 264,489,800 square kilometers of the Earth's surface. Find the square kilometers for each ocean.

35. Pacific Ocean   **36.** Atlantic Ocean   **37.** Indian Ocean   **38.** Arctic Ocean

Answer the question. See the Concept Check in this section.

39. True or false? The smaller a sector in a circle graph, the smaller the percent of the total it represents.

40. Can the data below be represented by a circle graph?

Type of Ice Cream Preferred:	
Vanilla	50%
Chocolate	46%

Explain.

Reading Graphs

The following pictograph shows the average number of pounds of beef and veal consumed per person per year in the United States. Use this graph to answer Exercises 1 through 4.

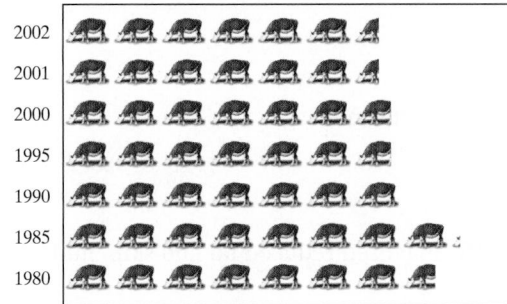

Beef and Veal Consumption

2002
2001
2000
1995
1990
1985
1980

Each 🐖 represents 10 pounds

Source: U.S. Department of Agriculture

1. Approximate the number of pounds of beef and veal consumed per person in 1995.

2. Approximate the number of pounds of beef and veal consumed per person in 1980.

3. How much more beef was consumed in 1980 than in 2002?

4. In what year(s) was the number of pounds consumed the least?

The following bar graph shows the highest U.S. dams. Use this graph to answer Exercises 5 through 8.

5. Name the U.S. dam with the greatest height and estimate its height.

6. Name the U.S. dam whose height is between 625 and 650 feet and estimate its height.

7. Estimate how much higher the Hoover Dam is than the Glen Canyon Dam.

8. How many U.S. dams have heights over 700 feet?

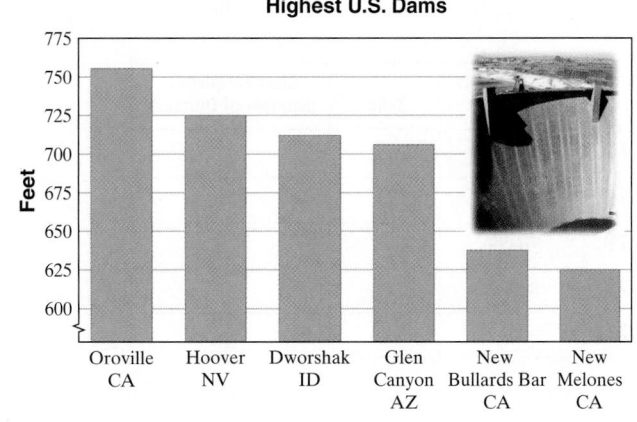

Highest U.S. Dams

Feet: 775, 750, 725, 700, 675, 650, 625, 600

Oroville CA · Hoover NV · Dworshak ID · Glen Canyon AZ · New Bullards Bar CA · New Melones CA

Source: Committee on Register of Dams

The following line graph shows the daily high temperatures for 1 week in Annapolis, Maryland. Use this graph to answer Exercises 9 through 12.

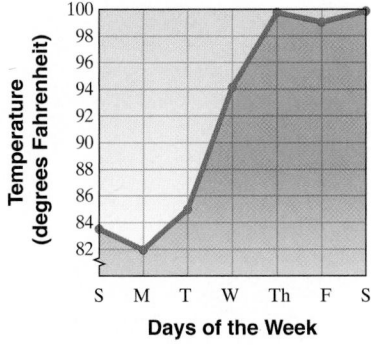

Temperature (degrees Fahrenheit): 100, 98, 96, 94, 92, 90, 88, 86, 84, 82

S M T W Th F S

Days of the Week

9. Name the day(s) of the week with the highest temperature and give that high temperature.

10. Name the day(s) of the week with the lowest temperature and give that low temperature.

11. On what days of the week was the temperature less than 90° Fahrenheit?

12. On what days of the week was the temperature greater than 90° Fahrenheit?

Answers

1. _____

2. _____

3. _____

4. _____

5. _____

6. _____

7. _____

8. _____

9. _____

10. _____

11. _____

12. _____

507

13. _____

14. _____

15. _____

16. _____

The following circle graph shows the type of beverage milk consumed in the United States. Use this graph for Exercises 13 through 16. If a store in Kerrville, Texas, sells 200 quart containers of milk per week, estimate how many quart containers are sold in each category below.

Types of Beverage Milk Consumed

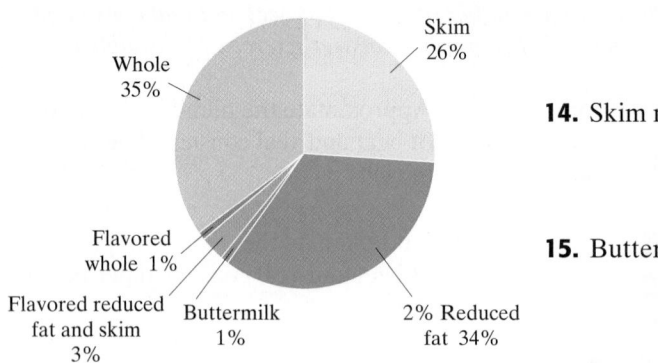

Source: U.S. Department of Agriculture

13. Whole milk

14. Skim milk

15. Buttermilk

16. Flavored reduced fat and skim milk

17. see table

18. see table

19. see table

20. see table

21. see table

22. see graph

The following list shows weekly quiz scores for a student in basic college mathematics. Use this list to complete the frequency distribution table.

50	80	71	83	86
67	89	93	88	97
	53	90		
75	80	78	93	99

	Class Intervals (Scores)	Tally	Class Frequency (Number of Quizzes)
17.	50–59		
18.	60–69		
19.	70–79		
20.	80–89		
21.	90–99		

22. Use the table from Exercises 17 through 21 to construct a histogram.

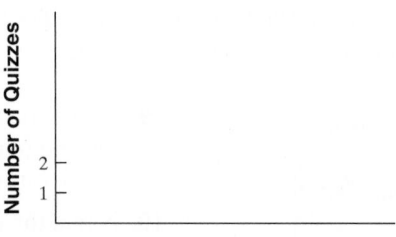

7.3 MEAN, MEDIAN, AND MODE

Objectives

A Find the Mean of a List of Numbers.

B Find the Median of a List of Numbers.

C Find the Mode of a List of Numbers.

Objective **A** Finding the Mean

Sometimes we want to summarize data by displaying them in a graph, but sometimes it is also desirable to be able to describe a set of data, or a set of numbers, by a single "middle" number. Three such **measures of central tendency** are the **mean**, the **median**, and the **mode**.

The most common measure of central tendency is the mean (sometimes called the "arithmetic mean" or the "average"). Recall that we first introduced finding the average of a list of numbers in Section 1.7.

> The **mean (average)** of a set of number items is the sum of the items divided by the number of items.
>
> $$\text{mean} = \frac{\text{sum of items}}{\text{number of items}}$$

EXAMPLE 1 Finding the Mean Time in an Experiment

Seven students in a psychology class conducted an experiment on mazes. Each student was given a pencil and asked to successfully complete the same maze. The timed results are below:

Student	Ann	Thanh	Carlos	Jesse	Melinda	Ramzi	Dayni
Time (Seconds)	13.2	11.8	10.7	16.2	15.9	13.8	18.5

a. Who completed the maze in the shortest time? Who completed the maze in the longest time?

b. Find the mean time.

c. How many students took longer than the mean time? How many students took shorter than the mean time?

Solution:

a. Carlos completed the maze in 10.7 seconds, the shortest time. Dayni completed the maze in 18.5 seconds, the longest time.

b. To find the mean (or average), we find the sum of the number items and divide by 7, the number of items.

$$\text{mean} = \frac{13.2 + 11.8 + 10.7 + 16.2 + 15.9 + 13.8 + 18.5}{7}$$

$$= \frac{100.1}{7} = 14.3$$

c. Three students, Jesse, Melinda, and Dayni, had times longer than the mean time. Four students, Ann, Thanh, Carlos, and Ramzi, had times shorter than the mean time.

▢ **Work Practice Problem 1**

✔ Concept Check Estimate the mean of the following set of data:

5, 10, 10, 10, 10, 15

Often in college, the calculation of a **grade point average** (GPA) is a **weighted mean** and is calculated as shown in Example 2.

PRACTICE PROBLEM 1

Find the mean of the following test scores: 77, 85, 86, 91, and 88.

Answer
1. 85.4

✔ **Concept Check Answer**
10

509

PRACTICE PROBLEM 2

Find the grade point average if the following grades were earned in one semester.

Grade	Credit Hours
A	2
C	4
B	5
D	2
A	2

EXAMPLE 2 **Calculating Grade Point Average (GPA)**

The following grades were earned by a student during one semester. Find the student's grade point average.

Course	Grade	Credit Hours
College mathematics	A	3
Biology	B	3
English	A	3
PE	C	1
Social studies	D	2

Solution: To calculate the grade point average, we need to know the point values for the different possible grades. The point values of grades commonly used in colleges and universities are given below:

A: 4, B: 3, C: 2, D: 1, F: 0

Now, to find the grade point average, we multiply the number of credit hours for each course by the point value of each grade. The grade point average is the sum of these products divided by the sum of the credit hours.

Course	Grade	Point Value of Grade	Credit Hours	Point Value · Credit Hours
College mathematics	A	4	3	12
Biology	B	3	3	9
English	A	4	3	12
PE	C	2	1	2
Social studies	D	1	2	2
		Totals:	12	37

$$\text{grade point average} = \frac{37}{12} \approx 3.08 \text{ rounded to two decimal places}$$

The student earned a grade point average of 3.08.

◼ **Work Practice Problem 2**

Objective **B** Finding the Median

You may have noticed that a very low number or a very high number can affect the mean of a list of numbers. Because of this, you may sometimes want to use another measure of central tendency. A second measure of central tendency is called the **median.** The median of a list of numbers is not affected by a low or high number in the list.

> The **median** of a set of numbers in numerical order is the middle number. If the number of items is odd, the median is the middle number. If the number of items is even, the median is the mean of the two middle numbers.

PRACTICE PROBLEM 3

Find the median of the list of numbers: 7, 9, 13, 23, 24, 35, 38, 41, 43

EXAMPLE 3 Find the median of the following list of numbers:

25, 54, 56, 57, 60, 71, 98

Solution: Because this list is in numerical order, the median is the middle number, 57.

◼ **Work Practice Problem 3**

Answers

2. 2.73, **3.** 24

EXAMPLE 4 Find the median of the following list of scores: 67, 91, 75, 86, 55, 91

Solution: First we list the scores in numerical order and then find the middle number.

55, 67, 75, 86, 91, 91

Since there is an even number of scores, there are two middle numbers, 75 and 86. The median is the mean of the two middle numbers.

$$\text{median} = \frac{75 + 86}{2} = 80.5$$

The median is 80.5.

◻ **Work Practice Problem 4**

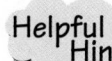

Helpful Hint Don't forget to write the numbers in order from smallest to largest before finding the median.

Objective **C** **Finding the Mode**

The last common measure of central tendency is called the **mode.**

> The **mode** of a set of numbers is the number that occurs most often. (It is possible for a set of numbers to have more than one mode or to have no mode.)

EXAMPLE 5 Find the mode of the list of numbers:

11, 14, 14, 16, 31, 56, 65, 77, 77, 78, 79

Solution: There are two numbers that occur the most often. They are 14 and 77. This list of numbers has two modes, 14 and 77.

◻ **Work Practice Problem 5**

EXAMPLE 6 Find the median and the mode of the following set of numbers. These numbers were high temperatures for 14 consecutive days in a city in Montana.

76, 80, 85, 86, 89, 87, 82, 77, 76, 79, 82, 89, 89, 92

Solution: First we write the numbers in numerical order.

76, 76, 77, 79, 80, 82, 82, 85, 86, 87, 89, 89, 89, 92

Since there is an even number of items, the median is the mean of the two middle numbers, 82 and 85.

$$\text{median} = \frac{82 + 85}{2} = 83.5$$

The mode is 89, since 89 occurs most often.

◻ **Work Practice Problem 6**

✔**Concept Check** True or false? Every set of numbers *must* have a mean, median, and mode. Explain your answer.

Helpful Hint Don't forget that it is possible for a list of numbers to have no mode. For example, the list

2, 4, 5, 6, 8, 9

has no mode. There is no number or numbers that occur more often than the others.

PRACTICE PROBLEM 4

Find the median of the list of scores:

43, 89, 78, 65, 95, 95, 88, 71

PRACTICE PROBLEM 5

Find the mode of the list of numbers:

9, 10, 10, 13, 15, 15, 15, 17, 18, 18, 20

PRACTICE PROBLEM 6

Find the median and the mode of the list of numbers:

26, 31, 15, 15, 26, 30, 16, 18, 15, 35

Answers
4. 83, **5.** 15, **6.** median: 22; mode: 15

✔ **Concept Check Answer**

false; a set of numbers may have no mode.

Mental Math

State the mean for each list of numbers.

1. 3, 5   **2.** 10, 20   **3.** 1, 3, 5   **4.** 7, 7, 7

7.3 EXERCISE SET

FOR EXTRA HELP

Student Solutions Manual   PH Math/Tutor Center   CD/Video for Review    MathXL®    MyMathLab

Objectives Ⓐ Ⓑ Ⓒ **Mixed Practice** *For each set of numbers, find the mean, the median, and the mode. If necessary, round the mean to one decimal place. See Examples 1 and 3 through 6.*

1. 21, 28, 16, 42, 38   **2.** 42, 35, 36, 40, 50   **3.** 7.6, 8.2, 8.2, 9.6, 5.7, 9.1   **4.** 4.9, 7.1, 6.8, 6.8, 5.3, 4.9

5. 0.2, 0.3, 0.5, 0.6, 0.6, 0.9, 0.2, 0.7, 1.1   **6.** 0.6, 0.6, 0.8, 0.4, 0.5, 0.3, 0.7, 0.8, 0.1

7. 231, 543, 601, 293, 588, 109, 334, 268   **8.** 451, 356, 478, 776, 892, 500, 467, 780

The eight tallest buildings in the world are listed in the following table. Use this table to answer Exercises 9 through 12. If necessary, round results to one decimal place. See Examples 1 and 3 through 6.

9. Find the mean height of the five tallest buildings.

10. Find the median height of the five tallest buildings.

11. Find the median height of the eight tallest buildings.

12. Find the mean height of the eight tallest buildings.

Building	Height (in Feet)
Petronas Tower 1, Kuala Lumpur	1483
Petronas Tower 2, Kuala Lumpur	1483
Sears Tower, Chicago	1450
Jin Mao Building, Shanghai	1381
Citic Plaza, Guangzhou	1283
Shun Hing Square, Shenzhen	1260
Empire State Building, New York	1250
Central Plaza, Hong Kong	1227
(*Source:* Council on Tall Buildings and Urban Habitat)	

13. Given the building heights, explain how you know, without calculating, that the answer to Exercise 10 is more than the answer to Exercise 11.

14. Given the building heights, explain how you know, without calculating, that the answer to Exercise 12 is less than the answer to Exercise 9.

512

For Exercises 15 through 18, the grades are given for a student for a particular semester. Find the grade point average. If necessary, round the grade point average to the nearest hundredth. See Example 2.

15.

Grade	Credit Hours
B	3
C	3
A	4
C	4

16.

Grade	Credit Hours
D	1
F	1
C	4
B	5

17.

Grade	Credit Hours
A	3
A	3
B	4
B	1
B	2

18.

Grade	Credit Hours
B	2
B	2
A	3
C	3
B	3

During an experiment, the following times (in seconds) were recorded:

$7.8, 6.9, 7.5, 4.7, 6.9, 7.0$

19. Find the mean. Round to the nearest tenth.

20. Find the median.

21. Find the mode.

In a mathematics class, the following test scores were recorded for a student: $86, 95, 91, 74, 77, 85.$

22. Find the mean. Round to the nearest hundredth.

23. Find the median.

24. Find the mode.

The following pulse rates were recorded for a group of 15 students: $78, 80, 66, 68, 71, 64, 82, 71, 70, 65, 70, 75, 77, 86, 72.$

25. Find the mean.

26. Find the median.

27. Find the mode.

28. How many rates were higher than the mean?

29. How many rates were lower than the mean?

Review

Write each fraction in simplest form. See Section 2.3.

30. $\dfrac{12}{20}$ **31.** $\dfrac{6}{18}$ **32.** $\dfrac{4}{36}$ **33.** $\dfrac{18}{30}$ **34.** $\dfrac{35}{100}$ **35.** $\dfrac{55}{75}$

Concept Extensions

Find the missing numbers in each set of numbers.

36. 16, 18, _____, _____, _____. The mode is 21. The median is 20.

37. _____, _____, _____, 40, _____. The mode is 35. The median is 37. The mean is 38.

38. Write a list of numbers for which you feel the median would be a better measure of central tendency than the mean.

STUDY SKILLS BUILDER

Tips for Studying for an Exam

To prepare for an exam, try the following study techniques.

- Start the study process days before your exam.
- Make sure that you are up-to-date on your assignments.
- If there is a topic that you are unsure of, use one of the many resources that are available to you. For example,

  See your instructor.

  Visit a learning resource center on campus.

  Read the textbook material and examples on the topic.

  View a video on the topic.

- Reread your notes and carefully review the Chapter Highlights at the end of any chapter.
- Work the review exercises at the end of the chapter. Check your answers and correct any mistakes. If you have trouble, use a resource listed above.
- Find a quiet place to take the Chapter Test found at the end of the chapter. Do not use any resources when taking this sample test. This way, you will have a clear indication of how prepared you are for your exam.

Check your answers and make sure that you correct any missed exercises.

- Get lots of rest the night before the exam. It's hard to show how well you know the material if your brain is foggy from lack of sleep.

Good luck and keep a positive attitude.

Let's see how you did on your last exam.

1. How many days before your last exam did you start studying?
2. Were you up-to-date on your assignments at that time or did you need to catch up on assignments?
3. List the most helpful text supplement (if you used one).
4. List the most helpful campus supplement (if you used one).
5. List your process for preparing for a mathematics test.
6. Was this process helpful? In other words, were you satisfied with your performance on your exam?
7. If not, what changes can you make in your process that will make it more helpful to you?

7.4 COUNTING AND INTRODUCTION TO PROBABILITY

Objectives

A Use a Tree Diagram to Count Outcomes.

B Find the Probability of an Event.

Objective **A** Using a Tree Diagram

In our daily conversations, we often talk about the likelihood or the **probability** of a given result occurring. For example:

The *chance* of thundershowers is 70 percent.

What are the *odds* that the Saints will go to the Super Bowl?

What is the *probability* that you will finish cleaning your room today?

Each of these chance happenings—thundershowers, the New Orleans Saints playing in the Super Bowl, and cleaning your room today—is called an **experiment.** The possible results of an experiment are called **outcomes.** For example, flipping a coin is an experiment, and the possible outcomes are heads (H) or tails (T).

One way to picture the outcomes of an experiment is to draw a **tree diagram.** Each outcome is shown on a separate branch. For example, the outcomes of flipping a coin are

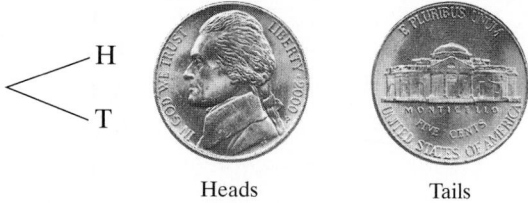

Heads   Tails

EXAMPLE 1 Draw a tree diagram for tossing a coin twice. Then use the diagram to find the number of possible outcomes.

Solution: There are 4 possible outcomes when tossing a coin twice.

First Coin Toss	Second Coin Toss	Outcomes
H	H	H, H
	T	H, T
T	H	T, H
	T	T, T

Work Practice Problem 1

PRACTICE PROBLEM 1

Draw a tree diagram for tossing a coin three times. Then use the diagram to find the number of possible outcomes.

Answer

1. 8 outcomes

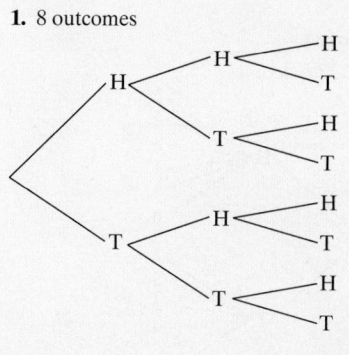

PRACTICE PROBLEM 2

Draw a tree diagram for an experiment consisting of tossing a coin and then rolling a die. Then use the diagram to find the number of possible outcomes.

EXAMPLE 2 Draw a tree diagram for an experiment consisting of rolling a die and then tossing a coin. Then use the diagram to find the number of possible outcomes.

Die

Solution: Recall that a die has six sides and that each side represents a number, 1 through 6.

Roll a Die	Toss a coin	Outcomes
1	H	1, H
	T	1, T
2	H	2, H
	T	2, T
3	H	3, H
	T	3, T
4	H	4, H
	T	4, T
5	H	5, H
	T	5, T
6	H	6, H
	T	6, T

There are 12 possible outcomes for rolling a die and then tossing a coin.

■ **Work Practice Problem 2**

Any number of outcomes considered together are called an **event.** For example, when tossing a coin twice, H, H is an event. The event is tossing heads first and tossing heads second. Another event would be tossing tails first and then heads (T, H), and so on.

Objective B Finding the Probability of an Event

As we mentioned earlier, the **probability of an event is a measure of the chance or likelihood of it occurring.** For example, if a coin is tossed, what is the probability that heads occurs? Since one of two equally likely possible outcomes is heads, the probability is $\frac{1}{2}$.

The Probability of an Event

$$\text{probability of an event} = \frac{\text{number of ways that the event can occur}}{\text{number of possible outcomes}}$$

Helpful Hint

Note from the definition of probability that the probability of an event is always between 0 and 1, inclusive (i.e., including 0 and 1). A probability of 0 means that an event won't occur, and a probability of 1 means that an event is certain to occur.

Answer

2. 12 outcomes

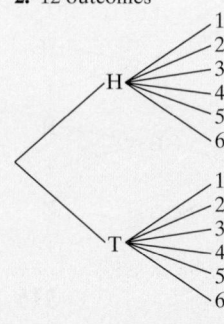

EXAMPLE 3 If a coin is tossed twice, find the probability of tossing heads and then heads (H, H).

Solution: 1 way the event can occur

$$\overbrace{\quad}$$

H, T, H, H, T, H, T, T

$\underbrace{\qquad\qquad\qquad\qquad\qquad}_{\text{4 possible outcomes}}$

probability $= \dfrac{1}{4}$ Number of ways the event can occur
              Number of possible outcomes

The probability of tossing heads and then heads is $\dfrac{1}{4}$.

◉ **Work Practice Problem 3**

PRACTICE PROBLEM 3

If a coin is tossed three times, find the probability of tossing heads, then tails, then tails (H, T, T).

EXAMPLE 4 If a die is rolled one time, find the probability of rolling a 3 or a 4.

Solution: Recall that there are 6 possible outcomes when rolling a die.

2 ways that the event can occur
$\downarrow \quad \downarrow$

possible outcomes: $\underbrace{1, \quad 2, \quad 3, \quad 4, \quad 5, \quad 6}$
                    6 possible outcomes

probability of a 3 or a 4 $= \dfrac{2}{6}$ Number of ways the event can occur
                            Number of possible outcomes

$= \dfrac{1}{3}$ Simplest form

◉ **Work Practice Problem 4**

PRACTICE PROBLEM 4

If a die is rolled one time, find the probability of rolling a 1 or a 2.

✔**Concept Check** Suppose you have calculated a probability of $\dfrac{11}{9}$. How do you know that you have made an error in your calculation?

EXAMPLE 5 Find the probability of choosing a red marble from a box containing 1 red, 1 yellow, and 2 blue marbles.

Solution: 1 way that event can occur
$\downarrow$

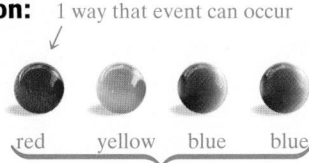

$\underbrace{\text{red} \quad \text{yellow} \quad \text{blue} \quad \text{blue}}$
4 possible outcomes

probability $= \dfrac{1}{4}$

◉ **Work Practice Problem 5**

PRACTICE PROBLEM 5

Use the diagram from Example 5 and find the probability of choosing a blue marble from the box.

Answers

3. $\dfrac{1}{8}$, 4. $\dfrac{1}{3}$, 5. $\dfrac{1}{2}$

✔ **Concept Check Answer**

The number of ways an event can occur can't be larger than the number of possible outcomes.

Mental Math

If a coin is tossed once, find the probability of each event.

1. The coin lands heads up.

2. The coin lands tails up.

If the spinner shown is spun once, find the probability of each event.

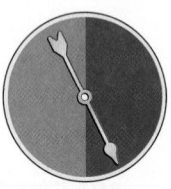

3. The spinner stops on red.

4. The spinner stops on blue.

7.4 EXERCISE SET

FOR EXTRA HELP

Student Solutions Manual   PH Math/Tutor Center   CD/Video for Review   Math XL MathXL®   MyMathLab MyMathLab

Objective Ⓐ *Draw a tree diagram for each experiment. Then use the diagram to find the number of possible outcomes. See Examples 1 and 2.*

1. Choosing a vowel (a, e, i, o, u) and then a number (1, 2, or 3)

2. Choosing a number (1 or 2) and then a vowel (a, e, i, o, u)

3. Spinning Spinner A once

4. Spinning Spinner B once

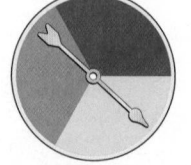

Spinner A   Spinner B

518

5. Spinning Spinner B twice

6. Spinning Spinner A twice

7. Spinning Spinner A and then Spinner B

8. Spinning Spinner B and then Spinner A

9. Tossing a coin and then spinning Spinner B

10. Tossing a coin and then spinning Spinner A

Objective B *If a single die is tossed once, find the probability of each event. See Examples 3 through 5.*

11. A 5

12. A 7

13. A 1 or a 4

14. A 2 or a 3

15. An even number

16. An odd number

17. A number greater than 1

18. A number less than 5

Suppose the spinner shown is spun once. Find the probability of each event. See Examples 3 through 5.

19. The result of the spin is 2.

20. The result of the spin is 3.

21. The result of a spin is 1, 2, or 3.

22. The result of a spin is not 3.

23. The result of the spin is an odd number.

24. The result of the spin is an even number.

If a single choice is made from the bag of marbles shown, find the probability of each event. See Examples 3 through 5.

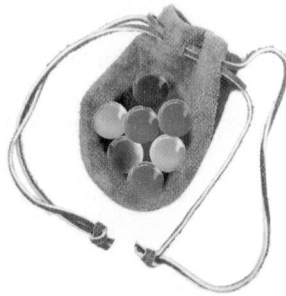

25. A red marble is chosen.

26. A blue marble is chosen.

27. A yellow marble is chosen.

28. A green marble is chosen.

29. A blue or red marble is chosen.

30. A red or yellow marble is chosen.

A new drug is being tested that is supposed to lower blood pressure. This drug was given to 200 people and the results are below.

Lower Blood Pressure	Higher Blood Pressure	Blood Pressure Not Changed
152	38	10

31. If a person is testing this drug, what is the probability that their blood pressure will be higher?

32. If a person is testing this drug, what is the probability that their blood pressure will be lower?

33. If a person is testing this drug, what is the probability that their blood pressure will not change?

34. What is the sum of the answers to exercises 25, 26, and 27? In your own words, explain why.

Review

Perform each indicated operation. See Sections 2.4, 2.5, and 3.3.

35. $\dfrac{1}{2} + \dfrac{1}{3}$

36. $\dfrac{7}{10} - \dfrac{2}{5}$

37. $\dfrac{1}{2} \cdot \dfrac{1}{3}$

38. $\dfrac{7}{10} \div \dfrac{2}{5}$

39. $5 \div \dfrac{3}{4}$

40. $\dfrac{3}{5} \cdot 10$

Concept Extensions

Recall that a deck of cards contains 52 cards. These cards consist of four suits (hearts, spades, clubs, and diamonds) of each of the following: 2, 3, 4, 5, 6, 7, 8, 9, 10, jack, queen, king, and ace. If a card is chosen from a deck of cards, find the probability of each event.

41. The king of hearts

42. The 10 of spades

43. A king

44. A 10

45. A heart

46. A club

47. A red card

48. A king or queen

Two dice are tossed. Find the probability of each sum of the dice. (Hint: Draw a tree diagram of the possibilities of two tosses of a die, and then find the sum of the numbers on each branch.)

49. A sum of 4

50. A sum of 11

51. A sum of 13

52. A sum of 2

Solve. See the Concept Check in this section.

53. In your own words, explain why the probability of an event cannot be greater than 1.

54. In your own words, explain when the probability of an event is 0.

 CHAPTER 7   Group Activity

Sections 7.1, 7.3

This activity may be completed by working in groups or individually.

How often have you read an article in a newspaper or in a magazine that included results from a survey or poll? Surveys seem to have become very popular ways of getting feedback on anything from a political candidate, to a new product, to services offered by a health club. In this activity, you will conduct a survey and analyze the results.

1. Conduct a survey of 30 students in one of your classes. Ask each student to report his or her age.

2. Classify each age according to the following categories: under 20, 20 to 24, 25 to 29, 30 to 39, 40 to 49, and 50 or

over. Tally the number of your survey respondents that fall into each category. Make a bar graph of your results. What does this graph tell you about the ages of your survey respondents?

3. Find the average age of your survey respondents.

4. Find the median age of your survey respondents.

5. Find the mode of the ages of your survey respondents.

6. Compare the mean, median, and mode of your age data. Are these measures similar? Which is largest? Which is smallest? If there is a noticeable difference between any of these measures, can you explain why?

Chapter 7 Vocabulary Check

Fill in each blank with one of the words or phrases listed below.

outcomes	bar	experiment	mean	tree diagram
pictograph	line	class interval	median	probability
histogram	circle	class frequency	mode	

1. A _____ graph presents data using vertical or horizontal bars.

2. The _____ of a set of number items is $\dfrac{\text{sum of items}}{\text{number of items}}$.

3. The possible results of an experiment are the _____.

4. A _____ is a graph in which pictures or symbols are used to visually present data.

5. The _____ of a set of numbers is the number that occurs most often.

6. A _____ graph displays information with a line that connects data points.

7. The _____ of an ordered set of numbers is the middle number.

8. A _____ is one way to picture and count outcomes.

9. An _____ is an activity being considered, such as tossing a coin or rolling a die.

10. In a _____ graph, each section (shaped like a piece of pie) shows a category and the relative size of the category.

11. The _____ of an event is $\dfrac{\text{number of ways that the event can occur}}{\text{number of possible outcomes}}$.

12. A _____ is a special bar graph in which the width of each bar represents a _____ and the height of each bar represents the _____.

Helpful Hint

Are you preparing for your test? Don't forget to take the Chapter 7 Test on page 530. Then check your answers at the back of your text and use the Chapter Test Prep Video CD to see the fully worked-out solutions to any of the exercises you want to review.

7 Chapter Highlights

DEFINITIONS AND CONCEPTS	**EXAMPLES**
Section 7.1 Reading Pictographs, Bar Graphs, Histograms, and Line Graphs	

A **pictograph** is a graph in which pictures or symbols are used to visually present data.

A **line graph** displays information with a line that connects data points.

A **bar graph** presents data using vertical or horizontal bars.

The bar graph on the right shows the number of acres of wheat harvested in 1996 for leading states.

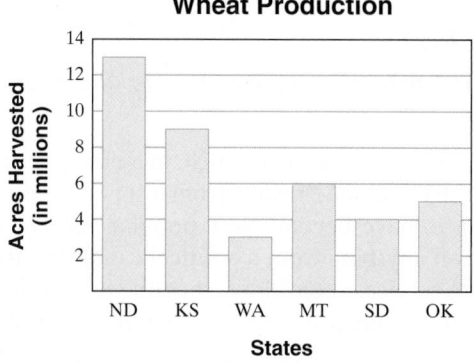

Wheat Production

Source: U.S. Department of Agriculture

1. Approximately how many acres of wheat were harvested in Kansas?

9,000,000 acres

DEFINITIONS AND CONCEPTS	**EXAMPLES**
Section 7.1 Reading Pictographs, Bar Graphs, Histograms, and Line Graphs (*continued*)	

	2. About how many more acres of wheat were harvested in North Dakota than South Dakota?
	$$\begin{aligned} & 13 \text{ million} \\ - \;& \;\;4 \text{ million} \\ \hline & \;\;9 \text{ million} \quad \text{or } 9{,}000{,}000 \text{ acres} \end{aligned}$$
A **histogram** is a special bar graph in which the width of each bar represents a **class interval** and the height of each bar represents the **class frequency.** The histogram on the right shows student quiz scores.	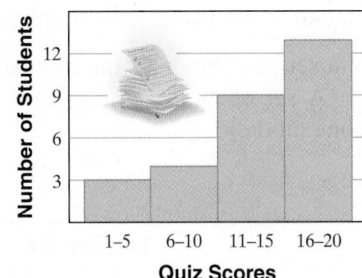
	1. How many students received a score of 6–10?
	4 students
	2. How many students received a score of 11–20?
	9 + 13 = 22 students

Section 7.2 Reading Circle Graphs	

In a **circle graph,** each section (shaped like a piece of pie) shows a category and the relative size of the category.	**Tornado Wind Speeds**
The circle graph on the right classifies tornadoes by wind speed.	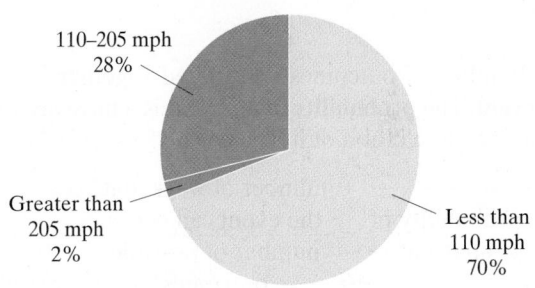
	Source: National Oceanic and Atmospheric Administration
	1. What percent of tornadoes have wind speeds of 110 mph or greater?
	28% + 2% = 30%
	2. If there were 1235 tornadoes in the United States in 1995, how many of these might we expect to have had wind speeds less than 110 mph? Find 70% of 1235.
	$70\%(1235) = 0.70(1235) = 864.5 \approx 865$
	Around 865 tornadoes would be expected to have had wind speeds of less than 110 mph.

DEFINITIONS AND CONCEPTS	**EXAMPLES**

Section 7.3   Mean, Median, and Mode

The **mean** (or **average**) of a set of number items is

$$\text{mean} = \frac{\text{sum of items}}{\text{number of items}}$$

The **median** of a set of numbers in numerical order is the middle number. If the number of items is even, the median is the mean of the two middle numbers.

The **mode** of a set of numbers is the number that occurs most often. (A set of numbers may have no mode or more than one mode.)

Find the mean, median, and mode of the following set of numbers: 33, 35, 35, 43, 68, 68

$$\text{mean} = \frac{33 + 35 + 35 + 43 + 68 + 68}{6} = 47$$

The median is the mean of the two middle numbers, 35 and 43

$$\text{median} = \frac{35 + 43}{2} = 39$$

There are two modes because there are two numbers that occur twice:

35 and 68

Section 7.4   Counting and Introduction to Probability

An **experiment** is an activity being considered, such as tossing a coin or rolling a die. The possible results of an experiment are the **outcomes**. A **tree diagram** is one way to picture and count outcomes.

Draw a tree diagram for tossing a coin and then choosing a number from 1 to 4.

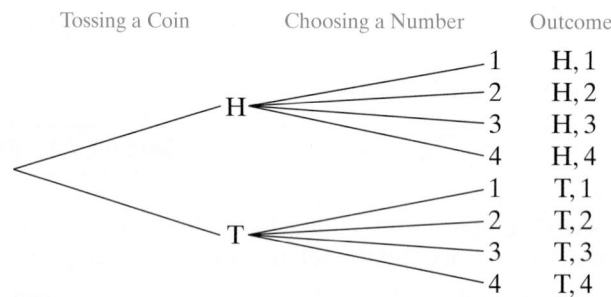

Any number of outcomes considered together is called an **event**. The **probability** of an event is a measure of the chance or likelihood of it occurring.

$$\begin{array}{c}\text{probability of} \\ \text{an event}\end{array} = \frac{\begin{array}{c}\text{number of ways that} \\ \text{the event can occur}\end{array}}{\begin{array}{c}\text{number of possible} \\ \text{outcomes}\end{array}}$$

Find the probability of tossing a coin twice and tails occurring each time.

1 way the event can occur

HH,   HT,   TH,   TT

4 possible outcomes

$$\text{probability} = \frac{1}{4}$$

STUDY SKILLS BUILDER

Are You Prepared for a Test on Chapter 7?

Below I have listed some *common trouble areas* for students in Chapter 7. After studying for your test—but before taking your test—read these.

• Do you remember that a set of numbers can have no mode, 1 mode, or even more than 1 mode?

    2, 5, 8, 9   no mode
    2, 2, 8, 9   mode: 2
    2, 2, 3, 3, 5, 7, 7   mode: 2, 3, 7

• Do you remember how to find the median of an even-numbered set of numbers?

    2, 5, 8, 9 $\dfrac{5 + 8}{2} = 6.5$ The median is the average of the two "middle" numbers.

• Don't forget that the probability of an event is always between 0 and 1 inclusive (including 0 and 1).

• What is the probability of an event that won't occur? 0

• What is the probability of an event that is certain to occur? 1

7 CHAPTER REVIEW

(7.1) *The following pictograph shows the number of new homes constructed in 2003, by region. Use this graph to answer Exercises 1 through 6.*

2003 Housing Starts by Region of United States

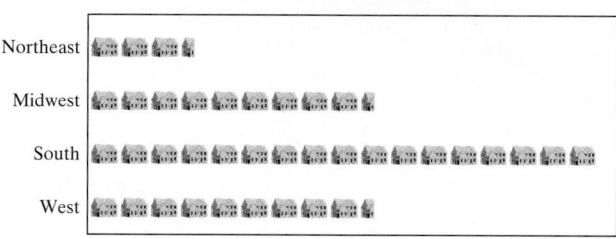

Each 🏠 represents 50,000 homes

Source: U.S. Census Bureau

1. How many housing starts were there in the Midwest in 2003?

2. How many housing starts were there in the Northeast in 2003?

3. Find the total housing starts in the Midwest and Northeast.

4. How many more housing starts were in the South than in the West?

5. Which region(s) had 400,000 or more housing starts?

6. Which region(s) had fewer than 400,000 housing starts?

The following bar graph shows the percent of persons age 25 or over who completed four or more years of college. Use this graph to answer Exercises 7 through 10.

Four or More Years of College by Persons Age 25 or Over

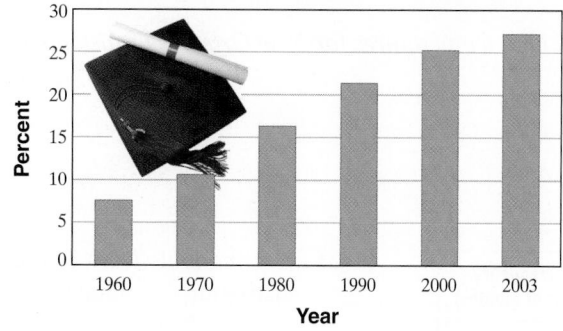

Source: U.S. Census Bureau

7. Approximate the percent of persons who completed four or more years of college in 1960.

8. What year shown had the greatest percent of persons completing four or more years of college?

9. What years shown had 15% or more of persons completing four or more years of college?

10. Describe any patterns you notice in this graph.

The following line graph shows the average price of a 30-second television advertisement during the Super Bowl for the years shown. Use this graph to answer Exercises 11 through 15.

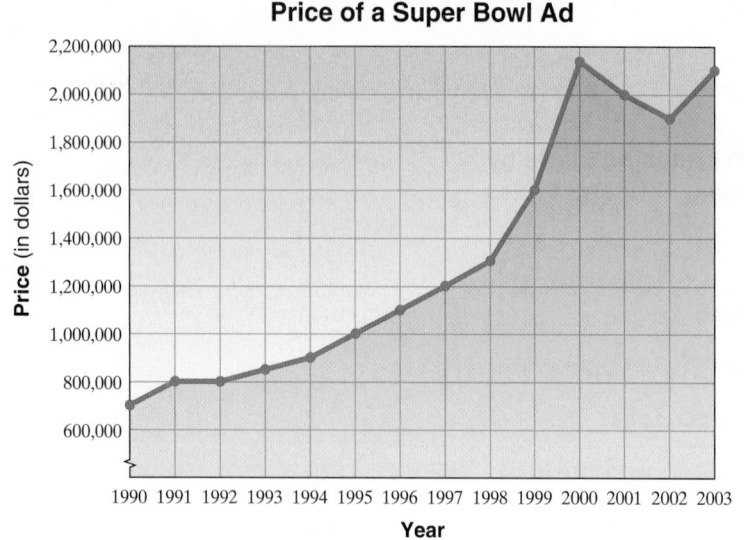

Price of a Super Bowl Ad

Sources: Nielsen Media Research and *Advertising Age* research

11. Approximate the price of a Super Bowl ad in 2003.

12. Approximate the price of a Super Bowl ad in 1997.

13. Between which two years did the price of a Super Bowl ad *not* increase?

14. Between which two years did the price of a Super Bowl ad increase the most?

15. During which years was the price of a Super Bowl ad *less than* $1,000,000?

The following histogram shows the hours worked per week by the employees of Southern Star Furniture. Use this histogram to answer Exercises 16 through 19.

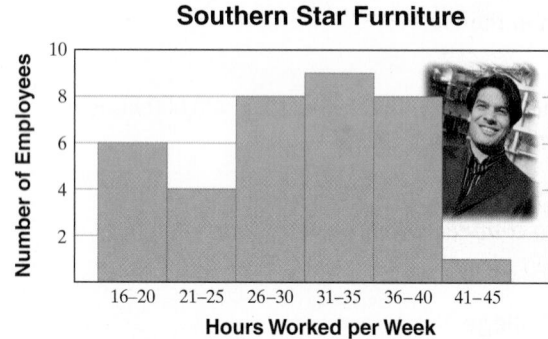

Southern Star Furniture

16. How many employees work 21–25 hours per week?

17. How many employees work 41–45 hours per week?

18. How many employees work 36 hours or more per week?

19. How many employees work 30 hours or less per week?

Following is a list of monthly record high temperatures for New Orleans, Louisiana. Use this list to complete the frequency distribution table below.

83	96	101	92
85	100	92	102
89	101	87	84

	Class Intervals (Temperatures)	Tally	Class Frequency (Number of Months)
20.	80°–89°		
21.	90°–99°		
22.	100°–109°		

23. Use the table from Exercises 20, 21, and 22 to draw a histogram.

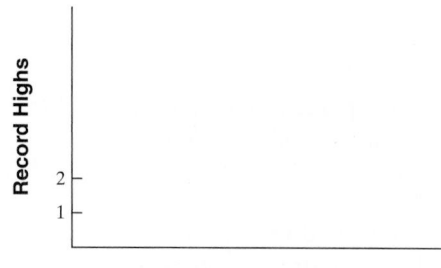

Record Highs

Temperatures

(7.2) *The following circle graph shows a family's $4000 monthly budget. Use this graph to answer Exercises 24 through 30. Write all ratios as fractions in simplest form.*

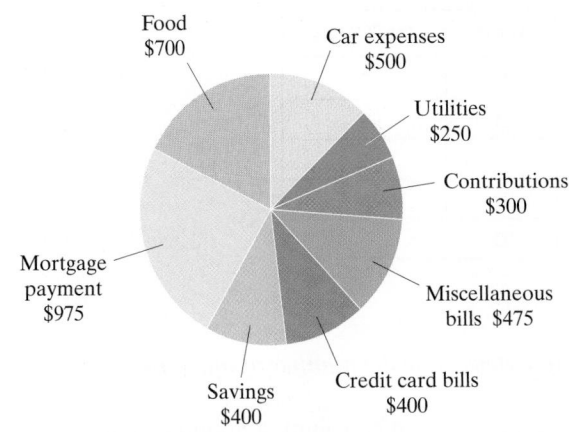

24. What is the largest budget item?

25. What is the smallest budget item?

26. How much money is budgeted for the mortgage payment and utilities?

27. How much money is budgeted for savings and contributions?

28. Find the ratio of the mortgage payment to the total monthly budget.

29. Find the ratio of food to the total monthly budget.

30. Find the ratio of car expenses to food.

The following circle graph shows the percent of the 50 states with various rural interstate highway speed limits in 2000. Use this graph to determine the number of states with each speed limit in Exercises 31 through 34.

Percent of States with Rural Interstate Highway Speed Limit

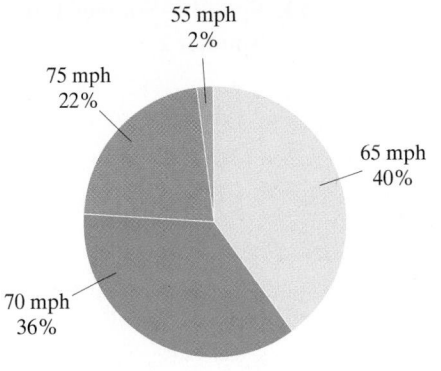

Source: Insurance Institute for Highway Safety

31. How many states had a rural interstate highway speed limit of 65 mph?

32. How many states had a rural interstate highway speed limit of 75 mph?

33. How many states had a rural interstate highway speed limit of 55 mph?

34. How many states had a rural interstate highway speed limit of 70 mph or 75 mph?

(7.3) *Find the mean, median, and any mode(s) for each list of numbers. If necessary, round to the nearest tenth.*

35. 13, 23, 33, 14, 6

36. 45, 86, 21, 60, 86, 64, 45

37. 14,000, 20,000, 12,000, 20,000, 36,000, 45,000

38. 560, 620, 123, 400, 410, 300, 400, 780, 430, 450

For Exercises 39 and 40, the grades are given for a student for a particular semester. Find each grade point average. If necessary, round the grade point average to the nearest hundredth.

39.

Grade	Credit Hours
A	3
A	3
C	2
B	3
C	1

40.

Grade	Credit Hours
B	3
B	4
C	2
D	2
B	3

(7.4) *Draw a tree diagram for each experiment. Then use the diagram to determine the number of outcomes.*

Spinner 1

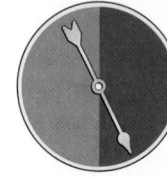

Spinner 2

41. Tossing a coin and then spinning Spinner 1

42. Spinning Spinner 2 and then tossing a coin

43. Spinning Spinner 1 twice

44. Spinning Spinner 2 twice

45. Spinning Spinner 1 and then Spinner 2

Find the probability of each event.

46. Rolling a 4 on a die

47. Rolling a 3 on a die

48. Spinning a 4 on the spinner

49. Spinning a 3 on the spinner

50. Spinning either a 1, 3, or 5 on the spinner

51. Spinning either a 2 or a 4 on the spinner

52. Rolling an even number on a die

53. Rolling a number greater than 3 on a die

Mixed Review

Find the mean, median, and any mode(s) for each list of numbers. If needed round answers to two decimal places.

54. 73, 82, 95, 68, 54

55. 25, 27, 32, 98, 62

56. 750, 500, 427, 322, 500, 225

57. 952, 327, 566, 814, 327, 729

Given a bag containing 2 red marbles, 2 blue marbles, 3 yellow marbles, and 1 green marble, find the following:

58. The probability of choosing a blue marble from the bag

59. The probability of choosing a yellow marble from the bag

60. The probability of choosing a red marble from the bag

61. The probability of choosing a green marble from the bag

7 CHAPTER TEST

 Remember to use the Chapter Test Prep Video CD to see the fully worked-out solutions to any of the exercises you want to review.

The following pictograph shows the money collected each week from a wrapping paper fundraiser. Use this graph to answer Exercises 1 through 3.

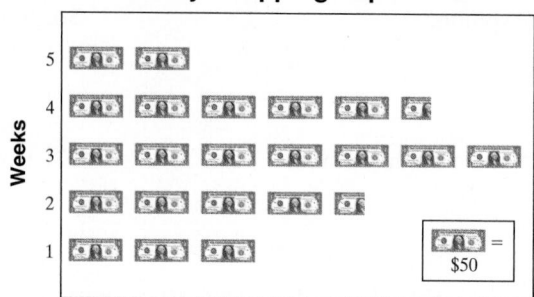

Weekly Wrapping Paper Sales

1. How much money was collected during the second week?

2. During which week was the most money collected? How much money was collected during that week?

3. What was the total money collected for the fundraiser?

The bar graph shows the normal monthly precipitation in centimeters for Chicago, Illinois. Use this graph to answer Exercises 4 through 6.

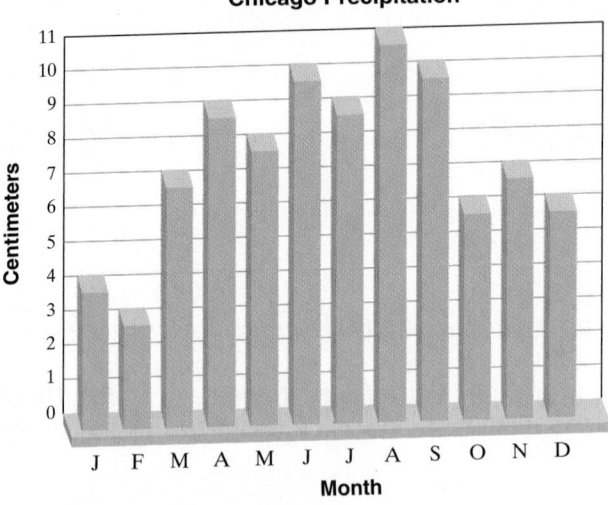

Chicago Precipitation

Source: U.S. National Oceanic and Atmospheric Administration, *Climatography of the United States*, No. 81

4. During which month(s) does Chicago normally have more than 9 centimeters of precipitation?

5. During which month does Chicago normally have the least amount of precipitation? How much precipitation occurs during that month?

6. During which month(s) does 7 centimeters of precipitation normally occur?

7. Use the information in the table to draw a bar graph. Clearly label each bar.

Countries with the Highest Newspaper Circulations	
Country	Average Daily Circulation (in millions)
Japan	72
US	56
China	50
India	31
Germany	24
Russia	24
UK	19

(*Source:* World Association of Newspapers)

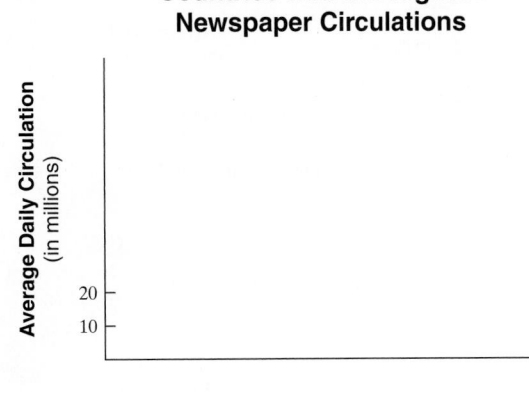

Countries with the Highest Newspaper Circulations

The following line graph shows the annual inflation rate in the United States for the years 1990–2003. Use this graph to answer Exercises 8 through 10.

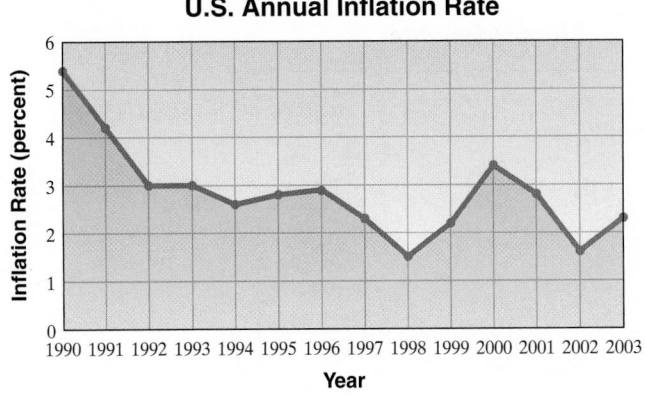

Source: Bureau of Labor Statistics

8. Approximate the annual inflation rate in 2002.

9. During which of the years shown was the inflation rate greater than 3%?

10. During which sets of years was the inflation rate increasing?

The result of a survey of 200 people is shown in the following circle graph. Each person was asked to tell his or her favorite type of music. Use this graph to answer Exercises 11 and 12.

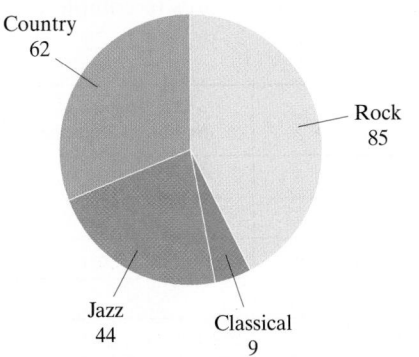

11. Find the ratio of those who prefer rock music to the total number surveyed.

12. Find the ratio of those who prefer country music to those who prefer jazz.

13. _____

14. _____

15. _____

16. _____

17. see table

The following circle graph shows the U.S. labor force employment by industry for 2000. There were approximately 132,000,000 people employed by these industries in the United States in 2000. Use the graph to find how many people were employed by the industries given in Exercises 13 and 14.

U.S. Labor Force Employment by Industry

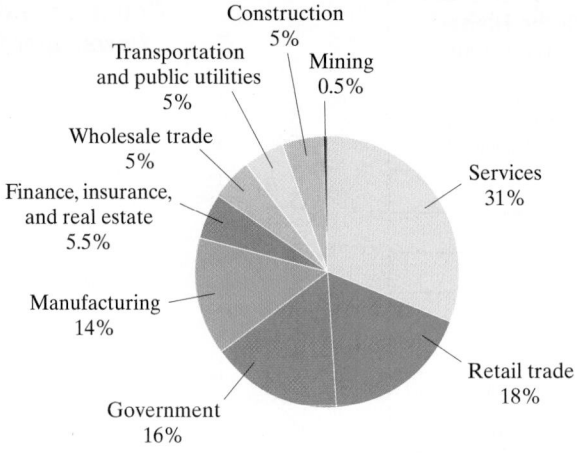

Source: Bureau of Labor Statistics

13. Services

14. Government

A professor measures the heights of the students in her class. The results are shown in the following histogram. Use this histogram to answer Exercises 15 and 16.

Student Heights

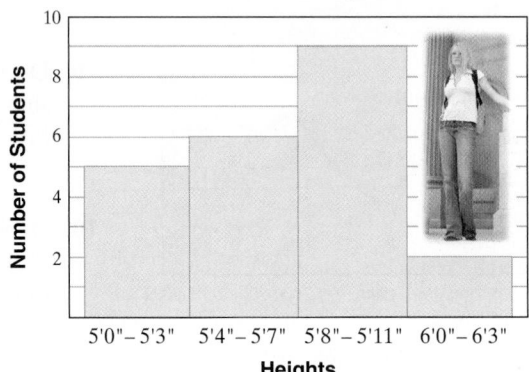

15. How many students are 5′8″–5′11″ tall?

16. How many students are 5′7″ or shorter?

17. The history test scores of 25 students are shown below. Use these scores to complete the frequency distribution table.

70	86	81	65	92
43	72	85	69	97
82	51	75	50	68
88	83	85	77	99
77	63	59	84	90

Class Intervals (Scores)	Tally	Class Frequency (Number of Students)
40–49		
50–59		
60–69		
70–79		
80–89		
90–99		

18. Use the results of Exercise 17 to draw a histogram.

Find the mean, median, and mode of each list of numbers.

19. 26, 32, 42, 43, 49

20. 8, 10, 16, 16, 14, 12, 12, 13

Find the grade point average. If necessary, round to the nearest hundredth.

21.

Grade	Credit Hours
A	3
B	3
C	3
B	4
A	1

22. Draw a tree diagram for the experiment of spinning the spinner twice. State the number of outcomes.

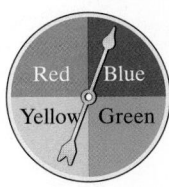

23. Draw a tree diagram for the experiment of tossing a coin twice. State the number of outcomes.

Suppose that the numbers 1 to 10 are each written on a scrap of paper and placed in a bag. You then select one number from the bag.

24. What is the probability of choosing a 6 from the bag?

25. What is the probability of choosing a 3 or a 4 from the bag?

18. see graph

19. _____

20. _____

21. _____

22. _____

23. _____

24. _____

25. _____

1. Simplify: $(8 - 6)^2 + 2^3 \cdot 3$

2. Simplify: $48 \div 8 \cdot 2$

3. Write $\dfrac{30}{108}$ in simplest form.

4. Subtract: $\dfrac{19}{40} - \dfrac{3}{10}$

5. Add: $1\dfrac{4}{5} + 4 + 2\dfrac{1}{2}$

6. Multiply: $5\dfrac{1}{3} \cdot 2\dfrac{1}{8}$

△ **7.** The formula for finding the area of a triangle is Area = $\dfrac{1}{2} \cdot$ base $\cdot$ height. Find the area of a triangle with height 3 feet and length 5.6 feet.

8. Find the perimeter of a rectangle with length $3\dfrac{1}{2}$ meters and width $1\dfrac{1}{2}$ meters.

9. Subtract. Check each answer by adding.
  a. $12 - 9$
  b. $11 - 6$
  c. $5 - 5$
  d. $7 - 0$

10. Multiply
  a. $20 \cdot 0$
  b. $20 \cdot 1$
  c. $0 \cdot 20$
  d. $1 \cdot 20$

11. Round 248,982 to the nearest hundred.

12. Round 248,982 to the nearest thousand.

13. Multiply:
  a. $\begin{array}{r} 25 \\ \times\ 8 \\ \hline \end{array}$
  b. $\begin{array}{r} 246 \\ \times\ 5 \\ \hline \end{array}$

14. Divide: $10{,}468 \div 28$

Answers

1. _____
2. _____
3. _____
4. _____
5. _____
6. _____
7. _____
8. _____
9. **a.** _____
   b. _____
   c. _____
   d. _____
10. **a.** _____
    b. _____
    c. _____
    d. _____
11. _____
12. _____
13 **a.** _____
   b. _____
14. _____

15. The director of a learning lab at a local community college is working on next year's budget. Thirty-three new DVD players are needed at a cost of $187 each. What is the total cost of these DVD players?

16. A study is being conducted for erecting soundproof walls along the interstate of a metropolitan area. The following feet of walls are part of the proposal. Find their total: 4800 feet, 3270 feet, 2761 feet, 5760 feet.

17. Find the prime factorization of 45.

18. Find $\sqrt{64}$.

Write each percent as a decimal.

19. 4.6%

20. 0.29%

21. 190%

22. 452%

Write each percent as a fraction in simplest form.

23. 40%

24. 27%

25. $33\dfrac{1}{3}\%$

26. $61\dfrac{1}{7}\%$

27. Translate to an equation: Five is what percent of 20?

28. Translate to a proportion: Five is what percent of 20?

29. Find the sales tax and the total price on the purchase of an $85.50 trench coat in a city where the sales tax rate is 7.5%.

30. A salesperson makes a 7% commission rate on her total sales. If her total sales are $23,000, what is her commission?

31. An accountant invested $2000 at a simple interest rate of 10% for 2 years. What total amount of money will she have from her investment in 2 years?

32. Find the mean (or average) of 28, 35, 40, and 32.

15. _____

16. _____

17. _____

18. _____

19. _____

20. _____

21. _____

22. _____

23. _____

24. _____

25. _____

26. _____

27. _____

28. _____

29. _____

30. _____

31. _____

32. _____

33. _____

34. _____

35. _____

36. _____

37. _____

38. _____

39. _____

40. _____

33. Find the complement of a 48° angle.

34. Find the supplement of a 48° angle.

35. Find $\sqrt{\dfrac{1}{36}}$.

36. Find: $\sqrt{\dfrac{1}{25}}$

37. Find the mode of the list of numbers:

11, 14, 14, 16, 31, 56, 65, 77, 77, 78, 79

38. Find the median of the numbers in Exercise 47.

39. If a coin is tossed twice, find the probability of tossing heads and then heads.

40. A bag contains 3 red marbles and 2 blue marbles. Find the probability of choosing a red marble.

8

Real Numbers and Introduction to Algebra

In this chapter, we begin with a review of the basic symbols—the language—of mathematics. We then introduce algebra by using a variable in place of a number. From there, we translate phrases to algebraic expressions and sentences to equations. This is the beginning of problem solving, which we formally study in Chapter 9.

The apparent magnitude of a star is the measure of its brightness as seen by someone on Earth. The smaller the apparent magnitude, the brighter the star. Below, the apparent magnitudes of some stars are listed.

Star	Apparent Magnitude	Star	Apparent Magnitude
Arcturus	−0.04	Spica	0.98
Sirius	−1.46	Rigel	0.12
Vega	0.03	Regulus	1.35
Antares	0.96	Canopus	−0.72
Sun	−26.7	Hadar	0.61

(*Source: Norton's 2000.0: Star Atlas and Reference Handbook*, 18th ed., Longman Group, UK, 1989)

The stars have been a source of interest to different cultures for centuries. Polaris, the North Star, guided ancient sailors. The Egyptians honored Sirius, the brightest star in the sky, in temples. Around 150 B.C., a Greek astronomer, Hipparchus, devised a system of classifying the brightness of stars. Hipparchus's system is the basis of the apparent magnitude scale used by modern astronomers. In Exercises 85 through 90, Section 8.1, we shall see how this scale is used to describe the brightness of objects such as the sun, the moon, and some planets.

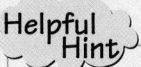 Define the Meaning of the
Symbols $=, \neq, <, >, \leq,$ and $\geq$.

B Translate Sentences into
Mathematical Statements.

C Identify Integers, Rational
Numbers, Irrational Numbers, and
Real Numbers.

D Find the Absolute Value of a Real
Number.

Helpful Hint

The three dots (an ellipsis) at the end of the list of elements of a set means that the list continues in the same manner indefinitely.

8.1 SYMBOLS AND SETS OF NUMBERS

We begin with a review of the set of natural numbers and the set of whole numbers and how we use symbols to compare these numbers. A **set** is a collection of objects, each of which is called a **member** or **element** of the set. A pair of brace symbols { } encloses the list of elements and is translated as "the set of" or "the set containing."

Natural Numbers

$$\{1, 2, 3, 4, 5, 6, \ldots\}$$

Whole Numbers

$$\{0, 1, 2, 3, 4, 5, 6, \ldots\}$$

These numbers can be pictured on a **number line.** To draw a number line, first draw a line. Choose a point on the line and label it 0. To the right of 0, label any other point 1. Being careful to use the same distance as from 0 to 1, mark off equally spaced distances to the right of 1. Label these points 2, 3, 4, 5, and so on. Since the whole numbers continue indefinitely, it is not possible to show every whole number on the number line. The arrow at the right end of the line indicates that the pattern continues indefinitely.

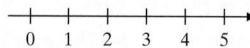

Objective A Equality and Inequality Symbols

Picturing natural numbers and whole numbers on a number line helps us to see the order of the numbers. Symbols can be used to describe in writing the order of two quantities. We will use equality symbols and inequality symbols to compare quantities.

Below is a review of these symbols. The letters a and b are used to represent quantities. Letters such as a and b that are used to represent numbers or quantities are called **variables.**

Equality and Inequality Symbols

		Meaning
Equality symbol:	$a = b$	a is equal to b.
Inequality symbols:	$a \neq b$	a is not equal to b.
	$a < b$	a is less than b.
	$a > b$	a is greater than b.
	$a \leq b$	a is less than or equal to b.
	$a \geq b$	a is greater than or equal to b.

These symbols may be used to form **mathematical statements** such as

$$2 = 2 \quad \text{and} \quad 2 \neq 6$$

On the number line, we see that a number **to the right of** another number is **larger.** Similarly, a number **to the left of** another number is **smaller.** For example, 3 is to the left of 5 on the number line, which means that 3 is less than 5, or $3 < 5$. Similarly, 2 is to the right of 0 on the number line, which means 2 is greater than 0, or $2 > 0$. Since 0 is to the left of 2, we can also say that 0 is less than 2, or $0 < 2$.

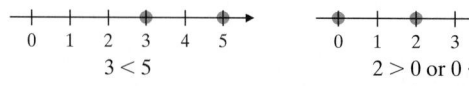

Helpful Hint

Notice that $2 > 0$ has exactly the same meaning as $0 < 2$. Switching the order of the numbers and reversing the "direction of the inequality symbol" does not change the meaning of the statement.

$5 > 3$ has the same meaning as $3 < 5$.

Also notice that when the statement is true, the inequality arrow points to the smaller number.

Our discussion above can be generalized in the order property below.

Order Property for Real Numbers

For any two real numbers a and b, a is less than b if a is to the left of b on the number line.

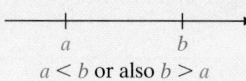

$a < b$ or also $b > a$

EXAMPLES Determine whether each statement is true or false.

1. $2 < 3$ True.   Since 2 is to the left of 3 on the number line
2. $72 < 27$ False.   72 is to the right of 27 on the number line, so $72 > 27$.
3. $8 \geq 8$ True.   Since $8 = 8$ is true
4. $8 \leq 8$ True.   Since $8 = 8$ is true
5. $23 \leq 0$ False.   Since neither $23 < 0$ nor $23 = 0$ is true
6. $0 \leq 23$ True.   Since $0 < 23$ is true

▬ Work Practice Problems 1–6

Objective B Translating Sentences into Mathematical Statements

Now, let's use the symbols discussed above to translate sentences into mathematical statements.

EXAMPLE 7 Translate each sentence into a mathematical statement.

a. Nine is less than or equal to eleven.   b. Eight is greater than one.
c. Three is not equal to four.

Solution:

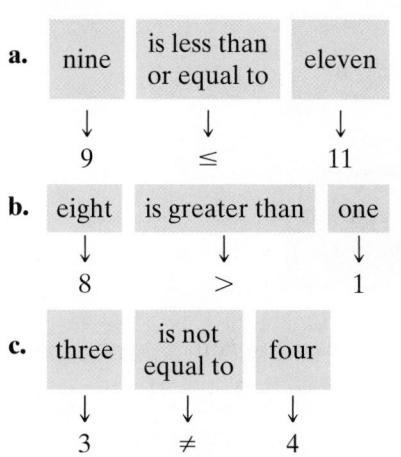

a.

nine	is less than or equal to	eleven
↓	↓	↓
9	≤	11

b.

eight	is greater than	one
↓	↓	↓
8	>	1

c.

three	is not equal to	four
↓	↓	↓
3	≠	4

▬ Work Practice Problem 7

PRACTICE PROBLEMS 1–6

Determine whether each statement is true or false.

1. $8 < 6$ 2. $100 > 10$
3. $21 \leq 21$ 4. $21 \geq 21$
5. $0 \geq 5$ 6. $25 \geq 22$

Helpful Hint

If either $3 < 3$ or $3 = 3$ is true, then $3 \leq 3$ is true.

PRACTICE PROBLEM 7

Translate each sentence into a mathematical statement.

a. Fourteen is greater than or equal to fourteen.
b. Zero is less than five.
c. Nine is not equal to ten.

Answers

1. false,   2. true,   3. true,
4. true,   5. false,   6. true,
7. a. $14 \geq 14$,   b. $0 < 5$,   c. $9 \neq 10$

Objective 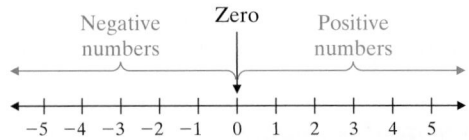 Identifying Common Sets of Numbers

Whole numbers are not sufficient to describe many situations in the real world. For example, quantities smaller than zero must sometimes be represented, such as temperatures less than 0 degrees.

We can place numbers less than zero on the number line as follows: Numbers less than 0 are to the left of 0 and are labeled −1, −2, −3, and so on. The numbers we have labeled on the number line below are called the set of **integers.**

Negative numbers   Zero   Positive numbers

−5 −4 −3 −2 −1 0 1 2 3 4 5

Integers to the left of 0 are called **negative integers;** integers to the right of 0 are called **positive integers.** The integer 0 is neither positive nor negative.

Integers

$$\{\ldots, -3, -2, -1, 0, 1, 2, 3, \ldots\}$$

Helpful Hint

A − sign, such as the one in −2, tells us that the number is to the left of 0 on the number line.

−2 is read "negative two."

A + sign or no sign tells us that a number lies to the right of 0 on the number line. For example, 3 and +3 both mean positive three.

PRACTICE PROBLEM 8

Use an integer to express the number in the following. Recently, due to hurricane Katrina the city of New Orleans suffered massive flooding. Under normal conditions, its elevation is 8 feet below sea level. (*Source: The World Almanac,* 2005)

Answer

8. −8

EXAMPLE 8

Use an integer to express the number in the following. "The lowest temperature ever recorded at South Pole Station, Antarctica, occurred during the month of June. The record-low temperature was 117 degrees below zero." (*Source:* The National Oceanic and Atmospheric Administration)

Solution: The integer −117 represents 117 degrees below zero.

Work Practice Problem 8

A problem with integers in real-life settings arises when quantities are smaller than some integer but greater than the next smallest integer. On the number line, these quantities may be visualized by points between integers. Some of these quantities between integers can be represented as a quotient of integers. For example,

The point on the number line halfway between 0 and 1 can be represented by $\frac{1}{2}$, a quotient of integers.

The point on the number line halfway between 0 and −1 can be represented by $-\frac{1}{2}$. Other quotients of integers and their graphs are shown below.

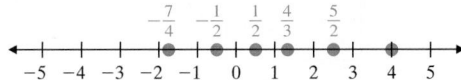

These numbers, each of which can be represented as a quotient of integers, are examples of **rational numbers.** It's not possible to list the set of rational numbers using the notation that we have been using. For this reason, we will use a different notation.

Rational Numbers

$$\left\{ \frac{a}{b} \,\middle|\, a \text{ and } b \text{ are integers and } b \neq 0 \right\}$$

We read this set as "the set of numbers $\frac{a}{b}$ such that a and b are integers and **b is not equal to 0.**"

> **Helpful Hint**
>
> We commonly refer to rational numbers as fractions.

Notice that every integer is also a rational number since each integer can be written as a quotient of integers. For example, the integer 5 is also a rational number since $5 = \frac{5}{1}$. For the rational number $\frac{5}{1}$, recall that the top number, 5, is called the numerator and the bottom number, 1, is called the denominator.

Let's practice **graphing** numbers on a number line.

EXAMPLE 9 Graph the numbers on a number line.

$$-\frac{4}{3}, \quad \frac{1}{4}, \quad \frac{3}{2}, \quad -2\frac{1}{8}, \quad 3.5$$

Solution: To help graph the improper fractions in the list, we first write them as mixed numbers.

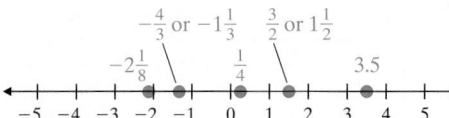

📖 **Work Practice Problem 9**

Every rational number has a point on the number line that corresponds to it. But not every point on the number line corresponds to a rational number. Those points that do not correspond to rational numbers correspond instead to **irrational numbers.**

PRACTICE PROBLEM 9

Graph the numbers on the number line.

$$-2\frac{1}{2}, \quad -\frac{2}{3}, \quad \frac{1}{5}, \quad \frac{5}{4}, \quad 2.25$$

Answer

9.

Irrational Numbers

{Nonrational numbers that correspond to points on the number line}

An irrational number that you have probably seen is π. Also, $\sqrt{2}$, the length of the diagonal of the square shown below, is an irrational number.

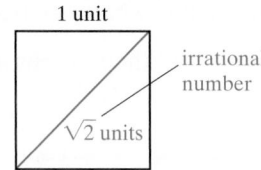

1 unit

irrational number

$\sqrt{2}$ units

Both rational and irrational numbers can be written as decimal numbers. The decimal equivalent of a rational number will either terminate or repeat in a pattern. For example, upon dividing we find that

$$\frac{3}{4} = 0.75 \qquad \text{(Decimal number terminates or ends.)}$$

$$\frac{2}{3} = 0.66666\ldots \quad \text{(Decimal number repeats in a pattern.)}$$

The decimal representation of an irrational number will neither terminate nor repeat. (For further review of decimals, see Chapter 4.)

The set of numbers, each of which corresponds to a point on the number line, is called the set of **real numbers.** One and only one point on the number line corresponds to each real number.

Real Numbers

{All numbers that correspond to points on the number line}

Several different sets of numbers have been discussed in this section. The following diagram shows the relationships among these sets of real numbers. Notice that, together, the rational numbers and the irrational numbers make up the real numbers.

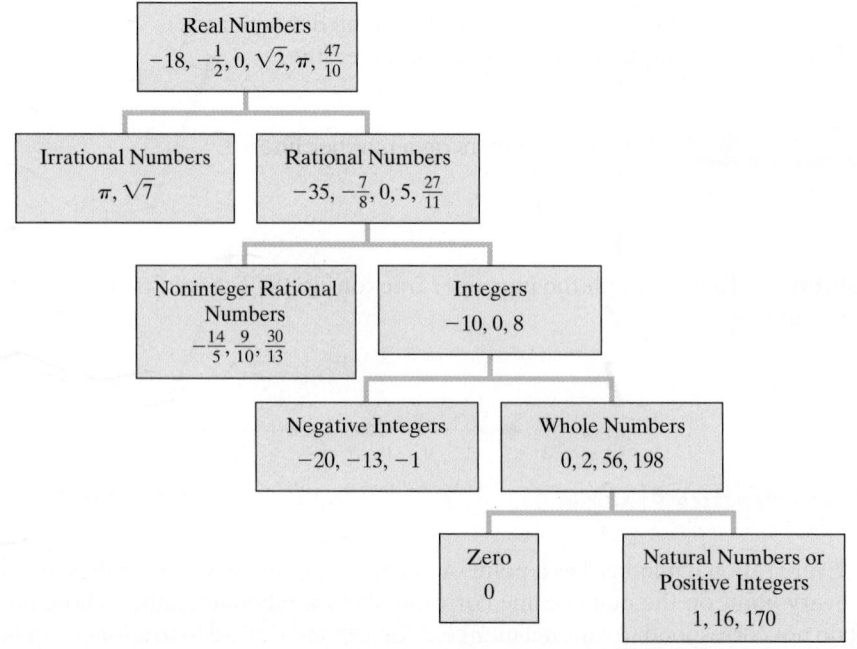

Now that other sets of numbers have been reviewed, let's continue our practice of comparing numbers.

EXAMPLE 10 Insert $<$, $>$, or $=$ between the pairs of numbers to form true statements.

a. $-5 \quad -6$ **b.** $3.195 \quad 3.2$ **c.** $\dfrac{1}{4} \quad \dfrac{1}{3}$

Solution:

a. $-5 > -6$ since -5 lies to the right of -6 on the number line.

b. By comparing digits in the same place values, we find that $3.195 < 3.2$. Since $0.1 < 0.2$.

c. By dividing, we find that $\dfrac{1}{4} = 0.25$ and $\dfrac{1}{3} = 0.33\ldots$ Since $0.25 < 0.33\ldots$, then $\dfrac{1}{4} < \dfrac{1}{3}$.

■ **Work Practice Problem 10**

EXAMPLE 11 Given the set $\left\{-2, 0, \dfrac{1}{4}, 112, -3, 11, \sqrt{2}\right\}$, list the numbers in this set that belong to the set of:

a. Natural numbers **b.** Whole numbers **c.** Integers
d. Rational numbers **e.** Irrational numbers **f.** Real numbers

Solution:

a. The natural numbers are 11 and 112.

b. The whole numbers are 0, 11, and 112.

c. The integers are $-3, -2, 0, 11,$ and 112.

d. Recall that integers are rational numbers also. The rational numbers are $-3, -2, 0, \dfrac{1}{4}, 11,$ and 112.

e. The irrational number is $\sqrt{2}$.

f. All numbers in the given set are real numbers.

■ **Work Practice Problem 11**

Objective D Finding the Absolute Value of a Number

The number line not only gives us a picture of the real numbers, it also helps us visualize the distance between numbers. The distance between a real number a and 0 is given a special name called the **absolute value** of a. "The absolute value of a" is written in symbols as $|a|$.

Absolute Value

The **absolute value** of a real number a, denoted by $|a|$, is the distance between a and 0 on the number line.

For example, $|3| = 3$ and $|-3| = 3$ since both 3 and -3 are a distance of 3 units from 0 on the number line.

PRACTICE PROBLEM 10

Insert $<$, $>$, or $=$ between pairs of numbers to form true statements.
a. $-11 \quad -9$
b. $4.511 \quad 4.151$
c. $\dfrac{7}{8} \quad \dfrac{2}{3}$

PRACTICE PROBLEM 11

Given the set $\left\{-100, -\dfrac{2}{5}, 0, \pi, 6, 913\right\}$, list the numbers in this set that belong to the set of:

a. Natural numbers
b. Whole numbers
c. Integers
d. Rational numbers
e. Irrational numbers
f. Real numbers

Helpful Hint

Since $|a|$ is a distance, $|a|$ is always either positive or 0. It is never negative. That is, **for any real number a, $|a| \geq 0$.**

Answers

10. **a.** $<$, **b.** $>$, **c.** $>$,
11. **a.** $6, 913$, **b.** $0, 6, 913$,
c. $-100, 0, 6, 913$,
d. $-100, -\dfrac{2}{5}, 0, 6, 913$, **e.** π,
f. all numbers in the given set

PRACTICE PROBLEM 12

Find the absolute value of each number.

a. $|7|$, **b.** $|-8|$, **c.** $\left|\dfrac{2}{3}\right|$,

d. $|0|$, **e.** $|-3.06|$

EXAMPLE 12 Find the absolute value of each number.

a. $|4|$ **b.** $|-5|$ **c.** $|0|$

d. $\left|-\dfrac{2}{9}\right|$ **e.** $|4.93|$

Solution:

a. $|4| = 4$ since 4 is 4 units from 0 on the number line.

b. $|-5| = 5$ since -5 is 5 units from 0 on the number line.

c. $|0| = 0$ since 0 is 0 units from 0 on the number line.

d. $\left|-\dfrac{2}{9}\right| = \dfrac{2}{9}$

e. $|4.93| = 4.93$

▣ **Work Practice Problem 12**

PRACTICE PROBLEM 13

Insert $<$, $>$, or $=$ in the appropriate space to make each statement true.

a. $|-4|$ 4,

b. -3 $|0|$,

c. $|-2.7|$ $|-2|$,

d. $|-6|$ $|-16|$

e. $|10|$ $\left|-10\dfrac{1}{3}\right|$

EXAMPLE 13 Insert $<$, $>$, or $=$ in the appropriate space to make each statement true.

a. $|0|$ 2 **b.** $|-5|$ 5 **c.** $|-3|$ $|-2|$

d. $|-9|$ $|-9.7|$ **e.** $\left|-7\dfrac{1}{6}\right|$ $|7|$

Solution:

a. $|0| < 2$ since $|0| = 0$ and $0 < 2$.

b. $|-5| = 5$.

c. $|-3| > |-2|$ since $3 > 2$.

d. $|-9| < |-9.7|$ since $9 < 9.7$.

e. $\left|-7\dfrac{1}{6}\right| > |7|$ since $7\dfrac{1}{6} > 7$.

▣ **Work Practice Problem 13**

Answers

12. a. 7, **b.** 8, **c.** $\dfrac{2}{3}$, **d.** 0, **e.** 3.06,

13. a. $=$, **b.** $<$, **c.** $>$, **d.** $<$,

e. $<$

Objectives Ⓐ Ⓒ **Mixed Practice** *Insert* $<$, $>$, *or* $=$ *in the space between the paired numbers to make each statement true. See Examples 1 through 6, and 10.*

1. 4   10

2. 8   5

3. 7   3

4. 9   15

5. 6.26   6.26

6. 1.13   1.13

7. 0   7

8. 20   0

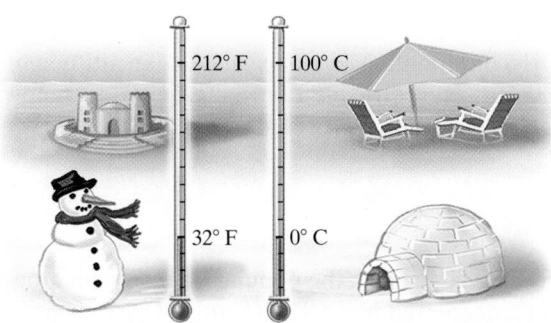

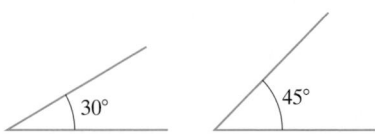

9. The freezing point of water is 32° Fahrenheit. The boiling point of water is 212° Fahrenheit. Write an inequality statement using $<$ or $>$ comparing the numbers 32 and 212.

10. The freezing point of water is 0° Celsius. The boiling point of water is 100° Celsius. Write an inequality statement using $<$ or $>$ comparing the numbers 0 and 100.

△ **11.** An angle measuring 30° and an angle measuring 45° are shown. Use the inequality symbols $\leq$ or $\geq$ to write a statement comparing the numbers 30 and 45.

△ **12.** The sum of the measures of the angles of a triangle is 180°. The sum of the measures of the angles of a parallelogram is 360°. Use the inequality symbols $\leq$ or $\geq$ to write a statement comparing the numbers 360 and 180.

30°   45°

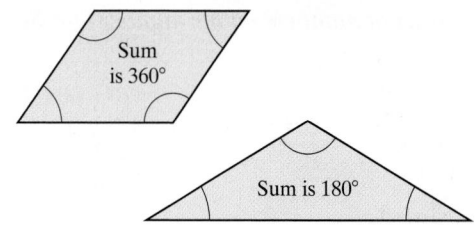

Determine whether each statement is true or false. See Examples 1 through 6 and 10.

13. $11 \leq 11$

14. $8 \geq 9$

15. $-11 > -10$

16. $-16 > -17$

17. $5.092 < 5.902$

18. $1.02 > 1.021$

19. $\dfrac{9}{10} \leq \dfrac{8}{9}$

20. $\dfrac{4}{5} \leq \dfrac{9}{11}$

Rewrite each inequality so that the inequality symbol points in the opposite direction and the resulting statement has the same meaning as the given one.

21. $25 \geq 20$

22. $-13 \leq 13$

23. $0 < 6$

24. $5 > 3$

25. $-10 > -12$

26. $-4 < -2$

Objectives **B** **C** **Mixed Practice** *Write each sentence as a mathematical statement. See Examples 7, 10, and 11.*

27. Seven is less than eleven.

28. Twenty is greater than two.

29. Five is greater than or equal to four.

30. Negative ten is less than or equal to thirty-seven.

31. Fifteen is not equal to negative two.

32. Negative seven is not equal to seven.

Use integers to represent the values in each statement. See Example 8.

33. The highest elevation in California is Mt. Whitney with an altitude of 14,494 feet. The lowest elevation in California is Death Valley with an altitude of 282 feet below sea level. (*Source:* U.S. Geological Survey)

34. Driskill Mountain, in Louisiana, has an altitude of 535 feet. New Orleans, Louisiana, lies 8 feet below sea level. (*Source:* U.S. Geological Survey)

35. The number of students admitted to the Class of 2008 at UCLA was 43,413 fewer students than the number that applied. (*Source:* UCLA)

36. From 1990 to 2000, the population of Washington, D.C., decreased by 34,841. (*Source:* U.S. Census Bureau)

37. Gretchen Bertani deposited $475 in her savings account. She later withdrew $195.

38. David Lopez was deep-sea diving. During his dive, he ascended 17 feet and later descended 15 feet.

Graph each set of numbers on the number line. See Example 9.

39. $-4, 0, 2, -2$

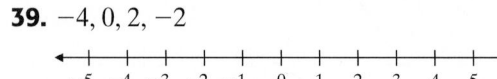

40. $-3, 0, 1, -5$

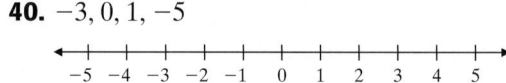

41. $-2, 4, \dfrac{1}{3}, -\dfrac{1}{4}$

42. $-5, 3, -\dfrac{1}{3}, \dfrac{7}{8}$

43. $-4.5, \dfrac{7}{4}, 3.25, -\dfrac{3}{2}$

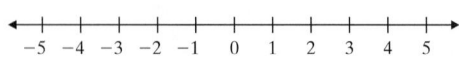

44. $4.5, -\dfrac{9}{4}, 1.75, -\dfrac{7}{2}$

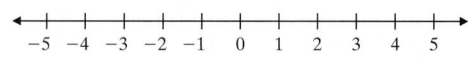

Tell which set or sets each number belongs to: natural numbers, whole numbers, integers, rational numbers, irrational numbers, and real numbers. See Example 11.

45. 0

46. $\dfrac{1}{4}$

47. -7

48. $-\dfrac{1}{7}$

49. 265

50. 7941

51. $\dfrac{2}{3}$

52. $\sqrt{3}$

Determine whether each statement is true or false.

53. Every rational number is also an integer.

54. Every natural number is positive.

55. 0 is a real number.

56. $\frac{1}{2}$ is an integer.

57. Every negative number is also a rational number.

58. Every rational number is also a real number.

59. Every real number is also a rational number.

60. Every whole number is an integer.

Objective **D** *Find each absolute value. See Example 12.*

61. $|8.9|$

62. $|11.2|$

63. $|-20|$

64. $|-17|$

65. $\left|\frac{9}{2}\right|$

66. $\left|\frac{10}{7}\right|$

67. $\left|-\frac{12}{13}\right|$

68. $\left|-\frac{1}{15}\right|$

Insert $<, >,$ or $=$ in the appropriate space to make each statement true. See Examples 12 and 13.

69. $|-5|$ ____ -4

70. $|-12|$ ____ $|0|$

71. $\left|-\frac{5}{8}\right|$ ____ $\left|\frac{5}{8}\right|$

72. $\left|\frac{2}{5}\right|$ ____ $\left|-\frac{2}{5}\right|$

73. $|-2|$ ____ $|-2.7|$

74. $|-5.01|$ ____ $|-5|$

75. $|0|$ ____ $|-8|$

76. $|-12|$ ____ $\frac{-24}{2}$

Review

Perform each indicated operation. See Section 1.9.

77. $90 + 12^2 - 5^3$

78. $3 \cdot (7 - 4) + 2 \cdot 5^2$

79. $12 \div 4 - 2 + 7$

80. $12 \div (4 - 2) + 7$

Concept Extensions

The graph below is called a bar graph. This graph shows apple production in Massachusetts from 1994 through 2003. Each bar represents a different year, and the height of each bar represents the apple production for that year in thousands of bushels. (A bushel is 42 lb.)

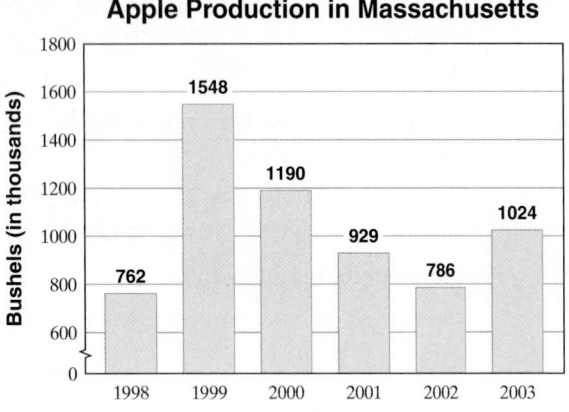

Apple Production in Massachusetts

(Note: The ⅟ symbol means that some numbers are missing. Along the vertical data line, notice the numbers between 0 and 600 are missing or not shown.) (Source: New England Agriculture Statistical Service.)

81. Write an inequality comparing the apple production in 1998 with the apple production in 1999.

82. Write an inequality comparing the apple production in 2003 with the apple production in 2002.

83. Determine the change in apple production between 2000 and 2001.

84. According to the bar graph, which year produced the largest crops?

The apparent magnitude of a star is the measure of its brightness as seen by someone on Earth. The smaller the apparent magnitude, the brighter the star. Below, the apparent magnitudes of some stars are listed. Use this table to answer Exercises 85 through 90.

Star	Apparent Magnitude	Star	Apparent Magnitude
Arcturus	−0.04	Spica	0.98
Sirius	−1.46	Rigel	0.12
Vega	0.03	Regulus	1.35
Antares	0.96	Canopus	−0.72
Sun	−26.7	Hadar	0.61

(Source: Norton's 2000.0: Star Atlas and Reference Handbook, 18th ed., Longman Group, UK, 1989)

85. The apparent magnitude of the sun is −26.7. The apparent magnitude of the star Arcturus is −0.04. Write an inequality statement comparing the numbers −0.04 and −26.7.

86. The apparent magnitude of Antares is 0.96. The apparent magnitude of Spica is 0.98. Write an inequality statement comparing the numbers 0.96 and 0.98.

87. Which is brighter, the sun or Arcturus?

88. Which is dimmer, Antares or Spica?

89. Which star listed is the brightest?

90. Which star listed is the dimmest?

91. In your own words, explain how to find the absolute value of a number.

92. Give an example of a real-life situation that can be described with integers but not with whole numbers.

8.2 EXPONENTS, ORDER OF OPERATIONS, AND VARIABLE EXPRESSIONS

Objectives

A Define and Use Exponents and the Order of Operations.

B Evaluate Algebraic Expressions, Given Replacement Values for Variables.

C Determine Whether a Number Is a Solution of a Given Equation.

D Translate Phrases into Expressions and Sentences into Equations.

Objective **A** Exponents and the Order of Operations

Exponents and order of operations were first introduced in Section 1.9. Recall that the volume of a cube whose sides each measure 2 centimeters is $(2 \cdot 2 \cdot 2)$ cubic centimeters. We may use **exponential notation** to write such products in a more compact form. For example,

$2 \cdot 2 \cdot 2$ may be written as 2^3.

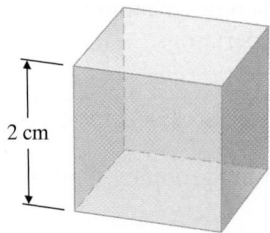

2 cm

Volume is $(2 \cdot 2 \cdot 2)$
cubic centimeters.

The 2 in 2^3 is called the **base;** it is the repeated factor. The 3 in 2^3 is called the **exponent** and is the number of times the base is used as a factor. The expression 2^3 is called an **exponential expression.**

$$\overset{\text{exponent}}{2^{\overset{\downarrow}{3}}} = 2 \cdot 2 \cdot 2 = 8$$

base ————⤴ 2 is a factor 3 times.

EXAMPLE 1 Evaluate (find the value of) each expression.

a. 3^2 [read as "3 squared" or as "3 to the second power"]
b. 5^3 [read as "5 cubed" or as "5 to the third power"]
c. 2^4 [read as "2 to the fourth power"]
d. 7^1
e. $\left(\dfrac{3}{7}\right)^2$

Solution:

a. $3^2 = 3 \cdot 3 = 9$
b. $5^3 = 5 \cdot 5 \cdot 5 = 125$
c. $2^4 = 2 \cdot 2 \cdot 2 \cdot 2 = 16$
d. $7^1 = 7$
e. $\left(\dfrac{3}{7}\right)^2 = \left(\dfrac{3}{7}\right)\left(\dfrac{3}{7}\right) = \dfrac{3 \cdot 3}{7 \cdot 7} = \dfrac{9}{49}$

▣ **Work Practice Problem 1**

PRACTICE PROBLEM 1

Evaluate each expression.
a. 4^2
b. 2^2
c. 3^4
d. 9^1
e. $\left(\dfrac{2}{5}\right)^3$

Helpful Hint

$2^3 \neq 2 \cdot 3$ since 2^3 indicates **repeated multiplication of the same factor.**

$2^3 = 2 \cdot 2 \cdot 2 = 8$, whereas $2 \cdot 3 = 6$

Answers
1. a. 16, **b.** 4, **c.** 81, **d.** 9, **e.** $\dfrac{8}{125}$

549

Using symbols for mathematical operations is a great convenience. The more operation symbols presented in an expression, the more careful we must be when performing the indicated operation. For example, in the expression $2 + 3 \cdot 7$, do we add first or multiply first? To eliminate confusion, **grouping symbols** are used. Examples of grouping symbols are parentheses ( ), brackets [ ], braces { }, absolute value bars | |, and the fraction bar. If we wish $2 + 3 \cdot 7$ to be simplified by adding first, we enclose $2 + 3$ in parentheses.

$$(2 + 3) \cdot 7 = 5 \cdot 7 = 35$$

If we wish to multiply first, $3 \cdot 7$ may be enclosed in parentheses.

$$2 + (3 \cdot 7) = 2 + 21 = 23$$

To eliminate confusion when no grouping symbols are present, we use the following agreed-upon order of operations.

Order of Operations

1. Perform all operations within grouping symbols first, starting with the innermost set.

2. Evaluate exponential expressions.

3. Multiply or divide in order from left to right.

4. Add or subtract in order from left to right.

Using this order of operations, we now simplify $2 + 3 \cdot 7$. There are no grouping symbols and no exponents, so we multiply and then add.

$$2 + 3 \cdot 7 = 2 + 21 \quad \text{Multiply.}$$
$$= 23 \quad \text{Add.}$$

EXAMPLES Simplify each expression.

2. $6 \div 3 + 5^2 = 6 \div 3 + 25 \quad$ Evaluate 5^2
$$= 2 + 25 \quad \text{Divide.}$$
$$= 27 \quad \text{Add.}$$

3. $20 \div 5 \cdot 4 = 4 \cdot 4$
$$= 16$$

> **Helpful Hint**
> Remember to multiply or divide in order from left to right.

4. $\dfrac{3}{2} \cdot \dfrac{1}{2} - \dfrac{1}{2} = \dfrac{3}{4} - \dfrac{1}{2} \quad$ Multiply.
$$= \dfrac{3}{4} - \dfrac{2}{4} \quad \text{The least common denominator is 4.}$$
$$= \dfrac{1}{4} \quad \text{Subtract.}$$

5. $1 + 2[5(2 \cdot 3 + 1) - 10] = 1 + 2[5(7) - 10] \quad$ Simplify the expression in the innermost set of parentheses. $2 \cdot 3 + 1 = 6 + 1 = 7$.
$$= 1 + 2[35 - 10] \quad \text{Multiply 5 and 7.}$$
$$= 1 + 2[25] \quad \text{Subtract inside the brackets.}$$
$$= 1 + 50 \quad \text{Multiply 2 and 25.}$$
$$= 51 \quad \text{Add.}$$

■ **Work Practice Problems 2–5**

In the next example, the fraction bar serves as a grouping symbol and separates the numerator and denominator. Simplify each separately.

PRACTICE PROBLEMS 2–5

Simplify each expression.

2. $3 \cdot 2 + 4^2$

3. $28 \div 7 \cdot 2$

4. $\dfrac{9}{5} \cdot \dfrac{1}{3} - \dfrac{1}{3}$

5. $5 + 3[2(3 \cdot 4 + 1) - 20]$

Answers

2. 22, **3.** 8, **4.** $\dfrac{4}{15}$, **5.** 23

EXAMPLE 8 Decide whether 2 is a solution of $3x + 10 = 8x$.

Solution: Replace x with 2 and see if a true statement results.

$$3x + 10 = 8x \quad \text{Original equation}$$
$$3(2) + 10 \stackrel{?}{=} 8(2) \quad \text{Replace } x \text{ with 2.}$$
$$6 + 10 \stackrel{?}{=} 16 \quad \text{Simplify each side.}$$
$$16 = 16 \quad \text{True}$$

Since we arrived at a true statement after replacing x with 2 and simplifying both sides of the equation, 2 is a solution of the equation.

Work Practice Problem 8

Objective D Translating Words to Symbols

Now that we know how to represent an unknown number by a variable, let's practice translating phrases into algebraic expressions and sentences into equations. Oftentimes solving problems involves the ability to translate word phrases and sentences into symbols. Below is a list of key words and phrases to help us translate.

Helpful Hint

Order matters when subtracting and also dividing, so be especially careful with these translations.

Addition (+)	Subtraction (−)	Multiplication (·)	Division (÷)	Equality (=)
Sum	Difference of	Product	Quotient	Equals
Plus	Minus	Times	Divide	Gives
Added to	Subtracted from	Multiply	Into	Is/was/ should be
More than	Less than	Twice	Ratio	Yields
Increased by	Decreased by	Of	Divided by	Amounts to
Total	Less			Represents Is the same as

EXAMPLE 9 Write an algebraic expression that represents each phrase. Let the variable x represent the unknown number.

a. The sum of a number and 3
b. The product of 3 and a number
c. The quotient of 7.3 and a number
d. 10 decreased by a number
e. 5 times a number, increased by 7

Solution:

a. $x + 3$ since "sum" means to add
b. $3 \cdot x$ and $3x$ are both ways to denote the product of 3 and x
c. $7.3 \div x$ or $\dfrac{7.3}{x}$
d. $10 - x$ because "decreased by" means to subtract
e. $\underbrace{5x}_{\substack{5 \text{ times} \\ \text{a number}}} + 7$

Work Practice Problem 9

PRACTICE PROBLEM 8

Decide whether 3 is a solution of $5x - 10 = x + 2$.

PRACTICE PROBLEM 9

Write an algebraic expression that represents each phrase. Let the variable x represent the unknown number.

a. The product of 5 and a number
b. A number added to 7
c. A number divided by 11.2
d. A number subtracted from 8
e. Twice a number, plus 1

Answers
8. It is a solution.,
9. a. $5 \cdot x$ or $5x$, **b.** $7 + x$,
c. $x \div 11.2$ or $\dfrac{x}{11.2}$, **d.** $8 - x$,
e. $2x + 1$

Helpful Hint

Make sure you understand the difference when translating phrases containing "decreased by," "subtracted from," and "less than."

Phrase	Translation	
A number decreased by 10	$x - 10$	
A number subtracted from 10	$10 - x$	Notice the order.
10 less than a number	$x - 10$	
A number less 10	$x - 10$	

Now let's practice translating sentences into equations.

EXAMPLE 10 Write each sentence as an equation. Let x represent the unknown number.

a. The quotient of 15 and a number is 4.

b. Three subtracted from 12 is a number.

c. 17 added to four times a number is 21.

Solution:

a. In words:

the quotient of 15 and a number	is	4
↓	↓	↓

Translate: $\dfrac{15}{x} = 4$

b. In words:

three subtracted **from** 12	is	a number
↓	↓	↓

Translate: $12 - 3 = x$

Care must be taken when the operation is subtraction. The expression $3 - 12$ would be incorrect. Notice that $3 - 12 \neq 12 - 3$.

c. In words:

17	added to	four times a number	is	21
↓	↓	↓	↓	↓

Translate: $17 + 4x = 21$

◼ **Work Practice Problem 10**

PRACTICE PROBLEM 10

Write each sentence as an equation. Let x represent the unknown number.

a. The ratio of a number and 6 is 24.

b. The difference of 10 and a number is 18.

c. One less than twice a number is 99.

Answers

10. a. $\dfrac{x}{6} = 24$, **b.** $10 - x = 18$,

c. $2x - 1 = 99$

Exponents

To evaluate exponential expressions on a calculator, find the key marked $\boxed{y^x}$ or $\boxed{\wedge}$. To evaluate, for example, 6^5, press the following keys: $\boxed{6}\ \boxed{y^x}\ \boxed{5}\ \boxed{=}$ or $\boxed{6}\ \boxed{\wedge}\ \boxed{5}\ \boxed{=}$.

↕ or
$\boxed{\text{ENTER}}$

The display should read $\boxed{\qquad 7776\ }$.

Order of Operations

Some calculators follow the order of operations, and others do not. To see whether or not your calculator has the order of operations built in, use your calculator to find $2 + 3 \cdot 4$. To do this, press the following sequence of keys:

$\boxed{2}\ \boxed{+}\ \boxed{3}\ \boxed{\times}\ \boxed{4}\ \boxed{=}$.

↕ or
$\boxed{\text{ENTER}}$

The correct answer is 14 because the order of operations is to multiply before we add. If the calculator displays $\boxed{\qquad 14\ }$, then it has the order of operations built in.

Even if the order of operations is built in, parentheses must sometimes be inserted. For example, to simplify $\dfrac{5}{12 - 7}$, press the keys

$\boxed{5}\ \boxed{\div}\ \boxed{(}\ \boxed{1}\ \boxed{2}\ \boxed{-}\ \boxed{7}\ \boxed{)}\ \boxed{=}$.

↕ or
$\boxed{\text{ENTER}}$

The display should read $\boxed{\qquad 1\ }$.

Use a calculator to evaluate each expression.

1. 5^3 **2.** 7^4

3. 9^5 **4.** 8^6

5. $2(20 - 5)$ **6.** $3(14 - 7) + 21$

7. $24(862 - 455) + 89$

8. $99 + (401 + 962)$

9. $\dfrac{4623 + 129}{36 - 34}$

10. $\dfrac{956 - 452}{89 - 86}$

8.2 EXERCISE SET

FOR EXTRA HELP

Student Solutions Manual   PH Math/Tutor Center   CD/Video for Review   Math XL MathXL®   MyMathLab MyMathLab

Objective A *Evaluate. See Example 1.*

1. 3^5 **2.** 5^4  **3.** 3^3 **4.** 4^4 **5.** 1^5 **6.** 1^8

7. 5^1 **8.** 8^1 **9.** 7^2 **10.** 9^2 **11.** $\left(\dfrac{2}{3}\right)^4$ **12.** $\left(\dfrac{6}{11}\right)^2$

13. $\left(\dfrac{1}{5}\right)^3$ **14.** $\left(\dfrac{1}{2}\right)^5$ **15.** $(1.2)^2$ **16.** $(1.5)^2$ **17.** $(0.7)^3$ **18.** $(0.4)^3$

△ **19.** The area of a square whose sides each measure 5 meters is $(5 \cdot 5)$ square meters. Write this area using exponential notation.

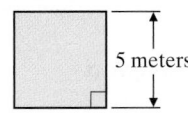

5 meters

△ **20.** The area of a circle whose radius is 9 meters is $(9 \cdot 9 \cdot \pi)$ square meters. Write this area using exponential notation.

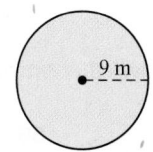

9 m

555

Simplify each expression. See Examples 2 through 6.

21. $5 + 6 \cdot 2$

22. $8 + 5 \cdot 3$

23. $4 \cdot 8 - 6 \cdot 2$

24. $12 \cdot 5 - 3 \cdot 6$

25. $18 \div 3 \cdot 2$

26. $48 \div 6 \cdot 2$

27. $2 + (5 - 2) + 4^2$

28. $6 - 2 \cdot 2 + 2^5$

29. $5 \cdot 3^2$

30. $2 \cdot 5^2$

31. $\dfrac{1}{4} \cdot \dfrac{2}{3} - \dfrac{1}{6}$

32. $\dfrac{3}{4} \cdot \dfrac{1}{2} + \dfrac{2}{3}$

33. $\dfrac{6 - 4}{9 - 2}$

34. $\dfrac{8 - 5}{24 - 20}$

35. $2[5 + 2(8 - 3)]$

36. $3[4 + 3(6 - 4)]$

37. $\dfrac{19 - 3 \cdot 5}{6 - 4}$

38. $\dfrac{14 - 2 \cdot 3}{12 - 8}$

39. $\dfrac{|6 - 2| + 3}{8 + 2 \cdot 5}$

40. $\dfrac{15 - |3 - 1|}{12 - 3 \cdot 2}$

41. $\dfrac{3 + 3(5 + 3)}{3^2 + 1}$

42. $\dfrac{3 + 6(8 - 5)}{4^2 + 2}$

43. $\dfrac{6 + |8 - 2| + 3^2}{18 - 3}$

44. $\dfrac{16 + |13 - 5| + 4^2}{17 - 5}$

45. $2 + 3[10(4 \cdot 5 - 16) - 30]$

46. $3 + 4[8(5 \cdot 5 - 20) - 41]$

47. $\left(\dfrac{2}{3}\right)^3 + \dfrac{1}{9} + \dfrac{1}{3} \cdot \dfrac{4}{3}$

48. $\left(\dfrac{3}{8}\right)^2 + \dfrac{1}{4} + \dfrac{1}{8} \cdot \dfrac{3}{2}$

Objective **B** *Evaluate each expression when $x = 1$, $y = 3$, and $z = 5$. See Example 7.*

49. $3y$

50. $4x$

51. $\dfrac{z}{5x}$

52. $\dfrac{y}{2z}$

53. $3x - 2$

54. $6y - 8$

55. $|2x + 3y|$

56. $|5z - 2y|$

57. $xy + z$

58. $yz - x$

59. $5y^2$

60. $2z^2$

Evaluate each expression when $x = 2$, $y = 6$, and $z = 3$. See Example 7.

61. $5z$

62. $7x$

63. $\dfrac{z}{xy}$

64. $\dfrac{x}{yz}$

65. $\dfrac{y}{x} + \dfrac{y}{x}$

66. $\dfrac{9}{z} + \dfrac{4z}{y}$

Objective **C** *Decide whether the given number is a solution of the given equation. See Example 8.*

67. $3x - 6 = 9; 5$

68. $2x + 7 = 3x; 6$

69. $2x + 6 = 5x - 1; 0$

70. $4x + 2 = x + 8; 2$

71. $2x - 5 = 5; 8$ **72.** $3x - 10 = 8; 6$ **73.** $x + 6 = x + 6; 2$ **74.** $x + 6 = x + 6; 10$

75. $x = 5x + 15; 0$ **76.** $4 = 1 - x; 1$ **77.** $\frac{1}{3}x = 9; 27$ **78.** $\frac{2}{7}x = \frac{3}{14}; 6$

Objective **D** *Write each phrase as an algebraic expression. Let x represent the unknown number. See Example 9.*

79. Fifteen more than a number

80. A number increased by 9

81. Five subtracted from a number

82. Five decreased by a number

83. The ratio of a number and 4

84. The quotient of a number and 9

85. Three times a number, increased by 22

86. Twice a number, decreased by 72

Write each sentence as an equation. Use x to represent any unknown number. See Example 10.

87. One increased by two equals the quotient of nine and three.

88. Four subtracted from eight is equal to two squared.

89. Three is not equal to four divided by two.

90. The difference of sixteen and four is greater than ten.

91. The sum of 5 and a number is 20.

92. Seven subtracted from a number is 0.

93. The product of 7.6 and a number is 17.

94. 9.1 times a number equals 4

95. Thirteen minus three times a number is 13.

96. Eight added to twice a number is 42.

Review

Add. See Section 1.3.

97. $15 + 20$

98. $20 + 15$

99. $47 + 236 + 77$

100. $362 + 37 + 90$

Concept Extensions

101. Are parentheses necessary in the expression $2 + (3 \cdot 5)$? Explain your answer.

102. Are parentheses necessary in the expression $(2 + 3) \cdot 5$? Explain your answer.

For Exercises 103 and 104, match each expression in the first column with its value in the second column.

103.
a. $(6 + 2) \cdot (5 + 3)$	19
b. $(6 + 2) \cdot 5 + 3$	22
c. $6 + 2 \cdot 5 + 3$	64
d. $6 + 2 \cdot (5 + 3)$	43

104.
a. $(1 + 4) \cdot 6 - 3$	15
b. $1 + 4 \cdot (6 - 3)$	13
c. $1 + 4 \cdot 6 - 3$	27
d. $(1 + 4) \cdot (6 - 3)$	22

Recall that perimeter measures the distance around a plane figure and area measures the amount of surface of a plane figure. The expression $2l + 2w$ gives the perimeter of the rectangle below, and the expression lw gives its area (measured in square units).

105. Complete the chart below for the given lengths and widths. Be sure to include units.

Length: *l*	Width: *w*	Perimeter of Rectangle: *2l + 2w*	Area of Rectangle: *lw*
4 in.	3 in.		
6 in.	1 in.		
5 in.	2 in.		

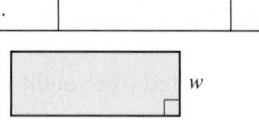

106. Study the perimeters and areas found in the chart to the left. Do you notice any trends?

107. Insert one set of parentheses so that the following expression simplifies to 32.

$$20 - 4 \cdot 4 \div 2$$

108. Insert parentheses so that the following expression simplifies to 28.

$$2 \cdot 5 + 3^2$$

109. In your own words, explain the difference between an expression and an equation.

Determine whether each is an expression or an equation. See the Concept Check in this section.

110.
a. $3x^2 - 26$
b. $3x^2 - 26 = 1$
c. $2x - 5 = 7x - 5$
d. $9y + x - 8$
e. $3^2 - 4(5 - 3)$

111.
a. $5x + 6$
b. $2a = 7$
c. $3a + 2 = 9$
d. $4x + 3y - 8z$
e. $5^2 - 2(6 - 2)$

112. Why is 8^2 usually read as "eight squared"? (*Hint:* What is the area of the **square** below?)

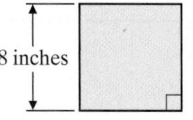

8 inches

113. Why is 4^3 usually read as "four cubed"? (*Hint:* What is the volume of the **cube** below?)

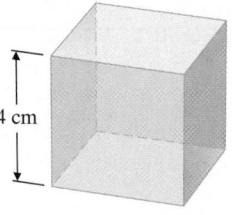

4 cm

114. Write any expression, using 4 or more numbers, that simplifies to 7.

8.3 ADDING REAL NUMBERS

Objectives

A Add Real Numbers.

B Find the Opposite of a Number.

C Solve Problems That Involve Addition of Real Numbers.

Real numbers can be added, subtracted, multiplied, divided, and raised to powers, just as whole numbers can.

Objective A Adding Real Numbers

Adding real numbers can be visualized by using a number line. A positive number can be represented on the number line by an arrow of appropriate length pointing to the right, and a negative number by an arrow of appropriate length pointing to the left.

Both arrows represent 2 or +2.
They both point to the right, and they are both 2 units long.

Both arrows represent −3.
They both point to the left, and they are both 3 units long.

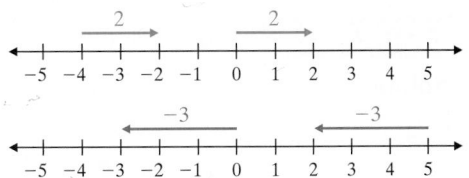

To add signed numbers such as $5 + (-2)$ on a number line, we start at 0 on the number line and draw an arrow representing 5. From the tip of this arrow, we draw another arrow representing −2. The tip of the second arrow ends at their sum, 3.

$$5 + (-2) = 3$$

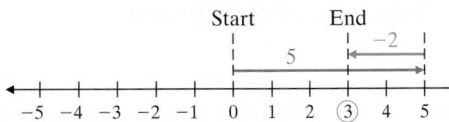

To add $-1 + (-4)$ on the number line, we start at 0 and draw an arrow representing −1. From the tip of this arrow, we draw another arrow representing −4. The tip of the second arrow ends at their sum, −5.

$$-1 + (-4) = -5$$

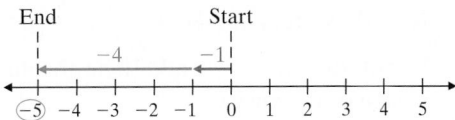

EXAMPLE 1 Add: $-1 + (-2)$

Solution:

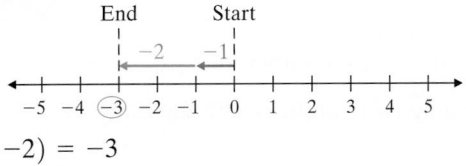

$$-1 + (-2) = -3$$

■ Work Practice Problem 1

Thinking of integers as money earned or lost might help make addition more meaningful. Earnings can be thought of as positive numbers. If $1 is earned and later another $3 is earned, the total amount earned is $4. In other words, $1 + 3 = 4$.

On the other hand, losses can be thought of as negative numbers. If $1 is lost and later another $3 is lost, a total of $4 is lost. In other words, $(-1) + (-3) = -4$.

In Example 1, we added numbers with the same sign. Adding numbers whose signs are not the same can be pictured on a number line also.

PRACTICE PROBLEM 1

Add using a number line:
$-2 + (-4)$

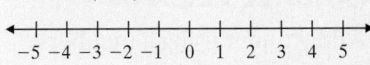

Answer

1. −6

559

PRACTICE PROBLEM 2

Add using a number line:
$-5 + 8$

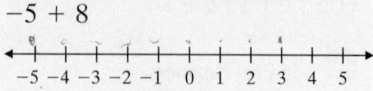

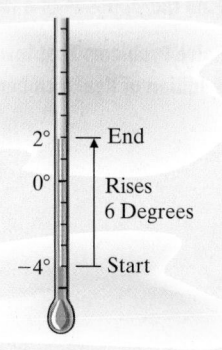

PRACTICE PROBLEM 3

Add using a number line:
$5 + (-4)$

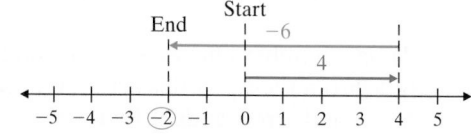

PRACTICE PROBLEM 4

Add without using a number line: $(-8) + (-5)$

PRACTICE PROBLEM 5

Add without using a number line: $(-14) + 6$

EXAMPLE 2 Add: $-4 + 6$

Solution:

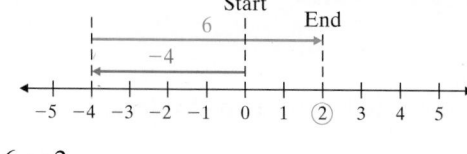

$-4 + 6 = 2$

▣ **Work Practice Problem 2**

Let's use temperature as an example. If the thermometer registers 4 degrees below 0 degrees and then rises 6 degrees, the new temperature is 2 degrees above 0 degrees. Thus, it is reasonable that $-4 + 6 = 2$. (See the diagram in the margin.)

EXAMPLE 3 Add: $4 + (-6)$

Solution:

$4 + (-6) = -2$

▣ **Work Practice Problem 3**

Using a number line each time we add two numbers can be time consuming. Instead, we can notice patterns in the previous examples and write rules for adding real numbers.

> ### Adding Real Numbers
>
> To add two real numbers
>
> **1.** with the *same sign,* add their absolute values. Use their common sign as the sign of the answer.
>
> **2.** with *different signs,* subtract their absolute values. Give the answer the same sign as the number with the larger absolute value.

EXAMPLE 4 Add without using a number line: $(-7) + (-6)$

Solution: Here, we are adding two numbers with the same sign.

$(-7) + (-6) = -13$

↑↖ sum of absolute values ($|-7| = 7, |-6| = 6, 7 + 6 = 13$)
same sign

▣ **Work Practice Problem 4**

EXAMPLE 5 Add without using a number line: $(-10) + 4$

Solution: Here, we are adding two numbers with different signs.

$(-10) + 4 = -6$

↑↖ difference of absolute values ($|-10| = 10, |4| = 4, 10 - 4 = 6$)
sign of number with larger absolute value, −10

▣ **Work Practice Problem 5**

EXAMPLES Add without using a number line.

6. $(-8) + (-11) = -19$

7. $(-2) + 10 = 8$

8. $0.2 + (-0.5) = -0.3$

9. $-\dfrac{7}{10} + \left(-\dfrac{1}{10}\right) = -\dfrac{8}{10} = -\dfrac{\overset{1}{\cancel{2}} \cdot 4}{\underset{1}{\cancel{2}} \cdot 5} = -\dfrac{4}{5}$

10. $11.4 + (-4.7) = 6.7$

11. $-\dfrac{3}{8} + \dfrac{2}{5} = -\dfrac{15}{40} + \dfrac{16}{40} = \dfrac{1}{40}$

▣ **Work Practice Problems 6–11**

EXAMPLE 12 Find each sum.

a. $3 + (-7) + (-8)$

b. $[7 + (-10)] + [-2 + (-4)]$

Solution:

a. Perform the additions from left to right.

$3 + (-7) + (-8) = -4 + (-8)$ Adding numbers with different signs

$= -12$ Adding numbers with like signs

b. Simplify inside the brackets first.

$[7 + (-10)] + [-2 + (-4)] = [-3] + [-6]$

$= -9$ Add.

▣ **Work Practice Problem 12**

Objective **B** Finding Opposites

To help us subtract real numbers in the next section, we first review what we mean by opposites. The graphs of 4 and −4 are shown on the number line below.

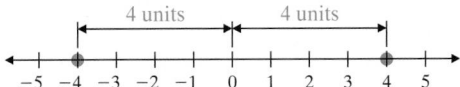

Notice that the graph of 4 and −4 lie on opposite sides of 0, and each is 4 units away from 0. Such numbers are known as **opposites** or **additive inverses** of each other.

Opposite or Additive Inverse

Two numbers that are the same distance from 0 but lie on opposite sides of 0 are called **opposites** or **additive inverses** of each other.

EXAMPLES Find the opposite of each number.

13. 10 The opposite of 10 is −10.

14. -3 The opposite of −3 is 3.

15. $\dfrac{1}{2}$ The opposite of $\dfrac{1}{2}$ is $-\dfrac{1}{2}$.

16. -4.5 The opposite of −4.5 is 4.5.

▣ **Work Practice Problems 13–16**

PRACTICE PROBLEMS 6–11

Add without using a number line.

6. $(-17) + (-10)$

7. $(-4) + 12$

8. $1.5 + (-3.2)$

9. $-\dfrac{6}{12} + \left(-\dfrac{3}{12}\right)$

10. $12.1 + (-3.6)$

11. $-\dfrac{4}{5} + \dfrac{2}{3}$

PRACTICE PROBLEM 12

Find each sum.

a. $16 + (-9) + (-9)$

b. $[3 + (-13)] + [-4 + (-7)]$

Helpful Hint

Don't forget that brackets are grouping symbols. We simplify within them first.

PRACTICE PROBLEMS 13–16

Find the opposite of each number.

13. -35 14. 12

15. $-\dfrac{3}{11}$ 16. 1.9

Answers

6. -27,   **7.** 8,   **8.** -1.7,   **9.** $-\dfrac{3}{4}$,

10. 8.5,   **11.** $-\dfrac{2}{15}$,   **12. a.** -2,

b. -21,   **13.** 35,   **14.** -12,   **15.** $\dfrac{3}{11}$,

16. -1.9

We use the symbol "−" to represent the phrase "the opposite of" or "the additive inverse of." In general, if a is a number, we write the opposite or additive inverse of a as $-a$. We know that the opposite of -3 is 3. Notice that this translates as

the opposite of	−3	is	3
↓	↓	↓	↓
−	(−3)	=	3

This is true in general.

If a is a number, then $-(-a) = a$.

PRACTICE PROBLEM 17

PRACTICE PROBLEM 17

Simplify each expression.

a. $-(-22)$

b. $-\left(-\dfrac{2}{7}\right)$

c. $-(-x)$

d. $-|-14|$

e. $-|2.3|$

EXAMPLE 17 Simplify each expression.

a. $-(-10)$ **b.** $-\left(-\dfrac{1}{2}\right)$ **c.** $-(-2x)$

d. $-|-6|$ **e.** $-|4.1|$

Solution:

a. $-(-10) = 10$ **b.** $-\left(-\dfrac{1}{2}\right) = \dfrac{1}{2}$

c. $-(-2x) = 2x$

d. $-|-6| = -6$ Since $|-6| = 6$.

e. $-|4.1| = -4.1$ Since $|4.1| = 4.1$

Work Practice Problem 17

Let's discover another characteristic about opposites. Notice that the sum of a number and its opposite is 0.

$$10 + (-10) = 0$$
$$-3 + 3 = 0$$
$$\frac{1}{2} + \left(-\frac{1}{2}\right) = 0$$

In general, we can write the following:

The sum of a number a and its opposite $-a$ is 0.

$$a + (-a) = 0 \qquad \text{Also,} \qquad -a + a = 0.$$

Notice that this means that the opposite of 0 is then 0 since $0 + 0 = 0$.

Answers

17. a. 22,   **b.** $\dfrac{2}{7}$,   **c.** x,   **d.** -14,

e. -2.3

Objective C Solving Problems That Involve Addition

Positive and negative numbers are used in everyday life. Stock market returns show gains and losses as positive and negative numbers. Temperatures in cold climates often dip into the negative range, commonly referred to as "below zero" temperatures. Bank statements report deposits and withdrawals as positive and negative numbers.

EXAMPLE 18 Calculating Gain or Loss

During a three-day period, a share of Lamplighter's International stock recorded the following gains and losses:

Monday	**Tuesday**	**Wednesday**
a gain of $2	a loss of $1	a loss of $3

Find the overall gain or loss for the stock for the three days.

Solution: Gains can be represented by positive numbers. Losses can be represented by negative numbers. The overall gain or loss is the sum of the gains and losses.

In words: | gain | plus | loss | plus | loss |

Translate: $2 + (-1) + (-3) = -2$

The overall loss is $2.

Work Practice Problem 18

PRACTICE PROBLEM 18

During a four-day period, a share of Walco stock recorded the following gains and losses:

Tuesday	**Wednesday**
a loss of $2	a loss of $1
Thursday	**Friday**
a gain of $3	a gain of $3

Find the overall gain or loss for the stock for the four days.

Answer
18. a gain of $3

8.3 EXERCISE SET

FOR EXTRA HELP

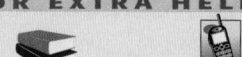
Student Solutions Manual

PH Math/Tutor Center

CD/Video for Review

Math XL
MathXL®

MyMathLab
MyMathLab

Objective Ⓐ *Add. See Examples 1 through 12.*

1. $6 + (-3)$

2. $9 + (-12)$

3. $-6 + (-8)$

4. $-6 + (-14)$

5. $8 + (-7)$

6. $16 + (-4)$

7. $-14 + 2$

8. $-10 + 5$

9. $-2 + (-3)$

10. $-7 + (-4)$

11. $-9 + (-3)$

12. $-11 + (-5)$

13. $-7 + 3$

14. $-5 + 9$

15. $10 + (-3)$

16. $8 + (-6)$

17. $5 + (-7)$

18. $3 + (-6)$

19. $-16 + 16$

20. $23 + (-23)$

21. $27 + (-46)$

22. $53 + (-37)$

23. $-18 + 49$

24. $-26 + 14$

25. $-33 + (-14)$

26. $-18 + (-26)$

27. $6.3 + (-8.4)$

28. $9.2 + (-11.4)$

29. $117 + (-79)$

30. $144 + (-88)$

31. $-9.6 + (-3.5)$

32. $-6.7 + (-7.6)$

33. $-\dfrac{3}{8} + \dfrac{5}{8}$

34. $-\dfrac{5}{12} + \dfrac{7}{12}$

35. $-\dfrac{7}{16} + \dfrac{1}{4}$

36. $-\dfrac{5}{9} + \dfrac{1}{3}$

37. $-\dfrac{7}{10} + \left(-\dfrac{3}{5}\right)$

38. $-\dfrac{5}{6} + \left(-\dfrac{2}{3}\right)$

39. $|-8| + (-16)$

40. $|-6| + (-61)$

41. $-15 + 9 + (-2)$

42. $-9 + 15 + (-5)$

43. $-21 + (-16) + (-22)$

44. $-18 + (-6) + (-40)$

45. $-23 + 16 + (-2)$

46. $-14 + (-3) + 11$

47. $|5 + (-10)|$

48. $|7 + (-17)|$

49. $6 + (-4) + 9$

50. $8 + (-2) + 7$

51. $[-17 + (-4)] + [-12 + 15]$

52. $[-2 + (-7)] + [-11 + 22]$

53. $|9 + (-12)| + |-16|$

54. $|43 + (-73)| + |-20|$

55. $-13 + [5 + (-3) + 4]$

56. $-30 + [1 + (-6) + 8]$

57. Find the sum of -38 and 12.

58. Find the sum of -44 and 16.

564

Objective B *Find each additive inverse or opposite. See Examples 13 through 17.*

59. 6

60. 4

61. −2

62. −8

63. 0

64. $-\dfrac{1}{4}$

65. $|-6|$

66. $|-11|$

Simplify each of the following. See Example 17.

67. $-|-2|$

68. $-|-5|$

69. $-(-7)$

70. $-(-14)$

71. $-(-7.9)$

72. $-(-8.4)$

73. $-(-5z)$

74. $-(-7m)$

75. $\left|-\dfrac{2}{3}\right|$

76. $-\left|-\dfrac{2}{3}\right|$

Objective C *Solve each of the following. See Example 18.*

77. The lowest temperature ever recorded in Massachusetts was −35°F. The highest recorded temperature in Massachusetts was 142° higher than the record low temperature. Find Massachusetts' highest recorded temperature. (*Source:* National Climatic Data Center)

78. On January 2, 1943, the temperature was −4° at 7:30 a.m. in Spearfish, South Dakota. Incredibly, it got 49° warmer in the next 2 minutes. To what temperature did it rise by 7:32?

79. The lowest elevation on Earth is −411 meters (that is, 411 meters below sea level) at the Dead Sea. If you are standing 316 meters above the Dead Sea, what is your elevation? (*Source:* National Geographic Society)

80. The lowest elevation in Australia is −52 feet at Lake Eyre. If you are standing at a point 439 feet above Lake Eyre, what is your elevation? (*Source:* National Geographic Society)

81. When checking the stock listing in the newspaper, LaTonda finds that one of her stocks posted net changes of −2.50 points and −0.86 point over the last two days. What is the combined change?

82. Yesterday your stock posted a net change of +0.93 point, but today it showed a loss of −1.25 points. Find the overall change for two days.

83. In golf, scores that are under par for the entire round are shown as negative scores; scores that are over par are positive, and par is 0. Vijay Singh won the 2004 PGA championship with round scores of −5, −4, −3, +4. What was his total overall score? (*Source:* PGA of America)

84. Annika Sorenstam won the 2004 LPGA Samsung World Championship with the following round scores: −6, −4, −3, and −5. What was her total overall score? (*Source:* LPGA of America)

85. A negative net income results when a company spends more money than it brings in. KMart had the following quarterly net incomes during its 2004 fiscal year. (*Source:* Yahoo finance)

Quarter of Fiscal 2004	Net Income (in millions)
First	−23
Second	−581
Third	93
Fourth	155

What was the total net income for fiscal year 2004?

86. Northwest Airlines had the following quarterly net incomes during its 2004 fiscal year. (*Source:* Yahoo finance)

Quarter of Fiscal 2004	Net Income (in millions)
First	13
Second	−1724
Third	−177
Fourth	34

What was the total net income for fiscal year 2004?

Review

Subtract. See Sections 1.4 and 4.3.

87. 76.1 − 4.09

88. 93.7 − 10.08

89. 200 − 59

90. 400 − 18

Concept Extensions

The following bar graph shows each month's average daily low temperature in degrees Fahrenheit for Barrow, Alaska. Use this graph to answer Exercises 91 through 94.

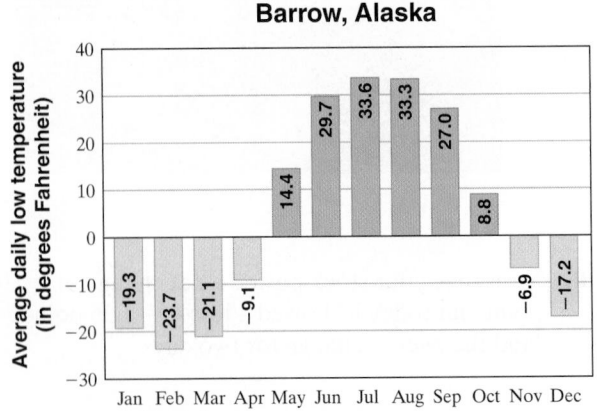

Source: National Climatic Data Center

91. Give any two numbers whose sum is −5.

92. Give two numbers, one positive and one negative whose sum is −10.

93. For what month is the graphed temperature the highest?

94. For what month is the graphed temperature the lowest?

95. For what month is the graphed temperature positive *and* closest to 0°?

96. For what month is the graphed temperature negative *and* closest to 0°?

97. Find the average of the temperatures shown for the months of April, May, and October. (To find the average of three temperatures, find their sum and divide by 3.)

98. Find the average of the temperatures shown for the months of January, September, and October.

If p is a positive number and n is a negative number, fill in the blanks with the words positive or negative.

99. $-p$ is a _____ number.

100. $-n$ is a _____ number.

101. $p + p$ is a _____ number.

102. $n + n$ is a _____ number.

103. Explain why adding a negative number to another negative number always gives a negative sum.

104. When a positive and a negative number are added, sometimes the sum is positive, sometimes it is zero, and sometimes it is negative. Explain why this happens.

105. In your own words, explain how to find the opposite of a number.

106. In your own words, explain why 0 is the only number that is its own opposite.

A Subtract Real Numbers.

B Evaluate Algebraic Expressions Using Real Numbers.

C Determine Whether a Number Is a Solution of a Given Equation.

D Solve Problems That Involve Subtraction of Real Numbers.

E Find Complementary and Supplementary Angles.

8.4 SUBTRACTING REAL NUMBERS

Objective **A** Subtracting Real Numbers

Now that addition of real numbers has been discussed, we can explore subtraction. We know that $9 - 7 = 2$. Notice that $9 + (-7) = 2$, also. This means that

$$9 - 7 = 9 + (-7)$$

Notice that the *difference* of 9 and 7 is the same as the *sum* of 9 and the opposite of 7. This is how we can subtract real numbers.

Subtracting Real Numbers

If a and b are real numbers, then $a - b = a + (-b)$.

In other words, to find the difference of two numbers, we add the opposite of the number being subtracted.

PRACTICE PROBLEM 1

Subtract.
a. $-20 - 6$
b. $3 - (-5)$
c. $7 - 17$
d. $-4 - (-9)$

EXAMPLE 1 Subtract.

a. $-13 - 4$ **b.** $5 - (-6)$ **c.** $3 - 6$ **d.** $-1 - (-7)$

Solution:

a. $-13 - 4 = -13 + (-4)$ Add -13 to the opposite of 4, which is -4.

$\qquad\qquad = -17$

b. $5 - (-6) = 5 + (6)$ Add 5 to the opposite of -6, which is 6.

$\qquad\qquad = 11$

c. $3 - 6 = 3 + (-6)$ Add 3 to the opposite of 6, which is -6.

$\qquad\qquad = -3$

d. $-1 - (-7) = -1 + (7) = 6$

◼ **Work Practice Problem 1**

Helpful Hint

Study the patterns indicated.

No change — Change to addition. Change to opposite.

$5 - 11 = 5 + (-11) = -6$

$-3 - 4 = -3 + (-4) = -7$

$7 - (-1) = 7 + (1) = 8$

PRACTICE PROBLEMS 2–4

Subtract.
2. $9.6 - (-5.7)$
3. $-\dfrac{4}{9} - \dfrac{2}{9}$
4. $-\dfrac{1}{4} - \left(-\dfrac{2}{5}\right)$

Answers

1. a. -26, **b.** 8, **c.** -10, **d.** 5,

2. 15.3, **3.** $-\dfrac{2}{3}$, **4.** $\dfrac{3}{20}$

EXAMPLES Subtract.

2. $5.3 - (-4.6) = 5.3 + (4.6) = 9.9$

3. $-\dfrac{3}{10} - \dfrac{5}{10} = -\dfrac{3}{10} + \left(-\dfrac{5}{10}\right) = -\dfrac{8}{10} = -\dfrac{4}{5}$

4. $-\dfrac{2}{3} - \left(-\dfrac{4}{5}\right) = -\dfrac{2}{3} + \left(\dfrac{4}{5}\right) = -\dfrac{10}{15} + \dfrac{12}{15} = \dfrac{2}{15}$

◼ **Work Practice Problems 2–4**

EXAMPLE 5 Write each phrase as an expression and simplify.

a. Subtract 8 from −4.   **b.** Decrease 10 by −20.

Solution: Be careful when interpreting these. The order of numbers in subtraction is important.

a. 8 is to be subtracted **from** −4.

$$-4 - 8 = -4 + (-8) = -12$$

b. To decrease 10 by −20, we find 10 **minus** −20.

$$10 - (-20) = 10 + 20 = 30$$

◻ **Work Practice Problem 5**

If an expression contains additions and subtractions, just write the subtractions as equivalent additions. Then simplify from left to right.

EXAMPLE 6 Simplify each expression.

a. $-14 - 8 + 10 - (-6)$ **b.** $1.6 - (-10.3) + (-5.6)$

Solution:

a. $-14 - 8 + 10 - (-6) = -14 + (-8) + 10 + 6 = -6$

b. $1.6 - (-10.3) + (-5.6) = 1.6 + 10.3 + (-5.6) = 6.3$

◻ **Work Practice Problem 6**

When an expression contains parentheses and brackets, remember the order of operations. Start with the innermost set of parentheses or brackets and work your way outward.

EXAMPLE 7 Simplify each expression.

a. $-3 + [(-2 - 5) - 2]$ **b.** $2^3 - 10 + [-6 - (-5)]$

Solution:

a. Start with the innermost set of parentheses. Rewrite $-2 - 5$ as an addition.

$$-3 + [(-2 - 5) - 2] = -3 + [(-2 + (-5)) - 2]$$
$$= -3 + [(-7) - 2] \qquad \text{Add: } -2 + (-5).$$
$$= -3 + [-7 + (-2)] \qquad \text{Write } -7 - 2 \text{ as an addition.}$$
$$= -3 + [-9] \qquad \text{Add.}$$
$$= -12 \qquad \text{Add.}$$

b. Start simplifying the expression inside the brackets by writing $-6 - (-5)$ as an addition.

$$2^3 - 10 + [-6 - (-5)] = 2^3 - 10 + [-6 + 5]$$
$$= 2^3 - 10 + [-1] \qquad \text{Add.}$$
$$= 8 - 10 + (-1) \qquad \text{Evaluate } 2^3.$$
$$= 8 + (-10) + (-1) \qquad \text{Write } 8 - 10 \text{ as an addition.}$$
$$= -2 + (-1) \qquad \text{Add.}$$
$$= -3 \qquad \text{Add.}$$

◻ **Work Practice Problem 7**

Objective B Evaluating Algebraic Expressions

It is important to be able to evaluate expressions for given replacement values. This helps, for example, when checking solutions of equations.

PRACTICE PROBLEM 5

Write each phrase as an expression and simplify.

a. Subtract 7 from −11.

b. Decrease 35 by −25.

PRACTICE PROBLEM 6

Simplify each expression.

a. $-20 - 5 + 12 - (-3)$

b. $5.2 - (-4.4) + (-8.8)$

PRACTICE PROBLEM 7

Simplify each expression.

a. $-9 + [(-4 - 1) - 10]$

b. $5^2 - 20 + [-11 - (-3)]$

Answers

5. a. −18, **b.** 60, **6. a.** −10,
b. 0.8, **7. a.** −24, **b.** −3

PRACTICE PROBLEM 8

Find the value of each expression when $x = 1$ and $y = -4$.

a. $\dfrac{x - y}{14 + x}$

b. $x^2 - y$

EXAMPLE 8   Find the value of each expression when $x = 2$ and $y = -5$.

a. $\dfrac{x - y}{12 + x}$ b. $x^2 - y$

Solution:

a. Replace x with 2 and y with -5. Be sure to put parentheses around -5 to separate signs. Then simplify the resulting expression.

$$\frac{x - y}{12 + x} = \frac{2 - (-5)}{12 + 2} = \frac{2 + 5}{14} = \frac{7}{14} = \frac{1}{2}$$

b. Replace the x with 2 and y with -5 and simplify.

$$x^2 - y = 2^2 - (-5) = 4 - (-5) = 4 + 5 = 9$$

⬛ **Work Practice Problem 8**

> **Helpful Hint**
>
> For additional help when replacing variables with replacement values, first place parentheses about any variables.
>
> For Example 8b above, we have
>
> $$x^2 - y = \underbrace{(x)^2 - (y)}_{\substack{\text{Place parentheses} \\ \text{about variables}}} = \underbrace{(2)^2 - (-5)}_{\substack{\text{Replace variables} \\ \text{with values}}} = 4 - (-5) = 4 + 5 = 9$$

Objective C Solutions of Equations

Recall from section 8.2 that a solution of an equation is a value for the variable that makes the equation true.

PRACTICE PROBLEM 9

Determine whether -2 is a solution of $-1 + x = 1$.

EXAMPLE 9   Determine whether -4 is a solution of $x - 5 = -9$.

Solution: Replace x with -4 and see if a true statement results.

$$x - 5 = -9 \quad \text{Original equation}$$
$$-4 - 5 \stackrel{?}{=} -9 \quad \text{Replace } x \text{ with } -4.$$
$$-4 + (-5) \stackrel{?}{=} -9$$
$$-9 = -9 \quad \text{True}$$

Thus -4 is a solution of $x - 5 = -9$.

⬛ **Work Practice Problem 9**

Objective D Solving Problems That Involve Subtraction

Another use of real numbers is in recording altitudes above and below sea level, as shown in the next example.

PRACTICE PROBLEM 10

At 6:00 p.m., the temperature at the Winter Olympics was 14°; by morning the temperature dropped to $-23°$. Find the overall change in temperature.

EXAMPLE 10   **Finding the Difference in Elevations**

The lowest point on the surface of the Earth is the Dead Sea, at an elevation of 1349 feet below sea level. The highest point is Mt. Everest, at an elevation of 29,035 feet. What is the difference in elevation between these two world extremes? (*Source:* National Geographic Society)

Solution: To find the difference in elevation between the two heights, find the difference of the high point and the low point.

Answers

8. a. $\dfrac{1}{3}$,   b. 5,   9. -2 is not a solution.,

10. $-37°$

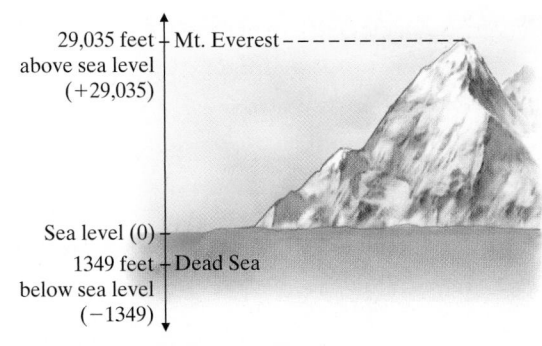

29,035 feet - Mt. Everest
above sea level
(+29,035)

Sea level (0)
1349 feet - Dead Sea
below sea level
(−1349)

In words: | high point | minus | low point |

Translate: 29,035   −   (−1349)   = 29,035 + 1349 feet
= 30,384 feet

Thus, the variation in elevation is 30,384 feet.

Work Practice Problem 10

Objective **E** Finding Complementary and Supplementary Angles

A knowledge of geometric concepts is needed by many professionals, such as doctors, carpenters, electronic technicians, gardeners, machinists, and pilots, just to name a few. With this in mind, we review the geometric concepts of **complementary** and **supplementary angles.**

Complementary and Supplementary Angles

Two angles are **complementary** if the sum of their measures is 90°.

Two angles are **supplementary** if the sum of their measures is 180°.

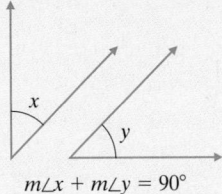

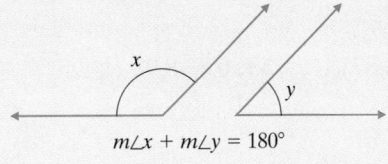

$m\angle x + m\angle y = 90°$

$m\angle x + m\angle y = 180°$

EXAMPLE 11 Find the measure of each unknown complementary or supplementary angle.

a.

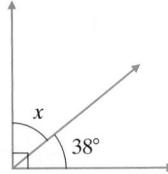

x
38°

b.

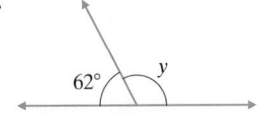

62° y

Solution:

a. These angles are complementary, so their sum is 90°. This means that the measure of angle x, $m\angle x$, is 90° − 38°.

$m\angle x = 90° − 38° = 52°$

b. These angles are supplementary, so their sum is 180°. This means that $m\angle y$ is 180° − 62°.

$m\angle y = 180° − 62° = 118°$

Work Practice Problem 11

PRACTICE PROBLEM 11

Find the measure of each unknown complementary or supplementary angle.

a.

x 78°

b.

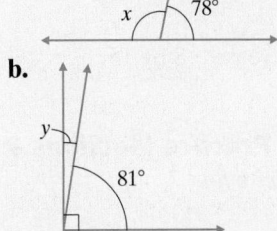

y
81°

Answers
11. a. 102°,   **b.** 9°

8.4 EXERCISE SET

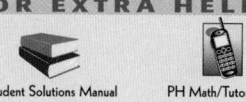

Student Solutions Manual   PH Math/Tutor Center   CD/Video for Review   MathXL   MathXL®   MyMathLab   MyMathLab

Objective Ⓐ *Subtract. See Examples 1 through 4.*

1. $-6 - 4$

2. $-12 - 8$

3. $4 - 9$

4. $8 - 11$

5. $16 - (-3)$

6. $12 - (-5)$

7. $7 - (-4)$

8. $3 - (-6)$

9. $-26 - (-18)$

10. $-60 - (-48)$

11. $-6 - 5$

12. $-8 - 4$

13. $16 - (-21)$

14. $15 - (-33)$

15. $-6 - (-11)$

16. $-4 - (-16)$

17. $-44 - 27$

18. $-36 - 51$

19. $-21 - (-21)$

20. $-17 - (-17)$

21. $-\dfrac{3}{11} - \left(-\dfrac{5}{11}\right)$

22. $-\dfrac{4}{7} - \left(-\dfrac{1}{7}\right)$

23. $9.7 - 16.1$

24. $8.3 - 11.2$

25. $-2.6 - (-6.7)$

26. $-6.1 - (-5.3)$

27. $\dfrac{1}{2} - \dfrac{2}{3}$

28. $\dfrac{3}{4} - \dfrac{7}{8}$

29. $-\dfrac{1}{6} - \dfrac{3}{4}$

30. $-\dfrac{1}{10} - \dfrac{7}{8}$

31. $8.3 - (-0.62)$

32. $4.3 - (-0.87)$

33. $0 - 8.92$

34. $0 - (-4.21)$

Write each phrase as an expression and simplify. See Example 5.

35. Subtract -5 from 8.

36. Subtract -2 from 3.

37. Find the difference between -6 and -1.

38. Find the difference between -17 and -1.

39. Subtract 8 from 7.

40. Subtract 9 from -4.

41. Decrease -8 by 15.

42. Decrease 11 by -14.

Mixed Practice (*Sections 8.2, 8.3, 8.4*) *Simplify each expression. (Remember the order of operations.) See Examples 6 and 7.*

43. $-10 - (-8) + (-4) - 20$

44. $-16 - (-3) + (-11) - 14$

572

45. $5 - 9 + (-4) - 8 - 8$

46. $7 - 12 + (-5) - 2 + (-2)$

47. $-6 - (2 - 11)$

48. $-9 - (3 - 8)$

49. $3^3 - 8 \cdot 9$

50. $2^3 - 6 \cdot 3$

51. $2 - 3(8 - 6)$

52. $4 - 6(7 - 3)$

53. $(3 - 6) + 4^2$

54. $(2 - 3) + 5^2$

55. $-2 + [(8 - 11) - (-2 - 9)]$

56. $-5 + [(4 - 15) - (-6) - 8]$

57. $|-3| + 2^2 + [-4 - (-6)]$

58. $|-2| + 6^2 + (-3 - 8)$

Objective **B** *Evaluate each expression when $x = -5$, $y = 4$, and $t = 10$. See Example 8.*

59. $x - y$

60. $y - x$

61. $\dfrac{9 - x}{y + 6}$

62. $\dfrac{15 - x}{y + 2}$

63. $|x| + 2t - 8y$

64. $|y| + 3x - 2t$

65. $y^2 - x$

66. $t^2 - x$

67. $\dfrac{|x - (-10)|}{2t}$

68. $\dfrac{|5y - x|}{6t}$

Objective **C** *Decide whether the given number is a solution of the given equation. See Example 9.*

69. $x - 9 = 5$; -4

70. $x - 10 = -7$; 3

71. $-x + 6 = -x - 1$; -2

72. $-x - 6 = -x - 1$; -10

73. $-x - 13 = -15$; 2

74. $4 = 1 - x$; 5

Objectives **D** **E** **Mixed Practice** *Solve. See Examples 10 and 11.*

75. Within 24 hours in 1916, the temperature in Browning, Montana, fell from 44° to −56°. How large a drop in temperature was this?

76. The coldest temperature ever recorded in Louisiana was −16°F. The hottest temperature ever recorded in Louisiana was 114°F. How much of a difference in temperature is there between these two extremes? (*Source:* National Climatic Data Center)

77. In a series of plays, the San Francisco 49ers gain 2 yards, lose 5 yards, and then lose another 20 yards. What is their total gain or loss of yardage?

78. In some card games, it is possible to have a negative score. Lavonne Schultz currently has a score of 15 points. She then loses 24 points. What is her new score?

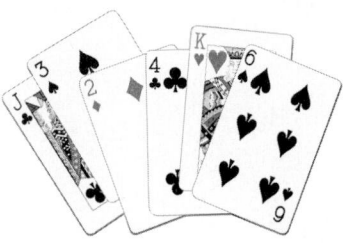

79. Pythagoras died in the year −475 (or 475 B.C.). When was he born, if he was 94 years old when he died?

80. The Greek astronomer and mathematician Geminus died in 60 A.D. at the age of 70. When was he born?

△ **81.** Find x if the angles below are complementary angles.

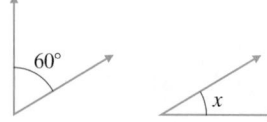

△ **82.** Find x if the angles below are supplementary angles.

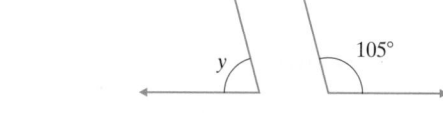

83. A commercial jet liner hits an air pocket and drops 250 feet. After climbing 120 feet, it drops another 178 feet. What is its overall vertical change?

84. Tyson Industries stock posted a loss of 1.625 points yesterday. If it drops another 0.75 point today, find its overall change for the two days.

85. The highest point in Africa is Mt. Kilimanjaro, Tanzania, at an elevation of 19,340 feet. The lowest point is Lake Assal, Djibouti, at 512 feet below sea level. How much higher is Mt. Kilimanjaro than Lake Assal? (*Source:* National Geographic Society)

86. The airport in Bishop, California, is at an elevation of 4101 feet above sea level. The nearby Furnace Creek Airport in Death Valley, California, is at an elevation of 226 feet below sea level. How much higher in elevation is the Bishop Airport than the Furnace Creek Airport? (*Source:* National Climatic Data Center)

Find each unknown complementary or supplementary angle.

△ **87.**

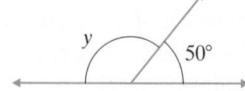

△ **88.**

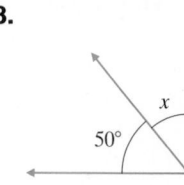

Review

Multiply as divide as indicated. See Sections 2.4 and 2.5.

89. $\frac{5}{8} \cdot 0$

90. $\frac{2}{3} \div \frac{3}{2}$

91. $1\frac{2}{3} \div 2\frac{1}{6}$

92. $3\frac{1}{2} \cdot \frac{11}{14}$

Concept Extensions

The following bar graph shows each month's average daily low temperature in degrees Fahrenheit for Barrow, Alaska. Use this graph to answer Exercises 93 through 95.

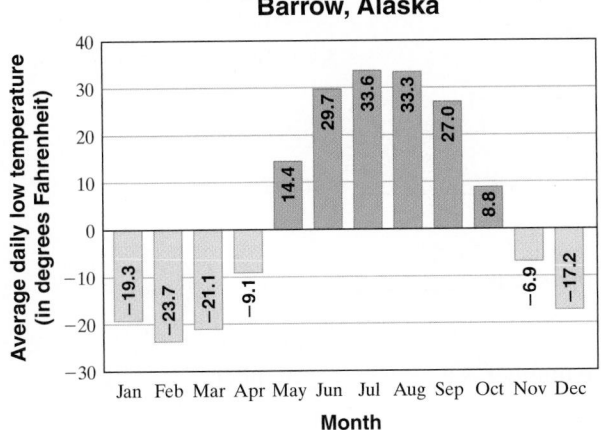

Barrow, Alaska

Source: National Climatic Data Center

93. Record the monthly increases and decreases in the low temperature from the previous month.

Month	Monthly Increase or Decrease
February	
March	
April	
May	
June	
July	
August	
September	
October	
November	
December	

94. Which month had the greatest increase in temperature?

95. Which month had the greatest decrease in temperature?

96. Find two numbers whose difference is −5.

97. Find two numbers whose difference is −9.

If p is a positive number and n is a negative number, determine whether each statement is true or false. Explain your answer.

98. $p - n$ is always a positive number.

99. $n - p$ is always a negative number.

100. $|n| - |p|$ is always a positive number.

101. $|n - p|$ is always a positive number.

Without calculating, determine whether each answer is positive or negative. Then use a calculator to find the exact difference.

102. $56{,}875 - 87{,}262$

103. $4.362 - 7.0086$

104. If a and b are positive numbers, then is $a - b$ always positive, always negative, or sometimes positive and sometimes negative?

105. If a and b are negative numbers, then is $a - b$ always positive, always negative, or sometimes positive and sometimes negative?

Operations on Real Numbers

Answer the following with positive, negative, or 0.

1. The opposite of a positive number is a _____ number.

2. The sum of two negative numbers is a _____ number.

3. The absolute value of a negative number is a _____ number.

4. The absolute value of zero is _____.

5. The reciprocal of a positive number is a _____ number.

6. The sum of a number and its opposite is _____.

7. The absolute value of a positive number is a _____ number.

8. The opposite of a negative number is a _____ number.

Fill in the chart:

	Number	Opposite	Absolute Value
9.	$\frac{1}{7}$		
10.	$-\frac{12}{5}$		
11.		-3	
12.		$\frac{9}{11}$	

Perform each indicated operation and simplify.

13. $-19 + (-23)$ **14.** $7 - (-3)$ **15.** $-15 + 17$ **16.** $-8 - 10$

17. $18 + (-25)$ **18.** $-2 + (-37)$ **19.** $-14 - (-12)$ **20.** $5 - 14$

21. $4.5 - 7.9$ **22.** $-8.6 - 1.2$ **23.** $-\frac{3}{4} - \frac{1}{7}$ **24.** $\frac{2}{3} - \frac{7}{8}$

25. $-9 - (-7) + 4 - 6$ **26.** $11 - 20 + (-3) - 12$ **27.** $24 - 6(14 - 11)$

28. $30 - 5(10 - 8)$ **29.** $(7 - 17) + 4^2$ **30.** $9^2 + (10 - 30)$

31. $|-9| + 3^2 + (-4 - 20)$ **32.** $|-4 - 5| + 5^2 + (-50)$

33. $-7 + [(1 - 2) + (-2 - 9)]$ **34.** $-6 + [(-3 + 7) + (4 - 15)]$

35. Subtract 5 from 1.   **36.** Subtract -2 from -3.

37. Subtract $-\dfrac{2}{5}$ from $\dfrac{1}{4}$.   **38.** Subtract $\dfrac{1}{10}$ from $-\dfrac{5}{8}$.

39. $2(19 - 17)^3 - 3(-7 + 9)^2$ **40.** $3(10 - 9)^2 + 6(20 - 19)^3$

Evaluate each expression when $x = -2$, $y = -1$, *and* $z = 9$.

41. $x - y$ **42.** $x + y$

43. $y + z$ **44.** $z - y$

45. $\dfrac{|5z - x|}{y - x}$ **46.** $\dfrac{|-x - y + z|}{2z}$

25.
26.
27.
28.
29.
30.
31.
32.
33.
34.
35.
36.
37.
38.
39.
40.
41.
42.
43.
44.
45.
46.

(A) Multiply Real Numbers.

(B) Find the Reciprocal of a Real Number.

(C) Divide Real Numbers.

(D) Evaluate Expressions Using Real Numbers.

(E) Determine Whether a Number is a Solution of a Given Equation.

8.5 MULTIPLYING AND DIVIDING REAL NUMBERS

Objective **(A)** Multiplying Real Numbers

Multiplication of real numbers is similar to multiplication of whole numbers. We just need to determine when the answer is positive, when it is negative, and when it is zero. To discover sign patterns for multiplication, recall that multiplication is repeated addition. For example, 3(2) means that 2 is added to itself three times, or

$$3(2) = 2 + 2 + 2 = 6$$

Also,

$$3(-2) = (-2) + (-2) + (-2) = -6$$

Since $3(-2) = -6$, this suggests that the product of a positive number and a negative number is a negative number.

What about the product of two negative numbers? To find out, consider the following pattern.

Factor decreases by 1 each time.
$$-3 \cdot 2 = -6$$
$$-3 \cdot 1 = -3 \quad \text{Product increases by 3 each time.}$$
$$-3 \cdot 0 = 0$$
$$-3 \cdot -1 = 3$$
$$-3 \cdot -2 = 6$$

This suggests that the product of two negative numbers is a positive number. Our results are given below.

Multiplying Real Numbers

1. The product of two numbers with the *same* sign is a positive number.

2. The product of two numbers with *different* signs is a negative number.

EXAMPLES Multiply.

1. $-7(6) = -42$ Different signs, so the product is negative.

2. $2(-10) = -20$

3. $-2(-14) = 28$ Same sign, so the product is positive.

4. $-\dfrac{2}{3} \cdot \dfrac{4}{7} = -\dfrac{2 \cdot 4}{3 \cdot 7} = -\dfrac{8}{21}$

5. $5(-1.7) = -8.5$

6. $-18(-3) = 54$

▢ Work Practice Problems 1–6

We already know that the product of 0 and any whole number is 0. This is true of all real numbers.

Products Involving Zero

If b is a real number, then $b \cdot 0 = 0$. Also $0 \cdot b = 0$.

PRACTICE PROBLEMS 1–6

Multiply.

1. $-8(3)$ **2.** $5(-30)$

3. $-4(-12)$ **4.** $-\dfrac{5}{6} \cdot \dfrac{1}{4}$

5. $6(-2.3)$ **6.** $-15(-2)$

Answers

1. -24,   **2.** -150,   **3.** 48,   **4.** $-\dfrac{5}{24}$,

5. -13.8,   **6.** 30

EXAMPLE 7 Multiply.

a. $7(0)(-6)$ **b.** $(-2)(-3)(-4)$ **c.** $(-1)(5)(-9)$

Solution:

a. By the order of operations, we multiply from left to right. Notice that because one of the factors is 0, the product is 0.

$$7(0)(-6) = 0(-6) = 0$$

b. Multiply two factors at a time, from left to right.

$$(-2)(-3)(-4) = (6)(-4) \quad \text{Multiply } (-2)(-3).$$
$$= -24$$

c. Multiply from left to right.

$$(-1)(5)(-9) = (-5)(-9) \quad \text{Multiply } (-1)(5).$$
$$= 45$$

▣ **Work Practice Problem 7**

PRACTICE PROBLEM 7

Multiply.
a. $5(0)(-3)$
b. $(-1)(-6)(-7)$
c. $(-2)(4)(-8)$

⟶ *Helpful Hint*

You may have noticed from the example that if we multiply:

- an *even* number of negative numbers, the product is *positive*.
- an *odd* number of negative numbers, the product is *negative*.

Now that we know how to multiply positive and negative numbers, let's see how we find the values of $(-5)^2$ and -5^2, for example. Although these two expressions look similar, the difference between the two is the parentheses. In $(-5)^2$, the parentheses tell us that the base, or repeated factor, is -5. In -5^2, only 5 is the base. Thus,

$$(-5)^2 = (-5)(-5) = 25 \quad \text{The base is } -5.$$
$$-5^2 = -(5 \cdot 5) = -25 \quad \text{The base is } 5.$$

EXAMPLE 8 Evaluate.

a. $(-2)^3$ **b.** -2^3 **c.** $(-3)^2$ **d.** -3^2 **e.** $\left(-\dfrac{2}{3}\right)^2$

Solution:

a. $(-2)^3 = (-2)(-2)(-2) = -8$ The base is -2.
b. $-2^3 = -(2 \cdot 2 \cdot 2) = -8$ The base is 2.
c. $(-3)^2 = (-3)(-3) = 9$ The base is -3.
d. $-3^2 = -(3 \cdot 3) = -9$ The base is 3.
e. $\left(-\dfrac{2}{3}\right)^2 = \left(-\dfrac{2}{3}\right)\left(-\dfrac{2}{3}\right) = \dfrac{4}{9}$ The base is $-\dfrac{2}{3}$.

▣ **Work Practice Problem 8**

PRACTICE PROBLEM 8

Evaluate.
a. $(-2)^4$ **b.** -2^4
c. $(-1)^5$ **d.** -1^5
e. $\left(-\dfrac{7}{9}\right)^2$

⟶ *Helpful Hint*

Be careful when identifying the base of an exponential expression.

$(-3)^2$ -3^2

Base is -3 Base is 3

$(-3)^2 = (-3)(-3) = 9$ $-3^2 = -(3 \cdot 3) = -9$

Answers

7. a. 0, **b.** -42, **c.** 64, **8. a.** 16,
b. -16, **c.** -1, **d.** -1, **e.** $\dfrac{49}{81}$

Objective **B** Finding Reciprocals

Addition and subtraction are related. Every difference of two numbers $a - b$ can be written as the sum $a + (-b)$. Multiplication and division are related also. For example, the quotient $6 \div 3$ can be written as the product $6 \cdot \frac{1}{3}$. Recall that the pair of numbers 3 and $\frac{1}{3}$ has a special relationship. Their product is 1 and they are called **reciprocals** or **multiplicative inverses** of each other.

Reciprocal or Multiplicative Inverse

Two numbers whose product is 1 are called **reciprocals** or **multiplicative inverses** of each other.

PRACTICE PROBLEM 9

Find the reciprocal of each number.

a. 13   **b.** $\frac{7}{15}$

c. -5 **d.** $-\frac{8}{11}$

e. 7.9

EXAMPLE 9 Find the reciprocal of each number.

a. 22   Reciprocal is $\frac{1}{22}$ since $22 \cdot \frac{1}{22} = 1$.

b. $\frac{3}{16}$ Reciprocal is $\frac{16}{3}$ since $\frac{3}{16} \cdot \frac{16}{3} = 1$.

c. -10 Reciprocal is $-\frac{1}{10}$ since $-10 \cdot -\frac{1}{10} = 1$.

d. $-\frac{9}{13}$ Reciprocal is $-\frac{13}{9}$ since $-\frac{9}{13} \cdot -\frac{13}{9} = 1$.

e. 1.7   Reciprocal is $\frac{1}{1.7}$ since $1.7 \cdot \frac{1}{1.7} = 1$.

■ **Work Practice Problem 9**

Helpful Hint

The fraction $\frac{1}{1.7}$ is not simplified since the denominator is a decimal number. For the purpose of finding a reciprocal, we will leave the fraction as is.

Does the number 0 have a reciprocal? If it does, it is a number n such that $0 \cdot n = 1$. Notice that this can never be true since $0 \cdot n = 0$. This means that 0 has no reciprocal.

Quotients Involving Zero

The number 0 does not have a reciprocal.

Objective **C** Dividing Real Numbers

We may now write a quotient as an equivalent product.

Quotient of Two Real Numbers

If a and b are real numbers and b is not 0, then

$$a \div b = \frac{a}{b} = a \cdot \frac{1}{b}$$

Answers

9. a. $\frac{1}{13}$,   **b.** $\frac{15}{7}$,   **c.** $-\frac{1}{5}$,

d. $-\frac{11}{8}$,   **e.** $\frac{1}{7.9}$

In other words, the quotient of two real numbers is the product of the first number and the multiplicative inverse or reciprocal of the second number.

EXAMPLE 10 Use the definition of the quotient of two numbers to find each quotient.

a. $-18 \div 3$ **b.** $\dfrac{-14}{-2}$ **c.** $\dfrac{20}{-4}$

Solution:

a. $-18 \div 3 = -18 \cdot \dfrac{1}{3} = -6$

b. $\dfrac{-14}{-2} = -14 \cdot -\dfrac{1}{2} = 7$

c. $\dfrac{20}{-4} = 20 \cdot -\dfrac{1}{4} = -5$

▢ **Work Practice Problem 10**

Since the quotient $a \div b$ can be written as the product $a \cdot \dfrac{1}{b}$, it follows that sign patterns for dividing two real numbers are the same as sign patterns for multiplying two real numbers.

Dividing Real Numbers

1. The quotient of two numbers with the same sign is a positive number.
2. The quotient of two numbers with different signs is a negative number.

EXAMPLE 11 Divide.

a. $\dfrac{-30}{-10} = 3$ Same sign, so the quotient is positive.

b. $\dfrac{-100}{5} = -20$

c. $\dfrac{20}{-2} = -10$ Different signs, so the quotient is negative.

d. $\dfrac{42}{-0.6} = -70$ $0.6\overline{)42.0}$ $70.$

▢ **Work Practice Problem 11**

In the examples above, we divided mentally or by long division. When we divide by a fraction, it is usually easier to multiply by its reciprocal.

EXAMPLES Divide.

12. $\dfrac{2}{3} \div \left(-\dfrac{5}{4}\right) = \dfrac{2}{3} \cdot \left(-\dfrac{4}{5}\right) = -\dfrac{8}{15}$

13. $-\dfrac{1}{6} \div \left(-\dfrac{2}{3}\right) = -\dfrac{1}{6} \cdot \left(-\dfrac{3}{2}\right) = \dfrac{3}{12} = \dfrac{\overset{1}{\cancel{3}}}{\underset{1}{\cancel{3} \cdot 4}} = \dfrac{1}{4}$

▢ **Work Practice Problems 12–13**

PRACTICE PROBLEM 10

Use the definition of the quotient of two numbers to find each quotient.

a. $-12 \div 4$ **b.** $\dfrac{-20}{-10}$

c. $\dfrac{36}{-4}$

PRACTICE PROBLEM 11

Divide.

a. $\dfrac{-25}{5}$ **b.** $\dfrac{-48}{-6}$

c. $\dfrac{50}{-2}$ **d.** $\dfrac{-72}{0.2}$

PRACTICE PROBLEMS 12–13

Divide.

12 $-\dfrac{5}{9} \div \dfrac{2}{3}$ **13** $-\dfrac{2}{7} \div \left(-\dfrac{1}{5}\right)$

Answers
10. a. -3, **b.** 2, **c.** -9,
11. a. -5, **b.** 8, **c.** -25, **d.** -360,
12. $-\dfrac{5}{6}$, **13.** $\dfrac{10}{7}$

Our definition of the quotient of two real numbers does not allow for division by 0 because 0 does not have a reciprocal. How then do we interpret $\frac{3}{0}$? We say that an expression such as this one is **undefined.** Can we divide 0 by a number other than 0? Yes; for example,

$$\frac{0}{3} = 0 \cdot \frac{1}{3} = 0$$

Division Involving Zero

If a is a nonzero number, then $\frac{0}{a} = 0$ and $\frac{a}{0}$ is undefined.

PRACTICE PROBLEM 14

Divide if possible.

a. $\dfrac{-7}{0}$ **b.** $\dfrac{0}{-2}$

EXAMPLE 14 Divide, if possible.

a. $\dfrac{1}{0}$ is undefined.   **b.** $\dfrac{0}{-3} = 0$

🔲 **Work Practice Problem 14**

Notice that $\dfrac{12}{-2} = -6, -\dfrac{12}{2} = -6$, and $\dfrac{-12}{2} = -6$. This means that

$$\frac{12}{-2} = -\frac{12}{2} = \frac{-12}{2}$$

In other words, a single negative sign in a fraction can be written in the denominator, in the numerator, or in front of the fraction without changing the value of the fraction.

If a and b are real numbers, and $b \neq 0$, then $\dfrac{a}{-b} = \dfrac{-a}{b} = -\dfrac{a}{b}$.

Objective D Evaluating Expressions

Examples combining basic arithmetic operations along with the principles of the order of operations help us to review these concepts of multiplying and dividing real numbers.

PRACTICE PROBLEM 15

Use order of operations to evaluate each expression.

a. $\dfrac{0(-5)}{3}$

b. $-3(-9) - 4(-4)$

c. $(-3)^2 + 2[(5 - 15) - |-4 - 1|]$

d. $\dfrac{-7(-4) + 2}{-10 - (-5)}$

e. $\dfrac{5(-2)^3 + 52}{-4 + 1}$

EXAMPLE 15 Use order of operations to evaluate each expression.

a. $\dfrac{0(-8)}{2}$

b. $-4(-11) - 5(-2)$

c. $(-2)^2 + 3[(-3 - 2) - |4 - 6|]$

d. $\dfrac{(-12)(-3) + 4}{-7 - (-2)}$

e. $\dfrac{2(-3)^2 - 20}{|-5| + 4}$

Solution:

a. $\dfrac{0(-8)}{2} = \dfrac{0}{2} = 0$

b. $(-4)(-11) - 5(-2) = 44 - (-10)$ Find the products.

$\qquad\qquad\qquad\qquad\quad = 44 + 10$ Add 44 to the opposite of -10.

$\qquad\qquad\qquad\qquad\quad = 54$ Add.

Answers

14. a. undefined, **b.** 0, **15. a.** 0,
b. 43, **c.** −21, **d.** −6, **e.** −4

c. $(-2)^2 + 3[(-3-2) - |4-6|] = (-2)^2 + 3[(-5) - |-2|]$ Simplify within innermost sets of grouping symbols.

$$= (-2)^2 + 3[-5 - 2]$$ Write $|-2|$ as 2.
$$= (-2)^2 + 3(-7)$$ Combine.
$$= 4 + (-21)$$ Evaluate $(-2)^2$ and then multiply $3(-7)$.
$$= -17$$ Add.

For parts d and e, first simplify the numerator and denominator separately; then divide.

d. $\dfrac{(-12)(-3) + 4}{-7 - (-2)} = \dfrac{36 + 4}{-7 + 2}$

$$= \dfrac{40}{-5}$$

$$= -8$$ Divide.

e. $\dfrac{2(-3)^2 - 20}{|-5| + 4} = \dfrac{2 \cdot 9 - 20}{5 + 4} = \dfrac{18 - 20}{9} = \dfrac{-2}{9} = -\dfrac{2}{9}$

▣ **Work Practice Problem 15**

Using what we have learned about multiplying and dividing real numbers, we continue to practice evaluating algebraic expressions.

EXAMPLE 16 Evaluate each expression when $x = -2$ and $y = -4$.

a. $\dfrac{3x}{2y}$ **b.** $x^3 - y^2$ **c.** $\dfrac{x-y}{-x}$

Solution: Replace x with -2 and y with -4 and simplify.

a. $\dfrac{3x}{2y} = \dfrac{3(-2)}{2(-4)} = \dfrac{-6}{-8} = \dfrac{6}{8} = \dfrac{\overset{1}{\cancel{2}} \cdot 3}{\underset{1}{\cancel{2}} \cdot 4} = \dfrac{3}{4}$

b. Replace x with -2 and y with -4.

$$x^3 - y^2 = (-2)^3 - (-4)^2$$ Substitute the given values for the variables.
$$= -8 - (16)$$ Evaluate $(-2)^3$ and $(-4)^2$.
$$= -8 + (-16)$$ Write as a sum.
$$= -24$$ Add.

c. $\dfrac{x-y}{-x} = \dfrac{-2 - (-4)}{-(-2)} = \dfrac{-2 + 4}{2} = \dfrac{2}{2} = 1$

▣ **Work Practice Problem 16**

Helpful Hint

Remember: For additional help when replacing variables with replacement values, first place parentheses about any variables.
Evaluate $3x - y^2$ when $x = 5$ and $y = -4$.

$$3x - y^2 = 3(x) - (y)^2$$ Place parentheses about variables only.
$$= 3(5) - (-4)^2$$ Replace variables with values.
$$= 15 - 16$$ Simplify.
$$= -1$$

PRACTICE PROBLEM 16

Evaluate each expression when $x = -1$ and $y = -5$.

a. $\dfrac{3y}{45x}$

b. $x^2 - y^3$

c. $\dfrac{x+y}{3x}$

Answers

16. a. $\dfrac{1}{3}$,   **b.** 126,   **c.** 2

Objective E Solutions of Equations

We use our skills in multiplying and dividing real numbers to check possible solutions of an equation.

PRACTICE PROBLEM 17

Determine whether -8 is a solution of $\dfrac{x}{4} - 3 = x + 3$.

EXAMPLE 17 Determine whether -10 is a solution of $\dfrac{-20}{x} + 15 = 2x$.

Solution:

$$\dfrac{-20}{x} + 15 = 2x \qquad \text{Original equation}$$

$$\dfrac{-20}{-10} + 15 \overset{?}{=} 2(-10) \qquad \text{Replace } x \text{ with } -10.$$

$$2 + 15 \overset{?}{=} -20 \qquad \text{Divide and multiply.}$$

$$17 = -20 \qquad \text{False}$$

Since we have a false statement, -10 is *not* a solution of the equation.

■ **Work Practice Problem 17**

Answer

17. -8 is a solution.

🖩 CALCULATOR EXPLORATIONS

Entering Negative Numbers on a Scientific Calculator

To enter a negative number on a scientific calculator, find a key marked ⎡ +/− ⎤. (On some calculators, this key is marked ⎡ CHS ⎤ for "change sign.") To enter −8, for example, press the keys ⎡ 8 ⎤ ⎡ +/− ⎤. The display will read ⎡ −8 ⎤.

Entering Negative Numbers on a Graphing Calculator

To enter a negative number on a graphing calculator, find a key marked ⎡ (−) ⎤. Do not confuse this key with the key ⎡ − ⎤, which is used for subtraction. To enter −8, for example, press the keys ⎡ (−) ⎤ ⎡ 8 ⎤. The display will read ⎡ −8 ⎤.

Operations with Real Numbers

To evaluate $-2(7 - 9) - 20$ on a calculator, press the keys

⎡ 2 ⎤ ⎡ +/− ⎤ ⎡ × ⎤ ⎡ (⎤ ⎡ 7 ⎤ ⎡ − ⎤ ⎡ 9 ⎤ ⎡) ⎤ ⎡ − ⎤ ⎡ 2 ⎤ ⎡ 0 ⎤
⎡ = ⎤, or ⎡ (−) ⎤ ⎡ 2 ⎤ ⎡ (⎤ ⎡ 7 ⎤ ⎡ − ⎤ ⎡ 9 ⎤ ⎡) ⎤ ⎡ − ⎤ ⎡ 2 ⎤ ⎡ 0 ⎤
⎡ ENTER ⎤.

The display will read ⎡ −16 ⎤ or

$$\begin{array}{r} -2(7 - 9) - 20 \\ -16 \end{array}$$

Use a calculator to simplify each expression.

1. $-38(26 - 27)$
2. $-59(-8) + 1726$
3. $134 + 25(68 - 91)$
4. $45(32) - 8(218)$
5. $\dfrac{-50(294)}{175 - 205}$
6. $\dfrac{-444 - 444.8}{-181 - (-181)}$
7. $9^5 - 4550$
8. $5^8 - 6259$
9. $(-125)^2$ (Be careful.)
10. -125^2 (Be careful.)

Mental Math

Answer the following with positive or negative.

1. The product of two negative numbers is a _____ number.

2. The quotient of two negative numbers is a _____ number.

3. The quotient of a positive number and a negative number is a _____ number.

4. The product of a positive number and a negative number is a _____ number.

5. The reciprocal of a positive number is a _____ number.

6. The opposite of a positive number is a _____ number.

8.5 EXERCISE SET

Objective A *Multiply. See Examples 1 through 6.*

1. $-6(4)$

2. $-8(5)$

3. $2(-1)$

4. $7(-4)$

5. $-5(-10)$

6. $-6(-11)$

7. $-3 \cdot 15$

8. $-2 \cdot 37$

9. $-\dfrac{1}{2}\left(-\dfrac{3}{5}\right)$

10. $-\dfrac{1}{8}\left(-\dfrac{1}{3}\right)$

11. $5(-1.4)$

12. $6(-2.5)$

Evaluate. See Examples 7 and 8.

13. $(-1)(-3)(-5)$

14. $(-2)(-3)(-4)$

15. $(2)(-1)(-3)(0)$

16. $(3)(-5)(-2)(0)$

17. $(-4)^2$

18. $(-3)^3$

19. -4^2

20. -6^2

21. $\left(-\dfrac{3}{4}\right)^2$

22. $\left(-\dfrac{2}{7}\right)^2$

23. -0.7^2

24. -0.8^2

Objective B *Find each reciprocal. See Example 9.*

25. $\dfrac{2}{3}$

26. $\dfrac{1}{7}$

27. -14

28. -8

29. $-\dfrac{3}{11}$

30. $-\dfrac{6}{13}$

31. 0.2

32. 1.5

Objective [C] *Divide. See Examples 10 through 14.*

33. $\dfrac{18}{-2}$

34. $\dfrac{36}{-9}$

35. $-48 \div 12$

36. $-60 \div 5$

37. $\dfrac{0}{-4}$

38. $\dfrac{0}{-9}$

39. $\dfrac{5}{0}$

40. $\dfrac{8}{0}$

41. $\dfrac{6}{7} \div \left(-\dfrac{1}{3}\right)$

42. $\dfrac{4}{5} \div \left(-\dfrac{1}{2}\right)$

43. $-3.2 \div -0.02$

44. $-4.9 \div -0.07$

Objectives [A] [C] **Mixed Practice** *Perform the indicated operation. See Examples 1 through 14.*

45. $(-8)(-8)$

46. $(-7)(-7)$

47. $\dfrac{2}{3}\left(-\dfrac{4}{9}\right)$

48. $\dfrac{2}{7}\left(-\dfrac{2}{11}\right)$

49. $\dfrac{-12}{-4}$

50. $\dfrac{-45}{-9}$

51. $\dfrac{30}{-2}$

52. $\dfrac{14}{-2}$

53. $(-5)^3$

54. $(-2)^5$

55. $(-0.2)^3$

56. $(-0.3)^3$

57. $-\dfrac{3}{4}\left(-\dfrac{8}{9}\right)$

58. $-\dfrac{5}{6}\left(-\dfrac{3}{10}\right)$

59. $-\dfrac{5}{9} \div \left(-\dfrac{3}{4}\right)$

60. $-\dfrac{1}{10} \div \left(-\dfrac{8}{11}\right)$

61. $-2.1(-0.4)$

62. $-1.3(-0.6)$

63. $\dfrac{-48}{1.2}$

64. $\dfrac{-86}{2.5}$

65. $(-3)^4$

66. -3^4

67. -1^7

68. $(-1)^7$

69. Multiply -11 by 11.

70. Multiply -12 by 12.

71. Find the quotient of $-\dfrac{4}{9}$ and $\dfrac{4}{9}$.

72. Find the quotient of $-\dfrac{5}{12}$ and $\dfrac{5}{12}$.

Mixed Practice (*Sections 8.3, 8.4, 8.5*) *Perform the indicated operation.*

73. $-9 - 10$

74. $-8 - 11$

75. $-9(-10)$

76. $-8(-11)$

77. $7(-12)$

78. $6(-15)$

79. $7 + (-12)$

80. $6 + (-15)$

Objective D *Evaluate each expression. See Example 15.*

81. $\dfrac{-9(-3)}{-6}$

82. $\dfrac{-6(-3)}{-4}$

83. $-3(2-8)$

84. $-4(3-9)$

85. $-7(-2)-3(-1)$

86. $-8(-3)-4(-1)$

87. $2^2-3[(2-8)-(-6-8)]$

88. $3^2-2[(3-5)-(2-9)]$

89. $\dfrac{-6^2+4}{-2}$

90. $\dfrac{3^2+4}{5}$

91. $\dfrac{-3-5^2}{2(-7)}$

92. $\dfrac{-2-4^2}{3(-6)}$

93. $\dfrac{22+(3)(-2)^2}{-5-2}$

94. $\dfrac{-20+(-4)^2(3)}{1-5}$

95. $\dfrac{(-4)^2-16}{4-12}$

96. $\dfrac{(-2)^2-4}{4-9}$

97. $\dfrac{6-2(-3)}{4-3(-2)}$

98. $\dfrac{8-3(-2)}{2-5(-4)}$

99. $\dfrac{|5-9|+|10-15|}{|2(-3)|}$

100. $\dfrac{|-3+6|+|-2+7|}{|-2\cdot2|}$

101. $\dfrac{-7(-1)+(-3)4}{(-2)(5)+(-6)(-8)}$

102. $\dfrac{8(-7)+(-2)(-6)}{(-9)(3)+(-10)(-11)}$

Evaluate each expression when $x = -5$ and $y = -3$. See Example 16.

103. $\dfrac{2x-5}{y-2}$

104. $\dfrac{2y-12}{x-4}$

105. $\dfrac{6-y}{x-4}$

106. $\dfrac{10-y}{x-8}$

107. $\dfrac{4-2x}{y+3}$

108. $\dfrac{2y+3}{-5-x}$

109. $\dfrac{x^2+y}{3y}$

110. $\dfrac{y^2-x}{2x}$

Objective E *Decide whether the given number is a solution of the given equation. See Example 17.*

111. $-3x-5=-20;\quad 5$

112. $17-4x=x+27;\quad -2$

113. $\dfrac{x}{5}+2=-1;\quad 15$

114. $\dfrac{x}{6}-3=5;\quad 48$

115. $\dfrac{x-3}{7}=-2;\quad -11$

116. $\dfrac{x+4}{5}=-6;\quad -30$

Review

Find the perimeter of each figure. See Section 6.3.

△ **117.** Square

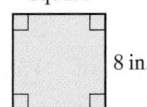
8 in.

△ **118.** Parallelogram

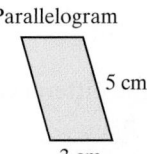
5 cm
3 cm

△ **119.** Rectangle

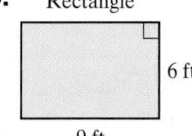
6 ft
9 ft

△ **120.** Triangle

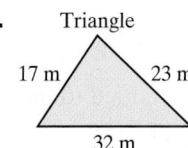
17 m   23 m
32 m

Concept Extensions

State whether each statement is true or false.

121. The product of three negative integers is negative.

122. The product of three positive integers is positive.

123. The product of four negative integers is negative.

124. The product of four positive integers is positive.

Study the bar graph below showing the average surface temperatures of planets. Use Exercises 125 and 126 to complete the planet temperatures on the graph.

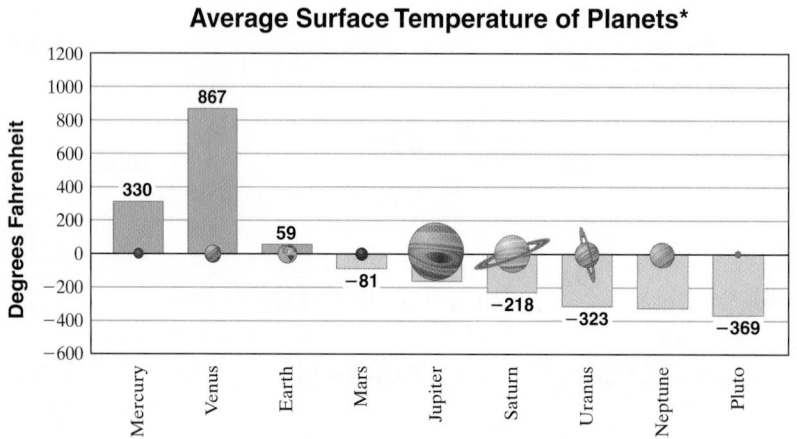

Average Surface Temperature of Planets*

*(For some planets, the temperature given is the temperature where the atmosphere pressure equals 1 Earth atmosphere; Source: The World Almanac, 2005)

125. The surface temperature of Jupiter is twice the temperature of Mars. Find this temperature.

126. The surface temperature of Neptune is equal to the temperature of Mercury divided by −1. Find this temperature.

127. Explain why the product of an even number of negative numbers is a positive number.

128. If a and b are any real numbers, is the statement $a \cdot b = b \cdot a$ always true? Why or why not?

129. Find any real numbers that are their own reciprocal.

130. Explain why 0 has no reciprocal.

Write each as an algebraic expression. Then simplify the expression.

131. 7 subtracted from the quotient of 0 and 5

132. Twice the sum of −3 and −4

133. −1 added to the product of −8 and −5

134. The difference of −9 and the product of −4 and −6

THE BIGGER PICTURE Simplifying Expressions

In this chapter, we increase our discussion of algebra. For this reason, and to keep your outlines manageable, we start a second outline. Don't forget that although suggestions are given, this outline should be in your own words. Once you complete the new portion of your outline, try the exercises below. Remember: Study your outline often as you proceed through this portion of your text.

I. Simplifying Expressions

   A. Real Numbers

      1. Add:

        $-1.7 + (-0.21) = -1.91$ Adding like signs. Add absolute values. Attach the common sign.

        $-7 + 3 = -4$ Adding unlike signs. Subtract absolute values. Attach the sign of the number with the larger absolute value.

      2. Subtract: Add the first number to the opposite of the second number.

$$\frac{1}{7} - \frac{1}{3} = \frac{3}{21} + \left(-\frac{7}{21}\right) = -\frac{4}{21}$$

      3. Multiply or Divide: Multiply or divide as usual. If the signs of the two numbers are the same, the answer is positive. If the signs of the two numbers are different, the answer is negative.

$$-\frac{3}{8} \cdot \frac{7}{11} = -\frac{21}{88}, \qquad -42 \div (-10) = 4.2$$

Perform the indicated operations.

1. $-0.2(25)$

2. $86 - 100$

3. $-\dfrac{1}{7} + \left(-\dfrac{3}{5}\right)$

4. $\dfrac{-40}{-5}$

5. $(-7)^2$

6. -7^2

7. $\dfrac{|-42|}{-|-2|}$

8. $\dfrac{8.6}{0}$

9. $\dfrac{0}{8.6}$

10. $-25 - (-13)$

11. $-8.3 - 8.3$

12. $-\dfrac{8}{9}\left(-\dfrac{3}{16}\right)$

13. $2 + 3(8 - 11)^3$

14. $-2\dfrac{1}{2} \div \left(-3\dfrac{1}{4}\right)$

15. $20 \div 2 \cdot 5$

16. $-2[(1 - 5) - (7 - 17)]$

8.6 PROPERTIES OF REAL NUMBERS

Objective **A** Using the Commutative and Associative Properties

In this section we give names to properties of real numbers with which we are already familiar. Throughout this section, the variables a, b, and c represent real numbers.

Recall that order does not matter when adding numbers. For example, we know that $7 + 5$ is the same as $5 + 7$. This property is given a special name—the **commutative property of addition.** We also know that order does not matter when multiplying numbers. For example, we know that $-5(6) = 6(-5)$. This property means that multiplication is commutative also and is called the **commutative property of multiplication.**

Commutative Properties

Addition:	$a + b = b + a$
Multiplication:	$a \cdot b = b \cdot a$

These properties state that the *order* in which any two real numbers are added or multiplied does not change their sum or product. For example, if we let $a = 3$ and $b = 5$, then the commutative properties guarantee that

$$3 + 5 = 5 + 3 \quad \text{and} \quad 3 \cdot 5 = 5 \cdot 3$$

Helpful Hint

Is subtraction also commutative? Try an example. Is $3 - 2 = 2 - 3$? **No!** The left side of this statement equals 1; the right side equals -1. There is no commutative property of subtraction. Similarly, there is no commutative property of division. For example, $10 \div 2$ does not equal $2 \div 10$.

PRACTICE PROBLEM 1

Use a commutative property to complete each statement.

a. $7 \cdot y = $ _____

b. $4 + x = $ _____

EXAMPLE 1 Use a commutative property to complete each statement.

a. $x + 5 = $ _____   **b.** $3 \cdot x = $ _____

Solution:

a. $x + 5 = 5 + x$ By the commutative property of addition

b. $3 \cdot x = x \cdot 3$ By the commutative property of multiplication

▨ **Work Practice Problem 1**

✔ **Concept Check** Which of the following pairs of actions are commutative?

a. "raking the leaves" and "bagging the leaves"

b. "putting on your left glove" and "putting on your right glove"

c. "putting on your coat" and "putting on your shirt"

d. "reading a novel" and "reading a newspaper"

Answers

1. **a.** $y \cdot 7$,   **b.** $x + 4$

✔ **Concept Check Answer**

b, d

Let's now discuss grouping numbers. When we add three numbers, the way in which they are grouped or associated does not change their sum. For example, we know that $2 + (3 + 4) = 2 + 7 = 9$. This result is the same if we group the numbers differently. In other words, $(2 + 3) + 4 = 5 + 4 = 9$, also. Thus, $2 + (3 + 4) = (2 + 3) + 4$. This property is called the **associative property of addition.**

In the same way, changing the grouping of numbers when multiplying does not change their product. For example, $2 \cdot (3 \cdot 4) = (2 \cdot 3) \cdot 4$ (check it). This is the **associative property of multiplication.**

Associative Properties

Addition:	$(a + b) + c = a + (b + c)$
Multiplication:	$(a \cdot b) \cdot c = a \cdot (b \cdot c)$

These properties state that the way in which three numbers are *grouped* does not change their sum or their product.

EXAMPLE 2 Use an associative property to complete each statement.

a. $5 + (4 + 6) =$ _____

b. $(-1 \cdot 2) \cdot 5 =$ _____

c. $(m + n) + 9 =$ _____

d. $(xy) \cdot 12 =$ _____

Solution:

a. $5 + (4 + 6) = (5 + 4) + 6$ By the associative property of addition

b. $(-1 \cdot 2) \cdot 5 = -1 \cdot (2 \cdot 5)$ By the associative property of multiplication

c. $(m + n) + 9 = m + (n + 9)$ By the associative property of addition

d. $(xy) \cdot 12 = x \cdot (y \cdot 12)$ Recall that xy means $x \cdot y$.

🖱 **Work Practice Problem 2**

> **Helpful Hint**
>
> Remember the difference between the commutative properties and the associative properties. The commutative properties have to do with the *order* of numbers and the associative properties have to do with the *grouping* of numbers.

EXAMPLES

Determine whether each statement is true by an associative property or a commutative property.

3. $(7 + 10) + 4 = (10 + 7) + 4$ Since the order of two numbers was changed and their grouping was not, this is true by the commutative property of addition.

4. $2 \cdot (3 \cdot 1) = (2 \cdot 3) \cdot 1$ Since the grouping of the numbers was changed and their order was not, this is true by the associative property of multiplication.

🖱 **Work Practice Problems 3–4**

Let's now illustrate how these properties can help us simplify expressions.

PRACTICE PROBLEM 2

Use an associative property to complete each statement.

a. $5 \cdot (-3 \cdot 6) =$ _____

b. $(-2 + 7) + 3 =$ _____

c. $(q + r) + 17 =$ _____

d. $(ab) \cdot 21 =$ _____

PRACTICE PROBLEMS 3–4

Determine whether each statement is true by an associative property or a commutative property.

3. $5 \cdot (4 \cdot 7) = 5 \cdot (7 \cdot 4)$

4. $-2 + (4 + 9)$
$= (-2 + 4) + 9$

Answers

2. a. $(5 \cdot -3) \cdot 6$,   **b.** $-2 + (7 + 3)$,
c. $q + (r + 17)$,   **d.** $a \cdot (b \cdot 21)$,
3. commutative,   **4.** associative

CHAPTER 8 | REAL NUMBERS AND INTRODUCTION TO ALGEBRA

PRACTICE PROBLEMS 5–6

Simplify each expression.

5. $(-3 + x) + 17$

6. $4(5x)$

EXAMPLES Simplify each expression.

5. $10 + (x + 12) = 10 + (12 + x)$ By the commutative property of addition

$\qquad\qquad\qquad = (10 + 12) + x$ By the associative property of addition

$\qquad\qquad\qquad = 22 + x$ Add.

6. $-3(7x) = (-3 \cdot 7)x$ By the associative property of multiplication

$\qquad\qquad = -21x$ Multiply.

◻ **Work Practice Problems 5–6**

Objective B Using the Distributive Property

The **distributive property of multiplication over addition** is used repeatedly throughout algebra. It is useful because it allows us to write a product as a sum or a sum as a product.

We know that $7(2 + 4) = 7(6) = 42$. Compare that with

$$7(2) + 7(4) = 14 + 28 = 42$$

Since both original expressions equal 42, they must equal each other, or

$$7(2 + 4) = 7(2) + 7(4)$$

This is an example of the distributive property. The product on the left side of the equal sign is equal to the sum on the right side. We can think of the 7 as being distributed to each number inside the parentheses.

Distributive Property of Multiplication Over Addition

$$a(b + c) = ab + ac$$

Since multiplication is commutative, this property can also be written as

$$(b + c)a = ba + ca$$

The distributive property can also be extended to more than two numbers inside the parentheses. For example,

$$3(x + y + z) = 3(x) + 3(y) + 3(z)$$
$$= 3x + 3y + 3z$$

Since we define subtraction in terms of addition, the distributive property is also true for subtraction. For example,

$$2(x - y) = 2(x) - 2(y)$$
$$= 2x - 2y$$

PRACTICE PROBLEMS 7–12

Use the distributive property to write each expression without parentheses. Then simplify the result.

7. $5(x + y)$

8. $-3(2 + 7x)$

9. $4(x + 6y - 2z)$

10. $-1(3 - a)$

11. $-(8 + a - b)$

12. $\dfrac{1}{2}(2x + 4) + 9$

EXAMPLES Use the distributive property to write each expression without parentheses. Then simplify the result.

7. $2(x + y) = 2(x) + 2(y)$
$$= 2x + 2y$$

8. $-5(-3 + 2z) = -5(-3) + (-5)(2z)$
$$= 15 - 10z$$

9. $5(x + 3y - z) = 5(x) + 5(3y) - 5(z)$
$$= 5x + 15y - 5z$$

Answers

5. $14 + x$,   **6.** $20x$,   **7.** $5x + 5y$,

8. $-6 - 21x$,   **9.** $4x + 24y - 8z$,

10. $-3 + a$,   **11.** $-8 - a + b$,

12. $x + 11$

Copyright 2007 Pearson Education, Inc.

10. $-1(2 - y) = (-1)(2) - (-1)(y)$
$\qquad = -2 + y$

11. $-(3 + x - w) = -1(3 + x - w)$
$\qquad = (-1)(3) + (-1)(x) - (-1)(w)$
$\qquad = -3 - x + w$

> **Helpful Hint**
>
> Notice in Example 11 that $-(3 + x - w)$ is first rewritten as $-1(3 + x - w)$.

12. $\dfrac{1}{2}(6x + 14) + 10 = \dfrac{1}{2}(6x) + \dfrac{1}{2}(14) + 10$ Apply the distributive property.
$\qquad\qquad\qquad\qquad = 3x + 7 + 10$ Multiply.
$\qquad\qquad\qquad\qquad = 3x + 17$ Add.

▶ **Work Practice Problems 7–12**

The distributive property can also be used to write a sum as a product.

EXAMPLES Use the distributive property to write each sum as a product.

13. $8 \cdot 2 + 8 \cdot x = 8(2 + x)$

14. $7s + 7t = 7(s + t)$

▶ **Work Practice Problems 13–14**

Objective C Using the Identity and Inverse Properties

Next, we look at the **identity properties.**

The number 0 is called the identity for addition because when 0 is added to any real number, the result is the same real number. In other words, the *identity* of the real number is not changed.

The number 1 is called the identity for multiplication because when a real number is multiplied by 1, the result is the same real number. In other words, the *identity* of the real number is not changed.

Identities for Addition and Multiplication

0 is the identity element for addition.

$\qquad a + 0 = a \quad \text{and} \quad 0 + a = a$

1 is the identity element for multiplication.

$\qquad a \cdot 1 = a \quad \text{and} \quad 1 \cdot a = a$

Notice that 0 is the *only* number that can be added to any real number with the result that the sum is the same real number. Also, 1 is the *only* number that can be multiplied by any real number with the result that the product is the same real number.

Additive inverses or **opposites** were introduced in Section 8.3. Two numbers are called additive inverses or opposites if their sum is 0. The additive inverse or opposite of 6 is -6 because $6 + (-6) = 0$. The additive inverse or opposite of -5 is 5 because $-5 + 5 = 0$.

Reciprocals or **multiplicative inverses** were introduced in Section 2.5. Two nonzero numbers are called reciprocals or multiplicative inverses if their product is 1. The reciprocal or multiplicative inverse of $\dfrac{2}{3}$ is $\dfrac{3}{2}$ because $\dfrac{2}{3} \cdot \dfrac{3}{2} = 1$. Likewise, the reciprocal of -5 is $-\dfrac{1}{5}$ because $-5\left(-\dfrac{1}{5}\right) = 1$.

PRACTICE PROBLEMS 13–14

Use the distributive property to write each sum as a product.

13. $9 \cdot 3 + 9 \cdot y$

14. $4x + 4y$

Answers

13. $9(3 + y)$,   **14.** $4(x + y)$

Additive or Multiplicative Inverses

The numbers a and $-a$ are additive inverses or opposites of each other because their sum is 0; that is,

$$a + (-a) = 0$$

The numbers b and $\dfrac{1}{b}$ (for $b \neq 0$) are reciprocals or multiplicative inverses of each other because their product is 1; that is,

$$b \cdot \dfrac{1}{b} = 1$$

✔ **Concept Check** Which of the following is the

a. opposite of $-\dfrac{3}{10}$, and which is the

b. reciprocal of $-\dfrac{3}{10}$?

$$1, -\dfrac{10}{3}, \dfrac{3}{10}, 0, \dfrac{10}{3}, -\dfrac{3}{10}$$

PRACTICE PROBLEMS 15–21

Name the property illustrated by each true statement.

15. $7(a + b) = 7 \cdot a + 7 \cdot b$

16. $12 + y = y + 12$

17. $-4 \cdot (6 \cdot x) = (-4 \cdot 6) \cdot x$

18. $6 + (z + 2) = 6 + (2 + z)$

19. $3\left(\dfrac{1}{3}\right) = 1$

20. $(x + 0) + 23 = x + 23$

21. $(7 \cdot y) \cdot 10 = y \cdot (7 \cdot 10)$

EXAMPLES Name the property illustrated by each true statement.

15. $3(x + y) = 3 \cdot x + 3 \cdot y$ Distributive property

16. $(x + 7) + 9 = x + (7 + 9)$ Associative property of addition (grouping changed)

17. $(b + 0) + 3 = b + 3$ Identity element for addition

18. $2 \cdot (z \cdot 5) = 2 \cdot (5 \cdot z)$ Commutative property of multiplication (order changed)

19. $-2 \cdot \left(-\dfrac{1}{2}\right) = 1$ Multiplicative inverse property

20. $-2 + 2 = 0$ Additive inverse property

21. $-6 \cdot (y \cdot 2) = (-6 \cdot 2) \cdot y$ Commutative and associative properties of multiplication (order and grouping changed)

▨ **Work Practice Problems 15–21**

Answers

15. distributive property,
16. commutative property of addition,
17. associative property of multiplication, **18.** commutative property of addition,
19. multiplicative inverse property,
20. identity element for addition,
21. commutative and associative properties of multiplication

✔ **Concept Check Answers**

a. $\dfrac{3}{10}$,   b. $-\dfrac{10}{3}$

8.6 EXERCISE SET

Objective A *Use a commutative property to complete each statement. See Examples 1 and 3.*

1. $x + 16 =$ _____

2. $8 + y =$ _____

3. $-4 \cdot y =$ _____

4. $-2 \cdot x =$ _____

5. $xy =$ _____

6. $ab =$ _____

7. $2x + 13 =$ _____

8. $19 + 3y =$ _____

Use an associative property to complete each statement. See Examples 2 and 4.

9. $(xy) \cdot z =$ _____

10. $3 \cdot (x \cdot y) =$ _____

11. $2 + (a + b) =$ _____

12. $(y + 4) + z =$ _____

13. $4 \cdot (ab) =$ _____

14. $(-3y) \cdot z =$ _____

15. $(a + b) + c =$ _____

16. $6 + (r + s) =$ _____

Use the commutative and associative properties to simplify each expression. See Examples 5 and 6.

17. $8 + (9 + b)$

18. $(r + 3) + 11$

19. $4(6y)$

20. $2(42x)$

21. $\frac{1}{5}(5y)$

22. $\frac{1}{8}(8z)$

23. $(13 + a) + 13$

24. $7 + (x + 4)$

25. $-9(8x)$

26. $-3(12y)$

27. $\frac{3}{4}\left(\frac{4}{3}s\right)$

28. $\frac{2}{7}\left(\frac{7}{2}r\right)$

29. $-\frac{1}{2}(5x)$

30. $-\frac{1}{3}(7x)$

Objective B *Use the distributive property to write each expression without parentheses. Then simplify the result, if possible. See Examples 7 through 12.*

31. $4(x + y)$

32. $7(a + b)$

33. $9(x - 6)$

34. $11(y - 4)$

35. $2(3x + 5)$

36. $5(7 + 8y)$

37. $7(4x - 3)$

38. $3(8x - 1)$

39. $3(6 + x)$

40. $2(x + 5)$

41. $-2(y - z)$

42. $-3(z - y)$

43. $-\frac{1}{3}(3y + 5)$

44. $-\frac{1}{2}(2r + 11)$

45. $5(x + 4m + 2)$

46. $8(3y + z - 6)$

47. $-4(1 - 2m + n) + 4$

48. $-4(4 + 2p + 5) + 16$

49. $-(5x + 2)$

50. $-(9r + 5)$

51. $-(r - 3 - 7p) + 3$

52. $-(q - 2 + 6r) + 2$

53. $\frac{1}{2}(6x + 7) + \frac{1}{2}$

54. $\frac{1}{4}(4x - 2) - \frac{7}{2}$

55. $-\dfrac{1}{3}(3x - 9y)$ **56.** $-\dfrac{1}{5}(10a - 25b)$ **57.** $3(2r + 5) - 7$ **58.** $10(4s + 6) - 40$

59. $-9(4x + 8) + 2$ **60.** $-11(5x + 3) + 10$ **61.** $-0.4(4x + 5) - 0.5$ **62.** $-0.6(2x + 1) - 0.1$

Use the distributive property to write each sum as a product. See Examples 13 and 14.

63. $4 \cdot 1 + 4 \cdot y$ **64.** $14 \cdot z + 14 \cdot 5$ **65.** $11x + 11y$ **66.** $9a + 9b$

67. $(-1) \cdot 5 + (-1) \cdot x$ **68.** $(-3)a + (-3)y$ **69.** $30a + 30b$ **70.** $25x + 25y$

Objectives Ⓐ Ⓒ *Name the properties illustrated by each true statement. See Examples 15 through 21.*

71. $3 \cdot 5 = 5 \cdot 3$ **72.** $4(3 + 8) = 4 \cdot 3 + 4 \cdot 8$

73. $2 + (x + 5) = (2 + x) + 5$ **74.** $9 \cdot (x \cdot 7) = (9 \cdot x) \cdot 7$

75. $(x + 9) + 3 = (9 + x) + 3$ **76.** $1 \cdot 9 = 9$

77. $(4 \cdot y) \cdot 9 = 4 \cdot (y \cdot 9)$ **78.** $-4 \cdot (8 \cdot 3) = (8 \cdot 3) \cdot (-4)$

79. $0 + 6 = 6$ **80.** $(a + 9) + 6 = a + (9 + 6)$

81. $-4(y + 7) = -4 \cdot y + (-4) \cdot 7$ **82.** $(11 + r) + 8 = (r + 11) + 8$

83. $6 \cdot \dfrac{1}{6} = 1$ **84.** $r + 0 = r$

85. $-6 \cdot 1 = -6$ **86.** $-\dfrac{3}{4}\left(-\dfrac{4}{3}\right) = 1$

Review

Perform each indicated operation. See Sections 1.3, 1.4, 1.6, and 1.7.

87. $45 \cdot 90$ **88.** $90 \div 45$ **89.** $90 - 45$ **90.** $45 + 90$

Concept Extensions

Fill in the table with the opposite (additive inverse), the reciprocal (multiplicative inverse), or the expression. Assume that the value of each expression is not 0.

	91.	**92.**	**93.**	**94.**	**95.**	**96.**
Expression	8	$-\dfrac{2}{3}$	x	$4y$		
Opposite						$7x$
Reciprocal				$\dfrac{1}{2x}$		

Decide whether each statement is true or false. See the Concept Check in this section.

97. The opposite of $-\dfrac{a}{2}$ is $-\dfrac{2}{a}$.

98. The reciprocal of $-\dfrac{a}{2}$ is $\dfrac{a}{2}$.

Determine which pairs of actions are commutative. See the Concept Check in this section.

99. "taking a test" and "studying for the test"

100. "putting on your shoes" and "putting on your socks"

101. "putting on your left shoe" and "putting on your right shoe"

102. "reading the sports section" and "reading the comics section"

103. "mowing the lawn" and "trimming the hedges"

104. "baking a cake" and "eating the cake"

105. "feeding the dog" and "feeding the cat"

106. "dialing a number" and "turning on the cell phone"

Name the property illustrated by each step.

107. a. $\triangle + (\square + \bigcirc) = (\square + \bigcirc) + \triangle$

   b. $ = (\bigcirc + \square) + \triangle$

   c. $ = \bigcirc + (\square + \triangle)$

108. a. $(x + y) + z = x + (y + z)$

   b. $ = (y + z) + x$

   c. $ = (z + y) + x$

109. Explain why 0 is called the identity element for addition.

110. Explain why 1 is called the identity element for multiplication.

111. Write an example that shows that division is not commutative.

112. Write an example that shows that subtraction is not commutative.

STUDY SKILLS BUILDER

Are You Familiar with Your Textbook Supplements?

There are many student supplements available for additional study. Below, I have listed some of these. See the preface of this text or your instructor for further information.

Chapter Test Prep Video CD. This material is found in your textbook and is fully explained there. The CD contains video clips of solutions to the Chapter Test exercises in this text and is excellent help when studying for chapter tests.

Lecture Video CDs. These video segments are keyed to each section of the text. The material is presented by me, Elayn Martin-Gay, and I have placed a video icon by the exercises in the text that I have worked on the video.

The Student Solutions Manual. This contains worked out solutions to odd-numbered exercises as well as every exercise in the Integrated Reviews, Chapter Reviews, Chapter Tests, and Cumulative Reviews.

Prentice Hall Tutor Center. Mathematics questions may be phoned, faxed, or emailed to this center.

MyMathLab, MathXL, and Interact Math. These are computer and Internet tutorials. This supplement may already be available to you somewhere on campus, for example at your local learning resource lab. Take a moment and find the name and location of any such lab on campus.

As usual, your instructor is your best source of information.

Let's see how you are doing with textbook supplements:

1. Name one way the Chapter Test Prep Video can help you prepare for a chapter test.

2. List any textbook supplements that you have found useful.

3. Have you located and visited a learning resource lab located on your campus?

4. List the textbook supplements that are currently housed in your campus' learning resource lab.

8.7 SIMPLIFYING EXPRESSIONS

As we explore in this section, we will see that an expression such as $3x + 2x$ is not written as simply as possible. This is because—even without replacing x by a value—we can perform the indicated addition.

Objective **A** Identifying Terms, Like Terms, and Unlike Terms

Before we practice simplifying expressions, we must learn some new language. A **term** is a number or the product of a number and variables raised to powers.

Terms

$$-y, \quad 2x^3, \quad -5, \quad 3xz^2, \quad \frac{2}{y}, \quad 0.8z$$

The **numerical coefficient** of a term is the numerical factor. The numerical coefficient of $3x$ is 3. Recall that $3x$ means $3 \cdot x$.

Term	Numerical Coefficient
$3x$	3
$\dfrac{y^3}{5}$	$\dfrac{1}{5}$ since $\dfrac{y^3}{5}$ means $\dfrac{1}{5} \cdot y^3$
$-0.7ab^3c^5$	-0.7
z	1
$-y$	-1
-5	-5

> **Helpful Hint**
>
> The term z means $1z$ and thus has a numerical coefficient of 1.
> The term $-y$ means $-1y$ and thus has a numerical coefficient of -1.

PRACTICE PROBLEM 1

Identify the numerical coefficient of each term.

a. $-4x$ **b.** $15y^3$ **c.** x

d. $-y$ **e.** $\dfrac{z}{4}$

Answers

1. **a.** -4, **b.** 15, **c.** 1,
d. -1, **e.** $\dfrac{1}{4}$

EXAMPLE 1 Identify the numerical coefficient of each term.

a. $-3y$ **b.** $22z^4$ **c.** y **d.** $-x$ **e.** $\dfrac{x}{7}$

Solution:

a. The numerical coefficient of $-3y$ is -3.

b. The numerical coefficient of $22z^4$ is 22.

c. The numerical coefficient of y is 1, since y is $1y$.

d. The numerical coefficient of $-x$ is -1, since $-x$ is $-1x$.

e. The numerical coefficient of $\dfrac{x}{7}$ is $\dfrac{1}{7}$, since $\dfrac{x}{7}$ is $\dfrac{1}{7} \cdot x$.

■ **Work Practice Problem 1**

Terms with the same variables raised to exactly the same powers are called **like terms.** Terms that aren't like terms are called **unlike terms.**

Like Terms	Unlike Terms	Reason Why
$3x, 2x$	$5x, 5x^2$	Why? Same variable x, but different powers of x and x^2
$-6x^2y, 2x^2y, 4x^2y$	$7y, 3z, 8x^2$	Why? Different variables
$2ab^2c^3, ac^3b^2$	$6abc^3, 6ab^2$	Why? Different variables and different powers

Helpful Hint

In like terms, each variable and its exponent must match exactly, but these factors don't need to be in the same order.

$2x^2y$ and $3yx^2$ are like terms.

EXAMPLE 2 Determine whether the terms are like or unlike.

a. $2x, 3x^2$ 　　　　　　**b.** $4x^2y, x^2y, -2x^2y$ 　　　　　　**c.** $-2yz, -3zy$
d. $-x^4, x^4$ 　　　　　　**e.** $-8a^5, 8a^5$

Solution:

a. Unlike terms, since the exponents on x are not the same.
b. Like terms, since each variable and its exponent match.
c. Like terms, since $zy = yz$ by the commutative property.
d. Like terms. The variable and its exponent match.
e. Like terms. The variable and its exponent match.

▣ **Work Practice Problem 2**

PRACTICE PROBLEM 2

Determine whether the terms are like or unlike.
a. $7x^2, -6x^3$
b. $3x^2y^2, -x^2y^2, 4x^2y^2$
c. $-5ab, 3ba$
d. $2x^3, 4y^3$
e. $-7m^4, 7m^4$

Objective B Combining Like Terms

An algebraic expression containing the sum or difference of like terms can be simplified by applying the distributive property. For example, by the distributive property, we rewrite the sum of the like terms $6x + 2x$ as

$$6x + 2x = (6 + 2)x = 8x$$

Also,

$$-y^2 + 5y^2 = (-1 + 5)y^2 = 4y^2$$

Simplifying the sum or difference of like terms is called **combining like terms.**

EXAMPLE 3 Simplify each expression by combining like terms.

a. $7x - 3x$ 　　　　　　**b.** $10y^2 + y^2$
c. $8x^2 + 2x - 3x$ 　　　　　　**d.** $9n^2 - 5n^2 + n^2$

Solution:

a. $7x - 3x = (7 - 3)x = 4x$
b. $10y^2 + y^2 = (10 + 1)y^2 = 11y^2$
c. $8x^2 + 2x - 3x = 8x^2 + (2 - 3)x = 8x^2 - 1x$ 　or　 $8x^2 - x$
d. $9n^2 - 5n^2 + n^2 = (9 - 5 + 1)n^2 = 5n^2$

▣ **Work Practice Problem 3**

PRACTICE PROBLEM 3

Simplify each expression by combining like terms.
a. $9y - 4y$
b. $11x^2 + x^2$
c. $5y - 3x + 4x$
d. $14m^2 - m^2 + 3m^2$

Answers

2. a. unlike, **b.** like, **c.** like, **d.** unlike, **e.** like, **3. a.** $5y$, **b.** $12x^2$, **c.** $5y + x$, **d.** $16m^2$

The preceding examples suggest the following.

Combining Like Terms

To **combine like terms,** combine the numerical coefficients and multiply the result by the common variable factors.

PRACTICE PROBLEMS 4–7

Simplify each expression by combining like terms.
4. $7y + 2y + 6 + 10$
5. $-2x + 4 + x - 11$
6. $3z - 3z^2$
7. $8.9y + 4.2y - 3$

EXAMPLES Simplify each expression by combining like terms.

4. $2x + 3x + 5 + 2 = (2 + 3)x + (5 + 2)$
$$= 5x + 7$$

5. $-5a - 3 + a + 2 = -5a + 1a + (-3 + 2)$
$$= (-5 + 1)a + (-3 + 2)$$
$$= -4a - 1$$

6. $4y - 3y^2$ These two terms cannot be combined because they are unlike terms.

7. $2.3x + 5x - 6 = (2.3 + 5)x - 6$
$$= 7.3x - 6$$

⬛ **Work Practice Problems 4–7**

Objective ⓒ **Simplifying Expressions Containing Parentheses**

In simplifying expressions we make frequent use of the distributive property to remove parentheses.

It may be helpful to study the examples below.

$$+(3a + 2) = +1(3a + 2) = +1(3a) + (+1)(2) = 3a + 2$$
means

$$-(3a + 2) = -1(3a + 2) = -1(3a) + (-1)(2) = -3a - 2$$
means

PRACTICE PROBLEMS 8–10

Find each product by using the distributive property to remove parentheses.
8. $3(11y + 6)$
9. $-4(x + 0.2y - 3)$
10. $-(3x + 2y + z - 1)$

EXAMPLES Find each product by using the distributive property to remove parentheses.

8. $5(3x + 2) = 5(3x) + 5(2)$ Apply the distributive property.
$$= 15x + 10$$ Multiply.

9. $-2(y + 0.3z - 1) = -2(y) + (-2)(0.3z)$ Apply the distributive property.
$$- (-2)(1)$$
$$= -2y - 0.6z + 2$$ Multiply.

10. $-(9x + y - 2z + 6) = -1(9x + y - 2z + 6)$ Distribute -1 over each term.
$$= -1(9x) + (-1)(y) - (-1)(2z) + (-1)(6)$$
$$= -9x - y + 2z - 6$$

⬛ **Work Practice Problems 8–10**

Answers

4. $9y + 16$, **5.** $-x - 7$,
6. $3z - 3z^2$, **7.** $13.1y - 3$,
8. $33y + 18$, **9.** $-4x - 0.8y + 12$,
10. $-3x - 2y - z + 1$

Helpful Hint

If a "−" sign precedes parentheses, the sign of each term inside the parentheses is changed when the distributive property is applied to remove the parentheses.

Examples:

$$-(2x + 1) = -2x - 1$$
$$-(x - 2y) = -x + 2y$$
$$-(-5x + y - z) = 5x - y + z$$
$$-(-3x - 4y - 1) = 3x + 4y + 1$$

When simplifying an expression containing parentheses, we often use the distributive property first to remove parentheses and then again to combine any like terms.

EXAMPLES Simplify each expression.

11. $3(2x - 5) + 1 = 6x - 15 + 1$ Apply the distributive property.
$$= 6x - 14 \quad \text{Combine like terms.}$$

12. $8 - (7x + 2) + 3x = 8 - 7x - 2 + 3x$ Apply the distributive property.
$$= -7x + 3x + 8 - 2$$
$$= -4x + 6 \quad \text{Combine like terms.}$$

13. $-2(4x + 7) - (3x - 1) = -8x - 14 - 3x + 1$ Apply the distributive property.
$$= -11x - 13 \quad \text{Combine like terms.}$$

14. $9 + 3(4x - 10) = 9 + 12x - 30$ Apply the distributive property.
$$= -21 + 12x \quad \text{Combine like terms.}$$
$$\text{or } 12x - 21$$

Work Practice Problems 11–14

EXAMPLE 15 Subtract $4x - 2$ from $2x - 3$.

Solution: We first note that "subtract $4x - 2$ **from** $2x - 3$" translates to $(2x - 3) - (4x - 2)$. Notice that parentheses were placed around each given expression. This is to ensure that the entire expression after the subtraction sign is subtracted. Next, we simplify the algebraic expression.

$$(2x - 3) - (4x - 2) = 2x - 3 - 4x + 2 \quad \text{Apply the distributive property.}$$
$$= -2x - 1 \quad \text{Combine like terms.}$$

Work Practice Problem 15

Objective D Writing Algebraic Expressions

To prepare for problem solving, we next practice writing word phrases as algebraic expressions.

PRACTICE PROBLEMS 11–14

Simplify each expression.
11. $4(4x - 6) + 20$
12. $5 - (3x + 9) + 6x$
13. $-3(7x + 1) - (4x - 2)$
14. $8 + 11(2y - 9)$

Helpful Hint Don't forget to use the distributive property and multiply before adding or subtracting like terms.

PRACTICE PROBLEM 15

Subtract $9x - 10$ from $4x - 3$.

Answers
11. $16x - 4$, **12.** $3x - 4$,
13. $-25x - 1$, **14.** $-91 + 22y$,
15. $-5x + 7$

PRACTICE PROBLEMS 16–19

Write each phrase as an algebraic expression and simplify if possible. Let x represent the unknown number.

16. Three times a number, subtracted from 10
17. The sum of a number and 2, divided by 5
18. Three times a number, added to the sum of a number and 6
19. Seven times the difference of a number and 4.

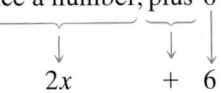 Write each phrase as an algebraic expression and simplify if possible. Let x represent the unknown number.

16. Twice a number, plus 6

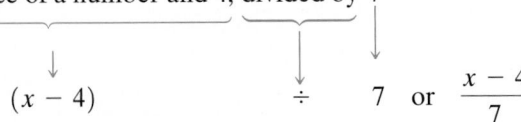

$$2x \qquad + \quad 6$$

This expression cannot be simplified.

17. The difference of a number and 4, divided by 7

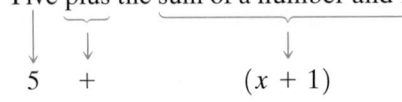

$$(x - 4) \qquad \div \quad 7 \quad \text{or} \quad \frac{x-4}{7}$$

This expression cannot be simplified.

18. Five plus the sum of a number and 1

$$5 \quad + \qquad (x + 1)$$

We can simplify this expression.

$$5 + (x + 1) = 5 + x + 1$$
$$= 6 + x$$

19. Four times the sum of a number and 3

$$4 \quad \cdot \qquad (x + 3)$$

Use the distributive property to simplify the expression.

$$4 \cdot (x + 3) = 4(x + 3)$$
$$= 4 \cdot x + 4 \cdot 3$$
$$= 4x + 12$$

▣ **Work Practice Problems 16–19**

Answers

16. $10 - 3x$,   17. $(x + 2) \div 5$ or $\dfrac{x+2}{5}$,
18. $4x + 6$,   19. $7x - 28$

Mental Math

Objective A *Identify the numerical coefficient of each term. See Example 1.*

1. $-7y$ **2.** $3x$ **3.** x **4.** $-y$ **5.** $17x^2y$ **6.** $1.2xyz$

Indicate whether the terms in each list are like or unlike. See Example 2.

7. $5y, -y$ **8.** $-2x^2y, 6xy$ **9.** $2z, 3z^2$

10. $ab^2, -7ab^2$ **11.** $8wz, \frac{1}{7}zw$ **12.** $7.4p^3q^2, 6.2p^3q^2r$

8.7 EXERCISE SET

FOR EXTRA HELP

Student Solutions Manual   PH Math/Tutor Center   CD/Video for Review   MathXL®   MyMathLab

Objective B *Simplify each expression by combining any like terms. See Examples 3 through 7.*

1. $7y + 8y$ **2.** $3x + 2x$ **3.** $8w - w + 6w$

4. $c - 7c + 2c$ **5.** $3b - 5 - 10b - 4$ **6.** $6g + 5 - 3g - 7$

7. $m - 4m + 2m - 6$ **8.** $a + 3a - 2 - 7a$ **9.** $5g - 3 - 5 - 5g$

10. $8p + 4 - 8p - 15$ **11.** $6.2x - 4 + x - 1.2$ **12.** $7.9y - 0.7 - y + 0.2$

13. $2k - k - 6$ **14.** $7c - 8 - c$ **15.** $-9x + 4x + 18 - 10x$

16. $5y - 14 + 7y - 20y$ **17.** $6x - 5x + x - 3 + 2x$ **18.** $8h + 13h - 6 + 7h - h$

19. $7x^2 + 8x^2 - 10x^2$ **20.** $8x^3 + x^3 - 11x^3$ **21.** $3.4m - 4 - 3.4m - 7$

22. $2.8w - 0.9 - 0.5 - 2.8w$ **23.** $6x + 0.5 - 4.3x - 0.4x + 3$ **24.** $0.4y - 6.7 + y - 0.3 - 2.6y$

Objective C *Simplify each expression. Use the distributive property to remove any parentheses. See Examples 8 through 10.*

25. $5(y + 4)$ **26.** $7(r + 3)$ **27.** $-2(x + 2)$ **28.** $-4(y + 6)$

29. $-5(2x - 3y + 6)$ **30.** $-2(4x - 3z - 1)$ **31.** $-(3x - 2y + 1)$ **32.** $-(y + 5z - 7)$

Objectives **B** **C** **Mixed Practice** *Remove parentheses and simplify each expression. See Examples 8 through 14.*

33. $7(d - 3) + 10$

34. $9(z + 7) - 15$

35. $-4(3y - 4) + 12y$

36. $-3(2x + 5) - 6x$

37. $3(2x - 5) - 5(x - 4)$

38. $2(6x - 1) - (x - 7)$

39. $-2(3x - 4) + 7x - 6$

40. $8y - 2 - 3(y + 4)$

41. $5k - (3k - 10)$

42. $-11c - (4 - 2c)$

43. Subtract $6x - 1$ from $3x + 4$

44. Subtract $4 + 3y$ from $8 - 5y$

45. $5(x + 2) - (3x - 4)$

46. $4(2x - 3) - (x + 1)$

47. $\frac{1}{3}(7y - 1) + \frac{1}{6}(4y + 7)$

48. $\frac{1}{5}(9y + 2) + \frac{1}{10}(2y - 1)$

49. $2 + 4(6x - 6)$

50. $8 + 4(3x - 4)$

51. $0.5(m + 2) + 0.4m$

52. $0.2(k + 8) - 0.1k$

53. $10 - 3(2x + 3y)$

54. $14 - 11(5m + 3n)$

55. $6(3x - 6) - 2(x + 1) - 17x$

56. $7(2x + 5) - 4(x + 2) - 20x$

57. $\frac{1}{2}(12x - 4) - (x + 5)$

58. $\frac{1}{3}(9x - 6) - (x - 2)$

Perform each indicated operation. Don't forget to simplify if possible. See Example 15.

59. Add $6x + 7$ to $4x - 10$.

60. Add $3y - 5$ to $y + 16$.

61. Subtract $7x + 1$ from $3x - 8$.

62. Subtract $4x - 7$ from $12 + x$.

63. Subtract $5m - 6$ from $m - 9$.

64. Subtract $m - 3$ from $2m - 6$.

Objective **D** *Write each phrase as an algebraic expression and simplify if possible. Let x represent the unknown number. See Examples 16 through 19.*

65. Twice a number, decreased by four

66. The difference of a number and two, divided by five

67. Three-fourths of a number, increased by twelve

68. Eight more than triple a number

69. The sum of 5 times a number and −2, added to 7 times the number

70. The sum of 3 times a number and 10, **subtracted from** 9 times the number

71. Eight times the sum of a number and six

72. Six times the difference of a number and five

73. Double a number minus the sum of the number and ten

74. Half a number minus the product of the number and eight

Review

Evaluate each expression for the given values. See Section 8.4.

75. If $x = -1$ and $y = 3$, find $y - x^2$

76. If $g = 0$ and $h = -4$, find $gh - h^2$

77. If $a = 2$ and $b = -5$, find $a - b^2$

78. If $x = -3$, find $x^3 - x^2 + 4$

79. If $y = -5$ and $z = 0$, find $yz - y^2$

80. If $x = -2$, find $x^3 - x^2 - x$

Concept Extensions

Given the following information, determine whether each scale is balanced or not.

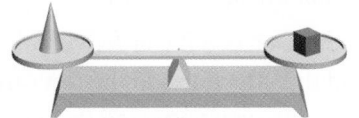

1 cone balances 1 cube

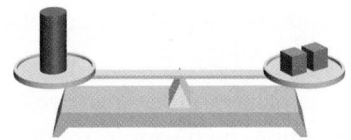

1 cylinder balances 2 cubes

81.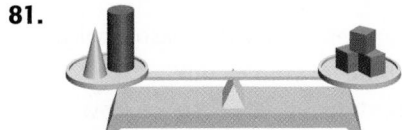

82.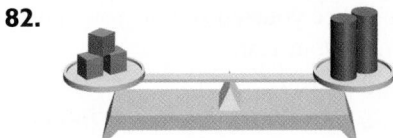

83.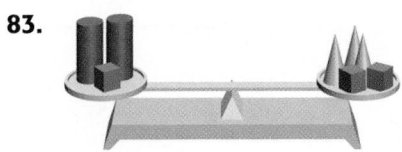

84.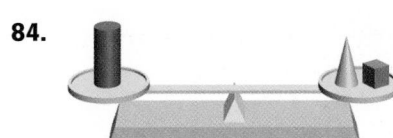

Write each algebraic expression described.

85. Write an expression with 4 terms that simplifies to $3x - 4$.

86. Write an expression of the form
_____ (_____ + _____) whose product is $6x + 24$.

△ **87.** Recall that the perimeter of a figure is the total distance around the figure. Given the following rectangle, express the perimeter as an algebraic expression containing the variable *x*.

5*x* feet

(4*x* − 1) feet   (4*x* − 1) feet

5*x* feet

△ **88.** Given the following triangle, express its perimeter as an algebraic expression containing the variable *x*.

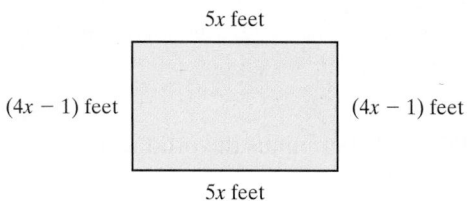

5 centimeters   (3*x* − 1) centimeters

(2*x* + 5) centimeters

△ **89.** To convert from feet to inches, we multiply by 12. For example, the number of inches in 2 feet is 12 · 2 inches. If one board has a length of (*x* + 2) *feet* and a second board has a length of (3*x* − 1) *inches*, express their total length in inches as an algebraic expression.

90. The value of 7 nickels is 5 · 7 cents. Likewise, the value of *x* nickels is 5*x* cents. If the money box in a drink machine contains *x nickels*, 3*x dimes*, and (30*x* − 1) *quarters*, express their total value in cents as an algebraic expression.

 91. In your own words, explain how to combine like terms.

92. Do like terms contain the same numerical coefficients? Explain your answer.

STUDY SKILLS BUILDER

What to Do the Day of an Exam?

Your first exam may be soon. On the day of an exam, don't forget to try the following:

- Allow yourself plenty of time to arrive.
- Read the directions on the test carefully.
- Read each problem carefully as you take your test. Make sure that you answer the question asked.
- Watch your time and pace yourself so that you may attempt each problem on your test.
- Check your work and answers.
- **_Do not turn your test in early._** If you have extra time, spend it double-checking your work.

Good luck!

Answer the following questions based on your most recent mathematics exam, whenever that was.

1. How soon before class did you arrive?
2. Did you read the directions on the test carefully?
3. Did you make sure you answered the question asked for each problem on the exam?
4. Were you able to attempt each problem on your exam?
5. If your answer to question 4 is no, list reasons why.
6. Did you have extra time on your exam?
7. If your answer to question 6 is yes, describe how you spent that extra time.

CHAPTER 8   Group Activity

Sections 8.2, 8.3, 8.4

Magic Squares

A magic square is a set of numbers arranged in a square table so that the sum of the numbers in each column, row, and diagonal is the same. For instance, in the magic square below, the sum of each column, row, and diagonal is 15. Notice that no number is used more than once in the magic square.

2	9	4
7	5	3
6	1	8

The properties of magic squares have been known for a very long time and once were thought to be good luck charms. The ancient Egyptians and Greeks understood their patterns. A magic square even made it into a famous work of art. The engraving titled *Melencolia I,* created by German artist Albrecht Dürer in 1514, features the following four-by-four magic square on the building behind the central figure.

16	3	2	13
5	10	11	8
9	6	7	12
4	15	14	1

Group Exercises

1. Verify that what is shown in the Dürer engraving is, in fact, a magic square. What is the common sum of the columns, rows, and diagonals?

2. Negative numbers can also be used in magic squares. Complete the following magic square:

3. Use the numbers $-12, -9, -6, -3, 0, 3, 6, 9,$ and 12 to form a magic square.

Chapter 8 Vocabulary Check

Fill in each blank with one of the words or phrases listed below.

inequality symbols	exponent	term	numerical coefficient
grouping symbols	solution	like terms	unlike terms
equation	absolute value	numerator	denominator
opposites	base	reciprocals	variable

1. The symbols $\neq$, $<$, and $>$ are called _____.
2. A mathematical statement that two expressions are equal is called an _____.
3. The _____ of a number is the distance between that number and 0 on the number line.
4. A symbol used to represent a number is called a _____.
5. Two numbers that are the same distance from 0 but lie on opposite sides of 0 are called _____.
6. The number in a fraction above the fraction bar is called the _____.
7. A _____ of an equation is a value for the variable that makes the equation a true statement.
8. Two numbers whose product is 1 are called _____.
9. In 2^3, the 2 is called the _____ and the 3 is called the _____.
10. The _____ of a term is its numerical factor.
11. The number in a fraction below the fraction bar is called the _____.
12. Parentheses and brackets are examples of _____.
13. A _____ is a number or the product of a number and variables raised to powers.
14. Terms with the same variables raised to the same powers are called _____.
15. If terms are not like terms, then they are _____.

> **Helpful Hint**
>
> Are you preparing for your test? Don't forget to take the Chapter 8 Test on page 617. Then check your answers at the back of the text and use the Chapter Test Prep Video CD to see the fully worked-out solutions to any of the exercises you want to review.

8 Chapter Highlights

DEFINITIONS AND CONCEPTS	EXAMPLES
Section 8.1 Symbols and Sets of Numbers	

A **set** is a collection of objects, called **elements**, enclosed in braces.	$\{a, c, e\}$
Natural numbers: $\{1, 2, 3, 4, \ldots\}$	Given the set $\left\{-3.4, \sqrt{3}, 0, \dfrac{2}{3}, 5, -4\right\}$ list the numbers that belong to the set of
Whole numbers: $\{0, 1, 2, 3, 4, \ldots\}$	Natural numbers: 5
Integers: $\{\ldots, -3, -2, -1, 0, 1, 2, 3, \ldots\}$	Whole numbers: 0, 5
Rational numbers: {real numbers that can be expressed as a quotient of integers}	Integers: $-4, 0, 5$
Irrational numbers: {real numbers that cannot be expressed as a quotient of integers}	Rational numbers: $-3.4, 0, \dfrac{2}{3}, 5, -4$
A line used to picture numbers is called a **number line.**	Irrational numbers: $\sqrt{3}$
Real numbers: {all numbers that correspond to a point on the number line}	$\begin{array}{c} \leftarrow\!\!+\!\!+\!\!+\!\!+\!\!+\!\!+\!\!+\!\!+\!\!+\!\!+\!\!+\!\!\rightarrow \\ \;\;-5\;-4\;-3\;-2\;-1\;\;\;0\;\;\;1\;\;\;2\;\;\;3\;\;\;4\;\;\;5 \end{array}$
	Real numbers: $-3.4, \sqrt{3}, 0, \dfrac{2}{3}, 5, -4$

DEFINITIONS AND CONCEPTS	**EXAMPLES**

Section 8.1   Symbols and Sets of Numbers (*continued*)

The **absolute value** of a real number a denoted by $\lvert a \rvert$ is the distance between a and 0 on the number line.	$\lvert 5 \rvert = 5 \quad \lvert 0 \rvert = 0 \quad \lvert -2 \rvert = 2$

SYMBOLS: $=$ is equal to
$\neq$ is not equal to
$>$ is greater than
$<$ is less than
$\leq$ is less than or equal to
$\geq$ is greater than or equal to

$-7 = -7$
$3 \neq -3$
$4 > 1$
$1 < 4$
$6 \leq 6$
$18 \geq -\dfrac{1}{3}$

ORDER PROPERTY FOR REAL NUMBERS

For any two real numbers a and b, a is less than b if a is to the left of b on the number line.

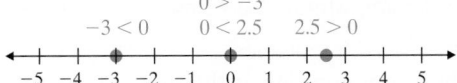
$$0 > -3$$
$$-3 < 0 \qquad 0 < 2.5 \qquad 2.5 > 0$$

Section 8.2   Exponents, Order of Operations, and Variable Expressions

The expression a^n is an **exponential expression.** The number a is called the **base;** it is the repeated factor. The number n is called the **exponent;** it is the number of times that the base is a factor.

$4^3 = 4 \cdot 4 \cdot 4 = 64$
$7^2 = 7 \cdot 7 = 49$

ORDER OF OPERATIONS

1. Perform all operations within grouping symbols first, starting with the innermost set.
2. Evaluate exponential expressions.
3. Multiply or divide in order from left to right.
4. Add or subtract in order from left to right.

$$\frac{8^2 + 5(7 - 3)}{3 \cdot 7} = \frac{8^2 + 5(4)}{21}$$
$$= \frac{64 + 5(4)}{21}$$
$$= \frac{64 + 20}{21}$$
$$= \frac{84}{21}$$
$$= 4$$

A symbol used to represent a number is called a **variable.**

Examples of variables are
$$q, x, z$$

An **algebraic expression** is a collection of numbers, variables, operation symbols, and grouping symbols.

Examples of algebraic expressions are
$$5x, \quad 2(y - 6), \quad \frac{q^2 - 3q + 1}{6}$$

To **evaluate an algebraic expression** containing a variable, substitute a given number for the variable and simplify.

Evaluate $x^2 - y^2$ when $x = 5$ and $y = 3$.
$$x^2 - y^2 = (5)^2 - 3^2$$
$$= 25 - 9$$
$$= 16$$

A mathematical statement that two expressions are equal is called an **equation.**

Equations:
$$3x - 9 = 20$$
$$A = \pi r^2$$

continued

DEFINITIONS AND CONCEPTS	**EXAMPLES**

Section 8.2   Exponents, Order of Operations, and Variable Expressions (*continued*)

A **solution** of an equation is a value for the variable that makes the equation a true statement.	Determine whether 4 is a solution of $5x + 7 = 27$. $$5x + 7 = 27$$ $$5(4) + 7 \overset{?}{=} 27$$ $$20 + 7 \overset{?}{=} 27$$ $$27 = 27 \text{ True}$$ 4 is a solution.

Section 8.3   Adding Real Numbers

TO ADD TWO NUMBERS WITH THE SAME SIGN **1.** Add their absolute values. **2.** Use their common sign as the sign of the sum.	Add. $$10 + 7 = 17$$ $$-3 + (-8) = -11$$
TO ADD TWO NUMBERS WITH DIFFERENT SIGNS **1.** Subtract their absolute values. **2.** Use the sign of the number whose absolute value is larger as the sign of the sum.	$$-25 + 5 = -20$$ $$14 + (-9) = 5$$
Two numbers that are the same distance from 0 but lie on opposite sides of 0 are called **opposites** or **additive inverses**. The opposite of a number a is denoted by $-a$.	The opposite of -7 is 7. The opposite of 123 is -123.

Section 8.4   Subtracting Real Numbers

To subtract two numbers a and b, add the first number a to the opposite of the second number, b. $$a - b = a + (-b)$$	Subtract. $$3 - (-44) = 3 + 44 = 47$$ $$-5 - 22 = -5 + (-22) = -27$$ $$-30 - (-30) = -30 + 30 = 0$$

Section 8.5   Multiplying and Dividing Real Numbers

MULTIPLYING REAL NUMBERS The product of two numbers with the same sign is a positive number. The product of two numbers with different signs is a negative number.	Multiply. $$7 \cdot 8 = 56 \qquad -7 \cdot (-8) = 56$$ $$-2 \cdot 4 = -8 \qquad 2 \cdot (-4) = -8$$
PRODUCTS INVOLVING ZERO The product of 0 and any number is 0. $$b \cdot 0 = 0 \quad \text{and} \quad 0 \cdot b = 0$$	$$-4 \cdot 0 = 0 \qquad 0 \cdot \left(-\frac{3}{4}\right) = 0$$
QUOTIENT OF TWO REAL NUMBERS $$\frac{a}{b} = a \cdot \frac{1}{b}$$	Divide. $$\frac{42}{2} = 42 \cdot \frac{1}{2} = 21$$

DEFINITIONS AND CONCEPTS	**EXAMPLES**

Section 8.5   Multiplying and Dividing Real Numbers (*continued*)

DIVIDING REAL NUMBERS

The quotient of two numbers with the same sign is a positive number. The quotient of two numbers with different signs is a negative number.

$$\frac{90}{10} = 9 \qquad \frac{-90}{-10} = 9$$

$$\frac{42}{-6} = -7 \qquad \frac{-42}{6} = -7$$

QUOTIENTS INVOLVING ZERO

Let a be a nonzero number. $\dfrac{0}{a} = 0$ and $\dfrac{a}{0}$ is undefined.

$$\frac{0}{18} = 0 \qquad \frac{0}{-47} = 0 \qquad \frac{-85}{0} \text{ is undefined.}$$

Section 8.6   Properties of Real Numbers

COMMUTATIVE PROPERTIES

Addition: $a + b = b + a$
Multiplication: $a \cdot b = b \cdot a$

$$3 + (-7) = -7 + 3$$
$$-8 \cdot 5 = 5 \cdot (-8)$$

ASSOCIATIVE PROPERTIES

Addition: $(a + b) + c = a + (b + c)$
Multiplication: $(a \cdot b) \cdot c = a \cdot (b \cdot c)$

$$(5 + 10) + 20 = 5 + (10 + 20)$$
$$(-3 \cdot 2) \cdot 11 = -3 \cdot (2 \cdot 11)$$

Two numbers whose product is 1 are called **multiplicative inverses** or **reciprocals**. The reciprocal of a nonzero number a is $\dfrac{1}{a}$ because $a \cdot \dfrac{1}{a} = 1$.

The reciprocal of 3 is $\dfrac{1}{3}$.

The reciprocal of $-\dfrac{2}{5}$ is $-\dfrac{5}{2}$.

DISTRIBUTIVE PROPERTY

$$a(b + c) = a \cdot b + a \cdot c$$

$$5(6 + 10) = 5 \cdot 6 + 5 \cdot 10$$
$$-2(3 + x) = -2 \cdot 3 + (-2)(x)$$

IDENTITIES

$$a + 0 = a \qquad 0 + a = a$$
$$a \cdot 1 = a \qquad 1 \cdot a = a$$

$$5 + 0 = 5 \qquad 0 + (-2) = -2$$
$$-14 \cdot 1 = -14 \qquad 1 \cdot 27 = 27$$

INVERSES

Additive or opposite: $a + (-a) = 0$

Multiplicative or reciprocal: $b \cdot \dfrac{1}{b} = 1, \qquad b \neq 0$

$$7 + (-7) = 0$$
$$3 \cdot \frac{1}{3} = 1$$

Section 8.7   Simplifying Expressions

The **numerical coefficient** of a **term** is its numerical factor.

TERM	NUMERICAL COEFFICIENT
$-7y$	-7
x	1
$\dfrac{1}{5}a^2b$	$\dfrac{1}{5}$

continued

Definitions and Concepts	**Examples**
Section 8.7 **Simplifying Expressions** (*continued*)	

Terms with the same variables raised to exactly the same powers are **like terms**.	**Like Terms** **Unlike Terms** $12x, -x$ $3y, 3y^2$ $-2xy, 5yx$ $7a^2b, -2ab^2$
To combine like terms, add the numerical coefficients and multiply the result by the common variable factor.	$9y + 3y = 12y$ $-4z^2 + 5z^2 - 6z^2 = -5z^2$
To remove parentheses, apply the distributive property.	$-4(x + 7) + 10(3x - 1)$ $= -4x - 28 + 30x - 10$ $= 26x - 38$

STUDY SKILLS BUILDER

Are You Prepared for a Test on Chapter 8?

Below I have listed some *common trouble areas* for students in Chapter 8. After studying for your test—but before taking your test—read these.

- Do you know the difference between $|-3|$, $-|-3|$, and $-(-3)$?

  $|-3| = 3$; $-|-3| = -3$;   and $-(-3) = 3$

                       (Section 8.1)

- Evaluate $x - y$ if $x = 7$ and $y = -3$.

  $x - y = 7 - (-3) = 10$ (Section 8.4)

- Make sure you are familiar with order of operations. Sometimes the simplest-looking expressions can give you the most trouble.

  $1 + 2(3 + 6) = 1 + 2(9) = 1 + 18 = 19$

                       (Section 8.2)

- Do you know the difference between $(-3)^2$ and -3^2?

  $(-3)^2 = 9$ and $-3^2 = -9$ (Section 8.5)

- Do you know that these fractions are equivalent?

  $$-\frac{1}{3} = \frac{-1}{3} = \frac{1}{-3}$$ (Section 8.5)

Remember: This is simply a checklist of selected topics given to check your understanding. For a review of Chapter 8 in the text, see the material at the end of Chapter 8.

8 CHAPTER REVIEW

(8.1) *Insert* $<$, $>$, *or* $=$ *in the appropriate space to make each statement true.*

1. 8   10

2. 7   2

3. -4 -5

4. $\dfrac{12}{2}$ -8

5. $|-7|$ $|-8|$

6. $|-9|$ -9

7. $-|-1|$ -1

8. $|-14|$ $-(-14)$

9. 1.2   1.02

10. $-\dfrac{3}{2}$ $-\dfrac{3}{4}$

Translate each statement into symbols.

11. Four is greater than or equal to negative three.

12. Six is not equal to five.

13. 0.03 is less than 0.3.

14. New York City has 155 museums and 400 art galleries. Write an inequality comparing the numbers 155 and 400. (*Source:* Absolute Trivia.com)

Given the sets of numbers below, list the numbers in each set that also belong to the set of:

a. Natural numbers
b. Whole numbers
c. Integers
d. Rational numbers
e. Irrational numbers
f. Real numbers

15. $\left\{-6, 0, 1, 1\dfrac{1}{2}, 3, \pi, 9.62\right\}$

16. $\left\{-3, -1.6, 2, 5, \dfrac{11}{2}, 15.1, \sqrt{5}, 2\pi\right\}$

The following chart shows the gains and losses in dollars of Density Oil and Gas stock for a particular week. Use this chart to answer Exercises 17 and 18.

Day	Gain or Loss (in dollars)
Monday	+1
Tuesday	−2
Wednesday	+5
Thursday	+1
Friday	−4

17. Which day showed the greatest loss?

18. Which day showed the greatest gain?

(8.2) *Choose the correct answer for each statement.*

19. The expression $6 \cdot 3^2 + 2 \cdot 8$ simplifies to
   a. -52 **b.** 440   **c.** 70   **d.** 64

20. The expression $68 - 5 \cdot 2^3$ simplifies to
   a. -232 **b.** 28   **c.** 38   **d.** 504

Simplify each expression.

21. $3(1 + 2 \cdot 5) + 4$ **22.** $8 + 3(2 \cdot 6 - 1)$ **23.** $\dfrac{4 + |6 - 2| + 8^2}{4 + 6 \cdot 4}$ **24.** $5[3(2 + 5) - 5]$

Translate each word statement to symbols.

25. The difference of twenty and twelve is equal to the product of two and four.

26. The quotient of nine and two is greater than negative five.

Evaluate each expression when $x = 6$, $y = 2$, and $z = 8$.

27. $2x + 3y$ **28.** $x(y + 2z)$ **29.** $\dfrac{x}{y} + \dfrac{z}{2y}$ **30.** $x^2 - 3y^2$

△ **31.** The expression $180 - a - b$ represents the measure of the unknown angle of the given triangle. Replace a with 37 and b with 80 to find the measure of the unknown angle.

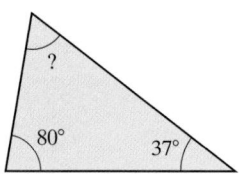

Decide whether the given number is a solution to the given equation.

32. $7x - 3 = 18$;   3   **33.** $3x^2 + 4 = x - 1$;   1

(8.3) *Find the additive inverse or opposite of each number.*

34. -9 **35.** $\dfrac{2}{3}$ **36.** $|-2|$ **37.** $-|-7|$

Add.

38. $-15 + 4$ **39.** $-6 + (-11)$ **40.** $\dfrac{1}{16} + \left(-\dfrac{1}{4}\right)$

41. $-8 + |-3|$ **42.** $-4.6 + (-9.3)$ **43.** $-2.8 + 6.7$

(8.4) *Perform each indicated operation.*

44. $6 - 20$ **45.** $-3.1 - 8.4$ **46.** $-6 - (-11)$

47. $4 - 15$ **48.** $-21 - 16 + 3(8 - 2)$ **49.** $\dfrac{11 - (-9) + 6(8 - 2)}{2 + 3 \cdot 4}$

Evaluate each expression for x = 3, y = −6, and z = −9. Then choose the correct evaluation.

50. $2x^2 - y + z$

    a. 15 **b.** 3 **c.** 27 **d.** −3

51. $\dfrac{|y - 4x|}{2x}$

    a. 3 **b.** 1 **c.** −1 **d.** −3

52. At the beginning of the week the price of Density Oil and Gas stock from Exercises 17 and 18 is $50 per share. Find the price of a share of stock at the end of the week.

Find each multiplicative inverse or reciprocal.

53. −6

54. $\dfrac{3}{5}$

(8.5) *Simplify each expression.*

55. $6(-8)$

56. $(-2)(-14)$

57. $\dfrac{-18}{-6}$

58. $\dfrac{42}{-3}$

59. $-3(-6)(-2)$

60. $(-4)(-3)(0)(-6)$

61. $\dfrac{4(-3) + (-8)}{2 + (-2)}$

62. $\dfrac{3(-2)^2 - 5}{-14}$

(8.6) *Name the property illustrated in each equation.*

63. $-6 + 5 = 5 + (-6)$

64. $6 \cdot 1 = 6$

65. $3(8 - 5) = 3 \cdot 8 + 3 \cdot (-5)$

66. $4 + (-4) = 0$

67. $2 + (3 + 9) = (2 + 3) + 9$

68. $2 \cdot 8 = 8 \cdot 2$

69. $6(8 + 5) = 6 \cdot 8 + 6 \cdot 5$

70. $(3 \cdot 8) \cdot 4 = 3 \cdot (8 \cdot 4)$

71. $4 \cdot \dfrac{1}{4} = 1$

72. $8 + 0 = 8$

73. $4(8 + 3) = 4(3 + 8)$

74. $5(2 + 1) = 5 \cdot 2 + 5 \cdot 1$

(8.7) *Simplify each expression.*

75. $5x - x + 2x$

76. $0.2z - 4.6z - 7.4z$

77. $\dfrac{1}{2}x + 3 + \dfrac{7}{2}x - 5$

78. $\frac{4}{5}y + 1 + \frac{6}{5}y + 2$

79. $2(n - 4) + n - 10$

80. $3(w + 2) - (12 - w)$

81. Subtract $7x - 2$ from $x + 5$.

82. Subtract $1.4y - 3$ from $y - 0.7$.

Write each phrase as an algebraic expression. Simplify if possible.

83. Three times a number decreased by 7

84. Twice the sum of a number and 2.8, added to 3 times the number

Mixed Review

Insert $<$, $>$, or $=$ in the space between each pair of numbers.

85. $-|-11|$ $|11.4|$

86. $-1\frac{1}{2}$ $-2\frac{1}{2}$

Perform the indicated operations.

87. $-7.2 + (-8.1)$

88. $14 - 20$

89. $4(-20)$

90. $\frac{-20}{4}$

91. $-\frac{4}{5}\left(\frac{5}{16}\right)$

92. $-0.5(-0.3)$

93. $8 \div 2 \cdot 4$

94. $(-2)^4$

95. $\frac{-3 - 2(-9)}{-15 - 3(-4)}$

96. $5 + 2[(7 - 5)^2 + (1 - 3)]$

97. $-\frac{5}{8} \div \frac{3}{4}$

98. $\frac{-15 + (-4)^2 + |-9|}{10 - 2 \cdot 5}$

Remove parentheses and simplify each expression.

99. $7(3x - 3) - 5(x + 4)$

100. $8 + 2(9x - 10)$

8 CHAPTER TEST

 Remember to use the Chapter Test Prep Video CD to see the fully worked-out solutions to any of the exercises you want to review.

Answers

Translate each statement into symbols.

1. The absolute value of negative seven is greater than five.

2. The sum of nine and five is greater than or equal to four.

Simplify each expression.

3. $-13 + 8$

4. $-13 - (-2)$

5. $6 \cdot 3 - 8 \cdot 4$

6. $13(-3)$

7. $(-6)(-2)$

8. $\dfrac{|-16|}{-8}$

9. $\dfrac{-8}{0}$

10. $\dfrac{|-6| + 2}{5 - 6}$

11. $\dfrac{1}{2} - \dfrac{5}{6}$

12. $-1\dfrac{1}{8} + 5\dfrac{3}{4}$

13. $-\dfrac{3}{5} + \dfrac{15}{8}$

14. $3(-4)^2 - 80$

15. $6[5 + 2(3 - 8) - 3]$

16. $\dfrac{-12 + 3 \cdot 8}{4}$

17. $\dfrac{(-2)(0)(-3)}{-6}$

Insert $<$, $>$, or $=$ in the appropriate space to make each statement true.

18. $-3 \quad -7$

19. $4 \quad -8$

20. $|-3| \quad 2$

21. $|-2| \quad -1 - (-3)$

---

1. _____

2. _____

3. _____

4. _____

5. _____

6. _____

7. _____

8. _____

9. _____

10. _____

11. _____

12. _____

13. _____

14. _____

15. _____

16. _____

17. _____

18. _____

19. _____

20. _____

21. _____

617

22. a. _____

b. _____

c. _____

d. _____

e. _____

f. _____

23. _____

24. _____

25. _____

26. _____

27. _____

28. _____

29. _____

30. _____

31. _____

32. _____

33. _____

34. _____

35. _____

36. _____

37. _____

38. _____

39. _____

40. _____

22. Given $\left\{ -5, -1, \frac{1}{4}, 0, 1, 7, 11.6, \sqrt{7}, 3\pi \right\}$, list the numbers in this set that also belong to the set of:

 a. Natural numbers   **b.** Whole numbers
 c. Integers   **d.** Rational numbers
 e. Irrational numbers   **f.** Real numbers

Evaluate each expression when $x = 6$, $y = -2$, and $z = -3$.

23. $x^2 + y^2$ **24.** $x + yz$ **25.** $2 + 3x - y$ **26.** $\dfrac{y + z - 1}{x}$

Identify the property illustrated by each expression.

27. $8 + (9 + 3) = (8 + 9) + 3$ **28.** $6 \cdot 8 = 8 \cdot 6$

29. $-6(2 + 4) = -6 \cdot 2 + (-6) \cdot 4$ **30.** $\dfrac{1}{6}(6) = 1$

31. Find the opposite of -9.   **32.** Find the reciprocal of $-\dfrac{1}{3}$.

The New Orleans Saints were 22 yards from the goal when the series of gains and losses shown in the chart occurred. Use this chart to answer Exercises 33 and 34.

	Gains and Losses (in yards)
First down	5
Second down	-10
Third down	-2
Fourth down	29

33. During which down did the greatest loss of yardage occur?

34. Was a touchdown scored?

35. The temperature at the Winter Olympics was a frigid 14° below zero in the morning, but by noon it had risen 31°. What was the temperature at noon?

36. Jean Avarez decided to sell 280 shares of stock, which decreased in value by $1.50 per share yesterday. How much money did she lose?

Simplify each expression.

37. $2y - 6 - y - 4$ **38.** $2.7x + 6.1 + 3.2x - 4.9$

39. $4(x - 2) - 3(2x - 6)$ **40.** $-5(y + 1) + 2(3 - 5y)$

1. Add: $1647 + 246 + 32 + 85$

2. Subtract: $2000 - 469$

3. Find the prime factorization of 945.

4. Find the area of the rectangle.

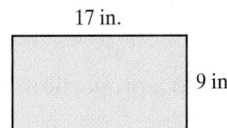

17 in.

9 in.

5. Find the LCM of 11 and 33.

6. Subtract: $\dfrac{8}{21} - \dfrac{2}{9}$

7. Add: $3\dfrac{4}{5} + 1\dfrac{4}{15}$

8. Multiply: $2\dfrac{1}{2} \cdot 4\dfrac{2}{15}$

Write each decimal as a fraction or mixed number in simplest form.

9. 0.125

10. 1.2

11. 105.083

12. Evaluate: $\left(\dfrac{2}{3}\right)^3$

13. Insert $<$, $>$, or $=$ to form a true statement.

0.052   0.236

14. Evaluate: $30 \div 6 \cdot 5$

15. Subtract $85 - 17.31$. Check your answer.

16. Add: $27.9 + 8.07 + 103.261$

Multiply.

17. 42.1×0.1

18. 186.04×1000

19. 9.2×0.001

20. Find the average of 6.8, 9.7, and 0.9.

21. Divide: $60.24 \div 8$. Check your answer.

22. Add: $\dfrac{3}{10} + \dfrac{3}{4}$

23. Write $2\dfrac{3}{16}$ as a decimal.

24. Round 7.2846 to the nearest tenth.

25. Write $\dfrac{2}{3}$ as a decimal.

26. Simplify: $\dfrac{0.12 + 0.96}{0.5}$

Answers

1. _____

2. _____

3. _____

4. _____

5. _____

6. _____

7. _____

8. _____

9. _____

10. _____

11. _____

12. _____

13. _____

14. _____

15. _____

16. _____

17. _____

18. _____

19. _____

20. _____

21. _____

22. _____

23. _____

24. _____

25. _____

26. _____

27. _____

28. _____

29. _____

30. _____

31. _____

32. _____

33. _____

34. _____

35. _____

36. _____

37. _____

38. _____

39. _____

40. _____

27. Write 23% as a decimal.

28. Write $\dfrac{7}{8}$ as a percent.

29. Write $\dfrac{1}{12}$ as a percent. Round to the nearest hundredth percent.

30. 108 is what percent of 450?

31. What number is 35% of 40?

32. Write 23% as a fraction.

33. Translate to a proportion. What percent of 30 is 75?

34. Add: $-1.8 + (-2.7)$

35. In response to a decrease in sales, a company with 1500 employees reduces the number of employees to 1230. What is the percent decrease?

36. Subtract: $1.8 - 2.7$

37. A speaker that normally sells for $65 is on sale for 25% off. What is the discount and what is the sale price?

38. Find 47% of 200.

39. Find the simple interest after 2 years on $500 at an interest rate of 12%.

40. The number of faculty at a local community college was recently increased from 240 to 276. What is the percent increase?

9

Equations, Inequalities, and Problem Solving

In this chapter, we solve equations and inequalities. Once we know how to solve equations and inequalities, we may solve word problems. Of course, problem solving is an integral topic in algebra and its discussion is continued throughout this text.

Since 1948, when NASCAR began, the cars have been transformed from the original "stock" cars, or road models, into the technologically advanced racing machines on the tracks today. In fact, auto manufacturers are creating more advanced street vehicles that can also be used for racing. NASCAR is an increasingly popular sport, with the audience growing daily. In Exercise 35 on page 659 (Section 9.4), you will find the number of points accumulated by the top two finishers for a recent Winston Cup.

Most Money Won Each Year

Dollars (in millions)

Year and Driver

1975 Richard Petty
1980 Dale Earnhardt
1985 Bill Elliott
1990 Dale Earnhardt
1995 Jeff Gordon
2000 Dale Jarrett
2004 Dale Earnhardt, Jr.

Source: NASCAR

A Use the Addition Property of Equality to Solve Linear Equations.

B Simplify an Equation and Then Use the Addition Property of Equality.

C Write Word Phrases as Algebraic Expressions.

9.1 THE ADDITION PROPERTY OF EQUALITY

Objective **A** Using the Addition Property

Recall from Section 8.2 that an equation is a statement in which two expressions have the same value. Also, a value of the variable that makes an equation a true statement is called a solution or root of the equation. The process of finding the solution of an equation is called **solving** the equation for the variable. In this section, we concentrate on solving *linear equations* in one variable.

Linear Equation in One Variable

A **linear equation in one variable** can be written in the form

$$Ax + B = C$$

where A, B, and C are real numbers and $A \neq 0$.

Evaluating a linear equation for a given value of the variable, as we did in Section 8.2, can tell us whether that value is a solution. But we can't rely on evaluating an equation as our method of solving it—with what value would we start?

Instead, to solve a linear equation in x, we write a series of simpler equations, all *equivalent* to the original equation, so that the final equation has the form

$$x = \text{number} \qquad \text{or} \qquad \text{number} = x$$

Equivalent equations are equations that have the same solution. This means that the "number" above is the solution to the original equation.

The first property of equality that helps us write simpler equivalent equations is the **addition property of equality.**

Addition Property of Equality

If a, b, and c are real numbers, then

$$a = b \qquad \text{and} \qquad a + c = b + c$$

are equivalent equations.

This property guarantees that adding the same number to both sides of an equation does not change the solution of the equation. Since subtraction is defined in terms of addition, we may also **subtract the same number from both sides** without changing the solution.

A good way to picture a true equation is as a balanced scale. Since it is balanced, each side of the scale weighs the same amount.

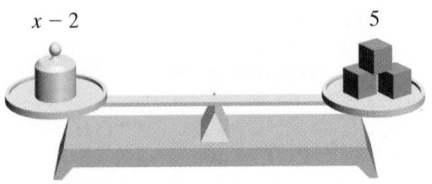

$x - 2$ 5

If the same weight is added to or subtracted from each side, the scale remains balanced.

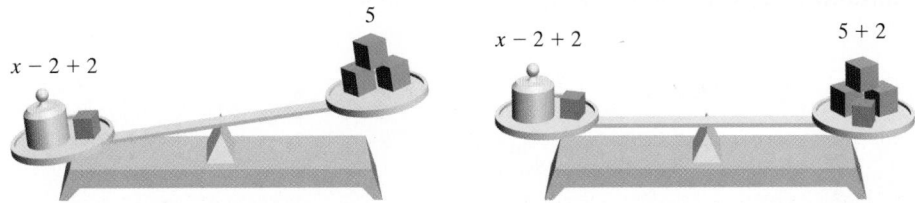

We use the addition property of equality to write equivalent equations until the variable is alone (by itself on one side of the equation) and the equation looks like "x = number" or "number = x."

✔**Concept Check** Use the addition property to fill in the blanks so that the middle equation simplifies to the last equation.

$$x - 5 = 3$$
$$x - 5 + \underline{} = 3 + 5$$
$$x = 8$$

EXAMPLE 1 Solve $x - 7 = 10$ for x.

Solution: To solve for x, we first get x alone on one side of the equation. To do this, we add 7 to both sides of the equation.

$$x - 7 = 10$$
$$x - 7 + 7 = 10 + 7 \quad \text{Add 7 to both sides.}$$
$$x = 17 \qquad \text{Simplify.}$$

The solution of the equation $x = 17$ is obviously 17.
Since we are writing equivalent equations, the solution of the equation $x - 7 = 10$ is also 17.

Check: To check, replace x with 17 in the original equation.

$$x - 7 = 10 \quad \text{Original equation.}$$
$$17 - 7 \overset{?}{=} 10 \quad \text{Replace } x \text{ with 17.}$$
$$10 = 10 \quad \text{True}$$

Since the statement is true, 17 is the solution.

▣ **Work Practice Problem 1**

PRACTICE PROBLEM 1
Solve $x - 5 = 8$ for x.

EXAMPLE 2 Solve: $y + 0.6 = -1.0$

Solution: To solve for y (get y alone on one side of the equation), we subtract 0.6 from both sides of the equation.

$$y + 0.6 = -1.0$$
$$y + 0.6 - 0.6 = -1.0 - 0.6 \quad \text{Subtract 0.6 from both sides.}$$
$$y = -1.6 \qquad \text{Combine like terms.}$$

Check: $\quad y + 0.6 = -1.0 \quad \text{Original equation.}$
$$-1.6 + 0.6 \overset{?}{=} -1.0 \quad \text{Replace } y \text{ with } -1.6.$$
$$-1.0 = -1.0 \quad \text{True}$$

The solution is -1.6.

▣ **Work Practice Problem 2**

PRACTICE PROBLEM 2
Solve: $y + 1.7 = 0.3$

Answers
1. $x = 13$, **2.** $y = -1.4$

✔ **Concept Check Answer**
5

Solve: $\frac{7}{8} = y - \frac{1}{3}$

EXAMPLE 3 Solve: $\frac{1}{2} = x - \frac{3}{4}$

Solution: To get x alone, we add $\frac{3}{4}$ to both sides.

$$\frac{1}{2} = x - \frac{3}{4}$$

$$\frac{1}{2} + \frac{3}{4} = x - \frac{3}{4} + \frac{3}{4} \quad \text{Add } \frac{3}{4} \text{ to both sides.}$$

$$\frac{1}{2} \cdot \frac{2}{2} + \frac{3}{4} = x \quad \text{The LCD is 4.}$$

$$\frac{2}{4} + \frac{3}{4} = x \quad \text{Add the fractions.}$$

$$\frac{5}{4} = x$$

Check: $\frac{1}{2} = x - \frac{3}{4}$ — Original equation.

$\frac{1}{2} \stackrel{?}{=} \frac{5}{4} - \frac{3}{4}$ — Replace x with $\frac{5}{4}$.

$\frac{1}{2} \stackrel{?}{=} \frac{2}{4}$ — Subtract.

$\frac{1}{2} = \frac{1}{2}$ — True

The solution is $\frac{5}{4}$.

■ **Work Practice Problem 3**

Helpful Hint

We may solve an equation so that the variable is alone on *either* side of the equation. For example, $\frac{5}{4} = x$ is equivalent to $x = \frac{5}{4}$.

PRACTICE PROBLEM 4

Solve: $3x + 10 = 4x$

EXAMPLE 4 Solve: $5t - 5 = 6t$

Solution: To solve for t, we first want all terms containing t on one side of the equation and numbers on the other side. Notice that if we subtract $5t$ from both sides of the equation, then variable terms will be on one side of the equation and the number -5 will be alone on the other side.

$$5t - 5 = 6t$$

$$5t - 5 - 5t = 6t - 5t \quad \text{Subtract } 5t \text{ from both sides.}$$

$$-5 = t \quad \text{Combine like terms.}$$

Check: $5t - 5 = 6t$ — Original equation.

$5(-5) - 5 \stackrel{?}{=} 6(-5)$ — Replace t with -5.

$-25 - 5 \stackrel{?}{=} -30$

$-30 = -30$ — True

The solution is -5.

■ **Work Practice Problem 4**

Helpful Hint

For Example 4, why not subtract $6t$ from both sides? The addition property allows us to do this, and we would have $-t - 5 = 0$. We are just no closer to our goal of having variable terms on one side of the equation and numbers on the other.

Answers

3. $y = \frac{29}{24}$, **4.** $x = 10$

Objective B Simplifying Equations

Many times, it is best to simplify one or both sides of an equation before applying the addition property of equality.

EXAMPLE 5 Solve: $2x + 3x - 5 + 7 = 10x + 3 - 6x - 4$

Solution: First we simplify both sides of the equation.

$$2x + 3x - 5 + 7 = 10x + 3 - 6x - 4$$
$$5x + 2 = 4x - 1 \qquad \text{Combine like terms on each side of the equation.}$$

Next, we want all terms with a variable on one side of the equation and all numbers on the other side.

$$5x + 2 - 4x = 4x - 1 - 4x \quad \text{Subtract } 4x \text{ from both sides.}$$
$$x + 2 = -1 \qquad \text{Combine like terms.}$$
$$x + 2 - 2 = -1 - 2 \qquad \text{Subtract 2 from both sides to get } x \text{ alone.}$$
$$x = -3 \qquad \text{Combine like terms.}$$

Check:
$$2x + 3x - 5 + 7 = 10x + 3 - 6x - 4 \qquad \text{Original equation.}$$
$$2(-3) + 3(-3) - 5 + 7 \stackrel{?}{=} 10(-3) + 3 - 6(-3) - 4 \quad \text{Replace } x \text{ with } -3.$$
$$-6 - 9 - 5 + 7 \stackrel{?}{=} -30 + 3 + 18 - 4 \qquad \text{Multiply.}$$
$$-13 = -13 \qquad \text{True}$$

The solution is -3.

⬛ **Work Practice Problem 5**

If an equation contains parentheses, we use the distributive property to remove them, as before. Then we combine any like terms.

EXAMPLE 6 Solve: $6(2a - 1) - (11a + 6) = 7$

Solution: $6(2a - 1) - 1(11a + 6) = 7$

$$6(2a) + 6(-1) - 1(11a) - 1(6) = 7 \qquad \text{Apply the distributive property.}$$
$$12a - 6 - 11a - 6 = 7 \qquad \text{Multiply.}$$
$$a - 12 = 7 \qquad \text{Combine like terms.}$$
$$a - 12 + 12 = 7 + 12 \qquad \text{Add 12 to both sides.}$$
$$a = 19 \qquad \text{Simplify.}$$

Check: Check by replacing a with 19 in the original equation.

⬛ **Work Practice Problem 6**

EXAMPLE 7 Solve: $3 - x = 7$

Solution: First we subtract 3 from both sides.

$$3 - x = 7$$
$$3 - x - 3 = 7 - 3 \quad \text{Subtract 3 from both sides.}$$
$$-x = 4 \qquad \text{Simplify.}$$

We have not yet solved for x since x is not alone. However, this equation does say that the opposite of x is 4. If the opposite of x is 4, then x is the opposite of 4, or $x = -4$.

If $\quad -x = 4,$

then $\quad x = -4.$

Continued on next page

PRACTICE PROBLEM 5

Solve:
$$10w + 3 - 4w + 4 = -2w + 3 + 7w$$

PRACTICE PROBLEM 6

Solve:
$$3(2w - 5) - (5w + 1) = -3$$

PRACTICE PROBLEM 7

Solve: $12 - y = 9$

Answers

5. $w = -4$, **6.** $w = 13$, **7.** $y = 3$

Check: $3 - x = 7$ Original equation.

$$3 - (-4) \overset{?}{=} 7$$ Replace x with -4.

$$3 + 4 \overset{?}{=} 7$$ Add.

$$7 = 7$$ True

The solution is -4.

▣ **Work Practice Problem 7**

Objective C Writing Algebraic Expressions

In this section, we continue to practice writing algebraic expressions.

PRACTICE PROBLEM 8

a. The sum of two numbers is 11. If one number is 4, find the other number.

b. The sum of two numbers is 11. If one number is x, write an expression representing the other number.

c. The sum of two numbers is 56. If one number is a, write an expression representing the other number.

EXAMPLE 8

a. The sum of two numbers is 8. If one number is 3, find the other number.

b. The sum of two numbers is 8. If one number is x, write an expression representing the other number.

Solution:

a. If the sum of two numbers is 8 and one number is 3, we find the other number by subtracting 3 from 8. The other number is $8 - 3$, or 5.

b. If the sum of two numbers is 8 and one number is x, we find the other number by subtracting x from 8. The other number is represented by $8 - x$.

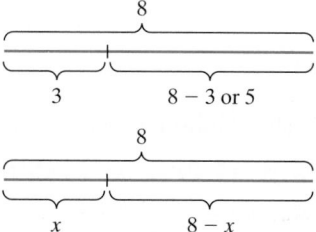

▣ **Work Practice Problem 8**

PRACTICE PROBLEM 9

In a recent House of Representatives race in California, Lucille Roybal-Allard received 49,489 more votes than Wayne Miller. If Wayne received n votes, how many did Lucille receive? (*Source:* Voter News Service)

EXAMPLE 9 The Verrazano-Narrows Bridge in New York City is the longest suspension bridge in North America. The Golden Gate Bridge in San Francisco is 60 feet shorter than the Verrazano-Narrows Bridge. If the length of the Verrazano-Narrows Bridge is m feet, express the length of the Golden Gate Bridge as an algebraic expression in m. (*Source:* Survey of State Highway Engineers)

Solution: Since the Golden Gate is 60 feet shorter than the Verrazano-Narrows Bridge, we have that its length is

In words:	Length of Verrazano-Narrows Bridge	minus	60
Translate:	m	$-$	60

The Golden Gate Bridge is $(m - 60)$ feet long.

▣ **Work Practice Problem 9**

Answers

8. a. $11 - 4$ or 7,   **b.** $11 - x$,   **c.** $56 - a$,   **9.** $(n + 49,489)$ votes

Mental Math

Solve each equation mentally. See Examples 1 and 2.

1. $x + 4 = 6$

2. $x + 7 = 17$

3. $n + 18 = 30$

4. $z + 22 = 40$

5. $b - 11 = 6$

6. $d - 16 = 5$

9.1 EXERCISE SET

FOR EXTRA HELP

Student Solutions Manual   PH Math/Tutor Center   CD/Video for Review   Math XL MathXL®   MyMathLab MyMathLab

Objective  *Solve each equation. Check each solution. See Examples 1 through 4.*

1. $x + 7 = 10$

2. $x + 14 = 25$

 **3.** $x - 2 = -4$

4. $y - 9 = 1$

5. $-11 = 3 + x$

6. $-8 = 8 + z$

7. $r - 8.6 = -8.1$

8. $t - 9.2 = -6.8$

9. $x - \dfrac{2}{5} = -\dfrac{3}{20}$

10. $y - \dfrac{4}{7} = -\dfrac{3}{14}$

11. $\dfrac{1}{3} + f = \dfrac{3}{4}$

12. $c + \dfrac{1}{6} = \dfrac{3}{8}$

Objective **B** *Solve each equation. Don't forget to first simplify each side of the equation, if possible. Check each solution. See Examples 5 through 7.*

13. $7x + 2x = 8x - 3$

14. $3n + 2n = 7 + 4n$

15. $\dfrac{5}{6}x + \dfrac{1}{6}x = -9$

16. $\dfrac{13}{11}y - \dfrac{2}{11}y = -3$

17. $2y + 10 = 5y - 4y$

18. $4x - 4 = 10x - 7x$

19. $-5(n - 2) = 8 - 4n$

20. $-4(z - 3) = 2 - 3z$

21. $\dfrac{3}{7}x + 2 = -\dfrac{4}{7}x - 5$

22. $\dfrac{1}{5}x - 1 = -\dfrac{4}{5}x - 13$

23. $5x - 6 = 6x - 5$

24. $2x + 7 = x - 10$

25. $8y + 2 - 6y = 3 + y - 10$

26. $4p - 11 - p = 2 + 2p - 20$

27. $-3(x - 4) = -4x$

28. $-2(x - 1) = -3x$

29. $\dfrac{3}{8}x - \dfrac{1}{6} = -\dfrac{5}{8}x - \dfrac{2}{3}$

30. $\dfrac{2}{5}x - \dfrac{1}{12} = -\dfrac{3}{5}x - \dfrac{3}{4}$

31. $2(x - 4) = x + 3$

32. $3(y + 7) = 2y - 5$

33. $3(n - 5) - (6 - 2n) = 4n$

34. $5(3 + z) - (8z + 9) = -4z$

35. $-2(x + 6) + 3(2x - 5) = 3(x - 4) + 10$

36. $-5(x + 1) + 4(2x - 3) = 2(x + 2) - 8$

627

Objectives **A** **B** **Mixed Practice** *Solve. See Examples 1 through 7.*

37. $13x - 3 = 14x$

38. $18x - 9 = 19x$

39. $5b - 0.7 = 6b$

40. $9x + 5.5 = 10x$

41. $3x - 6 = 2x + 5$

42. $7y + 2 = 6y + 2$

43. $13x - 9 + 2x - 5 = 12x - 1 + 2x$

44. $15x + 20 - 10x - 9 = 25x + 8 - 21x - 7$

45. $7(6 + w) = 6(2 + w)$

46. $6(5 + c) = 5(c - 4)$

47. $n + 4 = 3.6$

48. $m + 2 = 7.1$

49. $10 - (2x - 4) = 7 - 3x$

50. $15 - (6 - 7k) = 2 + 6k$

51. $\dfrac{1}{3} = x + \dfrac{2}{3}$

52. $\dfrac{1}{11} = y + \dfrac{10}{11}$

53. $-6.5 - 4x - 1.6 - 3x = -6x + 9.8$

54. $-1.4 - 7x - 3.6 - 2x = -8x + 4.4$

Objective **C** *Write each algebraic expression described. See Examples 8 and 9.*

55. A 10-foot board is cut into two pieces. If one piece is x feet long, express the other length in terms of x.

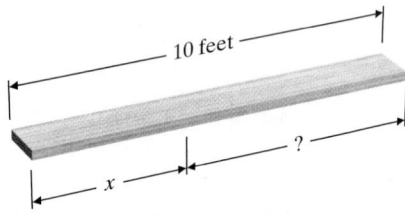

56. A 5-foot piece of string is cut into two pieces. If one piece is x feet long, express the other length in terms of x.

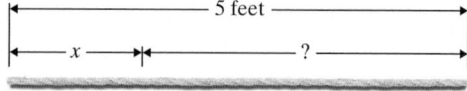

△ **57.** Recall that two angles are *supplementary* if their sum is 180°. If one angle measures $x°$, express the measure of its supplement in terms of x.

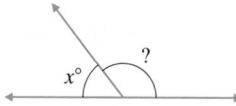

△ **58.** Recall that two angles are *complementary* if their sum is 90°. If one angle measures $x°$, express the measure of its complement in terms of x.

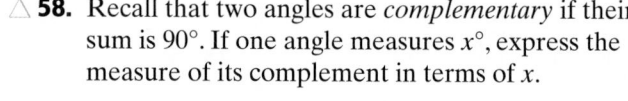

59. In 2004, the number of graduate students at the University of Texas at Austin was approximately 28,000 fewer than the number of undergraduate students. If the number of undergraduate students was n, how many graduate students attend UT Austin? (*Source:* www.utexas.edu)

60. The longest interstate highway in the U.S. is I-90, which connects Seattle, Washington, and Boston, Massachusetts. The second longest interstate highway, I-80 (connecting San Francisco, California, and Teaneck, New Jersey), is 178.5 miles shorter than I-90. If the length of I-80 is m miles, express the length of I-90 as an algebraic expression in m. (*Source:* U.S. Department of Transportation—Federal Highway Administration)

61. The area of the Sahara Desert in Africa is 7 times the area of the Gobi Desert in Asia. If the area of the Gobi Desert is x square miles, express the area of the Sahara Desert as an algebraic expression in x.

62. The largest meteorite in the world is the Hoba West located in Namibia. Its weight is 3 times the weight of the Armanty meteorite located in Outer Mongolia. If the weight of the Armanty meteorite is y kilograms, express the weight of the Hoba West meteorite as an algebraic expression in y.

Review

Find each multiplicative inverse or reciprocal. See Section 8.6.

63. $\dfrac{5}{8}$ **64.** $\dfrac{7}{6}$ **65.** 2   **66.** 5   **67.** $-\dfrac{1}{9}$ **68.** $-\dfrac{3}{5}$

Perform each indicated operation and simplify. See Sections 8.4 and 8.5.

69. $\dfrac{3x}{3}$ **70.** $\dfrac{-2y}{-2}$ **71.** $-5\left(-\dfrac{1}{5}y\right)$ **72.** $7\left(\dfrac{1}{7}r\right)$ **73.** $\dfrac{3}{5}\left(\dfrac{5}{3}x\right)$ **74.** $\dfrac{9}{2}\left(\dfrac{2}{9}x\right)$

Concept Extensions

75. Write two terms whose sum is $-3x$.

76. Write four terms whose sum is $2y - 6$.

Use the addition property to fill in the blank so that the middle equation simplifies to the last equation. See the Concept Check in this section.

77. $x - 4 = -9$
  $x - 4 + (\quad) = -9 + (\quad)$
         $x = -5$

78. $a + 9 = 15$
  $a + 9 + (\quad) = 15 + (\quad)$
         $a = 6$

Fill in the blanks with numbers of your choice so that each equation has the given solution. Note: Each blank may be replaced with a different number.

79. ____ $+ x =$ ____ ; Solution: -3

80. $x -$ ____ $=$ ____ ; Solution: -10

Solve.

△ **81.** The sum of the angles of a triangle is 180°. If one angle of a triangle measures $x°$ and a second angle measures $(2x + 7)°$, express the measure of the third angle in terms of x. Simplify the expression.

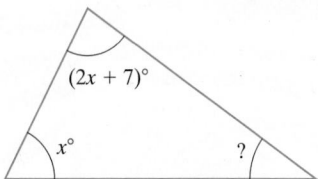

△ **82.** A quadrilateral is a four-sided figure (like the one shown in the figure) whose angle sum is 360°. If one angle measures $x°$, a second angle measures $3x°$, and a third angle measures $5x°$, express the measure of the fourth angle in terms of x. Simplify the expression.

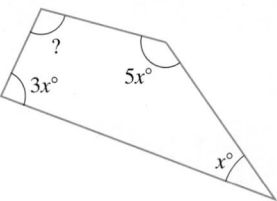

83. In your own words, explain what is meant by the solution of an equation.

84. In your own words, explain how to check a solution of an equation.

Use a calculator to determine the solution of each equation.

 85. $36.766 + x = -108.712$

86. $-85.325 = x - 97.985$

STUDY SKILLS BUILDER

Have You Decided to Complete This Course Successfully?

This Study Skills Builder was first located in Section 2.1. Now that we are later in this text, it's time to look at it again.

Ask yourself if one of your current goals is to complete this course successfully.

If it is not a goal of yours, ask yourself why? One common reason is fear of failure. Amazingly enough, fear of failure alone can be strong enough to keep many of us from doing our best in any endeavor.

Another common reason is that you simply haven't taken the time to make successfully completing this course one of your goals. How do you do this? Start by writing this goal in your mathematics notebook. Then list steps you will take to ensure success. A great first step is to read or reread Section 1.1 and make a commitment to try the suggestions in that section.

Good luck, and don't forget that a positive attitude will make a big difference.

Let's see how you are doing.

1. Have you decided to make "successfully completing this course" a goal of yours? If no, please list reasons why this has not happened. Study your list and talk to your instructor about this.

2. If your answer to question 1 is yes, take a moment and list in your notebook further specific goals that will help you achieve this major goal of successfully completing this course. (For example, "My goal this semester is not to miss any of my mathematics classes.")

3. Rate your commitment to this course with a number between 1 and 5. Use the diagram below to help.

High Commitment		Average Commitment		Not committed at all
5	4	3	2	1

4. If you have rated your personal commitment level (from the exercise above) as a 1, 2, or 3, list the reasons why this is so. Then determine whether it is possible to increase your commitment level to a 4 or 5.

9.2 THE MULTIPLICATION PROPERTY OF EQUA

Objective Using the Multiplication Property

As useful as the addition property of equality is, it cannot help us solve eve
linear equation in one variable. For example, adding or subtracting a value
sides of the equation does not help solve

$$\frac{5}{2}x = 15$$

because the variable x is being multiplied by a number (other than 1). Instead,
apply another important property of equality, the **multiplication property of equal**

Multiplication Property of Equality

If a, b, and c are real numbers and $c \neq 0$, then

$$a = b \quad \text{and} \quad ac = bc$$

are equivalent equations.

This property guarantees that multiplying both sides of an equation by the same
nonzero number does not change the solution of the equation. Since division is defined in terms of multiplication, we may also **divide both sides of the equation by the
same nonzero number** without changing the solution.

EXAMPLE 1 Solve: $\frac{5}{2}x = 15$

Solution: To get x alone, we multiply both sides of the equation by the reciprocal
(or multiplicative inverse) of $\frac{5}{2}$, which is $\frac{2}{5}$.

$$\frac{5}{2}x = 15$$

$$\frac{2}{5} \cdot \left(\frac{5}{2}x\right) = \frac{2}{5} \cdot 15 \quad \text{Multiply both sides by } \frac{2}{5}.$$

$$\left(\frac{2}{5} \cdot \frac{5}{2}\right)x = \frac{2}{5} \cdot 15 \quad \text{Apply the associative property.}$$

$$1x = 6 \quad \text{Simplify.}$$

or

$$x = 6$$

Check: Replace x with 6 in the original equation.

$$\frac{5}{2}x = 15 \quad \text{Original equation.}$$

$$\frac{5}{2}(6) \overset{?}{=} 15 \quad \text{Replace } x \text{ with 6.}$$

$$15 = 15 \quad \text{True}$$

The solution is 6.

■ **Work Practice Problem 1**

PRACTICE PROBLEM 1

Solve: $\frac{3}{7}x = 9$

Answer
1. $x = 21$

In the equation $\frac{5}{2}x = 15$, $\frac{5}{2}$ is the coefficient of x. When the coefficient of x is a *fraction*, we will get x alone by multiplying by the reciprocal. When the coefficient of x is an integer or a decimal, it is usually more convenient to divide both sides by the coefficient. (Dividing by a number is, of course, the same as multiplying by the reciprocal of the number.)

EXAMPLE 2 Solve: $5x = 30$

Solution: To get x alone, we divide both sides of the equation by 5, the coefficient of x.

$$5x = 30$$
$$\frac{5x}{5} = \frac{30}{5} \quad \text{Divide both sides by 5.}$$
$$1 \cdot x = 6 \quad \text{Simplify.}$$
$$x = 6$$

Check: $\quad 5x = 30 \quad$ Original equation.
$$5 \cdot 6 \stackrel{?}{=} 30 \quad \text{Replace } x \text{ with 6.}$$
$$30 = 30 \quad \text{True}$$

The solution is 6.

Work Practice Problem 2

EXAMPLE 3 Solve: $-3x = 33$

Solution: Recall that $-3x$ means $-3 \cdot x$. To get x alone, we divide both sides by the coefficient of x, that is, -3.

$$-3x = 33$$
$$\frac{-3x}{-3} = \frac{33}{-3} \quad \text{Divide both sides by } -3.$$
$$1x = -11 \quad \text{Simplify.}$$
$$x = -11$$

Check: $\quad -3x = 33 \quad$ Original equation.
$$-3(-11) \stackrel{?}{=} 33 \quad \text{Replace } x \text{ with } -11.$$
$$33 = 33 \quad \text{True}$$

The solution is -11.

Work Practice Problem 3

EXAMPLE 4 Solve: $\frac{y}{7} = 20$

Solution: Recall that $\frac{y}{7} = \frac{1}{7}y$. To get y alone, we multiply both sides of the equation by 7, the reciprocal of $\frac{1}{7}$.

$$\frac{y}{7} = 20$$
$$\frac{1}{7}y = 20$$
$$7 \cdot \frac{1}{7}y = 7 \cdot 20 \quad \text{Multiply both sides by 7.}$$
$$1y = 140 \quad \text{Simplify.}$$
$$y = 140$$

PRACTICE PROBLEM 2

ve: $\quad 7x = 42$

PRACTICE PROBLEM 3

Solve: $\quad -4x = 52$

PRACTICE PROBLEM 4

Solve: $\quad \frac{y}{5} = 13$

Answers

2. $x = 6$, **3.** $x = -13$, **4.** $y = 65$

Check: $\dfrac{y}{7} = 20$ Original equation.

$\dfrac{140}{7} \overset{?}{=} 20$ Replace y with 140.

$20 = 20$ True

The solution is 140.

◼ **Work Practice Problem 4**

EXAMPLE 5 Solve: $3.1x = 4.96$

Solution: $3.1x = 4.96$

$\dfrac{3.1x}{3.1} = \dfrac{4.96}{3.1}$ Divide both sides by 3.1.

$1x = 1.6$ Simplify.

$x = 1.6$

Check: Check by replacing x with 1.6 in the original equation. The solution is 1.6.

◼ **Work Practice Problem 5**

EXAMPLE 6 Solve: $-\dfrac{2}{3}x = -\dfrac{5}{2}$

Solution: To get x alone, we multiply both sides of the equation by $-\dfrac{3}{2}$, the reciprocal of the coefficient of x.

$-\dfrac{2}{3}x = -\dfrac{5}{2}$

$-\dfrac{3}{2} \cdot -\dfrac{2}{3}x = -\dfrac{3}{2} \cdot -\dfrac{5}{2}$ Multiply both sides by $-\dfrac{3}{2}$, the reciprocal of $-\dfrac{2}{3}$.

$x = \dfrac{15}{4}$ Simplify.

Check: Check by replacing x with $\dfrac{15}{4}$ in the original equation. The solution is $\dfrac{15}{4}$.

◼ **Work Practice Problem 6**

Objective B Using Both the Addition and Multiplication Properties

We are now ready to combine the skills learned in the last section with the skills learned from this section to solve equations by applying more than one property.

EXAMPLE 7 Solve: $-z - 4 = 6$

Solution: First, let's get $-z$, the term containing the variable, alone. To do so, we add 4 to both sides of the equation.

$-z - 4 + 4 = 6 + 4$ Add 4 to both sides.

$-z = 10$ Simplify.

Next, recall that $-z$ means $-1 \cdot z$. Thus to get z alone, we either multiply or divide both sides of the equation by -1. In this example, we divide.

$-z = 10$

$\dfrac{-z}{-1} = \dfrac{10}{-1}$ Divide both sides by the coefficient -1.

$1z = -10$ Simplify.

$z = -10$

Continued on next page

PRACTICE PROBLEM 5

Solve: $2.6x = 13.52$

PRACTICE PROBLEM 6

Solve: $-\dfrac{5}{6}y = -\dfrac{3}{5}$

PRACTICE PROBLEM 7

Solve: $-x + 7 = -12$

Answers

5. $x = 5.2$, **6.** $y = \dfrac{18}{25}$, **7.** $x = 19$

Check: $-z - 4 = 6$ Original equation.

$-(-10) - 4 \overset{?}{=} 6$ Replace z with -10.

$10 - 4 \overset{?}{=} 6$

$6 = 6$ True

The solution is -10.

◻ **Work Practice Problem 7**

Don't forget to first simplify one or both sides of an equation, if possible.

PRACTICE PROBLEM 8

Solve:

$-7x + 2x + 3 - 20 = -2$

EXAMPLE 8 Solve: $a + a - 10 + 7 = -13$

Solution: First, we simplify both sides of the equation by combining like terms.

$a + a - 10 + 7 = -13$

$2a - 3 = -13$ Combine like terms.

$2a - 3 + 3 = -13 + 3$ Add 3 to both sides.

$2a = -10$ Simplify.

$\dfrac{2a}{2} = \dfrac{-10}{2}$ Divide both sides by 2.

$a = -5$ Simplify.

Check: To check, replace a with -5 in the original equation. The solution is -5.

◻ **Work Practice Problem 8**

PRACTICE PROBLEM 9

Solve: $10x - 4 = 7x + 14$

EXAMPLE 9 Solve: $7x - 3 = 5x + 9$

Solution: To get x alone, let's first use the addition property to get variable terms on one side of the equation and numbers on the other side. One way to get variable terms on one side is to subtract $5x$ from both sides.

$7x - 3 = 5x + 9$

$7x - 3 - 5x = 5x + 9 - 5x$ Subtract $5x$ from both sides.

$2x - 3 = 9$ Simplify.

Now, to get numbers on the other side, let's add 3 to both sides.

$2x - 3 + 3 = 9 + 3$ Add 3 to both sides.

$2x = 12$ Simplify.

Use the multiplication property to get x alone.

$\dfrac{2x}{2} = \dfrac{12}{2}$ Divide both sides by 2.

$x = 6$ Simplify.

Check: To check, replace x with 6 in the original equation to see that a true statement results. The solution is 6.

◻ **Work Practice Problem 9**

If an equation has parentheses, don't forget to use the distributive property to remove them. Then combine any like terms.

Answers

8. $x = -3$, **9.** $x = 6$

EXAMPLE 10 Solve: $5(2x + 3) = -1 + 7$

Solution:

$$5(2x + 3) = -1 + 7$$
$$5(2x) + 5(3) = -1 + 7 \quad \text{Apply the distributive property.}$$
$$10x + 15 = 6 \quad \text{Multiply and write } -1 + 7 \text{ as } 6.$$
$$10x + 15 - 15 = 6 - 15 \quad \text{Subtract 15 from both sides.}$$
$$10x = -9 \quad \text{Simplify.}$$
$$\frac{10x}{10} = -\frac{9}{10} \quad \text{Divide both sides by 10.}$$
$$x = -\frac{9}{10} \quad \text{Simplify.}$$

Check: To check, replace x with $-\dfrac{9}{10}$ in the original equation to see that a true statement results. The solution is $-\dfrac{9}{10}$.

■ **Work Practice Problem 10**

PRACTICE PROBLEM 10

Solve: $4(3x - 2) = -1 + 4$

Objective **C** **Writing Algebraic Expressions**

We continue to sharpen our problem-solving skills by writing algebraic expressions.

EXAMPLE 11 **Writing an Expression for Consecutive Integers**

If x is the first of three consecutive integers, express the sum of the three integers in terms of x. Simplify if possible.

Solution: An example of three consecutive integers is 7, 8, and 9.

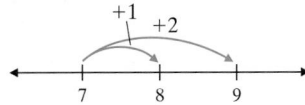

The second consecutive integer is always 1 more than the first, and the third consecutive integer is 2 more than the first. If x is the first of three consecutive integers, the three consecutive integers are x, $x + 1$, and $x + 2$.

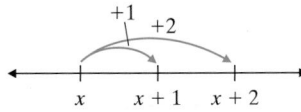

Their sum is shown below.

In words: | first integer | + | second integer | + | third integer |

Translate: x + $(x + 1)$ + $(x + 2)$

This simplifies to $3x + 3$.

■ **Work Practice Problem 11**

PRACTICE PROBLEM 11

a. If x is the first of two consecutive integers, express the sum of the first and the second integer in terms of x. Simplify if possible.

b. If x is the first of two consecutive even integers (see next page), express the sum of the first and second integer in terms of x. Simplify if possible.

Study these examples of consecutive even and consecutive odd integers.

Consecutive even integers:

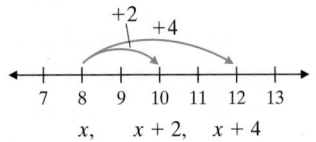

Consecutive odd integers:

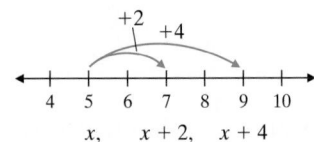

> **Helpful Hint**
>
> If x is an odd integer, then $x + 2$ is the next odd integer. This 2 simply means that odd integers are always 2 units from each other.
>
>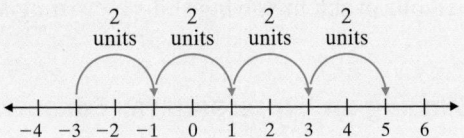

Mental Math

Solve each equation mentally. See Examples 2 and 3.

1. $3a = 27$ **2.** $9c = 54$ **3.** $5b = 10$ **4.** $7t = 14$ **5.** $6x = -30$ **6.** $8r = -64$

9.2 EXERCISE SET

FOR EXTRA HELP

Student Solutions Manual   PH Math/Tutor Center   CD/Video for Review    MathXL®   MyMathLab

Objective A *Solve each equation. Check each solution. See Examples 1 through 6.*

1. $-5x = -20$ **2.** $-7x = -49$ **3.** $3x = 0$ **4.** $2x = 0$

5. $-x = -12$ **6.** $-y = 8$ **7.** $\dfrac{2}{3}x = -8$ **8.** $\dfrac{3}{4}n = -15$

9. $\dfrac{1}{6}d = \dfrac{1}{2}$ **10.** $\dfrac{1}{8}v = \dfrac{1}{4}$ **11.** $\dfrac{a}{2} = 1$ **12.** $\dfrac{d}{15} = 2$

13. $\dfrac{k}{-7} = 0$ **14.** $\dfrac{f}{-5} = 0$ **15.** $1.7x = 10.71$ **16.** $8.5y = 19.55$

Objective B *Solve each equation. Check each solution. See Examples 7 and 8.*

17. $2x - 4 = 16$ **18.** $3x - 1 = 26$ **19.** $-x + 2 = 22$ **20.** $-x + 4 = -24$

21. $6a + 3 = 3$ **22.** $8t + 5 = 5$ **23.** $\dfrac{x}{3} - 2 = -5$ **24.** $\dfrac{b}{4} - 1 = -7$

25. $6z - 8 - z + 3 = 0$ **26.** $4a + 1 + a - 11 = 0$ **27.** $1 = 0.4x - 0.6x - 5$ **28.** $19 = 0.4x - 0.9x - 6$

29. $\dfrac{2}{3}y - 11 = -9$ **30.** $\dfrac{3}{5}x - 14 = -8$ **31.** $\dfrac{3}{4}t - \dfrac{1}{2} = \dfrac{1}{3}$ **32.** $\dfrac{2}{7}z - \dfrac{1}{5} = \dfrac{1}{2}$

Solve each equation. See Examples 9 and 10.

33. $8x + 20 = 6x + 18$ **34.** $11x + 13 = 9x + 9$ **35.** $3(2x + 5) = -18 + 9$ **36.** $2(4x + 1) = -12 + 6$

37. $2x - 5 = 20x + 4$ **38.** $6x - 4 = -2x - 10$ **39.** $2 + 14 = -4(3x - 4)$ **40.** $8 + 4 = -6(5x - 2)$

41. $-6y - 3 = -5y - 7$

42. $-17z - 4 = -16z - 20$

43. $\frac{1}{2}(2x - 1) = -\frac{1}{7} - \frac{3}{7}$

44. $\frac{1}{3}(3x - 1) = -\frac{1}{10} - \frac{2}{10}$

45. $-10z - 0.5 = -20z + 1.6$

46. $-14y - 1.8 = -24y + 3.9$

47. $-4x + 20 = 4x - 20$

48. $-3x + 15 = 3x - 15$

Objectives **A** **B** **Mixed Practice** *See Examples 1 through 10.*

49. $42 = 7x$

50. $81 = 3x$

51. $4.4 = -0.8x$

52. $6.3 = -0.6x$

53. $6x + 10 = -20$

54. $10y + 15 = -5$

55. $5 - 0.3k = 5$

56. $2 - 0.4p = 2$

57. $13x - 5 = 11x - 11$

58. $20x - 20 = 16x - 40$

59. $9(3x + 1) = 4x - 5x$

60. $7(2x + 1) = 18x - 19x$

61. $-\frac{3}{7}p = -2$

62. $-\frac{4}{5}r = -5$

63. $-\frac{4}{3}x = 12$

64. $-\frac{10}{3}x = 30$

65. $-2x - \frac{1}{2} = \frac{7}{2}$

66. $-3n - \frac{1}{3} = \frac{8}{3}$

67. $10 = 2x - 1$

68. $12 = 3j - 4$

69. $10 - 3x - 6 - 9x = 7$

70. $12x + 30 + 8x - 6 = 10$

71. $z - 5z = 7z - 9 - z$

72. $t - 6t = -13 + t - 3t$

73. $-x - \frac{4}{5} = x + \frac{1}{2} + \frac{2}{5}$

74. $x + \frac{3}{7} = -x + \frac{1}{3} + \frac{4}{7}$

75. $-15 + 37 = -2(x + 5)$

76. $-19 + 74 = -5(x + 3)$

Objective **C** *Write each algebraic expression described. Simplify if possible. See Example 11.*

77. If x represents the first of two consecutive odd integers, express the sum of the two integers in terms of x.

78. If x is the first of three consecutive even integers, write their sum as an algebraic expression in x.

79. If x is the first of four consecutive integers, express the sum of the first integer and the third integer as an algebraic expression containing the variable x.

80. If x is the first of two consecutive integers, express the sum of 20 and the second consecutive integer as an algebraic expression containing the variable x.

81. Classrooms on one side of the science building are all numbered with consecutive even integers. If the first room on this side of the building is numbered x, write an expression in x for the sum of five classroom numbers in a row. Then simplify this expression.

82. Two sides of a quadrilateral have the same length, x, while the other two sides have the same length, both being the next consecutive odd integer. Write the sum of these lengths. Then simplify this expression.

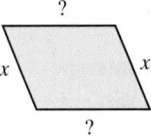

Review

Simplify each expression. See Section 8.7.

83. $5x + 2(x - 6)$

84. $-7y + 2y - 3(y + 1)$

85. $6(2z + 4) + 20$

86. $-(3a - 3) + 2a - 6$

87. $-(x - 1) + x$

88. $8(z - 6) + 7z - 1$

Concept Extensions

Fill in the blank with a number of your choice so that each equation has the given solution.

89. $6x = $ _____; solution: -8

90. _____ $x = 10$; solution: $\dfrac{1}{2}$

91. The equation $3x + 6 = 2x + 10 + x - 4$ is true for all real numbers. Substitute a few real numbers for x to see that this is so and then try solving the equation. Describe what happens.

92. The equation $6x + 2 - 2x = 4x + 1$ has no solution. Try solving this equation for x and describe what happens.

93. From the results of Exercises 91 and 92, when do you think an equation has all real numbers as its solutions?

94. From the results of Exercises 91 and 92, when do you think an equation has no solution?

Solve.

95. $0.07x - 5.06 = -4.92$

96. $0.06y + 2.63 = 2.5562$

 STUDY SKILLS BUILDER

How Are Your Homework Assignments Going?

It is very important in mathematics to keep up with homework. Why? Many concepts build on each other. Often your understanding of a day's concepts depends on an understanding of the previous day's material.

Remember that completing your homework assignment involves a lot more than attempting a few of the problems assigned.

To complete a homework assignment, remember these four things:

- Attempt all of it.
- Check it.
- Correct it.
- If needed, ask questions about it.

Take a moment and review your completed homework assignments. Answer the questions below based on this review.

1. Approximate the fraction of your homework you have attempted.

2. Approximate the fraction of your homework you have checked (if possible).

3. If you are able to check your homework, have you corrected it when errors have been found?

4. When working homework, if you do not understand a concept, what do you do?

9.3 FURTHER SOLVING LINEAR EQUATIONS

Objective A Solving Linear Equations

We now combine our knowledge from the previous sections into a general strategy for solving linear equations. One new piece in this strategy is a suggestion to "clear an equation of fractions" as a first step. Doing so makes the equation more manageable, since working with integers is more convenient than working with fractions. We will discuss this further in Example 3.

To Solve Linear Equations in One Variable

Step 1: If an equation contains fractions, multiply both sides by the LCD to clear the equation of fractions.

Step 2: Use the distributive property to remove parentheses if they occur.

Step 3: Simplify each side of the equation by combining like terms.

Step 4: Get all variable terms on one side and all numbers on the other side by using the addition property of equality.

Step 5: Get the variable alone by using the multiplication property of equality.

Step 6: Check the solution by substituting it into the original equation.

PRACTICE PROBLEM 1

Solve:

$5(3x - 1) + 2 = 12x + 6$

EXAMPLE 1 Solve: $4(2x - 3) + 7 = 3x + 5$

Solution: There are no fractions, so we begin with Step 2.

$$4(2x - 3) + 7 = 3x + 5$$

Step 2: $8x - 12 + 7 = 3x + 5$ Use the distributive property.

Step 3: $8x - 5 = 3x + 5$ Combine like terms.

Step 4:   Get all variable terms on one side of the equation and all numbers on the other side. One way to do this is by subtracting $3x$ from both sides and then adding 5 to both sides.

$$8x - 5 - 3x = 3x + 5 - 3x$$ Subtract $3x$ from both sides.

$$5x - 5 = 5$$ Simplify.

$$5x - 5 + 5 = 5 + 5$$ Add 5 to both sides.

$$5x = 10$$ Simplify.

Step 5:   Use the multiplication property of equality to get x alone.

$$\frac{5x}{5} = \frac{10}{5}$$ Divide both sides by 5.

$$x = 2$$ Simplify.

Step 6:   Check.

$$4(2x - 3) + 7 = 3x + 5$$ Original equation

$$4[2(2) - 3] + 7 \stackrel{?}{=} 3(2) + 5$$ Replace x with 2.

$$4(4 - 3) + 7 \stackrel{?}{=} 6 + 5$$

$$4(1) + 7 \stackrel{?}{=} 11$$

$$4 + 7 \stackrel{?}{=} 11$$

$$11 = 11$$ True

The solution is 2.

Answer

1. $x = 3$

■ **Work Practice Problem 1**

EXAMPLE 2 Solve: $8(2 - t) = -5t$

Solution: First, we apply the distributive property.

$$8(2 - t) = -5t$$

Step 2: $16 - 8t = -5t$ Use the distributive property.

Step 4: $16 - 8t + 8t = -5t + 8t$ Add $8t$ to both sides.
$$16 = 3t$$ Combine like terms.

Step 5: $\dfrac{16}{3} = \dfrac{3t}{3}$ Divide both sides by 3.

$$\dfrac{16}{3} = t$$ Simplify.

Step 6: Check.

$$8(2 - t) = -5t$$ Original equation

$$8\left(2 - \dfrac{16}{3}\right) \stackrel{?}{=} -5\left(\dfrac{16}{3}\right)$$ Replace t with $\dfrac{16}{3}$.

$$8\left(\dfrac{6}{3} - \dfrac{16}{3}\right) \stackrel{?}{=} -\dfrac{80}{3}$$ The LCD is 3.

$$8\left(-\dfrac{10}{3}\right) \stackrel{?}{=} -\dfrac{80}{3}$$ Subtract fractions.

$$-\dfrac{80}{3} = -\dfrac{80}{3}$$ True

The solution is $\dfrac{16}{3}$.

Work Practice Problem 2

Objective B Solving Equations Containing Fractions or Decimals

If an equation contains fractions, we can clear the equation of fractions by multiplying both sides by the LCD of all denominators. By doing this, we avoid working with time-consuming fractions.

EXAMPLE 3 Solve: $\dfrac{x}{2} - 1 = \dfrac{2}{3}x - 3$

Solution: We begin by clearing fractions. To do this, we multiply both sides of the equation by the LCD of 2 and 3, which is 6.

$$\dfrac{x}{2} - 1 = \dfrac{2}{3}x - 3$$

Step 1: $6\left(\dfrac{x}{2} - 1\right) = 6\left(\dfrac{2}{3}x - 3\right)$ Multiply both sides by the LCD, 6.

Step 2: $6\left(\dfrac{x}{2}\right) - 6(1) = 6\left(\dfrac{2}{3}x\right) - 6(3)$ Use the distributive property.

$$3x - 6 = 4x - 18$$ Simplify.

There are no longer grouping symbols and no like terms on either side of the equation, so we continue with Step 4.

Continued on next page

PRACTICE PROBLEM 2
Solve: $9(5 - x) = -3x$

Helpful Hint
When checking solutions, use the original equation.

PRACTICE PROBLEM 3
Solve: $\dfrac{5}{2}x - 1 = \dfrac{3}{2}x - 4$

Helpful Hint
Don't forget to multiply *each* term by the LCD.

Answers
2. $x = \dfrac{15}{2}$, **3.** $x = -3$

$$3x - 6 = 4x - 18$$

Step 4: $3x - 6 - 3x = 4x - 18 - 3x$ Subtract $3x$ from both sides.

$$-6 = x - 18$$ Simplify.

$$-6 + 18 = x - 18 + 18$$ Add 18 to both sides.

$$12 = x$$ Simplify.

Step 5: The variable is now alone, so there is no need to apply the multiplication property of equality.

Step 6: Check.

$$\frac{x}{2} - 1 = \frac{2}{3}x - 3$$ Original equation

$$\frac{12}{2} - 1 \stackrel{?}{=} \frac{2}{3} \cdot 12 - 3$$ Replace x with 12.

$$6 - 1 \stackrel{?}{=} 8 - 3$$ Simplify.

$$5 = 5$$ True

The solution is 12.

◻ **Work Practice Problem 3**

PRACTICE PROBLEM 4

Solve: $\dfrac{3(x - 2)}{5} = 3x + 6$

EXAMPLE 4 Solve: $\dfrac{2(a + 3)}{3} = 6a + 2$

Solution: We clear the equation of fractions first.

$$\frac{2(a + 3)}{3} = 6a + 2$$

Step 1: $3 \cdot \dfrac{2(a + 3)}{3} = 3(6a + 2)$ Clear the fraction by multiplying both sides by the LCD, 3.

$$2(a + 3) = 3(6a + 2)$$ Simplify.

Step 2: Next, we use the distributive property to remove parentheses.

$$2a + 6 = 18a + 6$$ Use the distributive property.

Step 4: $2a + 6 - 18a = 18a + 6 - 18a$ Subtract $18a$ from both sides.

$$-16a + 6 = 6$$ Simplify.

$$-16a + 6 - 6 = 6 - 6$$ Subtract 6 from both sides.

$$-16a = 0$$

Step 5: $\dfrac{-16a}{-16} = \dfrac{0}{-16}$ Divide both sides by -16.

$$a = 0$$ Simplify.

Step 6: To check, replace a with 0 in the original equation. The solution is 0.

◻ **Work Practice Problem 4**

> Helpful Hint
>
> Remember: When solving an equation, it makes no difference on which side of the equation variable terms lie. Just make sure that constant terms lie on the other side.

When solving a problem about money, you may need to solve an equation containing decimals. If you choose, you may multiply to clear the equation of decimals.

Answer

4. $x = -3$

EXAMPLE 5 Solve: $0.25x + 0.10(x - 3) = 1.1$

Solution: First we clear this equation of decimals by multiplying both sides of the equation by 100. Recall that multiplying a decimal number by 100 has the effect of moving the decimal point 2 places to the right.

$$0.25x + 0.10(x - 3) = 1.1$$

Step 1: $0.25x + 0.10(x - 3) = 1.10$ Multiply both sides by 100

$$25x + 10(x - 3) = 110$$

Step 2: $25x + 10x - 30 = 110$ Apply the distributive property.

Step 3: $35x - 30 = 110$ Combine like terms.

Step 4: $35x - 30 + 30 = 110 + 30$ Add 30 to both sides.

$$35x = 140$$ Combine like terms.

Step 5: $\dfrac{35x}{35} = \dfrac{140}{35}$ Divide both sides by 35.

$$x = 4$$

Step 6: To check, replace x with 4 in the original equation. The solution is 4.

■ **Work Practice Problem 5**

Objective C Recognizing Identities and Equations with No Solution

So far, each equation that we have solved has had a single solution. However, not every equation in one variable has a single solution. Some equations have no solution, while others have an infinite number of solutions. For example,

$$x + 5 = x + 7$$

has **no solution** since no matter which real number we replace x with, the equation is false.

real number $+ 5 =$ same real number $+ 7$ **FALSE**

On the other hand,

$$x + 6 = x + 6$$

has infinitely many solutions since x can be replaced by any real number and the equation is always true.

real number $+ 6 =$ same real number $+ 6$ **TRUE**

The equation $x + 6 = x + 6$ is called an **identity.** The next few examples illustrate special equations like these.

EXAMPLE 6 Solve: $-2(x - 5) + 10 = -3(x + 2) + x$

Solution:

$$-2(x - 5) + 10 = -3(x + 2) + x$$

$$-2x + 10 + 10 = -3x - 6 + x$$ Apply the distributive property on both sides.

$$-2x + 20 = -2x - 6$$ Combine like terms.

$$-2x + 20 + 2x = -2x - 6 + 2x$$ Add $2x$ to both sides.

$$20 = -6$$ Combine like terms.

The final equation contains no variable terms, and the result is the false statement $20 = -6$. This means that there is no value for x that makes $20 = -6$ a true equation. Thus, we conclude that there is **no solution** to this equation.

■ **Work Practice Problem 6**

PRACTICE PROBLEM 5

Solve:

$$0.06x - 0.10(x - 2) = -0.16$$

Helpful Hint

If you have trouble with this step, try removing parentheses first.

$$0.25x + 0.10(x - 3) = 1.1$$

$$0.25x + 0.10x - 0.3 = 1.1$$

$$0.25x + 0.10x - 0.30 = 1.10$$

$$25x + 10x - 30 = 110$$

Then continue.

PRACTICE PROBLEM 6

Solve:

$$5(2 - x) + 8x = 3(x - 6)$$

Answers

5. $x = 9$,   **6.** no solution

PRACTICE PROBLEM 7

Solve:

$-6(2x + 1) - 14$
$\quad = -10(x + 2) - 2x$

EXAMPLE 7 Solve: $3(x - 4) = 3x - 12$

Solution: $3(x - 4) = 3x - 12$

$\qquad 3x - 12 = 3x - 12$ Apply the distributive property.

The left side of the equation is now identical to the right side. Every real number may be substituted for x and a true statement will result. We arrive at the same conclusion if we continue.

$$3x - 12 = 3x - 12$$

$$3x - 12 - 3x = 3x - 12 - 3x \quad \text{Subtract } 3x \text{ from both sides.}$$

$$-12 = -12 \qquad\qquad \text{Combine like terms.}$$

Again, the final equation contains no variables, but this time the result is the true statement $-12 = -12$. This means that one side of the equation is identical to the other side. Thus, $3(x - 4) = 3x - 12$ is an **identity** and **every real number** is a solution.

◼ **Work Practice Problem 7**

Answer

7. Every real number is a solution.

✔ **Concept Check Answer**

a. Every real number is a solution.
b. The solution is 0.
c. There is no solution.

✔ **Concept Check** Suppose you have simplified several equations and obtain the following results. What can you conclude about the solutions to the original equation?

a. $7 = 7$ **b.** $x = 0$ **c.** $7 = -4$

▦ **CALCULATOR EXPLORATIONS** Checking Equations

We can use a calculator to check possible solutions of equations. To do this, replace the variable by the possible solution and evaluate both sides of the equation separately.

Equation: $3x - 4 = 2(x + 6)$ Solution: $x = 16$

$\qquad\qquad 3x - 4 = 2(x + 6)$ Original equation

$\qquad 3(16) - 4 \overset{?}{=} 2(16 + 6)$ Replace x with 16.

Now evaluate each side with your calculator.

Evaluate left side: ☐3☐ ☐×☐ ☐16☐ ☐−☐ ☐4☐ ☐=☐

$\qquad\qquad\qquad\qquad$ or

Display: ☐ 44 ☐   ☐ENTER☐

Evaluate right side: ☐2☐ ☐(☐ ☐16☐ ☐+☐ ☐6☐ ☐)☐ ☐=☐

$\qquad\qquad\qquad\qquad$ or

Display: ☐ 44 ☐   ☐ENTER☐

Since the left side equals the right side, the equation checks.

Use a calculator to check the possible solutions to each equation.

1. $2x = 48 + 6x;$ $x = -12$

2. $-3x - 7 = 3x - 1;$ $x = -1$

3. $5x - 2.6 = 2(x + 0.8);$ $x = 4.4$

4. $-1.6x - 3.9 = -6.9x - 25.6;$ $x = 5$

5. $\dfrac{564x}{4} = 200x - 11(649);$ $x = 121$

6. $20(x - 39) = 5x - 432;$ $x = 23.2$

Objective [A] *Solve each equation. See Examples 1 and 2.*

1. $-4y + 10 = -2(3y + 1)$

2. $-3x + 1 = -2(4x + 2)$

3. $15x - 8 = 10 + 9x$

4. $15x - 5 = 7 + 12x$

5. $-2(3x - 4) = 2x$

6. $-(5x - 10) = 5x$

7. $5(2x - 1) - 2(3x) = 1$

8. $3(2 - 5x) + 4(6x) = 12$

9. $-6(x - 3) - 26 = -8$

10. $-4(n - 4) - 23 = -7$

11. $8 - 2(a + 1) = 9 + a$

12. $5 - 6(2 + b) = b - 14$

13. $4x + 3 = -3 + 2x + 14$

14. $6y - 8 = -6 + 3y + 13$

15. $-2y - 10 = 5y + 18$

16. $-7n + 5 = 8n - 10$

Objective [B] *Solve each equation. See Examples 3 through 5.*

17. $\frac{2}{3}x + \frac{4}{3} = -\frac{2}{3}$

18. $\frac{4}{5}x - \frac{8}{5} = -\frac{16}{5}$

19. $\frac{3}{4}x - \frac{1}{2} = 1$

20. $\frac{2}{9}x - \frac{1}{3} = 1$

21. $0.50x + 0.15(70) = 35.5$

22. $0.40x + 0.06(30) = 9.8$

23. $\frac{2(x + 1)}{4} = 3x - 2$

24. $\frac{3(y + 3)}{5} = 2y + 6$

25. $x + \frac{7}{6} = 2x - \frac{7}{6}$

26. $\frac{5}{2}x - 1 = x + \frac{1}{4}$

27. $0.12(y - 6) + 0.06y = 0.08y - 0.7$

28. $0.60(z - 300) + 0.05z = 0.70z - 205$

Objective [C] *Solve each equation. See Examples 6 and 7.*

29. $4(3x + 2) = 12x + 8$

30. $14x + 7 = 7(2x + 1)$

31. $\frac{x}{4} + 1 = \frac{x}{4}$

32. $\frac{x}{3} - 2 = \frac{x}{3}$

33. $3x - 7 = 3(x + 1)$

34. $2(x - 5) = 2x + 10$

35. $-2(6x - 5) + 4 = -12x + 14$

36. $-5(4y - 3) + 2 = -20y + 17$

Objectives Ⓐ Ⓑ Ⓒ **Mixed Practice** *Solve. See Examples 1 through 7.*

37. $\dfrac{6(3-z)}{5} = -z$

38. $\dfrac{4(5-w)}{3} = -w$

39. $-3(2t-5) + 2t = 5t - 4$

40. $-(4a-7) - 5a = 10 + a$

41. $5y + 2(y-6) = 4(y+1) - 2$

42. $9x + 3(x-4) = 10(x-5) + 7$

43. $\dfrac{3(x-5)}{2} = \dfrac{2(x+5)}{3}$

44. $\dfrac{5(x-1)}{4} = \dfrac{3(x+1)}{2}$

45. $0.7x - 2.3 = 0.5$

46. $0.9x - 4.1 = 0.4$

47. $5x - 5 = 2(x+1) + 3x - 7$

48. $3(2x-1) + 5 = 6x + 2$

49. $4(2n+1) = 3(6n+3) + 1$

50. $4(4y+2) = 2(1+6y) + 8$

51. $x + \dfrac{5}{4} = \dfrac{3}{4}x$

52. $\dfrac{7}{8}x + \dfrac{1}{4} = \dfrac{3}{4}x$

53. $\dfrac{x}{2} - 1 = \dfrac{x}{5} + 2$

54. $\dfrac{x}{5} - 7 = \dfrac{x}{3} - 5$

55. $2(x+3) - 5 = 5x - 3(1+x)$

56. $4(2+x) + 1 = 7x - 3(x-2)$

57. $0.06 - 0.01(x+1) = -0.02(2-x)$

58. $-0.01(5x+4) = 0.04 - 0.01(x+4)$

59. $\dfrac{9}{2} + \dfrac{5}{2}y = 2y - 4$

60. $3 - \dfrac{1}{2}x = 5x - 8$

Review

Write each algebraic expression described. See Section 9.1.

△ **61.** A plot of land is in the shape of a triangle. If one side is x meters, a second side is $(2x - 3)$ meters, and a third side is $(3x - 5)$ meters, express the perimeter of the lot as a simplified expression in x.

62. A portion of a board has length x feet. The other part has length $(7x - 9)$ feet. Express the total length of the board as a simplified expression in x.

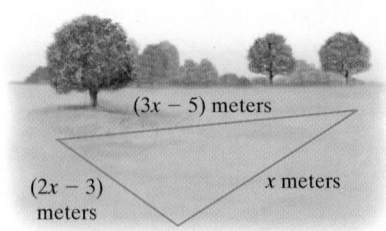

(3x − 5) meters

(2x − 3) meters   x meters

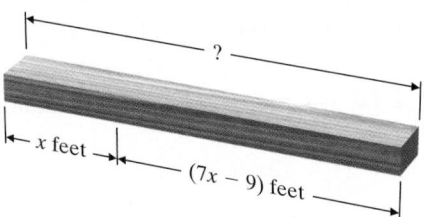

Write each phrase as an algebraic expression. Use x for the unknown number. See Section 9.1.

63. A number subtracted from -8

64. Three times a number

65. The sum of -3 and twice a number

66. The difference of 8 and twice a number

67. The product of 9 and the sum of a number and 20

68. The quotient of -12 and the difference of a number and 3

Concept Extensions

See the Concept Check in this section.

69. a. Solve: $x + 3 = x + 3$
b. If you simplify an equation and get $0 = 0$, what can you conclude about the solution(s) of the original equation?
c. On your own, construct an equation for which every real number is a solution.

70. a. Solve: $x + 3 = x + 5$
b. If you simplify an equation and get $3 = 5$, what can you conclude about the solution(s) of the original equation?
c. On your own, construct an equation that has no solution.

Match each equation in the first column with its solution in the second column. Items in the second column may be used more than once.

71. $5x + 1 = 5x + 1$

72. $3x + 1 = 3x + 2$

73. $2x - 6x - 10 = -4x + 3 - 10$

74. $x - 11x - 3 = -10x - 1 - 2$

75. $9x - 20 = 8x - 20$

76. $-x + 15 = x + 15$

a. all real numbers
b. no solution
c. 0

77. Explain the difference between simplifying an expression and solving an equation.

78. On your own, write an expression and then an equation. Label each.

For Exercises 79 and 80, **a.** *Write an equation for perimeter.* **b.** *Solve the equation in part (a).* **c.** *Find the length of each side.*

79. The perimeter of a geometric figure is the sum of the lengths of its sides. If the perimeter of the following pentagon (five-sided figure) is 28 centimeters, find the length of each side.

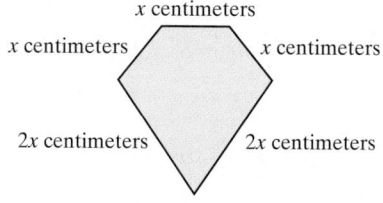

x centimeters
x centimeters   *x* centimeters
2*x* centimeters   2*x* centimeters

80. The perimeter of the following triangle is 35 meters. Find the length of each side.

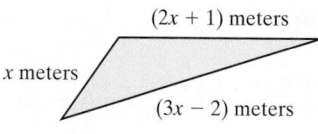

$(2x + 1)$ meters
x meters
$(3x - 2)$ meters

Fill in the blanks with numbers of your choice so that each equation has the given solution. Note: Each blank may be replaced by a different number.

81. $x + \underline{\quad} = 2x - \underline{\quad}$; solution: 9

82. $-5x - \underline{\quad} = \underline{\quad}$; solution: 2

Solve.

83. $1000(7x - 10) = 50(412 + 100x)$

84. $1000(x + 40) = 100(16 + 7x)$

85. $0.035x + 5.112 = 0.010x + 5.107$

86. $0.127x - 2.685 = 0.027x - 2.38$

1. _____

2. _____

3. _____

4. _____

5. _____

6. _____

7. _____

8. _____

9. _____

10. _____

11. _____

12. _____

13. _____

14. _____

15. _____

16. _____

17. _____

18. _____

19. _____

20. _____

21. _____

22. _____

INTEGRATED REVIEW   Sections 9.1–9.3

Solving Linear Equations

Solve. Feel free to use the steps given in Section 9.3.

1. $x - 10 = -4$

2. $y + 14 = -3$

3. $9y = 108$

4. $-3x = 78$

5. $-6x + 7 = 25$

6. $5y - 42 = -47$

7. $\dfrac{2}{3}x = 9$

8. $\dfrac{4}{5}z = 10$

9. $\dfrac{r}{-4} = -2$

10. $\dfrac{y}{-8} = 8$

11. $6 - 2x + 8 = 10$

12. $-5 - 6y + 6 = 19$

13. $2x - 7 = 6x - 27$

14. $3 + 8y = 3y - 2$

15. $9(3x - 1) = -4 + 49$

16. $12(2x + 1) = -6 + 66$

17. $-3a + 6 + 5a = 7a - 8a$

18. $4b - 8 - b = 10b - 3b$

19. $-\dfrac{2}{3}x = \dfrac{5}{9}$

20. $-\dfrac{3}{8}y = -\dfrac{1}{16}$

21. $10 = -6n + 16$

22. $-5 = -2m + 7$

23. $3(5c - 1) - 2 = 13c + 3$

24. $4(3t + 4) - 20 = 3 + 5t$

25. $\dfrac{2(z + 3)}{3} = 5 - z$

26. $\dfrac{3(w + 2)}{4} = 2w + 3$

27. $-2(2x - 5) = -3x + 7 - x + 3$

28. $-4(5x - 2) = -12x + 4 - 8x + 4$

29. $0.02(6t - 3) = 0.04(t - 2) + 0.02$

30. $0.03(m + 7) = 0.02(5 - m) + 0.03$

31. $-3y = \dfrac{4(y - 1)}{5}$

32. $-4x = \dfrac{5(1 - x)}{6}$

33. $\dfrac{5}{3}x - \dfrac{7}{3} = x$

34. $\dfrac{7}{5}n + \dfrac{3}{5} = -n$

35. $\dfrac{1}{10}(3x - 7) = \dfrac{3}{10}x + 5$

36. $\dfrac{1}{7}(2x - 5) = \dfrac{2}{7}x + 1$

37. $5 + 2(3x - 6) = -4(6x - 7)$

38. $3 + 5(2x - 4) = -7(5x + 2)$

23. _____

24. _____

25. _____

26. _____

27. _____

28. _____

29. _____

30. _____

31. _____

32. _____

33. _____

34. _____

35. _____

36. _____

37. _____

38. _____

9.4 AN INTRODUCTION TO PROBLEM SOLVING

Objective

A Translate a Problem to an Equation, Then Use the Equation to Solve the Problem.

In the preceding sections, we practiced translating phrases into expressions and sentences into equations as well as solving linear equations. We are now ready to put our skills to practical use. To begin, we present a general strategy for problem solving.

General Strategy for Problem Solving

1. UNDERSTAND the problem. During this step, become comfortable with the problem. Some ways of doing this are:

   Read and reread the problem.

   Choose a variable to represent the unknown.

   Construct a drawing.

   Propose a solution and check. Pay careful attention to how you check your proposed solution. This will help when writing an equation to model the problem.

2. TRANSLATE the problem into an equation.

3. SOLVE the equation.

4. INTERPRET the results: *Check* the proposed solution in the stated problem and *state* your conclusion.

Objective **A** Translating and Solving Problems

Much of problem solving involves a direct translation from a sentence to an equation.

EXAMPLE 1 Finding an Unknown Number

Twice the sum of a number and 4 is the same as four times the number, decreased by 12. Find the number.

Solution:

1. UNDERSTAND. Read and reread the problem. If we let x = the unknown number, then
   "the sum of a number and 4" translates to "$x + 4$" and
   "four times the number" translates to "$4x$"

2. TRANSLATE.

twice	sum of a number and 4	is the same as	four times the number	decreased by	12
↓	↓	↓	↓	↓	↓
2	$(x + 4)$	=	$4x$	−	12

3. SOLVE

$$2(x + 4) = 4x - 12$$
$$2x + 8 = 4x - 12 \qquad \text{Apply the distributive property.}$$
$$2x + 8 - 4x = 4x - 12 - 4x \qquad \text{Subtract } 4x \text{ from both sides.}$$
$$-2x + 8 = -12$$
$$-2x + 8 - 8 = -12 - 8 \qquad \text{Subtract 8 from both sides.}$$
$$-2x = -20$$
$$\frac{-2x}{-2} = \frac{-20}{-2} \qquad \text{Divide both sides by } -2.$$
$$x = 10$$

PRACTICE PROBLEM 1

Three times the difference of a number and 5 is the same as twice the number decreased by 3. Find the number.

Answer

1. The number is 12.

4. INTERPRET.

Check: Check this solution in the problem as it was originally stated. To do so, replace "number" with 10. Twice the sum of "10" and 4 is 28, which is the same as 4 times "10" decreased by 12.

State: The number is 10.

◾ **Work Practice Problem 1**

The next example has to do with consecutive integers. For a review, see Section 9.2.

EXAMPLE 2

Some states have a single area code for the entire state. Two such states have area codes that are consecutive odd integers. If the sum of these integers is 1208, find the two area codes. (*Source: World Almanac*)

Solution:

1. UNDERSTAND. Read and reread the problem. If we let

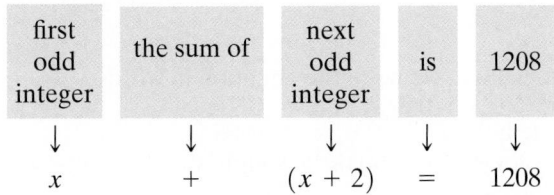

x = the first odd integer, then

$x + 2$ = the next odd integer

2. TRANSLATE.

first odd integer	the sum of	next odd integer	is	1208
↓	↓	↓	↓	↓
x	$+$	$(x + 2)$	$=$	1208

3. SOLVE.

$$x + x + 2 = 1208$$
$$2x + 2 = 1208$$
$$2x + 2 - 2 = 1208 - 2$$
$$2x = 1206$$
$$\frac{2x}{2} = \frac{1206}{2}$$
$$x = 603$$

4. INTERPRET.

Check: If $x = 603$, then the next odd integer $x + 2 = 603 + 2 = 605$. Notice their sum, $603 + 605 = 1208$, as needed.

State: The area codes are 603 and 605.

Note: New Hampshire's area code is 603 and South Dakota's area code is 605.

◾ **Work Practice Problem 2**

During the next example, we expand our discussion of the UNDERSTAND part of the problem-solving process.

PRACTICE PROBLEM 2

The sum of three consecutive even integers is 144. Find the integers.

Helpful Hint

Remember, the 2 here means that odd integers are 2 units apart, for example, the odd integers 13 and $13 + 2 = 15$.

Answer

2. 46, 48, 50

PRACTICE PROBLEM 3

An 18-foot wire is to be cut so that the longer piece is 5 times longer than the shorter piece. Find the length of each piece.

EXAMPLE 3 **Finding the Length of a Board**

A 10-foot board is to be cut into two pieces so that the longer piece is 4 times the shorter. Find the length of each piece.

Solution:

1. UNDERSTAND the problem. To do so, read and reread the problem. You may also want to propose a solution. For example, if 3 feet represents the length of the shorter piece, then $4(3) = 12$ feet is the length of the longer piece, since it is 4 times the length of the shorter piece. This guess gives a total board length of 3 feet + 12 feet = 15 feet, which is too long. However, the purpose of proposing a solution is not to guess correctly, but to help better understand the problem and how to model it.

In general, if we let

x = length of shorter piece, then

$4x$ = length of longer piece

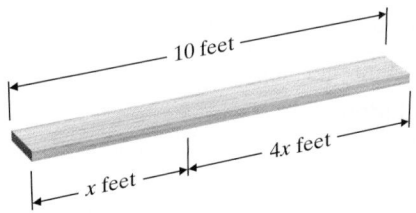

2. TRANSLATE the problem. First, we write the equation in words.

length of shorter piece	added to	length of longer piece	equals	total length of board
↓	↓	↓	↓	↓
x	$+$	$4x$	$=$	10

3. SOLVE.

$$x + 4x = 10$$
$$5x = 10 \quad \text{Combine like terms.}$$
$$\frac{5x}{5} = \frac{10}{5} \quad \text{Divide both sides by 5.}$$
$$x = 2$$

4. INTERPRET.

Check: Check the solution in the stated problem. If the shorter piece of board is 2 feet, the longer piece is $4 \cdot (2 \text{ feet}) = 8$ feet and the sum of the two pieces is 2 feet + 8 feet = 10 feet.

State: The shorter piece of board is 2 feet and the longer piece of board is 8 feet.

☐ **Work Practice Problem 3**

Helpful Hint

Make sure that units are included in your answer, if appropriate.

Answer

3. shorter piece: 3 feet; longer piece: 15 feet

EXAMPLE 4 Finding the Number of Republican and Democratic Senators

In a recent year, the U.S. House of Representatives had a total of 431 Democrats and Republicans. There were 15 more Republican representatives than Democratic. Find the number of representatives from each party. (*Source:* Office of the Clerk of the U.S. House of Representatives)

Solution:

1. UNDERSTAND the problem. Read and reread the problem. Let's suppose that there are 200 Democratic representatives. Since there are 15 more Republicans than Democrats, there must be 200 + 15 = 215 Republicans. The total number of Democrats and Republicans is then 200 + 215 = 415. This is incorrect since the total should be 431, but we now have a better understanding of the problem.
   In general, if we let

   x = number of Democrats, then

   $x + 15$ = number of Republicans

2. TRANSLATE the problem. First, we write the equation in words.

number of Democrats	added to	number of Republicans	equals	431
↓	↓	↓	↓	↓
x	$+$	$(x + 15)$	$=$	431

3. SOLVE.

$$x + (x + 15) = 431$$
$$2x + 15 = 431 \quad \text{Combine like terms.}$$
$$2x + 15 - 15 = 431 - 15 \quad \text{Subtract 15 from both sides.}$$
$$2x = 416$$
$$\frac{2x}{2} = \frac{416}{2} \quad \text{Divide both sides by 2.}$$
$$x = 208$$

4. INTERPRET.

Check: If there were 208 Democratic representatives, then there were 208 + 15 = 223 Republican representatives. The total number of representatives is then 208 + 223 = 431. The results check.

State: There were 208 Democratic and 223 Republican representatives in Congress.

⬛ **Work Practice Problem 4**

EXAMPLE 5 Calculating Hours on Job

A computer science major at a local university has a part-time job working on computers for his clients. He charges $20 to come to your home or office and then $25 per hour. During one month he visited 10 homes or offices and his total income was $575. How many hours did he spend working on computers?

Solution:

1. UNDERSTAND. Read and reread the problem. Let's propose that the student spent 20 hours working on computers. Pay careful attention as to how his income is calculated. For 20 hours and 10 visits, his income is 20($25) + 10($20) = $700, more than $575. We now have a better understanding of the problem and know that the time working on computers is less than 20 hours.

Continued on next page

Let's let

x = hours working on computers. Then

$25x$ = amount of money made while working on computers

2. TRANSLATE.

money made while working on computers	plus	money made for visits	is equal to	575
↓	↓	↓	↓	↓
$25x$	$+$	$10(20)$	$=$	575

3. SOLVE.

$$25x + 200 = 575$$
$$25x + 200 - 200 = 575 - 200 \qquad \text{Subtract 200 from both sides.}$$
$$25x = 375 \qquad \text{Simplify.}$$
$$\frac{25x}{25} = \frac{375}{25} \qquad \text{Divide both sides by 25.}$$
$$x = 15 \qquad \text{Simplify.}$$

4. INTERPRET.

Check: If the student works 15 hours and makes 10 visits, his income is $15(\$25) + 10(\$20) = \$575$.

State: The student spent 15 hours working on computers.

⬛ **Work Practice Problem 5**

PRACTICE PROBLEM 6

The measure of the second angle of a triangle is twice the measure of the smallest angle. The measure of the third angle of the triangle is three times the measure of the smallest angle. Find the measures of the angles.

△ **EXAMPLE 6** **Finding Angle Measures**

If the two walls of the Vietnam Veterans Memorial in Washington, D.C., were connected, an isosceles triangle would be formed. The measure of the third angle is 97.5° more than the measure of either of the two equal angles. Find the measure of the third angle. (*Source:* National Park Service)

Solution:

1. UNDERSTAND. Read and reread the problem. We then draw a diagram (recall that an isosceles triangle has two angles with the same measure) and let

x = degree measure of one angle

x = degree measure of the second equal angle

$x + 97.5$ = degree measure of the third angle

Answer

6. smallest: 30°; second: 60°; third: 90°

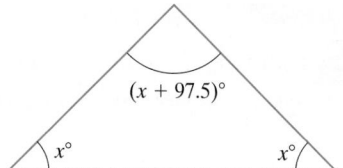

2. TRANSLATE. Recall that the sum of the measures of the angles of a triangle equals 180.

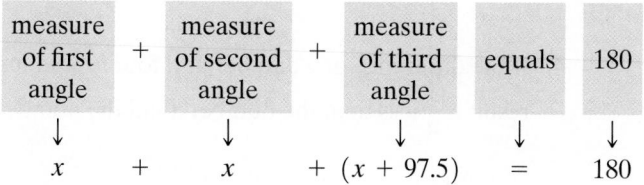

3. SOLVE.

$$x + x + (x + 97.5) = 180$$

$$3x + 97.5 = 180 \qquad \text{Combine like terms.}$$

$$3x + 97.5 - 97.5 = 180 - 97.5 \qquad \text{Subtract 97.5 from both sides.}$$

$$3x = 82.5$$

$$\frac{3x}{3} = \frac{82.5}{3} \qquad \text{Divide both sides by 3.}$$

$$x = 27.5$$

4. INTERPRET.

Check: If $x = 27.5$, then the measure of the third angle is $x + 97.5 = 125$. The sum of the angles is then $27.5 + 27.5 + 125 = 180$, the correct sum.

State: The third angle measures $125°$.*

■ **Work Practice Problem 6**

---

*The two walls actually meet at an angle of 125 degrees 12 minutes. The measurement of $97.5°$ given in the problem is an approximation.

9.4 EXERCISE SET

FOR EXTRA HELP

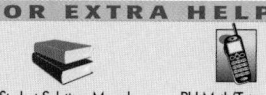
Student Solutions Manual

PH Math/Tutor Center

CD/Video for Review

Math XL
MathXL®

MyMathLab
MyMathLab

Objective **A** *Solve. See Example 1.*

1. Twice the difference of a number and 8 is equal to three times the sum of the number and 3. Find the number.

2. Five times the sum of a number and −1 is the same as 6 times the number. Find the number.

3. The product of twice a number and three is the same as the difference of five times the number and $\frac{3}{4}$. Find the number.

4. If the difference of a number and four is doubled, the result is $\frac{1}{4}$ less than the number. Find the number.

Solve. See Example 2.

5. The left and right page numbers of an open book are two consecutive integers whose sum is 469. Find these page numbers.

6. The room numbers of two adjacent classrooms are two consecutive even numbers. If their sum is 654, find the classroom numbers.

7. To make an international telephone call, you need the code for the country you are calling. The codes for Belgium, France, and Spain are three consecutive integers whose sum is 99. Find the code for each country. (*Source: The World Almanac and Book of Facts*)

8. The code to unlock a student's combination lock happens to be three consecutive odd integers whose sum is 51. Find the integers.

Solve. See Examples 3 and 4.

9. A 25-inch piece of steel is cut into three pieces so that the second piece is twice as long as the first piece, and the third piece is one inch more than five times the length of the first piece. Find the lengths of the pieces.

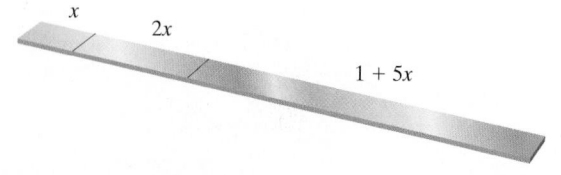

10. A 46-foot piece of rope is cut into three pieces so that the second piece is three times as long as the first piece, and the third piece is two feet more than seven times the length of the first piece. Find the lengths of the pieces.

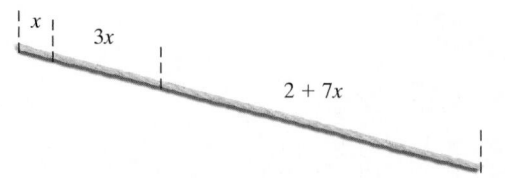

11. A 40-inch board is to be cut into three pieces so that the second piece is twice as long as the first piece and the third piece is 5 times as long as the first piece. If x represents the length of the first piece, find the lengths of all three pieces.

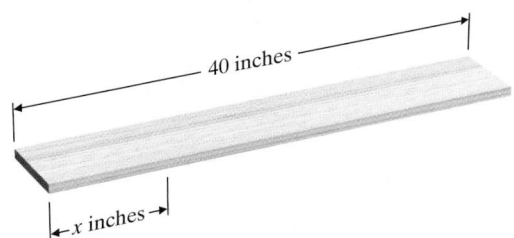

40 inches

x inches

12. A 21-foot beam is to be divided so that the longer piece is 1 foot more than 3 times the shorter piece. If x represents the length of the shorter piece, find the lengths of both pieces.

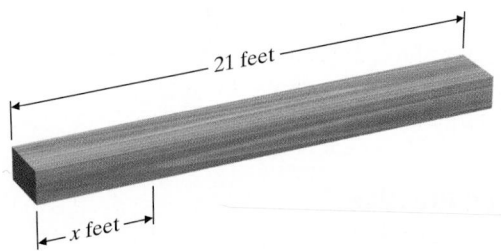

21 feet

x feet

13. The governor of California earns $50,425 more than the governor of Florida. If the total of their salaries is $299,575, find the salaries of each. (*Source: The World Almanac, 2005*)

14. In the 2004 Summer Olympics, the United States team won 3 more gold medals than the Chinese team. If the total number of gold medals won by both teams was 67, find the number of gold medals won by each team. (*Source:* Wikipedia)

Solve. See Example 5.

15. A car rental agency advertised renting a Buick Century for $24.95 per day and $0.29 per mile. If you rent this car for 2 days, how many whole miles can you drive on a $100 budget?

16. A plumber gave an estimate for the renovation of a kitchen. Her hourly pay is $27 per hour and the plumbing parts will cost $80. If her total estimate is $404, how many hours does she expect this job to take?

17. In one U.S. city, the taxi cost is $3 plus $0.80 per mile. If you are traveling from the airport, there is an additional charge of $4.50 for tolls. How far can you travel from the airport by taxi for $27.50?

18. A professional carpet cleaning service charges $30 plus $25.50 per hour to come to your home. If your total bill from this company is $119.25 before taxes, for how many hours were you charged?

Solve. See Example 6.

△ **19.** The flag of Equatorial Guinea contains an isosceles triangle. (Recall that an isosceles triangle contains two angles with the same measure.) If the measure of the third angle of the triangle is 30° more than twice the measure of either of the other two angles, find the measure of each angle of the triangle. (*Hint:* Recall that the sum of the measures of the angles of a triangle is 180°.)

△ **20.** The flag of Brazil contains a parallelogram. One angle of the parallelogram is 15° less than twice the measure of the angle next to it. Find the measure of each angle of the parallelogram. (*Hint:* Recall that opposite angles of a parallelogram have the same measure and that the sum of the measures of the angles is 360°.)

21. The sum of the measures of the angles of a parallelogram is 360°. In the parallelogram below, angles A and D have the same measure as well as angles C and B. If the measure of angle C is twice the measure of angle A, find the measure of each angle.

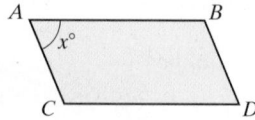

22. Recall that the sum of the measures of the angles of a triangle is 180°. In the triangle below, angle C has the same measure as angle B, and angle A measures 42° less than angle B. Find the measure of each angle.

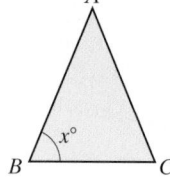

Mixed Practice

23. A 17-foot piece of string is cut into two pieces so that the longer piece is 2 feet longer than twice the shorter piece. Find the lengths of both pieces.

24. A 25-foot wire is to be cut so that the longer piece is one foot longer than 5 times the shorter piece. Find the length of each piece.

25. From 1997 to 2001, the number of prescriptions written for ADHD drugs increased by 5.5 million. If the sum of the number of prescriptions for these two years is 35.7 million, find the number of prescriptions for each year. Check to see that your results agree with the heights of the bars in the graph.

26. The Pentagon Building in Washington, D.C., is the headquarters for the U.S. Department of Defense. The Pentagon is also the world's largest office building in terms of ground space with a floor area of over 6.5 million square feet. This is three times the floor area of the Empire State Building. About how much floor space does the Empire State Building have? Round to the nearest tenth.

Number of Prescriptions Written for ADHD Drugs

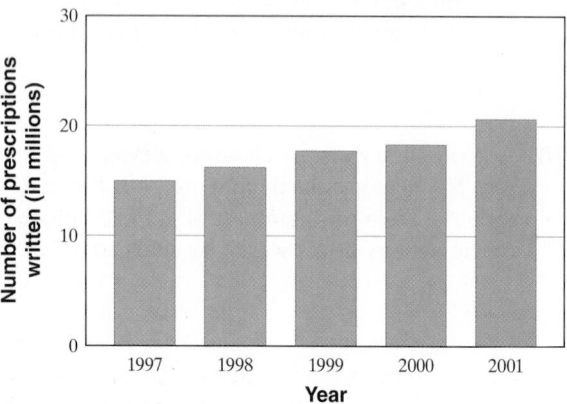

Source: IMS Health

27. Two angles are supplementary if their sum is 180°. One angle measures three times the measure of a smaller angle. If x represents the measure of the smaller angle and these two angles are supplementary, find the measure of each angle.

28. Two angles are complementary if their sum is 90°. Given the measures of the complementary angles shown, find the measure of each angle.

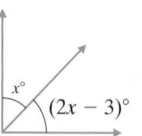

29. The measures of the angles of a triangle are 3 consecutive even integers. Find the measure of each angle.

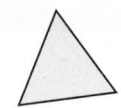

30. A quadrilateral is a polygon with 4 sides. The sum of the measures of the 4 angles in a quadrilateral is 360°. If the measures of the angles of a quadrilateral are consecutive odd integers, find the measures.

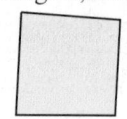

31. The sum of $\frac{1}{5}$ and twice a number is equal to $\frac{4}{5}$ subtracted from three times the number. Find the number.

32. The sum of $\frac{2}{3}$ and four times a number is equal to $\frac{5}{6}$ subtracted from five times the number. Find the number.

33. Hertz Car Rental charges a daily rate of $39 plus $0.20 per mile for a certain car. Suppose that you rent that car for a day and your bill (before taxes) is $95. How many miles did you drive?

34. A woman's $15,000 estate is to be divided so that her husband receives twice as much as her son. Find the amount of money that her husband receives and the amount of money that her son receives.

35. The winner of the NASCAR Winston Cup in 2003 was Matt Kenseth. Kenseth earned 90 more points than his closest rival, Jimmie Johnson. Together they earned 9954 points. How many points did each driver accumulate during the 2003 Winston Cup Series?

36. During the 2004 Houston Bowl, University of Colorado beat University of Texas–El Paso by 5 points. If their combined scores totaled 61, find the individual team scores. (*Source:* ESPN)

37. The number of counties in California and the number of counties in Montana are consecutive even integers whose sum is 114. If California has more counties than Montana, how many counties does each state have? (*Source: The World Almanac and Book of Facts*, 2005)

38. After a recent election, there were 2 more Republican governors than Democratic governors in the United States. How many Democrats and how many Republicans held governor's offices after this election? (*Source: The World Almanac and Book of Facts*)

39. Over the past few years the satellite Voyager II has passed by the planets Saturn, Uranus, and Neptune, continually updating information about these planets, including the number of moons for each. Uranus is now believed to have 13 more moons than Neptune. Also, Saturn is now believed to have 2 more than twice the number of moons of Neptune. If the total number of moons for these planets is 47, find the number of moons for each planet. (*Source:* National Space Science Data Center)

40. On April 7, 2001, the Mars Odyssey spacecraft was launched, beginning a multi-year mission to observe and map the planet Mars. Mars Odyssey was launched on Boeing's Delta II 7925 launch vehicle using nine strap-on solid rocket motors. Each solid rocket motor has a height that is 8 meters more than 5 times its diameter. If the sum of the height and the diameter for a single solid rocket motor is 14 meters, find each dimension. (*Source:* NASA)

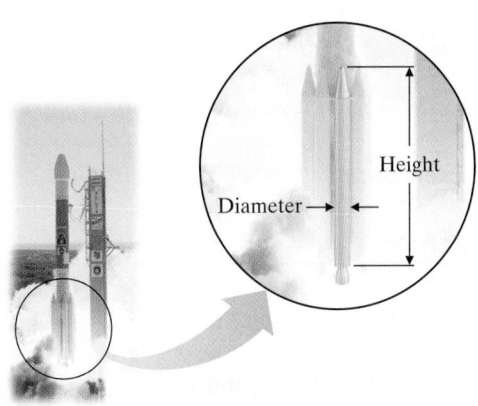

41. If the sum of a number and five is tripled, the result is one less than twice the number. Find the number.

42. Twice the sum of a number and six equals three times the sum of the number and four. Find the number.

43. The area of the Sahara Desert is 7 times the area of the Gobi Desert. If the sum of their areas is 4,000,000 square miles, find the area of each desert.

44. The largest meteorite in the world is the Hoba West located in Namibia. Its weight is 3 times the weight of the Armanty meteorite located in Outer Mongolia. If the sum of their weights is 88 tons, find the weight of each.

45. In the 2004 summer Olympics, France won more gold medals than Italy, who won more gold medals than Korea. If the total number of gold medals won by these three countries is three consecutive integers whose sum is 30, find the number of gold medals won by each. (*Source: The World Almanac, 2005*)

46. To make an international telephone call, you need the code for the country you are calling. The codes for Mali Republic, Côte d'Ivoire, and Niger are three consecutive odd integers whose sum is 675. Find the code for each country.

47. In a recent election in Florida for a seat in the United States House of Representatives, Corrine Brown received 13,288 more votes than Bill Randall. If the total number of votes was 119,436, find the number of votes for each candidate.

48. In a recent election in Texas for a seat in the United States House of Representatives, Max Sandlin received 25,557 more votes than opponent Dennis Boerner. If the total number of votes was 135,821, find the number of votes for each candidate. (*Source:* Voter News Service)

The graph below shows the states with the highest tourism budgets. Use the graph for Exercises 49 through 52.

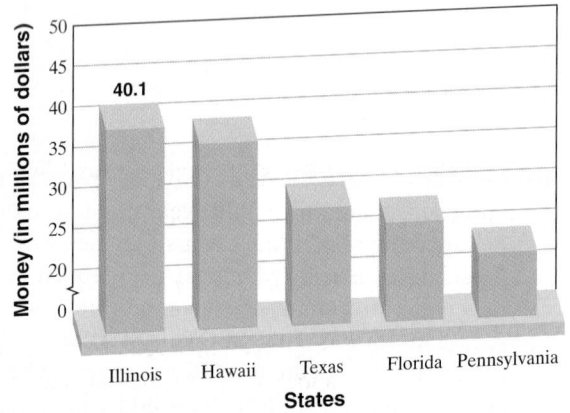

Source: Travel Industry Association of America

49. Which state spends the most money on tourism?

50. Which states spend between $25 and $30 million on tourism?

51. The states of Texas and Florida spend a total of $56.6 million for tourism. The state of Texas spends $2.2 million more than the state of Florida. Find the amount that each state spends on tourism.

52. The states of Hawaii and Pennsylvania spend a total of $60.9 million for tourism. The state of Hawaii spends $8.1 million less than twice the amount of money that the state of Pennsylvania spends. Find the amount that each state spends on tourism.

Compare the heights of the bars in the graph with your results of the exercises below. Are your answers reasonable?

53. Exercise 51

54. Exercise 52

Review

Evaluate each expression for the given values. See Section 8.2.

55. $2W + 2L$; $W = 7$ and $L = 10$

56. $\frac{1}{2}Bh$; $B = 14$ and $h = 22$

57. πr^2; $r = 15$

58. $r \cdot t$; $r = 15$ and $t = 2$

Concept Extensions

△ **59.** A golden rectangle is a rectangle whose length is approximately 1.6 times its width. The early Greeks thought that a rectangle with these dimensions was the most pleasing to the eye and examples of the golden rectangle are found in many early works of art. For example, the Parthenon in Athens contains many examples of golden rectangles.

Mike Hallahan would like to plant a rectangular garden in the shape of a golden rectangle. If he has 78 feet of fencing available, find the dimensions of the garden.

60. Dr. Dorothy Smith gave the students in her geometry class at the University of New Orleans the following question. Is it possible to construct a triangle such that the second angle of the triangle has a measure that is twice the measure of the first angle and the measure of the third angle is 3 times the measure of the first? If so, find the measure of each angle. (*Hint:* Recall that the sum of the measures of the angles of a triangle is 180°.)

▦ **61.** The human eye blinks once every 5 seconds on average. How many times does the average eye blink in one hour? In one 16-hour day while awake? In one year?

✎ **62.** Give an example of how you recently solved a problem using mathematics.

✎ **63.** In your own words, explain why a solution of a word problem should be checked using the original wording of the problem and not the equation written from the wording.

Recall from Exercise 59 that a golden rectangle is a rectangle whose length is approximately 1.6 times its width.

△ **64.** It is thought that for about 75% of adults, a rectangle in the shape of the golden rectangle is the most pleasing to the eye. Draw three rectangles, one in the shape of the golden rectangle, and poll your class. Do the results agree with the percentage given above?

△ **65.** Examples of golden rectangles can be found today in architecture and manufacturing packaging. Find an example of a golden rectangle in your home. A few suggestions: the front face of a book, the floor of a room, the front of a box of food.

△ **66.** Measure the dimensions of each rectangle and decide which one best approximates the shape of a golden rectangle.

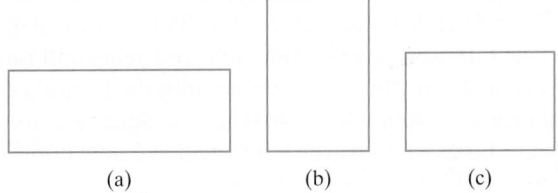

(a)   (b)   (c)

9.5 FORMULAS AND PROBLEM SOLVING

Objective **A** Using Formulas to Solve Problems

A **formula** describes a known relationship among quantities. Many formulas are given as equations. For example, the formula

$$d = r \cdot t$$

stands for the relationship

$$\text{distance} = \text{rate} \cdot \text{time}$$

Let's look at one way that we can use this formula.

If we know we traveled a distance of 100 miles at a rate of 40 miles per hour, we can replace the variables d and r in the formula $d = rt$ and find our travel time, t.

$$d = rt \qquad \text{Formula}$$
$$100 = 40t \qquad \text{Replace } d \text{ with 100 and } r \text{ with 40.}$$

To solve for t, we divide both sides of the equation by 40.

$$\frac{100}{40} = \frac{40t}{40} \qquad \text{Divide both sides by 40.}$$

$$\frac{5}{2} = t \qquad \text{Simplify.}$$

The travel times was $\frac{5}{2}$ hours, or $2\frac{1}{2}$ hours, or 2.5 hours.

In this section, we solve problems that can be modeled by known formulas. We use the same problem-solving strategy that was introduced in the previous section.

PRACTICE PROBLEM 1

A family is planning their vacation to visit relatives. They will drive from Cincinnati, Ohio to Rapid City, South Dakota, a distance of 1180 miles. They plan to average a rate of 50 miles per hour. How much time will they spend driving?

EXAMPLE 1 Finding Time Given Rate and Distance

A glacier is a giant mass of rocks and ice that flows downhill like a river. Portage Glacier in Alaska is about 6 miles, or 31,680 *feet,* long and moves 400 *feet* per year. Icebergs are created when the front end of the glacier flows into Portage Lake. How long does it take for ice at the head (beginning) of the glacier to reach the lake?

Solution:

1. UNDERSTAND. Read and reread the problem. The appropriate formula needed to solve this problem is the distance formula, $d = rt$. To become familiar with this formula, let's find the distance that ice traveling at a rate of 400 feet per year travels in 100 years. To do so, we let time t be 100 years and rate r be the given 400 feet per year, and substitute these values into the formula $d = rt$. We then have that distance $d = 400(100) = 40,000$ feet. Since we are interested in finding how long it takes ice to travel 31,680 feet, we now know that it is less than 100 years.

Since we are using the formula $d = rt$, we let

t = the time in years for ice to reach the lake

r = rate or speed of ice

d = distance from beginning of glacier to lake

2. TRANSLATE. To translate to an equation, we use the formula $d = rt$ and let distance d = 31,680 feet and rate r = 400 feet per year.

$$d = r \cdot t$$

$$31,680 = 400 \cdot t \quad \text{Let } d = 31,680 \text{ and } r = 400.$$

3. SOLVE. Solve the equation for t. To solve for t, divide both sides by 400.

$$\frac{31,680}{400} = \frac{400 \cdot t}{400} \quad \text{Divide both sides by 400.}$$

$$79.2 = t \quad \text{Simplify.}$$

4. INTERPRET.

Check: To check, substitute 79.2 for t and 400 for r in the distance formula and check to see that the distance is 31,680 feet.

State: It takes 79.2 years for the ice at the head of Portage Glacier to reach the lake.

Helpful Hint

Don't forget to include units, if appropriate.

🔲 **Work Practice Problem 1**

△ **EXAMPLE 2** **Calculating the Length of a Garden**

Charles Pecot can afford enough fencing to enclose a rectangular garden with a perimeter of 140 feet. If the width of his garden is to be 30 feet, find the length.

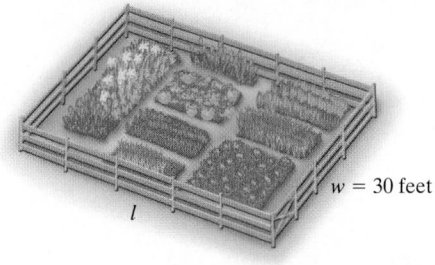
$w = 30$ feet
l

Solution:

1. UNDERSTAND. Read and reread the problem. The formula needed to solve this problem is the formula for the perimeter of a rectangle, $P = 2l + 2w$. Before continuing, let's become familar with this formula.

l = the length of the rectangular garden

w = the width of the rectangular garden

P = perimeter of the garden

2. TRANSLATE. To translate to an equation, we use the formula $P = 2l + 2w$ and let perimeter P = 140 feet and width w = 30 feet.

$$P = 2l + 2w \quad \text{Let } P = 140 \text{ and } w = 30.$$

$$140 = 2l + 2(30)$$

△ **PRACTICE PROBLEM 2**

A wood deck is being built behind a house. The width of the deck must be 18 feet because of the shape of the house. If there is 450 square feet of decking material, find the length of the deck.

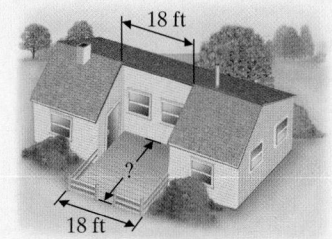
18 ft
?
18 ft

Continued on next page

Answer

2. 25 feet

3. SOLVE.

$$140 = 2l + 2(30)$$
$$140 = 2l + 60 \qquad \text{Multiply } 2(30).$$
$$140 - 60 = 2l + 60 - 60 \qquad \text{Subtract 60 from both sides.}$$
$$80 = 2l \qquad \text{Combine like terms.}$$
$$40 = l \qquad \text{Divide both sides by 2.}$$

4. INTERPRET.

Check: Substitute 40 for l and 30 for w in the perimeter formula and check to see that the perimeter is 140 feet.

State: The length of the rectangular garden is 40 feet.

▣ **Work Practice Problem 2**

PRACTICE PROBLEM 3

Convert the temperature 5°C to Fahrenheit.

EXAMPLE 3 **Finding an Equivalent Temperature**

The average maximum temperature for January in Algerias, Algeria, is 59° Fahrenheit. Find the equivalent temperature in degrees Celsius.

Solution:

1. UNDERSTAND. Read and reread the problem. A formula that can be used to solve this problem is the formula for converting degrees Celsius to degrees Fahrenheit, $F = \frac{9}{5}C + 32$. Before continuing, become familiar with this formula. Using this formula, we let

$C =$ temperature in degrees Celsius, and

$F =$ temperature in degrees Fahrenheit.

2. TRANSLATE. To translate to an equation, we use the formula $F = \frac{9}{5}C + 32$ and let degrees Fahrenheit $F = 59$.

Formula: $\qquad F = \frac{9}{5}C + 32$

Substitute: $\qquad 59 = \frac{9}{5}C + 32 \quad \text{Let } F = 59.$

3. SOLVE.

$$59 = \frac{9}{5}C + 32$$

$$59 - 32 = \frac{9}{5}C + 32 - 32 \qquad \text{Subtract 32 from both sides.}$$

$$27 = \frac{9}{5}C \qquad \text{Combine like terms.}$$

$$\frac{5}{9} \cdot 27 = \frac{5}{9} \cdot \frac{9}{5}C \qquad \text{Multiply both sides by } \frac{5}{9}.$$

$$15 = C \qquad \text{Simplify.}$$

4. INTERPRET.

Check: To check, replace C with 15 and F with 59 in the formula and see that a true statement results.

State: Thus, 59° Fahrenheit is equivalent to 15° Celsius.

▣ **Work Practice Problem 3**

Answer

3. 41°F

In the next example, we again use the formula for perimeter of a rectangle as in Example 2. In Example 2, we knew the width of the rectangle. In this example, both the length and width are unknown.

EXAMPLE 4 **Finding Road Sign Dimensions**

The length of a rectangular road sign is 2 feet less than three times its width. Find the dimensions if the perimeter is 28 feet.

PRACTICE PROBLEM 4

The length of a rectangle is one more meter than 4 times its width. Find the dimensions if the perimeter is 52 meters.

Solution:

1. UNDERSTAND. Read and reread the problem. Recall that the formula for the perimeter of a rectangle is $P = 2l + 2w$. Draw a rectangle and guess the solution. If the width of the rectangular sign is 5 feet, its length is 2 feet less than 3 times the width or 3(5 feet) − 2 feet = 13 feet. The perimeter P of the rectangle is then 2(13 feet) + 2(5 feet) = 36 feet, too much. We now know that the width is less than 5 feet.

    Proposed rectangle:

    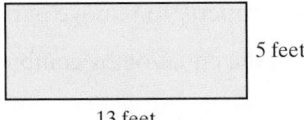

    5 feet

    13 feet

    Let

    w = the width of the rectangular sign; then

    $3w - 2$ = the length of the sign.

    Draw a rectangle and label it with the assigned variables.

    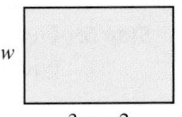

    w

    $3w - 2$

2. TRANSLATE.

    Formula: $P = 2l + 2w$

    Substitute: $28 = 2(3w - 2) + 2w.$

3. SOLVE.

    $28 = 2(3w - 2) + 2w$

    $28 = 6w - 4 + 2w$ Apply the distributive property.

    $28 = 8w - 4$

    $28 + 4 = 8w - 4 + 4$ Add 4 to both sides.

    $32 = 8w$

    $\dfrac{32}{8} = \dfrac{8w}{8}$ Divide both sides by 8.

    $4 = w$

4. INTERPRET.

    Check: If the width of the sign is 4 feet, the length of the sign is 3(4 feet) − 2 feet = 10 feet. This gives a perimeter of $P = 2(4$ feet$) + 2(10$ feet$) = 28$ feet, the correct perimeter.

    State: The width of the sign is 4 feet and the length of the sign is 10 feet.

Work Practice Problem 4

Objective B Solving a Formula for a Variable

We say that the formula

$$d = rt$$

is solved for d because d is alone on one side of the equation and the other side contains no d's. Suppose that we have a large number of problems to solve where we are given distance d and rate r and asked to find time t. In this case, it may be easier to first solve the formula $d = rt$ for t. To solve for t, we divide both sides of the equation by r.

$$d = rt$$

$$\frac{d}{r} = \frac{rt}{r} \quad \text{Divide both sides by } r.$$

$$\frac{d}{r} = t \quad \text{Simplify.}$$

To solve a formula or an equation for a specified variable, we use the same steps as for solving a linear equation except that we treat the specified variable as the only variable in the equation. These steps are listed next.

Solving Equations for a Specified Variable

Step 1: Multiply on both sides to clear the equation of fractions if they occur.

Step 2: Use the distributive property to remove parentheses if they occur.

Step 3: Simplify each side of the equation by combining like terms.

Step 4: Get all terms containing the specified variable on one side and all other terms on the other side by using the addition property of equality.

Step 5: Get the specified variable alone by using the multiplication property of equality.

PRACTICE PROBLEM 5

Solve $C = 2\pi r$ for r. (This formula is used to find the circumference C of a circle given its radius r.)

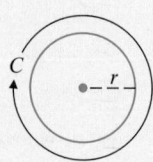

EXAMPLE 5 Solve $V = lwh$ for l.

Solution: This formula is used to find the volume of a box. To solve for l, we divide both sides by wh.

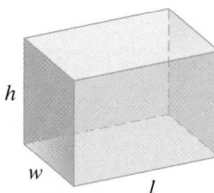

$$V = lwh$$

$$\frac{V}{wh} = \frac{lwh}{wh} \quad \text{Divide both sides by } wh.$$

$$\frac{V}{wh} = l \quad \text{Simplify.}$$

Since we have l alone on one side of the equation, we have solved for l in terms of $V, w,$ and h. Remember that it does not matter on which side of the equation we get the variable alone.

■ **Work Practice Problem 5**

Answer

5. $r = \dfrac{C}{2\pi}$

EXAMPLE 6 Solve $y = mx + b$ for x.

Solution: First we get mx alone by subtracting b from both sides.

$$y = mx + b$$
$$y - b = mx + b - b \quad \text{Subtract } b \text{ from both sides.}$$
$$y - b = mx \quad \text{Combine like terms.}$$

Next we solve for x by dividing both sides by m.

$$\frac{y - b}{m} = \frac{mx}{m}$$
$$\frac{y - b}{m} = x \quad \text{Simplify.}$$

Work Practice Problem 6

✔ **Concept Check** Solve:

a.  ◯ = ▢ − ▢ for ▢

b. ◯ = ▢ · △ − ▢ for ▢

PRACTICE PROBLEM 6

Solve $P = 2l + 2w$ for l.

EXAMPLE 7 Solve $P = 2l + 2w$ for w.

Solution: This formula relates the perimeter of a rectangle to its length and width. Find the term containing the variable w. To get this term, $2w$, alone subtract $2l$ from both sides.

$$P = 2l + 2w$$
$$P - 2l = 2l + 2w - 2l \quad \text{Subtract } 2l \text{ from both sides.}$$
$$P - 2l = 2w \quad \text{Combine like terms.}$$
$$\frac{P - 2l}{2} = \frac{2w}{2} \quad \text{Divide both sides by 2.}$$
$$\frac{P - 2l}{2} = w \quad \text{Simplify.}$$

Work Practice Problem 7

PRACTICE PROBLEM 7

Solve: $P = 2a + b - c$ for a.

Helpful Hint

The 2's may *not* be divided out here. Although 2 is a factor of the denominator, 2 is *not* a factor of the numerator since it is not a factor of both terms in the numerator.

The next example has an equation containing a fraction. We will first clear the equation of fractions and then solve for the specified variable.

EXAMPLE 8 Solve $F = \frac{9}{5}C + 32$ for C.

Solution:

$$F = \frac{9}{5}C + 32$$
$$5(F) = 5\left(\frac{9}{5}C + 32\right) \quad \text{Clear the fraction by multiplying both sides by the LCD.}$$
$$5F = 9C + 160 \quad \text{Distribute the 5.}$$
$$5F - 160 = 9C + 160 - 160 \quad \text{To get the term containing the variable } C \text{ alone, subtract 160 from both sides.}$$
$$5F - 160 = 9C \quad \text{Combine like terms.}$$
$$\frac{5F - 160}{9} = \frac{9C}{9} \quad \text{Divide both sides by 9.}$$
$$\frac{5F - 160}{9} = C \quad \text{Simplify.}$$

Work Practice Problem 8

PRACTICE PROBLEM 8

Solve $A = \frac{a + b}{2}$ for b.

Answers

6. $l = \dfrac{P - 2w}{2}$, **7.** $a = \dfrac{P - b + c}{2}$,

8. $b = 2A - a$

✔ **Concept Check Answer**

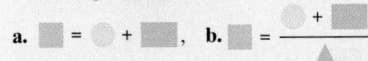

a. ▢ = ◯ + ▢, **b.** ▢ = $\dfrac{◯ + ▢}{△}$

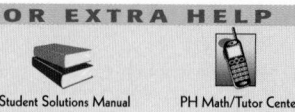  
Objective Ⓐ *Substitute the given values into each given formula and solve for the unknown variable. If necessary, round to one decimal place. See Examples 1 through 4.*

△ **1.** $A = bh$; $A = 45, b = 15$ (Area of a parallelogram)

2. $d = rt$; $d = 195, t = 3$ (Distance formula)

△ **3.** $S = 4lw + 2wh$; $S = 102, l = 7, w = 3$ (Surface area of a special rectangular box)

△ **4.** $V = lwh$; $l = 14, w = 8, h = 3$ (Volume of a rectangular box)

△ **5.** $A = \frac{1}{2}h(B + b)$; $A = 180, B = 11, b = 7$ (Area of a trapezoid)

△ **6.** $A = \frac{1}{2}h(B + b)$; $A = 60, B = 7, b = 3$ (Area of a trapezoid)

△ **7.** $P = a + b + c$; $P = 30, a = 8, b = 10$ (Perimeter of a triangle)

△ **8.** $V = \frac{1}{3}Ah$; $V = 45, h = 5$ (Volume of a pyramid)

△ **9.** $C = 2\pi r$; $C = 15.7$ (Circumference of a circle) (use the approximation 3.14 for π)

△ **10.** $A = \pi r^2$; $r = 4$ (Area of a circle) (use the approximation 3.14 for π)

Objective Ⓑ *Solve each formula for the specified variable. See Examples 5 through 8.*

11. $f = 5gh$ for h

△ **12.** $C = 2\pi r$ for r

13. $V = lwh$ for w

14. $T = mnr$ for n

15. $3x + y = 7$ for y

16. $-x + y = 13$ for y

17. $A = P + PRT$ for R

18. $A = P + PRT$ for T

19. $V = \frac{1}{3}Ah$ for A

20. $D = \frac{1}{4}fk$ for k

21. $P = a + b + c$ for a

22. $PR = x + y + z + w$ for z

23. $S = 2\pi rh + 2\pi r^2$ for h

△ **24.** $S = 4lw + 2wh$ for h

Solve. See Examples 1 through 4.

25. For the purpose of purchasing new baseboard and carpet,
  a. Find the area and perimeter of the room below (neglecting doors).
  b. Identify whether baseboard has to do with area or perimeter and the same with carpet.

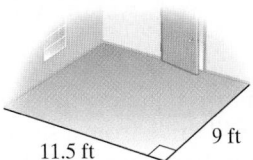
9 ft
11.5 ft

26. For the purpose of purchasing lumber for a new fence and seed to plant grass,
  a. Find the area and perimeter of the yard below.
  b. Identify whether a fence has to do with area or perimeter and the same with grass seed.

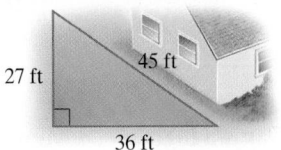
27 ft   45 ft
36 ft

27. A frame shop charges according to both the amount of framing needed to surround the picture and the amount of glass needed to cover the picture.
  a. Find the area and perimeter of the picture below.
  b. Identify whether the frame has to do with perimeter or area and the same with the glass.

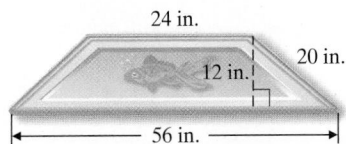
24 in.
12 in.   20 in.
56 in.

28. A decorator is painting and placing a border completely around the parallelogram-shaped wall.
  a. Find the area and perimeter of the wall below.
  b. Identify whether the border has to do with perimeter or area and the same with paint.

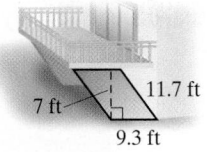
11.7 ft
7 ft
9.3 ft

29. The world's largest pink ribbon, the sign of the fight against breast cancer, was erected out of pink post-it notes on a billboard in New York City in October, 2004. If the area of the rectangular billboard covered by the ribbon is approximately 3990 sq ft, and the width of the ribbon was approximately 57 ft, what was the height of this gigantic symbol?

△ **30.** The world's largest sign for Coca-Cola is located in Arica, Chile. The rectangular sign has a length of 400 feet and has an area of 52,400 square feet. Find the width of the sign. (*Source:* Fabulous Facts about Coca-Cola, Atlanta, GA)

31. Convert Nome, Alaska's 14°F high temperature to Celsius.

32. Convert Paris, France's low temperature of −5°C to Fahrenheit.

33. The X-30 is a "space plane" that skims the edge of space at 4000 miles per hour. Neglecting altitude, if the circumference of the Earth is approximately 25,000 miles, how long will it take for the X-30 to travel around the Earth?

34. In the United States, a notable hang glider flight was a 303-mile, $8\frac{1}{2}$ hour flight from New Mexico to Kansas. What was the average rate during this flight?

△ **35.** An architect designs a rectangular flower garden such that the width is exactly two-thirds of the length. If 260 feet of antique picket fencing are to be used to enclose the garden, find the dimensions of the garden.

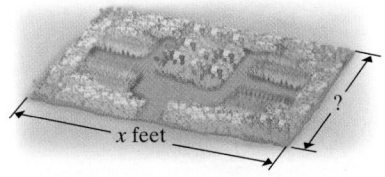
x feet

△ **36.** If the length of a rectangular parking lot is 10 meters less than twice its width, and the perimeter is 400 meters, find the length of the parking lot.

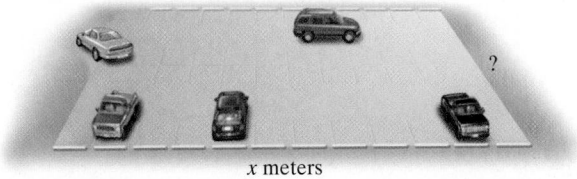
x meters

△ **37.** A flower bed is in the shape of a triangle with one side twice the length of the shortest side, and the third side is 30 feet more than the length of the shortest side. Find the dimensions if the perimeter is 102 feet.

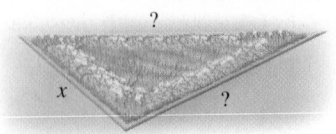

△ **38.** The perimeter of a yield sign in the shape of an isosceles triangle is 22 feet. If the shortest side is 2 feet less than the other two sides, find the length of the shortest side. (*Hint:* An isosceles triangle has two sides the same length.)

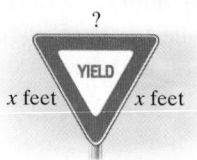

39. The Cat is a high-speed catamaran auto ferry that operates between Bar Harbor, Maine, and Yarmouth, Nova Scotia. The Cat can make the trip in about $2\frac{1}{2}$ hours at a speed of 55 mph. About how far apart are Bar Harbor and Yarmouth? (*Source:* Bay Ferries)

40. A family is planning their vacation to Disney World. They will drive from a small town outside New Orleans, Louisiana, to Orlando, Florida, a distance of 700 miles. They plan to average a rate of 55 mph. How long will this trip take?

△ **41.** Piranha fish require 1.5 cubic feet of water per fish to maintain a healthy environment. Find the maximum number of piranhas you could put in a tank measuring 8 feet by 3 feet by 6 feet.

△ **42.** Find the maximum number of goldfish you can put in a cylindrical tank whose diameter is 8 meters and whose height is 3 meters if each goldfish needs 2 cubic meters of water.

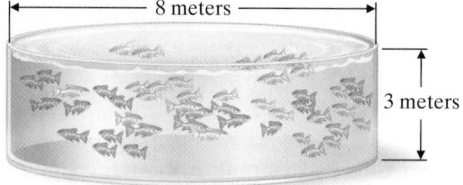

△ **43.** A lawn is in the shape of a trapezoid with a height of 60 feet and bases of 70 feet and 130 feet. How many bags of fertilizer must be purchased to cover the lawn if each bag covers 4000 square feet?

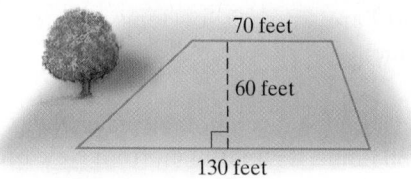

△ **44.** If the area of a right-triangularly shaped sail is 20 square feet and its base is 5 feet, find the height of the sail.

△ **45.** Maria's Pizza sells one 16-inch cheese pizza or two 10-inch cheese pizzas for $9.99. Determine which size gives more pizza.

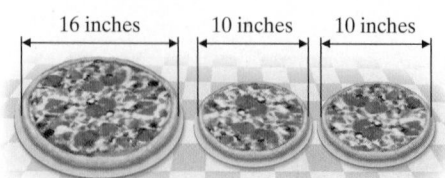

△ **46.** Find how much rope is needed to wrap around the Earth at the equator, if the radius of the Earth is 4000 miles. (*Hint:* Use 3.14 for π and the formula for circumference.)

47. A Japanese "bullet" train set a new world record for train speed at 552 kilometers per hour during a manned test run on the Yamanashi Maglev Test Line in April 1999. The Yamanashi Maglev Test Line is 42.8 kilometers long. How many *minutes* would a test run on the Yamanashi Line last at this record-setting speed? Round to the nearest hundredth of a minute. (*Source:* Japan Railways Central Co.)

48. In 1983, the Hawaiian volcano Kilauea began erupting in a series of episodes still occurring at the time of this writing. At times, the lava flows advanced at speeds of up to 0.5 kilometer per hour. In 1983 and 1984 lava flows destroyed 16 homes in the Royal Gardens subdivision, about 6 km away from the eruption site. Roughly how long did it take the lava to reach Royal Gardens? (*Source:* U.S. Geological Survey Hawaiian Volcano Observatory)

△ **49.** The perimeter of an equilateral triangle is 7 inches more than the perimeter of a square, and the side of the triangle is 5 inches longer than the side of the square. Find the side of the triangle. (*Hint:* An equilateral triangle has three sides the same length.)

△ **50.** A square animal pen and a pen shaped like an equilateral triangle have equal perimeters. Find the length of the sides of each pen if the sides of the triangular pen are fifteen less than twice a side of the square pen.

51. Find how long it takes Tran Nguyen to drive 135 miles on I-10 if he merges onto I-10 at 10 A.M. and drives nonstop with his cruise control set on 60 mph.

52. Beaumont, Texas, is about 150 miles from Toledo Bend. If Leo Miller leaves Beaumont at 4 A.M. and averages 45 mph, when should he arrive at Toledo Bend?

△ **53.** The longest runway at Los Angeles International Airport has the shape of a rectangle and an area of 1,813,500 square feet. This runway is 150 feet wide. How long is the runway? (*Source:* Los Angeles World Airports)

54. Bolts of lightning can travel at the speed of 270,000 miles per second. How many times can a lightning bolt travel around the world in one second? (See Exercise 46. Round to the nearest tenth.)

55. The highest temperature ever recorded in Europe was 122°F in Seville, Spain, in August of 1881. Convert this record high temperature to Celsius. (*Source:* National Climatic Data Center)

56. The lowest temperature ever recorded in Oceania was −10°C at the Haleakala Summit in Maui, Hawaii, in January 1961. Convert this record low temperature to Fahrenheit. (*Source:* National Climatic Data Center)

△ **57.** The CART FedEx Championship Series is an open-wheeled race car competition based in the United States. A CART car has a maximum length of 199 inches, a maximum width of 78.5 inches, and a maximum height of 33 inches. When the CART series travels to another country for a grand prix, teams must ship their cars. Find the volume of the smallest shipping crate needed to ship a CART car of maximum dimensions. (*Source:* Championship Auto Racing Teams, Inc.)

58. On a road course, a CART car's speed can average up to around 105 mph. Based on this speed, how long would it take a CART driver to travel from Los Angeles to New York City, a distance of about 2810 miles by road, without stopping? Round to the nearest tenth of an hour.

CART Racing Car

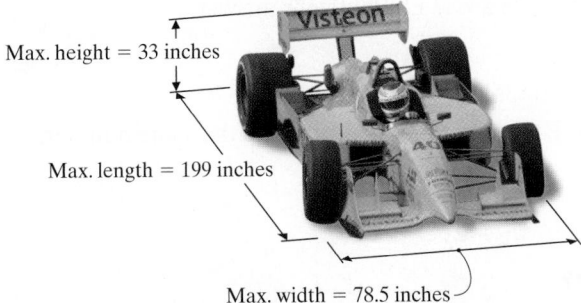

Max. height = 33 inches

Max. length = 199 inches

Max. width = 78.5 inches

59. The Hoberman Sphere is a toy ball that expands and contracts. When it is completely closed, it has a diameter of 9.5 inches. Find the volume of the Hoberman Sphere when it is completely closed. Use 3.14 for π. Round to the nearest whole cubic inch.
(*Hint:* volume of a sphere $= \frac{4}{3}\pi r^3$. *Source:* Hoberman Designs, Inc.)

60. When the Hoberman Sphere (see Exercise 59) is completely expanded, its diameter is 30 inches. Find the volume of the Hoberman Sphere when it is completely expanded. Use 3.14 for π. Round to the nearest whole cubic inch. (*Source:* Hoberman Designs, Inc.)

61. The average temperature on the planet Mercury is 167°C. Convert this temperature to degrees Fahrenheit. Round to the nearest degree. (*Source:* National Space Science Data Center)

62. The average temperature on the planet Jupiter is −227°F. Convert this temperature to degrees Celsius. Round to the nearest degree. (*Source:* National Space Science Data Center)

Review

Write each percent as a decimal. See Section 5.2.

63. 32%   **64.** 8%   **65.** 200%   **66.** 0.5%

Write each decimal as a percent. See Section 5.2.

67. 0.17   **68.** 0.03   **69.** 7.2   **70.** 5

Concept Extensions

Solve.

71. $N = R + \dfrac{V}{G}$ for V (Urban forestry: tree plantings per year)

72. $B = \dfrac{F}{P - V}$ for V (Business: break-even point)

73. The formula $V = lwh$ is used to find the volume of a box. If the length of a box is doubled, the width is doubled, and the height is doubled, how does this affect the volume? Explain your answer.

74. The formula $A = bh$ is used to find the area of a parallelogram. If the base of a parallelogram is doubled and its height is doubled, how does this affect the area? Explain your answer.

75. Find the temperature at which the Celsius measurement and Fahrenheit measurement are the same number.

Solve. See the Concept Check in this section.

76. ⬟ · ■ + ▲ = ● for ■

77. ■ − ● · ■ = ▲ for ●

78. A glacier is a giant mass of rocks and ice that flows downhill like a river. Exit Glacier, near Seward, Alaska, moves at a rate of 20 inches a day. Find the distance in feet the glacier moves in a year. (Assume 365 days a year. Round to two decimal places.)

79. Flying fish do not *actually* fly, but glide. They have been known to travel a distance of 1300 feet at a rate of 20 miles per hour. How many seconds did it take to travel this distance? (*Hint:* First convert miles per hour to feet per second. Recall that 1 mile = 5280 feet. Round to the nearest tenth of a second.)

Substitute the given values into each given formula and solve for the unknown variable. If necessary, round to one decimal place.

80. $I = PRT$; $I = 3750, P = 25,000, R = 0.05$ (Simple interest formula)

81. $I = PRT$; $I = 1,056,000, R = 0.055, T = 6$ (Simple interest formula)

82. $V = \dfrac{1}{3} \pi r^2 h$; $V = 565.2, r = 6$ (use a calculator approximation for π)(Volume of a cone)

83. $V = \dfrac{4}{3} \pi r^3$; $r = 3$ (use a calculator approximation for π) (Volume of a sphere)

 STUDY SKILLS BUILDER

Organizing a Notebook

It's never too late to get organized. If you need ideas about organizing a notebook for your mathematics course, try some of these:

- Use a spiral or ring binder notebook with pockets and use it for mathematics only.

- Start each page by writing the book's section number you are working on at the top.

- When your instructor is lecturing, take notes. *Always* include any examples your instructor works for you.

- Place your worked-out homework exercises in your notebook immediately after the lecture notes from that section. This way, a section's worth of material is together.

- Homework exercises: Attempt all assigned homework. For odd-numbered exercises, you are not through until you check your answers against the back of the book. Correct any exercises with incorrect answers. You may want to place a "?" by any homework exercises or notes that you need to ask questions about. Also, consider placing a "!" by any notes or exercises you feel are important.

- Place graded quizzes in the pockets of your notebook. If you are using a binder, you can place your quizzes in a special section of your binder.

Let's check your notebook organization by answering the following questions.

1. Do you have a spiral or ring binder notebook for your mathematics course only?

2. Have you ever had to flip through several sheets of notes and work in your mathematics notebook to determine what section's work you are in?

3. Are you now writing the textbook's section number at the top of each notebook page?

4. Have you ever lost or had trouble finding a graded quiz or test?

5. Are you now placing all your graded work in a dedicated place in your notebook?

6. Are you attempting all of your homework and placing all of your work in your notebook?

7. Are you checking and correcting your homework in your notebook? If not, why not?

8. Are you writing in your notebook the examples your instructor works for you in class?

9.6 PERCENT AND MIXTURE PROBLEM SOLVING

This section is devoted to solving problems in the categories listed. The same problem-solving steps used in previous sections are also followed in this section. They are listed below for review.

General Strategy for Problem Solving

1. UNDERSTAND the problem. During this step, become comfortable with the problem. Some ways of doing this are as follows:

    Read and reread the problem.

    Choose a variable to represent the unknown.

    Construct a drawing, whenever possible.

    Propose a solution and check. Pay careful attention to how you check your proposed solution. This will help writing an equation to model the problem.

2. TRANSLATE the problem into an equation.

3. SOLVE the equation.

4. INTERPRET the results: *Check* the proposed solution in the stated problem and *state* your conclusion.

Objective **A** Solving Percent Equations

Many of today's statistics are given in terms of percent: a basketball player's free throw percent, current interest rates, stock market trends, and nutrition labeling, just to name a few. In this section, we first explore percent, percent equations, and applications involving percents. See Section 5.2 if a further review of percents is needed.

PRACTICE PROBLEM 1

The number 22 is what percent of 40?

EXAMPLE 1 The number 63 is what percent of 72?

Solution:

1. UNDERSTAND. Read and reread the problem. Next, let's suppose that the percent is 80%. To check, we find 80% of 72.

    80% of 72 = 0.80(72) = 57.6

    This is close, but not 63. At this point, though, we have a better understanding of the problem, we know the correct answer is close to and greater than 80%, and we know how to check our proposed solution later.

    Let x = the unknown percent.

2. TRANSLATE. Recall that "is" means "equals" and "of" signifies multiplying. Let's translate the sentence directly.

the number 63	is	what percent	of	72
↓	↓	↓	↓	↓
63	=	x	·	72

3. SOLVE.

    $$63 = 72x$$
    $$0.875 = x \qquad \text{Divide both sides by 72.}$$
    $$87.5\% = x \qquad \text{Write as a percent.}$$

Answer

1. 55%

4. INTERPRET.

Check: Verify that 87.5% of 72 is 63.

State: The number 63 is 87.5% of 72.

◻ **Work Practice Problem 1**

EXAMPLE 2 The number 120 is 15% of what number?

Solution:

1. UNDERSTAND. Read and reread the problem.

Let x = the unknown number.

2. TRANSLATE.

the number 120	is	15%	of	what number
↓	↓	↓	↓	↓
120	=	15%	·	x

3. SOLVE.

$120 = 0.15x$ Write 15% as 0.15.

$800 = x$ Divide both sides by 0.15.

4. INTERPRET.

Check: Check the proposed solution by finding 15% of 800 and verifying that the result is 120.

State: Thus, 120 is 15% of 800.

◻ **Work Practice Problem 2**

EXAMPLE 3 The circle graph below shows the purpose of trips made by American travelers. Use this graph to answer the questions below.

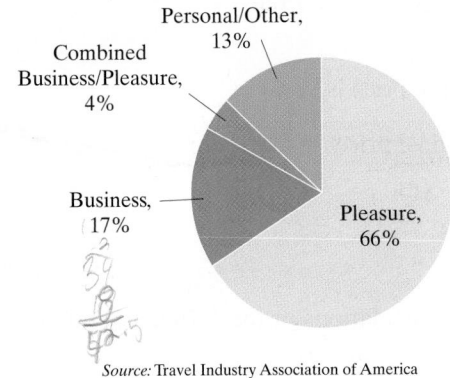

Purpose of Trip

Source: Travel Industry Association of America

a. What percent of trips made by American travelers are solely for the purpose of business?

b. What percent of trips made by American travelers are for the purpose of business or combined business/pleasure?

c. On an airplane flight of 253 Americans, how many of these people might we expect to be traveling solely for business?

Solution:

a. From the circle graph, we see that 17% of trips made by American travelers are solely for the purpose of business.

Continued on next page

PRACTICE PROBLEM 2

The number 150 is 40% of what number?

PRACTICE PROBLEM 3

Use the circle graph to answer each question.

a. What percent of trips made by American travelers are solely for pleasure?

b. What percent of trips made by American travelers are for the purpose of pleasure or combined business/pleasure?

c. On an airplane flight of 250 Americans, how many of these people might we expect to be traveling solely for pleasure?

Answers

2. 375, **3. a.** 66%, **b.** 70%,
c. 165 people

b. From the circle graph, we know that 17% of trips are solely for business and 4% of trips are for combined business/pleasure. The sum 17% + 4% or 21% of trips made by American travelers are for the purpose of business or combined business/pleasure.

c. Since 17% of trips made by American travelers are for business, we find 17% of 253. Remember that "of" translates to "multiplication."

17% of 253 = 0.17(253)   Replace "of" with the operation of multiplication.

= 43.01

We might then expect that about 43 American travelers on the flight are traveling solely for business.

▥ **Work Practice Problem 3**

Objective **B** Solving Discount and Mark-Up Problems

The next example has to do with discounting the price of a cell phone.

PRACTICE PROBLEM 4

A surfboard, originally purchased for $400, was sold on eBay at a discount of 40% of the original price. What is the discount and the new price?

EXAMPLE 4 Cell Phones Unlimited recently reduced the price of a $140 phone by 20%. What is the discount and the new price?

Solution:

1. UNDERSTAND. Read and reread the problem. Make sure you understand the meaning of the word "discount." Discount is the amount of money by which an item has been decreased. To find the discount, we simply find 20% of $140. In other words, we have the formulas,

discount = percent · original price   Then

new price = original price − discount

2, 3. TRANSLATE and SOLVE.

$$\begin{aligned} \text{discount} &= \text{percent} \cdot \text{original price} \\ &= 20\% \cdot \$140 \\ &= 0.20 \cdot \$140 \\ &= \$28 \end{aligned}$$

Thus, the discount in price is $28.

$$\begin{aligned} \text{new price} &= \text{original price} - \text{discount} \\ &= \$140 - \$28 \\ &= \$112 \end{aligned}$$

4. INTERPRET.

Check: Check your calculations in the formulas, and also see if our results are reasonable. They are.

State: The discount in price is $28 and the new price is $112.

▥ **Work Practice Problem 4**

A concept similar to discount is mark-up. What is the difference between the two? A discount is subtracted from the original price while a mark-up is added to the original price. For mark-ups,

mark-up = percent · original price

new price = original price + mark-up

Mark-up exercises can be found in Exercise Set 9.6.

Answer

4. discount: $160,   new price: $240

Objective C Solving Percent Increase and Percent Decrease Problems

Percent increase or percent decrease is a common way to describe how some measurement has increased or decreased. For example, crime increased by 8%, teachers received a 5.5% increase in salary, or a company decreased its employees by 10%. The next example is a review of percent increase.

EXAMPLE 5 Calculating the Percent Increase of Attending College

The tuition and fees cost of attending a public college rose from $1454 in 1990 to $2928 in 2003. Find the percent increase. (*Source:* National Center for Education Statistics and U.S. Department of Education) *Note:* These costs are an average of two-year and four-year colleges.

Solution:

1. UNDERSTAND. Read and reread the problem. Notice that the new tuition, $2928, is over double the old tuition of $1454. Because of that, we know that the percent increase is greater than 100%. To see this, let's guess that the percent increase is 100%. To check, we find 100% of $1454 to find the *increase* in cost. Then we add this increase to $1454 to find the *new cost*. In other words, 100% ($1454) = 1.00($1454) = $1454, the *increase* in cost. The *new cost* would be old cost + increase = $1454 + $1454 = $2908, very close to the actual new cost of $2928. We now know that the increase is close to, but greater than 100% and we know how to check our proposed solution.

   Let x = the percent increase.

2. TRANSLATE. First, find the **increase,** and then the **percent increase.** The increase in cost is found by:

   In words: increase   =   new cost   –   old cost   or

   Translate: increase   = $2928   – $1454

                        = $1474

   Next, find the percent increase. The percent increase or percent decrease is always a percent of the original number or in this case, the old cost.

   In words: increase   is   what percent increase   of   old cost

   Translate: $1474   = x · $1454

3. SOLVE.

   $$1474 = 1454x$$
   $$1.014 \approx x \qquad \text{Divide both sides by 1454 and round to 3 decimal places.}$$
   $$101.4\% \approx x \qquad \text{Write as a percent.}$$

4. INTERPRET.

Check: Check the proposed solution.

State: The percent increase in cost is approximately 101.4%.

🖱 **Work Practice Problem 5**

Percent decrease is found using a similar method. First find the decrease, then determine what percent of the original or first amount is that decrease.

Read the next example carefully. For Example 5, we were asked to find percent increase. In Example 6, we are given the percent increase and asked to find the number before the increase.

EXAMPLE 6 Most of the movie screens in the United States project analog films, but the number of cinemas using digital are increasing. Find the number of digital screens last year if after a 175% increase, the number this year is 124. Round to the nearest whole.

Solution:

1. UNDERSTAND. Read and reread the problem. Let's guess a solution and see how we would check our guess. If the number of digital screens last year was 50, we would see if 50 plus the increase is 124; that is,

$$50 + 175\%(50) = 50 + 1.75(50) = 50 + 87.5 = 137.50$$

Since 137.5 is too large, we know that our guess of 50 is too large. We also have a better understanding of the problem. Let

x = number of digital screens last year

2. TRANSLATE. To translate to an equation, we remember that

In words:	number of digital screen last year	plus	increase	equals	number of digital screens this year
Translate:	x	$+$	$1.75x$	$=$	124

3. SOLVE.

$$2.75x = 124$$
$$x = \frac{124}{2.75}$$
$$x \approx 45$$

4. INTERPRET.

Check: Recall that x represents the number of digital screens last year. If this number is approximately 45, let's see if 45 plus the increase is close to 124. (We use the word "close" since 45 is rounded.)

$$45 + 175\%(45) = 45 + 1.75(45) = 45 + 78.75 = 123.75,$$

which is close to 124.

State: There were approximately 45 digital screens last year.

▣ **Work Practice Problem 6**

Objective **D** Solving Mixture Problems

Mixture problems involve two or more different quantities being combined to form a new mixture. These applications range from Dow Chemical's need to form a chemical mixture of a required strength to Planter's Peanut Company's need to find the correct mixture of peanuts and cashews, given taste and price constraints.

EXAMPLE 7 **Calculating Percent for a Lab Experiment**

A chemist working on his doctoral degree at Massachusetts Institute of Technology needs 12 liters of a 50% acid solution for a lab experiment. The stockroom has only 40% and 70% solutions. How much of each solution should be mixed together to form 12 liters of a 50% solution?

Solution:

1. UNDERSTAND. First, read and reread the problem a few times. Next, guess a solution. Suppose that we need 7 liters of the 40% solution. Then we need $12 - 7 = 5$ liters of the 70% solution. To see if this is indeed the solution, find

the amount of pure acid in 7 liters of the 40% solution, in 5 liters of the 70% solution, and in 12 liters of a 50% solution, the required amount and strength.

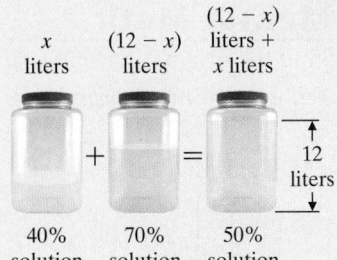

number of liters	×	acid strength	=	amount of pure acid
7 liters	×	40%	=	7(0.40) or 2.8 liters
5 liters	×	70%	=	5(0.70) or 3.5 liters
12 liters	×	50%	=	12(0.50) or 6 liters

Since 2.8 liters + 3.5 liters = 6.3 liters and not 6, our guess is incorrect, but we have gained some valuable insight into how to model and check this problem.
    Let

x = number of liters of 40% solution; then

$12 - x$ = number of liters of 70% solution.

2. TRANSLATE. To help us translate to an equation, the following table summarizes the information given. Recall that the amount of acid in each solution is found by multiplying the acid strength of each solution by the number of liters.

	No. of Liters	·	Acid Strength	=	Amount of Acid
40% Solution	x		40%		$0.40x$
70% Solution	$12 - x$		70%		$0.70(12 - x)$
50% Solution Needed	12		50%		$0.50(12)$

The amount of acid in the final solution is the sum of the amounts of acid in the two beginning solutions.

In words: acid in 40% solution   +   acid in 70% solution   =   acid in 50% mixture

Translate: $0.40x$ + $0.70(12 - x)$ = $0.50(12)$

3. SOLVE.

$$0.40x + 0.70(12 - x) = 0.50(12)$$

$0.4x + 8.4 - 0.7x = 6$ Apply the distributive property.

$-0.3x + 8.4 = 6$ Combine like terms.

$-0.3x = -2.4$ Subtract 8.4 from both sides.

$x = 8$ Divide both sides by −0.3.

4. INTERPRET.

Check: To check, recall how we checked our guess.

State: If 8 liters of the 40% solution are mixed with 12 − 8 or 4 liters of the 70% solution, the result is 12 liters of a 50% solution.

■ **Work Practice Problem 7**

Mental Math

Tell whether the percent labels in the circle graphs are correct.

1.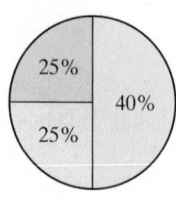

25%
40%
25%

2.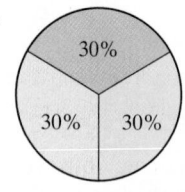

30%
30% 30%

3.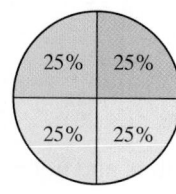

25% 25%
25% 25%

4.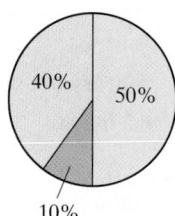

40% 50%
10%

9.6 EXERCISE SET

Objective A *Find each number described. See Examples 1 and 2.*

1. What number is 16% of 70?

2. What number is 88% of 1000?

3. The number 28.6 is what percent of 52?

4. The number 87.2 is what percent of 436?

5. The number 45 is 25% of what number?

6. The number 126 is 35% of what number?

The circle graph below shows the number of minutes that adults spend on their home phone each day. Use this graph for Exercises 7 through 10. See Example 3.

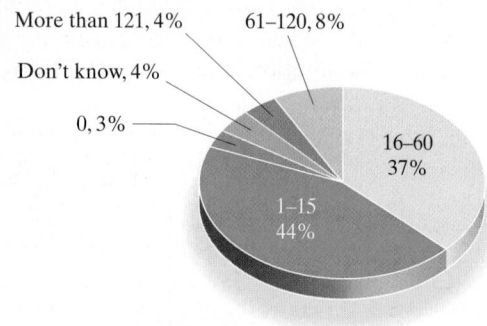

More than 121, 4%   61–120, 8%
Don't know, 4%
0, 3%
16–60
37%
1–15
44%

Source: Bruskin/Goldring Research for Sony Electronics

7. What percent of adults spend more than 121 minutes on the phone each day?

8. What percent of adults spend no time on the phone each day?

9. Florence is a town in Alabama whose adult population is approximately 27,000. How many of these adults might you expect to talk 16–60 minutes on the phone each day?

10. Columbus is a town in Indiana whose adult population is approximately 29,250. How many of these adults might you expect to talk 61–120 minutes on the phone each day?

Objective B *Solve. If needed, round answers to the nearest cent. See Example 4.*

11. A used automobile dealership recently reduced the price of a used sports car by 8%. If the price of the car before discount was $18,500, find the discount and the new price.

12. A music store is advertising a 25%-off sale on all new releases. Find the discount and the sale price of a newly released CD that regularly sells for $12.50.

13. A birthday celebration meal is $40.50 including tax. Find the total cost if a 15% tip is added to the cost.

14. A retirement dinner for two is $65.40 including tax. Find the total cost if a 20% tip is added to the cost.

Objective **C** *Solve. See Example 5.*

15. The number of fraud complaints (usually ID theft) rose from 220,000 in 2001 to 380,000 in 2002. Find the percent increase. Round to the nearest whole percent.

16. The number of text messages rose from 996 million in June to 1100 million in December. Find the percent increase. Round to the nearest whole percent.

17. By decreasing each dimension by 1 unit, the area of a rectangle decreased from 40 square feet (on the left) to 28 square feet (on the right). Find the percent decrease in area.

18. By decreasing the length of the side by one unit, the area of a square decreased from 100 square meters to 81 square meters. Find the percent decrease in area.

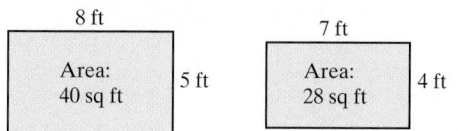

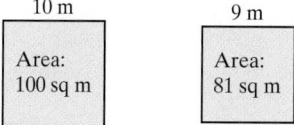

Solve. See Example 6.

19. Find the original price of a pair of shoes if the sale price is $78 after a 25% discount.

20. Find the original price of a popular pair of shoes if the increased price is $80 after a 25% increase.

21. Find last year's salary if after a 4% pay raise, this year's salary is $44,200.

22. Find last year's salary if after a 3% pay raise, this year's salary is $55,620.

Objective **D** *Solve. For each exercise, a table is given for you to complete and use to write an equation that models the situation. See Example 7.*

23. How much pure acid should be mixed with 2 gallons of a 40% acid solution in order to get a 70% acid solution?

	Number of Gallons	·	Acid Strength	=	Amount of Acid
Pure Acid			100%		
40% Acid Solution					
70% Acid Solution Needed					

24. How many cubic centimeters (cc) of a 25% antibiotic solution should be added to 10 cubic centimeters of a 60% antibiotic solution in order to get a 30% antibiotic solution?

	Number of Cubic cm	·	Antibiotic Strength	=	Amount of Antibiotic
25% Antibiotic Solution					
60% Antibiotic Solution					
30% Antibiotic Solution Needed					

25. Community Coffee Company wants a new flavor of Cajun coffee. How many pounds of coffee worth $7 a pound should be added to 14 pounds of coffee worth $4 a pound to get a mixture worth $5 a pound?

	Number of Pounds	·	Cost per Pound	=	Value
$7 per lb Coffee					
$4 per lb Coffee					
$5 per lb Coffee Wanted					

26. Planter's Peanut Company wants to mix 20 pounds of peanuts worth $3 a pound with cashews worth $5 a pound in order to make an experimental mix worth $3.50 a pound. How many pounds of cashews should be added to the peanuts?

	Number of Pounds	·	Cost per Pound	=	Value
$3 per lb Peanuts					
$5 per lb Cashews					
$3.50 per lb Mixture Wanted					

Objectives Ⓐ Ⓑ Ⓒ **Mixed Practice** *Solve. If needed, round money amounts to two decimal places and all other amounts to one decimal place. See Examples 1 through 6.*

27. Find 23% of 20.

28. Find 140% of 86.

29. The number 40 is 80% of what number?

30. The number 56.25 is 45% of what number?

31. The number 144 is what percent of 480?

32. The number 42 is what percent of 35?

The graph shows the communities in the United States that have the highest percentages of citizens that shop by catalog. Use the graph to answer Exercises 33 through 36.

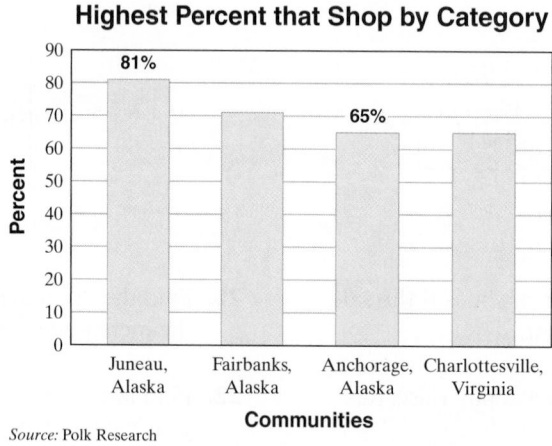

Highest Percent that Shop by Category

Source: Polk Research

33. Estimate the percent of the population in Fairbanks, Alaska, who shops by catalog?

34. Estimate the percent of the population in Charlottesville, Virginia, who shops by catalog?

35. According to the 2005 *World Almanac*, Anchorage has a population of 270,951. How many catalog shoppers might we predict live in Anchorage? Round to the nearest whole number.

36. According to the 2005 *World Almanac*, Juneau has a population of 31,187. How many catalog shoppers might we predict live in Juneau? Round to the nearest whole number.

For Exercises 37 and 38, fill in the percent column in each table. Each table contains a worked-out example.

37.

Ford Motor Company Model Year 2004 Vehicle Sales Worldwide		
	Thousands of Vehicles	**Percent of Total** **(Rounded to Nearest Percent)**
North America	3277	
Europe	1474	
Asia-Pacific	328	
Rest of the World	383	Example: $\frac{383}{5462} \approx 7\%$
Total	5462	

Source: Ford Motor Company

38.

Kraft Foods North America Year 2003 Volume Food Produced		
Food Group	**Volume** **(in pounds)**	**Percent** **(Round to Nearest Percent)**
Cheese, Meals, and Enhancers	6183	
Biscuits, Snacks, and Confectionaries	2083	Example: $\frac{2083}{13,741} \approx 15\%$
Beverages, Desserts, and Cereals	3905	
Oscar Mayer and Pizza	1570	
Total	13,741	

Source: Kraft Foods, North America

39. Iceberg lettuce is grown and shipped to stores for about 40 cents a head, and consumers purchase it for about 70 cents a head. Find the percent increase.

40. The lettuce consumption per capita in 1980 was about 25.6 pounds, and in 2002 the consumption dropped to 22.4 pounds. Find the percent decrease.

41. A student at the University of New Orleans makes money by buying and selling used cars. Charles bought a used car and later sold it for a 20% profit. If he sold it for $4680, how much did Charles pay for the car?

42. Smart Cards (cards with an embedded computer chip) have been growing in popularity in recent years. In 2006, 500 million Smart Cards are expected to be issued. This represents a 117% increase from the number of cards that were issued in 2001. How many Smart Cards were issued in 2001? Round to the nearest million. (*Source:* The Freedonia Group)

43. By doubling each dimension, the area of a parallelogram increased from 36 square centimeters to 144 square centimeters. Find the percent increase in area.

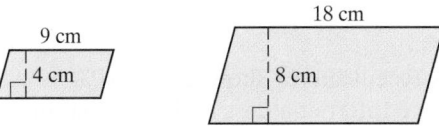

44. By doubling each dimension, the area of a triangle increased from 6 square miles to 24 square miles. Find the percent increase in area.

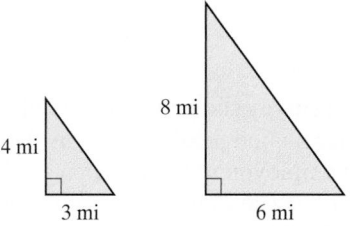

45. A gasoline station recently increased the price of one grade of gasoline by 5%. If this gasoline originally cost $2.20 per gallon, find the mark-up and the new price.

46. The price of a biology book recently increased by 10%. If this book originally cost $89.90, find the mark-up and the new price.

47. How much of an alloy that is 20% copper should be mixed with 200 ounces of an alloy that is 50% copper in order to get an alloy that is 30% copper?

48. How much water should be added to 30 gallons of a solution that is 70% antifreeze in order to get a mixture that is 60% antifreeze?

49. During the 1982–1983 term, the Supreme Court made 151 decisions while during the 2003–2004 term, they only made 73. Find the percent decrease in number of decisions. Round to the nearest tenth of a percent.

50. The number of farms in the United States is decreasing. In 1940, there were approximately 6.3 million farms, while in 2003 there were only 2.1 million. Find the percent decrease in the number of farms. Round to the nearest tenth of a percent.

51. A company recently downsized its number of employees by 35%. If there are still 78 employees, how many employees were there prior to the layoffs?

52. The average number of children born to each U.S. woman has decreased by 44% since 1920. If this average is now 1.9, find the average in 1920. Round to the nearest tenth.

53. Nordstrom advertised a 25%-off sale. If a London Fog coat originally sold for $256, find the decrease in price and the sale price.

54. A gasoline station decreased the price of a $0.95 cola by 15%. Find the decrease in price and the new price.

55. Scoville units are used to measure the hotness of a pepper. Measuring 577 thousand Scoville units, the "Red Savina" habañero pepper was known as the hottest chili pepper. That has recently changed with the discovery of Naga Jolokia pepper from India. It measures 48% hotter than the habañero. Find the measure of the Naga Jolokia pepper. Round to the nearest thousand units.

56. At this writing, the women's world record for throwing a disc (like a heavy Frisbee) was set by Jennifer Griffin of the United States in 2000. Her throw was 138.56 meters. The men's world record was set by Christian Sandstrom of Sweden in 2002. His throw was 80.4% farther than Jennifer's. Find the distance of his throw. Round to the nearest meter. (*Source:* World Flying Disc Federation)

57. A recent survey showed that 42% of recent college graduates named flexible hours as their most desired employment benefit. In a graduating class of 860 college students, how many would you expect to rank flexible hours as their top priority in job benefits? (Round to the nearest whole.) (*Source:* JobTrak.com)

58. A recent survey showed that 64% of U.S. colleges have Internet access in their classrooms. There are approximately 9800 post-secondary institutions in the United States. How many of these would you expect to have Internet access in their classrooms? (*Source:* Market Data Retrieval, National Center for Education Statistics)

59. A new self-tanning lotion for everyday use is to be sold. First, an experimental lotion mixture is made by mixing 800 ounces of everyday moisturizing lotion worth $0.30 an ounce with self-tanning lotion worth $3 per ounce. If the experimental lotion is to cost $1.20 per ounce, how many ounces of the self-tanning lotion should be in the mixture?

60. The owner of a local chocolate shop wants to develop a new trail mix. How many pounds of chocolate-covered peanuts worth $5 a pound should be mixed with 10 pounds of granola bites worth $2 a pound to get a mixture worth $3 per pound?

Review

Place <, >, or = in the appropriate space to make each a true statement. See Sections 8.1, 8.2, and 8.5.

61. -5 -7

62. $\dfrac{12}{3}$ 2^2

63. $|-5|$ $-(-5)$

64. -3^3 $(-3)^3$

65. $(-3)^2$ -3^2

66. $|-2|$ $-|-2|$

Concept Extensions

67. Is it possible to mix a 10% acid solution and a 40% acid solution to obtain a 60% acid solution? Why or why not?

68. Must the percents in a circle graph have a sum of 100%? Why or why not?

Standardized nutrition labels like the one below have been displayed on food items since 1994. The percent column on the right shows the percent of daily values (based on a 2000-calorie diet) shown at the bottom of the label. For example, a serving of this food contains 4 grams of total fat, where the recommended daily fat based on a 2000-calorie diet is less than 65 grams of fat. This means that $\frac{4}{65}$ or approximately 6% (as shown) of your daily recommended fat is taken in by eating a serving of this food. Use this nutrition label to answer Exercises 69 through 71.

Nutrition Facts

Serving Size   18 Crackers (31g)
Servings Per Container   About 9

Amount Per Serving

Calories 130   Calories from Fat 35

             % Daily Value*

Total Fat 4g	**6%**
Saturated Fat 0.5g	**3%**
Polyunsaturated Fat 0g	
Monounsaturated Fat 1.5g	
Cholesterol 0mg	**0%**
Sodium 230mg	*x*
Total Carbohydrate 23g	*y*
Dietary Fiber 2g	**8%**
Sugars 3g	
Protein 2g	

Vitamin A 0%   •   Vitamin C 0%
Calcium 2%   •   Iron 6%

* Percent Daily Values are based on a 2,000 calorie diet. Your daily values may be higher or lower depending on your calorie needs.

	Calories	2,000	2,500
Total Fat	Less than	65g	80g
Sat. Fat	Less than	20g	25g
Cholesterol	Less than	300mg	300mg
Sodium	Less than	2400mg	2400mg
Total Carbohydrate		300g	375g
Dietary Fiber		25g	30g

69. Based on a 2000-calorie diet, what percent of daily value of sodium is contained in a serving of this food? In other words, find *x* in the label. (Round to the nearest tenth of a percent.)

70. Based on a 2000-calorie diet, what percent of daily value of total carbohydrate is contained in a serving of this food? In other words, find *y* in the label. (Round to the nearest tenth of a percent.)

71. Notice on the nutrition label that one serving of this food contains 130 calories and 35 of these calories are from fat. Find the percent of calories from fat. (Round to the nearest tenth of a percent.) It is recommended that no more than 30% of calorie intake come from fat. Does this food satisfy this recommendation?

Use the nutrition label below to answer Exercises 72 through 74.

NUTRITIONAL INFORMATION PER SERVING

Serving Size: 9.8 oz.   Servings Per Container: 1

Calories 280	Polyunsaturated Fat 1g
Protein 12g	Saturated Fat 3g
Carbohydrate 45g	Cholesterol 20mg
Fat 6g	Sodium 520mg
Percent of Calories from Fat....?	Potassium 220mg

72. If fat contains approximately 9 calories per gram, find the percent of calories from fat in one serving of this food. (Round to the nearest tenth of a percent.)

73. If protein contains approximately 4 calories per gram, find the percent of calories from protein from one serving of this food. (Round to the nearest tenth of a percent.)

74. Find a food that contains more than 30% of its calories per serving from fat. Analyze the nutrition label and verify that the percents shown are correct.

A Graph Inequalities on a Number Line.

B Use the Addition Property of Inequality to Solve Inequalities.

C Use the Multiplication Property of Inequality to Solve Inequalities.

D Use Both Properties to Solve Inequalities.

E Solve Problems Modeled by Inequalities.

9.7 SOLVING LINEAR INEQUALITIES

In Chapter 8, we reviewed these inequality symbols and their meanings:

$<$ means "is less than" $\leq$ means "is less than or equal to"

$>$ means "is greater than" $\geq$ means "is greater than or equal to"

An **inequality** is a statement that contains one of the symbols above.

Equations	Inequalities
$x = 3$	$x \leq 3$
$5n - 6 = 14$	$5n - 6 > 14$
$12 = 7 - 3y$	$12 \leq 7 - 3y$
$\dfrac{x}{4} - 6 = 1$	$\dfrac{x}{4} - 6 > 1$

Objective **A** Graphing Inequalities on a Number Line

Recall that the single solution to the equation $x = 3$ is 3. The solutions of the inequality $x \leq 3$ include 3 and *all real numbers less than 3* (for example, $-10, \frac{1}{2}, 2$, and 2.9). Because we can't list all numbers less than 3, we show instead a picture of the solutions by graphing them on a number line.

To graph the solutions of $x \leq 3$, we shade the numbers to the left of 3 since they are less than 3. Then we place a closed circle on the point representing 3. The closed circle indicates that 3 *is* a solution: 3 *is* less than or equal to 3.

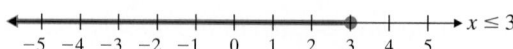

To graph the solutions of $x < 3$, we shade the numbers to the left of 3. Then we place an open circle on the point representing 3. The open circle indicates that 3 *is not* a solution: 3 *is not* less than 3.

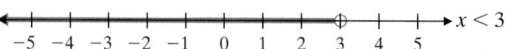

PRACTICE PROBLEM 1

Graph: $x \geq -2$

![number line from -5 to 5]

PRACTICE PROBLEM 2

Graph: $5 > x$

![number line from -5 to 5]

Answers

1. ![number line from -5 to 5, closed circle at -2 shaded right]

2. ![number line from -5 to 5, open circle at 5 shaded left]

686

EXAMPLE 1 Graph: $x \geq -1$

Solution: To graph the solutions of $x \geq -1$, we place a closed circle at -1 since the inequality symbol is $\geq$ and -1 is greater than or equal to -1. Then we shade to the right of -1.

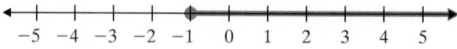

■ **Work Practice Problem 1**

EXAMPLE 2 Graph: $-1 > x$

Solution: Recall from Chapter 8 that $-1 > x$ means the same as $x < -1$. The graph of the solutions of $x < -1$ is shown below.

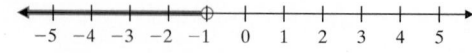

■ **Work Practice Problem 2**

EXAMPLE 3 Graph: $-4 < x \le 2$

Solution: We read $-4 < x \le 2$ as "-4 is less than x and x is less than or equal to 2," or as "x is greater than -4 and x is less than or equal to 2." To graph the solutions of this inequality, we place an open circle at -4 (-4 is not part of the graph), a closed circle at 2 (2 is part of the graph), and we shade all numbers between -4 and 2. Why? All numbers between -4 and 2 are greater than -4 *and* also less than 2.

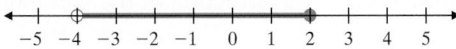

■ **Work Practice Problem 3**

Objective **B** Using the Addition Property

When solutions of a linear inequality are not immediately obvious, they are found through a process similar to the one used to solve a linear equation. Our goal is to get the variable alone on one side of the inequality. We use properties of inequality similar to properties of equality.

Addition Property of Inequality

If a, b, and c are real numbers, then

$$a < b \quad \text{and} \quad a + c < b + c$$

are equivalent inequalities.

This property also holds true for subtracting values, since subtraction is defined in terms of addition. In other words, adding or subtracting the same quantity from both sides of an inequality does not change the solutions of the inequality.

EXAMPLE 4 Solve $x + 4 \le -6$. Graph the solutions.

Solution: To solve for x, subtract 4 from both sides of the inequality.

$x + 4 \le -6$	Original inequality
$x + 4 - 4 \le -6 - 4$	Subtract 4 from both sides.
$x \le -10$	Simplify.

The graph of the solutions is shown below.

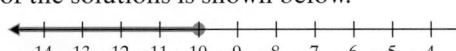

■ **Work Practice Problem 4**

Helpful Hint

Notice that any number less than or equal to -10 is a solution to $x \le -10$. For example, solutions include

$$-10, \quad -200, \quad -11\frac{1}{2}, \quad -\sqrt{130}, \quad \text{and} \quad -50.3$$

Objective **C** Using the Multiplication Property

An important difference between solving linear equations and solving linear inequalities is shown when we multiply or divide both sides of an inequality by a nonzero real number. For example, start with the true statement $6 < 8$ and multiply both sides by 2. As we see below, the resulting inequality is also true.

$6 < 8$	True
$2(6) < 2(8)$	Multiply both sides by 2.
$12 < 16$	True

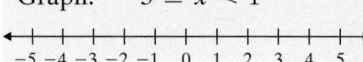
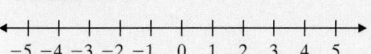
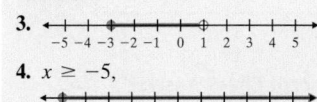

But if we start with the same true statement $6 < 8$ and multiply both sides by -2, the resulting inequality is not a true statement.

$$6 < 8 \qquad \text{True}$$
$$-2(6) < -2(8) \qquad \text{Multiply both sides by } -2.$$
$$-12 < -16 \qquad \text{False}$$

Notice, however, that if we reverse the direction of the inequality symbol, the resulting inequality is true.

$$-12 < -16 \qquad \text{False}$$
$$-12 > -16 \qquad \text{True}$$

This demonstrates the multiplication property of inequality.

Multiplication Property of Inequality

1. If a, b, and c are real numbers, and c is **positive**, then

$$a < b \qquad \text{and} \qquad ac < bc$$

are equivalent inequalities.

2. If a, b, and c are real numbers, and c is **negative**, then

$$a < b \quad \text{and} \quad ac > bc$$

are equivalent inequalities.

Because division is defined in terms of multiplication, this property also holds true when dividing both sides of an inequality by a nonzero number: If we multiply or divide both sides of an inequality by a negative number, **the direction of the inequality sign must be reversed for the inequalities to remain equivalent.**

✔ **Concept Check**   Fill in the box with $<$, $>$, $\leq$, or $\geq$.

a. Since $-8 < -4$, then $3(-8) \,\square\, 3(-4)$.

b. Since $5 \geq -2$, then $\dfrac{5}{-7} \,\square\, \dfrac{-2}{-7}$.

c. If $a < b$, then $2a \,\square\, 2b$.

d. If $a \geq b$, then $\dfrac{a}{-3} \,\square\, \dfrac{b}{-3}$.

PRACTICE PROBLEM 5

Solve $-3x \leq 12$. Graph the solutions.

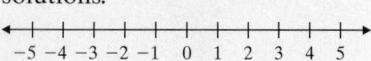

EXAMPLE 5   Solve $-2x \leq -4$. Graph the solutions.

Solution: Remember to reverse the direction of the inequality symbol when dividing by a negative number.

$$-2x \leq -4$$
$$\frac{-2x}{-2} \geq \frac{-4}{-2} \qquad \text{Divide both sides by } -2 \text{ and reverse the inequality sign.}$$
$$x \geq 2 \qquad \text{Simplify.}$$

The graph of the solutions is shown.

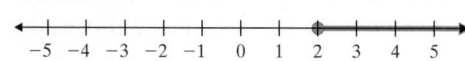

🔲 **Work Practice Problem 5**

Answer

5. $x \geq -4$,

EXAMPLE 6 Solve $2x < -4$. Graph the solutions.

Solution: $2x < -4$

$$\frac{2x}{2} < \frac{-4}{2} \quad \text{Divide both sides by 2. Do not reverse the inequality sign.}$$

$$x < -2 \quad \text{Simplify.}$$

The graph of the solutions is shown.

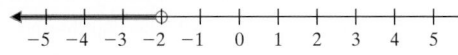

Work Practice Problem 6

Since we cannot list all solutions to an inequality such as $x < -2$, we will use the set notation $\{x \mid x < -2\}$. Recall from Section 8.1 that this is read "the set of all x such that x is less than -2." We will use this notation when solving inequalities.

Objective D Using Both Properties of Inequality

The following steps may be helpful when solving inequalities in one variable. Notice that these steps are similar to the ones given in Section 9.3 for solving equations.

To Solve Linear Inequalities in One Variable

Step 1: If an inequality contains fractions, multiply both sides by the LCD to clear the inequality of fractions.

Step 2: Use the distributive property to remove parentheses if they occur.

Step 3: Simplify each side of the inequality by combining like terms.

Step 4: Get all variable terms on one side and all numbers on the other side by using the addition property of inequality.

Step 5: Get the variable alone by using the multiplication property of inequality.

> **Helpful Hint**
>
> Don't forget that if both sides of an inequality are multiplied or divided by a negative number, the direction of the inequality sign must be reversed.

EXAMPLE 7 Solve $-4x + 7 \geq -9$. Graph the solution set.

Solution: $-4x + 7 \geq -9$

$$-4x + 7 - 7 \geq -9 - 7 \quad \text{Subtract 7 from both sides.}$$

$$-4x \geq -16 \quad \text{Simplify.}$$

$$\frac{-4x}{-4} \leq \frac{-16}{-4} \quad \text{Divide both sides by } -4 \text{ and reverse the direction of the inequality sign.}$$

$$x \leq 4 \quad \text{Simplify.}$$

The graph of the solution set $\{x \mid x \leq 4\}$ is shown.

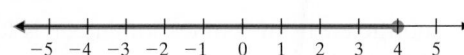

Work Practice Problem 7

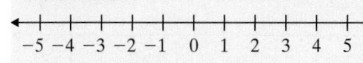
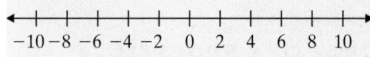
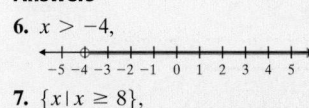

PRACTICE PROBLEM 8

Solve $2x - 3 > 4(x - 1)$.
Graph the solution set.

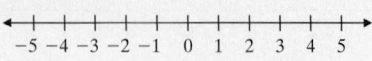

EXAMPLE 8 Solve $-5x + 7 < 2(x - 3)$. Graph the solution set.

Solution: $-5x + 7 < 2(x - 3)$

$-5x + 7 < 2x - 6$	Apply the distributive property.
$-5x + 7 - 2x < 2x - 6 - 2x$	Subtract $2x$ from both sides.
$-7x + 7 < -6$	Combine like terms.
$-7x + 7 - 7 < -6 - 7$	Subtract 7 from both sides.
$-7x < -13$	Combine like terms.
$\dfrac{-7x}{-7} > \dfrac{-13}{-7}$	Divide both sides by -7 and reverse the direction of the inequality sign.
$x > \dfrac{13}{7}$	Simplify.

The graph of the solution set $\left\{ x \mid x > \dfrac{13}{7} \right\}$ is shown.

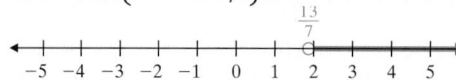

⬛ **Work Practice Problem 8**

PRACTICE PROBLEM 9

Solve:
$3(x + 5) - 1 \geq 5(x - 1) + 7$

EXAMPLE 9 Solve: $2(x - 3) - 5 \leq 3(x + 2) - 18$

Solution: $2(x - 3) - 5 \leq 3(x + 2) - 18$

$2x - 6 - 5 \leq 3x + 6 - 18$	Apply the distributive property.
$2x - 11 \leq 3x - 12$	Combine like terms.
$-x - 11 \leq -12$	Subtract $3x$ from both sides.
$-x \leq -1$	Add 11 to both sides.
$\dfrac{-x}{-1} \geq \dfrac{-1}{-1}$	Divide both sides by -1 and reverse the direction of the inequality sign.
$x \geq 1$	Simplify.

The solution set is $\{ x \mid x \geq 1 \}$.

⬛ **Work Practice Problem 9**

Objective E Solving Problems Modeled by Inequalities

Problems containing words such as "at least," "at most," "between," "no more than," and "no less than" usually indicate that an inequality should be solved instead of an equation. In solving applications involving linear inequalities, we use the same procedure we used to solve applications involving linear equations.

Some Inequality Translations			
≥	≤	<	>
at least	at most	is less than	is greater than
no less than	no more than		

PRACTICE PROBLEM 10

Twice a number, subtracted from 35 is greater than 15. Find all numbers that make this true.

EXAMPLE 10 12 subtracted from 3 times a number is less than 21. Find all numbers that make this true.

Solution:

1. UNDERSTAND. Read and reread the problem. This is a direct translation problem, and let's let

x = the unknown number

Answers

8. $\left\{ x \mid x < \dfrac{1}{2} \right\}$,

9. $\{ x \mid x \leq 6 \}$,
10. All numbers less than 10

2. TRANSLATE.

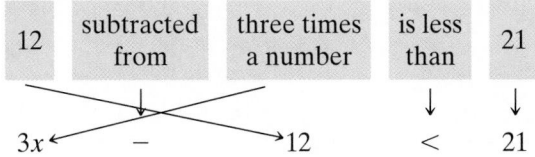

12	subtracted from	three times a number	is less than	21

$$3x \quad - \quad 12 \qquad < \qquad 21$$

3. SOLVE. $3x - 12 < 21$

$\qquad 3x < 33$ Add 12 to both sides.

$\qquad \dfrac{3x}{3} < \dfrac{33}{3}$ Divide both sides by 3 and do not reverse the direction of the inequality sign.

$\qquad x < 11$ Simplify.

4. INTERPRET.

Check: Check the translation; then let's choose a number less than 11 to see if it checks. For example, let's check 10. 12 subtracted from 3 times 10 is 12 subtracted from 30, or 18. Since 18 is less than 21, the number 10 checks.

State: All numbers less than 11 make the original statement true.

◻ Work Practice Problem 10

EXAMPLE 11 **Budgeting for a Wedding**

Marie Chase and Jonathan Edwards are having their wedding reception at the Gallery reception hall. They may spend at most $1000 for the reception. If the reception hall charges a $100 cleanup fee plus $14 per person, find the greatest number of people that they can invite and still stay within their budget.

Solution:

1. UNDERSTAND. Read and reread the problem. Suppose that 50 people attend the reception. The cost is then $100 + $14(50) = $100 + $700 = $800.

Let x = the number of people who attend the reception.

2. TRANSLATE.

cleanup fee	+	cost per person	times	number of people	must be less than or equal to	$1000
100	+	14	·	x	≤	1000

3. SOLVE.

$100 + 14x \le 1000$

$\qquad 14x \le 900$ Subtract 100 from both sides.

$\qquad x \le 64\dfrac{2}{7}$ Divide both sides by 14.

4. INTERPRET.

Check: Since x represents the number of people, we round down to the nearest whole, or 64. Notice that if 64 people attend, the cost is $100 + $14(64) = $996. If 65 people attend, the cost is $100 + $14(65) = $1010, which is more than the given $1000.

State: Marie Chase and Jonathan Edwards can invite at most 64 people to the reception.

◻ Work Practice Problem 11

PRACTICE PROBLEM 11

Alex earns $600 per month plus 4% of all his sales. Find the minimum sales that will allow Alex to earn at least $3000 per month.

Answer

11. $60,000

Mental Math

Solve each inequality.

1. $5x > 10$ **2.** $4x < 20$ **3.** $2x \geq 16$ **4.** $9x \leq 63$

Decide which number listed is not a solution to each given inequality.

5. $x \geq -3;$ $-3, 0, -5, \pi$ **6.** $x < 6;$ $-6, |-6|, 0, -3.2$

7. $x < 4.01;$ $4, -4.01, 4.1, -4.1$ **8.** $x \geq -3;$ $-4, -3, -2, -(-2)$

9.7 EXERCISE SET

FOR EXTRA HELP

Student Solutions Manual   PH Math/Tutor Center   CD/Video for Review   MathXL®   MyMathLab

Objective A *Graph each inequality on a number line. See Examples 1 and 2.*

1. $x \leq -1$

2. $y < 0$

3. $x > \dfrac{1}{2}$
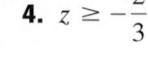

4. $z \geq -\dfrac{2}{3}$

5. $y < 4$
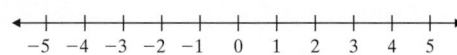

6. $x > 3$
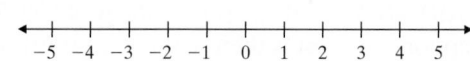

7. $-2 \leq m$
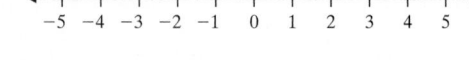

8. $-5 \geq x$
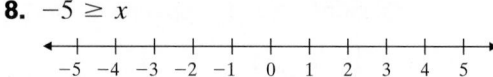

Graph each inequality on a number line. See Example 3.

9. $-1 < x < 3$
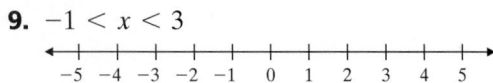

10. $-2 \leq x \leq 3$
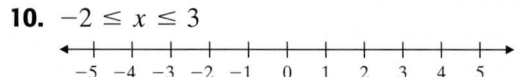

11. $0 \leq y < 2$

12. $-4 < x \leq 0$
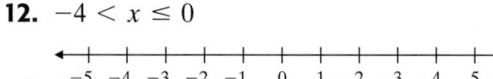

Objective B *Solve each inequality. Graph the solution set. See Example 4.*

13. $x - 2 \geq -7$
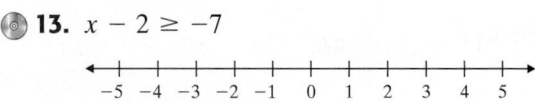

14. $x + 4 \leq 1$
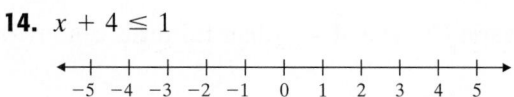

15. $-9 + y < 0$

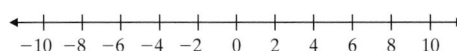

16. $-3 + m > 5$

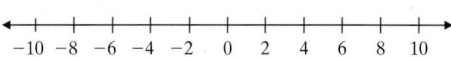

17. $3x - 5 > 2x - 8$

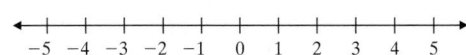

18. $3 - 7x \geq 10 - 8x$

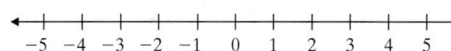

19. $4x - 1 \leq 5x - 2x$

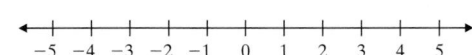

20. $7x + 3 < 9x - 3x$

Objective **C** *Solve each inequality. Graph the solution set. See Examples 5 and 6.*

21. $2x < -6$

22. $3x > -9$

23. $-8x \leq 16$

24. $-5x < 20$

25. $-x > 0$

26. $-y \geq 0$

27. $\dfrac{3}{4}y \geq -2$

28. $\dfrac{5}{6}x \leq -8$

29. $-0.6y < -1.8$

30. $-0.3x > -2.4$

Objectives **B** **C** **D** **Mixed Practice** *Solve each inequality. See Examples 4 through 9.*

31. $-8 < x + 7$

32. $-11 > x + 4$

33. $7(x + 1) - 6x \geq -4$

34. $10(x + 2) - 9x \leq -1$

35. $4x > 1$

36. $6x < 5$

37. $-\dfrac{2}{3}y \leq 8$

38. $-\dfrac{3}{4}y \geq 9$

39. $4(2z + 1) < 4$

40. $6(2 - z) \geq 12$

41. $3x - 7 < 6x + 2$

42. $2x - 1 \geq 4x - 5$

43. $5x - 7x \leq x + 2$

44. $4 - x < 8x + 2x$

45. $-6x + 2 \geq 2(5 - x)$

46. $-7x + 4 > 3(4 - x)$

47. $3(x - 5) < 2(2x - 1)$

48. $5(x - 2) \le 3(2x - 1)$

49. $4(3x - 1) \le 5(2x - 4)$

50. $3(5x - 4) \le 4(3x - 2)$

51. $3(x + 2) - 6 > -2(x - 3) + 14$

52. $7(x - 2) + x \le -4(5 - x) - 12$

53. $-5(1 - x) + x \le -(6 - 2x) + 6$

54. $-2(x - 4) - 3x < -(4x + 1) + 2x$

55. $\frac{1}{4}(x + 4) < \frac{1}{5}(2x + 3)$

56. $\frac{1}{2}(x - 5) < \frac{1}{3}(2x - 1)$

57. $-5x + 4 \le -4(x - 1)$

58. $-6x + 2 < -3(x + 4)$

Objective E *Solve the following. See Examples 10 and 11.*

59. Six more than twice a number is greater than negative fourteen. Find all numbers that make this statement true.

60. One more than five times a number is less than or equal to ten. Find all such numbers.

61. The perimeter of a rectangle is to be no greater than 100 centimeters and the width must be 15 centimeters. Find the maximum length of the rectangle.

62. One side of a triangle is four times as long as another side, and the third side is 12 inches long. If the perimeter can be no longer than 87 inches, find the maximum lengths of the other two sides.

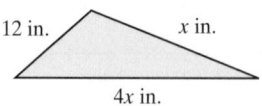
12 in.   x in.
4x in.

63. Ben Holladay bowled 146 and 201 in his first two games. What must he bowl in his third game to have an average of at least 180? (*Hint:* The average of a list of numbers is their sum divided by the number of numbers in the list.)

64. On an NBA team the two forwards measure 6'8" and 6'6" tall and the two guards measure 6'0" and 5'9" tall. How tall a center should they hire if they wish to have a starting team average height of at least 6'5"?

65. Dennis and Nancy Wood are celebrating their 30th wedding anniversary by having a reception at Tiffany Oaks reception hall. They have budgeted $3000 for their reception. If the reception hall charges a $50.00 cleanup fee plus $34 per person, find the greatest number of people that they may invite and still stay within their budget.

66. A surprise retirement party is being planned for Pratap Puri. A total of $860 has been collected for the event, which is to be held at a local reception hall. This reception hall charges a cleanup fee of $40 and $15 per person for drinks and light snacks. Find the greatest number of people that may be invited and still stay within the $860 budget.

67. A 150-pound person uses 5.8 calories per minute when walking at a speed of 4 mph. How long must a person walk at this speed to use at least 200 calories? (Round up to the nearest minute.) (*Source:* Home & Garden Bulletin No. 72)

68. A 170-pound person uses 5.3 calories per minute when bicycling at a speed of 5.5 mph. How long must a person ride a bike at this speed in order to use at least 200 calories? (Round up to the nearest minute.) (*Source:* Same as Exercise 67.)

Review

Evaluate each expression. See Section 8.2.

69. 3^4 **70.** 4^3 **71.** 1^8 **72.** 0^7 **73.** $\left(\dfrac{7}{8}\right)^2$ **74.** $\left(\dfrac{2}{3}\right)^3$

The graph shows the number of Krispy Kreme Doughnut locations from 1996 to 2004. The height of the graph for each year shown corresponds to the number of Krispy Kreme locations. Use this graph to answer Exercises 75 through 80.

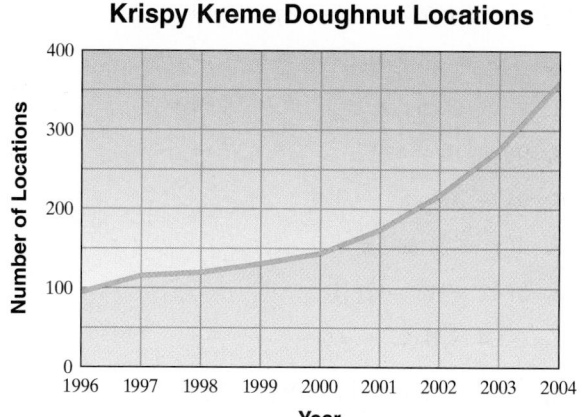

Krispy Kreme Doughnut Locations

75. How many Krispy Kreme locations were there in 1998?

76. How many Krispy Kreme locations were there in 2003?

77. Between which two years did the greatest increase in the number of Krispy Kreme locations occur?

78. In what year were there approximately 150 Krispy Kreme locations?

79. During which year did the number of Krispy Kreme locations rise above 200?

80. During which year did the number of Krispy Kreme locations rise above 300?

Concept Extensions

Fill in the box with $<, >, \leq, or \geq$. See the Concept Check in this section.

81. Since $3 < 5$, then $3(-4) \,\square\, 5(-4)$.

82. If $m \leq n$, then $2m \,\square\, 2n$.

83. If $m \leq n$, then $-2m \,\square\, -2n$.

84. If $-x < y$, then $x \,\square\, -y$.

85. When solving an inequality, when must you reverse the direction of an inequality symbol?

86. If both sides of the inequality $-3x < -30$ are divided by 3, do you reverse the direction of the inequality symbol? Why or why not?

Solve.

87. Eric Daly has scores of 75, 83, and 85 on his history tests. Use an inequality to find the scores he can make on his final exam to receive a B in the class. The final exam counts as **two** tests, and a B is received if the final course average is greater than or equal to 80.

88. Maria Lipco has scores of 85, 95, and 92 on her algebra tests. Use an inequality to find the scores she can make on her final exam to receive an A in the course. The final exam counts as three tests, and an A is received if the final course average is greater than or equal to 90. Round to one decimal place.

THE BIGGER PICTURE Simplifying Expressions and Solving Equations and Inequalities

Now we continue our outline started in Section 8.5. Although suggestions are given, this outline should be in your own words. Once you complete this new portion, try the exercises below.

I. Simplifying Expressions
   A. Real Numbers
      1. Add (Section 8.3)
      2. Subtract (Section 8.4)
      3. Multiply or Divide (Section 8.5)

II. **Solving Equations and Inequalities**
   A. **Linear Equations:** power on variable is 1 and there are no variables in the denominator

   $7(x - 3) = 4x + 6$ Linear equation. Simplify both sides, then get variable terms on one side, numbers on the other side.

   $7x - 21 = 4x + 6$ Use the distributive property.

   $7x = 4x + 27$ Add 21 to both sides.

   $3x = 27$ Subtract $4x$ from both sides.

   $x = 9$ Divide both sides by 3.

   B. **Linear Inequalities:** same as linear equation, except there are inequality symbols, $\leq, <, \geq, >$ Remember, if you multiply or divide by a negative number,

then reverse the direction of the inequality symbol.

$-4x - 11 \leq 1$ Linear inequality.

$-4x \leq 12$ Add 11 to both sides.

$\dfrac{-4x}{-4} \geq \dfrac{12}{-4}$ Divide both sides by -4 and reverse the direction of the inequality symbol.

$x \geq -3$ Simplify.

Solve each equation or inequality.

1. $-5x = 15$

2. $-5x > 15$

3. $9y - 14 = -12$

4. $9x - 3 = 5x - 4$

5. $4(x - 2) \leq 5x + 7$

6. $5(4x - 1) = 2(10x - 1)$

7. $-5.4 = 0.6x - 9.6$

8. $\dfrac{1}{3}(x - 4) < \dfrac{1}{4}(x + 7)$

9. $3y - 5(y - 4) = -2(y - 10)$

10. $\dfrac{7(x - 1)}{3} = \dfrac{2(x + 1)}{5}$

CHAPTER 9   Group Activity

Investigating Averages

Sections 9.1–9.7

Materials:

- small rubber ball or crumpled paper ball
- bucket or waste can

This activity may be completed by working in groups or individually.

1. Try shooting the ball into the bucket or waste can 5 times. Record your results below.

   Shots Made   **Shots Missed**

2. Find your shooting percent for the 5 shots (that is, the percent of the shots you actually made out of the number you tried).

3. Suppose you are going to try an additional 5 shots. How many of the next 5 shots will you have to make to have

a 50% shooting percent for all 10 shots? An 80% shooting percent?

4. Did you solve an equation in Question 3? If so, explain what you did. If not, explain how you could use an equation to find the answers.

5. Now suppose you are going to try an additional 22 shots. How many of the next 22 shots will you have to make to have at least a 50% shooting percent for all 27 shots? At least a 70% shooting percent?

6. Choose one of the sports played at your college that is currently in season. How many regular-season games are scheduled? What is the team's current percent of games won?

7. Suppose the team has a goal of finishing the season with a winning percent better than 110% of their current wins. At least how many of the remaining games must they win to achieve their goal?

Chapter 9 Vocabulary Check

Fill in each blank with one of the words or phrases listed below.

no solution	all real numbers	linear equation in one variable
equivalent equations	formula	reversed
linear inequality in one variable	the same	

1. A _____ can be written in the form $ax + b = c$.
2. Equations that have the same solution are called _____.
3. An equation that describes a known relationship among quantities is called a _____.
4. A _____ can be written in the form $ax + b < c$, (or $>$, $\leq$, $\geq$).
5. The solution(s) to the equation $x + 5 = x + 5$ is/are _____.
6. The solution(s) to the equation $x + 5 = x + 4$ is/are _____.
7. If both sides of an inequality are multiplied or divided by the same positive number, the direction of the inequality symbol is _____.
8. If both sides of an inequality are multiplied by the same negative number, the direction of the inequality symbol is _____.

Chapter Highlights

Helpful Hint

Are you preparing for your test? Don't forget to take the Chapter 9 Test on page 705. Then check your answers at the back of the text and use the Chapter Test Prep Video CD to see the fully worked-out solutions to any of the exercises you want to review.

DEFINITIONS AND CONCEPTS	EXAMPLES
Section 9.1 The Addition Property of Equality	
A **linear equation in one variable** can be written in the form $Ax + B = C$ where A, B, and C are real numbers and $A \neq 0$. **Equivalent equations** are equations that have the same solution.	$-3x + 7 = 2$ $3(x - 1) = -8(x + 5) + 4$ $x - 7 = 10$ and $x = 17$ are equivalent equations.
ADDITION PROPERTY OF EQUALITY Adding the same number to or subtracting the same number from both sides of an equation does not change its solution.	$y + 9 = 3$ $y + 9 - 9 = 3 - 9$ $y = -6$
Section 9.2 The Multiplication Property of Equality	
MULTIPLICATION PROPERTY OF EQUALITY Multiplying both sides or dividing both sides of an equation by the same nonzero number does not change its solution.	$\dfrac{2}{3}a = 18$ $\dfrac{3}{2}\left(\dfrac{2}{3}a\right) = \dfrac{3}{2}(18)$ $a = 27$

DEFINITIONS AND CONCEPTS	EXAMPLES
Section 9.3 Further Solving Linear Equations	

TO SOLVE LINEAR EQUATIONS

Solve: $\dfrac{5(-2x + 9)}{6} + 3 = \dfrac{1}{2}$

1. Clear the equation of fractions.

  1. $6 \cdot \dfrac{5(-2x + 9)}{6} + 6 \cdot 3 = 6 \cdot \dfrac{1}{2}$

2. Remove any grouping symbols such as parentheses.

  2. $5(-2x + 9) + 18 = 3$ Apply the distributive property.
  $-10x + 45 + 18 = 3$

3. Simplify each side by combining like terms.

  3. $-10x + 63 = 3$ Combine like terms.

4. Get all variable terms on one side and all numbers on the other side by using the addition property of equality.

  4. $-10x + 63 - 63 = 3 - 63$ Subtract 63.
  $-10x = -60$

5. Get the variable alone by using the multiplication property of equality.

  5. $\dfrac{-10x}{-10} = \dfrac{-60}{-10}$ Divide by -10.
  $x = 6$

6. Check the solution by substituting it into the original equation.

| **Section 9.4   An Introduction to Problem Solving** | |

PROBLEM-SOLVING STEPS

The height of the Hudson volcano in Chile is twice the height of the Kiska volcano in the Aleutian Islands. If the sum of their heights is 12,870 feet, find the height of each.

1. UNDERSTAND the problem.

  1. Read and reread the problem. Guess a solution and check your guess.
  Let x be the height of the Kiska volcano. Then $2x$ is the height of the Hudson volcano.

x $2x$

2. TRANSLATE the problem.

  2.
height of Kiska	added to	height of Hudson	is	12,870
↓	↓	↓	↓	↓
x	$+$	$2x$	$=$	12,870

3. SOLVE the equation.

  3. $x + 2x = 12{,}870$
  $3x = 12{,}870$
  $x = 4290$

4. INTERPRET the results.

  4. *Check:* If x is 4290, then $2x$ is 2(4290) or 8580. Their sum is $4290 + 8580$ or 12,870, the required amount.

  State: The Kiska volcano is 4290 feet high, and the Hudson volcano is 8580 feet high.

DEFINITIONS AND CONCEPTS	**EXAMPLES**
Section 9.5 Formulas and Problem Solving	

An equation that describes a known relationship among quantities is called a **formula.**	$A = lw$ (area of a rectangle) $I = PRT$ (simple interest)
To solve a formula for a specified variable, use the same steps as for solving a linear equation. Treat the specified variable as the only variable of the equation.	*Solve:* $P = 2l + 2w$ for l. $P = 2l + 2w$ $P - 2w = 2l + 2w - 2w$ Subtract $2w$. $P - 2w = 2l$ $\dfrac{P - 2w}{2} = \dfrac{2l}{2}$ Divide by 2. $\dfrac{P - 2w}{2} = l$

Section 9.6 Percent and Mixture Problem Solving	

Use the same problem-solving steps to solve a problem containing percents.	32% of what number is 36.8?
1. UNDERSTAND.	**1.** Read and reread. Propose a solution and check. Let x = the unknown number.
2. TRANSLATE.	**2.** 32% of what number is 36.8 $\downarrow$ $\downarrow$ $\downarrow$ $\downarrow$ $\downarrow$ 32% $\cdot$ x $=$ 36.8
3. SOLVE.	**3.** *Solve:* $32\% \cdot x = 36.8$ $0.32x = 36.8$ $\dfrac{0.32x}{0.32} = \dfrac{36.8}{0.32}$ Divide by 0.32. $x = 115$ Simplify.
4. INTERPRET.	**4.** *Check, then state:* 32% of 115 is 36.8.
	How many liters of a 20% acid solution must be mixed with a 50% acid solution in order to obtain 12 liters of a 30% solution?
1. UNDERSTAND.	**1.** Read and reread. Guess a solution and check. Let x = number of liters of 20% solution. Then $12 - x$ = number of liters of 50% solution.
2. TRANSLATE.	**2.**

	No. of Liters ·	Acid Strength =	Amount of Acid
20% Solution	x	20%	$0.20x$
50% Solution	$12 - x$	50%	$0.50(12 - x)$
30% Solution Needed	12	30%	$0.30(12)$

In words: acid in 20% solution $+$ acid in 50% solution $=$ acid in 30% solution

Translate: $0.20x$ $+ \ 0.50(12 - x)$ $=$ $0.30(12)$

continued

DEFINITIONS AND CONCEPTS	EXAMPLES
Section 9.6 Percent and Mixture Problem Solving (*continued*)	

3. SOLVE.

4. INTERPRET.

3. *Solve:* $0.20x + 0.50(12 - x) = 0.30(12)$

$0.20x + 6 - 0.50x = 3.6$ Apply the distributive property.

$-0.30x + 6 = 3.6$ Combine like terms.

$-0.30x = -2.4$ Subtract 6.

$x = 8$ Divide by -0.30.

4. *Check, then state:*
If 8 liters of a 20% acid solution are mixed with $12 - 8$ or 4 liters of a 50% acid solution, the result is 12 liters of a 30% solution.

Section 9.7 Solving Linear Inequalities	

Properties of inequalities are similar to properties of equations. However, if you multiply or divide both sides of an inequality by the same *negative* number, you must reverse the direction of the inequality symbol.

$-2x \leq 4$

$\dfrac{-2x}{-2} \geq \dfrac{4}{-2}$ Divide by -2; reverse the inequality symbol.

$x \geq -2$

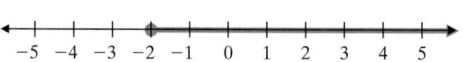

To Solve Linear Inequalities

1. Clear the inequality of fractions.

2. Remove grouping symbols.

3. Simplify each side by combining like terms.

4. Write all variable terms on one side and all numbers on the other side using the addition property of inequality.

5. Get the variable alone by using the multiplication property of inequality.

Solve: $3(x + 2) \leq -2 + 8$

1. $3(x + 2) \leq -2 + 8$ No fractions to clear.

2. $3x + 6 \leq -2 + 8$ Apply the distributive property.

3. $3x + 6 \leq 6$ Combine like terms.

4. $3x + 6 - 6 \leq 6 - 6$ Subtract 6.

$3x \leq 0$

5. $\dfrac{3x}{3} \leq \dfrac{0}{3}$ Divide by 3.

$x \leq 0$

The solution set is $\{x \mid x \leq 0\}$.

9 CHAPTER REVIEW

(9.1) *Solve each equation.*

1. $8x + 4 = 9x$

2. $5y - 3 = 6y$

3. $\dfrac{2}{7}x + \dfrac{5}{7}x = 6$

4. $3x - 5 = 4x + 1$

5. $2x - 6 = x - 6$

6. $4(x + 3) = 3(1 + x)$

7. $6(3 + n) = 5(n - 1)$

8. $5(2 + x) - 3(3x + 2) = -5(x - 6) + 2$

Choose the correct algebraic expression.

9. The sum of two numbers is 10. If one number is x, express the other number in terms of x.
  a. $x - 10$
  b. $10 - x$
  c. $10 + x$
  d. $10x$

10. Mandy is 5 inches taller than Melissa. If x inches represents the height of Mandy, express Melissa's height in terms of x.
  a. $x - 5$
  b. $5 - x$
  c. $5 + x$
  d. $5x$

△ **11.** If one angle measures $x°$, express the measure of its complement in terms of x.
  a. $(180 - x)°$
  b. $(90 - x)°$
  c. $(x - 180)°$
  d. $(x - 90)°$

△ **12.** If one angle measures $(x + 5)°$, express the measure of its supplement in terms of x.
  a. $(185 + x)°$
  b. $(95 + x)°$
  c. $(175 - x)°$
  d. $(x - 170)°$

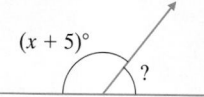

(9.2) *Solve each equation.*

13. $\dfrac{3}{4}x = -9$

14. $\dfrac{x}{6} = \dfrac{2}{3}$

15. $-5x = 0$

16. $-y = 7$

17. $0.2x = 0.15$

18. $\dfrac{-x}{3} = 1$

19. $-3x + 1 = 19$

20. $5x + 25 = 20$

21. $7(x - 1) + 9 = 5x$

22. $7x - 6 = 5x - 3$

23. $-5x + \dfrac{3}{7} = \dfrac{10}{7}$

24. $5x + x = 9 + 4x - 1 + 6$

25. Write the sum of three consecutive integers as an expression in x. Let x be the first integer.

26. Write the sum of the first and fourth of four consecutive even integers. Let x be the first even integer.

(9.3) *Solve each equation.*

27. $\dfrac{5}{3}x + 4 = \dfrac{2}{3}x$

28. $\dfrac{7}{8}x + 1 = \dfrac{5}{8}x$

29. $-(5x + 1) = -7x + 3$

30. $-4(2x + 1) = -5x + 5$

31. $-6(2x - 5) = -3(9 + 4x)$

32. $3(8y - 1) = 6(5 + 4y)$

33. $\dfrac{3(2 - z)}{5} = z$

34. $\dfrac{4(n + 2)}{5} = -n$

35. $0.5(2n - 3) - 0.1 = 0.4(6 + 2n)$

36. $-9 - 5a = 3(6a - 1)$

37. $\dfrac{5(c + 1)}{6} = 2c - 3$

38. $\dfrac{2(8 - a)}{3} = 4 - 4a$

▦ **39.** $200(70x - 3560) = -179(150x - 19{,}300)$

40. $1.72y - 0.04y = 0.42$

(9.4) *Solve each of the following.*

41. The height of the Washington Monument is 50.5 inches more than 10 times the length of a side of its square base. If the sum of these two dimensions is 7327 inches, find the height of the Washington Monument. (*Source:* National Park Service)

42. A 12-foot board is to be divided into two pieces so that one piece is twice as long as the other. If *x* represents the length of the shorter piece, find the length of each piece.

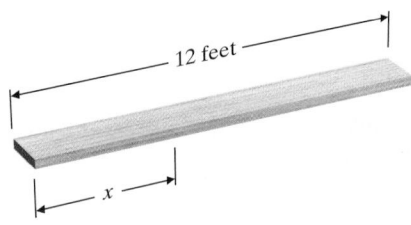

43. In a recent year, Kellogg Company acquired Keebler Foods Company. After the merger, the total number of Kellogg and Keebler manufacturing plants was 53. The number of Kellogg plants was one less than twice the number of Keebler plants. How many of each type of plant were there? (*Source: Kellogg Company 2000 Annual Report*)

44. Find three consecutive integers whose sum is −114.

45. The quotient of a number and 3 is the same as the difference of the number and two. Find the number.

46. Double the sum of a number and 6 is the opposite of the number. Find the number.

(9.5) *Substitute the given values into the given formulas and solve for the unknown variable.*

47. $P = 2l + 2w$; $P = 46, l = 14$

48. $V = lwh$; $V = 192, l = 8, w = 6$

Solve each equation for the indicated variable.

49. $y = mx + b$ for m

50. $r = vst - 5$ for s

51. $2y - 5x = 7$ for x

52. $3x - 6y = -2$ for y

△ **53.** $C = \pi D$ for π

△ **54.** $C = 2\pi r$ for π

△ **55.** A swimming pool holds 900 cubic meters of water. If its length is 20 meters and its height is 3 meters, find its width.

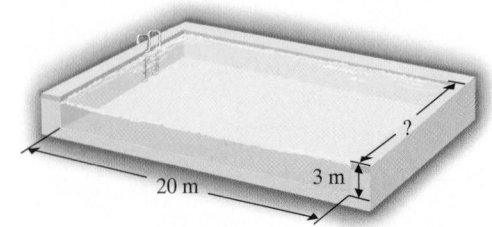

56. The perimeter of a rectangular billboard is 60 feet and has a length 6 feet longer than its width. Find the dimensions of the billboard.

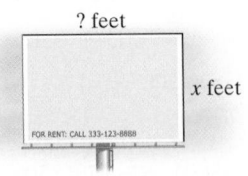

57. A charity 10K race is given annually to benefit a local hospice organization. How long will it take to run/walk a 10K race (10 kilometers or 10,000 meters) if your average pace is 125 **meters** per minute? Give your time in hours and minutes.

58. On April 28, 2001, the highest temperature recorded in the United States was 104°F, which occurred in Death Valley, California. Convert this temperature to degrees Celsius. (*Source:* National Weather Service)

(9.6) *Find each of the following.*

59. The number 9 is what percent of 45?

60. The number 59.5 is what percent of 85?

61. The number 137.5 is 125% of what number?

62. The number 768 is 60% of what number?

63. The price of a small diamond ring was recently increased by 11%. If the ring originally cost $1900, find the mark-up and the new price of the ring.

64. A recent survey found that 66.9% of Americans use the Internet. If a city has a population of 76,000 how many people in that city would you expect to use the Internet? (*Source:* UCLA Center for Communication Policy)

65. Thirty gallons of a 20% acid solution is needed for an experiment. Only 40% and 10% acid solutions are available. How much of each should be mixed to form the needed solution?

66. The ACT Assessment is a college entrance exam taken by about 60% of college-bound students. The national average score was 20.7 in 1993 and rose to 21.0 in 2001. Find the percent increase. (Round to the nearest hundredth of a percent.)

The graph below shows the percent(s) of cell phone users who have engaged in various behaviors while driving and talking on their cell phones. Use this graph to answer Exercises 67 through 70.

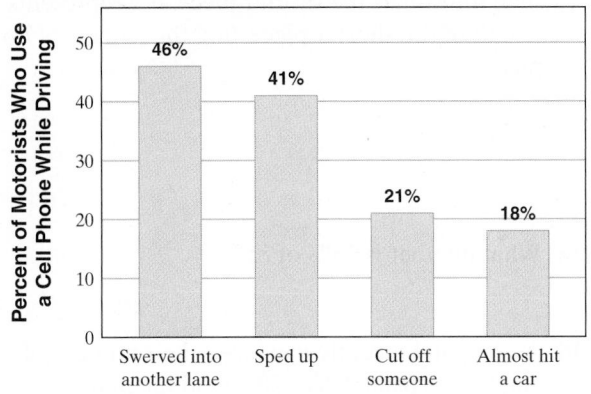

Effects of Cell Phone Use on Driving

Source: Progressive Insurance

67. What percent of motorists who use a cell phone while driving have almost hit another car?

68. What is the most common effect of cell phone use on driving?

69. If a cell-phone service has an estimated 4600 customers who use their cell phones while driving, how many of these customers would you expect to have cut someone off while driving and talking on their cell phones?

70. Do the percents in the graph to the left have a sum of 100%? Why or why not?

(9.7) *Graph on a number line.*

71. $x \leq -2$

```
<---+---+---+---+---+---+---+---+---+---+---+--->
   -5  -4  -3  -2  -1   0   1   2   3   4   5
```

72. $0 < x \leq 5$

```
<---+---+---+---+---+---+---+---+---+---+---+--->
   -5  -4  -3  -2  -1   0   1   2   3   4   5
```

Solve each inequality.

73. $x - 5 \leq -4$

74. $x + 7 > 2$

75. $-2x \geq -20$

76. $-3x > 12$

77. $5x - 7 > 8x + 5$

78. $x + 4 \geq 6x - 16$

79. $\frac{2}{3}y > 6$

80. $-0.5y \leq 7.5$

81. $-2(x - 5) > 2(3x - 2)$

82. $4(2x - 5) \leq 5x - 1$

83. Carol Abolafia earns \$175 per week plus a 5% commission on all her sales. Find the minimum amount of sales she must make to ensure that she earns at least \$300 per week.

84. Joseph Barrow shot rounds of 76, 82, and 79 golfing. What must he shoot on his next round so that his average will be below 80?

Mixed Review

Solve each equation.

85. $6x + 2x - 1 = 5x + 11$

86. $2(3y - 4) = 6 + 7y$

87. $4(3 - a) - (6a + 9) = -12a$

88. $\frac{x}{3} - 2 = 5$

89. $2(y + 5) = 2y + 10$

90. $7x - 3x + 2 = 2(2x - 1)$

Solve.

91. The sum of six and twice a number is equal to seven less than the number. Find the number.

92. A 23-inch piece of string is to be cut into two pieces so that the length of the longer piece is three more than four times the shorter piece. If x represents the length of the shorter piece, find the lengths of both pieces.

Solve for the specified variable.

93. $V = \frac{1}{3}Ah$ for h

94. What number is 26% of 85?

95. The number 72 is 45% of what number?

96. A company recently increased their number of employees from 235 to 282. Find the percent increase.

Solve each inequality. Graph the solution set.

97. $4x - 7 > 3x + 2$

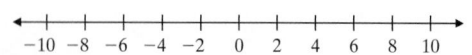

98. $-5x < 20$

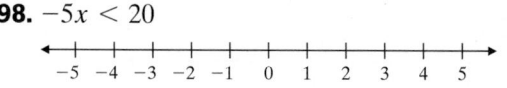

99. $-3(1 + 2x) + x \geq -(3 - x)$

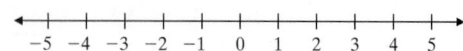

9 CHAPTER TEST

Remember to use the Chapter Test Prep Video CD to see the fully worked-out solutions to any of the exercises you want to review.

Solve each equation.

1. $-\dfrac{4}{5}x = 4$

2. $4(n - 5) = -(4 - 2n)$

3. $5y - 7 + y = -(y + 3y)$

4. $4z + 1 - z = 1 + z$

5. $\dfrac{2(x + 6)}{3} = x - 5$

6. $\dfrac{4(y - 1)}{5} = 2y + 3$

7. $\dfrac{1}{2} - x + \dfrac{3}{2} = x - 4$

8. $\dfrac{1}{3}(y + 3) = 4y$

9. $-0.3(x - 4) + x = 0.5(3 - x)$

10. $-4(a + 1) - 3a = -7(2a - 3)$

11. $-2(x - 3) = x + 5 - 3x$

Solve each application.

12. A number increased by two-thirds of the number is 35. Find the number.

△ **13.** A gallon of water seal covers 200 square feet. How many gallons are needed to paint two coats of water seal on a deck that measures 20 feet by 35 feet?

35 feet
20 feet

14. Find the value of x if $y = -14, m = -2$, and $b = -2$ in the formula $y = mx + b$.

Solve each equation for the indicated variable.

15. $V = \pi r^2 h$ for h

16. $3x - 4y = 10$ for y

Answers

1. _____

2. _____

3. _____

4. _____

5. _____

6. _____

7. _____

8. _____

9. _____

10. _____

11. _____

12. _____

13. _____

14. _____

15. _____

16. _____

17. _____

18. _____

19. _____

20. _____

21. _____

22. _____

23. _____

24. _____

25. _____

Solve each inequality. Graph the solution set.

17. $3x - 5 > 7x + 3$

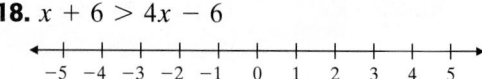

18. $x + 6 > 4x - 6$

Solve each inequality.

19. $-0.3x \geq 2.4$

20. $-5(x - 1) + 6 \leq -3(x + 4) + 1$

21. $\dfrac{2(5x + 1)}{3} > 2$

The following graph shows the breakdown of tornadoes occurring in the United States by strength. The corresponding Fujita Tornado Scale categories are shown in parentheses. Use this graph to answer Exercises 22 and 23.

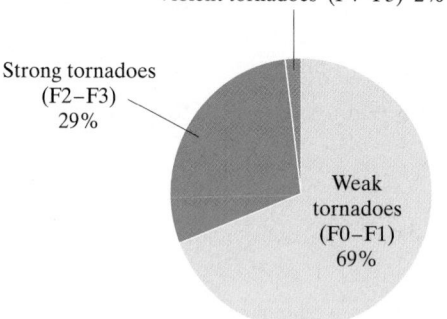

Violent tornadoes (F4–F5) 2%

Strong tornadoes
(F2–F3)
29%

Weak
tornadoes
(F0–F1)
69%

Source: National Climatic Data Center

22. What percent of tornadoes occurring in the United States are classified as "strong," that is, F2 or F3 on the Fujita Scale?

23. According to the National Climatic Data Center, in an average year, about 800 tornadoes are reported in the United States. How many of these would you expect to be classified as "weak" tornadoes?

24. The number 72 is what percent of 180?

25. New York State has more public libraries than any other state. It has 650 more public libraries than Indiana does. If the total number of public libraries for these states is 1504, find the number of public libraries in New York and the number in Indiana. (*Source: The World Almanac and Book of Facts,* 2001)

Determine whether each statement is true or false.

1. $8 \geq 8$

2. $-4 < -6$

3. $8 \leq 8$

4. $3 > -3$

5. $23 \leq 0$

6. $-8 \geq -8$

7. $0 \leq 23$

8. $-8 \leq -8$

9. Add: $2\frac{1}{3} + 5\frac{3}{8}$

10. Perform the indicated operation.

    a. $\dfrac{2}{5} + \dfrac{3}{10}$

    b. $\dfrac{7}{8} - \dfrac{1}{3}$

11. Simplify the expression

$$\frac{3 + |4 - 3| + 2^2}{6 - 3}.$$

12. $1 + 2(9 - 7)^3 + 4^2$

Add without using number lines.

13. $(-8) + (-11)$

14. $-2 + (-8)$

15. $(-2) + 10$

16. $-10 + 20$

17. $0.2 + (-0.5)$

18. $1.2 + (-1.2)$

19. Simplify each expression.

    a. $-3 + [(-2 - 5) - 2]$

    b. $2^3 - 10 + [-6 - (-5)]$

20. Simplify each expression.

    a. $-(-5)$ **c.** $-(-a)$

    b. $-\left(-\dfrac{2}{3}\right)$ **d.** $-|-3|$

Answers

1. _____
2. _____
3. _____
4. _____
5. _____
6. _____
7. _____
8. _____
9. _____
10. a. _____
   b. _____
11. _____
12. _____
13. _____
14. _____
15. _____
16. _____
17. _____
18. _____
19. a. _____
   b. _____
20. a. _____
   b. _____
   c. _____
   d. _____

21. a. _____

b. _____

c. _____

22. a. _____

b. _____

c. _____

23. a. _____

b. _____

c. _____

24. a. _____

b. _____

25. _____

26. _____

27. _____

28. _____

29. a. _____

b. _____

c. _____

d. _____

e. _____

30. a. _____

b. _____

c. _____

31. _____

32. _____

33. _____

21. Use order of operations and simplify each expression.

   a. $7(0)(-6)$

   b. $(-2)(-3)(-4)$

   c. $(-1)(5)(-9)$

22. Subtract

   a. $-2.7 - 8.4$

   b. $-\dfrac{4}{5} - \left(-\dfrac{3}{5}\right)$

   c. $\dfrac{1}{4} - \left(-\dfrac{1}{2}\right)$

23. Use the definition of the quotient of two numbers to find each quotient.

   a. $-18 \div 3$

   b. $\dfrac{-14}{-2}$

   c. $\dfrac{20}{-4}$

24. Find each product.

   a. $(4.5)(-0.08)$

   b. $-\dfrac{3}{4} \cdot -\dfrac{8}{17}$

Use the distributive property to write each expression without parentheses. Then simplify the result.

25. $-5(-3 + 2z)$

26. $2x(x^2 - 3x + 4)$

27. $\dfrac{1}{2}(6x + 14) + 10$

28. $-(x + 4) + 3(x + 4)$

29. Tell whether the terms are like or unlike.

   a. $2x, 3x^2$

   b. $4x^2y, x^2y, -2x^2y$

   c. $-2yz, -3zy$

   d. $-x^4, x^4$

   e. $-8a^5, 8a^5$

30. Find each quotient.

   a. $\dfrac{-32}{8}$ **b.** $\dfrac{-108}{-12}$

   c. $-\dfrac{5}{7} \div \left(-\dfrac{9}{2}\right)$

31. Subtract $4x - 2$ from $2x - 3$.

32. Subtract $10x + 3$ from $-5x + 1$.

33. Solve: $x - 7 = 10$

Solve.

34. $\dfrac{5}{6} + x = \dfrac{2}{3}$

35. Solve: $-z - 4 = 6$

36. $-3x + 1 - (-4x - 6) = 10$

37. Solve: $\dfrac{2(a + 3)}{3} = 6a + 2$

38. $\dfrac{x}{4} = 18$

39. In a recent year, the U.S. House of Representatives had a total of 431 Democrats and Republicans. There were 15 more Republican representatives than Democratic. Find the number of representatives from each party. (*Source:* Office of the Clerk of the U.S. House of Representatives)

40. $6x + 5 = 4(x + 4) - 1$

41. A glacier is a giant mass of rocks and ice that flows downhill like a river. Portage Glacier in Alaska is about 6 miles, or 31,680 feet, long and moves 400 feet per year. Icebergs are created when the front end of the glacier flows into Portage Lake. How long does it take for ice at the head (beginning) of the glacier to reach the lake?

42. A number increased by 4 is the same as 3 times the number decreased by 8. Find the number.

43. The number 63 is what percent of 72?

44. Solve $C = 2\pi r$ for r.

45. Solve: $5(2x + 3) = -1 + 7$

46. Solve: $x - 3 > 2$

47. Graph $-1 > x$.

48. Solve: $3x - 4 \le 2x - 14$

49. Solve: $2(x - 3) - 5 \le 3(x + 2) - 18$

50. Solve: $-3x \ge 9$

34. _____

35. _____

36. _____

37. _____

38. _____

39. _____

40. _____

41. _____

42. _____

43. _____

44. _____

45. _____

46. _____

47. see graph

48. _____

49. _____

50. _____

10

Graphing Equations and Inequalities

In Chapter 9 we learned to solve and graph the solutions of linear equations and inequalities in one variable on number lines. Now we define and present techniques for solving and graphing linear equations and inequalities in two variables on grids. Two-variable equations lead directly to the concept of *function*, perhaps the most important concept in all mathematics. Functions are introduced in Section 10.6.

CHECK YOUR PROGRESS

Vocabulary Check

Chapter Highlights

Chapter Review

Chapter Test

Cumulative Review

mericans enjoy pets more than ever before. Currently 62% of all U.S. households, or about 64.2 million households, have at least one pet. According to an American Pet Products Manufacturing Association survey, companionship, love, company, and affection eclipse all other benefits of pet ownership and are cited as the primary benefits of sharing their lives with their pet.

In Exercise 17, Section 10.1, we will examine the growth of these pet-related expenditures, such as food, veterinary care, supplies, and pet care and grooming.

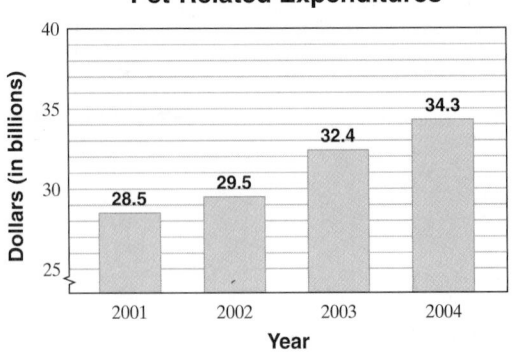

Pet-Related Expenditures

Objectives

A Plot Ordered Pairs of Numbers on the Rectangular Coordinate System.

B Graph Paired Data to Create a Scatter Diagram.

C Find the Missing Coordinate of an Ordered Pair Solution, Given One Coordinate of the Pair.

Recall from Chapter 7 that we practiced reading different types of graphs, including line graphs. Let's study the line graph below and discover that there are two numbers associated with each point of the graph.

The line graph shows the relationship between time spent smoking a cigarette and pulse rate. Time is recorded along the horizontal axis in minutes, with 0 minutes being the moment a smoker lights a cigarette. Pulse is recorded along the vertical axis in heartbeats per minute.

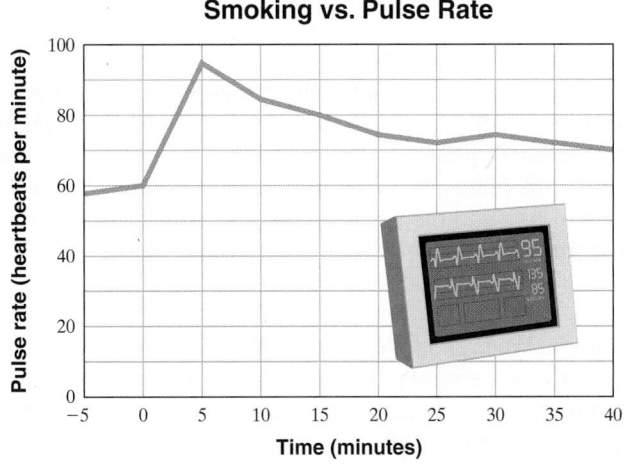

Notice in the graph that there are two numbers associated with each point of the graph. For example, can you see that 15 minutes after "lighting up," the pulse rate is 80 beats per minute? If we agree to write the time first and the pulse rate second, we can say there is a point on the graph corresponding to the **ordered pair** of numbers (15, 80). A few more ordered pairs are shown alongside their corresponding points.

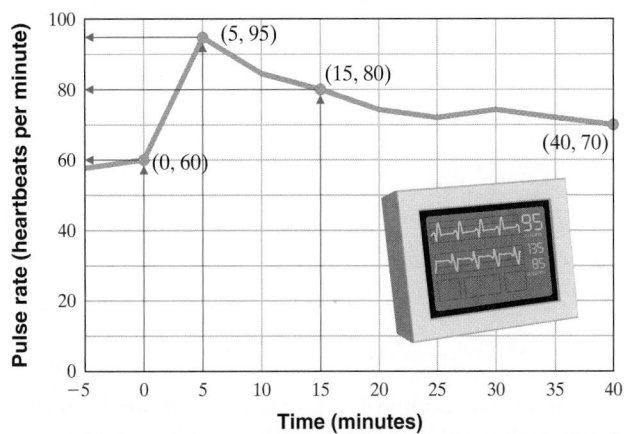

Objective **A** Plotting Ordered Pairs of Numbers

In general, we use the idea of ordered pairs to describe the location of a point in a plane (such as a piece of paper). We start with a horizontal and a vertical axis. Each axis is a number line, and for the sake of consistency we construct our axes to intersect at the 0 coordinate of both. This point of intersection is called the **origin.** Notice that these two number lines or axes divide the plane into four regions called

quadrants. The quadrants are usually numbered with Roman numerals as shown. The axes are not considered to be in any quadrant.

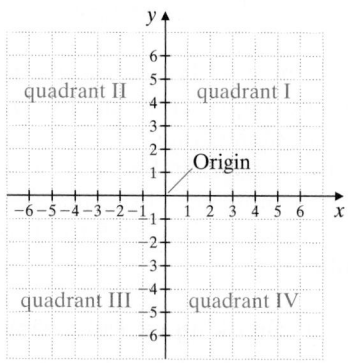

It is helpful to label axes, so we label the horizontal axis the **x-axis** and the vertical axis the **y-axis.** We call the system described above the **rectangular coordinate system,** or the **coordinate plane.** Just as with other graphs shown, we can then describe the locations of points by ordered pairs of numbers. We list the horizontal **x-axis** measurement first and the vertical **y-axis** measurement second.

To plot or graph the point corresponding to the ordered pair

(a, b)

we start at the origin. We then move a units left or right (right if a is positive, left if a is negative). From there, we move b units up or down (up if b is positive, down if b is negative). For example, to plot the point corresponding to the ordered pair $(3, 2)$, we start at the origin, move 3 units right, and from there move 2 units up. (See the figure on next page.) The x-value, 3, is also called the **x-coordinate** and the y-value, 2, is also called the **y-coordinate.** From now on, we will call the point with coordinates $(3, 2)$ simply the point $(3, 2)$. The point $(-2, 5)$ is also graphed below.

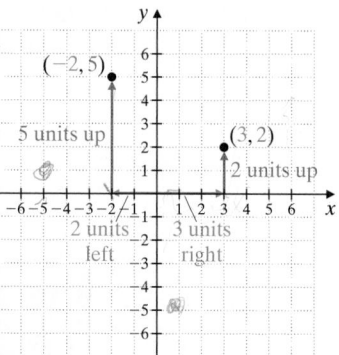

Helpful Hint

Don't forget that **each ordered pair corresponds to exactly one point in the plane and that each point in the plane corresponds to exactly one ordered pair.**

✔ **Concept Check**   Is the graph of the point $(-5, 1)$ in the same location as the graph of the point $(1, -5)$? Explain.   No

✔ Concept Check Answers

The graph of point $(-5, 1)$ lies in quadrant II and the graph of point $(1, -5)$ lies in quadrant IV. They are *not* in the same location.

EXAMPLE 1 On a single coordinate system, plot each ordered pair. State in which quadrant, or on which axis each point lies.

a. $(5, 3)$ **b.** $(-2, -4)$ **c.** $(1, -2)$ **d.** $(-5, 3)$ **e.** $(0, 0)$

f. $(0, 2)$ **g.** $(-5, 0)$ **h.** $\left(0, -5\frac{1}{2}\right)$ **i.** $\left(4\frac{2}{3}, -3\right)$

Solution:

a. Point $(5, 3)$ lies in quadrant I.
b. Point $(-2, -4)$ lies in quadrant III.
c. Point $(1, -2)$ lies in quadrant IV.
d. Point $(-5, 3)$ lies in quadrant II.

e.–h. Points $(0, 0), (0, 2),$ and $\left(0, -5\frac{1}{2}\right)$ lie on the y-axis. Points $(0, 0)$ and $(-5, 0)$ lie on the x-axis.

i. Point $\left(4\frac{2}{3}, -3\right)$ lies in quadrant IV.

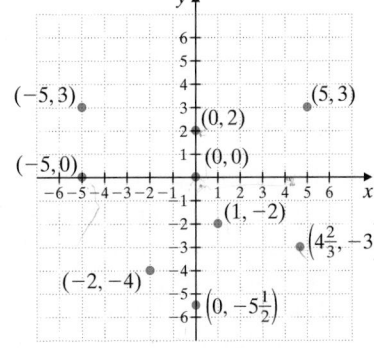

■ Work Practice Problem 1

Helpful Hint

In Example 1, notice that the point $(0, 0)$ lies on both the x-axis and the y-axis. It is the only point in the entire rectangular coordinate system that has this feature. Why? It is the only point of intersection of the x-axis and the y-axis.

✔ Concept Check For each description of a point in the rectangular coordinate system, write an ordered pair that represents it.

a. Point A is located three units to the left of the y-axis and five units above the x-axis.

b. Point B is located six units below the origin.

From Example 1, notice that the y-coordinate of any point on the x-axis is 0. For example, the point $(-5, 0)$ lies on the x-axis. Also, the x-coordinate of any point on the y-axis is 0. For example, the point $(0, 2)$ lies on the y-axis.

Objective **B** Creating Scatter Diagrams

Data that can be represented as ordered pairs are called **paired data.** Many types of data collected from the real world are paired data. For instance, the annual measurements of a child's height can be written as ordered pairs of the form (year, height in inches) and are paired data. The graph of paired data as points in the rectangular coordinate system is called a **scatter diagram.** Scatter diagrams can be used to look for patterns and trends in paired data.

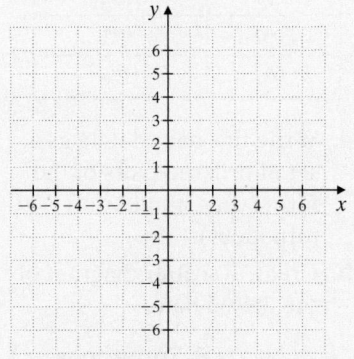
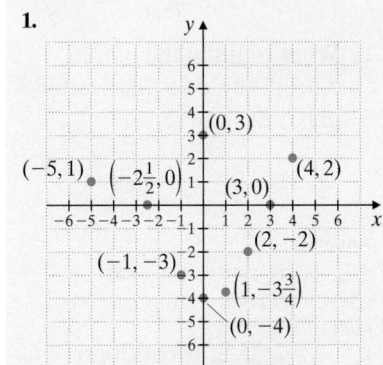

PRACTICE PROBLEM 2

The table gives the number of tornadoes that have occurred in the United States for the years shown. (*Source:* Storm Prediction Center, National Weather Service)

Year	Tornadoes
1998	1424
1999	1343
2000	997
2001	1216
2002	941
2003	1376

a. Write this paired data as a set of ordered pairs of the form (year, number of tornadoes).

b. Create a scatter diagram of the paired data.

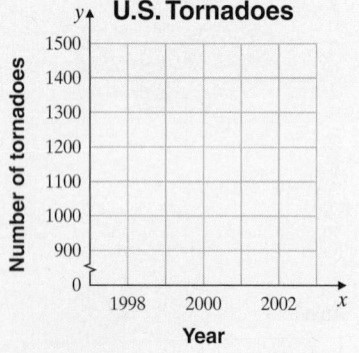

c. What trend in the paired data, if any, does the scatter diagram show?

EXAMPLE 2 The table gives the annual net sales for Target Stores for the years shown. (*Source:* TargetCorp.com)

a. Write this paired data as a set of ordered pairs of the form (year, net sales in billions of dollars).

b. Create a scatter diagram of the paired data.

c. What trend in the paired data does the scatter diagram show?

Year	Target Net Sales (in billions of dollars)
1999	34
2000	37
2001	40
2002	44
2003	48

Solution:

a. The ordered pairs are $(1999, 34), (2000, 37), (2001, 40), (2002, 44),$ and $(2003, 48)$.

b. We begin by plotting the ordered pairs. Because the x-coordinate in each ordered pair is a year, we label the x-axis "Year" and mark the horizontal axis with the years given. Then we label the y-axis or vertical axis "Target Net Sales (in billions of dollars)." In this case, it is convenient to mark the vertical axis in multiples of 5, starting with 0. In Practice Problem 2, since there are no years when the number of tornadoes is less than 900, we use the notation $\natural$ to skip to 900, then proceed by multiples of 100.

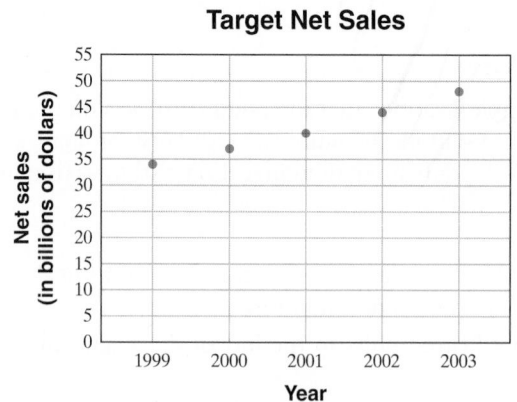

c. The scatter diagram shows that Target net sales steadily increased over the years 1999–2003.

🔲 **Work Practice Problem 2**

Objective C Completing Ordered Pair Solutions

Let's see how we can use ordered pairs to record solutions of equations containing two variables. An equation in one variable such as $x + 1 = 5$ has one solution, 4: the number 4 is the value of the variable x that makes the equation true.

An equation in two variables, such as $2x + y = 8$, has solutions consisting of two values, one for x and one for y. For example, $x = 3$ and $y = 2$ is a solution of $2x + y = 8$ because, if x is replaced with 3 and y with 2, we get a true statement.

$$2x + y = 8$$
$$2(3) + 2 \overset{?}{=} 8 \quad \text{Replace } x \text{ with 3 and } y \text{ with 2.}$$
$$8 = 8 \quad \text{True}$$

The solution $x = 3$ and $y = 2$ can be written as $(3, 2)$, an ordered pair of numbers.

Answers

2. a. $(1998, 1424), (1999, 1343),$ $(2000, 997), (2001, 1216), (2002, 941),$ $(2003, 1376)$

b.

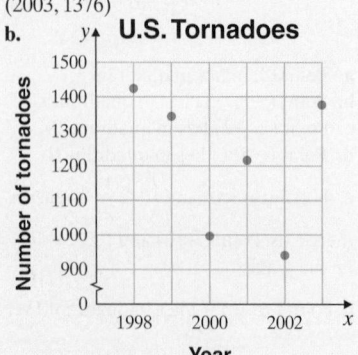

c. The number of tornadoes varies greatly from year to year.

In general, an ordered pair is a **solution** of an equation in two variables if replacing the variables by the values of the ordered pair results in a *true statement*.

For example, another ordered pair solution of $2x + y = 8$ is $(5, -2)$. Replacing x with 5 and y with -2 results in a true statement.

$$2x + y = 8$$
$$2(5) + (-2) \stackrel{?}{=} 8 \quad \text{Replace } x \text{ with 5 and } y \text{ with } -2.$$
$$10 - 2 \stackrel{?}{=} 8$$
$$8 = 8 \quad \text{True}$$

EXAMPLE 3 Complete each ordered pair so that it is a solution to the equation $3x + y = 12$.

a. $(0, \ )$ **b.** $(\ , 6)$ **c.** $(-1, \ )$

Solution:

a. In the ordered pair $(0, \ )$, the x-value is 0. We let $x = 0$ in the equation and solve for y.

$$3x + y = 12$$
$$3(0) + y = 12 \quad \text{Replace } x \text{ with 0.}$$
$$0 + y = 12$$
$$y = 12$$

The completed ordered pair is $(0, 12)$.

b. In the ordered pair $(\ , 6)$, the y-value is 6. We let $y = 6$ in the equation and solve for x.

$$3x + y = 12$$
$$3x + 6 = 12 \quad \text{Replace } y \text{ with 6.}$$
$$3x = 6 \quad \text{Subtract 6 from both sides.}$$
$$x = 2 \quad \text{Divide both sides by 3.}$$

The ordered pair is $(2, 6)$.

c. In the ordered pair $(-1, \ )$, the x-value is -1. We let $x = -1$ in the equation and solve for y.

$$3x + y = 12$$
$$3(-1) + y = 12 \quad \text{Replace } x \text{ with } -1.$$
$$-3 + y = 12$$
$$y = 15 \quad \text{Add 3 to both sides.}$$

The ordered pair is $(-1, 15)$.

☐ **Work Practice Problem 3**

Solutions of equations in two variables can also be recorded in a **table of paired values,** as shown in the next example.

PRACTICE PROBLEM 3

Complete each ordered pair so that it is a solution to the equation $x + 2y = 8$.

a. $(0, \ )$
b. $(\ , 3)$
c. $(-4, \ )$

PRACTICE PROBLEM 4

Complete the table for the equation $y = -2x$.

	x	y
a.	−3	
b.		0
c.		10

EXAMPLE 4 Complete the table for the equation $y = 3x$.

	x	y
a.	−1	
b.		0
c.		−9

Solution:

a. We replace x with -1 in the equation and solve for y.

$$y = 3x$$
$$y = 3(-1) \quad \text{Let } x = -1.$$
$$y = -3$$

The ordered pair is $(-1, -3)$.

b. We replace y with 0 in the equation and solve for x.

$$y = 3x$$
$$0 = 3x \quad \text{Let } y = 0.$$
$$0 = x \quad \text{Divide both sides by 3.}$$

The ordered pair is $(0, 0)$.

c. We replace y with -9 in the equation and solve for x.

$$y = 3x$$
$$-9 = 3x \quad \text{Let } y = -9.$$
$$-3 = x \quad \text{Divide both sides by 3.}$$

The ordered pair is $(-3, -9)$. The completed table is shown to the right.

x	y
−1	−3
0	0
−3	−9

■ **Work Practice Problem 4**

PRACTICE PROBLEM 5

Complete the table for the equation $y = \dfrac{1}{3}x - 1$.

	x	y
a.	−3	
b.	0	
c.		0

EXAMPLE 5 Complete the table for the equation

$$y = \frac{1}{2}x - 5.$$

	x	y
a.	−2	
b.	0	
c.		0

Solution:

a. Let $x = -2$.

$$y = \frac{1}{2}x - 5$$
$$y = \frac{1}{2}(-2) - 5$$
$$y = -1 - 5$$
$$y = -6$$

b. Let $x = 0$.

$$y = \frac{1}{2}x - 5$$
$$y = \frac{1}{2}(0) - 5$$
$$y = 0 - 5$$
$$y = -5$$

c. Let $y = 0$.

$$y = \frac{1}{2}x - 5$$
$$0 = \frac{1}{2}x - 5 \quad \text{Now, solve for } x.$$
$$5 = \frac{1}{2}x \quad \text{Add 5.}$$
$$10 = x \quad \text{Multiply by 2.}$$

Ordered Pairs: $(-2, -6)$ $(0, -5)$ $(10, 0)$

The completed table is

x	−2	0	10
y	−6	−5	0

■ **Work Practice Problem 5**

Answers

4.

	x	y
a.	−3	6
b.	0	0
c.	−5	10

5.

	x	y
a.	−3	−2
b.	0	−1
c.	3	0

By now, you have noticed that equations in two variables often have more than one solution. We discuss this more in the next section.

A table showing ordered pair solutions may be written vertically, or horizontally as shown in the next example.

EXAMPLE 6 A small business purchased a computer for $2000. The business predicts that the computer will be used for 5 years and the value in dollars y of the computer in x years is $y = -300x + 2000$. Complete the table.

x	0	1	2	3	4	5
y						

Solution:

To find the value of y when x is 0, we replace x with 0 in the equation. We use this same procedure to find y when x is 1 and when x is 2.

When $x = 0$,	**When $x = 1$,**	**When $x = 2$,**
$y = -300x + 2000$	$y = -300x + 2000$	$y = -300x + 2000$
$y = -300 \cdot 0 + 2000$	$y = -300 \cdot 1 + 2000$	$y = -300 \cdot 2 + 2000$
$y = 0 + 2000$	$y = -300 + 2000$	$y = -600 + 2000$
$y = 2000$	$y = 1700$	$y = 1400$

We have the ordered pairs (0, 2000), (1, 1700), and (2, 1400). This means that in 0 years the value of the computer is $2000, in 1 year the value of the computer is $1700, and in 2 years the value is $1400. To complete the table of values, we continue the procedure for $x = 3$, $x = 4$, and $x = 5$.

When $x = 3$,	**When $x = 4$,**	**When $x = 5$,**
$y = -300x + 2000$	$y = -300x + 2000$	$y = -300x + 2000$
$y = -300 \cdot 3 + 2000$	$y = -300 \cdot 4 + 2000$	$y = -300 \cdot 5 + 2000$
$y = -900 + 2000$	$y = -1200 + 2000$	$y = -1500 + 2000$
$y = 1100$	$y = 800$	$y = 500$

The completed table is shown below.

x	0	1	2	3	4	5
y	2000	1700	1400	1100	800	500

Work Practice Problem 6

The ordered pair solutions recorded in the completed table for Example 6 are another set of paired data. They are graphed next. Notice that this scatter diagram gives a visual picture of the decrease in value of the computer.

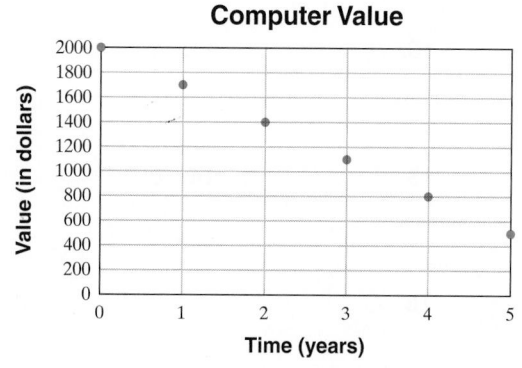

Computer Value

Value (in dollars) / Time (years)

Mental Math

Give two ordered pair solutions for each linear equation.

1. $x + y = 10$

2. $x + y = 6$

10.1 EXERCISE SET

Objective A *Plot each ordered pair. State in which quadrant or on which axis each point lies. See Example 1.*

1. a. $(1, 5)$ **b.** $(-5, -2)$ **c.** $(-3, 0)$ **d.** $(0, -1)$ **2. a.** $(2, 4)$ **b.** $(0, 2)$ **c.** $(-2, 1)$ **d.** $(-3, -3)$

e. $(2, -4)$ **f.** $\left(-1, 4\frac{1}{2}\right)$ **g.** $(3.7, 2.2)$ **h.** $\left(\frac{1}{2}, -3\right)$ **e.** $\left(3\frac{3}{4}, 0\right)$ **f.** $(5, -4)$ **g.** $(-3.4, 4.8)$ **h.** $\left(\frac{1}{3}, -5\right)$

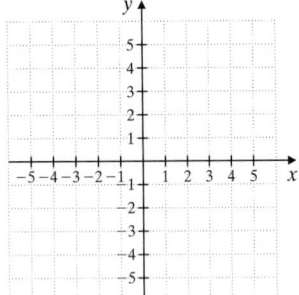   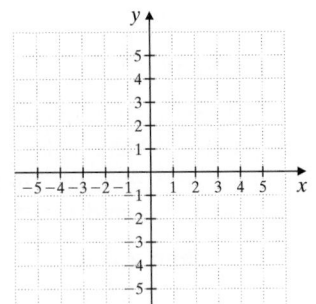

Find the x- and y-coordinates of each labeled point. See Example 1.

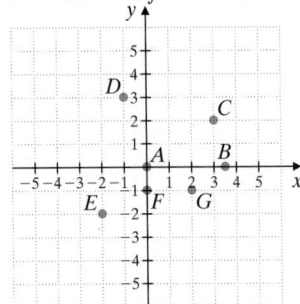   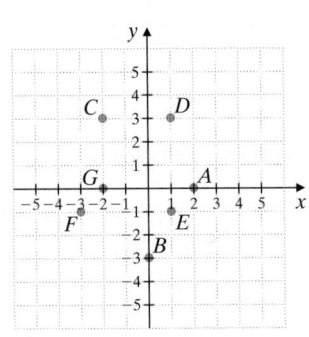

3. A **4.** B **5.** C **10.** A **11.** B **12.** C

6. D **7.** E **8.** F **13.** D **14.** E **15.** F

9. G **16.** G

Objective **B** *Solve. See Example 2.*

17. The table shows the amount of money (in billions of dollars) that Americans spent on their pets for the years shown. (*Source:* American Pet Products Manufacturers Association)

Year	Pet-Related Expenditures (in billions of dollars)
2001	28.5
2002	29.5
2003	32.4
2004	34.3

a. Write this paired data as a set of ordered pairs of the form (year, pet-related expenditures).

b. In your own words, write the meaning of the ordered pair (2004, 34.3).

c. Create a scatter diagram of the paired data. Be sure to label the axes appropriately.

Pet-Related Expenditures

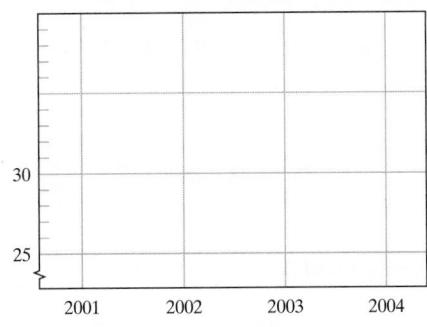

d. What trend in the paired data does the scatter diagram show?

18. The table shows the average farm size (in acres) in the United States during the years shown. (*Source:* National Agricultural Statistics Service)

Year	Average Farm Size (in acres)
1998	435
1999	432
2000	434
2001	438
2002	440
2003	441

a. Write this paired data as a set of ordered pairs of the form (year, average farm size).

b. In your own words, write the meaning of the ordered pair (2003, 441).

c. Create a scatter diagram of the paired data. Be sure to label the axes appropriately.

U.S. Average Farm Size

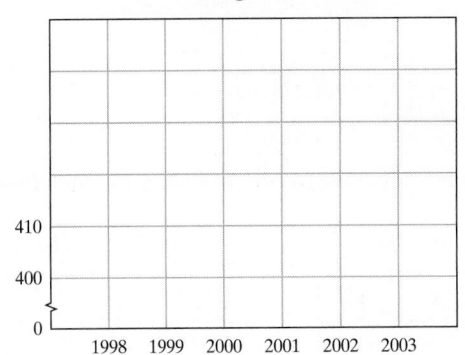

19. Minh, a psychology student, kept a record of how much time she spent studying for each of her 20-point psychology quizzes and her score on each quiz.

Hours Spent Studying	0.50	0.75	1.00	1.25	1.50	1.50	1.75	2.00
Quiz Score	10	12	15	16	18	19	19	20

a. Write each paired data as an ordered pair of the form (hours spent studying, quiz score).

b. In your own words, write the meaning of the ordered pair (1.25, 16).

c. Create a scatter diagram of the paired data. Be sure to label the axes appropriately.

d. What might Minh conclude from the scatter diagram?

Minh's Chart for Psychology

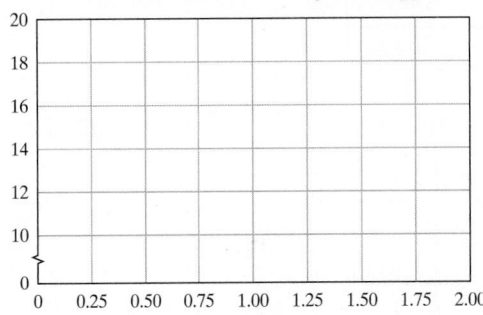

20. A local lumberyard uses quantity pricing. The table shows the price per board for different amounts of lumber purchased.

Price per Board (in dollars)	Number of Boards Purchased
8.00	1
7.50	10
6.50	25
5.00	50
2.00	100

a. Write each paired data as an ordered pair of the form (price per board, number of boards purchased).

b. In your own words, write the meaning of the ordered pair (2.00, 100).

c. Create a scatter diagram of the paired data. Be sure to label the axes appropriately.

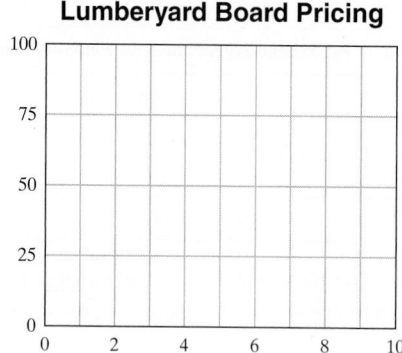

Lumberyard Board Pricing

d. What trend in the paired data does the scatter diagram show?

Objective **C** *Complete each ordered pair so that it is a solution of the given linear equation. See Example 3.*

21. $x - 4y = 4$; (, −2), (4,)

22. $x - 5y = -1$; (, −2), (4,)

23. $y = \dfrac{1}{4}x - 3$; (−8,), (, 1)

24. $y = \dfrac{1}{5}x - 2$; (−10,), (, 1)

Complete the table of ordered pairs for each linear equation. See Examples 4 and 5.

25. $y = -7x$

x	y
0	
−1	
	2

26. $y = -9x$

x	y
	0
−3	
	2

27. $y = -x + 2$

x	y
0	
	0
−3	

28. $x = -y + 4$

x	y
	0
0	
	−3

29. $y = \dfrac{1}{2}x$

x	y
0	
−6	
	1

30. $y = \dfrac{1}{3}x$

x	y
0	
−6	
	1

31. $x + 3y = 6$

x	y
0	
	0
	1

32. $2x + y = 4$

x	y
0	
	0
	2

33. $y = 2x - 12$

x	y
0	
	−2
3	

34. $y = 5x + 10$

x	y
	0
	5
0	

35. $2x + 7y = 5$

x	y
0	
	0
	1

36. $x - 6y = 3$

x	y
0	
1	
	-1

Objectives **A** **B** **C** **Mixed Practice** *Complete the table of ordered pairs for each equation. Then plot the ordered pair solutions. See Examples 1 through 5.*

37. $x = -5y$

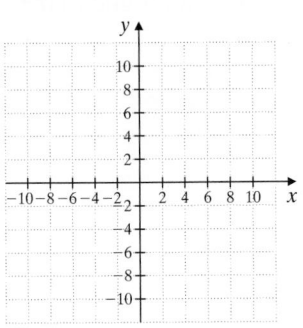

x	y
	0
	1
10	

38. $y = -3x$

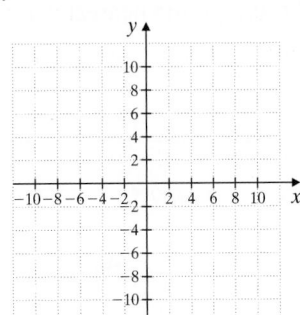

x	y
0	
-2	
	9

39. $y = \dfrac{1}{3}x + 2$

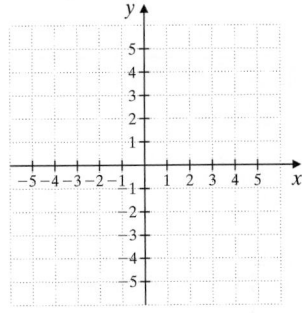

x	y
0	
-3	
	0

40. $y = \dfrac{1}{2}x + 3$

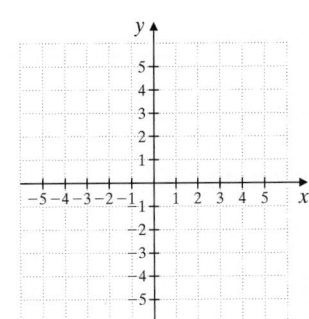

x	y
0	
-4	
	0

Solve. See Example 6.

41. The cost in dollars y of producing x computer desks is given by $y = 80x + 5000$.

   a. Complete the table.

x	100	200	300
y			

   b. Find the number of computer desks that can be produced for $8600. (*Hint:* Find x when $y = 8600$.)

42. The hourly wage y of an employee at a certain production company is given by $y = 0.25x + 9$ where x is the number of units produced by the employee in an hour.

   a. Complete the table.

x	0	1	5	10
y				

   b. Find the number of units that an employee must produce each hour to earn an hourly wage of $12.25. (*Hint:* Find x when $y = 12.25$.)

43. The percent y of recorded music sales that were in cassette format from 1998 through 2003 is given by $y = -2.4x + 13$. In the equation, x represents the number of years after 1998. (*Source:* Recording Industry Association of America)

   a. Complete the table.

x	1	3	5
y			

   b. Find the year in which approximately 3% of recorded music sales were cassettes. (*Hint:* Find x when $y = 3$ and round to the nearest whole number.)

44. The amount y of land occupied by farms in the United States (in million acres) from 1993 through 2003 is given by $y = -3.2x + 968$. In the equation, x represents the number of years after 1993. (*Source:* National Agricultural Statistics Service)

   a. Complete the table.

x	4	7	10
y			

   b. Find the year in which there were approximately 943 million acres of land occupied by farms. (*Hint:* Find x when $y = 943$ and round to the nearest whole number.)

Review

Solve each equation for y. See Section 9.5.

45. $x + y = 5$

46. $x - y = 3$

47. $2x + 4y = 5$

48. $5x + 2y = 7$

49. $10x = -5y$

50. $4y = -8x$

Concept Extensions

Answer each exercise with true or false.

51. Point $(-1, 5)$ lies in quadrant IV.

52. Point $(3, 0)$ lies on the y-axis.

53. For the point $\left(-\frac{1}{2}, 1.5\right)$, the first value, $-\frac{1}{2}$, is the x-coordinate and the second value, 1.5, is the y-coordinate.

54. The ordered pair $\left(2, \frac{2}{3}\right)$ is a solution of $2x - 3y = 6$.

For Exercises 55 through 59, fill in each blank with "0," "positive," or "negative." For Exercises 60 and 61, fill in each blank with "x" or "y."

	Point	Location
55.	(,)	quadrant III
56.	(,)	quadrant I
57.	(,)	quadrant IV
58.	(,)	quadrant II
59.	(,)	origin
60.	(number, 0)	-axis
61.	(0, number)	-axis

62. Give an example of an ordered pair whose location is in (or on)

   a. quadrant I   **b.** quadrant II   **c.** quadrant III

   d. quadrant IV   **e.** x-axis   **f.** y-axis

Solve. See the Concept Check in this section.

63. Is the graph of $(3, 0)$ in the same location as the graph of $(0, 3)$? Explain why or why not.

64. Give the coordinates of a point such that if the coordinates are reversed, their location is the same.

65. In general, what points can have coordinates reversed and still have the same location?

66. In your own words, describe how to plot or graph an ordered pair of numbers.

Write an ordered pair for each point described.

67. Point C is four units to the right of the y-axis and seven units below the x-axis.

68. Point D is three units to the left of the origin.

69. Find the perimeter of the rectangle whose vertices are the points with coordinates $(-1, 5)$, $(3, 5)$, $(3, -4)$, and $(-1, -4)$.

70. Find the area of the rectangle whose vertices are the points with coordinates $(5, 2)$, $(5, -6)$, $(0, -6)$, and $(0, 2)$.

The scatter diagram below shows Walt Disney Company's annual revenues. The horizontal axis represents the number of years after 1999.

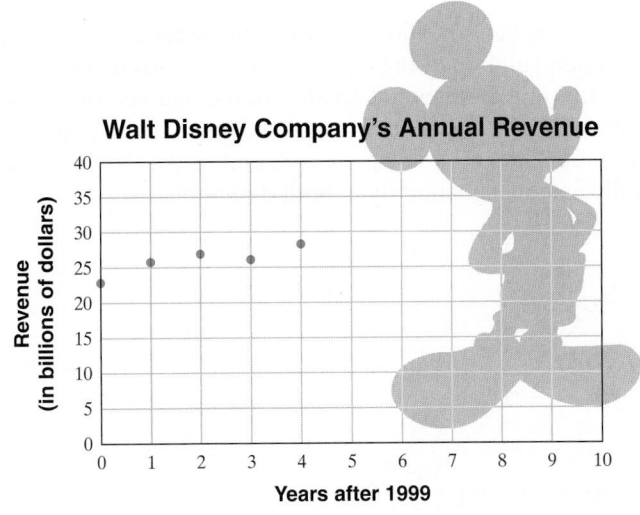

Walt Disney Company's Annual Revenue

71. Estimate the annual revenues for years 1, 2, 3, and 4.

72. Use a straight edge or ruler and this scatter diagram to predict Disney's revenue in the year 2008.

73. Discuss any similarities in the graphs of the ordered pair solutions for Exercises 37–40.

📖 **STUDY SKILLS BUILDER**

Are You Satisfied with Your Performance in This Course Thus Far?

To see if there is room for improvement, answer these questions:

1. Am I attending all classes and arriving on time?

2. Am I working and checking my homework assignments on time?

3. Am I getting help (from my instructor or a campus learning resource lab) when I need it?

4. In addition to my instructor, am I using the text supplements that might help me?

5. Am I satisfied with my performance on quizzes and exams?

If you answered no to any of these questions, read or reread Section 1.1 for suggestions in these areas. Also, you might want to contact your instructor for additional feedback.

10.2 GRAPHING LINEAR EQUATIONS

In the previous section, we found that equations in two variables may have more than one solution. For example, both $(2, 2)$ and $(0, 4)$ are solutions of the equation $x + y = 4$. In fact, this equation has an infinite number of solutions. Other solutions include $(-2, 6)$, $(4, 0)$, and $(6, -2)$. Notice the pattern that appears in the graph of these solutions.

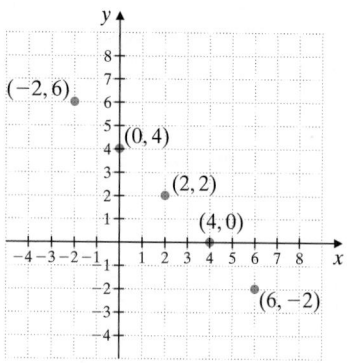

These solutions all appear to lie on the same line, as seen in the second graph. It can be shown that every ordered pair solution of the equation corresponds to a point on this line, and every point on this line corresponds to an ordered pair solution. Thus, we say that this line is the **graph of the equation** $x + y = 4$. Notice that we can only show a part of a line on a graph. The arrowheads on each end of the line below remind us that the line actually extends indefinitely in both directions.

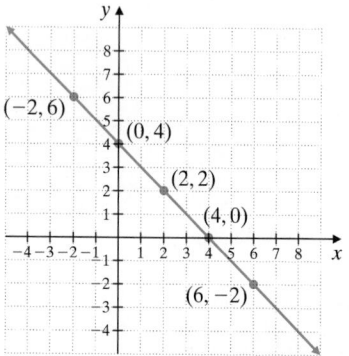

The equation $x + y = 4$ is called a *linear equation in two variables* and *the graph of every linear equation in two variables is a straight line.*

Linear Equation in Two Variables

A **linear equation in two variables** is an equation that can be written in the form

$$Ax + By = C$$

where A, B, and C are real numbers and A and B are not both 0. This form is called **standard form. The graph of a linear equation in two variables is a straight line.**

A linear equation in two variables may be written in many forms. Standard form, $Ax + By = C$, is just one of many of these forms.

Following are examples of linear equations in two variables.

$$2x + y = 8 \qquad -2x = 7y \qquad y = \frac{1}{3}x + 2 \qquad y = 7$$
(Standard Form)

Objective A Graphing Linear Equations

From geometry, we know that a straight line is determined by just two points. Thus, to graph a linear equation in two variables we need to find just two of its infinitely many solutions. Once we do so, we plot the solution points and draw the line connecting the points. Usually, we find a third solution as well, as a check.

EXAMPLE 1 Graph the linear equation $2x + y = 5$.

Solution: To graph this equation, we find three ordered pair solutions of $2x + y = 5$. To do this, we choose a value for one variable, x or y, and solve for the other variable. For example, if we let $x = 1$, then $2x + y = 5$ becomes

$$2x + y = 5$$
$$2(1) + y = 5 \quad \text{Replace } x \text{ with } 1.$$
$$2 + y = 5 \quad \text{Multiply.}$$
$$y = 3 \quad \text{Subtract 2 from both sides.}$$

Since $y = 3$ when $x = 1$, the ordered pair $(1, 3)$ is a solution of $2x + y = 5$. Next, we let $x = 0$.

$$2x + y = 5$$
$$2(0) + y = 5 \quad \text{Replace } x \text{ with } 0.$$
$$0 + y = 5$$
$$y = 5$$

The ordered pair $(0, 5)$ is a second solution.

The two solutions found so far allow us to draw the straight line that is the graph of all solutions of $2x + y = 5$. However, we will find a third ordered pair as a check. Let $y = -1$.

$$2x + y = 5$$
$$2x + (-1) = 5 \quad \text{Replace } y \text{ with } -1.$$
$$2x - 1 = 5$$
$$2x = 6 \quad \text{Add 1 to both sides.}$$
$$x = 3 \quad \text{Divide both sides by 2.}$$

The third solution is $(3, -1)$. These ordered pair solutions are listed in the table and plotted on the coordinate plane. The graph of $2x + y = 5$ is the line through the three points.

x	y
1	3
0	5
3	-1

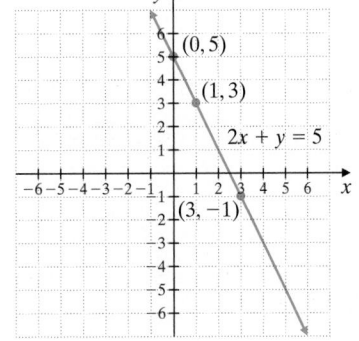

■ **Work Practice Problem 1**

PRACTICE PROBLEM 1

Graph the linear equation $x + 3y = 6$.

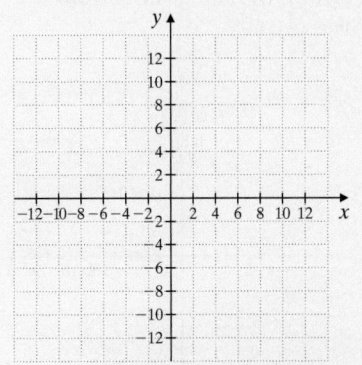

Helpful Hint

All three points should fall on the same straight line. If not, check your ordered pair solutions for a mistake.

Answer

1.

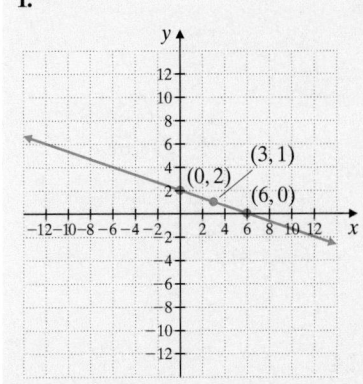

PRACTICE PROBLEM 2

Graph the linear equation $-2x + 4y = 8$.

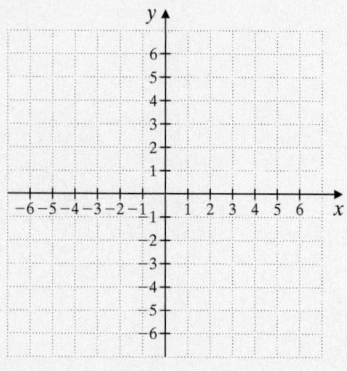

PRACTICE PROBLEM 3

Graph the linear equation $y = 2x$.

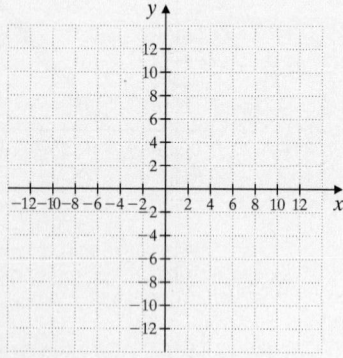

Answers

2.

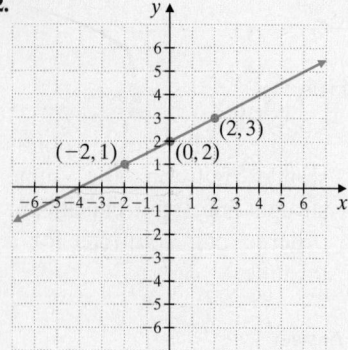

3.

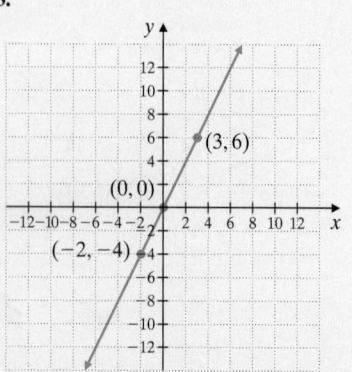

EXAMPLE 2 Graph the linear equation $-5x + 3y = 15$.

Solution: We find three ordered pair solutions of $-5x + 3y = 15$.

Let $x = 0$.	Let $y = 0$.	Let $x = -2$.
$-5x + 3y = 15$	$-5x + 3y = 15$	$-5x + 3y = 15$
$-5 \cdot 0 + 3y = 15$	$-5x + 3 \cdot 0 = 15$	$-5 \cdot -2 + 3y = 15$
$0 + 3y = 15$	$-5x + 0 = 15$	$10 + 3y = 15$
$3y = 15$	$-5x = 15$	$3y = 5$
$y = 5$	$x = -3$	$y = \frac{5}{3}$ or $1\frac{2}{3}$

The ordered pairs are $(0, 5)$, $(-3, 0)$, and $\left(-2, 1\frac{2}{3}\right)$. The graph of $-5x + 3y = 15$ is the line through the three points.

x	y
0	5
-3	0
-2	$1\frac{2}{3}$

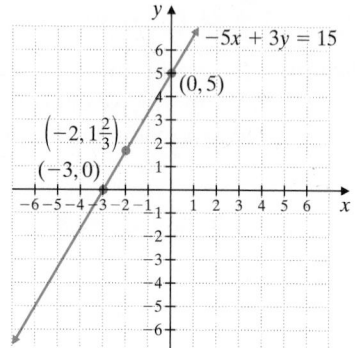

■ **Work Practice Problem 2**

EXAMPLE 3 Graph the linear equation $y = 3x$.

Solution: We find three ordered pair solutions. Since this equation is solved for y, we'll choose three x values.

If $x = 2$, $y = 3 \cdot 2 = 6$.

If $x = 0$, $y = 3 \cdot 0 = 0$.

If $x = -1$, $y = 3 \cdot -1 = -3$.

Next, we plot the ordered pair solutions and draw a line through the plotted points. The line is the graph of $y = 3x$.

Think about the following for a moment: A line is made up of an infinite number of points. Every point on the line defined by $y = 3x$ represents an ordered pair solution of the equation and every ordered pair solution is a point on this line.

x	y
2	6
0	0
-1	-3

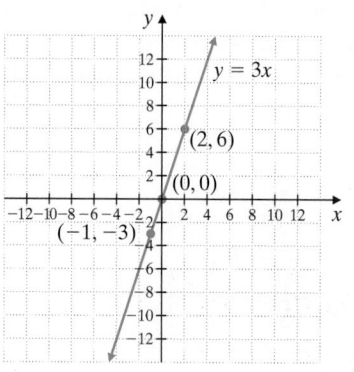

■ **Work Practice Problem 3**

Helpful Hint

When graphing a linear equation in two variables, if it is

- solved for y, it may be easier to find ordered-pair solutions by choosing x-values. If it is
- solved for x, it may be easier to find ordered-pair solutions by choosing y-values.

EXAMPLE 4 Graph the linear equation $y = -\dfrac{1}{3}x + 2$.

Solution: We find three ordered pair solutions, plot the solutions, and draw a line through the plotted solutions. To avoid fractions, we'll choose x values that are multiples of 3 to substitute into the equation.

If $x = 6$, then $y = -\dfrac{1}{3}\cdot 6 + 2 = -2 + 2 = 0$

If $x = 0$, then $y = -\dfrac{1}{3}\cdot 0 + 2 = 0 + 2 = 2$

If $x = -3$, then $y = -\dfrac{1}{3}\cdot -3 + 2 = 1 + 2 = 3$

x	y
6	0
0	2
-3	3

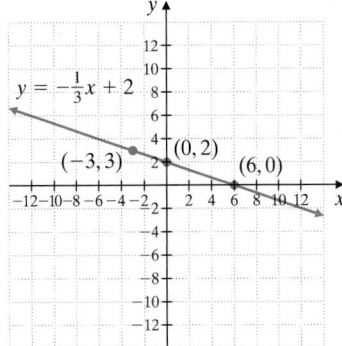

Work Practice Problem 4

Let's take a moment and compare the graphs in Examples 3 and 4. The graph of $y = 3x$ tilts upward (as we follow the line from left to right) and the graph of $y = -\dfrac{1}{3}x + 2$ tilts downward (as we follow the line from left to right). We will learn more about the tilt, or slope, of a line in Section 10.4.

EXAMPLE 5 Graph the linear equation $y = -2$.

Solution: The equation $y = -2$ can be written in standard form as $0x + y = -2$. No matter what value we replace x with, y is always -2.

x	y
0	-2
3	-2
-2	-2

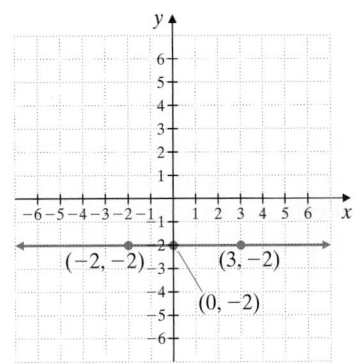

Notice that the graph of $y = -2$ is a horizontal line.

Work Practice Problem 5

Linear equations are often used to model real data, as seen in the next example.

PRACTICE PROBLEM 4

Graph the linear equation $y = -\dfrac{1}{2}x + 4$.

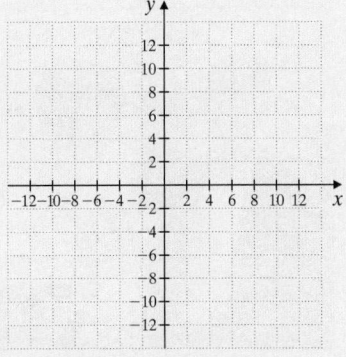

PRACTICE PROBLEM 5

Graph the linear equation $x = 3$.

Answers

4.

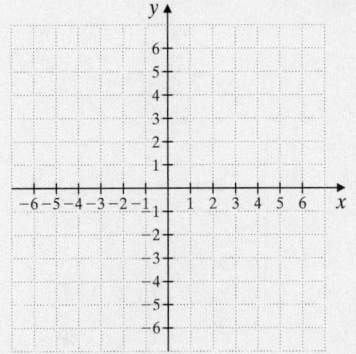

5.

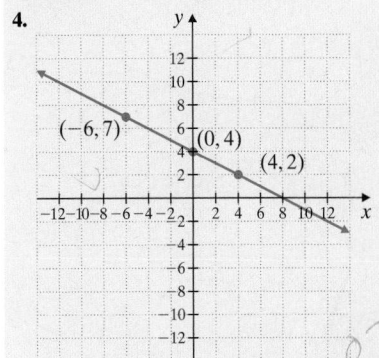

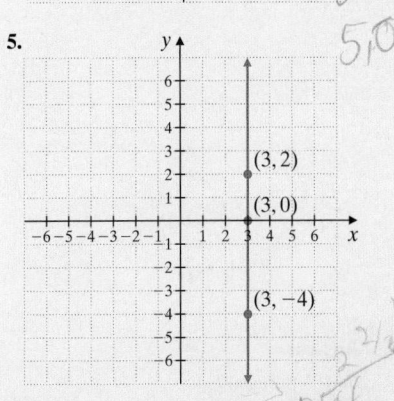

PRACTICE PROBLEM 6

Use the graph in Example 6 to predict the number of medical assistants in 2004.

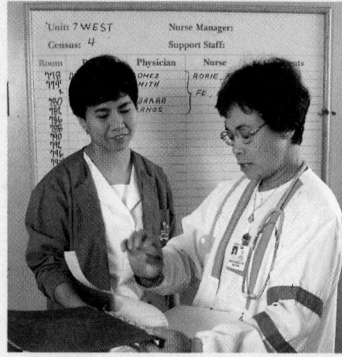

EXAMPLE 6 **Estimating the Number of Medical Assistants**

One of the occupations expected to have the most growth in the next few years is medical assistant. The number of people y (in thousands) employed as medical assistants in the United States can be estimated by the linear equation $y = 31.8x + 180$, where x is the number of years after the year 1995. (*Source:* Based on data from the Bureau of Labor Statistics)

a. Graph the equation.

b. Use the graph to predict the number of medical assistants in the year 2010.

Solution:

a. To graph $y = 31.8x + 180$, choose x-values and substitute in the equation.

If $x = 0$, then $y = 31.8(0) + 180 = 180$.

If $x = 2$, then $y = 31.8(2) + 180 = 243.6$.

If $x = 7$, then $y = 31.8(7) + 180 = 402.6$.

x	y
0	180
2	243.6
7	402.6

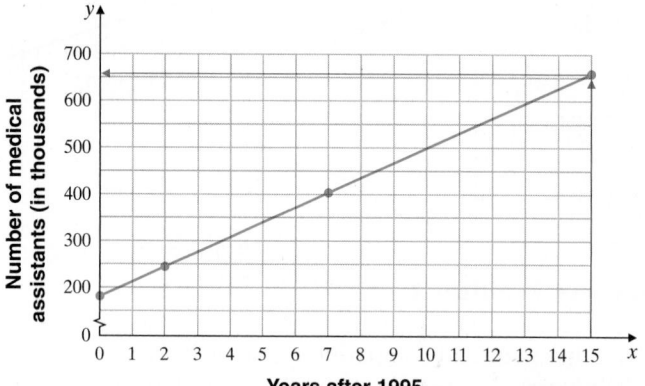

b. To use the graph to *predict* the number of medical assistants in the year 2010, we need to find the y-coordinate that corresponds to $x = 15$. (15 years after 1995 is the year 2010.) To do so, find 15 on the x-axis. Move vertically upward to the graphed line and then horizontally to the left. We approximate the number on the y-axis to be 655. Thus in the year 2010, we predict that there will be 655 thousand medical assistants. (The actual value, using 15 for x, is 657.)

▣ **Work Practice Problem 6**

> **Helpful Hint**
>
> Make sure you understand that models are mathematical approximations of the data for the known years. (For example, see the model in Example 6.) Any number of unknown factors can affect future years, so be cautious when using models to predict.

Answer

6. 465 thousand

▣ CALCULATOR EXPLORATIONS Graphing

In this section, we begin an optional study of graphing calculators and graphing software packages for computers. These graphers use the same point plotting technique that was introduced in this section. The advantage of this graphing technology is, of course, that graphing calculators and computers can find and plot ordered pair solutions much faster than we can. Note, however, that the features described in these boxes may not be available on all graphing calculators.

The rectangular screen where a portion of the rectangular coordinate system is displayed is called a **window.** We call it a **standard window** for graphing when both the x- and y-axes show coordinates between -10 and 10. This information is often displayed in the window menu on a graphing calculator as follows.

Xmin $= -10$
Xmax $= 10$
 Xscl $= 1$ The scale on the x-axis is one unit per tick mark.
Ymin $= -10$
Ymax $= 10$
 Yscl $= 1$ The scale on the y-axis is one unit per tick mark.

To use a graphing calculator to graph the equation $y = 2x + 3$, press the $\boxed{Y=}$ key and enter the keystrokes $\boxed{2}\ \boxed{x}\ \boxed{+}\ \boxed{3}$. The top row should now read $Y_1 = 2x + 3$. Next press the $\boxed{GRAPH}$ key, and the display should look like this:

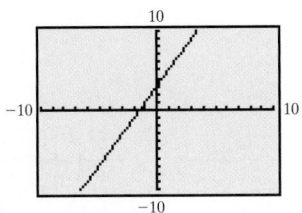

Graph the following linear equations. (Unless otherwise stated, use a standard window when graphing.)

1. $y = -3x + 7$

2. $y = -x + 5$

3. $y = 2.5x - 7.9$

4. $y = -1.3x + 5.2$

5. $y = -\dfrac{3}{10}x + \dfrac{32}{5}$

6. $y = \dfrac{2}{9}x - \dfrac{22}{3}$

Objective Ⓐ *For each equation, find three ordered pair solutions by completing the table. Then use the ordered pairs to graph the equation. See Examples 1 through 5.*

1. $x - y = 6$

x	y
	0
4	
	-1

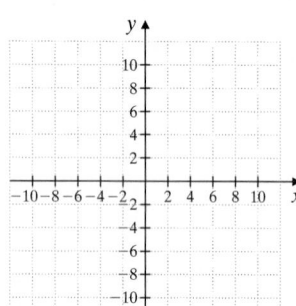

2. $x - y = 4$

x	y
0	
	2
-1	

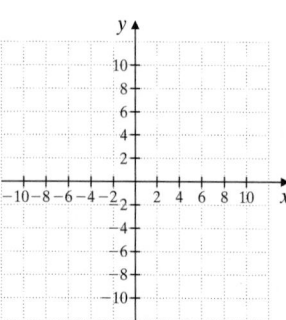

3. $y = -4x$

x	y
1	
0	
-1	

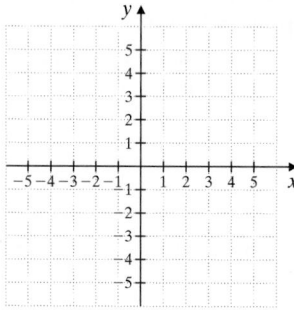

4. $y = -5x$

x	y
1	
0	
-1	

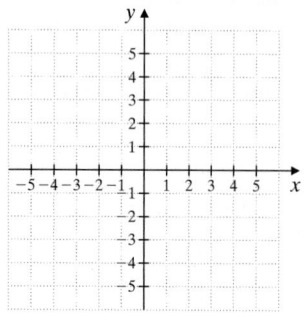

5. $y = \dfrac{1}{3}x$

x	y
0	
6	
-3	

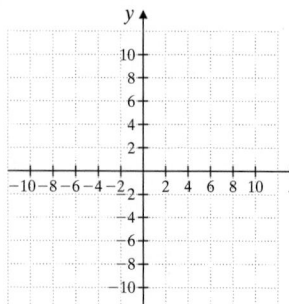

6. $y = \dfrac{1}{2}x$

x	y
0	
-4	
2	

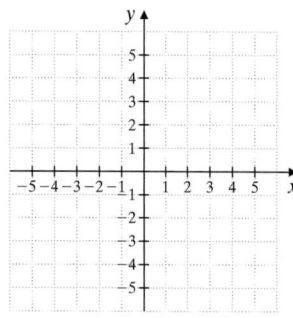

7. $y = -4x + 3$

x	y
0	
1	
2	

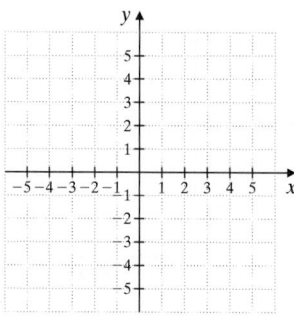

8. $y = -5x + 2$

x	y
0	
1	
2	

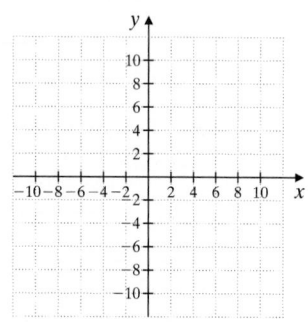

Graph each linear equation. See Examples 1 through 5.

9. $x + y = 1$

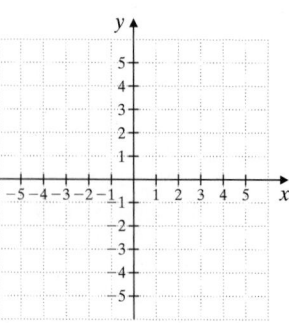

10. $x + y = 7$

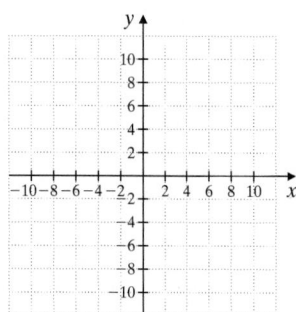

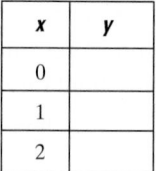 **11.** $x - y = -2$

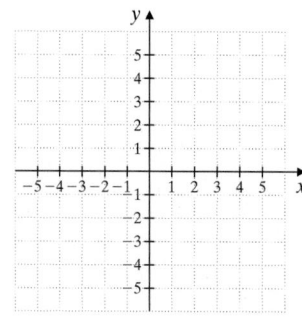

12. $-x + y = 6$

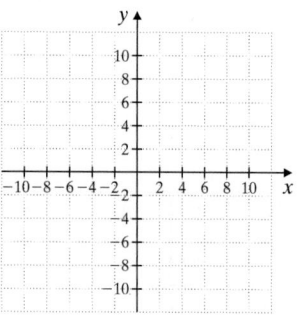

730

13. $x - 2y = 6$

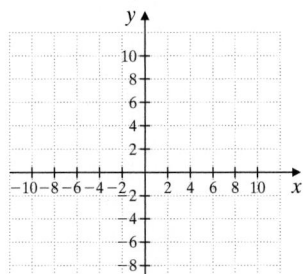

14. $-x + 5y = 5$

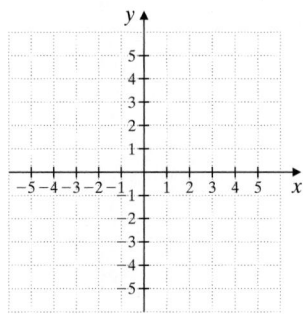

15. $y = 6x + 3$

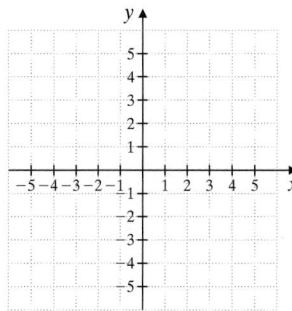

16. $y = -2x + 7$

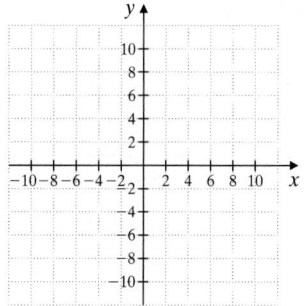

17. $x = -4$

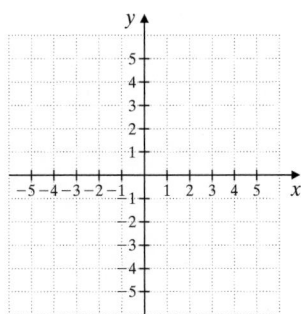

18. $y = 5$

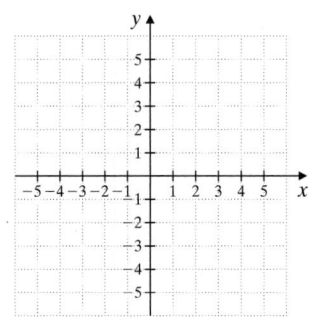

19. $y = 3$

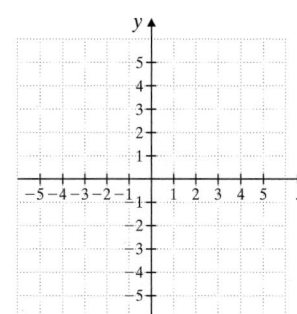

20. $x = -1$

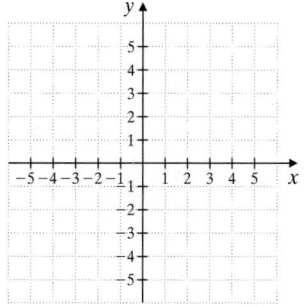

21. $y = x$

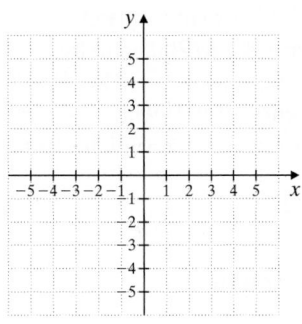

22. $y = -x$

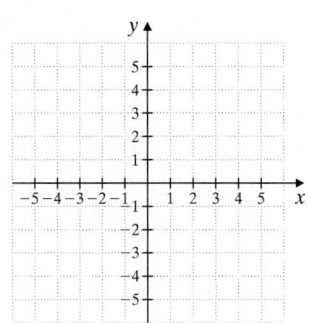

23. $y = 5x$

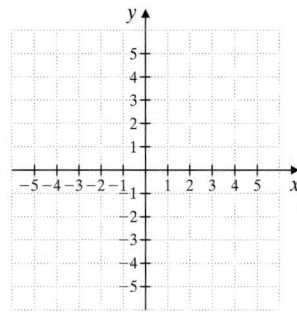

24. $y = 4x$

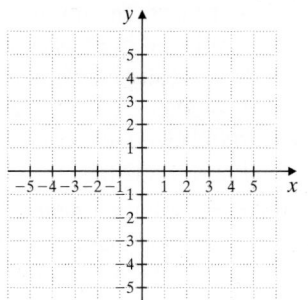

25. $x + 3y = 9$

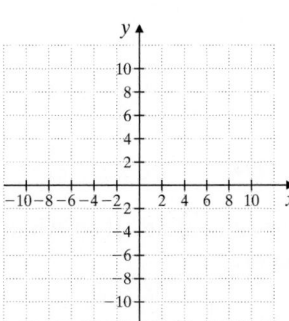

26. $2x + y = 2$

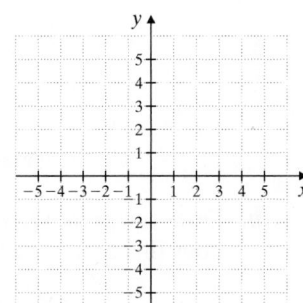

27. $y = \dfrac{1}{2}x - 1$

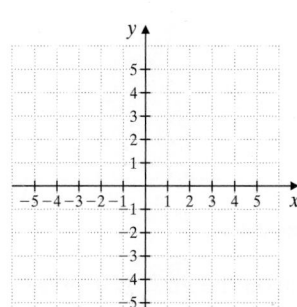

28. $y = \dfrac{1}{4}x + 3$

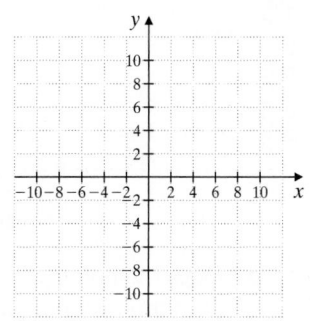

29. $3x - 2y = 12$

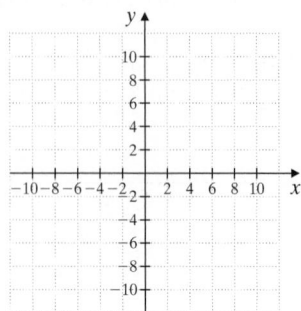

30. $2x - 7y = 14$

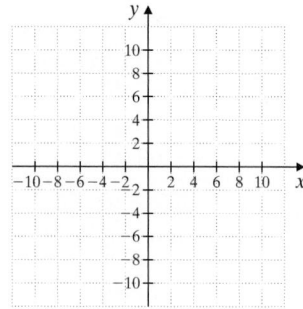

31. $y = -3.5x + 4$

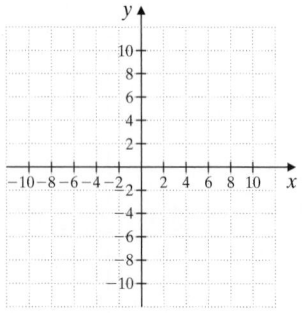

32. $y = -1.5x - 3$

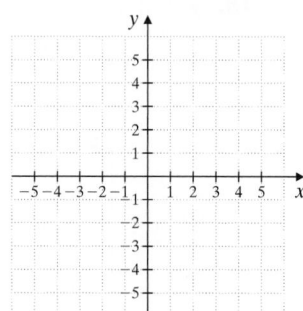

Solve. See Example 6.

33. One of the top five occupations in terms of growth in the next few years is expected to be physician's assistants. The number of people y (in hundreds) employed as physician's assistants in the United States can be estimated by the linear equation $y = 31x + 630$ where x is the number of years after 2002. (*Source:* Based on data from the Bureau of Labor Statistics)

    a. Graph the linear equation. The break in the vertical axis means that the numbers between 0 and 600 have been skipped.

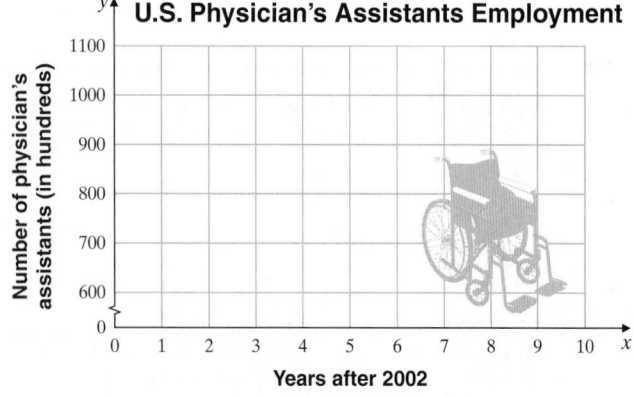

    b. Does the point $(6, 816)$ lie on the line? If so, what does this ordered pair mean?

34. Head Start is a comprehensive child development program serving young children in low-income families. The number of children y (in thousands) enrolled in Head Start from 1998 to 2003 can be approximated by the linear equation $y = 21x + 822$, where x is the number of years after 1998. (*Source:* Head Start Bureau, the Administration on Children, Youth and Families)

    a. Graph the linear equation.

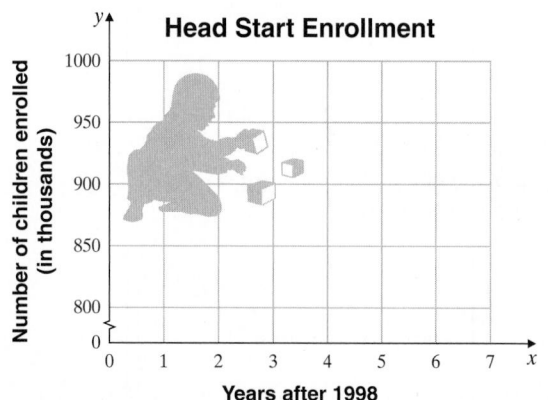

    b. Does the point $(3, 885)$ lie on the line? If so, what does this ordered pair mean?

35. The number of U.S. households y in millions that have at least one television set can be estimated by the linear equation $y = 1.5x + 99$ where x is the number of years after 1999. (*Source:* Nielsen Media Research)

a. Graph the linear equation.

U.S. Television Households

y-axis: TV households (in millions) — 108, 106, 104, 102, 100, 98

x-axis: Years after 1999 — 0, 1, 2, 3, 4, 5, 6

b. Complete the ordered pair (5,).
c. Write a sentence explaining the meaning of the ordered pair found in part b.

36. The restaurant industry is busier than ever. The yearly revenue for restaurants in the United States can be estimated by $y = 11.9x + 284$ where x is the number of years after 2001 and y is the revenue in billions of dollars. (*Source:* National Restaurant Assn.)

a. Graph the linear equation.

U.S. Restaurant Revenue

y-axis: Revenue (in billions of dollars) — 330, 320, 310, 300, 290, 280, 270

x-axis: Years after 2001 — 0, 1, 2, 3

b. Complete the ordered pair (3,).
c. Write a sentence explaining the meaning of the ordered pair found in part b.

Review

△ **37.** The coordinates of three vertices of a rectangle are $(-2, 5)$, $(4, 5)$, and $(-2, -1)$. Find the coordinates of the fourth vertex. See Section 10.1.

△ **38.** The coordinates of two vertices of a square are $(-3, -1)$ and $(2, -1)$. Find the coordinates of two pairs of points possible for the third and fourth vertices. See Section 10.1.

Complete each table. See Section 10.1.

39. $x - y = -3$

x	y
0	
	0

40. $y - x = 5$

x	y
0	
	0

41. $y = 2x$

x	y
0	
	0

42. $x = -3y$

x	y
0	
	0

Concept Extensions

Graph each pair of linear equations on the same set of axes. Discuss how the graphs are similar and how they are different.

43. $y = 5x$
$y = 5x + 4$

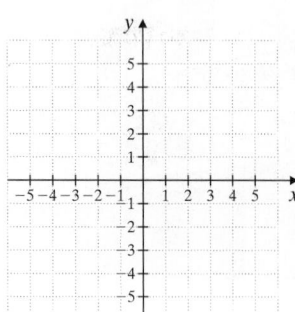

44. $y = 2x$
$y = 2x + 5$

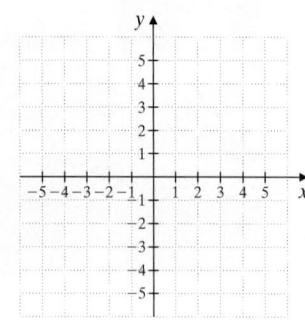

45. $y = -2x$
$y = -2x - 3$

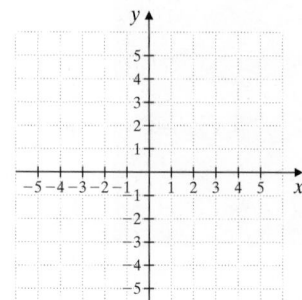

46. $y = x$
$y = x - 7$

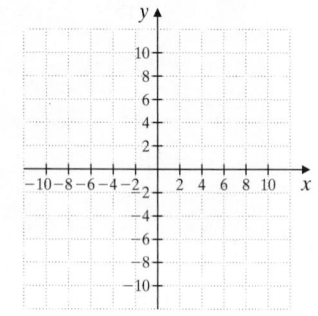

47. Graph the nonlinear equation $y = x^2$ by completing the table shown. Plot the ordered pairs and connect them with a smooth curve.

x	y
0	
1	
−1	
2	
−2	

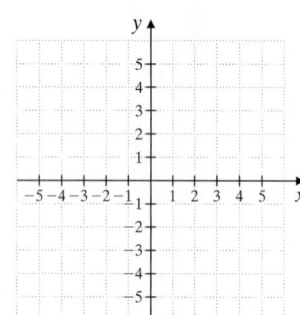

48. Graph the nonlinear equation $y = |x|$ by completing the table shown. Plot the ordered pairs and connect them. This curve is "V" shaped.

x	y
0	
1	
−1	
2	
−2	

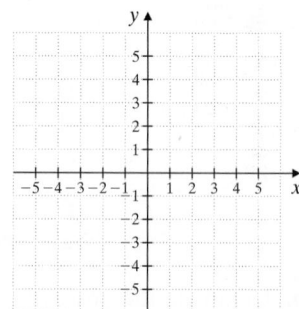

△ **49.** The perimeter of the trapezoid below is 22 centimeters. Write a linear equation in two variables for the perimeter. Find y if x is 3 centimeters.

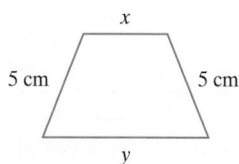

5 cm   5 cm

△ **50.** The perimeter of the rectangle below is 50 miles. Write a linear equation in two variables for the perimeter. Use this equation to find x when y is 20.

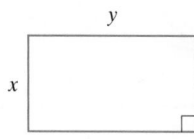

51. If (a, b) is an ordered pair solution of $x + y = 5$, is (b, a) also a solution? Explain why or why not.

10.3 INTERCEPTS

Objectives

A Identify Intercepts of a Graph.

B Graph a Linear Equation by Finding and Plotting Intercept Points.

C Identify and Graph Vertical and Horizontal Lines.

Objective **A** Identifying Intercepts

The graph of $y = 4x - 8$ is shown below. Notice that this graph crosses the y-axis at the point $(0, -8)$. This point is called the **y-intercept.** Likewise the graph crosses the x-axis at $(2, 0)$. This point is called the **x-intercept.**

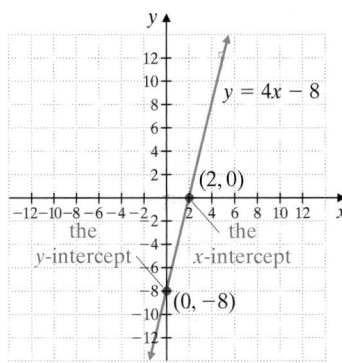

The intercepts are $(2, 0)$ and $(0, -8)$.

Helpful Hint

If a graph crosses the x-axis at $(2, 0)$ and the y-axis at $(0, -8)$, then

$$\underbrace{(2, 0)}_{x\text{-intercept}} \qquad \underbrace{(0, -8)}_{y\text{-intercept}}$$

Notice that for the x-intercept, the y-value is 0 and for the y-intercept, the x-value is 0.

Note: Sometimes in mathematics, you may see just the number -8 stated as the y-intercept, and 2 stated as the x-intercept.

EXAMPLES Identify the x- and y-intercepts.

1.

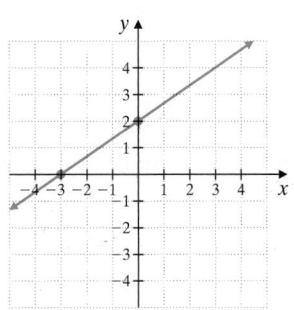

Solution:

x-intercept: $(-3, 0)$

y-intercept: $(0, 2)$

PRACTICE PROBLEM 1

Identify the x- and y-intercepts.

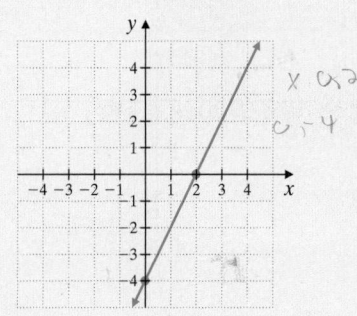

Answer

1. x-intercept: $(2, 0)$; y-intercept: $(0, -4)$

Continued on next page

735

PRACTICE PROBLEMS 2–3

Identify the *x*- and *y*-intercepts.

2.

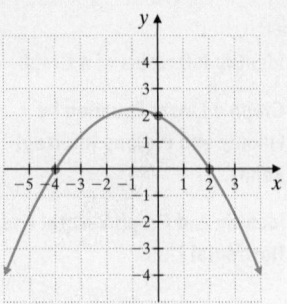

3.

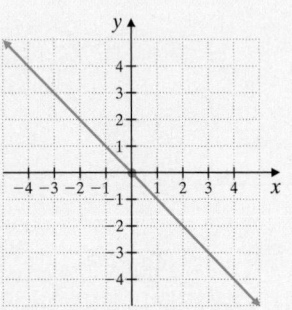

2.

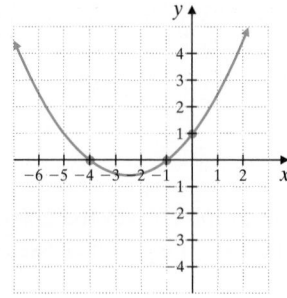

Solution:

x-intercepts: $(-4, 0)$, $(-1, 0)$

y-intercept: $(0, 1)$

3.

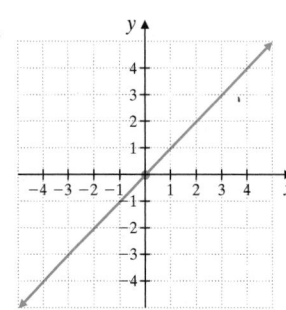

> **Helpful Hint**
> Notice that any time $(0, 0)$ is a point of a graph, then it is an *x*-intercept and a *y*-intercept. Why? It is the *only* point that lies on both axes.

Solution:

x-intercept: $(0, 0)$

y-intercept: $(0, 0)$

Here, the *x*- and *y*-intercept happen to be the same point.

⬛ **Work Practice Problems 1–3**

Objective **B** Finding and Plotting Intercepts

Given an equation of a line, we can usually find intercepts easily since one coordinate is 0.

To find the *x*-intercept of a line from its equation, let $y = 0$, since a point on the *x*-axis has a *y*-coordinate of 0. To find the *y*-intercept of a line from its equation, let $x = 0$, since a point on the *y*-axis has an *x*-coordinate of 0.

Finding x- and y-Intercepts

To find the *x*-intercept, let $y = 0$ and solve for *x*.
To find the *y*-intercept, let $x = 0$ and solve for *y*.

PRACTICE PROBLEM 4

Graph $2x - y = 4$ by finding and plotting its intercepts.

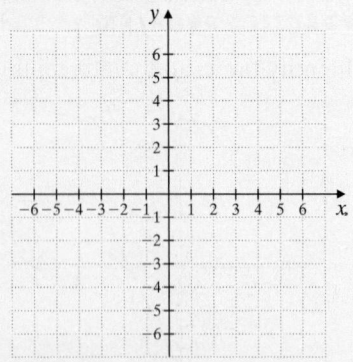

EXAMPLE 4 Graph $x - 3y = 6$ by finding and plotting its intercepts.

Solution: We let $y = 0$ to find the *x*-intercept and $x = 0$ to find the *y*-intercept.

Let $y = 0$.	Let $x = 0$.
$x - 3y = 6$	$x - 3y = 6$
$x - 3(0) = 6$	$0 - 3y = 6$
$x - 0 = 6$	$-3y = 6$
$x = 6$	$y = -2$

The *x*-intercept is $(6, 0)$ and the *y*-intercept is $(0, -2)$. We find a third ordered pair solution to check our work. If we let $y = -1$, then $x = 3$. We plot the points $(6, 0)$,

(0, −2), and (3, −1). The graph of $x - 3y = 6$ is the line drawn through these points as shown.

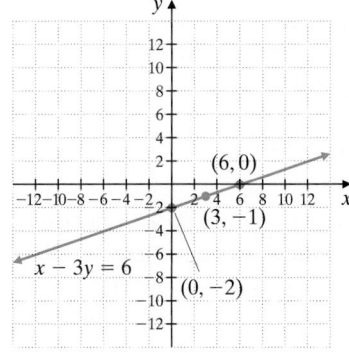

x	y
6	0
0	−2
3	−1

Work Practice Problem 4

EXAMPLE 5 Graph $x = -2y$ by finding and plotting its intercepts.

Solution: We let $y = 0$ to find the x-intercept and $x = 0$ to find the y-intercept.

Let $y = 0$.
$$x = -2y$$
$$x = -2(0)$$
$$x = 0$$

Let $x = 0$.
$$x = -2y$$
$$0 = -2y$$
$$0 = y$$

Both the x-intercept and y-intercept are $(0, 0)$. In other words, when $x = 0$, then $y = 0$, which gives the ordered pair $(0, 0)$. Also, when $y = 0$, then $x = 0$, which gives the same ordered pair $(0, 0)$. This happens when the graph passes through the origin. Since two points are needed to determine a line, we must find at least one more ordered pair that satisfies $x = -2y$. Since the equation is solved for x, we choose y-values so that there is no need to solve to find the corresponding x-value. We let $y = -1$ to find a second ordered pair solution and let $y = 1$ as a check point.

Let $y = -1$.
$$x = -2(-1)$$
$$x = 2 \qquad \text{Multiply.}$$
Let $y = 1$.
$$x = -2(1)$$
$$x = -2 \qquad \text{Multiply.}$$

The ordered pairs are $(0, 0)$, $(2, -1)$, and $(-2, 1)$. We plot these points to graph $x = -2y$.

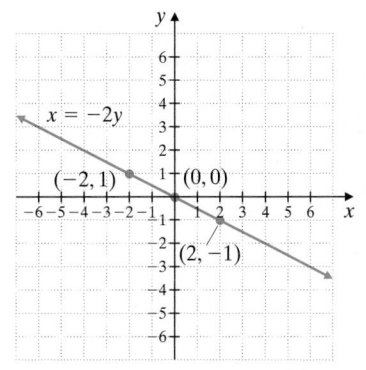

x	y
0	0
2	−1
−2	1

Work Practice Problem 5

PRACTICE PROBLEM 5

Graph $y = 3x$ by finding and plotting its intercepts.

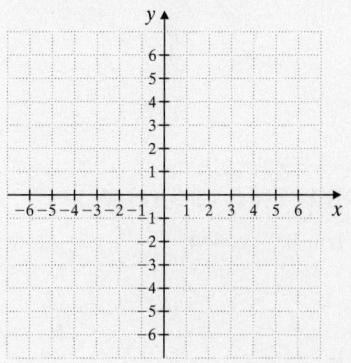

Answers

4.

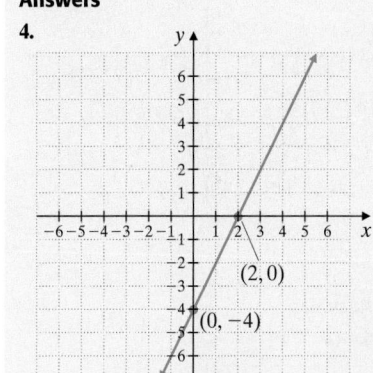

5.

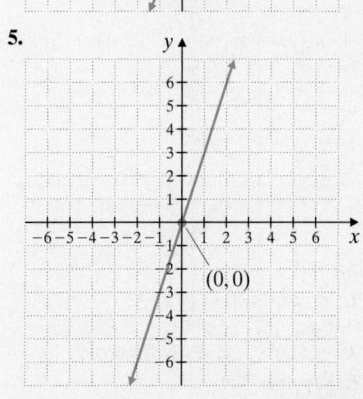

Objective C Graphing Vertical and Horizontal Lines

From Section 10.2, recall that the equation $x = 2$, for example, is a linear equation in two variables because it can be written in the form $x + 0y = 2$. The graph of this equation is a vertical line, as reviewed in the next example.

PRACTICE PROBLEM 6

Graph: $x = -3$

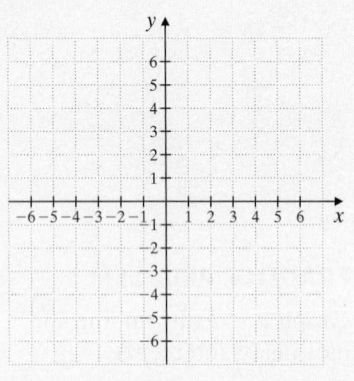

EXAMPLE 6 Graph: $x = 2$

Solution: The equation $x = 2$ can be written as $x + 0y = 2$. For any y-value chosen, notice that x is 2. No other value for x satisfies $x + 0y = 2$. Any ordered pair whose x-coordinate is 2 is a solution of $x + 0y = 2$. We will use the ordered pair solutions $(2, 3)$, $(2, 0)$, and $(2, -3)$ to graph $x = 2$.

x	y
2	3
2	0
2	-3

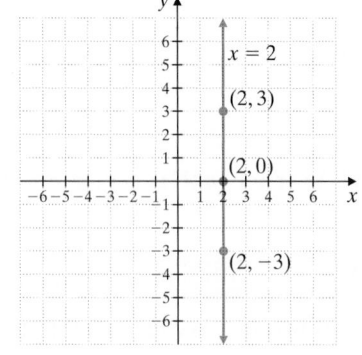

The graph is a vertical line with x-intercept 2. Note that this graph has no y-intercept because x is never 0.

🔲 **Work Practice Problem 6**

In general, we have the following.

Vertical Lines

The graph of $x = c$, where c is a real number, is a **vertical line** with x-intercept $(c, 0)$.

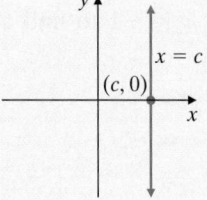

PRACTICE PROBLEM 7

Graph: $y = 4$

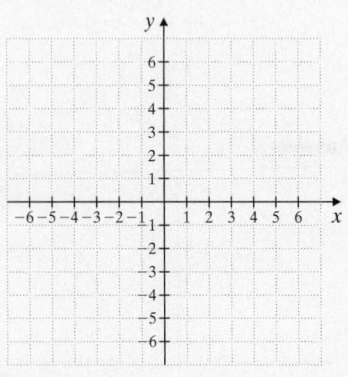

EXAMPLE 7 Graph: $y = -3$

Solution: The equation $y = -3$ can be written as $0x + y = -3$. For any x-value chosen, y is -3. If we choose 4, 1, and -2 as x-values, the ordered pair solutions are $(4, -3)$, $(1, -3)$, and $(-2, -3)$. We use these ordered pairs to graph $y = -3$. The graph is a horizontal line with y-intercept -3 and no x-intercept.

x	y
4	-3
1	-3
-2	-3

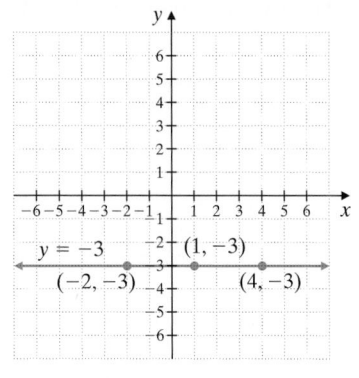

🔲 **Work Practice Problem 7**

Answers

6.

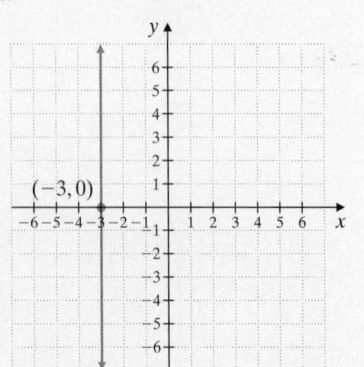

7. See page 739.

In general, we have the following.

Horizontal Lines

The graph of $y = c$, where c is a real number, is a **horizontal line** with y-intercept $(0, c)$.

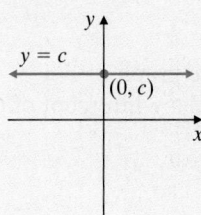

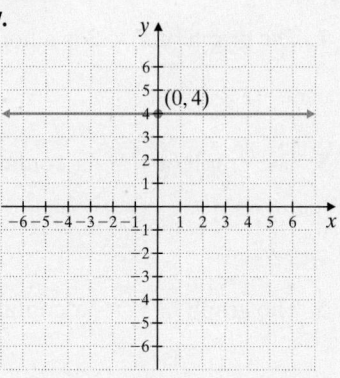

📟 CALCULATOR EXPLORATIONS Graphing

You may have noticed that to use the $\boxed{Y=}$ key on a graphing calculator to graph an equation, the equation must be solved for y. For example, to graph $2x + 3y = 7$, we solve this equation for y.

$$2x + 3y = 7$$

$$3y = -2x + 7 \qquad \text{Subtract } 2x \text{ from both sides.}$$

$$\frac{3y}{3} = -\frac{2x}{3} + \frac{7}{3} \qquad \text{Divide both sides by 3.}$$

$$y = -\frac{2}{3}x + \frac{7}{3} \qquad \text{Simplify.}$$

To graph $2x + 3y = 7$ or $y = -\dfrac{2}{3}x + \dfrac{7}{3}$, press the $\boxed{Y=}$ key and enter

$$Y_1 = -\frac{2}{3}x + \frac{7}{3}$$

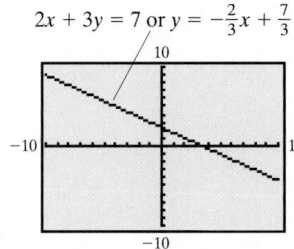

Graph each linear equation.

1. $x = 3.78y$

2. $-2.61y = x$

3. $3x + 7y = 21$

4. $-4x + 6y = 12$

5. $-2.2x + 6.8y = 15.5$

6. $5.9x - 0.8y = -10.4$

MentAl Math

Answer the following true or false.

1. The graph of $x = 2$ is a horizontal line.

2. All lines have an *x*-intercept *and* a *y*-intercept.

3. The graph of $y = 4x$ contains the point $(0, 0)$.

4. The graph of $x + y = 5$ has an *x*-intercept of $(5, 0)$ and a *y*-intercept of $(0, 5)$.

5. The graph of $y = 5x$ contains the point $(5, 1)$.

6. The graph of $y = 5$ is a horizontal line.

10.3 EXERCISE SET

FOR EXTRA HELP

Student Solutions Manual   PH Math/Tutor Center   CD/Video for Review   Math XL   MyMathLab
MathXL®   MyMathLab

Objective **A** *Identify the intercepts. See Examples 1 through 3.*

1.
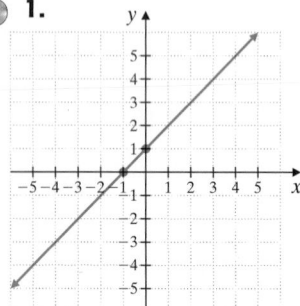

2.
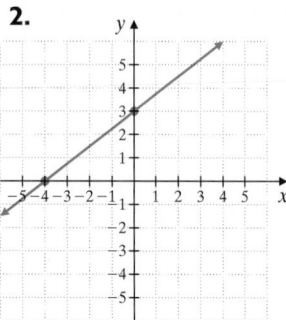

3.
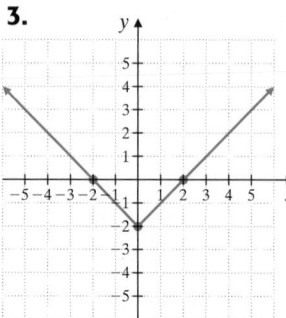

4.
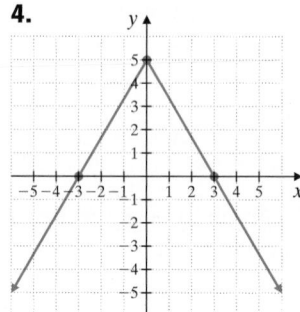

5.
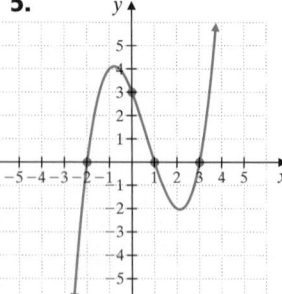

6.
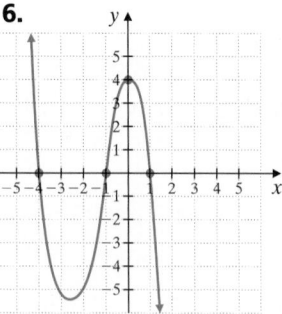

7.
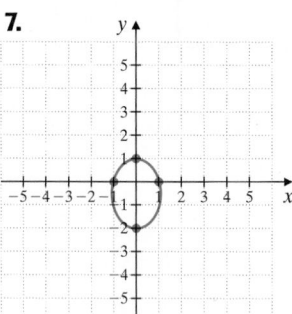

8.
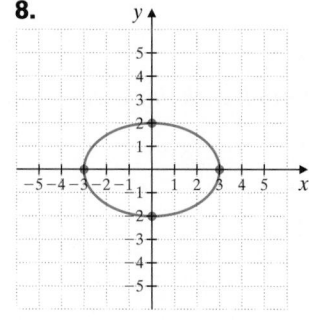

Objective **B** *Graph each linear equation by finding and plotting its intercepts. See Examples 4 and 5.*

9. $x - y = 3$

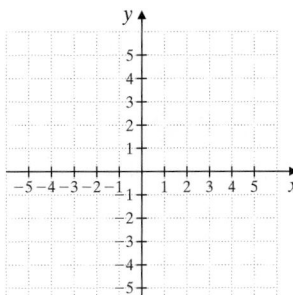

10. $x - y = -4$

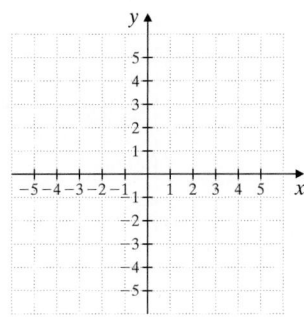

11. $x = 5y$

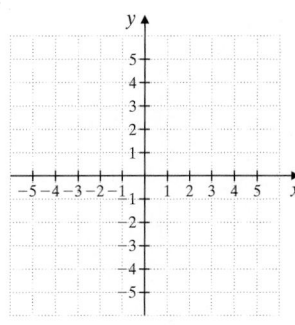

12. $x = 2y$

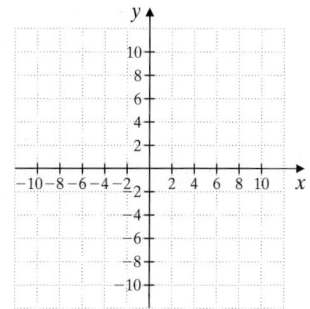

13. $-x + 2y = 6$

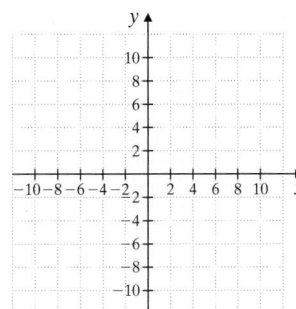

14. $x - 2y = -8$

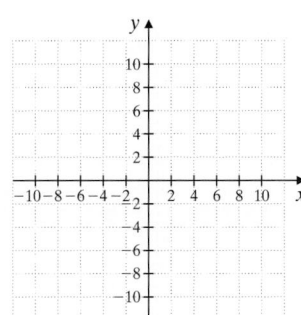

15. $2x - 4y = 8$

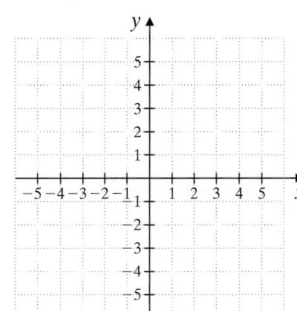

16. $2x + 3y = 6$

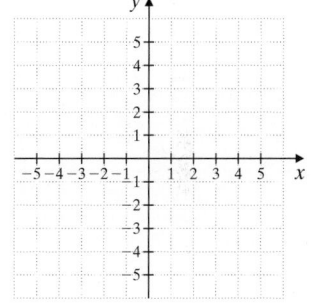

17. $2x - y = 0$

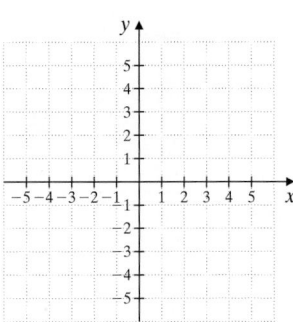

18. $-2x - y = 0$

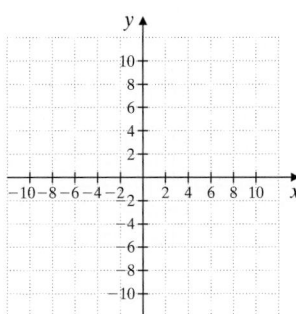

19. $y = 3x + 6$

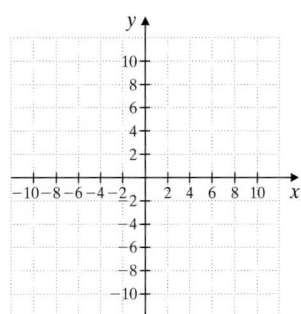

20. $y = 2x + 10$

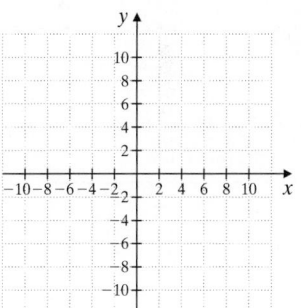

Objective **C** *Graph each linear equation. See Examples 6 and 7.*

21. $x = -1$

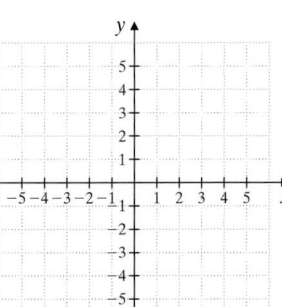

22. $y = 5$

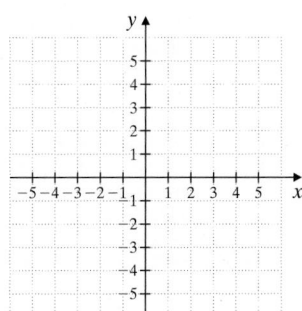

23. $y = 0$

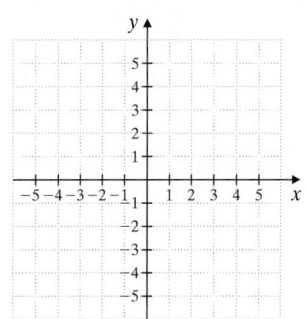

24. $x = 0$

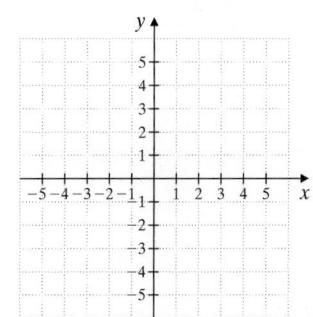

25. $y + 7 = 0$

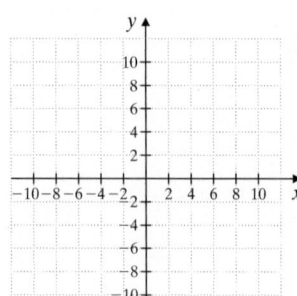

26. $x - 2 = 0$

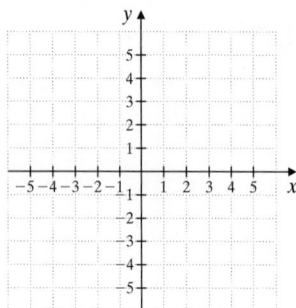

27. $x + 3 = 0$

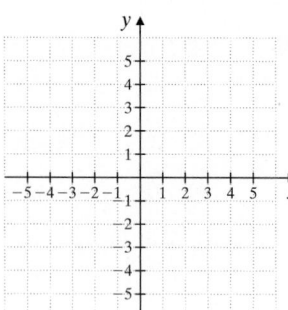

28. $y - 6 = 0$

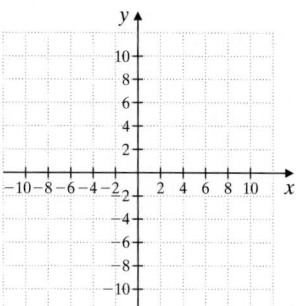

Objectives **B** **C** **Mixed Practice** *Graph each linear equation. See Examples 4 through 7.*

29. $x = y$

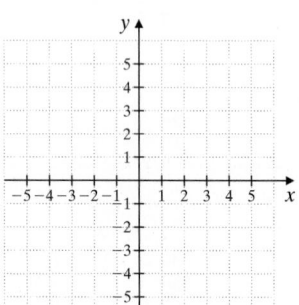

30. $x = -y$

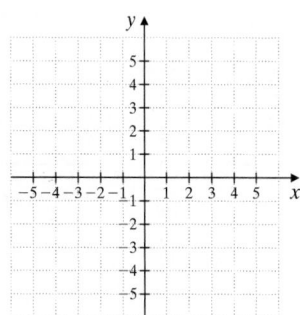

31. $x + 8y = 8$

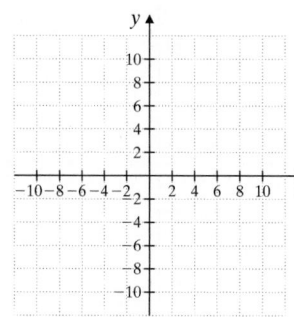

32. $x + 3y = 9$

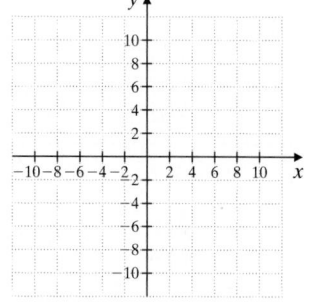

33. $5 = 6x - y$

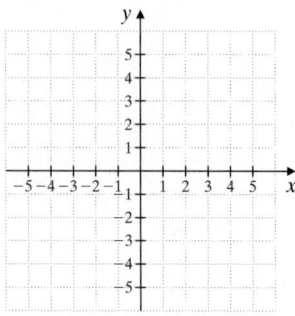

34. $4 = x - 3y$

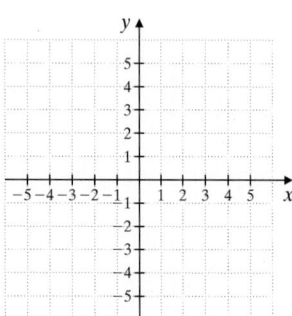

35. $-x + 10y = 11$

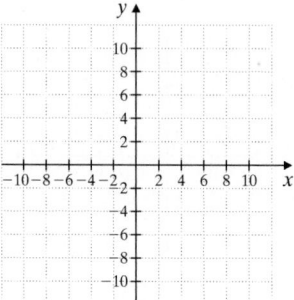

36. $-x + 9y = 10$

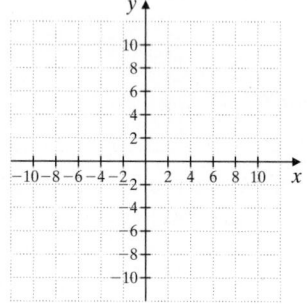

37. $x = -4\dfrac{1}{2}$

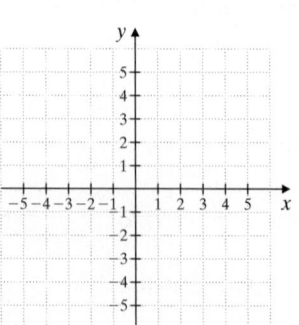

38. $x = -1\dfrac{3}{4}$

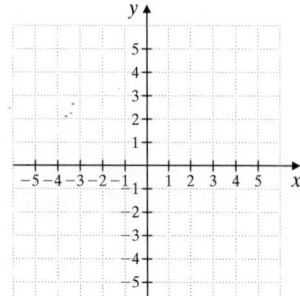

39. $y = 3\dfrac{1}{4}$

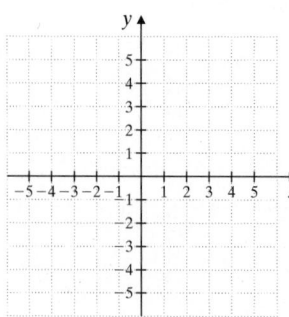

40. $y = 2\dfrac{1}{2}$

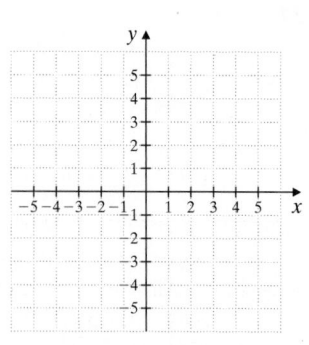

41. $y = -\dfrac{2}{3}x + 1$ **42.** $y = -\dfrac{3}{5}x + 3$ **43.** $4x - 6y + 2 = 0$ **44.** $9x - 6y + 3 = 0$

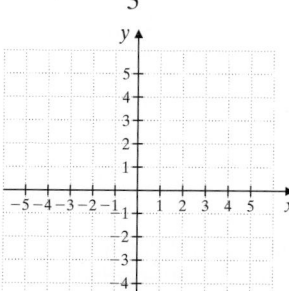   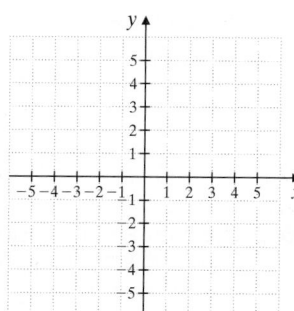   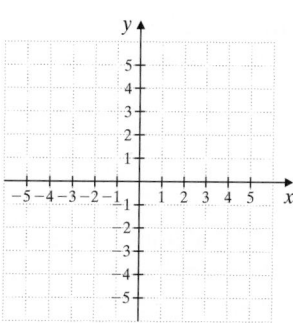   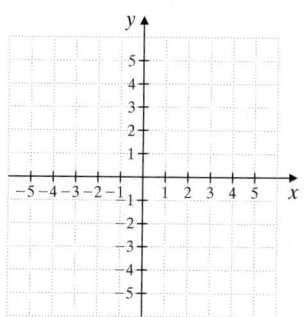

Review

Simplify. See Sections 8.4 and 8.5.

45. $\dfrac{-6 - 3}{2 - 8}$

46. $\dfrac{4 - 5}{-1 - 0}$

47. $\dfrac{-8 - (-2)}{-3 - (-2)}$

48. $\dfrac{12 - 3}{10 - 9}$

49. $\dfrac{0 - 6}{5 - 0}$

50. $\dfrac{2 - 2}{3 - 5}$

Concept Extensions

Match each equation with its graph.

51. $y = 3$ **52.** $y = 2x + 2$ **53.** $x = 3$ **54.** $y = 2x + 3$

a. 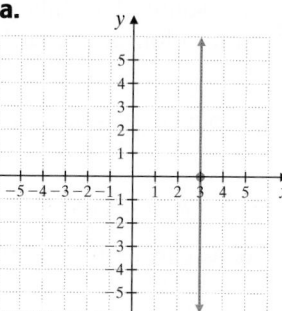   **b.** 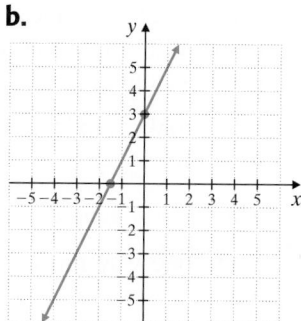   **c.** 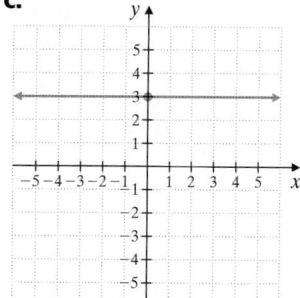   **d.**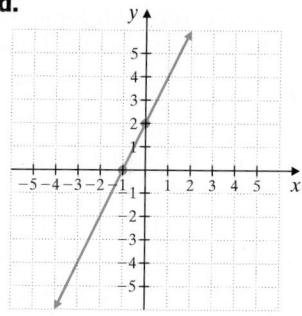

55. What is the greatest number of x- and y-intercepts that a line can have?

56. What is the smallest number of x- and y-intercepts that a line can have?

57. What is the smallest number of x- and y-intercepts that a circle can have?

58. What is the greatest number of x- and y-intercepts that a circle can have?

59. Discuss whether a vertical line ever has a y-intercept.

60. Discuss whether a horizontal line ever has an x-intercept.

61. The production supervisor at Alexandra's Office Products finds that it takes 3 hours to manufacture a particular office chair and 6 hours to manufacture an office desk. A total of 1200 hours is available to produce office chairs and desks of this style. The linear equation that models this situation is $3x + 6y = 1200$, where x represents the number of chairs produced and y the number of desks manufactured.

a. Complete the ordered pair solution $(0,\ )$ of this equation. Describe the manufacturing situation that corresponds to this solution.

b. Complete the ordered pair solution $(\ ,0)$ of this equation. Describe the manufacturing situation that corresponds to this solution.

c. If 50 desks are manufactured, find the greatest number of chairs that can be made.

*Two lines in the same plane that do not intersect are called **parallel lines.***

62. Use your own graph paper to draw a line parallel to the line $x = 5$ that intersects the x-axis at 1. What is the equation of this line?

63. Use your own graph paper to draw a line parallel to the line $y = -1$ that intersects the y-axis at -4. What is the equation of this line?

Solve.

64. The number of music videos y, in millions, shipped to retailers in the United States from 1998 to 2003 can be modeled by the equation $y = -2.71x + 25$, where x represents the number of years after 1998. (*Source:* Recording Industry Association of America)

    a. Find the x-intercept of this equation (round to the nearest tenth).

    b. What does this x-intercept mean?

65. The number of a certain chain of stores y for the years 1999–2003 can be modeled by the equation $y = 29.2x + 919$, where x represents the number of years after 1999. (*Source:* Limited Brands)

    a. Find the y-intercept of this equation.

    b. What does this y-intercept mean?

 STUDY SKILLS BUILDER

Are You Familiar with Your Textbook Supplements?

Below is a review of some of the student supplements available for additional study. Check to see if you are using the ones most helpful to you.

- Chapter Test Prep Videos on CD. This material is found with your textbook and is fully explained there. The CD contains video clip solutions to the Chapter Test exercises in this text and are excellent help when studying for chapter tests.

- Lecture Videos on CD-ROM. These video segments are keyed to each section of the text. The material is presented by me, Elayn Martin-Gay, and I have placed a ⊚ by the exercises in the text that I have worked on the video.

- The *Student Solutions Manual*. This contains worked out solutions to odd-numbered exercises as well as every exercise in the Integrated Reviews. Chapter Reviews, Chapter Tests, and Cumulative Reviews.

- Prentice Hall Tutor Center. Mathematics questions may be phoned, faxed, or emailed to this center.

- MyMathLab, MathXL, and Internet Math. These are computer and Internet tutorials. This supplement may already be available to you somewhere on campus, for example at your local learning resource lab. Take a moment and find the name and location of any such lab on campus.

    As usual, your instructor is your best source of information.

Let's see how you are doing with textbook supplements.

1. Name one way the Lecture Videos can be helpful to you.

2. Name one way the Chapter Test Prep Video can help you prepare for a chapter test.

3. List any textbook supplements that you have found useful.

4. Have you located and visited a learning resource lab located on your campus?

5. List the textbook supplements that are currently housed in your campus' learning resource lab.

10.4 SLOPE AND RATE OF CHANGE

Objective **A** Finding the Slope of a Line Given Two Points

Thus far, much of this chapter has been devoted to graphing lines. You have probably noticed by now that a key feature of a line is its slant or steepness. In mathematics, the slant or steepness of a line is formally known as its **slope.** We measure the slope of a line by the ratio of vertical change (rise) to the corresponding horizontal change (run) as we move along the line.

On the line below, for example, suppose that we begin at the point $(1, 2)$ and move to the point $(4, 6)$. The vertical change is the change in y-coordinates: $6 - 2$ or 4 units. The corresponding horizontal change is the change in x-coordinates: $4 - 1 = 3$ units. The ratio of these changes is

$$\text{slope} = \frac{\text{change in } y \text{ (vertical change or rise)}}{\text{change in } x \text{ (horizontal change or run)}} = \frac{4}{3}$$

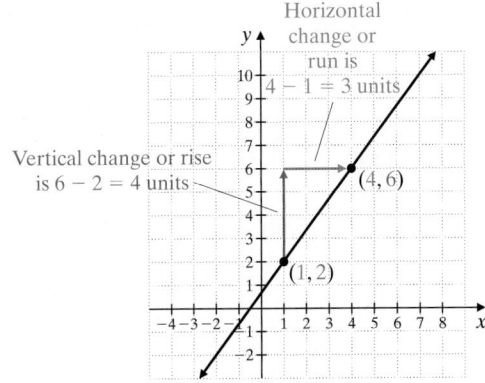

The slope of this line, then, is $\frac{4}{3}$. This means that for every 4 units of change in y-coordinates, there is a corresponding change of 3 units in x-coordinates.

> **Helpful Hint**
>
> It makes no difference what two points of a line are chosen to find its slope. The slope of a line is the same everywhere on the line.
>
>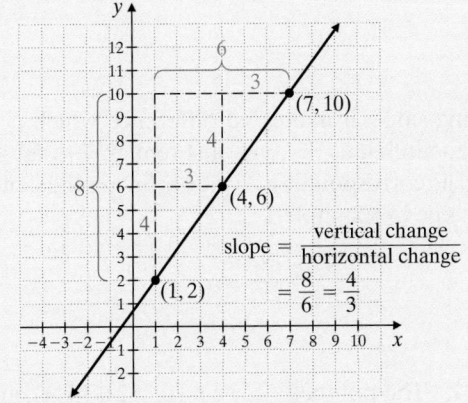

To find the slope of a line, then, choose two points of the line. Label the two x-coordinates of two points x_1 and x_2 (read "x sub one" and "x sub two"), and label the corresponding y-coordinates y_1 and y_2.

The vertical change or **rise** between these points is the difference in the y-coordinates: $y_2 - y_1$. The horizontal change or **run** between the points is the difference of the x-coordinates: $x_2 - x_1$. The slope of the line is the ratio of $y_2 - y_1$ to $x_2 - x_1$, and we traditionally use the letter m to denote slope $m = \dfrac{y_2 - y_1}{x_2 - x_1}$.

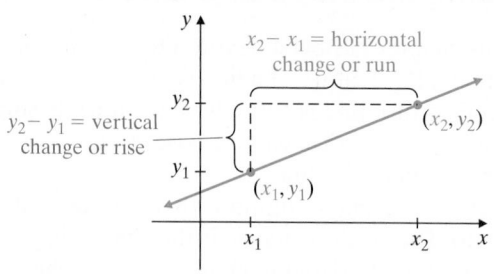

Slope of a Line

The slope m of the line containing the points (x_1, y_1) and (x_2, y_2) is given by

$$m = \frac{\text{rise}}{\text{run}} = \frac{\text{change in } y}{\text{change in } x} = \frac{y_2 - y_1}{x_2 - x_1}, \qquad \text{as long as } x_2 \neq x_1$$

PRACTICE PROBLEM 1

Find the slope of the line through $(-2, 3)$ and $(4, -1)$. Graph the line.

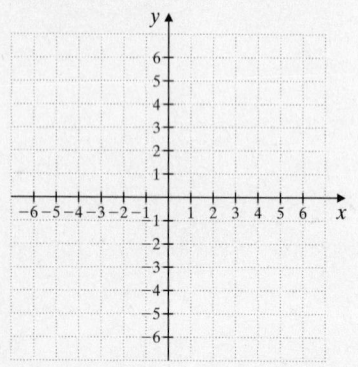

Answer

1. $-\dfrac{2}{3}$

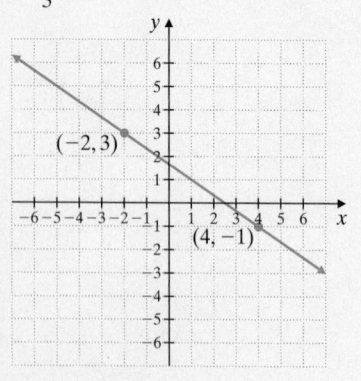

✔ Concept Check Answer

$m = \dfrac{3}{2}$

EXAMPLE 1 Find the slope of the line through $(-1, 5)$ and $(2, -3)$. Graph the line.

Solution: Let (x_1, y_1) be $(-1, 5)$ and (x_2, y_2) be $(2, -3)$. Then, by the definition of slope, we have the following.

$$m = \frac{y_2 - y_1}{x_2 - x_1}$$

$$= \frac{-3 - 5}{2 - (-1)}$$

$$= \frac{-8}{3} = -\frac{8}{3}$$

The slope of the line is $-\dfrac{8}{3}$.

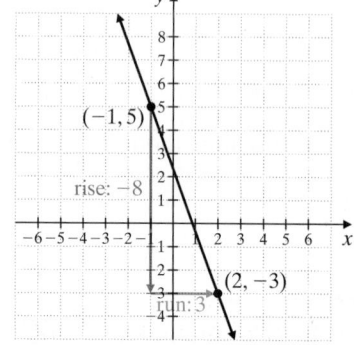

■ **Work Practice Problem 1**

Helpful Hint

When finding slope, it makes no difference which point is identified as (x_1, y_1) and which is identified as (x_2, y_2). Just remember that whatever y-value is first in the numerator, its corresponding x-value is first in the denominator. Another way to calculate the slope in Example 1 is

$$m = \frac{y_2 - y_1}{x_2 - x_1} = \frac{5 - (-3)}{-1 - 2} = \frac{8}{-3} \quad \text{or} \quad -\frac{8}{3} \leftarrow \text{Same slope as found in Example 1.}$$

✔ Concept Check The points $(-2, -5)$, $(0, -2)$, $(4, 4)$, and $(10, 13)$ all lie on the same line. Work with a partner and verify that the slope is the same no matter which points are used to find slope.

EXAMPLE 2 Find the slope of the line through $(-1, -2)$ and $(2, 4)$. Graph the line.

Solution: Let (x_1, y_1) be $(2, 4)$ and (x_2, y_2) be $(-1, -2)$.

$$m = \frac{y_2 - y_1}{x_2 - x_1}$$

$$= \frac{-2 - 4}{-1 - 2} \quad \begin{array}{l} y\text{-value} \\ \\ \text{corresponding } x\text{-value} \end{array}$$

$$= \frac{-6}{-3} = 2$$

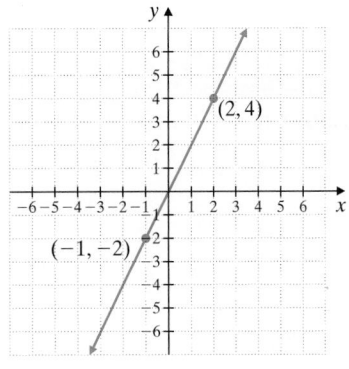

The slope is 2.

Work Practice Problem 2

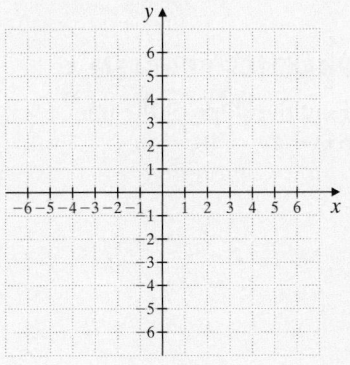
✔**Concept Check** What is wrong with the following slope calculation for the points $(3, 5)$ and $(-2, 6)$?

$$m = \frac{5 - 6}{-2 - 3} = \frac{-1}{-5} = \frac{1}{5}$$

Notice that the slope of the line in Example 1 is negative, and the slope of the line in Example 2 is positive. Let your eye follow the line with negative slope from left to right and notice that the line "goes down." If you follow the line with positive slope from left to right, you will notice that the line "goes up." This is true in general.

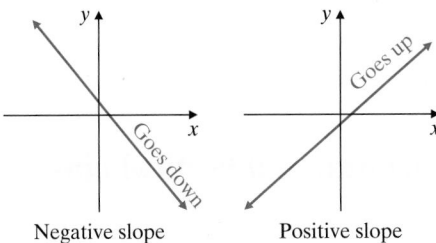

Negative slope   Positive slope

Helpful Hint
To decide whether a line "goes up" or "goes down," always follow the line from left to right.

Objective B Finding the Slope of a Line Given Its Equation

As we have seen, the slope of a line is defined by two points on the line. Thus, if we know the equation of a line, we can find its slope by finding two of its points. For example, let's find the slope of the line

$$y = 3x - 2$$

To find two points, we can choose two values for x and substitute to find corresponding y-values. If $x = 0$, for example, $y = 3 \cdot 0 - 2$ or $y = -2$. If $x = 1$, $y = 3 \cdot 1 - 2$ or $y = 1$. This gives the ordered pairs $(0, -2)$ and $(1, 1)$. Using the definition for slope, we have

$$m = \frac{1 - (-2)}{1 - 0} = \frac{3}{1} = 3 \quad \text{The slope is 3.}$$

Notice that the slope, 3, is the same as the coefficient of x in the equation $y = 3x - 2$. This is true in general.

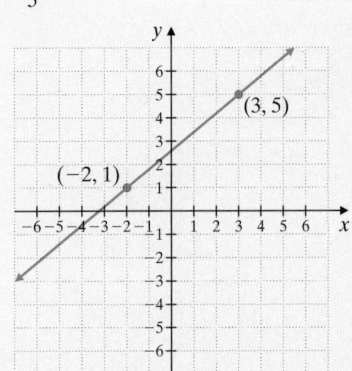

If a linear equation is solved for y, the coefficient of x is the line's slope. In other words, the slope of the line given by $y = mx + b$ is m, the coefficient of x.

$$y = mx + b$$

$\uparrow$ slope

PRACTICE PROBLEM 3

Find the slope of the line $5x + 4y = 10$.

EXAMPLE 3 Find the slope of the line $-2x + 3y = 11$.

Solution: When we solve for y, the coefficient of x is the slope.

$$-2x + 3y = 11$$
$$3y = 2x + 11 \qquad \text{Add } 2x \text{ to both sides.}$$
$$y = \frac{2}{3}x + \frac{11}{3} \qquad \text{Divide both sides by 3.}$$

The slope is $\frac{2}{3}$.

▣ **Work Practice Problem 3**

PRACTICE PROBLEM 4

Find the slope of the line $-y = -2x + 7$.

EXAMPLE 4 Find the slope of the line $-y = 5x - 2$.

Solution: Remember, the equation must be solved for y (not $-y$) in order for the coefficient of x to be the slope.

To solve for y, let's divide both sides of the equation by -1.

$$-y = 5x - 2$$
$$\frac{-y}{-1} = \frac{5x}{-1} - \frac{2}{-1} \qquad \text{Divide both sides by } -1.$$
$$y = -5x + 2 \qquad \text{Simplify.}$$

The slope is -5.

▣ **Work Practice Problem 4**

Objective **C** Finding Slopes of Horizontal and Vertical Lines

PRACTICE PROBLEM 5

Find the slope of $y = 3$.

EXAMPLE 5 Find the slope of the line $y = -1$.

Solution: Recall that $y = -1$ is a horizontal line with y-intercept -1. To find the slope, we find two ordered pair solutions of $y = -1$, knowing that solutions of $y = -1$ must have a y-value of -1. We will use $(2, -1)$ and $(-3, -1)$. We let (x_1, y_1) be $(2, -1)$ and (x_2, y_2) be $(-3, -1)$.

$$m = \frac{y_2 - y_1}{x_2 - x_1} = \frac{-1 - (-1)}{-3 - 2} = \frac{0}{-5} = 0$$

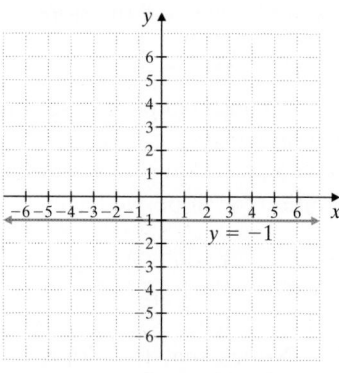

The slope of the line $y = -1$ is 0. Since the y-values will have a difference of 0 for every horizontal line, we can say that all **horizontal lines have a slope of 0.**

▣ **Work Practice Problem 5**

EXAMPLE 6 Find the slope of the line $x = 5$.

Solution: Recall that the graph of $x = 5$ is a vertical line with x-intercept 5. To find the slope, we find two ordered pair solutions of $x = 5$. Ordered pair solutions of $x = 5$ must have an x-value of 5. We will use $(5, 0)$ and $(5, 4)$. We let $(x_1, y_1) = (5, 0)$ and $(x_2, y_2) = (5, 4)$.

$$m = \frac{y_2 - y_1}{x_2 - x_1} = \frac{4 - 0}{5 - 5} = \frac{4}{0}$$

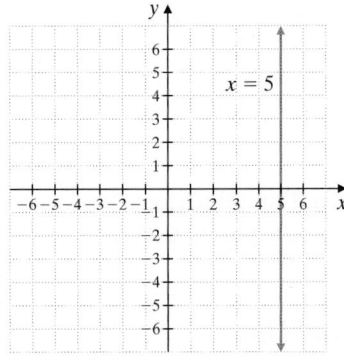

Since $\frac{4}{0}$ is undefined, we say the slope of the vertical line $x = 5$ is undefined.

Since the x-values will have a difference of 0 for every vertical line, we can say that all **vertical lines have undefined slope.**

■ **Work Practice Problem 6**

Here is a general review of slope.

Summary of Slope

Slope m of the line through (x_1, y_1) and (x_2, y_2) is given by the equation

$$m = \frac{y_2 - y_1}{x_2 - x_1}.$$

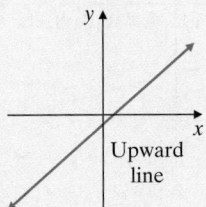
Upward line

Positive slope: $m > 0$

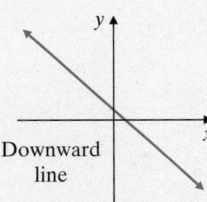
Downward line

Negative slope: $m < 0$

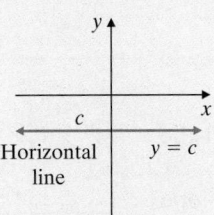
Horizontal line $y = c$

Zero slope: $m = 0$

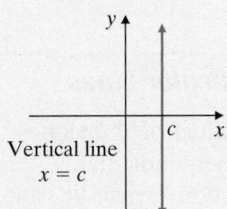
Vertical line $x = c$

No slope or undefined slope

Objective **D** Slopes of Parallel and Perpendicular Lines

Two lines in the same plane are **parallel** if they do not intersect. Slopes of lines can help us determine whether lines are parallel. Since parallel lines have the same steepness, it follows that they have the same slope.

PRACTICE PROBLEM 6

Find the slope of the line $x = -2$.

Helpful Hint
Slope of 0 and undefined slope are not the same. Vertical lines have undefined slope, while horizontal lines have a slope of 0.

Answer
6. undefined slope

For example, the graphs of

$$y = -2x + 4$$

and

$$y = -2x - 3$$

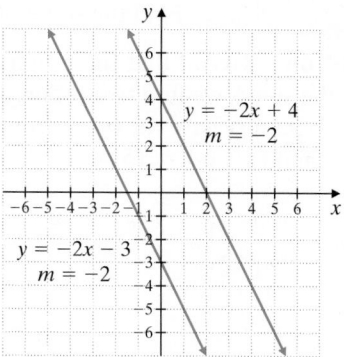

are shown. These lines have the same slope, -2. They also have different y-intercepts, so the lines are parallel. (If the y-intercepts were the same also, the lines would be the same.)

Parallel Lines

Nonvertical parallel lines have the same slope and different y-intercepts.

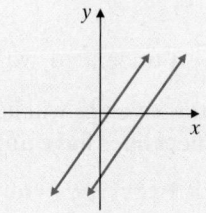

Two lines are **perpendicular** if they lie in the same plane and meet at a 90° (right) angle. How do the slopes of perpendicular lines compare? The product of the slopes of two perpendicular lines is -1.

For example, the graphs of

$$y = 4x + 1$$

and

$$y = -\frac{1}{4}x - 3$$

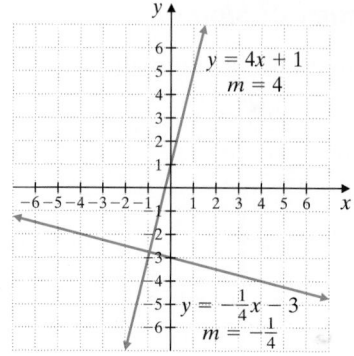

are shown. The slopes of the lines are 4 and $-\dfrac{1}{4}$. Their product is $4\left(-\dfrac{1}{4}\right) = -1$, so the lines are perpendicular.

Perpendicular Lines

If the product of the slopes of two lines is -1, then the lines are perpendicular.

(Two nonvertical lines are perpendicular if the slope of one is the negative reciprocal of the slope of the other.)

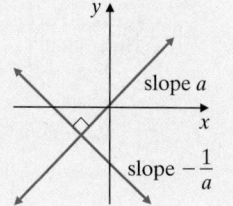

Helpful Hint

Here are examples of numbers that are negative (opposite) reciprocals.

Number	Negative Reciprocal	Their product is −1.
$\dfrac{2}{3}$	$-\dfrac{3}{2}$	$\dfrac{2}{3} \cdot -\dfrac{3}{2} = -\dfrac{6}{6} = -1$
-5 or $-\dfrac{5}{1}$	$\dfrac{1}{5}$	$-5 \cdot \dfrac{1}{5} = -\dfrac{5}{5} = -1$

Here are a few important points about vertical and horizontal lines.

- Two distinct vertical lines are parallel.
- Two distinct horizontal lines are parallel.
- A horizontal line and a vertical line are always perpendicular.

 **EXAMPLE 7** Determine whether each pair of lines is parallel, perpendicular, or neither.

a. $y = -\dfrac{1}{5}x + 1$ **b.** $x + y = 3$ **c.** $3x + y = 5$

$2x + 10y = 3$ $-x + y = 4$ $2x + 3y = 6$

Solution:

a. The slope of the line $y = -\dfrac{1}{5}x + 1$ is $-\dfrac{1}{5}$. We find the slope of the second line by solving its equation for y.

$2x + 10y = 3$

$\quad 10y = -2x + 3$ Subtract $2x$ from both sides.

$\quad\quad y = \dfrac{-2}{10}x + \dfrac{3}{10}$ Divide both sides by 10.

$\quad\quad y = -\dfrac{1}{5}x + \dfrac{3}{10}$ Simplify.

The slope of this line is $-\dfrac{1}{5}$ also. Since the lines have the same slope and different y-intercepts, they are parallel, as shown in the figure below.

b. To find each slope, we solve each equation for y.

$x + y = 3$ $-x + y = 4$

$\quad y = -x + 3$ $\quad y = x + 4$

The slope is -1.   The slope is 1.

The slopes are not the same, so the lines are not parallel. Next we check the product of the slopes: $(-1)(1) = -1$. Since the product is -1, the lines are perpendicular, as shown in the figure.

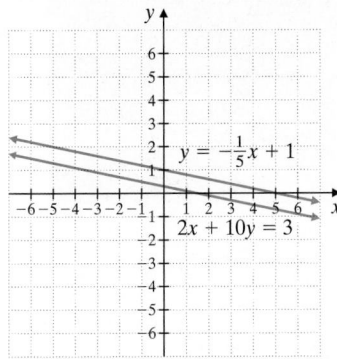

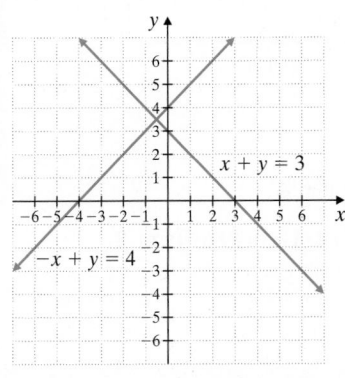

Continued on next page

PRACTICE PROBLEM 7

Determine whether each pair of lines is parallel, perpendicular, or neither.

a. $x + y = 5$

$\quad 2x + y = 5$

b. $5y = 2x - 3$

$\quad 5x + 2y = 1$

c. $y = 2x + 1$

$\quad 4x - 2y = 8$

Answers

7. a. neither,   **b.** perpendicular,   **c.** parallel

c. We solve each equation for y to find each slope. The slopes are -3 and $-\dfrac{2}{3}$. The slopes are not the same and their product is not -1. Thus, the lines are neither parallel nor perpendicular.

▭ **Work Practice Problem 7**

✔**Concept Check**   Consider the line $-6x + 2y = 1$.

a. Write the equations of two lines parallel to this line.

b. Write the equations of two lines perpendicular to this line.

Objective E Slope as a Rate of Change

Slope can also be interpreted as a rate of change. In other words, slope tells us how fast y is changing with respect to x. To see this, let's look at a few of the many real-world applications of slope. For example, the pitch of a roof, used by builders and architects, is its slope. The pitch of the roof on the left is $\dfrac{7}{10}\left(\dfrac{\text{rise}}{\text{run}}\right)$. This means that the roof rises vertically 7 feet for every horizontal 10 feet. The rate of change for the roof is 7 vertical feet (y) per 10 horizontal feet (x).

The grade of a road is its slope written as a percent. A 7% grade, as shown below, means that the road rises (or falls) 7 feet for every horizontal 100 feet. $\Big($Recall that $7\% = \dfrac{7}{100}.\Big)$ Here, the slope of $\dfrac{7}{100}$ gives us the rate of change. The road rises (in our diagram) 7 vertical feet (y) for every 100 horizontal feet (x).

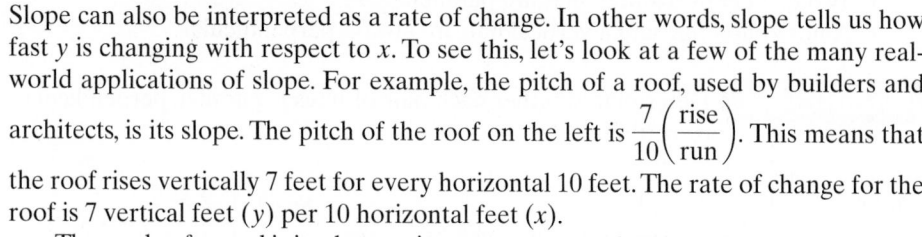

$\dfrac{7}{100} = 7\%\,\text{grade}$

7 feet

100 feet

PRACTICE PROBLEM 8

Find the grade of the road shown.

3 feet

20 feet

EXAMPLE 8 **Finding the Grade of a Road**

At one part of the road to the summit of Pike's Peak, the road rises 15 feet for a horizontal distance of 250 feet. Find the grade of the road.

Solution: Recall that the grade of a road is its slope written as a percent.

$$\text{grade} = \frac{\text{rise}}{\text{run}} = \frac{15}{250} = 0.06 = 6\%$$

15 feet

250 feet

The grade is 6%.

▭ **Work Practice Problem 8**

Answer

8. 15%

✔ **Concept Check Answers**

answers may vary; for example,

a. $y = 3x - 3$, $y = 3x - 1$,

b. $y = -\dfrac{1}{3}x$, $y = -\dfrac{1}{3}x + 1$

Slope can also be interpreted as a rate of change. In other words, slope tells us how fast *y* is changing with respect to *x*.

EXAMPLE 9 **Finding the Slope of a Line**

The following graph shows the cost *y* (in cents) of a nationwide long-distance telephone call from Texas with a certain telephone-calling plan, where *x* is the length of the call in minutes. Find the slope of the line and attach the proper units for the rate of change. Then write a sentence explaining the meaning of slope in this application.

Solution: Use (2, 34) and (6, 62) to calculate slope.

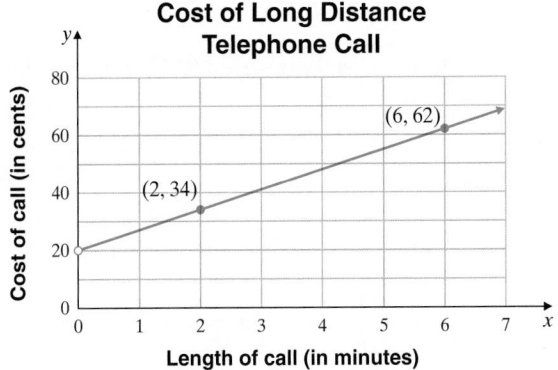

Cost of Long Distance Telephone Call

$$m = \frac{62 - 34}{6 - 2} = \frac{28}{4} = \frac{7 \text{ cents}}{1 \text{ minute}}$$

This means that the rate of change of a phone call is 7 cents per 1 minute or the cost of the phone call is 7 cents per minute.

☐ **Work Practice Problem 9**

PRACTICE PROBLEM 9

Find the slope of the line and write the slope as a rate of change. This graph represents annual food and drink sales *y* (in billions of dollars) for year *x*. Write a sentence explaining the meaning of slope in this application.

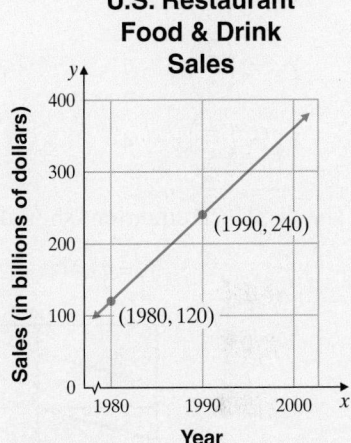

U.S. Restaurant Food & Drink Sales

Source: National Restaurant Assn.

Answer

9. *m* = 12; Each year the sales of food and drink from restaurants increases by $12 billion dollars per year.

CALCULATOR EXPLORATIONS Graphing

It is possible to use a graphing calculator and sketch the graph of more than one equation on the same set of axes. This feature can be used to see parallel lines with the same slope. For example, graph the equations $y = \frac{2}{5}x$, $y = \frac{2}{5}x + 7$, and $y = \frac{2}{5}x - 4$ on the same set of axes. To do so, press the $\boxed{Y=}$ key and enter the equations on the first three lines.

$$Y_1 = \left(\frac{2}{5}\right)x$$

$$Y_2 = \left(\frac{2}{5}\right)x + 7$$

$$Y_3 = \left(\frac{2}{5}\right)x - 4$$

The displayed equations should look like this:

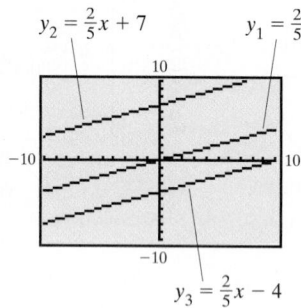

These lines are parallel as expected since they all have a slope of $\frac{2}{5}$. The graph of $y = \frac{2}{5}x + 7$ is the graph of $y = \frac{2}{5}x$ moved 7 units upward with a y-intercept of 7. Also, the graph of $y = \frac{2}{5}x - 4$ is the graph of $y = \frac{2}{5}x$ moved 4 units downward with a y-intercept of -4.

Graph the parallel lines on the same set of axes. Describe the similarities and differences in their graphs.

1. $y = 3.8x$, $y = 3.8x - 3$, $y = 3.8x + 9$

2. $y = -4.9x$, $y = -4.9x + 1$, $y = -4.9x + 8$

3. $y = \frac{1}{4}x$, $y = \frac{1}{4}x + 5$, $y = \frac{1}{4}x - 8$

4. $y = -\frac{3}{4}x$, $y = -\frac{3}{4}x - 5$, $y = -\frac{3}{4}x + 6$

Mental Math

State whether the slope of the line is positive, negative, 0, or is undefined.

1.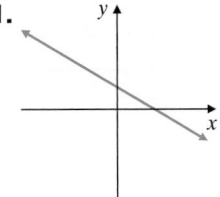

2.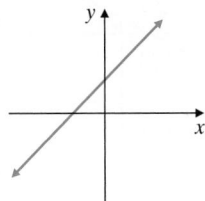

3.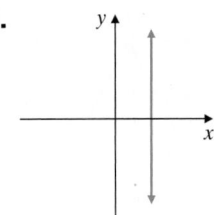

4.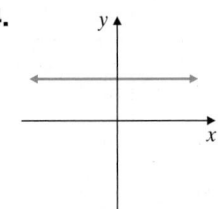

Decide whether a line with the given slope is upward sloping, downward sloping, horizontal, or vertical.

5. $m = \dfrac{7}{6}$

6. $m = -3$

7. $m = 0$

8. m is undefined

10.4 EXERCISE SET

FOR EXTRA HELP

Student Solutions Manual | PH Math/Tutor Center | CD/Video for Review | MathXL® | MyMathLab

Objective A *Find the slope of the line that passes through the given points. See Examples 1 and 2.*

1. $(-1, 5)$ and $(6, -2)$

2. $(-1, 16)$ and $(3, 4)$

3. $(1, 4)$ and $(5, 3)$

4. $(3, 1)$ and $(2, 6)$

5. $(5, 1)$ and $(-2, 1)$

6. $(-8, 3)$ and $(-2, 3)$

7. $(5, 4)$ and $(5, 0)$

8. $(-2, -3)$ and $(-2, 5)$

Use the points shown on each graph to find the slope of each line. See Examples 1 and 2.

9.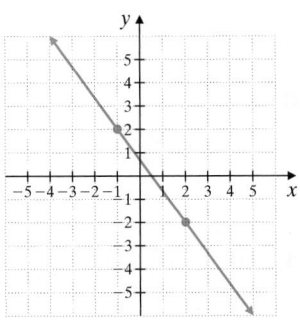

10.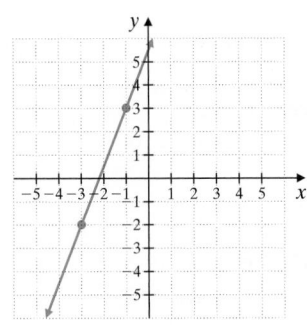

11.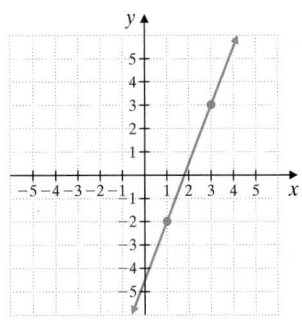

12.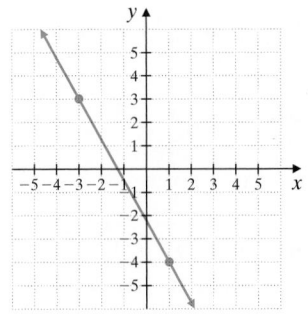

For each graph, determine which line has the greater slope.

13.

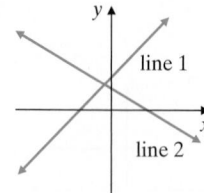

14.

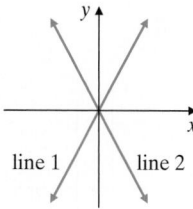

15.

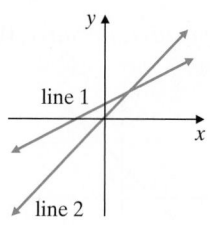

16.

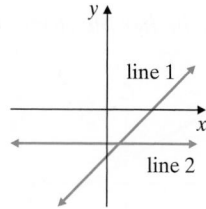

Objectives **B** **C** **Mixed Practice** *Find the slope of each line. See Examples 3 through 6.*

17. $y = 5x - 2$

18. $y = -2x + 6$

19. $y = -0.3x + 2.5$

20. $y = -7.6x - 0.1$

21. $2x + y = 7$

22. $-5x + y = 10$

23.

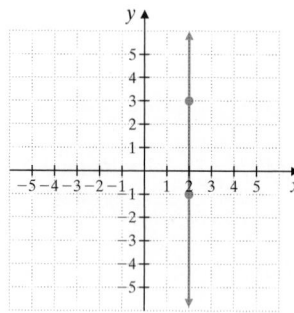

24.

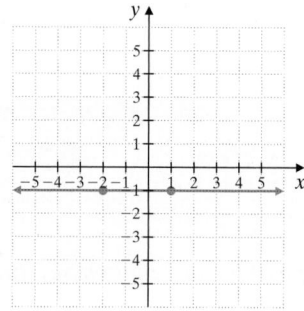

25. $2x - 3y = 10$

26. $3x - 5y = 1$

27. $x = 1$

28. $y = -2$

29. $x = 2y$

30. $x = -4y$

31. $y = -3$

32. $x = 5$

33. $-3x - 4y = 6$

34. $-4x - 7y = 9$

35. $20x - 5y = 1.2$

36. $24x - 3y = 5.7$

△ Objective **D** *Determine whether each pair of lines is parallel, perpendicular, or neither. See Example 7.*

37. $y = \dfrac{2}{9}x + 3$

$y = -\dfrac{2}{9}x$

38. $y = \dfrac{1}{5}x + 20$

$y = -\dfrac{1}{5}x$

39. $x - 3y = -6$

$y = 3x - 9$

40. $y = 4x - 2$

$4x + y = 5$

41. $6x = 5y + 1$

$-12x + 10y = 1$

42. $-x + 2y = -2$

$2x = 4y + 3$

43. $6 + 4x = 3y$

$3x + 4y = 8$

44. $10 + 3x = 5y$

$5x + 3y = 1$

△ *Find the slope of the line that is (**a**) parallel and (**b**) perpendicular to the line through each pair of points. See Example 7.*

45. $(-3, -3)$ and $(0, 0)$

46. $(6, -2)$ and $(1, 4)$

47. $(-8, -4)$ and $(3, 5)$

48. $(6, -1)$ and $(-4, -10)$

Objective **E** *The pitch of a roof is its slope. Find the pitch of each roof shown. See Example 8.*

49.

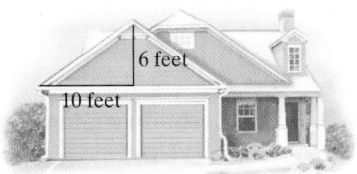
6 feet
10 feet

50.

5
10

The grade of a road is its slope written as a percent. Find the grade of each road shown. See Example 8.

51.

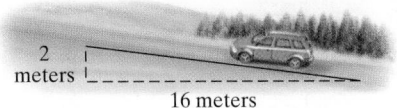
2 meters
16 meters

52.

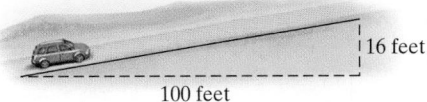
16 feet
100 feet

53. One of Japan's superconducting "bullet" trains is researched and tested at the Yamanashi Maglev Test Line near Otsuki City. The steepest section of the track has a rise of 2580 meters for a horizontal distance of 6450 meters. What is the grade of this section of track? (*Source:* Japan Railways Central Co.)

2580 meters
6450 meters

54. Professional plumbers suggest that a sewer pipe should rise 0.25 inch for every horizontal foot. Find the recommended slope for a sewer pipe. Round to the nearest hundredth.

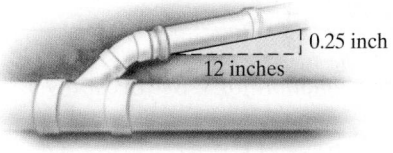
0.25 inch
12 inches

55. The steepest street is Baldwin Street in Dunedin, New Zealand. It has a maximum rise of 10 meters for a horizontal distance of 12.66 meters. Find the grade of this section of road. Round to the nearest whole percent. (*Source: The Guinness Book of Records*)

56. According to federal regulations, a wheelchair ramp should rise no more than 1 foot for a horizontal distance of 12 feet. Write the slope as a grade. Round to the nearest tenth of a percent.

Find the slope of each line and write the slope as a rate of change. Don't forget to attach the proper units. See Example 9.

57. This graph approximates the number of U.S. households that have personal computers y (in millions) for year x.

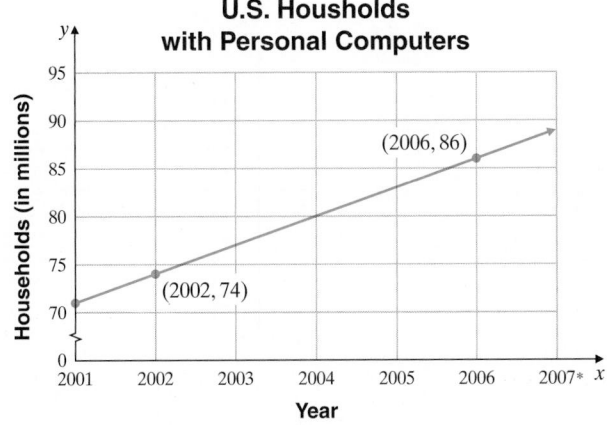

U.S. Housholds with Personal Computers
Households (in millions)
(2006, 86)
(2002, 74)
Year
2001 2002 2003 2004 2005 2006 2007*

Source: Statistical Abstract of the United States, *projected numbers

58. This graph approximates the total number of cosmetic surgeons for year x.

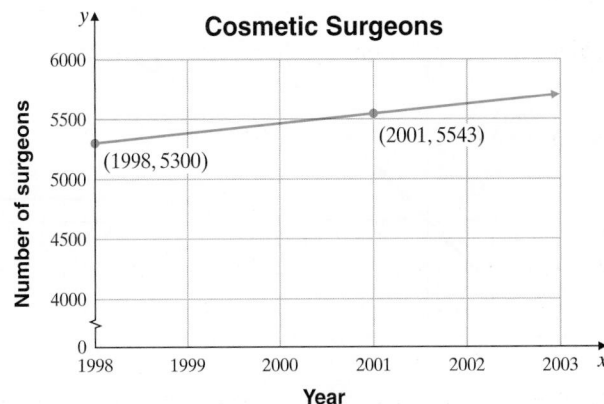

Cosmetic Surgeons
Number of surgeons
6000
5500
5000
4500
4000
(2001, 5543)
(1998, 5300)
Year
1998 1999 2000 2001 2002 2003

Source: CDC: National Center for Health Statistics

59. The graph below shows the total cost y (in dollars) of owning and operating a compact car where x is the number of miles driven.

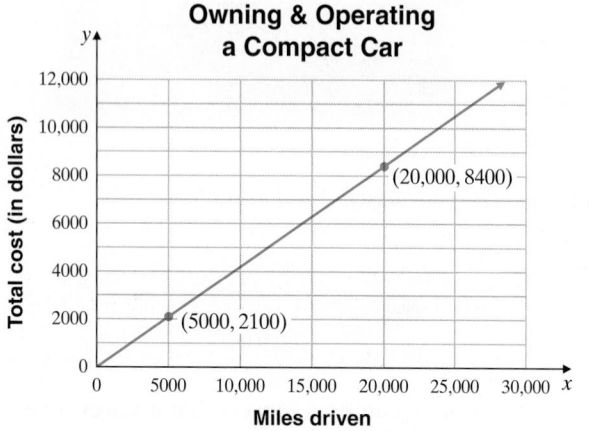

Owning & Operating a Compact Car

Total cost (in dollars) vs Miles driven

(5000, 2100)
(20,000, 8400)

Source: Federal Highway Administration

60. The graph below shows the total cost y (in dollars) of owning and operating a standard pickup truck, where x is the number of miles driven.

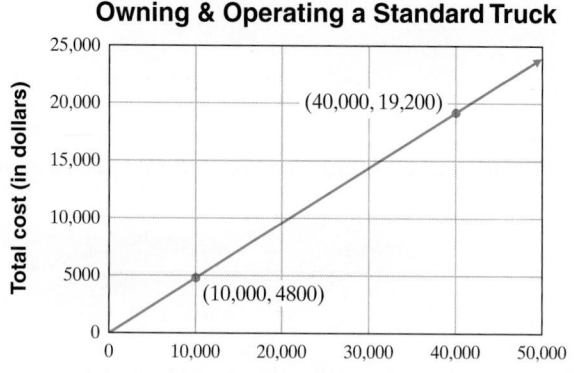

Owning & Operating a Standard Truck

Total cost (in dollars) vs Miles driven

(40,000, 19,200)
(10,000, 4800)

Source: Federal Highway Administration

Review

Solve each equation for y. See Section 9.5.

61. $y - (-6) = 2(x - 4)$

62. $y - 7 = -9(x - 6)$

63. $y - 1 = -6(x - (-2))$

64. $y - (-3) = 4(x - (-5))$

Concept Extensions

Match each line with its slope.

a. $m = 0$

b. undefined slope

c. $m = 3$

d. $m = 1$

e. $m = -\dfrac{1}{2}$

f. $m = -\dfrac{3}{4}$

65.

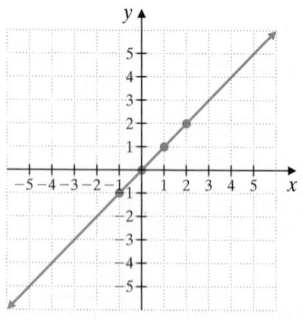

66.

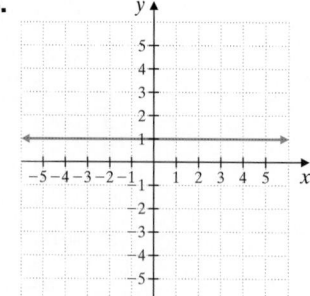

67.

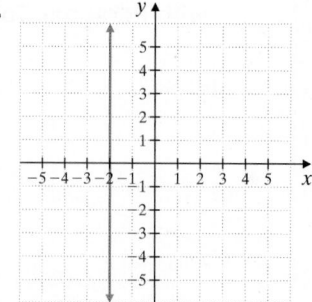

68.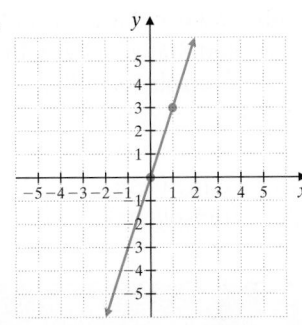

69.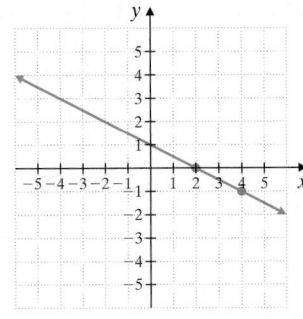

70.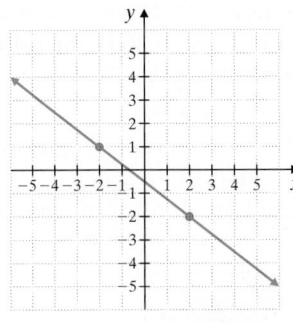

Solve. See a Concept Check in this section.

71. Verify that the points $(2, 1), (0, 0), (-2, -1)$ and $(-4, -2)$ are all on the same line by computing the slope between each pair of points. (See the first Concept Check.)

72. Given the points $(2, 3)$ and $(-5, 1)$, can the slope of the line through these points be calculated by $\dfrac{1 - 3}{2 - (-5)}$? Why or why not? (See the second Concept Check.)

73. Write the equations of three lines parallel to $10x - 5y = -7$. (See the third Concept Check.)

74. Write the equations of two lines perpendicular to $10x - 5y = -7$. (See the third Concept Check.)

The following line graph shows the average fuel economy (in miles per gallon) by passenger automobiles produced during each of the model years shown. Use this graph to answer Exercises 75 through 79.

75. What was the average fuel economy (in miles per gallon) for automobiles produced during 2001?

Average Fuel Economy for Autos

76. Find the decrease in average fuel economy for automobiles between the years 1998 to 2000.

77. During which of the model years shown was average fuel economy the lowest? What was the average fuel economy for that year?

Source: U.S. Environmental Protection Agency, Office of Transportation and Air Quality

78. During which of the model years shown was average fuel economy the highest? What was the average fuel economy for that year?

79. What line segment has the greatest slope?

80. Find x so that the pitch of the roof is $\dfrac{1}{3}$.

81. Find x so that the pitch of the roof is $\dfrac{2}{5}$.

82. The average price of an acre of U.S. farmland was $974 in 1998. In 2003, the price of an acre rose to approximately $1275. (*Source:* National Agricultural Statistics Services)

   a. Write two ordered pairs of the form (year, price of acre)

   b. Find the slope of the line through the two points.

   c. Write a sentence explaining the meaning of the slope as a rate of change.

83. There were approximately 10,359 kidney transplants performed in the United States in 1993. In 2003, the number of kidney transplants in the United States rose to 15,138. (*Source:* Organ Procurement and Transplantation Network)

   a. Write two ordered pairs of the form (year, number of kidney transplants).

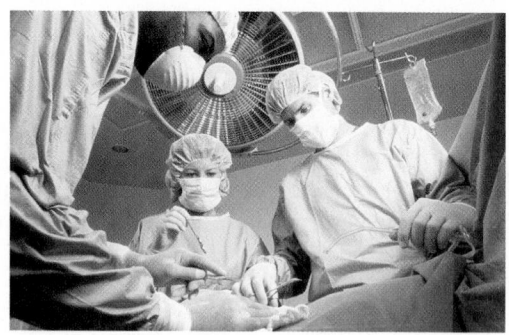

   b. Find the slope of the line between the two points.

   c. Write a sentence explaining the meaning of the slope as a rate of change.

84. Show that a triangle with vertices at the points $(1, 1)$, $(-4, 4)$, and $(-3, 0)$ is a right triangle.

85. Show that the quadrilateral with vertices $(1, 3)$, $(2, 1)$, $(-4, 0)$, and $(-3, -2)$ is a parallelogram.

Find the slope of the line through the given points.

86. $(2.1, 6.7)$ and $(-8.3, 9.3)$

87. $(-3.8, 1.2)$ and $(-2.2, 4.5)$

88. $(2.3, 0.2)$ and $(7.9, 5.1)$

89. $(14.3, -10.1)$ and $(9.8, -2.9)$

90. The graph of $y = -\frac{1}{3}x + 2$ has a slope of $-\frac{1}{3}$. The graph of $y = -2x + 2$ has a slope of -2. The graph of $y = -4x + 2$ has a slope of -4. Graph all three equations on a single coordinate system. As the absolute value of the slope becomes larger, how does the steepness of the line change?

91. The graph of $y = \frac{1}{2}x$ has a slope of $\frac{1}{2}$. The graph of $y = 3x$ has a slope of 3. The graph of $y = 5x$ has a slope of 5. Graph all three equations on a single coordinate system. As slope becomes larger, how does the steepness of the line change?

10.5 EQUATIONS OF LINES

A Use the Slope-Intercept Form to Write an Equation of a Line.

B Use the Slope-Intercept Form to Graph a Linear Equation.

C Use the Point-Slope Form to Find an Equation of a Line Given Its Slope and a Point of the Line.

D Use the Point-Slope Form to Find an Equation of a Line Given Two Points of the Line.

E Use the Point-Slope Form to Solve Problems.

We know that when a linear equation is solved for y, the coefficient of x is the slope of the line. For example, the slope of the line whose equation is $y = 3x + 1$ is 3. In this equation, $y = 3x + 1$, what does 1 represent? To find out, let $x = 0$ and watch what happens.

$$y = 3x + 1$$
$$y = 3 \cdot 0 + 1 \quad \text{Let } x = 0.$$
$$y = 1$$

We now have the ordered pair $(0, 1)$, which means that 1 is the y-intercept. This is true in general. To see this, let $x = 0$ and solve for y in $y = mx + b$.

$$y = m \cdot 0 + b \quad \text{Let } x = 0.$$
$$y = b$$

We obtain the ordered pair $(0, b)$, which means that point is the y-intercept.

The form $y = mx + b$ is appropriately called the *slope-intercept form* of a linear equation.

$$y = \underset{\uparrow}{mx} + \underset{\uparrow}{b}$$

slope y-intercept is $(0, b)$

Slope-Intercept Form

When a linear equation in two variables is written in **slope-intercept form,**

$$y = \underset{\uparrow}{m}x + \underset{\uparrow}{b}$$

slope $(0, b)$, y-intercept

then m is the slope of the line and $(0, b)$ is the y-intercept of the line.

Objective **A** Using the Slope-Intercept Form to Write an Equation

The slope-intercept form can be used to write the equation of a line when we know its slope and y-intercept.

EXAMPLE 1 Find an equation of the line with y-intercept $(0, -3)$ and slope of $\frac{1}{4}$.

Solution: We are given the slope and the y-intercept. We let $m = \frac{1}{4}$ and $b = -3$ and write the equation in slope-intercept form, $y = mx + b$.

$$y = mx + b$$
$$y = \frac{1}{4}x + (-3) \quad \text{Let } m = \frac{1}{4} \text{ and } b = -3.$$
$$y = \frac{1}{4}x - 3 \quad \text{Simplify.}$$

Work Practice Problem 1

Objective **B** Using the Slope-Intercept Form to Graph an Equation

We also can use the slope-intercept form of the equation of a line to graph a linear equation.

PRACTICE PROBLEM 1

Find an equation of the line with y-intercept $(0, -2)$ and slope of $\frac{3}{5}$.

Answer

1. $y = \frac{3}{5}x - 2$

761

762

PRACTICE PROBLEM 2

Graph the equation
$y = \dfrac{2}{3}x - 4$.

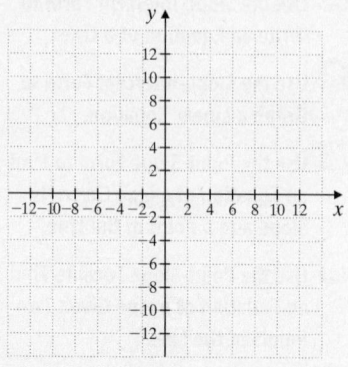

PRACTICE PROBLEM 3

Use the slope-intercept form to graph $3x + y = 2$.

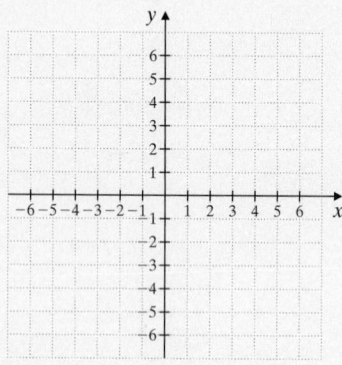

Answers

2.

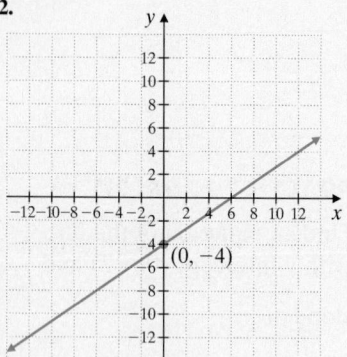

3.

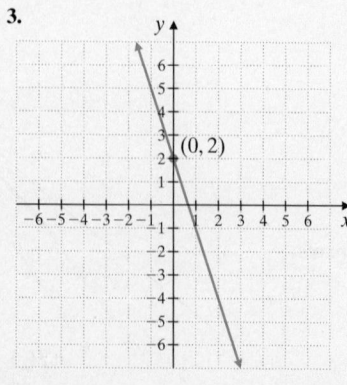

EXAMPLE 2 Use the slope-intercept form to graph the equation

$$y = \dfrac{3}{5}x - 2$$

Solution: Since the equation $y = \dfrac{3}{5}x - 2$ is written in slope-intercept form $y = mx + b$, the slope of its graph is $\dfrac{3}{5}$ and the y-intercept is $(0, -2)$. To graph this equation, we begin by plotting the point $(0, -2)$.

From this point, we can find another point of the graph by using the slope $\dfrac{3}{5}$ and recalling that slope is $\dfrac{\text{rise}}{\text{run}}$. We start at the y-intercept and move 3 units up since the numerator of the slope is 3; then we move 5 units to the right since the denominator of the slope is 5. We stop at the point $(5, 1)$. The line through $(0, -2)$ and $(5, 1)$ is the graph of $y = \dfrac{3}{5}x - 2$.

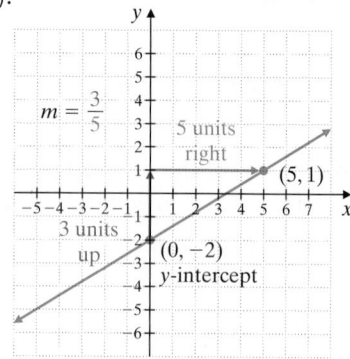

◼ **Work Practice Problem 2**

EXAMPLE 3 Use the slope-intercept form to graph the equation $4x + y = 1$.

Solution: First we write the given equation in slope-intercept form.

$$4x + y = 1$$
$$y = -4x + 1$$

The graph of this equation will have slope -4 and y-intercept $(0, 1)$. To graph this line, we first plot the point $(0, 1)$. To find another point of the graph, we use the slope -4, which can be written as $\dfrac{-4}{1}\left(\dfrac{4}{-1}\text{ could also be used}\right)$. We start at the point $(0, 1)$ and move 4 units down (since the numerator of the slope is -4), and then 1 unit to the right (since the denominator of the slope is 1).

We arrive at the point $(1, -3)$. The line through $(0, 1)$ and $(1, -3)$ is the graph of $4x + y = 1$.

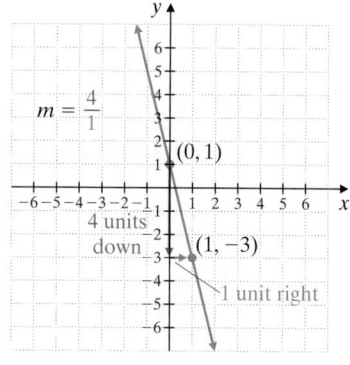

◼ **Work Practice Problem 3**

Helpful Hint

In Example 3, if we interpret the slope of -4 as $\dfrac{4}{-1}$, we arrive at $(-1, 5)$ for a second point. Notice that this point is also on the line.

Objective **C** Writing an Equation Given Its Slope and a Point

Thus far, we have seen that we can write an equation of a line if we know its slope and y-intercept. We can also write an equation of a line if we know its slope and any point on the line. To see how we do this, let m represent slope and (x_1, y_1) represent the point on the line. Then if (x, y) is any other point of the line, we have that

$$\frac{y - y_1}{x - x_1} = m$$

$$y - y_1 = m(x - x_1) \quad \text{Multiply both sides by } (x - x_1).$$

$\underset{\text{slope}}{\uparrow}$

This is the *point-slope form* of the equation of a line.

Point-Slope Form of the Equation of a Line

The **point-slope form** of the equation of a line is $y - y_1 = m(x - x_1)$, where m is the slope of the line and (x_1, y_1) is a point on the line.

EXAMPLE 4 Find an equation of the line with slope -2 that passes through $(-1, 5)$. Write the equation in slope-intercept form, $y = mx + b$, and in standard form, $Ax + By = C$.

Solution: Since the slope and a point on the line are given, we use point-slope form $y - y_1 = m(x - x_1)$ to write the equation. Let $m = -2$ and $(-1, 5) = (x_1, y_1)$.

$$y - y_1 = m(x - x_1)$$
$$y - 5 = -2[x - (-1)] \quad \text{Let } m = -2 \text{ and } (x_1, y_1) = (-1, 5).$$
$$y - 5 = -2(x + 1) \quad \text{Simplify.}$$
$$y - 5 = -2x - 2 \quad \text{Use the distributive property.}$$

To write the equation in slope-intercept form, $y = mx + b$, we simply solve the equation for y. To do this, we add 5 to both sides.

$$y - 5 = -2x - 2$$
$$y = -2x + 3 \quad \text{Slope-intercept form.}$$
$$2x + y = 3 \quad \text{Add } 2x \text{ to both sides and we have standard form.}$$

🔲 **Work Practice Problem 4**

Objective D Writing an Equation Given Two Points

We can also find the equation of a line when we are given any two points of the line.

EXAMPLE 5 Find an equation of the line through $(2, 5)$ and $(-3, 4)$. Write the equation in the form $Ax + By = C$.

Solution: First, use the two given points to find the slope of the line.

$$m = \frac{4 - 5}{-3 - 2} = \frac{-1}{-5} = \frac{1}{5}$$

Next we use the slope $\frac{1}{5}$ and either one of the given points to write the equation in point-slope form. We use $(2, 5)$. Let $x_1 = 2$, $y_1 = 5$, and $m = \frac{1}{5}$.

$$y - y_1 = m(x - x_1) \quad \text{Use point-slope form.}$$

$$y - 5 = \frac{1}{5}(x - 2) \quad \text{Let } x_1 = 2, y_1 = 5, \text{ and } m = \frac{1}{5}.$$

$$5(y - 5) = 5 \cdot \frac{1}{5}(x - 2) \quad \text{Multiply both sides by 5 to clear fractions.}$$

$$5y - 25 = x - 2 \quad \text{Use the distributive property and simplify.}$$

$$-x + 5y - 25 = -2 \quad \text{Subtract } x \text{ from both sides.}$$

$$-x + 5y = 23 \quad \text{Add 25 to both sides.}$$

🔲 **Work Practice Problem 5**

PRACTICE PROBLEM 4

Find an equation of the line with slope -3 that passes through $(2, -4)$. Write the equation in slope-intercept form $y = mx + b$.

PRACTICE PROBLEM 5

Find an equation of the line through $(1, 3)$ and $(5, -2)$. Write the equation in the form $Ax + By = C$.

Answers

4. $y = -3x + 2$, **5.** $5x + 4y = 17$

Copyright 2007 Pearson Education, Inc.

> **Helpful Hint**
>
> When you multiply both sides of the equation from Example 5, $-x + 5y = 23$ by -1, it becomes $x - 5y = -23$.
>
> Both $-x + 5y = 23$ and $x - 5y = -23$ are in the form $Ax + By = C$ and both are equations of the same line.

Objective E Using the Point-Slope Form to Solve Problems

Problems occurring in many fields can be modeled by linear equations in two variables. The next example is from the field of marketing and shows how consumer demand of a product depends on the price of the product.

EXAMPLE 6 The Whammo Company has learned that by pricing a newly released Frisbee at $6, sales will reach 2000 Frisbees per day. Raising the price to $8 will cause the sales to fall to 1500 Frisbees per day.

a. Assume that the relationship between sales price and number of Frisbees sold is linear and write an equation describing this relationship. Write the equation in slope-intercept form. Use ordered pairs of the form (sales price, number sold).

b. Predict the daily sales of Frisbees if the price is $7.50.

Solution:

a. We use the given information and write two ordered pairs. Our ordered pairs are $(6, 2000)$ and $(8, 1500)$. To use the point-slope form to write an equation, we find the slope of the line that contains these points.

$$m = \frac{2000 - 1500}{6 - 8} = \frac{500}{-2} = -250$$

Next we use the slope and either one of the points to write the equation in point-slope form. We use $(6, 2000)$.

$$y - y_1 = m(x - x_1) \qquad \text{Use point-slope form.}$$
$$y - 2000 = -250(x - 6) \qquad \text{Let } x_1 = 6, y_1 = 2000, \text{ and } m = -250.$$
$$y - 2000 = -250x + 1500 \qquad \text{Use the distributive property.}$$
$$y = -250x + 3500 \qquad \text{Write in slope-intercept form.}$$

b. To predict the sales if the price is $7.50, we find y when $x = 7.50$.

$$y = -250x + 3500$$
$$y = -250(7.50) + 3500 \qquad \text{Let } x = 7.50.$$
$$y = -1875 + 3500$$
$$y = 1625$$

If the price is $7.50, sales will reach 1625 Frisbees per day.

■ **Work Practice Problem 6**

PRACTICE PROBLEM 6

The Pool Entertainment Company learned that by pricing a new pool toy at $10, local sales will reach 200 a week. Lowering the price to $9 will cause sales to rise to 250 a week.

a. Assume that the relationship between sales price and number of toys sold is linear, and write an equation describing this relationship. Write the equation in slope-intercept form. Use ordered pairs of the form (sales price, number sold).

b. Predict the weekly sales of the toy if the price is $7.50.

Answers

6. a. $y = -50x + 700$, **b.** 325

We could have solved Example 6 by using ordered pairs of the form (number sold, sales price).

Here is a summary of our discussion on linear equations thus far.

Forms of Linear Equations

$Ax + By = C$	**Standard form** of a linear equation. A and B are not both 0.
$y = mx + b$	**Slope-intercept form** of a linear equation. The slope is m and the y-intercept is $(0, b)$.
$y - y_1 = m(x - x_1)$	**Point-slope form** of a linear equation. The slope is m and (x_1, y_1) is a point on the line.
$y = c$	**Horizontal line** The slope is 0 and the y-intercept is $(0, c)$.
$x = c$	**Vertical line** The slope is undefined and the x-intercept is $(c, 0)$.

Parallel and Perpendicular Lines

Nonvertical parallel lines have the same slope.
The product of the slopes of two nonvertical perpendicular lines is -1.

 CALCULATOR EXPLORATIONS Graphing

A graphing calculator is a very useful tool for discovering patterns. To discover the change in the graph of a linear equation caused by a change in slope, try the following. Use a standard window and graph a linear equation in the form $y = mx + b$. Recall that the graph of such an equation will have slope m and y-intercept $(0, b)$.

First graph $y = x + 3$. To do so, press the $\boxed{Y=}$ key and enter $Y_1 = x + 3$. Notice that this graph has slope 1 and that the y-intercept is 3. Next, on the same set of axes, graph $y = 2x + 3$ and $y = 3x + 3$ by pressing $\boxed{Y=}$ and entering $Y_2 = 2x + 3$ and $Y_3 = 3x + 3$.

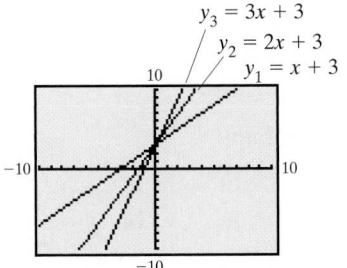

Notice the difference in the graph of each equation as the slope changes from 1 to 2 to 3. How would the graph of $y = 5x + 3$ appear? To see the change in the graph caused by a change in negative slope, try graphing $y = -x + 3$, $y = -2x + 3$, and $y = -3x + 3$ on the same set of axes.

Use a graphing calculator to graph the following equations. For each exercise, graph the first equation and use its

graph to predict the appearance of the other equations. Then graph the other equations on the same set of axes and check your prediction.

1. $y = x$; $y = 6x$, $y = -6x$

2. $y = -x$; $y = -5x$, $y = -10x$

3. $y = \dfrac{1}{2}x + 2$; $y = \dfrac{3}{4}x + 2$, $y = x + 2$

4. $y = x + 1$; $y = \dfrac{5}{4}x + 1$, $y = \dfrac{5}{2}x + 1$

Mental Math

Use the equation to identify the slope and the y-intercept of the graph of each equation.

1. $y = 2x - 1$

2. $y = -7x + 3$

3. $y = x + \dfrac{1}{3}$

4. $y = -x - \dfrac{2}{9}$

5. $y = \dfrac{5}{7}x - 4$

6. $y = -\dfrac{1}{4}x + \dfrac{3}{5}$

Use the equation to identify the slope and a point on the line.

7. $y - 8 = 3(x - 4)$

8. $y - 1 = 5(x - 2)$

9. $y + 3 = -2(x - 10)$

10. $y + 6 = -7(x - 2)$

11. $y = \dfrac{2}{5}(x + 1)$

12. $y = \dfrac{3}{7}(x + 4)$

10.5 EXERCISE SET

FOR EXTRA HELP

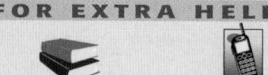 Student Solutions Manual   PH Math/Tutor Center   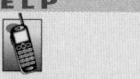 CD/Video for Review    Math XL   MathXL®   MyMathLab MyMathLab

Objective **A** *Write an equation of the line with each given slope, m, and y-intercept, (0, b). See Example 1.*

1. $m = 5, b = 3$

2. $m = -3, b = -3$

3. $m = -4, b = -\dfrac{1}{6}$

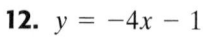 **4.** $m = 2, b = \dfrac{3}{4}$

5. $m = \dfrac{2}{3}, b = 0$

6. $m = -\dfrac{4}{5}, b = 0$

7. $m = 0, b = -8$

8. $m = 0, b = -2$

9. $m = -\dfrac{1}{5}, b = \dfrac{1}{9}$

10. $m = \dfrac{1}{2}, b = -\dfrac{1}{3}$

Objective **B** *Use the slope-intercept form to graph each equation. See Examples 2 and 3.*

11. $y = 2x + 1$

12. $y = -4x - 1$

13. $y = \dfrac{2}{3}x + 5$

14. $y = \dfrac{1}{4}x - 3$

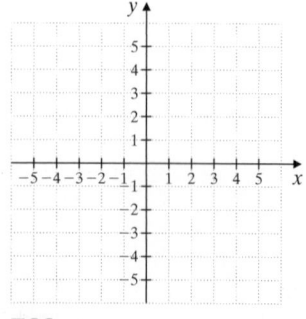
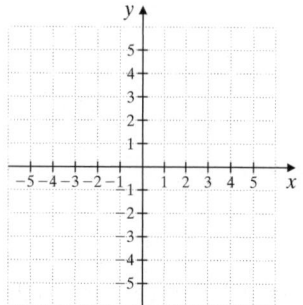
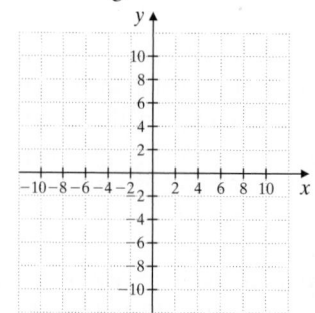
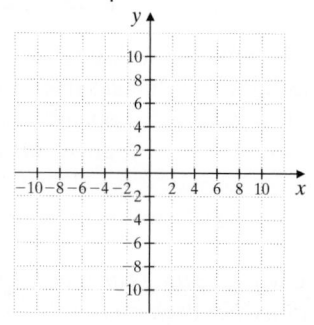

15. $y = -5x$

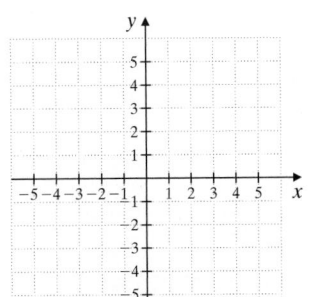

16. $y = -6x$

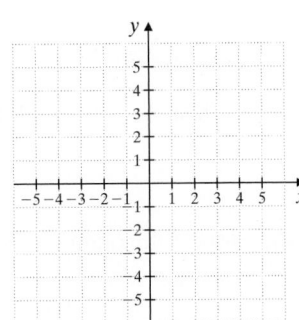

17. $4x + y = 6$

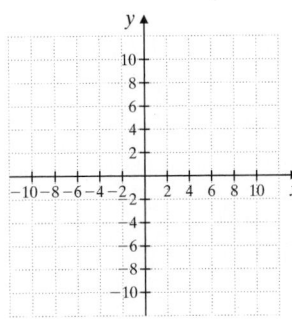

18. $-3x + y = 2$

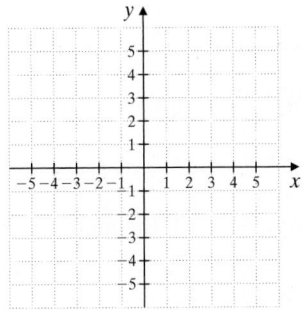

19. $4x - 7y = -14$

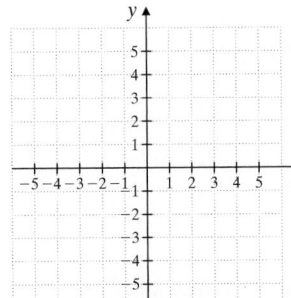

20. $3x - 4y = 4$

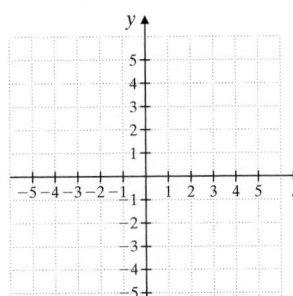

21. $x = \dfrac{5}{4}y$

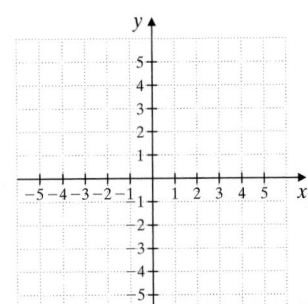

22. $x = \dfrac{3}{2}y$

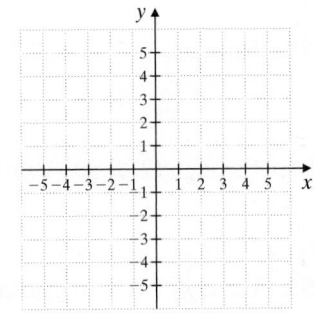

Objective **C** *Find an equation of each line with the given slope that passes through the given point. Write the equation in the form $Ax + By = C$. See Example 4.*

23. $m = 6;\quad (2, 2)$

24. $m = 4;\quad (1, 3)$

25. $m = -8;\quad (-1, -5)$

26. $m = -2;\quad (-11, -12)$

27. $m = \dfrac{3}{2};\quad (5, -6)$

28. $m = \dfrac{2}{3};\quad (-8, 9)$

29. $m = -\dfrac{1}{2};\quad (-3, 0)$

30. $m = -\dfrac{1}{5};\quad (4, 0)$

Objective **D** *Find an equation of the line passing through each pair of points. Write the equation in the form $Ax + By = C$. See Example 5.*

31. $(3, 2)$ and $(5, 6)$

32. $(6, 2)$ and $(8, 8)$

33. $(-1, 3)$ and $(-2, -5)$

34. $(-4, 0)$ and $(6, -1)$

35. $(2, 3)$ and $(-1, -1)$

36. $(7, 10)$ and $(-1, -1)$

37. $(0, 0)$ and $\left(-\dfrac{1}{8}, \dfrac{1}{13}\right)$

38. $(0, 0)$ and $\left(-\dfrac{1}{2}, \dfrac{1}{3}\right)$

Objectives **A** **C** **D** **Mixed Practice** *See Examples 1, 4, and 5. Find an equation of each line described. Write each equation in slope-intercept form when possible.*

39. With slope $-\dfrac{1}{2}$, through $\left(0, \dfrac{5}{3}\right)$

40. With slope $\dfrac{5}{7}$, through $(0, -3)$

41. Through $(10, 7)$ and $(7, 10)$

42. Through $(5, -6)$ and $(-6, 5)$

43. With undefined slope, through $\left(-\dfrac{3}{4}, 1\right)$

44. With slope 0, through $(6.7, 12.1)$

45. Slope 1, through $(-7, 9)$

46. Slope 5, through $(6, -8)$

47. Slope -5, y-intercept $(0, 7)$

48. Slope -2; y-intercept $(0, -4)$

49. Through $(6, 7)$, parallel to the x-axis

50. Through $(1, -5)$, parallel to the y-axis

51. Through $(2, 3)$ and $(0, 0)$

52. Through $(4, 7)$ and $(0, 0)$

53. Through $(-2, -3)$, perpendicular to the y-axis

54. Through $(0, 12)$, perpendicular to the x-axis

55. Slope $-\dfrac{4}{7}$, through $(-1, -2)$

56. Slope $-\dfrac{3}{5}$, through $(4, 4)$

Objective **E** *Solve. Assume each exercise describes a linear relationship. Write the equations in slope-intercept form. See Example 6.*

57. A rock is dropped from the top of a 400-foot cliff. After 1 second, the rock is traveling 32 feet per second. After 3 seconds, the rock is traveling 96 feet per second.

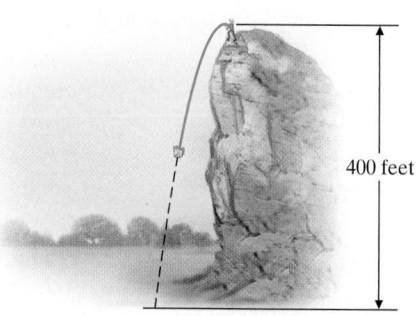

400 feet

a. Assume that the relationship between time and speed is linear and write an equation describing this relationship. Use ordered pairs of the form (time, speed).

b. Use this equation to determine the speed of the rock 4 seconds after it was dropped.

58. A Hawaiian fruit company is studying the sales of a pineapple sauce to see if this product is to be continued. At the end of its first year, profits on this product amounted to $30,000. At the end of the fourth year, profits were $66,000.

a. Assume that the relationship between years on the market and profit is linear and write an equation describing this relationship. Use ordered pairs of the form (years on the market, profit).

b. Use this equation to predict the profit at the end of 7 years.

59. In 2003 there were approximately 54,000 gas-electric hybrid vehicles sold in the United States. In 2001, there were only 22,000 such vehicles sold. (*Source:* Energy Information Administration, Department of Energy)

  a. Write an equation describing the relationship between time and the number of gas-electric hybrid vehicles sold. Use ordered pairs of the form (years past 2001, number of vehicles sold).

  b. Use this equation to predict the number of gas-electric hybrid sales in 2006.

60. In 2004, there were approximately 875 thousand restaurants in the United States. In 1972, there were 491 thousand restaurants. (*Source:* National Restaurant Association)

  a. Write an equation describing the relationship between time and the number of restaurants. Use ordered pairs of the form (years past 1972, numbers of restaurants in thousands).

  b. Use this equation to predict the number of eating establishments in 2012.

61. In 2003 there were approximately 5700 cinema sites in the United States. In 1999 there were 7032 cinema sites. (*Source:* National Association of Theater Owners)

  a. Write an equation describing this relationship. Use ordered pairs of the form (years past 1999, number of cinema sites).

  b. Use this equation to predict the number of cinema sites in 2007.

62. In 2000, the U.S. population per square mile of land area was 79.6. In 1990, this person per square mile population was 70.3.

  a. Write an equation describing the relationship between year and person per square mile. Use ordered pairs of the form (years past 1990, person per square mile).

  b. Use this equation to predict the person per square mile population in 2007.

63. In 1997 there were 1509 daily newspapers in the United States. By 2003, there were only 1456 daily newspapers. (*Source:* Statistical Abstract of the United States)

  a. Write two ordered pairs of the form (years after 1997, number of daily newspapers) for this situation.

  b. The relationship between years after 1997 and numbers of daily newspapers is linear over this period. Use the ordered pairs from part (a) to write an equation for the line relating year after 1997 to numbers of daily newspapers. (Round the slope to one decimal place.)

  c. Use the linear equation in part (b) to estimate numbers of daily newspapers in 1999. (Round to the nearest whole.)

64. In 1999, crude oil production by the European Union countries was 3803 thousand barrels per day. In 2002, European Union oil production had decreased to 3482 thousand barrels per day. (*Source:* Energy Information Administration)

  a. Write two ordered pairs of the form (years after 1999, crude oil production).

  b. Assume that the relationship between years after 1999 and crude oil production is linear over this period. Use the ordered pairs from part (a) to write an equation of the line relating year to crude oil production.

  c. Use the linear equation from part (b) to estimate the crude oil production by European Union countries in 2005, if this trend were to continue.

65. The Pool Fun Company has learned that, by pricing a newly released Fun Noodle at $3, sales will reach 10,000 Fun Noodles per day during the summer. Raising the price to $5 will cause the sales to fall to 8000 Fun Noodles per day.

  a. Assume that the relationship between sales price and number of Fun Noodles sold is linear and write an equation describing this relationship. Use ordered pairs of the form (sales price, number sold).

  b. Predict the daily sales of Fun Noodles if the price is $3.50.

66. The value of a building bought in 1990 may be depreciated (or decreased) as time passes for income tax purposes. Seven years after the building was bought, this value was $225,000 and 12 years after it was bought, this value was $195,000.

  a. If the relationship between number of years past 1990 and the depreciated value of the building is linear, write an equation describing this relationship. Use ordered pairs of the form (years past 1990, value of building).

  b. Use this equation to estimate the depreciated value of the building in 2008.

Review

Find the value of $x^2 - 3x + 1$ for each given value of x. See Section 8.5.

67. 2   **68.** 5   **69.** -1 **70.** -3

Concept Extensions

Match each linear equation with its graph.

71. $y = 2x + 1$ **72.** $y = -x + 1$ **73.** $y = -3x - 2$ **74.** $y = \dfrac{5}{3}x - 2$

a. 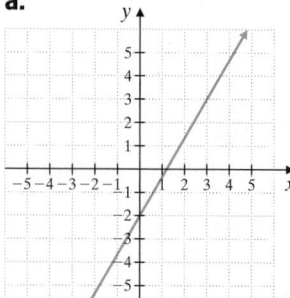   **b.** 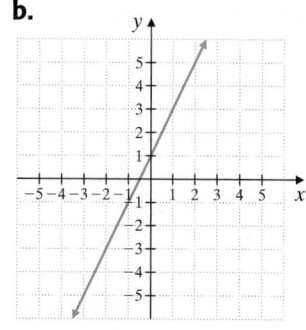   **c.** 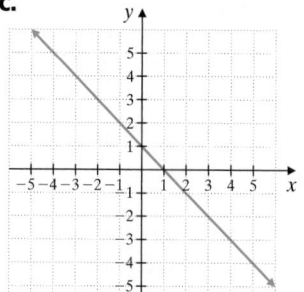   **d.**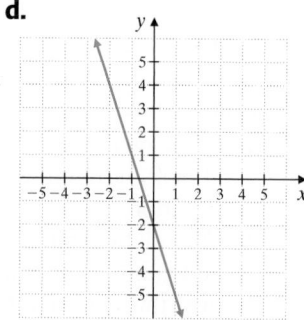

75. Write an equation of the line that contains the point $(-1, 2)$ and has the same slope as the line $y = 3x - 1$.

76. Write an equation of the line that contains the point $(4, 0)$ and has the same slope as the line $y = -2x + 3$.

△ **77.** Write an equation in standard form of the line that contains the point $(-1, 2)$ and is

  a. parallel to the line $y = 3x - 1$.

  b. perpendicular to the line $y = 3x - 1$.

△ **78.** Write an equation in standard form of the line that contains the point $(4, 0)$ and is

  a. parallel to the line $y = -2x + 3$.

  b. perpendicular to the line $y = -2x + 3$.

We could have solved Example 6 by using ordered pairs of the form (number sold, sales price).

Here is a summary of our discussion on linear equations thus far.

Forms of Linear Equations

$Ax + By = C$	**Standard form** of a linear equation. A and B are not both 0.
$y = mx + b$	**Slope-intercept form** of a linear equation. The slope is m and the y-intercept is $(0, b)$.
$y - y_1 = m(x - x_1)$	**Point-slope form** of a linear equation. The slope is m and (x_1, y_1) is a point on the line.
$y = c$	**Horizontal line** The slope is 0 and the y-intercept is $(0, c)$.
$x = c$	**Vertical line** The slope is undefined and the x-intercept is $(c, 0)$.

Parallel and Perpendicular Lines

Nonvertical parallel lines have the same slope.
The product of the slopes of two nonvertical perpendicular lines is -1.

CALCULATOR EXPLORATIONS Graphing

A graphing calculator is a very useful tool for discovering patterns. To discover the change in the graph of a linear equation caused by a change in slope, try the following. Use a standard window and graph a linear equation in the form $y = mx + b$. Recall that the graph of such an equation will have slope m and y-intercept $(0, b)$.

First graph $y = x + 3$. To do so, press the $\boxed{Y=}$ key and enter $Y_1 = x + 3$. Notice that this graph has slope 1 and that the y-intercept is 3. Next, on the same set of axes, graph $y = 2x + 3$ and $y = 3x + 3$ by pressing $\boxed{Y=}$ and entering $Y_2 = 2x + 3$ and $Y_3 = 3x + 3$.

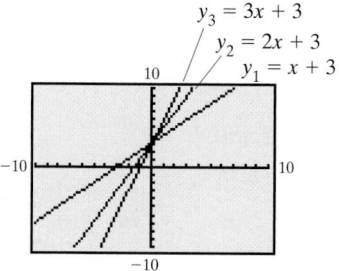

Notice the difference in the graph of each equation as the slope changes from 1 to 2 to 3. How would the graph of $y = 5x + 3$ appear? To see the change in the graph caused by a change in negative slope, try graphing $y = -x + 3$, $y = -2x + 3$, and $y = -3x + 3$ on the same set of axes.

Use a graphing calculator to graph the following equations. For each exercise, graph the first equation and use its graph to predict the appearance of the other equations. Then graph the other equations on the same set of axes and check your prediction.

1. $y = x$; $y = 6x$, $y = -6x$

2. $y = -x$; $y = -5x$, $y = -10x$

3. $y = \frac{1}{2}x + 2$; $y = \frac{3}{4}x + 2$, $y = x + 2$

4. $y = x + 1$; $y = \frac{5}{4}x + 1$, $y = \frac{5}{2}x + 1$

Mental Math

Use the equation to identify the slope and the y-intercept of the graph of each equation.

1. $y = 2x - 1$

2. $y = -7x + 3$

3. $y = x + \dfrac{1}{3}$

4. $y = -x - \dfrac{2}{9}$

5. $y = \dfrac{5}{7}x - 4$

6. $y = -\dfrac{1}{4}x + \dfrac{3}{5}$

Use the equation to identify the slope and a point on the line.

7. $y - 8 = 3(x - 4)$

8. $y - 1 = 5(x - 2)$

9. $y + 3 = -2(x - 10)$

10. $y + 6 = -7(x - 2)$

11. $y = \dfrac{2}{5}(x + 1)$

12. $y = \dfrac{3}{7}(x + 4)$

FOR EXTRA HELP

10.5 EXERCISE SET

 Student Solutions Manual    PH Math/Tutor Center    CD/Video for Review   *Math XL* MathXL®   **MyMathLab** MyMathLab

Objective A *Write an equation of the line with each given slope, m, and y-intercept, (0, b). See Example 1.*

1. $m = 5, b = 3$

2. $m = -3, b = -3$

3. $m = -4, b = -\dfrac{1}{6}$

4. $m = 2, b = \dfrac{3}{4}$

5. $m = \dfrac{2}{3}, b = 0$

6. $m = -\dfrac{4}{5}, b = 0$

7. $m = 0, b = -8$

8. $m = 0, b = -2$

9. $m = -\dfrac{1}{5}, b = \dfrac{1}{9}$

10. $m = \dfrac{1}{2}, b = -\dfrac{1}{3}$

Objective B *Use the slope-intercept form to graph each equation. See Examples 2 and 3.*

11. $y = 2x + 1$

12. $y = -4x - 1$

13. $y = \dfrac{2}{3}x + 5$

14. $y = \dfrac{1}{4}x - 3$

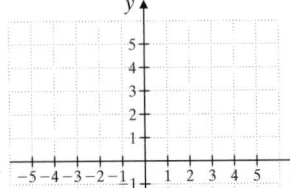
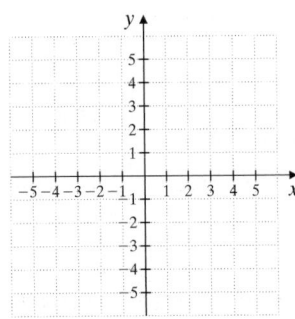
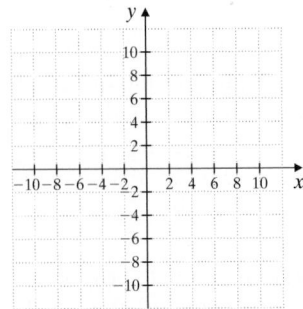
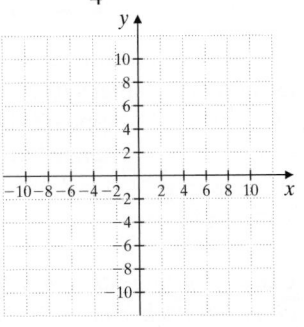

766

15. $y = -5x$

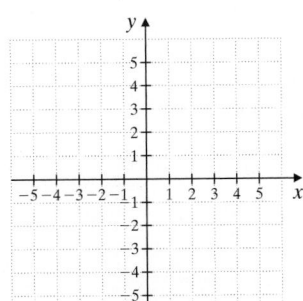

16. $y = -6x$

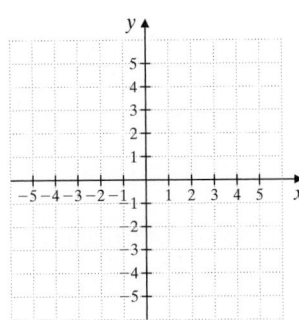

17. $4x + y = 6$

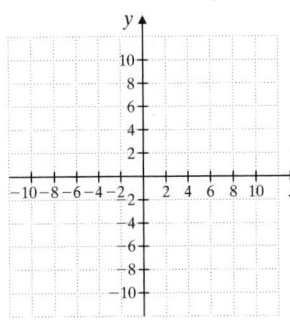

18. $-3x + y = 2$

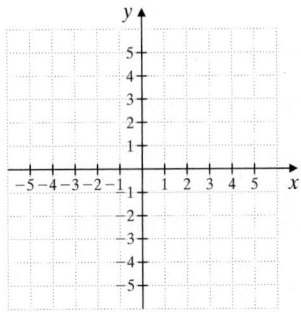

19. $4x - 7y = -14$

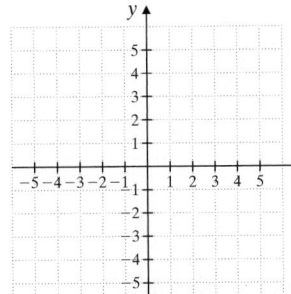

20. $3x - 4y = 4$

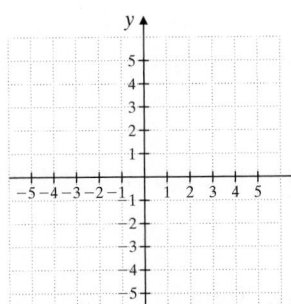

21. $x = \dfrac{5}{4}y$

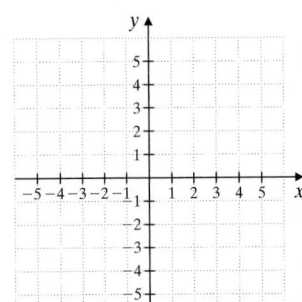

22. $x = \dfrac{3}{2}y$

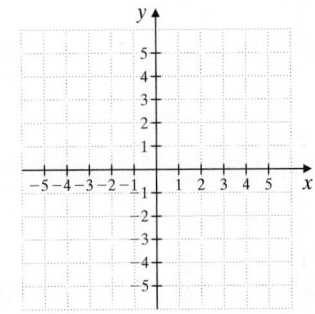

Objective **C** *Find an equation of each line with the given slope that passes through the given point. Write the equation in the form $Ax + By = C$. See Example 4.*

23. $m = 6$; $(2, 2)$

24. $m = 4$; $(1, 3)$

25. $m = -8$; $(-1, -5)$

26. $m = -2$; $(-11, -12)$

27. $m = \dfrac{3}{2}$; $(5, -6)$

28. $m = \dfrac{2}{3}$; $(-8, 9)$

29. $m = -\dfrac{1}{2}$; $(-3, 0)$

30. $m = -\dfrac{1}{5}$; $(4, 0)$

Objective **D** *Find an equation of the line passing through each pair of points. Write the equation in the form $Ax + By = C$. See Example 5.*

31. $(3, 2)$ and $(5, 6)$

32. $(6, 2)$ and $(8, 8)$

33. $(-1, 3)$ and $(-2, -5)$

34. $(-4, 0)$ and $(6, -1)$

35. $(2, 3)$ and $(-1, -1)$

36. $(7, 10)$ and $(-1, -1)$

37. $(0, 0)$ and $\left(-\dfrac{1}{8}, \dfrac{1}{13}\right)$

38. $(0, 0)$ and $\left(-\dfrac{1}{2}, \dfrac{1}{3}\right)$

Objectives **A** **C** **D** **Mixed Practice** *See Examples 1, 4, and 5. Find an equation of each line described. Write each equation in slope-intercept form when possible.*

39. With slope $-\dfrac{1}{2}$, through $\left(0, \dfrac{5}{3}\right)$

40. With slope $\dfrac{5}{7}$, through $(0, -3)$

41. Through $(10, 7)$ and $(7, 10)$

42. Through $(5, -6)$ and $(-6, 5)$

43. With undefined slope, through $\left(-\dfrac{3}{4}, 1\right)$

44. With slope 0, through $(6.7, 12.1)$

45. Slope 1, through $(-7, 9)$

46. Slope 5, through $(6, -8)$

47. Slope -5, y-intercept $(0, 7)$

48. Slope -2; y-intercept $(0, -4)$

49. Through $(6, 7)$, parallel to the x-axis

50. Through $(1, -5)$, parallel to the y-axis

51. Through $(2, 3)$ and $(0, 0)$

52. Through $(4, 7)$ and $(0, 0)$

53. Through $(-2, -3)$, perpendicular to the y-axis

54. Through $(0, 12)$, perpendicular to the x-axis

55. Slope $-\dfrac{4}{7}$, through $(-1, -2)$

56. Slope $-\dfrac{3}{5}$, through $(4, 4)$

Objective **E** *Solve. Assume each exercise describes a linear relationship. Write the equations in slope-intercept form. See Example 6.*

57. A rock is dropped from the top of a 400-foot cliff. After 1 second, the rock is traveling 32 feet per second. After 3 seconds, the rock is traveling 96 feet per second.

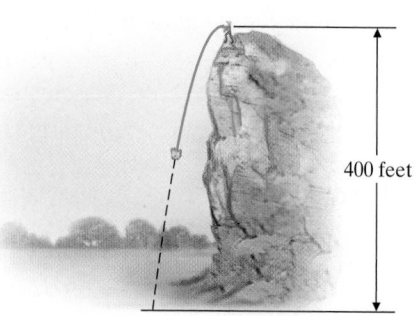

400 feet

  a. Assume that the relationship between time and speed is linear and write an equation describing this relationship. Use ordered pairs of the form (time, speed).

  b. Use this equation to determine the speed of the rock 4 seconds after it was dropped.

58. A Hawaiian fruit company is studying the sales of a pineapple sauce to see if this product is to be continued. At the end of its first year, profits on this product amounted to $30,000. At the end of the fourth year, profits were $66,000.

  a. Assume that the relationship between years on the market and profit is linear and write an equation describing this relationship. Use ordered pairs of the form (years on the market, profit).

  b. Use this equation to predict the profit at the end of 7 years.

59. In 2003 there were approximately 54,000 gas-electric hybrid vehicles sold in the United States. In 2001, there were only 22,000 such vehicles sold. (*Source:* Energy Information Administration, Department of Energy)

a. Write an equation describing the relationship between time and the number of gas-electric hybrid vehicles sold. Use ordered pairs of the form (years past 2001, number of vehicles sold).

b. Use this equation to predict the number of gas-electric hybrid sales in 2006.

60. In 2004, there were approximately 875 thousand restaurants in the United States. In 1972, there were 491 thousand restaurants. (*Source:* National Restaurant Association)

a. Write an equation describing the relationship between time and the number of restaurants. Use ordered pairs of the form (years past 1972, numbers of restaurants in thousands).

b. Use this equation to predict the number of eating establishments in 2012.

61. In 2003 there were approximately 5700 cinema sites in the United States. In 1999 there were 7032 cinema sites. (*Source:* National Association of Theater Owners)

a. Write an equation describing this relationship. Use ordered pairs of the form (years past 1999, number of cinema sites).

b. Use this equation to predict the number of cinema sites in 2007.

62. In 2000, the U.S. population per square mile of land area was 79.6. In 1990, this person per square mile population was 70.3.

a. Write an equation describing the relationship between year and person per square mile. Use ordered pairs of the form (years past 1990, person per square mile).

b. Use this equation to predict the person per square mile population in 2007.

63. In 1997 there were 1509 daily newspapers in the United States. By 2003, there were only 1456 daily newspapers. (*Source:* Statistical Abstract of the United States)

a. Write two ordered pairs of the form (years after 1997, number of daily newspapers) for this situation.

b. The relationship between years after 1997 and numbers of daily newspapers is linear over this period. Use the ordered pairs from part (a) to write an equation for the line relating year after 1997 to numbers of daily newspapers. (Round the slope to one decimal place.)

c. Use the linear equation in part (b) to estimate numbers of daily newspapers in 1999. (Round to the nearest whole.)

64. In 1999, crude oil production by the European Union countries was 3803 thousand barrels per day. In 2002, European Union oil production had decreased to 3482 thousand barrels per day. (*Source:* Energy Information Administration)

a. Write two ordered pairs of the form (years after 1999, crude oil production).

b. Assume that the relationship between years after 1999 and crude oil production is linear over this period. Use the ordered pairs from part (a) to write an equation of the line relating year to crude oil production.

c. Use the linear equation from part (b) to estimate the crude oil production by European Union countries in 2005, if this trend were to continue.

65. The Pool Fun Company has learned that, by pricing a newly released Fun Noodle at $3, sales will reach 10,000 Fun Noodles per day during the summer. Raising the price to $5 will cause the sales to fall to 8000 Fun Noodles per day.

   a. Assume that the relationship between sales price and number of Fun Noodles sold is linear and write an equation describing this relationship. Use ordered pairs of the form (sales price, number sold).

   b. Predict the daily sales of Fun Noodles if the price is $3.50.

66. The value of a building bought in 1990 may be depreciated (or decreased) as time passes for income tax purposes. Seven years after the building was bought, this value was $225,000 and 12 years after it was bought, this value was $195,000.

   a. If the relationship between number of years past 1990 and the depreciated value of the building is linear, write an equation describing this relationship. Use ordered pairs of the form (years past 1990, value of building).

   b. Use this equation to estimate the depreciated value of the building in 2008.

Review

Find the value of $x^2 - 3x + 1$ for each given value of x. See Section 8.5.

67. 2   **68.** 5   **69.** -1 **70.** -3

Concept Extensions

Match each linear equation with its graph.

71. $y = 2x + 1$ **72.** $y = -x + 1$ **73.** $y = -3x - 2$ **74.** $y = \dfrac{5}{3}x - 2$

a.

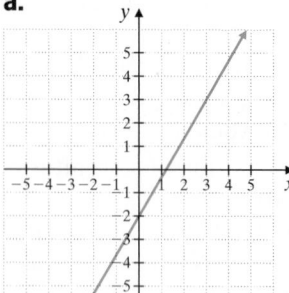

b.

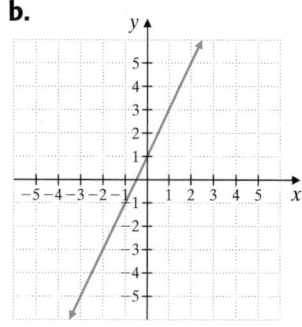

c.

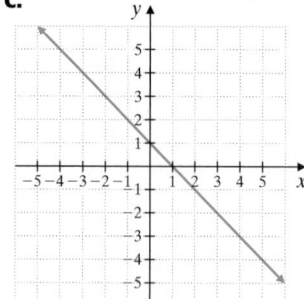

d.

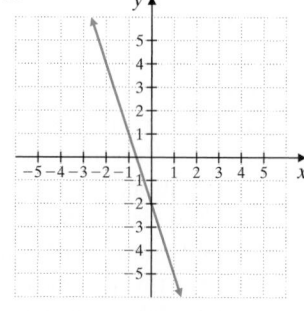

75. Write an equation of the line that contains the point $(-1, 2)$ and has the same slope as the line $y = 3x - 1$.

76. Write an equation of the line that contains the point $(4, 0)$ and has the same slope as the line $y = -2x + 3$.

△ **77.** Write an equation in standard form of the line that contains the point $(-1, 2)$ and is

   a. parallel to the line $y = 3x - 1$.

   b. perpendicular to the line $y = 3x - 1$.

△ **78.** Write an equation in standard form of the line that contains the point $(4, 0)$ and is

   a. parallel to the line $y = -2x + 3$.

   b. perpendicular to the line $y = -2x + 3$.

Summary on Linear Equations

Find the slope of each line.

1.

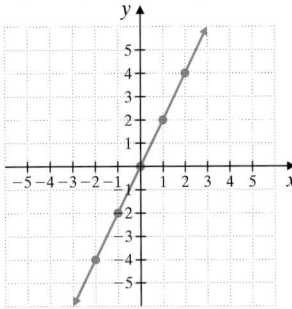

2.

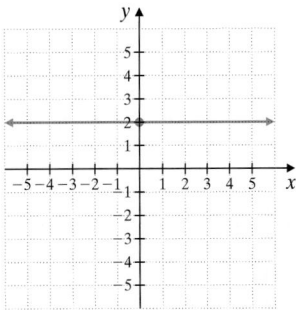

3.

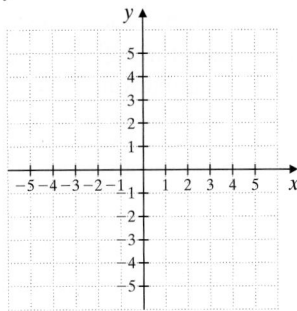

4.

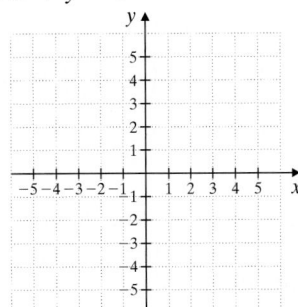

Graph each linear equation. For Exercises 11 and 12, label the intercepts.

5. $y = -2x$

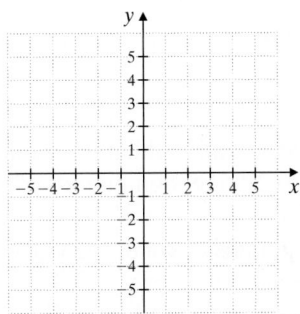

6. $x + y = 3$

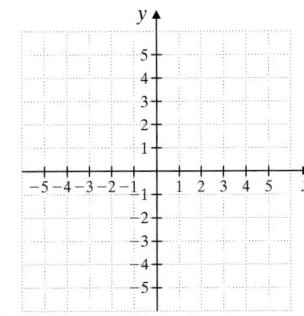

7. $x = -1$

8. $y = 4$

Answers

1. _____

2. _____

3. _____

4. _____

5. see graph

6. see graph

7. see graph

8. see graph

9. see graph

10. see graph

11. see graph

12. see graph

13. _____

14. _____

15. _____

16. _____

17. _____

18. _____

19. _____

20. _____

21. _____

22. _____

23. _____

24. a. _____

b. _____

c. _____

9. $x - 2y = 6$

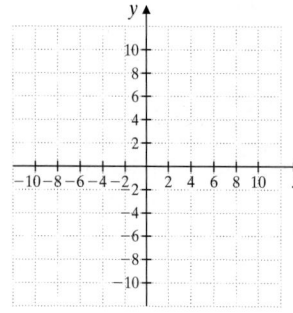

10. $y = 3x + 2$

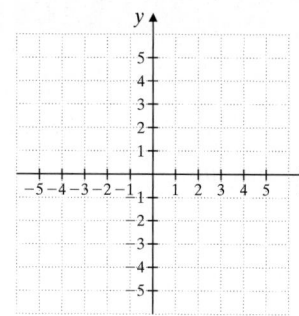

11. $y = -\dfrac{3}{4}x + 3$

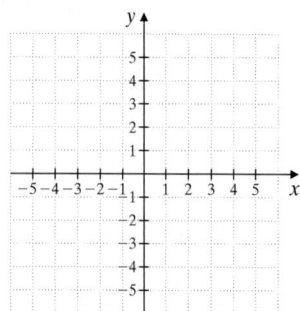

12. $5x - 2y = 8$

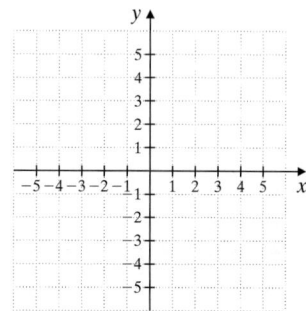

Find the slope of each line by writing the equation in slope-intercept form.

13. $y = 3x - 1$ **14.** $y = -6x + 2$ **15.** $7x + 2y = 11$ **16.** $2x - y = 0$

Find the slope of each line.

17. $x = 2$

18. $y = -4$

19. Write an equation of the line with slope $m = 2$ and y-intercept $\left(0, -\dfrac{1}{3}\right)$. Write the equation in the form $y = mx + b$.

20. Find an equation of the line with slope $m = -4$ that passes through the point $(-1, 3)$. Write the equation in the form $y = mx + b$.

21. Find an equation of the line that passes through the points $(2, 0)$ and $(-1, -3)$. Write the equation in the form $Ax + By = C$.

Determine whether each pair of lines is parallel, perpendicular, or neither.

22. $6x - y = 7$
    $2x + 3y = 4$

23. $3x - 6y = 4$
    $y = -2x$

24. Yogurt is an ever more popular food item. In 1998, American Dairy affiliates produced 1639 million pounds of yogurt. In 2002, this number rose to 2135 million pounds of yogurt.
   a. Write two ordered pairs of the form (year, millions of pounds of yogurt produced).
   b. Find the slope of the line between these two points.
   c. Write a sentence explaining the meaning of the slope as a rate of change.

10.6 INTRODUCTION TO FUNCTIONS

Objective **A** Identifying Relations, Domains, and Ranges

In this chapter, we have studied paired data in the form of ordered pairs. For example, when we list an ordered pair such as (3, 1), we are saying that when x is 3, then y is 1. In other words $x = 3$ and $y = 1$ are related to each other.

For this reason, we call a set of ordered pairs a **relation.** The set of all x-coordinates is called the **domain** of a relation, and the set of all y-coordinates is called the **range** of a relation.

EXAMPLE 1 Find the domain and the range of the relation $\{(0, 2), (3, 3), (-1, 0), (3, -2)\}$.

Solution: The domain is the set of all x-coordinates, or $\{-1, 0, 3\}$, and the range is the set of all y-coordinates, or $\{-2, 0, 2, 3\}$.

 Work Practice Problem 1

PRACTICE PROBLEM 1

Find the domain and range of the relation $\{(-3, 5), (-3, 1), (4, 6), (7, 0)\}$.

Objective **B** Identifying Functions

Paired data occur often in real-life applications. Some special sets of paired data, or ordered pairs, are called *functions*.

Function

A **function** is a set of ordered pairs in which each x-coordinate has exactly one y-coordinate.

In other words, a function cannot have two ordered pairs with the same x-coordinate but different y-coordinates.

EXAMPLE 2 Which of the following relations are also functions?

a. $\{(-1, 1), (2, 3), (7, 3), (8, 6)\}$
b. $\{(0, -2), (1, 5), (0, 3), (7, 7)\}$

Solution:

a. Although the ordered pairs (2, 3) and (7, 3) have the same y-value, each x-value is assigned to only one y-value, so this set of ordered pairs is a function.

b. The x-value 0 is paired with two y-values, -2 and 3, so this set of ordered pairs is not a function.

 Work Practice Problem 2

Relations and functions can be described by graphs of their ordered pairs.

PRACTICE PROBLEM 2

Are the following relations also functions?

a. $\{(2, 5), (-3, 7), (4, 5), (0, -1)\}$
b. $\{(1, 4), (6, 6), (1, -3), (7, 5)\}$

PRACTICE PROBLEM 3

Is each graph the graph of a function?

a.

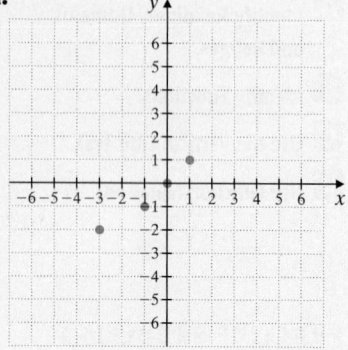

b.

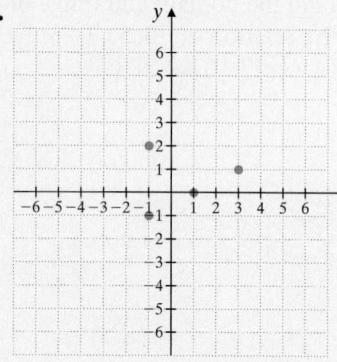

EXAMPLE 3 Which graph is the graph of a function?

a.

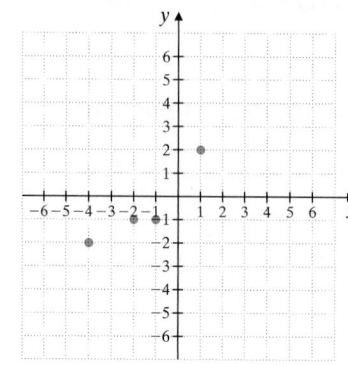

b.

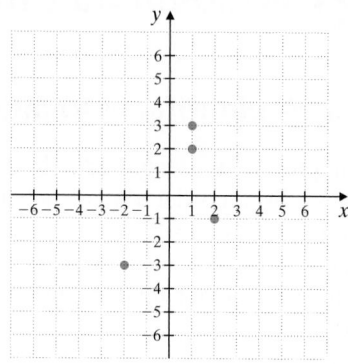

Solution:

a. This is the graph of the relation $\{(-4, -2), (-2, -1), (-1, -1), (1, 2)\}$. Each x-coordinate has exactly one y-coordinate, so this is the graph of a function.

b. This is the graph of the relation $\{(-2, -3), (1, 2), (1, 3), (2, -1)\}$. The x-coordinate 1 is paired with two y-coordinates, 2 and 3, so this is not the graph of a function.

■ **Work Practice Problem 3**

Objective C Using the Vertical Line Test

The graph in Example 3(b) was not the graph of a function because the x-coordinate 1 was paired with two y-coordinates, 2 and 3. Notice that when an x-coordinate is paired with more than one y-coordinate, a vertical line can be drawn that will intersect the graph at more than one point. We can use this fact to determine whether a relation is also a function. We call this the vertical line test.

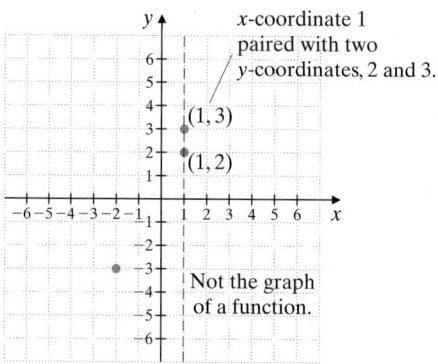

Vertical Line Test

If a vertical line can be drawn so that it intersects a graph more than once, the graph is not the graph of a function. (If no such vertical line can be drawn, the graph is that of a function.)

This vertical line test works for all types of graphs on the rectangular coordinate system.

Answers

3. a. a function, **b.** not a function

EXAMPLE 4 Use the vertical line test to determine whether each graph is the graph of a function.

a.

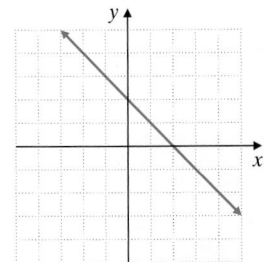

b.

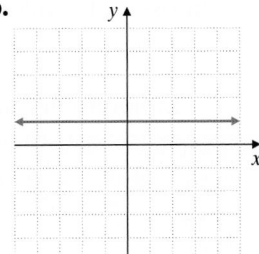

c.

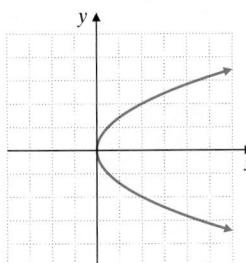

d.

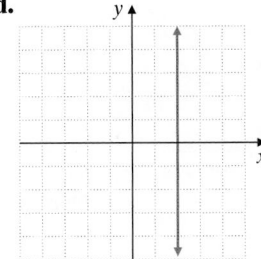

Solution:

a. This graph is the graph of a function since no vertical line will intersect this graph more than once.

b. This graph is also the graph of a function; no vertical line will intersect it more than once.

c. This graph is not the graph of a function. Vertical lines can be drawn that intersect the graph in two points. An example of one is shown.

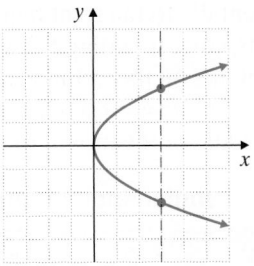

d. This graph is not the graph of a function. A vertical line can be drawn that intersects this line at every point.

🔲 **Work Practice Problem 4**

Examples of functions can often be found in magazines, newspapers, books, and other printed material in the form of tables or graphs such as that in Example 5.

PRACTICE PROBLEM 4

Determine whether each graph is the graph of a function.

a.

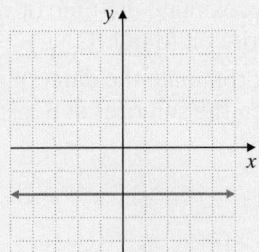

b.

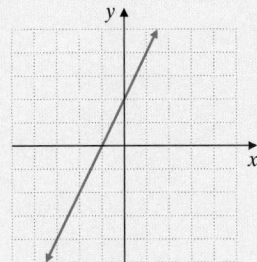

c.

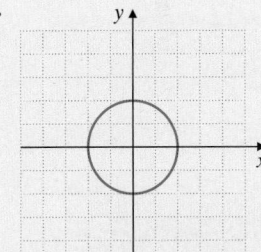

d.

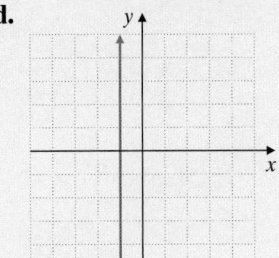

PRACTICE PROBLEM 5

Use the graph in Example 5 to answer the questions.

a. Approximate the time of sunrise on March 1.

b. Approximate the date(s) when the sun rises at 6 A.M.

EXAMPLE 5 The graph shows the sunrise time for Indianapolis, Indiana, for the year. Use this graph to answer the questions.

a. Approximate the time of sunrise on February 1.

b. Approximate the date(s) when the sun rises at 5 A.M.

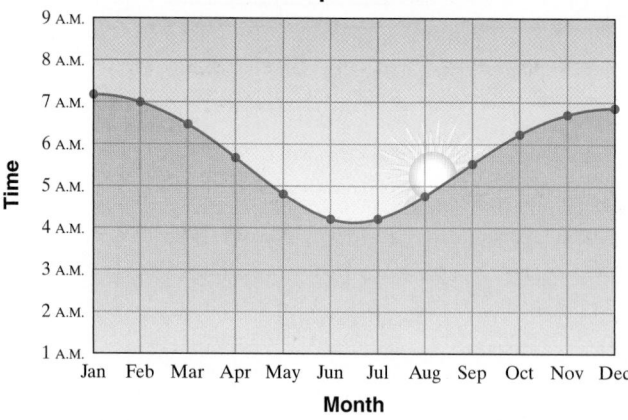

Source: Wolff World Atlas

c. Is this the graph of a function?

Solution:

a. To approximate the time of sunrise on February 1, we find the mark on the horizontal axis that corresponds to February 1. From this mark, we move vertically upward (shown in blue) until the graph is reached. From that point on the graph, we move horizontally to the left until the vertical axis is reached. The vertical axis there reads 7 A.M. as shown below.

b. To approximate the date(s) when the sun rises at 5 A.M., we find 5 A.M. on the time axis and move horizontally to the right (shown in red). Notice that we will hit the graph at two points, corresponding to two dates for which the sun rises at 5 A.M. We follow both points on the graph vertically downward until the horizontal axis is reached. The sun rises at 5 A.M. at approximately the end of the month of April and the middle of the month of August.

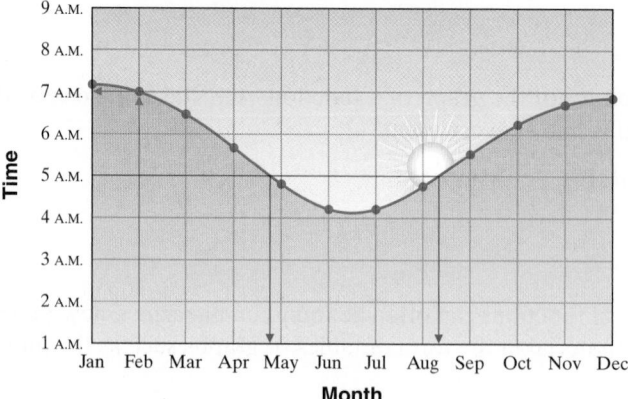

Source: Wolff World Atlas

c. The graph is the graph of a function since it passes the vertical line test. In other words, for every day of the year in Indianapolis, there is exactly one sunrise time.

■ **Work Practice Problem 5**

Answers

5. a. 6:30 A.M., **b.** middle of March and middle of September

Objective D Using Function Notation

The graph of the linear equation $y = 2x + 1$ passes the vertical line test, so we say that $y = 2x + 1$ is a function. In other words, $y = 2x + 1$ gives us a rule for writing ordered pairs where every x-coordinate is paired with at most one y-coordinate.

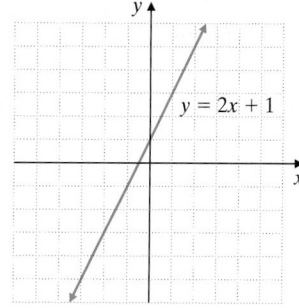

We often use letters such as f, g, and h to name functions. For example, the symbol $f(x)$ means *function of x* and is read "f of x." This notation is called **function notation.** The equation $y = 2x + 1$ can be written as $f(x) = 2x + 1$ using function notation, and these equations mean the same thing. In other words $y = f(x)$.

The notation $f(1)$ means to replace x with 1 and find the resulting y or function value. Since

$$f(x) = 2x + 1$$

then

$$f(1) = 2(1) + 1 = 3$$

This means that, when $x = 1$, y or $f(x) = 3$, and we have the ordered pair $(1, 3)$. Now let's find $f(2)$, $f(0)$, and $f(-1)$.

$$f(x) = 2x + 1 \qquad f(x) = 2x + 1 \qquad f(x) = 2x + 1$$
$$f(2) = 2(2) + 1 \qquad f(0) = 2(0) + 1 \qquad f(-1) = 2(-1) + 1$$
$$= 4 + 1 \qquad\qquad = 0 + 1 \qquad\qquad = -2 + 1$$
$$= 5 \qquad\qquad\quad = 1 \qquad\qquad\quad = -1$$

Ordered
Pair: $(2, 5)$ $(0, 1)$ $(-1, -1)$

> **Helpful Hint**
>
> Note that $f(x)$ is a special symbol in mathematics used to denote a function. The symbol $f(x)$ is read "f of x." It does **not** mean $f \cdot x$ (f times x).

EXAMPLE 6 Given $g(x) = x^2 - 3$, find the following and list the corresponding ordered pair.

a. $g(2)$ **b.** $g(-2)$ **c.** $g(0)$

Solution:

a. $g(x) = x^2 - 3$ **b.** $g(x) = x^2 - 3$ **c.** $g(x) = x^2 - 3$
     $g(2) = 2^2 - 3$ $g(-2) = (-2)^2 - 3$ $g(0) = 0^2 - 3$
        $= 4 - 3$ $= 4 - 3$ $= 0 - 3$
        $= 1$ $= 1$ $= -3$

Ordered
Pair: $(2, 1)$ $(-2, 1)$ $(0, -3)$

Work Practice Problem 6

✔**Concept Check** Suppose that the value of a function $f(x)$ is -7 when the function is evaluated at 2. Write this situation in function notation.

PRACTICE PROBLEM 6

Given $f(x) = x^2 + 1$, find the following and list the corresponding ordered pair.
a. $f(1)$
b. $f(-3)$
c. $f(0)$

FOR EXTRA HELP

Student Solutions Manual

PH Math/Tutor Center

CD/Video for Review

Math **XL**
MathXL®

MyMathLab
MyMathLab

Objective **A** *Find the domain and the range of each relation. See Example 1.*

1. $\{(2, 4), (0, 0), (-7, 10), (10, -7)\}$

2. $\{(3, -6), (1, 4), (-2, -2)\}$

3. $\{(0, -2), (1, -2), (5, -2)\}$

4. $\{(5, 0), (5, -3), (5, 4), (5, 3)\}$

Objective **B** *Determine whether each relation is also a function. See Example 2.*

5. $\{(1, 1), (2, 2), (-3, -3), (0, 0)\}$

6. $\{(11, 6), (-1, -2), (0, 0), (3, -2)\}$

7. $\{(-1, 0), (-1, 6), (-1, 8)\}$

8. $\{(1, 2), (3, 2), (1, 4)\}$

Objectives **B** **C** **Mixed Practice** *Determine whether each graph is the graph of a function. For Exercises 9 through 12, either write down the ordered pairs or use the vertical line test. See Examples 3 and 4.*

9.

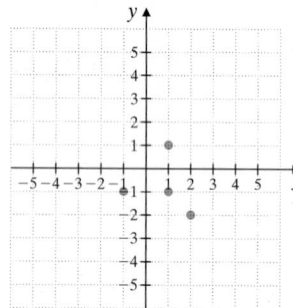

10.

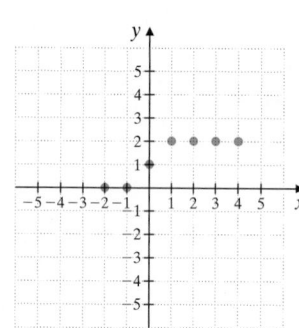

11.

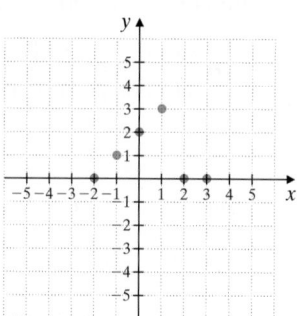

12.

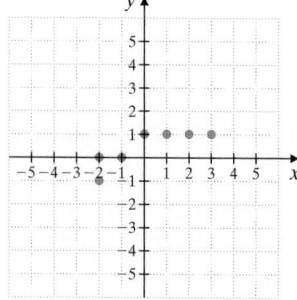

13.

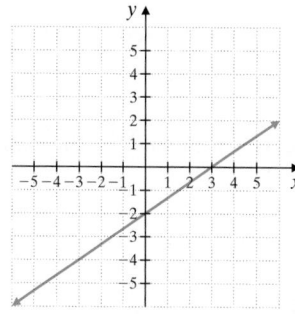

14.

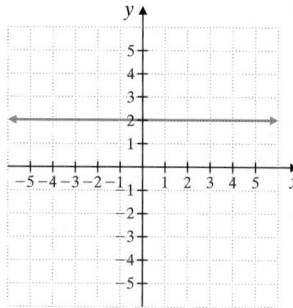

15.

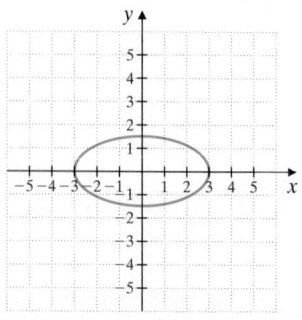

16.

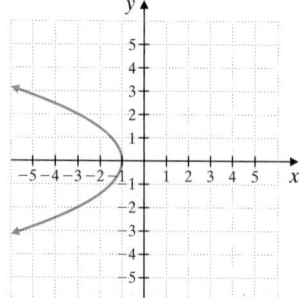

778

The graph shows the sunset times for Seward, Alaska. Use this graph to answer Exercises 17 through 22.

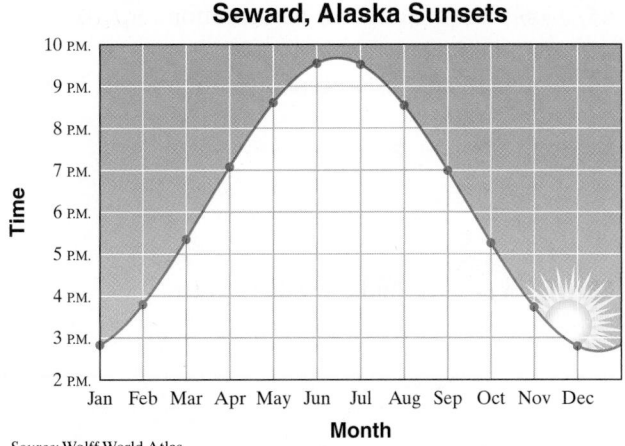

Seward, Alaska Sunsets

Source: Wolff World Atlas

17. Approximate the time of sunset on June 1.

18. Approximate the time of sunset on November 1.

19. Approximate the date(s) when the sunset is at 3 P.M.

20. Approximate the date(s) when the sunset is at 9 P.M.

21. Is this graph the graph of a function? Why or why not?

22. Do you think a graph of sunset times for any location will always be a function? Why or why not?

This graph shows the U.S. hourly minimum wage for each year shown. Use this graph to answer Exercises 23 through 28.

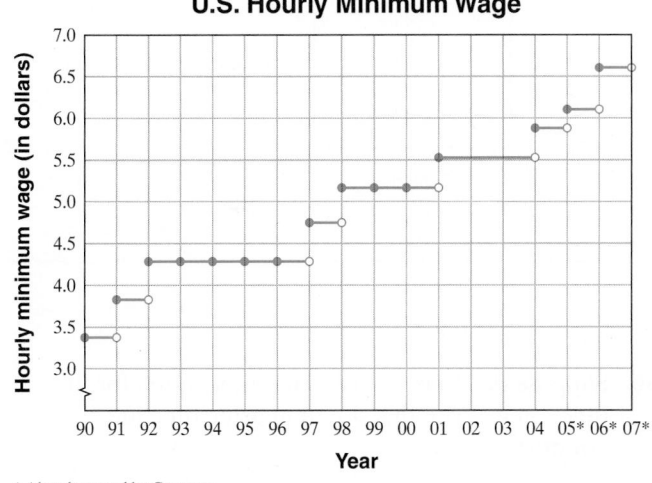

U.S. Hourly Minimum Wage

* Already passed by Congress

23. Approximate the minimum wage at the beginning of 1997.

24. Approximate the minimum wage at the beginning of 1999.

25. Approximate the year when the minimum wage will increase to over $5.75 per hour.

26. Approximate the year when the minimum wage increased to over $5.00 per hour.

27. Is this graph the graph of a function? Why or why not?

28. Do you think that a similar graph of your hourly wage on January 1 of every year (whether you are working or not) will be the graph of a function? Why or why not?

Objective D *Find $f(-2)$, $f(0)$, and $f(3)$ for each function. See Example 6.*

29. $f(x) = 2x - 5$

30. $f(x) = 3 - 7x$

31. $f(x) = x^2 + 2$

32. $f(x) = x^2 - 4$

33. $f(x) = 3x$

34. $f(x) = -3x$

35. $f(x) = |x|$

36. $f(x) = |2 - x|$

Find $h(-1)$, $h(0)$, and $h(4)$ for each function. See Example 6.

37. $h(x) = -5x$

38. $h(x) = -3x$

39. $h(x) = 2x^2 + 3$

40. $h(x) = 3x^2$

41. If $f(3) = 6$, write a corresponding ordered-pair solution.

42. If $f(7) = -2$, write a corresponding ordered-pair solution.

Use the graph of f below to answer Exercises 43 through 48.

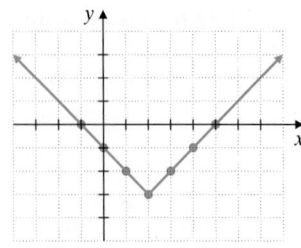

43. Complete the ordered-pair solution for f. $(0, \ )$

44. Complete the ordered-pair solution for f. $(3, \ )$

45. $f(0) = \underline{\quad}$?

46. $f(3) = \underline{\quad}$?

47. If $f(x) = 0$, find the value(s) of x.

48. If $f(x) = -1$, find the value(s) of x.

Review

Solve each inequality. See Section 9.7.

49. $2x + 5 < 7$

50. $3x - 1 \geq 11$

51. $-x + 6 \leq 9$

52. $-2x + 3 > 3$

Find the perimeter of each figure. See Section 6.3.

△ **53.**

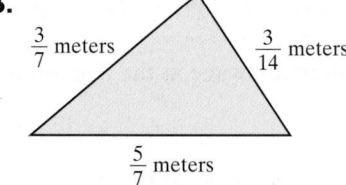

$\frac{3}{7}$ meters $\frac{3}{14}$ meters

$\frac{5}{7}$ meters

△ **54.**

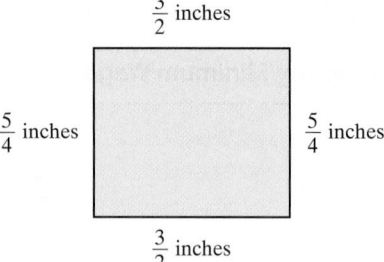

$\frac{3}{2}$ inches

$\frac{5}{4}$ inches $\frac{5}{4}$ inches

$\frac{3}{2}$ inches

Concept Extensions

Solve. See the Concept Check in this section.

55. If a function f is evaluated at -5, the value of the function is 12. Write this situation using function notation.

56. Suppose $(9, 20)$ is an ordered-pair solution for the function g. Write this situation using function notation.

57. In your own words define (a) function; (b) domain; (c) range.

58. Explain the vertical line test and how it is used.

59. Since $y = x + 7$ is a function, rewrite the equation using function notation.

60. Forensic scientists use the function
$$f(x) = 2.59x + 47.24$$
to estimate the height of a woman, in centimeters, given the length x of her femur bone in centimeters.

  a. Estimate the height of a woman whose femur measures 46 centimeters.

  b. Estimate the height of a woman whose femur measures 39 centimeters.

61. The dosage in milligrams of Ivermectin, a heartworm preventive for a dog who weighs x pounds, is given by the function
$$f(x) = \frac{136}{25}x$$

  a. Find the proper dosage for a dog that weighs 35 pounds.

  b. Find the proper dosage for a dog that weighs 70 pounds.

10.7 GRAPHING LINEAR INEQUALITIES IN TWO VARIABLES

A Determine Whether an Ordered Pair is a Solution of a Linear Inequality in Two Variables.

B Graph a Linear Inequality in Two Variables.

Recall that a linear equation in two variables is an equation that can be written in the form $Ax + By = C$, where A, B, and C are real numbers and A and B are not both 0. A **linear inequality in two variables** is an inequality that can be written in one of the forms

$$Ax + By < C \qquad Ax + By \leq C$$
$$Ax + By > C \qquad Ax + By \geq C$$

where A, B, and C are real numbers and A and B are not both 0.

Objective **A** Determining Solutions of Linear Inequalities in Two Variables

Just as for linear equations in x and y, an ordered pair is a **solution** of an inequality in x and y if replacing the variables with the coordinates of the ordered pair results in a true statement.

EXAMPLE 1 Determine whether each ordered pair is a solution of the inequality $2x - y < 6$.

a. $(5, -1)$ **b.** $(2, 7)$

Solution:

a. We replace x with 5 and y with -1 and see if a true statement results.

$$2x - y < 6$$
$$2(5) - (-1) < 6 \quad \text{Replace } x \text{ with 5 and } y \text{ with } -1.$$
$$10 + 1 < 6$$
$$11 < 6 \quad \text{False}$$

The ordered pair $(5, -1)$ is not a solution since $11 < 6$ is a false statement.

b. We replace x with 2 and y with 7 and see if a true statement results.

$$2x - y < 6$$
$$2(2) - (7) < 6 \quad \text{Replace } x \text{ with 2 and } y \text{ with 7.}$$
$$4 - 7 < 6$$
$$-3 < 6 \quad \text{True}$$

The ordered pair $(2, 7)$ is a solution since $-3 < 6$ is a true statement.

■ **Work Practice Problem 1**

Objective **B** Graphing Linear Inequalities in Two Variables

The linear equation $x - y = 1$ is graphed next. Recall that all points on the line correspond to ordered pairs that satisfy the equation $x - y = 1$.

Notice the line defined by $x - y = 1$ divides the rectangular coordinate system plane into 2 sides. All points on one side of the line satisfy the inequality $x - y < 1$ and all points on the other side satisfy the inequality $x - y > 1$. The graph on the next page shows a few examples of this.

PRACTICE PROBLEM 1

Determine whether each ordered pair is a solution of $x - 4y > 8$.

a. $(-3, 2)$

b. $(9, 0)$

Answers

1. a. no, **b.** yes

$x - y < 1$
$1 - 3 < 1$ True
$-2 - 1 < 1$ True
$-4 - (-4) < 1$ True

$x - y > 1$
$4 - 1 > 1$ True
$2 - (-2) > 1$ True
$0 - (-4) > 1$ True

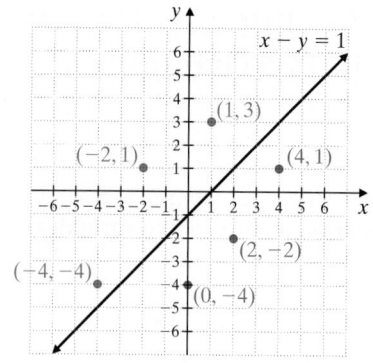

The graph of $x - y < 1$ is the region shaded blue and the graph of $x - y > 1$ is the region shaded red below.

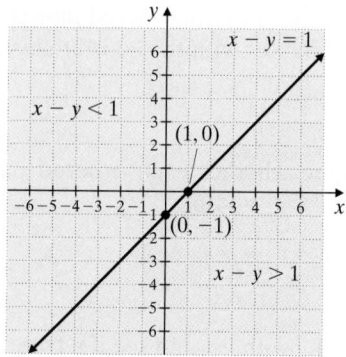

The region to the left of the line and the region to the right of the line are called **half-planes.** Every line divides the plane (similar to a sheet of paper extending indefinitely in all directions) into two half-planes; the line is called the **boundary.**

Recall that the inequality $x - y \le 1$ means

$$x - y = 1 \quad \text{or} \quad x - y < 1$$

Thus, the graph of $x - y \le 1$ is the half-plane $x - y < 1$ along with the boundary line $x - y = 1$.

To Graph a Linear Inequality in Two Variables

Step 1: Graph the boundary line found by replacing the inequality sign with an equal sign. If the inequality sign is $>$ or $<$, graph a dashed boundary line (indicating that the points on the line are not solutions of the inequality). If the inequality sign is $\ge$ or $\le$, graph a solid boundary line (indicating that the points on the line are solutions of the inequality).

Step 2: Choose a point, *not* on the boundary line, as a test point. Substitute the coordinates of this test point into the *original* inequality.

Step 3: If a true statement is obtained in Step 2, shade the half-plane that contains the test point. If a false statement is obtained, shade the half-plane that does not contain the test point.

EXAMPLE 2 Graph: $x + y < 7$

Solution:

Step 1: First we graph the boundary line by graphing the equation $x + y = 7$. We graph this boundary as a *dashed line* because the inequality sign is $<$, and thus the points on the line are not solutions of the inequality $x + y < 7$.

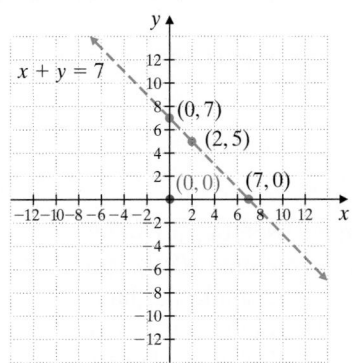

Step 2: Next we choose a test point, being careful *not* to choose a point on the boundary line. We choose $(0, 0)$, and substitute the coordinates of $(0, 0)$ into $x + y < 7$.

$x + y < 7$ Original inequality

$0 + 0 < 7$ Replace x with 0 and y with 0.

$0 < 7$ True

Step 3: Since the result is a true statement, $(0, 0)$ is a solution of $x + y < 7$, and every point in the same half-plane as $(0, 0)$ is also a solution. To indicate this, we shade the entire half-plane containing $(0, 0)$, as shown.

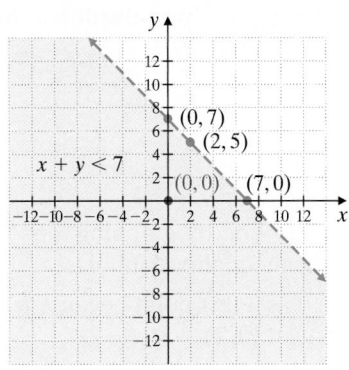

🔲 **Work Practice Problem 2**

✔ **Concept Check** Determine whether $(0, 0)$ is included in the graph of

a. $y \geq 2x + 3$

b. $x < 7$

c. $2x - 3y < 6$

PRACTICE PROBLEM 2

Graph: $x - y > 3$

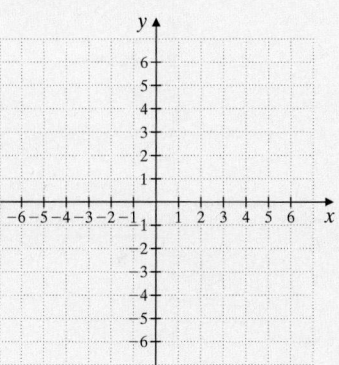

Answer

2.

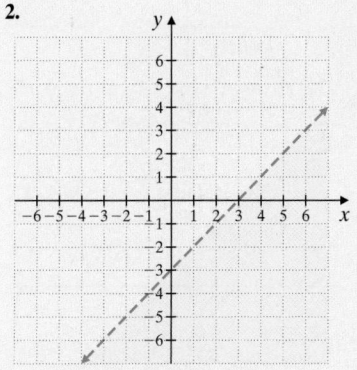

✔ **Concept Check Answers**

a. no,   **b.** yes,   **c.** yes

PRACTICE PROBLEM 3

Graph: $x - 4y \leq 4$

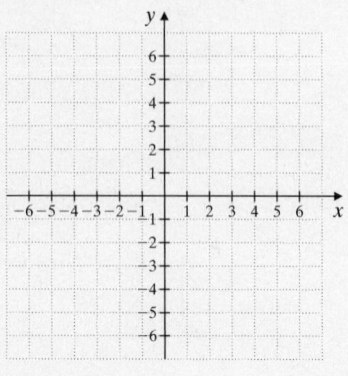

PRACTICE PROBLEM 4

Graph: $y < 3x$

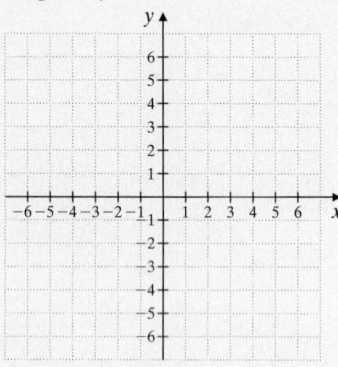

Answers

3.

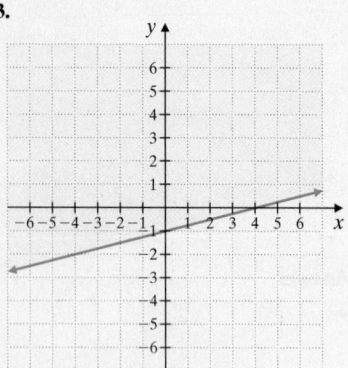

4.

EXAMPLE 3 Graph: $2x - y \geq 3$

Solution:

Step 1: We graph the boundary line by graphing $2x - y = 3$. We draw this line as a solid line because the inequality sign is $\geq$, and thus the points on the line are solutions of $2x - y \geq 3$.

Step 2: Once again, $(0, 0)$ is a convenient test point since it is not on the boundary line.

We substitute 0 for x and 0 for y into the original inequality.

$$2x - y \geq 3$$
$$2(0) - 0 \geq 3 \quad \text{Let } x = 0 \text{ and } y = 0.$$
$$0 \geq 3 \quad \text{False}$$

Step 3: Since the statement is false, no point in the half-plane containing $(0, 0)$ is a solution. Therefore, we shade the half-plane that does not contain $(0, 0)$. Every point in the shaded half-plane and every point on the boundary line is a solution of $2x - y \geq 3$.

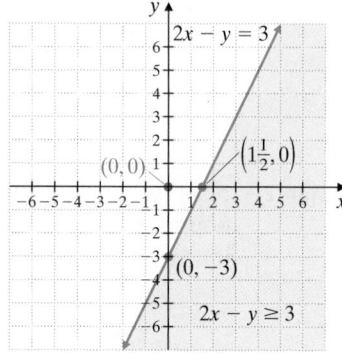

■ **Work Practice Problem 3**

Helpful Hint

When graphing an inequality, make sure the test point is substituted into the **original inequality.** For Example 3, we substituted the test point $(0, 0)$ into the **original inequality** $2x - y \geq 3$, *not* $2x - y = 3$.

EXAMPLE 4 Graph: $x > 2y$

Solution:

Step 1: We find the boundary line by graphing $x = 2y$. The boundary line is a dashed line since the inequality symbol is $>$.

Step 2: We cannot use $(0, 0)$ as a test point because it is a point on the boundary line. We choose instead $(0, 2)$.

$$x > 2y$$
$$0 > 2(2) \quad \text{Let } x = 0 \text{ and } y = 2.$$
$$0 > 4 \quad \text{False}$$

Step 3: Since the statement is false, we shade the half-plane that does not contain the test point $(0, 2)$, as shown.

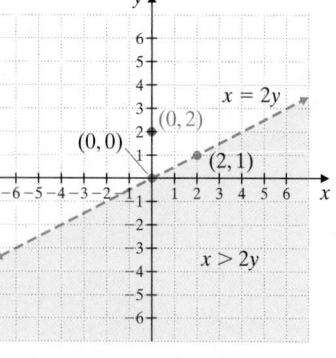

■ **Work Practice Problem 4**

EXAMPLE 5 Graph: $5x + 4y \leq 20$

Solution: We graph the solid boundary line $5x + 4y = 20$ and choose $(0, 0)$ as the test point.

$$5x + 4y \leq 20$$
$$5(0) + 4(0) \leq 20 \quad \text{Let } x = 0 \text{ and } y = 0.$$
$$0 \leq 20 \quad \text{True}$$

We shade the half-plane that contains $(0, 0)$, as shown.

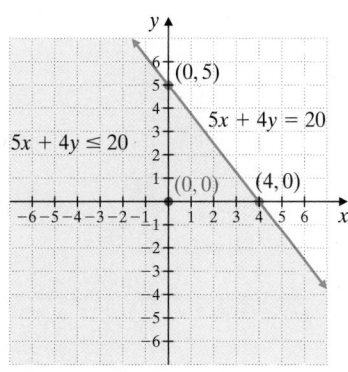

■ **Work Practice Problem 5**

EXAMPLE 6 Graph: $y > 3$

Solution: We graph the dashed boundary line $y = 3$ and choose $(0, 0)$ as the test point. (Recall that the graph of $y = 3$ is a horizontal line with y-intercept 3.)

$$y > 3$$
$$0 > 3 \quad \text{Let } y = 0.$$
$$0 > 3 \quad \text{False}$$

We shade the half-plane that does not contain $(0, 0)$, as shown.

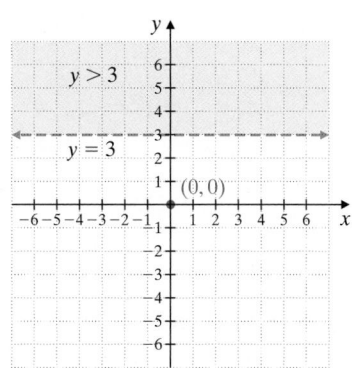

■ **Work Practice Problem 6**

PRACTICE PROBLEM 5

Graph: $3x + 2y \geq 12$

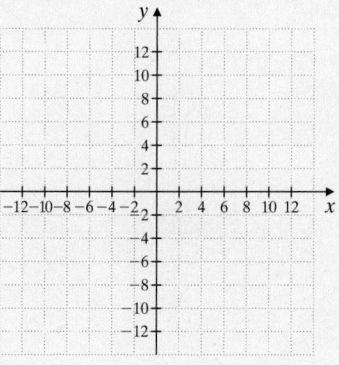

PRACTICE PROBLEM 6

Graph: $x < 2$

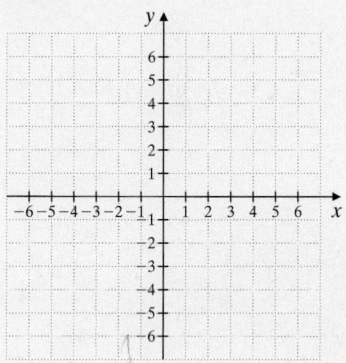

Answers

5.

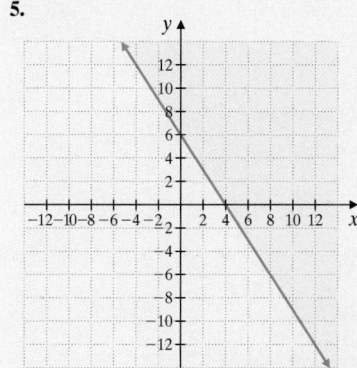

6.

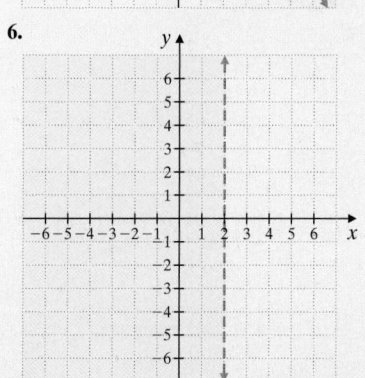

PRACTICE PROBLEM 7

Graph: $y \geq \dfrac{1}{4}x + 3$

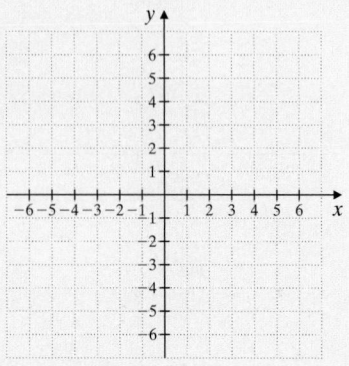

EXAMPLE 7 Graph: $y \leq \dfrac{2}{3}x - 4$

Solution: Graph the solid boundary line $y = \dfrac{2}{3}x - 4$. This equation is in slope-intercept form with slope $\dfrac{2}{3}$ and y-intercept -4.

We use this information to graph the line. Then we choose $(0, 0)$ as our test point.

$$y \leq \dfrac{2}{3}x - 4$$

$$0 \leq \dfrac{2}{3} \cdot 0 - 4$$

$$0 \leq -4 \quad \text{False}$$

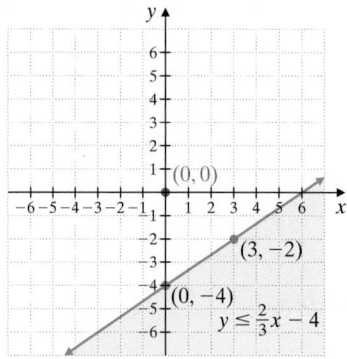

We shade the half-plane that does not contain $(0, 0)$, as shown.

▣ **Work Practice Problem 7**

Answer

7.

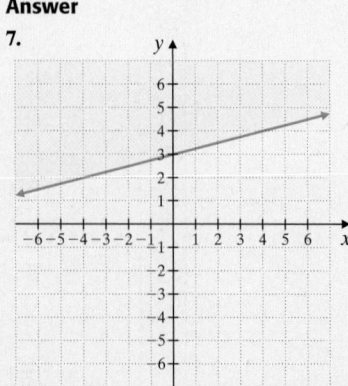

Mental Math

State whether the graph of each inequality includes its corresponding boundary line.

1. $y \geq x + 4$

2. $x - y > -7$

3. $y \geq x$

4. $x > 0$

Decide whether $(0, 0)$ is a solution of each given inequality.

5. $x + y > -5$

6. $2x + 3y < 10$

7. $x - y \leq -1$

8. $\dfrac{2}{3}x + \dfrac{5}{6}y > 4$

10.7 EXERCISE SET

Objective A Determine whether the ordered pairs given are solutions of the linear inequality in two variables. See Example 1.

1. $x - y > 3$; $(0, 3), (2, -1)$

2. $y - x < -2$; $(2, 1), (5, -1)$

3. $3x - 5y \leq -4$; $(2, 3), (-1, -1)$

4. $2x + y \geq 10$; $(0, 11), (5, 0)$

5. $x < -y$; $(0, 2), (-5, 1)$

6. $y > 3x$; $(0, 0), (1, 4)$

Objective B Graph each inequality. See Examples 2 through 7.

7. $x + y \leq 1$

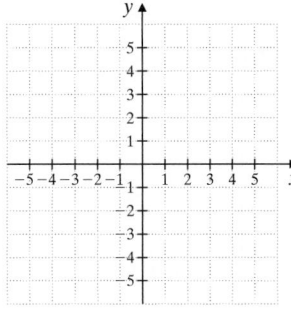

8. $x + y \geq -2$

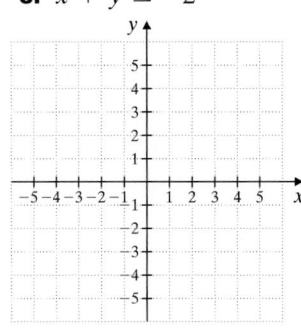

9. $2x - y > -4$

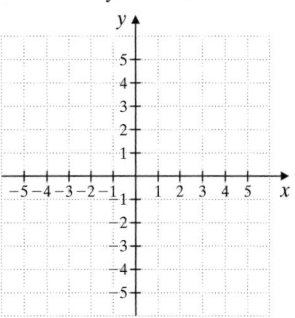

10. $x - 3y < 3$

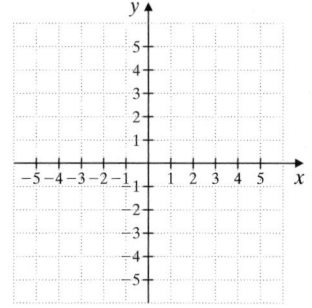

11. $y > 2x$

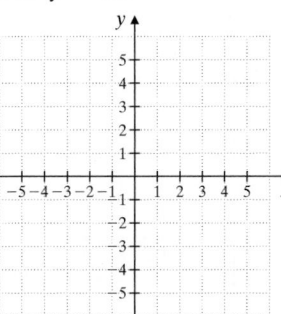

12. $y < 3x$

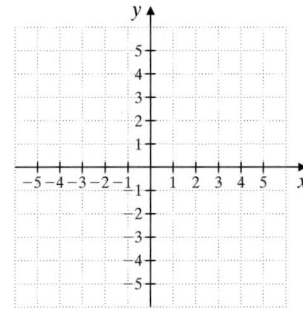

13. $x \leq -3y$

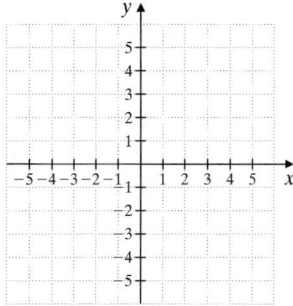

14. $x \geq -2y$

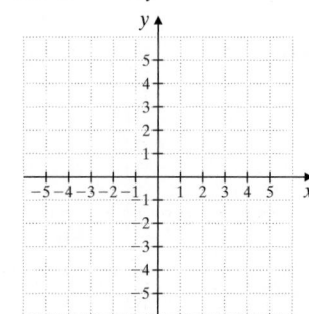

15. $y \geq x + 5$

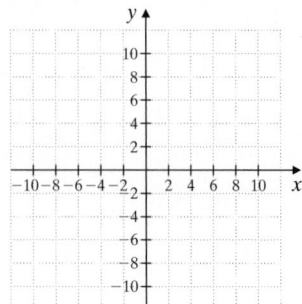

16. $y \leq x + 1$

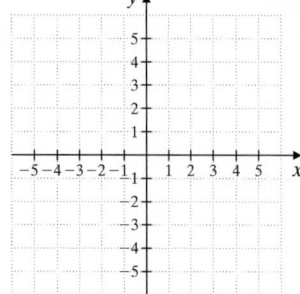

17. $y < 4$

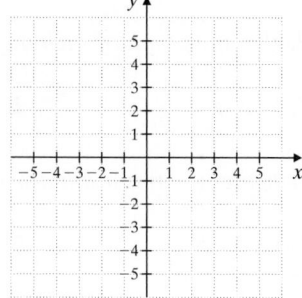

18. $y > 2$

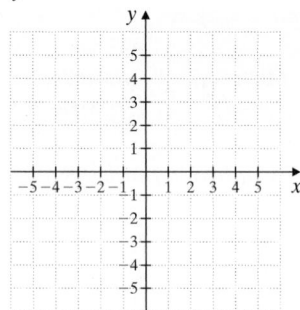

19. $x \geq -3$

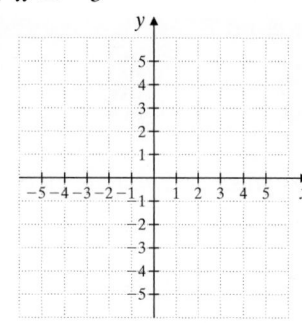

20. $x \leq -1$

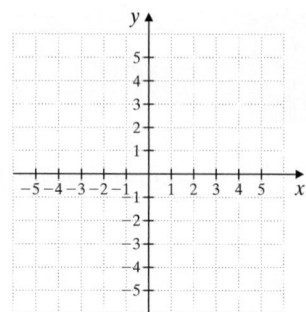

21. $5x + 2y \leq 10$

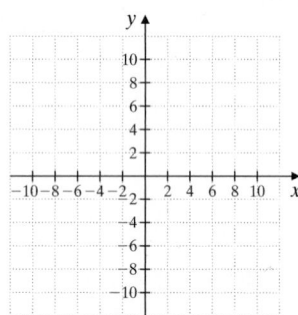

22. $4x + 3y \geq 12$

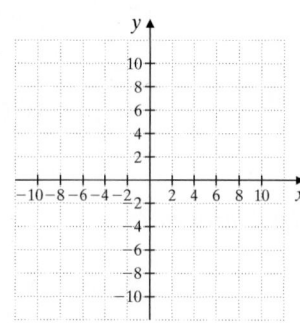

23. $x > y$

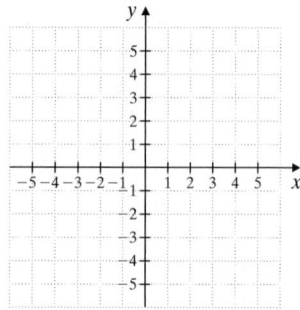

24. $x \leq -y$

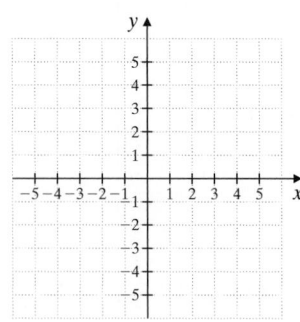

25. $x - y \leq 6$

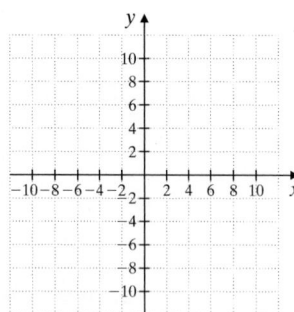

26. $x - y > 10$

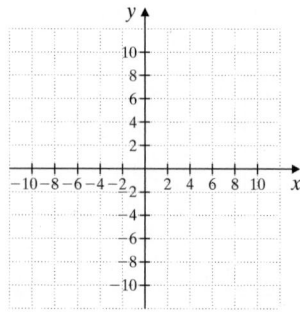

27. $x \geq 0$

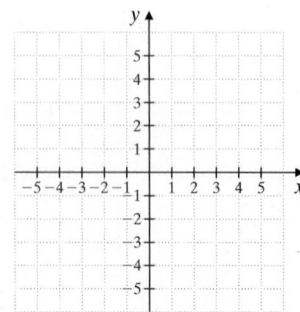

28. $y \leq 0$

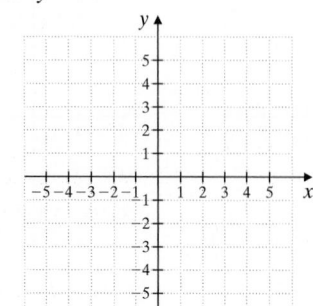

29. $2x + 7y > 5$

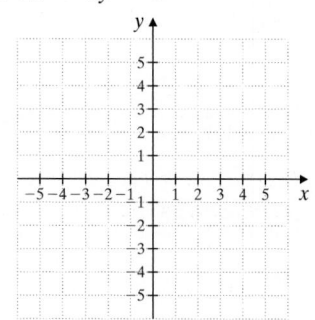

30. $3x + 5y \leq -2$

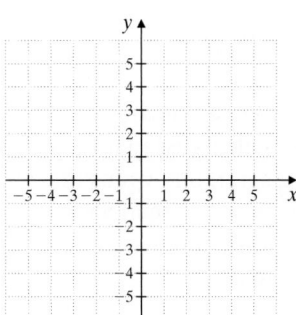

31. $y \geq \dfrac{1}{2}x - 4$

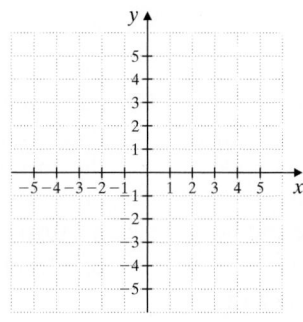

32. $y < \dfrac{2}{5}x - 3$

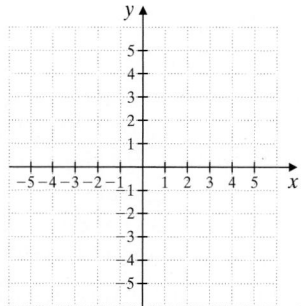

Review

Approximate the coordinates of each point of intersection. See Section 10.1.

33.

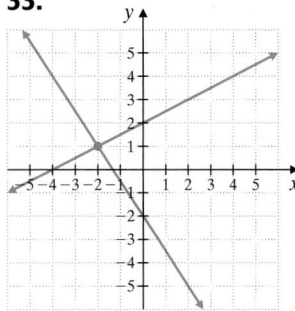

34.

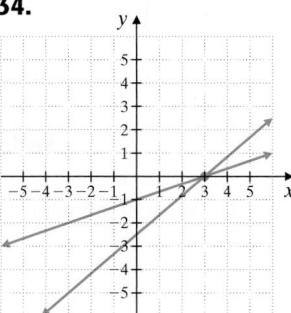

35.

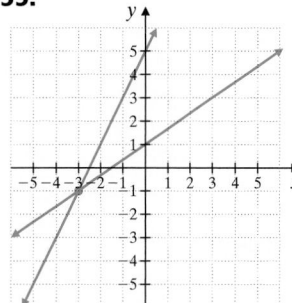

36.

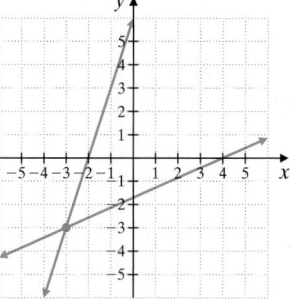

Concept Extensions

Match each inequality with its graph.

a. $x > 2$ **b.** $y < 2$ **c.** $y \leq 2x$ **d.** $y \leq -3x$

37.

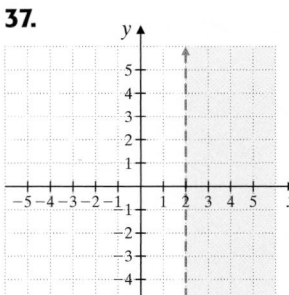

38.

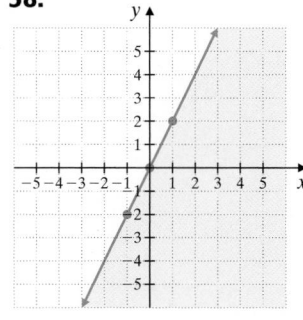

39.

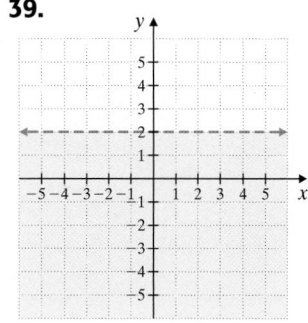

40.

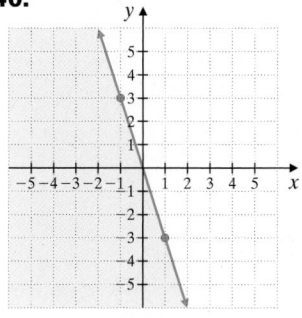

41. Explain why a point on the boundary line should not be chosen as the test point.

42. Write an inequality whose solutions are all points of numbers whose sum is at least 13.

Determine whether $(1, 1)$ *is included in each graph. See the Concept Check in this section.*

43. $3x + 4y < 8$ **44.** $y > 5x$ **45.** $y \geq -\dfrac{1}{2}x$ **46.** $x > 3$

47. It's the end of the budgeting period for Dennis Fernandes and he has $500 left in his budget for car rental expenses. He plans to spend this budget on a sales trip throughout southern Texas. He will rent a car that costs $30 per day and $0.15 per mile and he can spend no more than $500.

    a. Write an inequality describing this situation. Let x = number of days and let y = number of miles.

    b. Graph this inequality below.

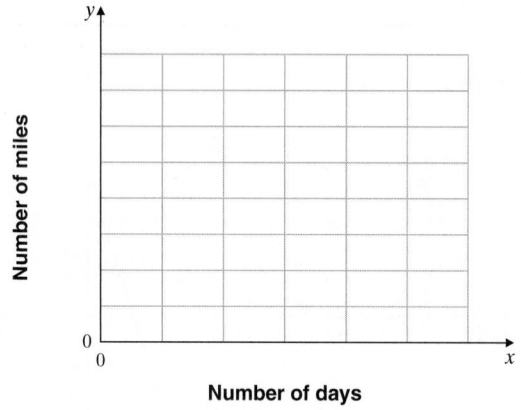

    c. Why is the grid showing quadrant I only?

48. Scott Sambracci and Sara Thygeson are planning their wedding. They have calculated that they want the cost of their wedding ceremony x plus the cost of their reception y to be no more than $5000.

    a. Write an inequality describing this relationship.

    b. Graph this inequality below.

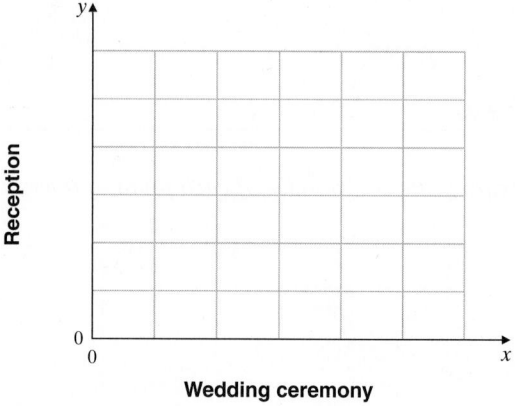

    c. Why is the grid showing quadrant I only?

10.8 DIRECT AND INVERSE VARIATION

In Chapter 9, we studied linear equations in two variables. Recall that such an equation can be written in the form $Ax + By = C$, where A and B are not both 0. Also recall that the graph of a linear equation in two variables is a line. In this section, we begin by looking at a particular family of linear equations—those that can be written in the form

$$y = kx$$

where k is a constant. This family of equations is called *direct variation*.

Objective **A** Solving Direct Variation Problems

Let's suppose that you are earning $7.25 per hour at a part-time job. The amount of money you earn depends on the number of hours you work. This is illustrated by the following table:

Hours Worked	0	1	2	3	4
Money Earned (before deductions)	0	7.25	14.50	21.75	29.00

and so on

In general, to calculate your earnings (before deductions), multiply the constant $7.25 by the number of hours you work. If we let y represent the amount of money earned and x represent the number of hours worked, we get the direct variation equation

$$y = 7.25 \cdot x$$

earnings $= \$7.25 \cdot$ hours worked

Notice that in this direct variation equation, as the number of hours increases, the pay increases as well.

Direct Variation

y varies directly as x, or **y is directly proportional to x,** if there is a nonzero constant k such that

$$y = kx$$

The number k is called the **constant of variation** or the **constant of proportionality.**

In our direct variation example, $y = 7.25x$, the constant of variation is 7.25.

Let's use the previous table to graph $y = 7.25x$. We begin our graph at the ordered-pair solution $(0, 0)$. Why? We assume that the least amount of hours worked is 0. If 0 hours are worked, then the pay is $0.

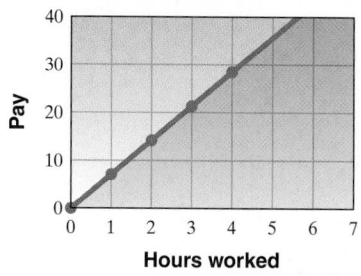

As illustrated in this graph, a direct variation equation $y = kx$ is linear. Also notice that $y = 7.25x$ is a function since its graph passes the vertical line test.

PRACTICE PROBLEM 1

Write a direct variation equation that satisfies:

x	4	$\frac{1}{2}$	1.5	6
y	8	1	3	12

EXAMPLE 1 Write a direct variation equation of the form $y = kx$ that satisfies the ordered pairs in the table below.

x	2	9	1.5	−1
y	6	27	4.5	−3

Solution: We are given that there is a direct variation relationship between x and y. This means that

$$y = kx$$

By studying the given values, you may be able to mentally calculate k. If not, to find k, we simply substitute one given ordered pair into this equation and solve for k. We'll use the given pair $(2, 6)$.

$$y = kx$$
$$6 = k \cdot 2$$
$$\frac{6}{2} = \frac{k \cdot 2}{2}$$
$$3 = k \qquad \text{Solve for } k.$$

Since $k = 3$, we have the equation $y = 3x$.
To check, see that each given y is 3 times the given x.

◼ **Work Practice Problem 1**

Let's try another type of direct variation example.

PRACTICE PROBLEM 2

Suppose that y varies directly as x. If y is 15 when x is 45, find the constant of variation and the direct variation equation. Then find y when x is 3.

EXAMPLE 2 Suppose that y varies directly as x. If y is 17 when x is 34, find the constant of variation and the direct variation equation. Then find y when x is 12.

Solution: Let's use the same method as in Example 1 to find k. Since we are told that y varies directly as x, we know the relationship is of the form

$$y = kx$$

Let $y = 17$ and $x = 34$ and solve for k.

$$17 = k \cdot 34$$
$$\frac{17}{34} = \frac{k \cdot 34}{34}$$
$$\frac{1}{2} = k \qquad \text{Solve for } k.$$

Thus, the constant of variation is $\frac{1}{2}$ and the equation is $y = \frac{1}{2}x$.

To find y when $x = 12$, use $y = \frac{1}{2}x$ and replace x with 12.

$$y = \frac{1}{2}x$$
$$y = \frac{1}{2} \cdot 12 \qquad \text{Replace } x \text{ with 12.}$$
$$y = 6$$

Thus, when x is 12, y is 6.

◼ **Work Practice Problem 2**

Answers
1. $y = 2x$, **2.** $k = \frac{1}{3}$; $y = \frac{1}{3}x$; $y = 1$

Let's review a few facts about linear equations of the form $y = kx$.

Direct Variation: y = kx

- There is a direct variation relationship between x and y.
- The graph is a line.
- The line will always go through the origin $(0, 0)$. Why?

    Let $x = 0$. Then $y = k \cdot 0$ or $y = 0$.

- The slope of the graph of $y = kx$ is k, the constant of variation. Why? Remember that the slope of an equation of the form $y = mx + b$ is m, the coefficient of x.
- The equation $y = kx$ describes a function. Each x has a unique y and its graph passes the vertical line test.

EXAMPLE 3 The line is the graph of a direct variation equation. Find the constant of variation and the direct variation equation.

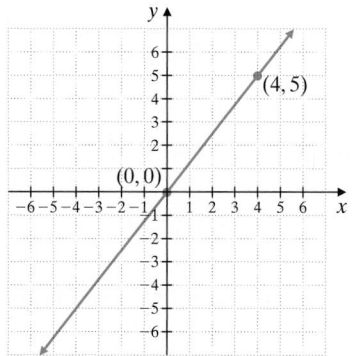

PRACTICAL PROBLEM 3

Find the constant of variation and the direct variation equation for the line below.

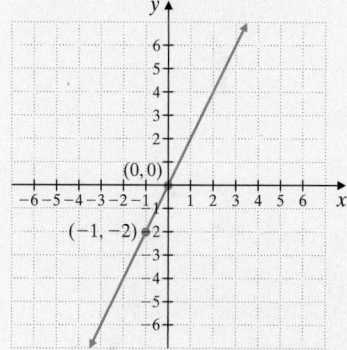

Solution: Recall that k, the constant of variation, is the same as the slope of the line. Thus, to find k, we use the slope formula and find slope.

Using the given points $(0, 0)$, and $(4, 5)$, we have

$$\text{slope} = \frac{5 - 0}{4 - 0} = \frac{5}{4}$$

Thus, $k = \dfrac{5}{4}$ and the variation equation is $y = \dfrac{5}{4}x$.

🔲 **Work Practice Problem 3**

Objective **B** Solving Inverse Variation Problems

In this section, we introduce another type of variation called inverse variation.

Let's suppose you need to drive a distance of 40 miles. You know that the faster you drive the distance, the sooner you arrive at your destination. Recall that there is a mathematical relationship between distance, rate, and time. It is $d = r \cdot t$. In our example, distance is a constant 40 miles, so we have $40 = r \cdot t$ or $t = \dfrac{40}{r}$.

For example, if you drive 10 mph, the time to drive the 40 miles is

$$t = \frac{40}{r} = \frac{40}{10} = 4 \text{ hours}$$

If you drive 20 mph, the time is

$$t = \frac{40}{r} = \frac{40}{20} = 2 \text{ hours}$$

Answer

3. $k = 2$; $y = 2x$

Again, notice that as speed increases, time decreases. Below are some ordered-pair solutions of $t = \dfrac{40}{r}$ and its graph.

Rate (mph)	r	5	10	20	40	60	80
Time (hr)	t	8	4	2	1	$\frac{2}{3}$	$\frac{1}{2}$

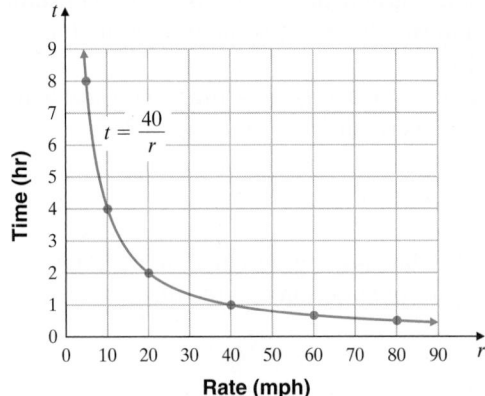

Notice that the graph of this variation is not a line, but it passes the vertical line test so $t = \dfrac{40}{r}$ does describe a function. This is an example of inverse variation.

Inverse Variation

y varies inversely as x, or **y is inversely proportional to x,** if there is a nonzero constant k such that

$$y = \frac{k}{x}$$

The number k is called the **constant of variation** or the **constant of proportionality.**

In our inverse variation example, $t = \dfrac{40}{r}$ or $y = \dfrac{40}{x}$, the constant of variation is 40.

We can immediately see differences and similarities in direct variation and inverse variation.

Direct Variation	$y = kx$	linear equation	both functions
Inverse Variation	$y = \frac{k}{x}$	nonlinear equation	

In Chapter 14 we will learn that $y = \dfrac{k}{x}$ is called a rational equation and is not a linear equation. Also notice that because x is in the denominator, x can be any value except 0.

We can still derive an inverse variation equation from a table of values.

EXAMPLE 4 Write an inverse variation equation of the form $y = \dfrac{k}{x}$ that satisfies the ordered pairs in the table below.

x	2	4	$\frac{1}{2}$
y	6	3	24

Solution: Since there is an inverse variation relationship between x and y, we know that $y = \dfrac{k}{x}$.

PRACTICE PROBLEM 4

Write an inverse variation equation of the form $y = \dfrac{k}{x}$ that satisfies:

x	4	10	40	-2
y	5	2	$\frac{1}{2}$	-10

Answer

4. $y = \dfrac{20}{x}$

To find k, choose one given ordered pair and substitute the values into the equation. We'll use $(2, 6)$.

$$y = \frac{k}{x}$$

$$6 = \frac{k}{2}$$

$$2 \cdot 6 = 2 \cdot \frac{k}{2} \quad \text{Multiply both sides by 2.}$$

$$12 = k \quad \text{Solve.}$$

Since $k = 12$, we have the equation $y = \frac{12}{x}$.

 **Work Practice Problem 4**

> ### Helpful Hint
>
> Multiply both sides of the inverse variation relationship equation $y = \frac{k}{x}$ by x (as long as x is not 0), and we have $xy = k$. This means that if y varies inversely as x, their product is always the constant of variation k. For an example of this, check the table from Example 4:
>
> | x | 2 | 4 | $\frac{1}{2}$ |
> |---|---|---|---|
> | y | 6 | 3 | 24 |
>
> $2 \cdot 6 = 12 \qquad 4 \cdot 3 = 12 \qquad \frac{1}{2} \cdot 24 = 12$

EXAMPLE 5 Suppose that y varies inversely as x. If $y = 0.02$ when $x = 75$, find the constant of variation and the inverse variation equation. Then find y when x is 30.

Solution: Since y varies inversely as x, the constant of variation may be found by simply finding the product of the given x and y.

$$k = xy = 75(0.02) = 1.5$$

To check, we will use the inverse variation equation

$$y = \frac{k}{x}$$

Let $y = 0.02$ and $x = 75$ and solve for k.

$$0.02 = \frac{k}{75}$$

$$75(0.02) = 75 \cdot \frac{k}{75} \quad \text{Multiply both sides by 75.}$$

$$1.5 = k \quad \text{Solve for } k.$$

Thus, the constant of variation is 1.5 and the equation is $y = \frac{1.5}{x}$. To find y when $x = 30$, use $y = \frac{1.5}{x}$ and replace x with 30.

$$y = \frac{1.5}{x}$$

$$y = \frac{1.5}{30} \quad \text{Replace } x \text{ with 30.}$$

$$y = 0.05$$

Thus, when x is 30, y is 0.05.

 **Work Practice Problem 5**

PRACTICE PROBLEM 5

Suppose that y varies inversely as x. If y is 4 when x is 0.8, find the constant of variation and the direct variation equation. Then find y when x is 20.

Answer

5. $k = 3.2$; $y = \frac{3.2}{x}$; $y = 0.16$

Objective C Solving Other Types of Direct and Inverse Variation Problems

It is possible for y to vary directly or inversely as powers of x.

Direct and Inverse Variation as nth Powers of x

y varies directly as a power of x if there is a nonzero constant k and a natural number n such that

$$y = kx^n$$

y varies inversely as a power of x if there is a nonzero constant k and a natural number n such that

$$y = \frac{k}{x^n}$$

PRACTICE PROBLEM 6

The area of a circle varies directly as the square of its radius. A circle with radius 7 inches has an area of 49π square inches. Find the area of a circle whose radius is 4 feet.

EXAMPLE 6 The surface area of a cube A varies directly as the square of a length of its sides. If A is 54 when s is 3, find A when $s = 4.2$.

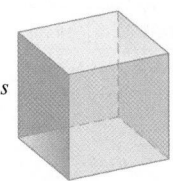

Solution: Since the surface area A varies directly as the square of side s, we have

$A = ks^2$

To find k, let $A = 54$ and $s = 3$.

$A = k \cdot s^2$

$54 = k \cdot 3^2$ Let $A = 54$ and $s = 3$.

$54 = 9k$ $3^2 = 9$.

$6 = k$ Divide by 9.

The formula for surface area of a cube is then

$A = 6s^2$ where s is the length of a side.

To find the surface area when $s = 4.2$, substitute.

$A = 6s^2$

$A = 6 \cdot (4.2)^2$

$A = 105.84$

The surface area of a cube whose side measures 4.2 units is 105.84 sq units.

💾 **Work Practice Problem 6**

Answer

6. 16π sq ft

Objective D Solving Applications of Variation

There are many real-life applications of direct and inverse variation.

EXAMPLE 7 The weight of a body w varies inversely with the square of its distance from the center of Earth, d. If a person weighs 160 pounds on the surface of Earth, what is the person's weight 200 miles above the surface? (Assume that the radius of Earth is 4000 miles.)

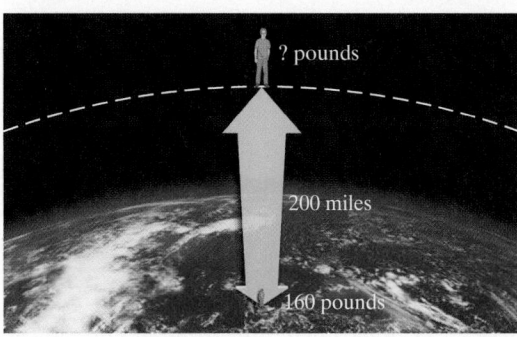

? pounds

200 miles

160 pounds

PRACTICE PROBLEM 7

The distance d that an object falls is directly proportional to the square of the time of the fall, t. If an object falls 144 feet in 3 seconds, find how far the object falls in 5 seconds.

Solution:

1. UNDERSTAND. Make sure you read and reread the problem.
2. TRANSLATE. Since we are told that weight w varies inversely with the square of its distance from the center of Earth, d, we have

$$w = \frac{k}{d^2}$$

3. SOLVE. To solve the problem, we first find k. To do so, use the fact that the person weighs 160 pounds on Earth's surface, which is a distance of 4000 miles from the Earth's center.

$$w = \frac{k}{d^2}$$

$$160 = \frac{k}{(4000)^2}$$

$$2{,}560{,}000{,}000 = k$$

Thus, we have $w = \dfrac{2{,}560{,}000{,}000}{d^2}$.

Since we want to know the person's weight 200 miles above the Earth's surface, we let $d = 4200$ and find w.

$$w = \frac{2{,}560{,}000{,}000}{d^2}$$

$$w = \frac{2{,}560{,}000{,}000}{(4200)^2}$$ A person 200 miles above the Earth's surface is 4200 miles from the Earth's center.

$$w \approx 145$$ Simplify.

4. INTERPRET. *Check:* Your answer is reasonable since the farther a person is from Earth, the less the person weighs. *State:* Thus, 200 miles above the surface of the Earth, a 160-pound person weighs approximately 145 pounds.

Work Practice Problem 7

Answer

7. 400 feet

Mental Math

State whether each equation represents direct or indirect variation.

1. $y = 5x$

2. $y = \dfrac{5}{x}$

3. $y = \dfrac{7}{x^2}$

4. $y = 6.5x^4$

5. $y = \dfrac{11}{x}$

6. $y = 18x$

7. $y = 12x^2$

8. $y = \dfrac{20}{x^3}$

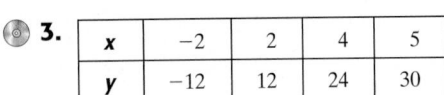

10.8 EXERCISE SET

FOR EXTRA HELP

Student Solutions Manual · PH Math/Tutor Center · CD/Video for Review · Math XL MathXL® · MyMathLab MyMathLab

Objective A *Write a direct variation equation, $y = kx$, that satisfies the ordered pairs in each table. See Example 1.*

1.

x	0	6	10
y	0	3	5

2.

x	0	2	−1	3
y	0	14	−7	21

3.

x	−2	2	4	5
y	−12	12	24	30

4.

x	3	9	−2	12
y	1	3	$-\dfrac{2}{3}$	4

Write a direct variation equation, $y = kx$, that describes each graph. See Example 3.

5.

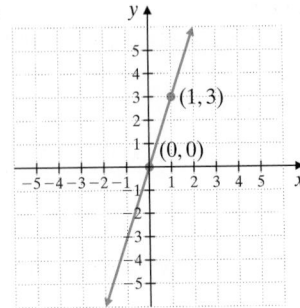

6.

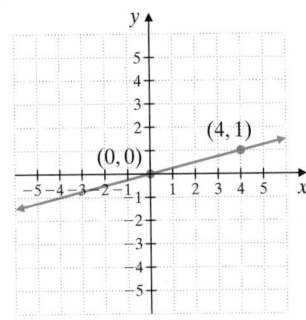

7.

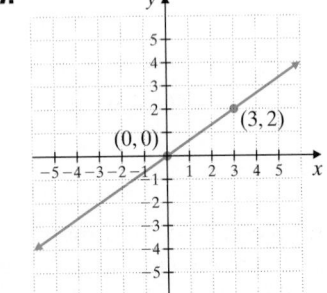

8.

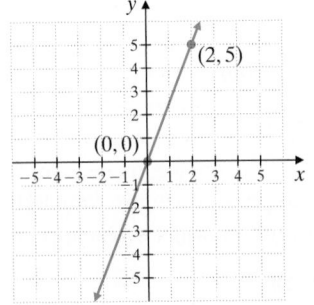

Objective **B** *Write an inverse variation equation,* $y = \dfrac{k}{x}$, *that satisfies the ordered pairs in each table. See Example 4.*

9.

x	1	−7	3.5	−2
y	7	−1	2	−3.5

10.

x	2	−11	4	−4
y	11	−2	5.5	−5.5

11.

x	10	$\dfrac{1}{2}$	$-\dfrac{1}{4}$
y	0.05	1	−2

12.

x	4	$\dfrac{1}{5}$	−8
y	0.1	2	−0.05

Objectives **A** **B** *Write an equation to describe each variation. Use k for the constant of proportionality. See Examples 1 through 5.*

13. y varies directly as x **14.** a varies directly as b **15.** h varies inversely as t **16.** s varies inversely as t

17. z varies directly as x^2 **18.** p varies inversely as x^2 **19.** y varies inversely as z^3 **20.** x varies directly as y^4

21. x varies inversely as $\sqrt{y}$ **22.** y varies directly as d^2

Objectives **A** **B** **C** *Solve. See Examples 2, 5, and 6.*

23. y varies directly as x. If $y = 20$ when $x = 5$, find y when x is 10.

24. y varies directly as x. If $y = 27$ when $x = 3$, find y when x is 2.

25. y varies inversely as x. If $y = 5$ when $x = 60$, find y when x is 100.

26. y varies inversely as x. If $y = 200$ when $x = 5$, find y when x is 4.

27. z varies directly as x^2. If $z = 96$ when $x = 4$, find z when $x = 3$.

28. s varies directly as t^3. If $s = 270$ when $t = 3$, find s when $x = 1$.

29. a varies inversely as b^3. If $a = \dfrac{3}{2}$ when $b = 2$, find a when b is 3.

30. p varies inversely as q^2. If $p = \dfrac{5}{16}$ when $q = 8$, find p when $q = \dfrac{1}{2}$.

Objectives **C** **D** *Solve. See Examples 1 through 7.*

31. Your paycheck (before deductions) varies directly as the number of hours you work. If your paycheck is $112.50 for 18 hours, find your pay for 10 hours.

32. If your paycheck (before deductions) is $244.50 for 30 hours, find your pay for 34 hours. (See Exercise 31.)

33. The cost of manufacturing a certain type of headphone varies inversely as the number of headphones increases. If 5000 headphones can be manufactured for $9.00 each, find the cost to manufacture 7500 headphones.

34. The cost of manufacturing a certain composition notebook varies inversely as the number of notebooks increases. If 10,000 notebooks can be manufactured for $0.50 each, find the cost to manufacture 18,000 notebooks. Round your answer to the nearest cent.

35. The distance a spring stretches varies directly with the weight attached to the spring. If a 60-pound weight stretches the spring 4 inches, find the distance that an 80-pound weight stretches the spring.

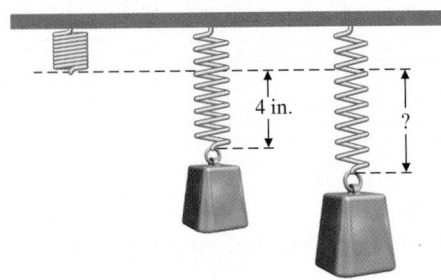

36. If a 30-pound weight stretches a spring 10 inches, find the distance a 20-pound weight stretches the spring. (See Exercise 35.)

37. The weight of an object varies inversely as the square of its distance from the *center* of the Earth. If a person weighs 180 pounds on Earth's surface, what is his weight 10 miles above the surface of the Earth? (Assume that the Earth's radius is 4000 miles and round your answer to one decimal place.)

38. For a constant distance, the rate of travel varies inversely as the time traveled. If a family travels 55 mph and arrives at a destination in 4 hours, how long will the return trip take traveling at 60 mph?

39. The distance d that an object falls is directly proportional to the square of the time of the fall, t. A person who is parachuting for the first time is told to wait ten seconds before opening the parachute. If the person falls 64 feet in 2 seconds, find how far he falls in 10 seconds.

40. The distance needed for a car to stop, d, is directly proportional to the square of its rate of travel, r. Under certain driving conditions, a car traveling 60 mph needs 300 feet to stop. With these same driving conditions, how long does it take a car to stop if the car is traveling 30 mph when the brakes are applied?

Review

Add the equations. See Section 8.7.

41. $-3x + 4y = 7$
$\underline{3x - 2y = 9}$

42. $x - y = -9$
$\underline{-x - y = -14}$

43. $5x - 0.4y = 0.7$
$\underline{-9x + 0.4y = -0.2}$

44. $1.9x - 2y = 5.7$
$\underline{-1.9x - 0.1y = 2.3}$

Concept Extensions

45. Suppose that y varies directly as x. If x is tripled, what is the effect on y?

46. Suppose that y varies directly as x^2. If x is tripled, what is the effect on y?

47. The period of a pendulum p (the time of one complete back-and-forth swing) varies directly with the square root of its length, ℓ. If the length of the pendulum is quadrupled, what is the effect on the period, p?

48. For a constant distance, the rate of travel r varies inversely with the time traveled, t. If a car traveling 100 mph completes a test track in 6 minutes, find the rate needed to complete the same test track in 4 minutes. (*Hint:* Convert minutes to hours.)

CHAPTER 10 Group Activity

Finding a Linear Model

This activity may be completed by working in groups or individually.

The following table shows the actual number of foreign visitors (in millions) to the United States for the years 2000 through 2003.

Year	Foreign Visitors to the United States (in millions)
2000	50.9
2001	44.8
2002	41.9
2003	40.4

(*Source:* Tourism Industries/International Trade Administration, U.S. Department of Commerce)

1. Make a scatter diagram of the paired data in the table.

2. Use what you have learned in this chapter to write an equation of the line representing the paired data in the table. Explain how you found the equation, and what each variable represents.

3. What is the slope of your line? What does the slope mean in this context?

4. Use your linear equation to predict the number of foreign visitors to the United States in 2010.

5. Compare your linear equation to that found by other students or groups. Is it the same, similar, or different? How?

6. Compare your prediction from Question 3 to that of other students or groups. Describe what you find.

7. The number of visitors to the United States for 2004 was estimated to be 45.7 million. If this data point is added to the chart above, how does it affect your results?

Chapter 10 Vocabulary Check

Fill in each blank with one of the words listed below.

y-axis	*x*-axis	solution	linear	standard	point-slope
x-intercept	*y*-intercept	*y*	*x*	slope	relation
domain	range	direct	inverse	slope-intercept	function

1. An ordered pair is a _____ of an equation in two variables if replacing the variables by the coordinates of the ordered pair results in a true statement.
2. The vertical number line in the rectangular coordinate system is called the _____.
3. A _____ equation can be written in the form $Ax + By = C$.
4. A(n) _____ is a point of the graph where the graph crosses the *x*-axis.
5. The form $Ax + By = C$ is called _____ form.
6. A(n) _____ is a point of the graph where the graph crosses the *y*-axis.
7. A set of ordered pairs that assigns to each *x*-value exactly one *y*-value is called a _____.
8. The equation $y = 7x - 5$ is written in _____ form.
9. The set of all *x*-coordinates of a relation is called the _____ of the relation.
10. The set of all *y*-coordinates of a relation is called the _____ of the relation.
11. A set of ordered pairs is called a _____.
12. The equation $y + 1 = 7(x - 2)$ is written in _____ form.
13. To find an *x*-intercept of a graph, let _____ = 0.
14. The horizontal number line in the rectangular coordinate system is called the _____.
15. To find a *y*-intercept of a graph, let _____ = 0.
16. The _____ of a line measures the steepness or tilt of a line.
17. The equation $y = kx$ is an example of _____ variation.
18. The equation $y = \dfrac{k}{x}$ is an example of _____ variation.

> **Helpful Hint**
>
> Are you preparing for your test? Don't forget to take the Chapter 10 Test on page 813. Then check your answers at the back of the text and use the Chapter Test Prep Video CD to see the fully worked-out solutions to any of the exercises you want to review.

10 Chapter Highlights

DEFINITIONS AND CONCEPTS	**EXAMPLES**

Section 10.1   Reading Graphs and the Rectangular Coordinate System

The **rectangular coordinate system** consists of a plane and a vertical and a horizontal number line intersecting at their 0 coordinate. The vertical number line is called the **y-axis** and the horizontal number line is called the **x-axis.** The point of intersection of the axes is called the **origin.**

To **plot** or **graph** an ordered pair means to find its corresponding point on a rectangular coordinate system.

To plot or graph an ordered pair such as $(3, -2)$, start at the origin. Move 3 units to the right and from there, 2 units down.

To plot or graph $(-3, 4)$; start at the origin. Move 3 units to the left and from there, 4 units up.

An ordered pair is a **solution** of an equation in two variables if replacing the variables with the coordinates of the ordered pair results in a true statement.

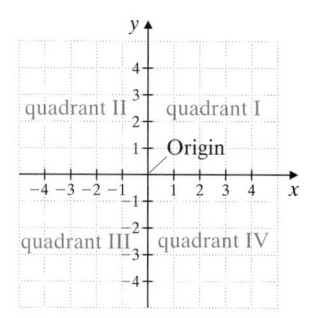

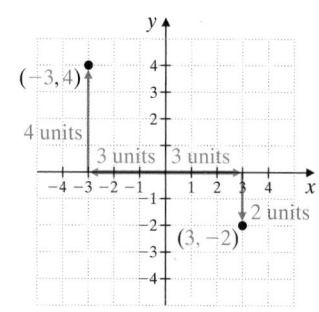

DEFINITIONS AND CONCEPTS	EXAMPLES

Section 10.1   Reading Graphs and The Rectangular Coordinate System (*continued*)

If one coordinate of an ordered pair solution is known, the other value can be determined by substitution.

Complete the ordered pair $(0, \ )$ for the equation $x - 6y = 12$.

$$x - 6y = 12$$
$$0 - 6y = 12 \quad \text{Let } x = 0.$$
$$\frac{-6y}{-6} = \frac{12}{-6} \quad \text{Divide by } -6.$$
$$y = -2$$

The ordered pair solution is $(0, -2)$.

Section 10.2   Graphing Linear Equations

A **linear equation in two variables** is an equation that can be written in the form $Ax + By = C$, where A and B are not both 0. The form $Ax + By = C$ is called **standard form.**

$$3x + 2y = -6 \qquad x = -5$$
$$y = 3 \qquad y = -x + 10$$

$x + y = 10$ is in standard form.

To graph a linear equation in two variables, find three ordered pair solutions. Plot the solution points and draw the line connecting the points.

Graph: $x - 2y = 5$

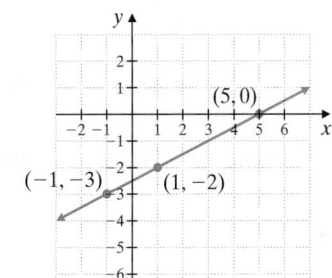

x	y
5	0
1	-2
-1	-3

Section 10.3   Intercepts

An **intercept** of a graph is a point where the graph intersects an axis. If a graph intersects the x-axis at a, then $(a, 0)$ is an **x-intercept.** If a graph intersects the y-axis at b, then $(0, b)$ is a **y-intercept.**

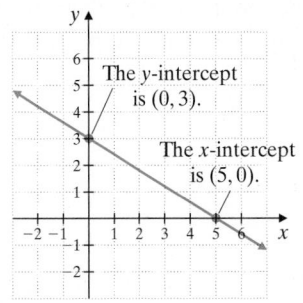

The y-intercept is $(0, 3)$.

The x-intercept is $(5, 0)$.

To find the x-intercept(s), let $y = 0$ and solve for x.
To find the y-intercept(s), let $x = 0$ and solve for y.

Find the intercepts for $2x - 5y = -10$.

If $y = 0$, then

$$2x - 5 \cdot 0 = -10$$
$$2x = -10$$
$$\frac{2x}{2} = \frac{-10}{2}$$
$$x = -5$$

If $x = 0$, then

$$2 \cdot 0 - 5y = -10$$
$$-5y = -10$$
$$\frac{-5y}{-5} = \frac{-10}{-5}$$
$$y = 2$$

continued

DEFINITIONS AND CONCEPTS	**EXAMPLES**

Section 10.3   Intercepts (*continued*)

	The x-intercept is $(-5, 0)$. The y-intercept is $(0, 2)$. 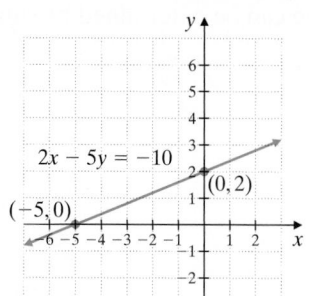
The graph of $x = c$ is a vertical line with x-intercept $(c, 0)$. The graph of $y = c$ is a horizontal line with y-intercept $(0, c)$.	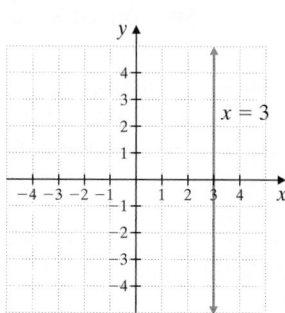 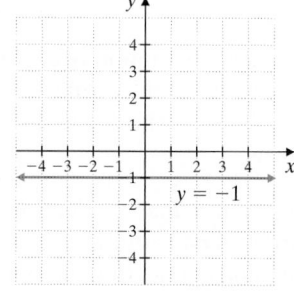

Section 10.4   Slope and Rate of Change

The **slope m** of the line through points (x_1, y_1) and (x_2, y_2) is given by

$$m = \frac{y_2 - y_1}{x_2 - x_1} \qquad \text{as long as } x_2 \neq x_1$$

A horizontal line has slope 0.
The slope of a vertical line is undefined.
Nonvertical parallel lines have the same slope.
Two nonvertical lines are perpendicular if the slope of one is the negative reciprocal of the slope of the other.

The slope of the line through points $(-1, 6)$ and $(-5, 8)$ is

$$m = \frac{y_2 - y_1}{x_2 - x_1} = \frac{8 - 6}{-5 - (-1)} = \frac{2}{-4} = -\frac{1}{2}$$

The slope of the line $y = -5$ is 0.
The line $x = 3$ has undefined slope.

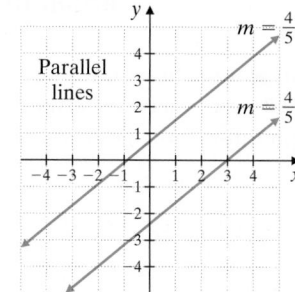   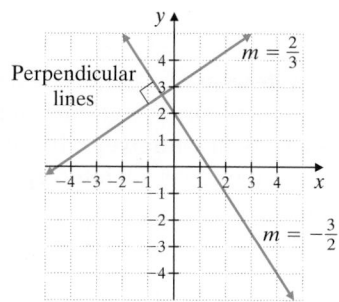

Section 10.5   Equations of Lines

SLOPE-INTERCEPT FORM

$$y = mx + b$$

m is the slope of the line.
$(0, b)$ is the y-intercept.

Find the slope and the y-intercept of the line $2x + 3y = 6$.
Solve for y:

$$2x + 3y = 6$$
$$3y = -2x + 6 \qquad \text{Subtract } 2x.$$
$$y = -\frac{2}{3}x + 2 \qquad \text{Divide by 3.}$$

The slope of the line is $-\frac{2}{3}$ and the y-intercept is $(0, 2)$.

DEFINITIONS AND CONCEPTS	**EXAMPLES**

Section 10.5   Equations of Lines (*continued*)

POINT-SLOPE FORM

$$y - y_1 = m(x - x_1)$$

m is the slope.
(x_1, y_1) is a point of the line.

Find an equation of the line with slope $\dfrac{3}{4}$ that contains the point $(-1, 5)$.

$$y - 5 = \frac{3}{4}[x - (-1)]$$

$4(y - 5) = 3(x + 1)$ Multiply by 4.

$4y - 20 = 3x + 3$ Distribute.

$-3x + 4y = 23$ Subtract $3x$ and add 20.

Section 10.6   Introduction to Functions

A set of ordered pairs is a **relation.** The set of all x-coordinates is called the **domain** of the relation and the set of all y-coordinates is called the **range** of the relation.

A **function** is a set of ordered pairs that assigns to each x-value exactly one y-value.

VERTICAL LINE TEST

If a vertical line can be drawn so that it intersects a graph more than once, the graph is not the graph of a function. (If no such line can be drawn, the graph is that of a function.)

The domain of the relation

$$\{(0, 5), (2, 5), (4, 5), (5, -2)\}$$

is $\{0, 2, 4, 5\}$. The range is $\{-2, 5\}$.

Which are graphs of functions?

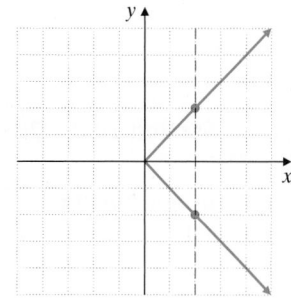   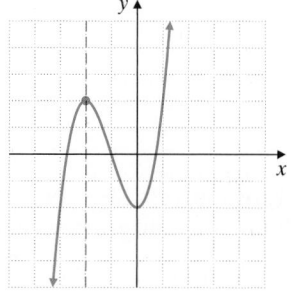

This graph is not the graph of a function.   This graph is the graph of a function.

The symbol $f(x)$ means **function of x.** This notation is called **function notation.**

If $f(x) = 3x - 7$, then

$$f(-1) = 3(-1) - 7$$
$$= -3 - 7$$
$$= -10$$

Section 10.7   Graphing Linear Inequalities in Two Variables

A **linear inequality in two variables** is an inequality that can be written in one of these forms:

$$Ax + By < C \qquad Ax + By \le C$$
$$Ax + By > C \qquad Ax + By \ge C$$

where A and B are not both 0.

$$2x - 5y < 6 \qquad x \ge -5$$
$$y > -8x \qquad y \le 2$$

continued

DEFINITIONS AND CONCEPTS	**EXAMPLES**
Section 10.7 Graphing Linear Inequalities in Two Variables (*continued*)	

TO GRAPH A LINEAR INEQUALITY

1. Graph the boundary line by graphing the related equation. Draw the line solid if the inequality symbol is $\leq$ or $\geq$. Draw the line dashed if the inequality symbol is $<$ or $>$.

2. Choose a test point not on the line. Substitute its coordinates into the original inequality.

3. If the resulting inequality is true, shade the half-plane that contains the test point. If the inequality is not true, shade the half-plane that does not contain the test point.

Graph: $2x - y \leq 4$

1. Graph $2x - y = 4$. Draw a solid line because the inequality symbol is $\leq$.

2. Check the test point $(0, 0)$ in the original inequality, $2x - y \leq 4$.

$$2 \cdot 0 - 0 \leq 4 \quad \text{Let } x = 0 \text{ and } y = 0.$$
$$0 \leq 4 \quad \text{True}$$

3. The inequality is true, so shade the half-plane containing $(0, 0)$ as shown.

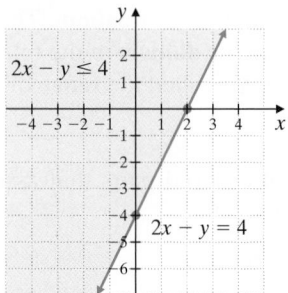

Section 10.8 Direct and Inverse Variation	

y **varies directly as** *x*, or *y* is **directly proportional to** *x*, if there is a nonzero constant k such that

$$y = kx$$

y **varies inversely as** *x*, or *y* is **inversely proportional to** *x*, if there is a nonzero constant k such that

$$y = \frac{k}{x}$$

The circumference of a circle C varies directly as its radius r.

$$C = \underbrace{2\pi}_{k} r$$

Pressure P varies inversely with volume V.

$$P = \frac{k}{V}$$

 STUDY SKILLS BUILDER

Are You Prepared for a Test on Chapter 10?

Below I have listed some common trouble areas for students in Chapter 10. After studying for your test—but before taking your test—read these.

- If you are having trouble with graphing, you might want to ask your instructor if you can use graph paper on your test. This will save you time and keep your graphs neat.

- Don't forget that the graph of an ordered pair is a *single* point in the rectangular coordinate system.

- Make sure you remember that to find the slope of a linear equation using its equation, *first* solve the equation for *y*. *Then* the coefficient of *x* is its slope.

$$2x + 3y = 7$$
$$3y = -2x + 7 \quad \text{Subtract } 2x \text{ from both sides.}$$
$$\frac{3y}{3} = -\frac{2}{3}x + \frac{7}{3} \quad \text{Divide both sides by 3.}$$
$$y = -\frac{2}{3}x + \frac{7}{3} \quad \leftarrow y\text{-intercept}$$

slope

- Remember that a point that is an *x*-intercept will have a *y*-value of 0 and a point that is a *y*-intercept will have an *x*-value of 0. Also—the point $(0, 0)$ will be both an *x*- and *y*-intercept.

- If you studied functions, remember that $f(x)$ *does not* mean $f \cdot x$. It is a special function notation. If $f(x) = x^2 - 6$, then $f(-3) = (-3)^2 - 6 = 9 - 6 = 3$.

10 CHAPTER REVIEW

(10.1) *Plot each pair on the same rectangular coordinate system.*

1. $(-7, 0)$

2. $\left(0, 4\frac{4}{5}\right)$

3. $(-2, -5)$

4. $(1, -3)$

5. $(0.7, 0.7)$

6. $(-6, 4)$

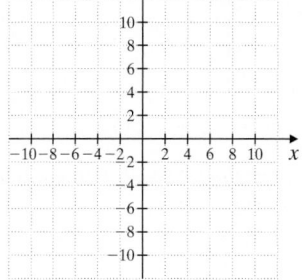

Complete each ordered pair so that it is a solution of the given equation.

7. $-2 + y = 6x; (7, \quad)$

8. $y = 3x + 5; (\quad, -8)$

Complete the table of values for each given equation.

9. $9 = -3x + 4y$

x	y
	0
	3
9	

10. $y = 5$

x	y
7	
-7	
0	

11. $x = 2y$

x	y
	0
	5
	-5

12. The cost in dollars of producing x compact disc holders is given by $y = 5x + 2000$.
   a. Complete the table.

x	1	100	1000
y			

b. Find the number of compact disc holders that can be produced for $6430.

(10.2) *Graph each linear equation.*

13. $x - y = 1$

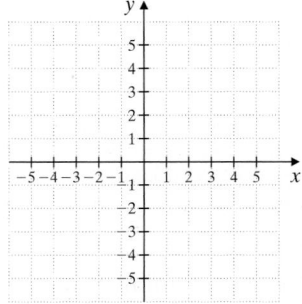

14. $x + y = 6$

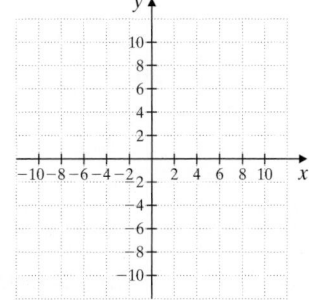

15. $x - 3y = 12$

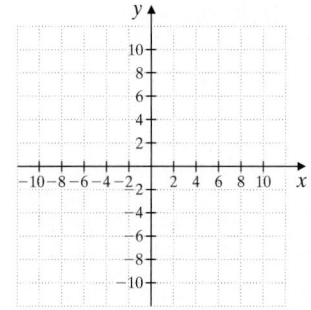

16. $5x - y = -8$

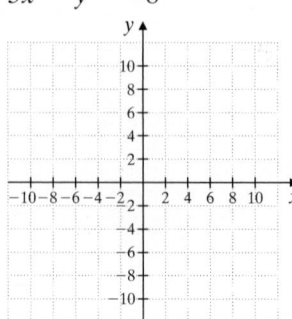

17. $x = 3y$

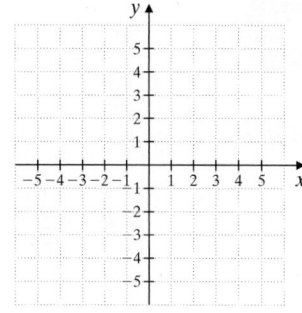

18. $y = -2x$

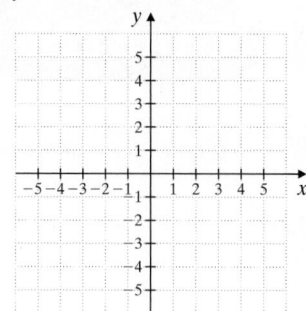

(10.3) *Identify the intercepts in each graph.*

19.

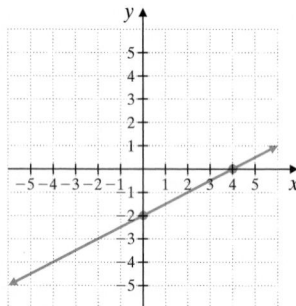

20.

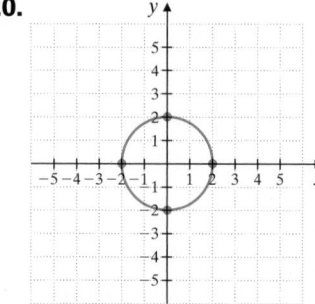

Graph each linear equation.

21. $y = -3$

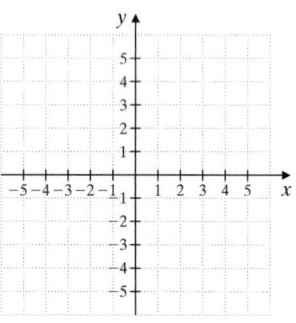

22. $x = 5$

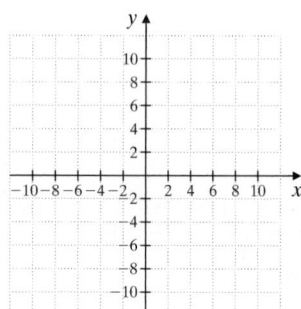

Find the intercepts of each equation.

23. $x - 3y = 12$

24. $-4x + y = 8$

(10.4) *Find the slope of each line.*

25.

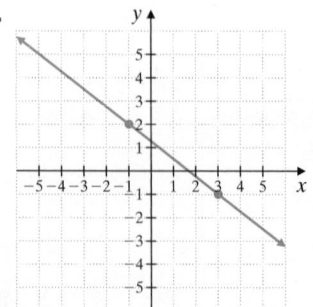

26.

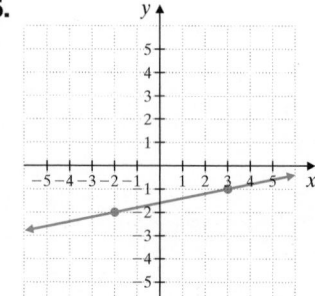

Match each line with its slope.

a.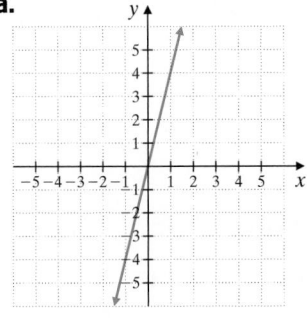

b.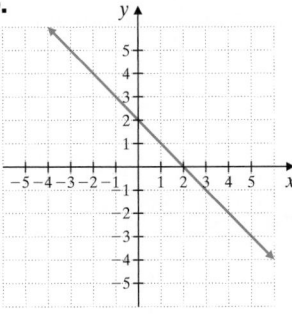

c.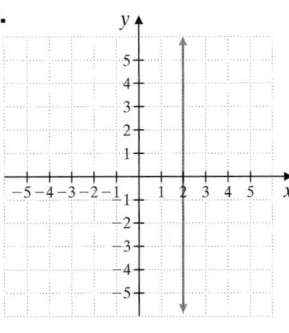

d.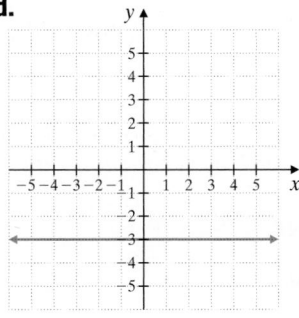

27. $m = 0$ **28.** $m = -1$ **29.** undefined slope   **30.** $m = 4$

Find the slope of the line that passes through each pair of points.

31. $(2, 5)$ and $(6, 8)$ **32.** $(4, 7)$ and $(1, 2)$ **33.** $(1, 3)$ and $(-2, -9)$ **34.** $(-4, 1)$ and $(3, -6)$

Find the slope of each line.

35. $y = 3x + 7$ **36.** $x - 2y = 4$ **37.** $y = -2$ **38.** $x = 0$

△ *Determine whether each pair of lines is parallel, perpendicular, or neither.*

39. $x - y = -6$
$x + y = 3$

40. $3x + y = 7$
$-3x - y = 10$

41. $y = 4x + \dfrac{1}{2}$
$4x + 2y = 1$

Find the slope of each line and write the slope as a rate of change. Don't forget to attach the proper units.

42. The graph below approximates the number of U.S. persons y (in millions) who have a bachelor's degree or higher per year x.

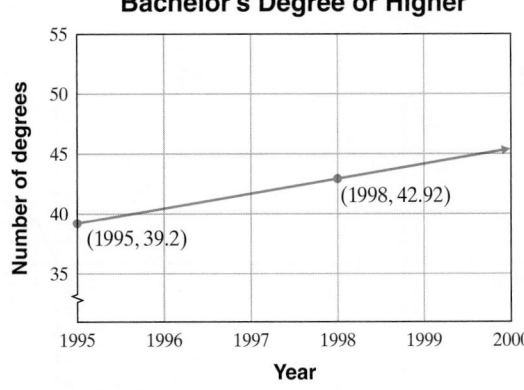

Bachelor's Degree or Higher

Source: U.S. Census Bureau

43. The graph below approximates the number of U.S. travelers y (in millions) that are vacationing per year x.

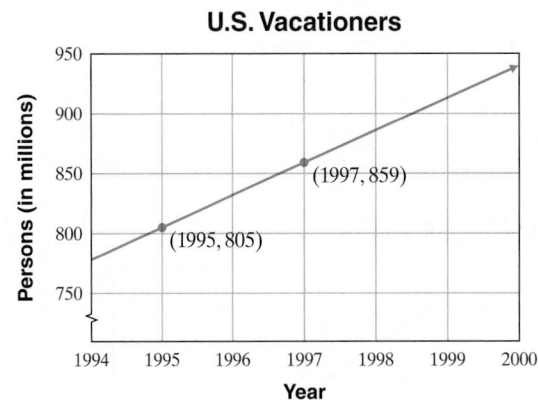

U.S. Vacationers

Source: TIA Research Dept., trips of 100 miles or more, one-way

(10.5) *Determine the slope and the y-intercept of the graph of each equation.*

44. $3x + y = 7$ **45.** $x - 6y = -1$

Write an equation of each line.

46. slope -5; y-intercept $\left(0, \dfrac{1}{2}\right)$

47. slope $\dfrac{2}{3}$; y-intercept $(0, 6)$

Match each equation with its graph.

48. $y = 2x + 1$ **49.** $y = -4x$ **50.** $y = 2x$ **51.** $y = 2x - 1$

a. 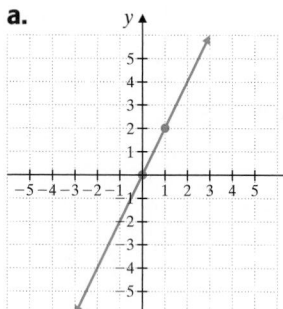   **b.** 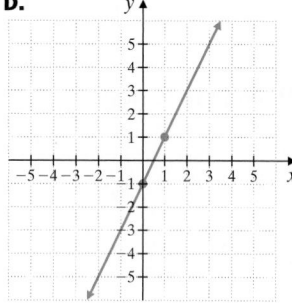   **c.** 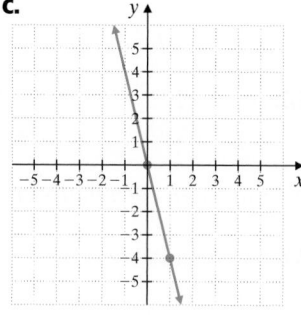   **d.**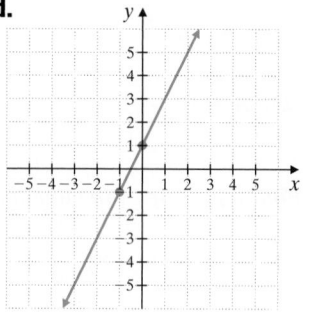

Write an equation of the line with the given slope that passes through the given point. Write the equation in the form $Ax + By = C$.

52. $m = 4$; $(2, 0)$ **53.** $m = -3$; $(0, -5)$ **54.** $m = \dfrac{3}{5}$; $(1, 4)$ **55.** $m = -\dfrac{1}{3}$; $(-3, 3)$

Write an equation of the line passing through each pair of points. Write the equation in the form $y = mx + b$.

56. $(1, 7)$ and $(2, -7)$

57. $(-2, 5)$ and $(-4, 6)$

(10.6) *Determine whether each relation or graph is a function.*

58. $\{(7, 1), (7, 5), (2, 6)\}$

59. $\{(0, -1), (5, -1), (2, 2)\}$

60. 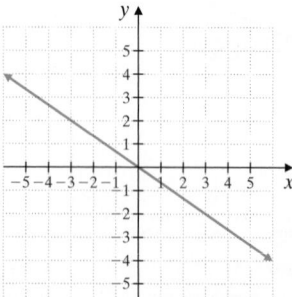   **61.** 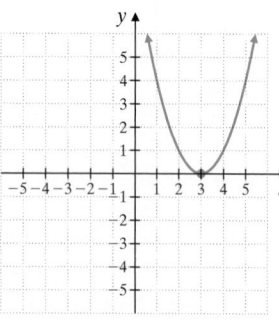   **62.** 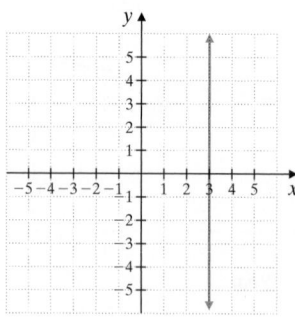   **63.**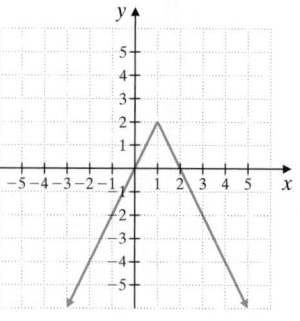

64. Find the indicated function value for the function, $f(x) = -2x + 6$.

a. $f(0)$ **b.** $f(-2)$ **c.** $f\left(\dfrac{1}{2}\right)$

(10.7) *Graph each inequality.*

65. $x + 6y < 6$

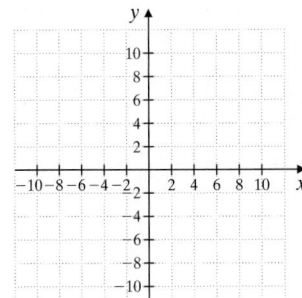

66. $x + y > -2$

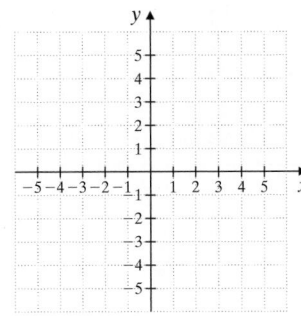

67. $y \geq -7$

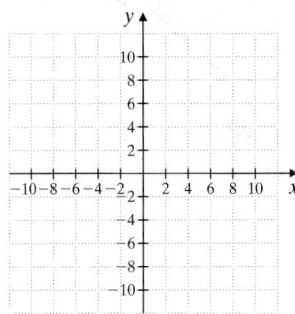

68. $y \leq -4$

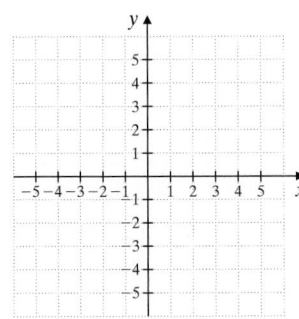

69. $-x \leq y$

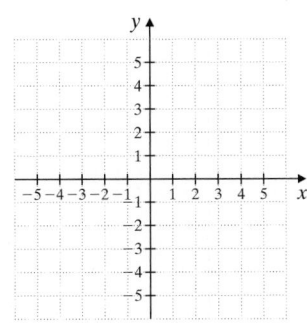

70. $x \geq -y$

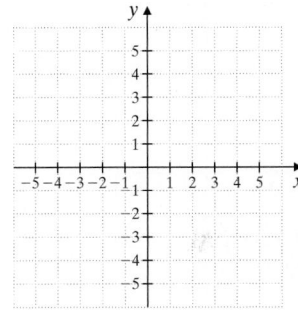

(10.8) *Solve.*

71. y varies directly as x. If $y = 40$ when $x = 4$, find y when x is 11.

72. y varies inversely as x. If $y = 4$ when $x = 6$, find y when x is 48.

73. y varies inversely as x^3. If $y = 12.5$ when $x = 2$, find y when x is 3.

74. y varies directly as x^2. If $y = 175$ when $x = 5$, find y when $x = 10$.

75. The cost of manufacturing a certain medicine varies inversely as the amount of medicine manufactured increases. If 3000 milliliters can be manufactured for $6600, find the cost to manufacture 5000 milliliters.

76. The distance a spring stretches varies directly with the weight attached to the spring. If a 150-pound weight stretches the spring 8 inches, find the distance that a 90-pound weight stretches the spring.

Mixed Review

Complete the table of values for each given equation.

77. $2x - 5y = 9$

x	y
	1
2	
	-3

78. $x = -3y$

x	y
0	
	1
6	

Find the intercepts for each equation.

79. $2x - 3y = 6$

80. $-5x + y = 10$

Graph each linear equation.

81. $x - 5y = 10$

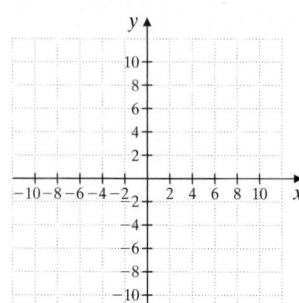

82. $x + y = 4$

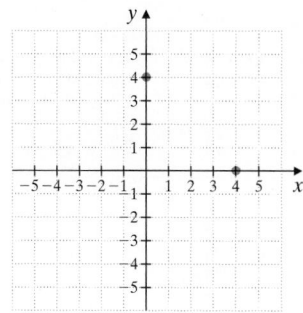

83. $y = -4x$

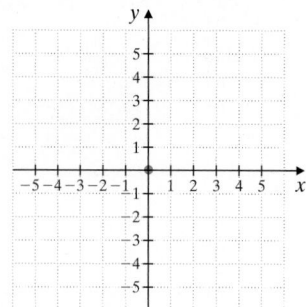

84. $2x + 3y = -6$

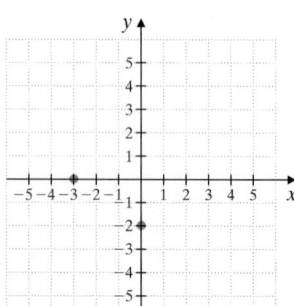

85. $x = 3$

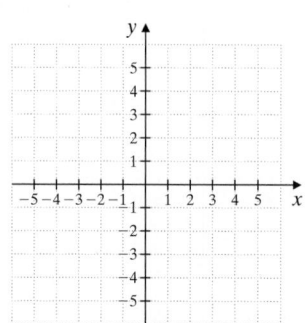

86. $y = -2$

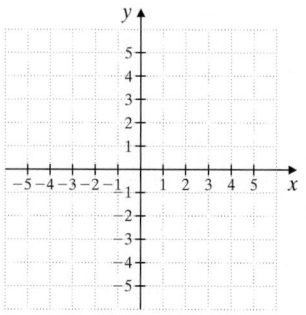

Find the slope of the line that passes through each pair of points.

87. $(3, -5)$ and $(-4, 2)$

88. $(1, 3)$ and $(-6, -8)$

Find the slope of each line.

89.

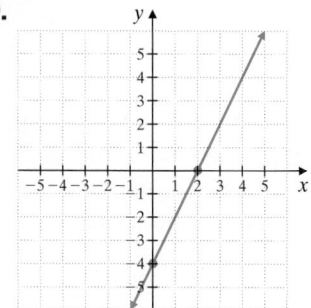

90.

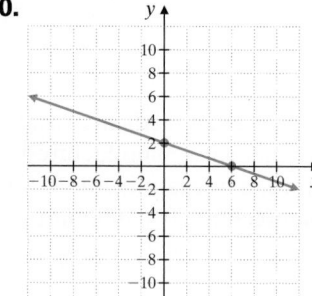

Determine the slope and y-intercept of the graph of each equation.

91. $-2x + 3y = -15$

92. $6x + y - 2 = 0$

Write an equation of the line with the given slope that passes through the given point. Write the equation in the form $Ax + By = C$.

93. $m = -5$; $(3, -7)$

94. $m = 3$; $(0, 6)$

Write an equation of the line passing through each pair of points. Write the equation in the form $Ax + By = C$.

95. $(-3, 9)$ and $(-2, 5)$

96. $(3, 1)$ and $(5, -9)$

10 CHAPTER TEST

 Remember to use the Chapter Test Prep Video CD to see the fully worked-out solutions to any of the exercises you want to review.

Complete each ordered pair so that it is a solution of the given equation.

1. $12y - 7x = 5; (1,\ \ )$

2. $y = 17; (-4,\ \ )$

Find the slope of each line.

1. _____

3.
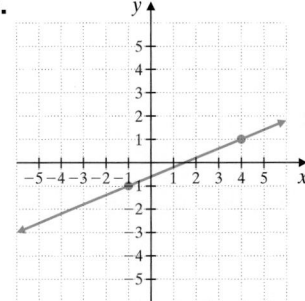

4.
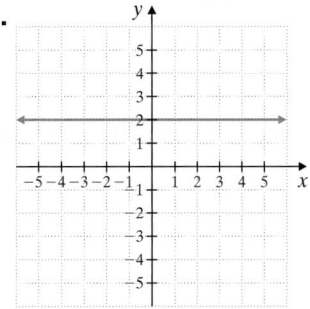

2. _____

3. _____

5. Passes through $(6, -5)$ and $(-1, 2)$

6. Passes through $(0, -8)$ and $(-1, -1)$

4. _____

7. $-3x + y = 5$

8. $x = 6$

5. _____

6. _____

Graph.

7. _____

9. $2x + y = 8$
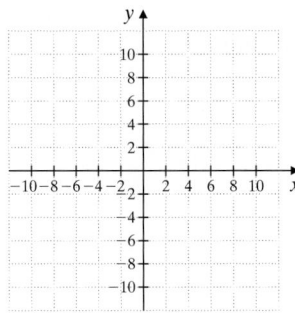

10. $-x + 4y = 5$
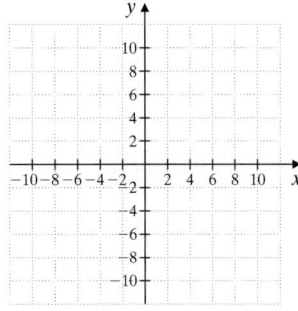

11. $x - y \geq -2$
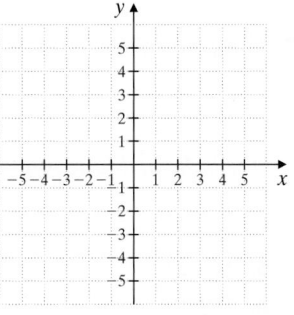

8. _____

9. see graph

10. see graph

12. $y \geq -4x$
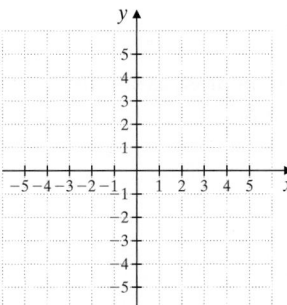

13. $5x - 7y = 10$
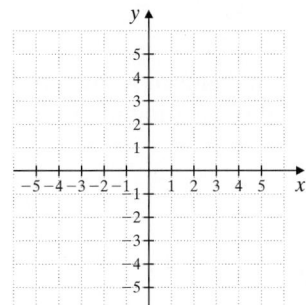

14. $2x - 3y > -6$
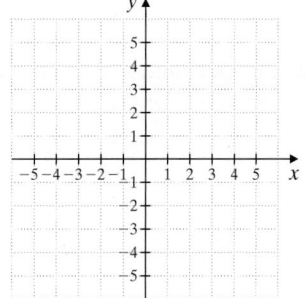

11. see graph

12. see graph

13. see graph

14. see graph

813

15. see graph

16. see graph

17. _____

18. _____

19. _____

20. _____

21. _____

22. _____

23. _____

24. _____

25. _____

26. a. _____

   b. _____

   c. _____

27. a. _____

   b. _____

   c. _____

28. _____

15. $6x + y > -1$

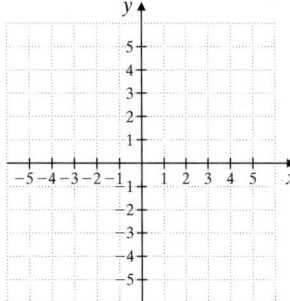

16. $y = -1$

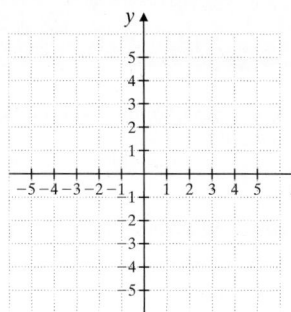

17. Determine whether the graphs of $y = 2x - 6$ and $-4x = 2y$ are parallel lines, perpendicular lines, or neither.

Find the equation of each line. Write the equation in the form $Ax + By = C$.

18. Slope $-\dfrac{1}{4}$, passes through $(2, 2)$

19. Passes through the origin and $(6, -7)$

20. Passes through $(2, -5)$ and $(1, 3)$

21. Slope $\dfrac{1}{8}$; y-intercept $(0, 12)$

Determine whether each relation is a function.

22. $\{(-1, 2), (-2, 4), (-3, 6), (-4, 8)\}$

23. $\{(-3, -3), (0, 5), (-3, 2), (0, 0)\}$

24. The graph shown in Exercise 3.

25. The graph shown in Exercise 4.

Find the indicated function values for each function.

26. $f(x) = 2x - 4$
   a. $f(-2)$
   b. $f(0.2)$
   c. $f(0)$

27. $f(x) = x^3 - x$
   a. $f(-1)$
   b. $f(0)$
   c. $f(4)$

△ **28.** The perimeter of the parallelogram below is 42 meters. Write a linear equation in two variables for the perimeter. Use this equation to find x when y is 8.

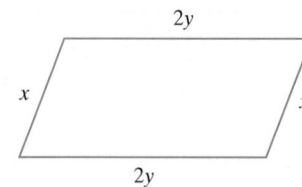

29. The table gives the number of basic cable TV subscribers (in millions) for the years shown. (*Source:* Cisco Systems)

Year	Basic Cable TV Subscribers (in millions)
2000	69.3
2001	70.0
2002	69.9
2003	70.1
2004	70.3
2005	70.5 (estimated)

a. Write this data as a set of ordered pairs of the form (year, number of basic cable TV subscribers in millions).

b. Create a scatter diagram of the data. Be sure to label the axes properly.

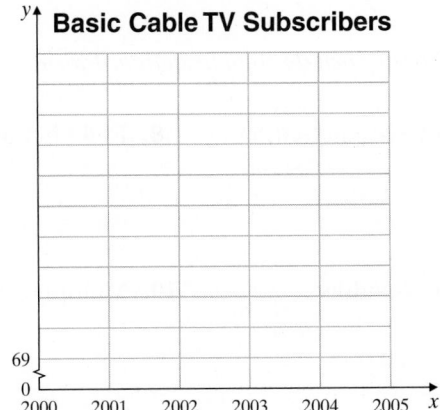

Basic Cable TV Subscribers

30. This graph approximates the movie ticket sales *y* (in millions) for the year *x*. Find the slope of the line and write the slope as a rate of change. Don't forget to attach the proper units.

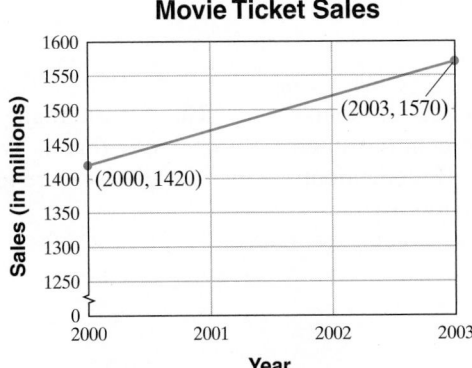

Movie Ticket Sales

Source: National Association of Theater Owners

31. *y* varies directly as *x*. If $y = 10$ when $x = 15$, find *y* when *x* is 42.

32. *y* varies inversely as x^2. If $y = 8$ when $x = 5$, find *y* when *x* is 15.

29. a. _____

b. see diagram

30. _____

31. _____

32. _____

Answers

1. _____

2. _____

3. _____

4. _____

5. _____

6. _____

7. _____

8. _____

9. _____

10. _____

11. _____

12. _____

13. _____

14. _____

15. _____

16. _____

17. _____

18. _____

19. _____

20. _____

816

1. Multiply: 631×125

2. Multiply: $\dfrac{5}{8} \cdot \dfrac{10}{11}$

3. Divide: $\dfrac{2}{5} \div \dfrac{1}{2}$

4. Divide: $2124 \div 9$

5. Add: $\dfrac{2}{3} + \dfrac{1}{7}$

6. Subtract: $9\dfrac{2}{7} - 7\dfrac{1}{2}$

For Exercises 7 through 9, write each decimal in standard form.

7. Forty-eight and twenty-six hundredths

8. Eight hundredths

9. Six and ninety-five thousandths

10. Multiply: 563.21×100

11. Subtract: $3.5 - 0.068$

12. Divide: $0.27 \div 0.02$

13. Simplify: $\dfrac{5.68 + (0.9)^2 \div 100}{0.2}$

14. Simplify: $50 \div 5 \cdot 2$

15. 46 out of every 100 college students live at home. What percent of students live at home? (*Source:* Independent Insurance Agents of America)

16. A basketball player made 4 out of 5 free throws. What percent of free throws were made?

Simplify each expression.

17. $6 \div 3 + 5^2$

18. $\dfrac{10}{3} + \dfrac{5}{21}$

19. $1 + 2[5(2 \cdot 3 + 1) - 10]$

20. $16 - 3 \cdot 3 + 2^4$

21. The lowest point on the surface of the Earth is the Dead Sea, at an elevation of 1349 feet below sea level. The highest point is Mt. Everest, at an elevation of 29,035 feet. What is the difference in elevation between these two world extremes? (*Source:* National Geographic Society)

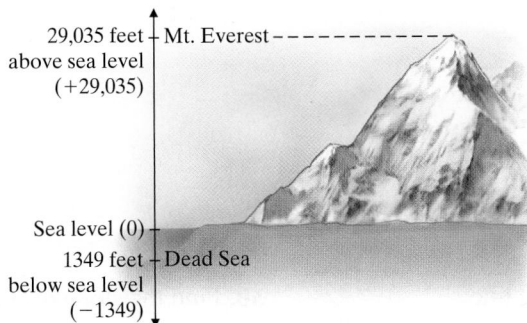

22. Simplify: $1.7x - 11 - 0.9x - 25$

Write each phrase as an algebraic expression and simplify if possible. Let x represent the unknown number.

23. Twice a number, plus 6.

24. The product of -15 and the sum of a number and $\frac{2}{3}$.

25. The difference of a number and 4, divided by 7.

26. The quotient of -9 and twice a number.

27. Five plus the sum of a number and 1.

28. A number subtracted from -86.

29. Solve for x: $\frac{5}{2}x = 15$

30. Solve for x: $\frac{x}{4} - 1 = -7$

31. Solve $2x < -4$. Graph the solutions.

$$\begin{array}{c} \leftarrow\!\!+\!\!\!+\!\!\!+\!\!\!+\!\!\!+\!\!\!+\!\!\!+\!\!\!+\!\!\!+\!\!\!+\!\!\!+\!\!\rightarrow \\ {\scriptstyle -5\ -4\ -3\ -2\ -1\quad 0\quad 1\quad 2\quad 3\quad 4\quad 5} \end{array}$$

32. Solve: $5(x + 4) \geq 4(2x + 3)$

33. Complete each ordered pair solution so that it is a solution to the equation $3x + y = 12$.
   a. $(0, \ )$
   b. $(\ , 6)$
   c. $(-1, \ )$

34. Complete the table for $y = -5x$.

x	y
0	
-1	
	-10

21. _____

22. _____

23. _____

24. _____

25. _____

26. _____

27. _____

28. _____

29. _____

30. _____

31. see graph _____

32. _____

33. a. _____

b. _____

c. _____

34. see table _____

35. see graph

36. _____

37. _____

38. _____

39. _____

40. _____

41. a. _____

b. _____

c. _____

42. _____

35. Graph: $2x + y = 5$

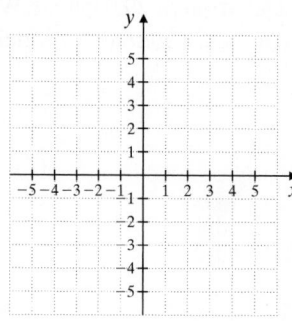

36. Find the slope of the line through $(0, 5)$ and $(-5, 4)$.

37. Find the slope of the line:
$-2x + 3y = 11$

38. Find the slope of the line $x = -10$.

39. Find an equation of the line with slope -2 that passes through $(-1, 5)$. Write the equation in slope-intercept form, $y = mx + b$.

40. Find the slope and y-intercept of the line whose equation is $2x - 5y = 10$.

41. Given $g(x) = x^2 - 3$, find each function value and list the corresponding ordered pair.
   a. $g(2)$ **b.** $g(-2)$ **c.** $g(0)$

42. Write an equation of the line through $(2, 3)$ and $(0, 0)$. Write the equation in standard form.

12

Exponents and Polynomials

Recall from Chapter 1 that an exponent is a shorthand notation for repeated factors. This chapter explores additional concepts about exponents and exponential expressions. An especially useful type of exponential expression is a polynomial. Polynomials model many real-world phenomena. Our goal in this chapter is to become proficient with operations on polynomials.

A popular use of the Internet is the World Wide Web. The World Wide Web was invented in 1989–1990 as an environment originally by which scientists could share information. It has grown into a medium containing text, graphics, audio, animation, and video. Each of the locations, or Web sites below, has an address and can be used to locate other Web sites. In Section 12.2, Exercise 95, you will have the opportunity to estimate the number of visitors of the most popular Web sites.

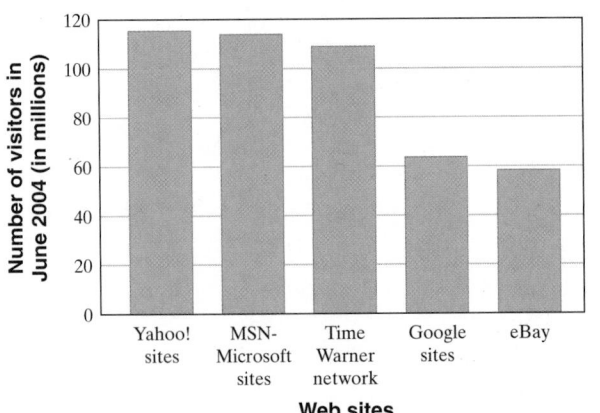

Most Visited Web Sites

12.1 EXPONENTS

Objective A Evaluating Exponential Expressions

In this section, we continue our work with integer exponents. For example,

$$2 \cdot 2 \cdot 2 \cdot 2 \cdot 2 = 2^5$$

Recall that the exponent 5 tells us how many times that 2 is a factor. The expression 2^5 is called an **exponential expression.** It is also called the fifth **power** of 2, or we can say that 2 is **raised** to the fifth power.

$$5^6 = \underbrace{5 \cdot 5 \cdot 5 \cdot 5 \cdot 5 \cdot 5}_{\text{6 factors; each factor is 5}} \quad \text{and} \quad (-3)^4 = \underbrace{(-3) \cdot (-3) \cdot (-3) \cdot (-3)}_{\text{4 factors; each factor is } -3}$$

The base of an exponential expression is the repeated factor. The exponent is the number of times that the base is used as a factor.

$$\overset{\text{exponent or power}}{a^n} = \underbrace{a \cdot a \cdot a \cdots a}_{\substack{\uparrow \\ \text{base}}}$$
$$n \text{ factors; each factor is } a$$

EXAMPLES Evaluate each expression.

1. $2^3 = 2 \cdot 2 \cdot 2 = 8$
2. $3^1 = 3$. To raise 3 to the first power means to use 3 as a factor only once. When no exponent is shown, the exponent is assumed to be 1.
3. $(-4)^2 = (-4)(-4) = 16$
4. $-4^2 = -(4 \cdot 4) = -16$
5. $\left(\dfrac{1}{2}\right)^4 = \dfrac{1}{2} \cdot \dfrac{1}{2} \cdot \dfrac{1}{2} \cdot \dfrac{1}{2} = \dfrac{1}{16}$
6. $4 \cdot 3^2 = 4 \cdot 9 = 36$

▨ Work Practice Problems 1–6

Notice how similar -4^2 is to $(-4)^2$ in the examples above. The difference between the two is the parentheses. In $(-4)^2$, the parentheses tell us that the base, or the repeated factor, is -4. In -4^2, only 4 is the base.

Helpful Hint

Be careful when identifying the base of an exponential expression. Pay close attention to the use of parentheses.

$(-3)^2$	-3^2	$2 \cdot 3^2$
The base is -3.	The base is 3.	The base is 3.
$(-3)^2 = (-3)(-3) = 9$	$-3^2 = -(3 \cdot 3) = -9$	$2 \cdot 3^2 = 2 \cdot 3 \cdot 3 = 18$

An exponent has the same meaning whether the base is a number or a variable. If x is a real number and n is a positive integer, then x^n is the product of n factors, each of which is x.

$$x^n = \underbrace{x \cdot x \cdot x \cdot x \cdot x \cdots x}_{n \text{ factors; each factor is } x}$$

Objectives

- **A** Evaluate Exponential Expressions.
- **B** Use the Product Rule for Exponents.
- **C** Use the Power Rule for Exponents.
- **D** Use the Power Rules for Products and Quotients.
- **E** Use the Quotient Rule for Exponents, and Define a Number Raised to the 0 Power.
- **F** Decide Which Rule(s) to Use to Simplify an Expression.

PRACTICE PROBLEMS 1–6

Evaluate each expression.

1. 3^4
2. 7^1
3. $(-2)^3$
4. -2^3
5. $\left(\dfrac{2}{3}\right)^2$
6. $5 \cdot 6^2$

Answers
1. 81, 2. 7, 3. -8, 4. -8, 5. $\dfrac{4}{9}$,
6. 180

Copyright 2007 Pearson Education, Inc.

PRACTICE PROBLEM 7

Evaluate each expression for the given value of x.

a. $3x^2$ when x is 4

b. $\dfrac{x^4}{-8}$ when x is -2

EXAMPLE 7 Evaluate each expression for the given value of x.

a. $2x^3$ when x is 5   b. $\dfrac{9}{x^2}$ when x is -3

Solution:

a. When x is 5, $2x^3 = 2 \cdot 5^3$

$$= 2 \cdot (5 \cdot 5 \cdot 5)$$
$$= 2 \cdot 125$$
$$= 250$$

b. When x is -3, $\dfrac{9}{x^2} = \dfrac{9}{(-3)^2}$

$$= \dfrac{9}{(-3)(-3)}$$
$$= \dfrac{9}{9} = 1$$

Work Practice Problem 7

Objective **B** **Using the Product Rule**

Exponential expressions can be multiplied, divided, added, subtracted, and themselves raised to powers. Let's see if we can discover a shortcut method for multiplying exponential expressions with the same base. By our definition of an exponent,

$$5^4 \cdot 5^3 = \underbrace{(5 \cdot 5 \cdot 5 \cdot 5)}_{4 \text{ factors of } 5} \cdot \underbrace{(5 \cdot 5 \cdot 5)}_{3 \text{ factors of } 5}$$

$$= \underbrace{5 \cdot 5 \cdot 5 \cdot 5 \cdot 5 \cdot 5 \cdot 5}_{7 \text{ factors of } 5}$$

$$= 5^7$$

Also,

$$x^2 \cdot x^3 = (x \cdot x) \cdot (x \cdot x \cdot x)$$
$$= x \cdot x \cdot x \cdot x \cdot x$$
$$= x^5$$

In both cases, notice that the result is exactly the same if the exponents are added.

$$5^4 \cdot 5^3 = 5^{4+3} = 5^7 \quad \text{and} \quad x^2 \cdot x^3 = x^{2+3} = x^5$$

This suggests the following rule.

Product Rule for Exponents

If m and n are positive integers and a is a real number, then

$$a^m \cdot a^n = a^{m+n} \quad \leftarrow \text{ Add exponents.}$$
$$\uparrow \underline{\hspace{1.5cm}} \text{ Keep common base.}$$

For example,

$$3^5 \cdot 3^7 = 3^{5+7} = 3^{12} \quad \leftarrow \text{ Add exponents.}$$
$$\uparrow \underline{\hspace{1.5cm}} \text{ Keep common base.}$$

Answers

7. a. 48,   **b.** -2

Helpful Hint

Don't forget that

$3^5 \cdot 3^7 \neq 9^{12}$ ← Add exponents.
↑ —— Common base *not* kept.

$3^5 \cdot 3^7 = \underbrace{3 \cdot 3 \cdot 3 \cdot 3 \cdot 3}_{\text{5 factors of 3}} \cdot \underbrace{3 \cdot 3 \cdot 3 \cdot 3 \cdot 3 \cdot 3 \cdot 3}_{\text{7 factors of 3}}$

$= 3^{12}$ 12 factors of 3, *not* 9.

In other words, to multiply two exponential expressions with the **same base,** we keep the base and add the exponents. We call this **simplifying** the exponential expression.

EXAMPLES Use the product rule to simplify each expression.

8. $4^2 \cdot 4^5 = 4^{2+5} = 4^7$ ← Add exponents.
↑ —— Keep common base.

9. $x^2 \cdot x^5 = x^{2+5} = x^7$

10. $y^3 \cdot y = y^3 \cdot y^1$
$= y^{3+1}$
$= y^4$

Helpful Hint
Don't forget that if no exponent is written, it is assumed to be 1.

11. $y^3 \cdot y^2 \cdot y^7 = y^{3+2+7} = y^{12}$

12. $(-5)^7 \cdot (-5)^8 = (-5)^{7+8} = (-5)^{15}$

Work Practice Problems 8–12

✔Concept Check Where possible, use the product rule to simplify the expression.

a. $z^2 \cdot z^{14}$ **b.** $x^2 \cdot z^{14}$ **c.** $9^8 \cdot 9^3$ **d.** $9^8 \cdot 2^7$

EXAMPLE 13 Use the product rule to simplify $(2x^2)(-3x^5)$.

Solution: Recall that $2x^2$ means $2 \cdot x^2$ and $-3x^5$ means $-3 \cdot x^5$.

$(2x^2)(-3x^5) = (2 \cdot x^2) \cdot (-3 \cdot x^5)$
$= (2 \cdot -3) \cdot (x^2 \cdot x^5)$ Group factors with common bases (using commutative and associative properties.)
$= -6x^7$ Simplify.

Work Practice Problem 13

EXAMPLES Simplify.

14. $(x^2y)(x^3y^2) = (x^2 \cdot x^3) \cdot (y^1 \cdot y^2)$ Group like bases and write y as y^1.
$= x^5 \cdot y^3$ or x^5y^3 Multiply.

15. $(-a^7b^4)(3ab^9) = (-1 \cdot 3) \cdot (a^7 \cdot a^1) \cdot (b^4 \cdot b^9)$
$= -3a^8b^{13}$

Work Practice Problems 14–15

PRACTICE PROBLEMS 8–12

Use the product rule to simplify each expression.

8. $7^3 \cdot 7^2$ **9.** $x^4 \cdot x^9$
10. $r^5 \cdot r$ **11.** $s^6 \cdot s^2 \cdot s^3$
12. $(-3)^9 \cdot (-3)$

PRACTICE PROBLEM 13

Use the product rule to simplify $(6x^3)(-2x^9)$.

PRACTICE PROBLEMS 14–15

Simplify.

14. $(m^5n^{10})(mn^8)$
15. $(-x^9y)(4x^2y^{11})$

Answers
8. 7^5, **9.** x^{13}, **10.** r^6, **11.** s^{11},
12. $(-3)^{10}$, **13.** $-12x^{12}$,
14. m^6n^{18}, **15.** $-4x^{11}y^{12}$

✔ Concept Check Answers
a. z^{16}, **b.** cannot be simplified,
c. 9^{11}, **d.** cannot be simplified

Helpful Hint

These examples will remind you of the difference between adding and multiplying terms.

Addition

$$5x^3 + 3x^3 = (5 + 3)x^3 = 8x^3 \qquad \text{By the distributive property.}$$

$$7x + 4x^2 = 7x + 4x^2 \qquad \text{Cannot be combined.}$$

Multiplication

$$(5x^3)(3x^3) = 5 \cdot 3 \cdot x^3 \cdot x^3 = 15x^{3+3} = 15x^6 \qquad \text{By the product rule.}$$

$$(7x)(4x^2) = 7 \cdot 4 \cdot x \cdot x^2 = 28x^{1+2} = 28x^3 \qquad \text{By the product rule.}$$

Objective **C** Using the Power Rule

Exponential expressions can themselves be raised to powers. Let's try to discover a rule that simplifies an expression like $(x^2)^3$. By the definition of a^n,

$$(x^2)^3 = (x^2)(x^2)(x^2) \qquad (x^2)^3 \text{ means 3 factors of } (x^2).$$

which can be simplified by the product rule for exponents.

$$(x^2)^3 = (x^2)(x^2)(x^2) = x^{2+2+2} = x^6$$

Notice that the result is exactly the same if we multiply the exponents.

$$(x^2)^3 = x^{2 \cdot 3} = x^6$$

The following rule states this result.

Power Rule for Exponents

If m and n are positive integers and a is a real number, then

$$(a^m)^n = a^{mn} \quad \leftarrow \text{Multiply exponents.}$$
$$\phantom{(a^m)^n = a^{mn}} \underset{\uparrow\text{—————}}{} \text{Keep common base.}$$

For example,

$$(7^2)^5 = 7^{2 \cdot 5} = 7^{10} \quad \leftarrow \text{Multiply exponents.}$$
$$\phantom{(7^2)^5 = 7^{2 \cdot 5} = 7^{10}} \underset{\uparrow\text{—————}}{} \text{Keep common base.}$$

In other words, to raise an exponential expression to a power, we keep the base and multiply the exponents.

PRACTICE PROBLEMS 16–17

Use the power rule to simplify each expression.

16. $(9^4)^{10}$ **17.** $(z^6)^3$

EXAMPLES Use the power rule to simplify each expression.

16. $(5^3)^6 = 5^{3 \cdot 6} = 5^{18}$

17. $(y^8)^2 = y^{8 \cdot 2} = y^{16}$

Work Practice Problems 16–17

Helpful Hint

Take a moment to make sure that you understand when to apply the product rule and when to apply the power rule.

Product Rule → Add Exponents	Power Rule → Multiply Exponents
$x^5 \cdot x^7 = x^{5+7} = x^{12}$	$(x^5)^7 = x^{5 \cdot 7} = x^{35}$
$y^6 \cdot y^2 = y^{6+2} = y^8$	$(y^6)^2 = y^{6 \cdot 2} = y^{12}$

Answers

16. 9^{40},   **17.** z^{18}

Objective D Using the Power Rules for Products and Quotients

When the base of an exponential expression is a product, the definition of a^n still applies. For example, simplify $(xy)^3$ as follows.

$$(xy)^3 = (xy)(xy)(xy) \quad \text{$(xy)^3$ means 3 factors of (xy).}$$
$$= x \cdot x \cdot x \cdot y \cdot y \cdot y \quad \text{Group factors with common bases.}$$
$$= x^3y^3 \quad \text{Simplify.}$$

Notice that to simplify the expression $(xy)^3$, we raise each factor within the parentheses to a power of 3.

$$(xy)^3 = x^3y^3$$

In general, we have the following rule.

Power of a Product Rule

If n is a positive integer and a and b are real numbers, then

$$(ab)^n = a^n b^n$$

For example,

$$(3x)^5 = 3^5 x^5$$

In other words, to raise a product to a power, we raise each factor to the power.

EXAMPLES Simplify each expression.

18. $(st)^4 = s^4 \cdot t^4 = s^4 t^4$ ⟶ Use the power of a product rule.

19. $(2a)^3 = 2^3 \cdot a^3 = 8a^3$ ⟶ Use the power of a product rule.

20. $(-5x^2y^3z)^2 = (-5)^2 \cdot (x^2)^2 \cdot (y^3)^2 \cdot (z^1)^2$ ⟶ Use the power of a product rule.

$\qquad = 25x^4y^6z^2$ ⟶ Use the power rule for exponents.

21. $(-xy^3)^5 = (-1xy^3)^5 = (-1)^5 \cdot x^5 \cdot (y^3)^5$

$\qquad\qquad\qquad = -1x^5y^{15} \quad \text{or} \quad -x^5y^{15}$

⊞ **Work Practice Problems 18–21**

Let's see what happens when we raise a quotient to a power. For example, we simplify $\left(\dfrac{x}{y}\right)^3$ as follows.

$$\left(\frac{x}{y}\right)^3 = \left(\frac{x}{y}\right)\left(\frac{x}{y}\right)\left(\frac{x}{y}\right) \quad \text{$\left(\frac{x}{y}\right)^3$ means 3 factors of $\left(\frac{x}{y}\right)$.}$$

$$= \frac{x \cdot x \cdot x}{y \cdot y \cdot y} \quad \text{Multiply fractions.}$$

$$= \frac{x^3}{y^3} \quad \text{Simplify.}$$

Notice that to simplify the expression, $\left(\dfrac{x}{y}\right)^3$, we raise both the numerator and the denominator to a power of 3.

$$\left(\frac{x}{y}\right)^3 = \frac{x^3}{y^3}$$

In general, we have the following rule.

PRACTICE PROBLEMS 18–21

Simplify each expression.
18. $(xy)^7$ **19.** $(3y)^4$
20. $(-2p^4q^2r)^3$ **21.** $(-a^4b)^7$

Answers
18. x^7y^7,   **19.** $81y^4$,   **20.** $-8p^{12}q^6r^3$,
21. $-a^{28}b^7$

Power of a Quotient Rule

If n is a positive integer and a and c are real numbers, then

$$\left(\frac{a}{c}\right)^n = \frac{a^n}{c^n}, \quad c \neq 0$$

For example,

$$\left(\frac{y}{7}\right)^3 = \frac{y^3}{7^3}$$

In other words, to raise a quotient to a power, we raise both the numerator and the denominator to the power.

PRACTICE PROBLEMS 22–23

Simplify each expression.

22. $\left(\dfrac{r}{s}\right)^6$ **23.** $\left(\dfrac{5x^6}{9y^3}\right)^2$

EXAMPLES Simplify each expression.

22. $\left(\dfrac{m}{n}\right)^7 = \dfrac{m^7}{n^7}, \quad n \neq 0$ Use the power of a quotient rule.

23. $\left(\dfrac{2x^4}{3y^5}\right)^4 = \dfrac{2^4 \cdot (x^4)^4}{3^4 \cdot (y^5)^4}$ Use the power of a quotient rule.

$\qquad\qquad = \dfrac{16x^{16}}{81y^{20}}, \quad y \neq 0$ Use the power rule for exponents.

Work Practice Problems 22–23

Objective **E** Using the Quotient Rule and Defining the Zero Exponent

Another pattern for simplifying exponential expressions involves quotients.

$$\frac{x^5}{x^3} = \frac{x \cdot x \cdot x \cdot x \cdot x}{x \cdot x \cdot x}$$

$$= \frac{x \cdot x \cdot x \cdot x \cdot x}{x \cdot x \cdot x}$$

$$= 1 \cdot 1 \cdot 1 \cdot x \cdot x$$

$$= x \cdot x$$

$$= x^2$$

Notice that the result is exactly the same if we subtract exponents of the common bases.

$$\frac{x^5}{x^3} = x^{5-3} = x^2$$

The following rule states this result in a general way.

Quotient Rule for Exponents

If m and n are positive integers and a is a real number, then

$$\frac{a^m}{a^n} = a^{m-n}, \quad a \neq 0$$

For example,

$$\frac{x^6}{x^2} = x^{6-2} = x^4, \quad x \neq 0$$

Answers

22. $\dfrac{r^6}{s^6}, \quad s \neq 0,$ **23.** $\dfrac{25x^{12}}{81y^6}, \quad y \neq 0$

In other words, to divide one exponential expression by another with a common base, we keep the base and subtract the exponents.

> **EXAMPLES** Simplify each quotient.
>
> **24.** $\dfrac{x^5}{x^2} = x^{5-2} = x^3$ Use the quotient rule.
>
> **25.** $\dfrac{4^7}{4^3} = 4^{7-3} = 4^4 = 256$ Use the quotient rule.
>
> **26.** $\dfrac{(-3)^5}{(-3)^2} = (-3)^3 = -27$ Use the quotient rule.
>
> **27.** $\dfrac{2x^5y^2}{xy} = 2 \cdot \dfrac{x^5}{x^1} \cdot \dfrac{y^2}{y^1}$
>
> $= 2 \cdot (x^{5-1}) \cdot (y^{2-1})$ Use the quotient rule.
>
> $= 2x^4y^1$ or $2x^4y$

◻ **Work Practice Problems 24–27**

Let's now give meaning to an expression such as x^0. To do so, we will simplify $\dfrac{x^3}{x^3}$ in two ways and compare the results.

$\dfrac{x^3}{x^3} = x^{3-3} = x^0$ Apply the quotient rule.

$\dfrac{x^3}{x^3} = \dfrac{x \cdot x \cdot x}{x \cdot x \cdot x} = 1$ Apply the fundamental principle for fractions.

Since $\dfrac{x^3}{x^3} = x^0$ and $\dfrac{x^3}{x^3} = 1$, we define that $x^0 = 1$ as long as x is not 0.

> **Zero Exponent**
>
> $a^0 = 1$, as long as a is not 0.
>
> For example, $5^0 = 1$.

In other words, a base raised to the 0 power is 1, as long as the base is not 0.

> **EXAMPLES** Simplify each expression.
>
> **28.** $3^0 = 1$
>
> **29.** $(5x^3y^2)^0 = 1$
>
> **30.** $(-4)^0 = 1$
>
> **31.** $-4^0 = -1 \cdot 4^0 = -1 \cdot 1 = -1$
>
> **32.** $5x^0 = 5 \cdot x^0 = 5 \cdot 1 = 5$

◻ **Work Practice Problems 28–32**

PRACTICE PROBLEMS 24–27

Simplify each quotient.

24. $\dfrac{y^7}{y^3}$ **25.** $\dfrac{5^9}{5^6}$

26. $\dfrac{(-2)^{14}}{(-2)^{10}}$ **27.** $\dfrac{7a^4b^{11}}{ab}$

PRACTICE PROBLEMS 28–32

Simplify each expression.

28. 8^0 **29.** $(2r^2s)^0$

30. $(-7)^0$ **31.** -7^0

32. $7y^0$

Answers

24. y^4,   **25.** 125,   **26.** 16,   **27.** $7a^3b^{10}$,

28. 1,   **29.** 1,   **30.** 1,   **31.** -1,

32. 7

✔**Concept Check** Suppose you are simplifying each expression. Tell whether you would *add* the exponents, *subtract* the exponents, *multiply* the exponents, *divide* the exponents, or *none of these*.

a. $\left(x^{63}\right)^{21}$ **b.** $\dfrac{y^{15}}{y^3}$ **c.** $z^{16} + z^8$ **d.** $w^{45} \cdot w^9$

Objective 🅕 Deciding Which Rule to Use

Let's practice deciding which rule to use to simplify. We will continue this discussion with more examples in the next section.

PRACTICE PROBLEM 33

Simplify each expression.

a. $\dfrac{x^7}{x^4}$ **b.** $(3y^4)^4$ **c.** $\left(\dfrac{x}{4}\right)^3$

EXAMPLE 33 Simplify each expression.

a. $x^7 \cdot x^4$ **b.** $\left(\dfrac{t}{2}\right)^4$ **c.** $(9y^5)^2$

Solution:

a. Here, we have a product, so we use the product rule to simplify.

$$x^7 \cdot x^4 = x^{7+4} = x^{11}$$

b. This is a quotient raised to a power, so we use the power of a quotient rule.

$$\left(\frac{t}{2}\right)^4 = \frac{t^4}{2^4} = \frac{t^4}{16}$$

c. This is a product raised to a power, so we use the power of a product rule.

$$(9y^5)^2 = 9^2(y^5)^2 = 81y^{10}$$

▫ **Work Practice Problem 33**

Answers

33. a. x^3,   **b.** $81y^{16}$,   **c.** $\dfrac{x^3}{64}$

✔ **Concept Check Answers**

a. multiply,   **b.** subtract,
c. none of these,   **d.** add

Mental Math

State the bases and the exponents for each expression.

1. 3^2 **2.** 5^4 **3.** $(-3)^6$ **4.** -3^7 **5.** -4^2

6. $(-4)^3$ **7.** $5 \cdot 3^4$ **8.** $9 \cdot 7^6$ **9.** $5x^2$ **10.** $(5x)^2$

12.1 EXERCISE SET

Objective A *Evaluate each expression. See Examples 1 through 6.*

 **1.** 7^2 **2.** -3^2 **3.** $(-5)^1$ **4.** $(-3)^2$ **5.** -2^4 **6.** -4^3

 **7.** $(-2)^4$ **8.** $(-4)^3$ **9.** $\left(\dfrac{1}{3}\right)^3$ **10.** $\left(-\dfrac{1}{9}\right)^2$ **11.** $7 \cdot 2^4$ **12.** $9 \cdot 2^2$

Evaluate each expression with the given replacement values. See Example 7.

13. x^2 when $x = -2$ **14.** x^3 when $x = -2$ **15.** $5x^3$ when $x = 3$

16. $4x^2$ when $x = 5$ **17.** $2xy^2$ when $x = 3$ and $y = -5$ **18.** $-4x^2y^3$ when $x = 2$ and $y = -1$

19. $\dfrac{5z^4}{7}$ when $z = -2$ **20.** $\dfrac{10}{3y^3}$ when $y = -3$

Objective B *Use the product rule to simplify each expression. Write the results using exponents. See Examples 8 through 13.*

21. $x^2 \cdot x^5$ **22.** $y^2 \cdot y$ **23.** $(-3)^3 \cdot (-3)^9$ **24.** $(-5)^7 \cdot (-5)^6$

25. $(5y^4)(3y)$ **26.** $(-2z^3)(-2z^2)$ **27.** $(x^9y)(x^{10}y^5)$ **28.** $(a^2b)(a^{13}b^{17})$

29. $(-8mn^6)(9m^2n^2)$ **30.** $(-7a^3b^3)(7a^{19}b)$ **31.** $(4z^{10})(-6z^7)(z^3)$ **32.** $(12x^5)(-x^6)(x^4)$

△ **33.** The rectangle below has width $4x^2$ feet and length $5x^3$ feet. Find its area as an expression in x.

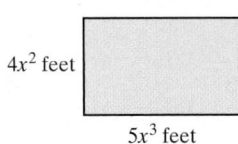

$4x^2$ feet

$5x^3$ feet

△ **34.** The parallelogram below has base length $9y^7$ meters and height $2y^{10}$ meters. Find its area as an expression in y.

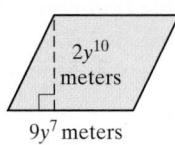

$2y^{10}$ meters

$9y^7$ meters

Objectives **C** **D** **Mixed Practice** *Use the power rule and the power of a product or quotient rule to simplify each expression. See Examples 16 through 23.*

35. $(x^9)^4$

36. $(y^7)^5$

37. $(pq)^8$

38. $(ab)^6$

39. $(2a^5)^3$

40. $(4x^6)^2$

41. $(x^2y^3)^5$

42. $(a^4b)^7$

43. $(-7a^2b^5c)^2$

44. $(-3x^7yz^2)^3$

45. $\left(\dfrac{r}{s}\right)^9$

46. $\left(\dfrac{q}{t}\right)^{11}$

47. $\left(\dfrac{mp}{n}\right)^9$

48. $\left(\dfrac{xy}{7}\right)^2$

49. $\left(\dfrac{-2xz}{y^5}\right)^2$

50. $\left(\dfrac{xy^4}{-3z^3}\right)^3$

△ **51.** The square shown has sides of length $8z^5$ decimeters. Find its area.

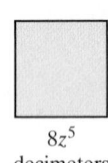

$8z^5$ decimeters

△ **52.** Given the circle below with radius $5y$ centimeters, find its area. Do not approximate π.

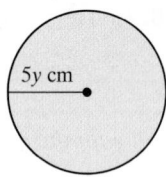

$5y$ cm

△ **53.** The vault below is in the shape of a cube. If each side is $3y^4$ feet, find its volume.

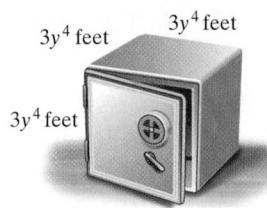

$3y^4$ feet $3y^4$ feet

$3y^4$ feet

△ **54.** The silo shown is in the shape of a cylinder. If its radius is $4x$ meters and its height is $5x^3$ meters, find its volume. Do not approximate π.

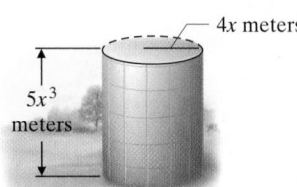

$4x$ meters

$5x^3$ meters

Objective **E** *Use the quotient rule and simplify each expression. See Examples 24 through 28.*

55. $\dfrac{x^3}{x}$

56. $\dfrac{y^{10}}{y^9}$

57. $\dfrac{(-4)^6}{(-4)^3}$

58. $\dfrac{(-6)^{13}}{(-6)^{11}}$

59. $\dfrac{p^7q^{20}}{pq^{15}}$

60. $\dfrac{x^8y^6}{xy^5}$

61. $\dfrac{7x^2y^6}{14x^2y^3}$

62. $\dfrac{9a^4b^7}{27ab^2}$

Simplify each expression. See Examples 28 through 32.

63. 7^0

64. 23^0

65. $(2x)^0$

66. $(4y)^0$

67. $-7x^0$

68. $-2x^0$

69. $5^0 + y^0$

70. $-3^0 + 4^0$

Objectives Ⓐ Ⓑ Ⓒ Ⓓ Ⓔ Ⓕ **Mixed Practice** *Simplify each expression. See Examples 1 through 6, and 8 through 33.*

71. -9^2

72. $(-9)^2$

73. $\left(\dfrac{1}{4}\right)^3$

74. $\left(\dfrac{2}{3}\right)^3$

75. $b^4 b^2$

76. $y^4 y$

77. $a^2 a^3 a^4$

78. $x^2 x^{15} x^9$

79. $(2x^3)(-8x^4)$

80. $(3y^4)(-5y)$

81. $(a^7 b^{12})(a^4 b^8)$

82. $(y^2 z^2)(y^{15} z^{13})$

83. $(-2mn^6)(-13m^8 n)$

84. $(-3s^5 t)(-7st^{10})$

85. $(z^4)^{10}$

86. $(t^5)^{11}$

87. $(4ab)^3$

88. $(2ab)^4$

89. $(-6xyz^3)^2$

90. $(-3xy^2 a^3)^3$

91. $\dfrac{z^{12}}{z^4}$

92. $\dfrac{b^4}{b}$

93. $\dfrac{3x^5}{x^4}$

94. $\dfrac{5x^9}{x^3}$

95. $(6b)^0$

96. $(5ab)^0$

97. $(9xy)^2$

98. $(2ab)^5$

99. $2^3 + 2^5$

100. $7^2 - 7^0$

101. $\left(\dfrac{3y^5}{6x^4}\right)^3$

102. $\left(\dfrac{2ab}{6yz}\right)^4$

103. $\dfrac{2x^3 y^2 z}{xyz}$

104. $\dfrac{x^{12} y^{13}}{x^5 y^7}$

Review

Subtract. See Section 8.4.

105. $5 - 7$

106. $9 - 12$

107. $3 - (-2)$

108. $5 - (-10)$

109. $-11 - (-4)$

110. $-15 - (-21)$

Concept Extensions

Solve. See the Concept Checks in this section. For Exercises 111 through 114, match the expression with the operation needed to simplify each. A letter may be used more than once and a letter may not be used at all.

111. $(x^{14})^{23}$

112. $x^{14} \cdot x^{23}$

113. $x^{14} + x^{23}$

114. $\dfrac{x^{35}}{x^{17}}$

a. Add the exponents

b. Subtract the exponents

c. Multiply the exponents

d. Divide the exponents

e. None of these

Fill in the boxes so that each statement is true. (More than one answer is possible for each exercise.)

115. $x^\square \cdot x^\square = x^{12}$

116. $(x^\square)^\square = x^{20}$

117. $\dfrac{y^\square}{y^\square} = y^7$

118. $(y^\square)^\square \cdot (y^\square)^\square = y^{30}$

119. The formula $V = x^3$ can be used to find the volume V of a cube with side length x. Find the volume of a cube with side length 7 meters. (Volume is measured in cubic units.)

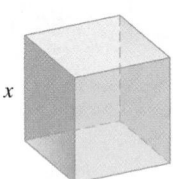

120. The formula $S = 6x^2$ can be used to find the surface area S of a cube with side length x. Find the surface area of a cube with side length 5 meters. (Surface area is measured in square units.)

121. To find the amount of water that a swimming pool in the shape of a cube can hold, do we use the formula for volume of the cube or surface area of the cube? (See Exercises 119 and 120.)

122. To find the amount of material needed to cover an ottoman in the shape of a cube, do we use the formula for volume of the cube or surface area of the cube? (See Exercises 119 and 120.)

123. Explain why $(-5)^4 = 625$, while $-5^4 = -625$.

124. Explain why $5 \cdot 4^2 = 80$, while $(5 \cdot 4)^2 = 400$.

125. In your own words, explain why $5^0 = 1$.

126. In your own words, explain when $(-3)^n$ is positive and when it is negative.

Simplify each expression. Assume that variables represent positive integers.

127. $x^{5a}x^{4a}$ **128.** $b^{9a}b^{4a}$ **129.** $(a^b)^5$ **130.** $(2a^{4b})^4$ **131.** $\dfrac{x^{9a}}{x^{4a}}$ **132.** $\dfrac{y^{15b}}{y^{6b}}$

STUDY SKILLS BUILDER

How Well Do You Know Your Textbook?

The questions below will determine whether you are familiar with your textbook. For help, see Section 1.1 in this text.

1. What does the ⊙ icon mean?
2. What does the ✎ icon mean?
3. What does the △ icon mean?
4. Where can you find a review for each chapter? What answers to this review can be found in the back of your text?
5. Each chapter contains an overview of the chapter along with examples. What is this feature called?

6. Each chapter contains a review of vocabulary. What is this feature called?
7. There is a CD in your text. What content is contained on this CD?
8. What is the location of the section that is entirely devoted to study skills?
9. There are Practice Problems that are contained in the margin of the text. What are they and how can they be used?

12.2 NEGATIVE EXPONENTS AND SCIENTIFIC NOTATION

Objectives

A Simplify Expressions Containing Negative Exponents.

B Use the Rules and Definitions for Exponents to Simplify Exponential Expressions.

C Write Numbers in Scientific Notation.

D Convert Numbers in Scientific Notation to Standard Form.

Objective **A** Simplifying Expressions Containing Negative Exponents

Our work with exponential expressions so far has been limited to exponents that are positive integers or 0. Here we will also give meaning to an expression like x^{-3}.

Suppose that we wish to simplify the expression $\dfrac{x^2}{x^5}$. If we use the quotient rule for exponents, we subtract exponents:

$$\frac{x^2}{x^5} = x^{2-5} = x^{-3}, \quad x \neq 0$$

But what does x^{-3} mean? Let's simplify $\dfrac{x^2}{x^5}$ using the definition of a^n.

$$\frac{x^2}{x^5} = \frac{x \cdot x}{x \cdot x \cdot x \cdot x \cdot x}$$

$$= \frac{\boxed{x} \cdot \boxed{x}}{\boxed{x} \cdot \boxed{x} \cdot x \cdot x \cdot x} \qquad \text{Divide numerator and denominator by common factors by applying the fundamental principle for fractions.}$$

$$= \frac{1}{x^3}$$

If the quotient rule is to hold true for negative exponents, then x^{-3} must equal $\dfrac{1}{x^3}$.

From this example, we state the definition for negative exponents.

Negative Exponents

If a is a real number other than 0 and n is an integer, then

$$a^{-n} = \frac{1}{a^n}$$

For example,

$$x^{-3} = \frac{1}{x^3}$$

In other words, another way to write a^{-n} is to take its reciprocal and change the sign of its exponent.

EXAMPLES Simplify by writing each expression with positive exponents only.

1. $3^{-2} = \dfrac{1}{3^2} = \dfrac{1}{9}$ \qquad Use the definition of negative exponents.

2. $2x^{-3} = 2^1 \cdot \dfrac{1}{x^3} = \dfrac{2^1}{x^3}$ or $\dfrac{2}{x^3}$ \qquad Use the definition of negative exponents.

3. $2^{-1} + 4^{-1} = \dfrac{1}{2} + \dfrac{1}{4} = \dfrac{2}{4} + \dfrac{1}{4} = \dfrac{3}{4}$

4. $(-2)^{-4} = \dfrac{1}{(-2)^4} = \dfrac{1}{(-2)(-2)(-2)(-2)} = \dfrac{1}{16}$

> **Helpful Hint**
> Don't forget that since there are no parentheses, only x is the base for the exponent -3.

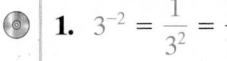 **Work Practice Problems 1–4**

PRACTICE PROBLEMS 1–4

Simplify by writing each expression with positive exponents only.

1. 5^{-3} \qquad **2.** $7x^{-4}$

3. $5^{-1} + 3^{-1}$ \qquad **4.** $(-3)^{-4}$

Answers

1. $\dfrac{1}{125}$, **2.** $\dfrac{7}{x^4}$, **3.** $\dfrac{8}{15}$, **4.** $\dfrac{1}{81}$

Helpful
Hint

A negative exponent *does not affect* the sign of its base.
Remember: Another way to write a^{-n} is to take its reciprocal and change the sign of its exponent: $a^{-n} = \dfrac{1}{a^n}$. For example,

$$x^{-2} = \frac{1}{x^2}, \qquad 2^{-3} = \frac{1}{2^3} \quad \text{or} \quad \frac{1}{8}$$

$$\frac{1}{y^{-4}} = \frac{1}{\dfrac{1}{y^4}} = y^4, \qquad \frac{1}{5^{-2}} = 5^2 \quad \text{or} \quad 25$$

From the preceding Helpful Hint, we know that $x^{-2} = \dfrac{1}{x^2}$ and $\dfrac{1}{y^{-4}} = y^4$. We can use this to include another statement in our definition of negative exponents.

Negative Exponents

If a is a real number other than 0 and n is an integer, then

$$a^{-n} = \frac{1}{a^n} \quad \text{and} \quad \frac{1}{a^{-n}} = a^n$$

PRACTICE PROBLEMS 5–8

Simplify each expression.
Write each result using positive exponents only.

5. $\left(\dfrac{6}{7}\right)^{-2}$ **6.** $\dfrac{x}{x^{-4}}$

7. $\dfrac{y^{-9}}{z^{-5}}$ **8.** $\dfrac{y^{-4}}{y^6}$

EXAMPLES Simplify each expression. Write each result using positive exponents only.

5. $\left(\dfrac{2}{x}\right)^{-3} = \dfrac{2^{-3}}{x^{-3}} = \dfrac{2^{-3}}{1} \cdot \dfrac{1}{x^{-3}} = \dfrac{1}{2^3} \cdot \dfrac{x^3}{1} = \dfrac{x^3}{2^3} = \dfrac{x^3}{8}$ Use the negative exponents rule.

6. $\dfrac{y}{y^{-2}} = \dfrac{y^1}{y^{-2}} = y^{1-(-2)} = y^3$ Use the quotient rule.

7. $\dfrac{p^{-4}}{q^{-9}} = p^{-4} \cdot \dfrac{1}{q^{-9}} = \dfrac{1}{p^4} \cdot q^9 = \dfrac{q^9}{p^4}$ Use the negative exponents rule.

8. $\dfrac{x^{-5}}{x^7} = x^{-5-7} = x^{-12} = \dfrac{1}{x^{12}}$

Work Practice Problems 5–8

Objective B Simplifying Exponential Expressions

All the previously stated rules for exponents apply for negative exponents also. Here is a summary of the rules and definitions for exponents.

Summary of Exponent Rules

If m and n are integers and a, b, and c are real numbers, then

Product rule for exponents:	$a^m \cdot a^n = a^{m+n}$
Power rule for exponents:	$(a^m)^n = a^{m \cdot n}$
Power of a product:	$(ab)^n = a^n b^n$
Power of a quotient:	$\left(\dfrac{a}{c}\right)^n = \dfrac{a^n}{c^n}, \quad c \neq 0$
Quotient rule for exponents:	$\dfrac{a^m}{a^n} = a^{m-n}, \quad a \neq 0$
Zero exponent:	$a^0 = 1, \quad a \neq 0$
Negative exponent:	$a^{-n} = \dfrac{1}{a^n}, \quad a \neq 0$

Answers

5. $\dfrac{49}{36}$, **6.** x^5, **7.** $\dfrac{z^5}{y^9}$, **8.** $\dfrac{1}{y^{10}}$

EXAMPLES Simplify each expression. Write each result using positive exponents only.

9. $\dfrac{(x^3)^4 x}{x^7} = \dfrac{x^{12} \cdot x}{x^7} = \dfrac{x^{12+1}}{x^7} = \dfrac{x^{13}}{x^7} = x^{13-7} = x^6$ Use the power rule.

10. $\left(\dfrac{3a^2}{b}\right)^{-3} = \dfrac{3^{-3}(a^2)^{-3}}{b^{-3}}$ Raise each factor in the numerator and the denominator to the -3 power.

$= \dfrac{3^{-3}a^{-6}}{b^{-3}}$ Use the power rule.

$= \dfrac{b^3}{3^3 a^6}$ Use the negative exponent rule.

$= \dfrac{b^3}{27a^6}$ Write 3^3 as 27.

11. $(y^{-3}z^6)^{-6} = (y^{-3})^{-6}(z^6)^{-6}$ Raise each factor to the -6 power.

$= y^{18}z^{-36} = \dfrac{y^{18}}{z^{36}}$

12. $\dfrac{(2x)^5}{x^3} = \dfrac{2^5 \cdot x^5}{x^3} = 2^5 \cdot x^{5-3} = 32x^2$ Raise each factor in the numerator to the fifth power.

13. $\dfrac{x^{-7}}{(x^4)^3} = \dfrac{x^{-7}}{x^{12}} = x^{-7-12} = x^{-19} = \dfrac{1}{x^{19}}$

14. $(5y^3)^{-2} = 5^{-2}(y^3)^{-2} = 5^{-2}y^{-6} = \dfrac{1}{5^2 y^6} = \dfrac{1}{25y^6}$

15. $-\dfrac{22a^7 b^{-5}}{11a^{-2} b^3} = -\dfrac{22}{11} \cdot a^{7-(-2)} b^{-5-3} = -2a^9 b^{-8} = -\dfrac{2a^9}{b^8}$

16. $\dfrac{(2xy)^{-3}}{(x^2 y^3)^2} = \dfrac{2^{-3}x^{-3}y^{-3}}{(x^2)^2(y^3)^2} = \dfrac{2^{-3}x^{-3}y^{-3}}{x^4 y^6} = 2^{-3}x^{-3-4}y^{-3-6}$

$= 2^{-3}x^{-7}y^{-9} = \dfrac{1}{2^3 x^7 y^9}$ or $\dfrac{1}{8x^7 y^9}$

🔲 **Work Practice Problems 9–16**

Objective **C** Writing Numbers in Scientific Notation

Both very large and very small numbers frequently occur in many fields of science. For example, the distance between the sun and the planet Pluto is approximately 5,906,000,000 kilometers, and the mass of a proton is approximately 0.000000000000000000000000165 gram. It can be tedious to write these numbers in this standard decimal notation, so **scientific notation** is used as a convenient shorthand for expressing very large and very small numbers.

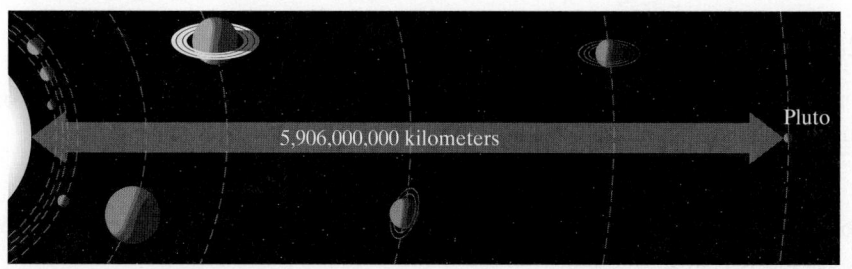

5,906,000,000 kilometers

Pluto

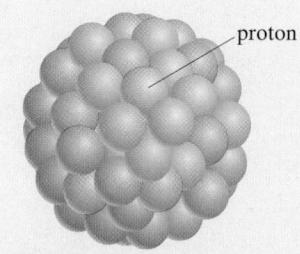

proton

Mass of proton is approximately 0.000000000000000000000000165 gram

Scientific Notation

A positive number is written in scientific notation if it is written as the product of a number a, where $1 \leq a < 10$, and an integer power r of 10: $a \times 10^r$

The following numbers are written in scientific notation. The $\times$ sign for multiplication is used as part of the notation.

$2.03 \times 10^2 \quad 7.362 \times 10^7 \quad 5.906 \times 10^9$ (Distance between the sun and Pluto)

$1 \times 10^{-3} \quad 8.1 \times 10^{-5} \quad 1.65 \times 10^{-24}$ (Mass of a proton)

The following steps are useful when writing numbers in scientific notation.

To Write a Number in Scientific Notation

Step 1: Move the decimal point in the original number so that the new number has a value between 1 and 10.

Step 2: Count the number of decimal places the decimal point is moved in Step 1. If the original number is 10 or greater, the count is positive. If the original number is less than 1, the count is negative.

Step 3: Multiply the new number in Step 1 by 10 raised to an exponent equal to the count found in Step 2.

PRACTICE PROBLEM 17

Write each number in scientific notation.

a. 420,000   **b.** 0.00017

c. 9,060,000,000   **d.** 0.000007

EXAMPLE 17 Write each number in scientific notation.

a. 367,000,000   **c.** 20,520,000,000

b. 0.000003   **d.** 0.00085

Solution:

a. Step 1: Move the decimal point until the number is between 1 and 10.

367,000,000.

8 places

Step 2: The decimal point is moved 8 places and the original number is 10 or greater, so the count is positive 8.

Step 3: $367,000,000 = 3.67 \times 10^8$.

b. Step 1: Move the decimal point until the number is between 1 and 10.

0.000003

6 places

Step 2: The decimal point is moved 6 places and the original number is less than 1, so the count is −6.

Step 3: $0.000003 = 3.0 \times 10^{-6}$

c. $20,520,000,000 = 2.052 \times 10^{10}$

d. $0.00085 = 8.5 \times 10^{-4}$

⬛ **Work Practice Problem 17**

Objective D Converting Numbers to Standard Form

A number written in scientific notation can be rewritten in standard form. For example, to write 8.63×10^3 in standard form, recall that $10^3 = 1000$.

$$8.63 \times 10^3 = 8.63(1000) = 8630$$

Notice that the exponent on the 10 is positive 3, and we moved the decimal point 3 places to the right.

Answers

17. a. 4.2×10^5,   **b.** 1.7×10^{-4},

c. 9.06×10^9,   **d.** 7×10^{-6}

To write 7.29×10^{-3} in standard form, recall that $10^{-3} = \dfrac{1}{10^3} = \dfrac{1}{1000}$.

$$7.29 \times 10^{-3} = 7.29\left(\frac{1}{1000}\right) = \frac{7.29}{1000} = 0.00729$$

The exponent on the 10 is negative 3, and we moved the decimal to the left 3 places.

In general, **to write a scientific notation number in standard form,** move the decimal point the same number of places as the exponent on 10. If the exponent is positive, move the decimal point to the right; if the exponent is negative, move the decimal point to the left.

✔ **Concept Check**   Which number in each pair is larger?

a. 7.8×10^3 or 2.1×10^5

b. 9.2×10^{-2} or 2.7×10^4

c. 5.6×10^{-4} or 6.3×10^{-5}

EXAMPLE 18   Write each number in standard notation, without exponents.

a. 1.02×10^5

b. 7.358×10^{-3}

c. 8.4×10^7

d. 3.007×10^{-5}

Solution:

a. Move the decimal point 5 places to the right.

$$1.02 \times 10^5 = 102,000.$$

b. Move the decimal point 3 places to the left.

$$7.358 \times 10^{-3} = 0.007358$$

c. $8.4 \times 10^7 = 84,000,000.$ 7 places to the right

d. $3.007 \times 10^{-5} = 0.00003007$ 5 places to the left

◻ **Work Practice Problem 18**

Performing operations on numbers written in scientific notation makes use of the rules and definitions for exponents.

EXAMPLE 19   Perform each indicated operation. Write each result in standard decimal notation.

a. $(8 \times 10^{-6})(7 \times 10^3)$

b. $\dfrac{12 \times 10^2}{6 \times 10^{-3}}$

Solution:

a. $(8 \times 10^{-6})(7 \times 10^3) = 8 \cdot 7 \cdot 10^{-6} \cdot 10^3$

$$= 56 \times 10^{-3}$$

$$= 0.056$$

b. $\dfrac{12 \times 10^2}{6 \times 10^{-3}} = \dfrac{12}{6} \times 10^{2-(-3)} = 2 \times 10^5 = 200,000$

◻ **Work Practice Problem 19**

PRACTICE PROBLEM 18

Write the numbers in standard notation, without exponents.

a. 3.062×10^{-4}

b. 5.21×10^4

c. 9.6×10^{-5}

d. 6.002×10^6

PRACTICE PROBLEM 19

Perform each indicated operation. Write each result in standard decimal notation.

a. $(9 \times 10^7)(4 \times 10^{-9})$

b. $\dfrac{8 \times 10^4}{2 \times 10^{-3}}$

Answers

18. a. 0.0003062,   **b.** 52,100,
c. 0.000096,   **d.** 6,002,000,
19. a. 0.36,   **b.** 40,000,000

✔ **Concept Check Answer**

a. 2.1×10^5,   **b.** 2.7×10^4,
c. 5.6×10^{-4}

To enter a number written in scientific notation on a scientific calculator, locate the scientific notation key, which may be marked ☐ EE ☐ or ☐ EXP ☐. To enter 3.1×10^7, press ☐ 3.1 ☐ ☐ EE ☐ ☐ 7 ☐. The display should read ☐ 3.1 ☐ 07 ☐.

Enter each number written in scientific notation on your calculator.

1. 5.31×10^3

2. -4.8×10^{14}

3. 6.6×10^{-9}

4. -9.9811×10^{-2}

Multiply each of the following on your calculator. Notice the form of the result.

5. $3,000,000 \times 5,000,000$

6. $230,000 \times 1,000$

Multiply each of the following on your calculator. Write the product in scientific notation.

7. $(3.26 \times 10^6)(2.5 \times 10^{13})$

8. $(8.76 \times 10^{-4})(1.237 \times 10^9)$

Mental Math

Write each expression using positive exponents only.

1. $5x^{-2}$ **2.** $3x^{-3}$ **3.** $\dfrac{1}{y^{-6}}$ **4.** $\dfrac{1}{x^{-3}}$ **5.** $\dfrac{4}{y^{-3}}$ **6.** $\dfrac{16}{y^{-7}}$

12.2 EXERCISE SET

Objective  *Simplify each expression. Write each result using positive exponents only. See Examples 1 through 8.*

1. 4^{-3} **2.** 6^{-2} **3.** $7x^{-3}$ **4.** $(7x)^{-3}$ **5.** $\left(-\dfrac{1}{4}\right)^{-3}$ **6.** $\left(-\dfrac{1}{8}\right)^{-2}$

7. $3^{-1} + 2^{-1}$ **8.** $4^{-1} + 4^{-2}$ **9.** $\dfrac{1}{p^{-3}}$ **10.** $\dfrac{1}{q^{-5}}$ **11.** $\dfrac{p^{-5}}{q^{-4}}$ **12.** $\dfrac{r^{-5}}{s^{-2}}$

13. $\dfrac{x^{-2}}{x}$ **14.** $\dfrac{y}{y^{-3}}$ **15.** $\dfrac{z^{-4}}{z^{-7}}$ **16.** $\dfrac{x^{-4}}{x^{-1}}$ **17.** $3^{-2} + 3^{-1}$ **18.** $4^{-2} - 4^{-3}$

19. $(-3)^{-2}$ **20.** $(-2)^{-6}$ **21.** $\dfrac{-1}{p^{-4}}$ **22.** $\dfrac{-1}{y^{-6}}$ **23.** $-2^0 - 3^0$ **24.** $5^0 + (-5)^0$

Objective  *Simplify each expression. Write each result using positive exponents only. See Examples 9 through 16.*

25. $\dfrac{x^2 x^5}{x^3}$ **26.** $\dfrac{y^4 y^5}{y^6}$ **27.** $\dfrac{p^2 p}{p^{-1}}$ **28.** $\dfrac{y^3 y}{y^{-2}}$ **29.** $\dfrac{(m^5)^4 m}{m^{10}}$ **30.** $\dfrac{(x^2)^8 x}{x^9}$

31. $\dfrac{r}{r^{-3}r^{-2}}$

32. $\dfrac{p}{p^{-3}q^{-5}}$

33. $(x^5y^3)^{-3}$

34. $(z^5x^5)^{-3}$

35. $\dfrac{(x^2)^3}{x^{10}}$

36. $\dfrac{(y^4)^2}{y^{12}}$

37. $\dfrac{(a^5)^2}{(a^3)^4}$

38. $\dfrac{(x^2)^5}{(x^4)^3}$

39. $\dfrac{8k^4}{2k}$

40. $\dfrac{27r^6}{3r^4}$

41. $\dfrac{-6m^4}{-2m^3}$

42. $\dfrac{15a^4}{-15a^5}$

43. $\dfrac{-24a^6b}{6ab^2}$

44. $\dfrac{-5x^4y^5}{15x^4y^2}$

45. $\dfrac{6x^2y^3}{-7x^2y^5}$

46. $\dfrac{-8xa^2b}{-5xa^5b}$

47. $(3a^2b^{-4})^3$

48. $(5x^3y^{-2})^2$

49. $(a^{-5}b^2)^{-6}$

50. $(4^{-1}x^5)^{-2}$

51. $\left(\dfrac{x^{-2}y^4}{x^3y^7}\right)^2$

52. $\left(\dfrac{a^5b}{a^7b^{-2}}\right)^{-3}$

53. $\dfrac{4^2z^{-3}}{4^3z^{-5}}$

54. $\dfrac{5^{-1}z^7}{5^{-2}z^9}$

55. $\dfrac{3^{-1}x^4}{3^3x^{-7}}$

56. $\dfrac{2^{-3}x^{-4}}{2^2x}$

57. $\dfrac{7ab^{-4}}{7^{-1}a^{-3}b^2}$

58. $\dfrac{6^{-5}x^{-1}y^2}{6^{-2}x^{-4}y^4}$

59. $\dfrac{-12m^5n^{-7}}{4m^{-2}n^{-3}}$

60. $\dfrac{-15r^{-6}s}{5r^{-4}s^{-3}}$

61. $\left(\dfrac{a^{-5}b}{ab^3}\right)^{-4}$

62. $\left(\dfrac{r^{-2}s^{-3}}{r^{-4}s^{-3}}\right)^{-3}$

63. $(5^2)(8)(2^0)$

64. $(3^4)(7^0)(2)$

65. $\dfrac{(xy^3)^5}{(xy)^{-4}}$

66. $\dfrac{(rs)^{-3}}{(r^2s^3)^2}$

67. $\dfrac{(-2xy^{-3})^{-3}}{(xy^{-1})^{-1}}$

68. $\dfrac{(-3x^2y^2)^{-2}}{(xyz)^{-2}}$

69. $\dfrac{(a^4b^{-7})^{-5}}{(5a^2b^{-1})^{-2}}$

70. $\dfrac{(a^6b^{-2})^4}{(4a^{-3}b^{-3})^3}$

△ **71.** Find the volume of the cube.

△ **72.** Find the area of the triangle.

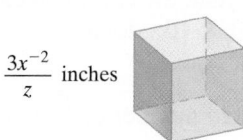
$\dfrac{3x^{-2}}{z}$ inches

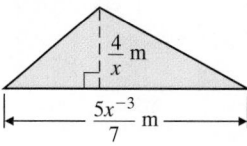
$\dfrac{4}{x}$ m

$\dfrac{5x^{-3}}{7}$ m

Objective **C** *Write each number in scientific notation. See Example 17.*

73. 78,000

74. 9,300,000,000

75. 0.00000167

76. 0.00000017

77. 0.00635

78. 0.00194

79. 1,160,000

80. 700,000

81. At this writing, the world's largest optical telescopes are the twin Keck Telescopes located near the summit of Mauna Kea in Hawaii. The elevation of the Keck Telescopes is about 13,600 feet above sea level. Write 13,600 in scientific notation. (*Source:* W.M. Keck Observatory)

82. After more than 30 years, the *Pioneer 10* spacecraft sent its last signal to Earth. Launched on March 2, 1972, it became the first spacecraft to leave our solar system. When it transmitted its last signal, in January 2003, it was approximately 8,000,000,000 miles from Earth. Write 8,000,000,000 in scientific notation. (*Source:* NASA Ames Research Center)

Objective **D** *Write each number in standard notation. See Example 18.*

83. 8.673×10^{-10}

84. 9.056×10^{-4}

85. 3.3×10^{-2}

86. 4.8×10^{-6}

87. 2.032×10^{4}

88. 9.07×10^{10}

89. Each second, the Sun converts 7.0×10^{8} tons of hydrogen into helium and energy in the form of gamma rays. Write this number in standard notation. (*Source:* Students for the Exploration and Development of Space)

90. In chemistry, Avogadro's number is the number of atoms in one mole of an element. Avogadro's number is $6.02214199 \times 10^{23}$. Write this number in standard notation. (*Source:* National Institute of Standards and Technology)

Objectives **C** **D** **Mixed Practice** *See Examples 17 and 18. Below are some interesting facts about the Internet. If a number is written in standard form, write it in scientific notation. If a number is written in scientific notation, write it in standard form.*

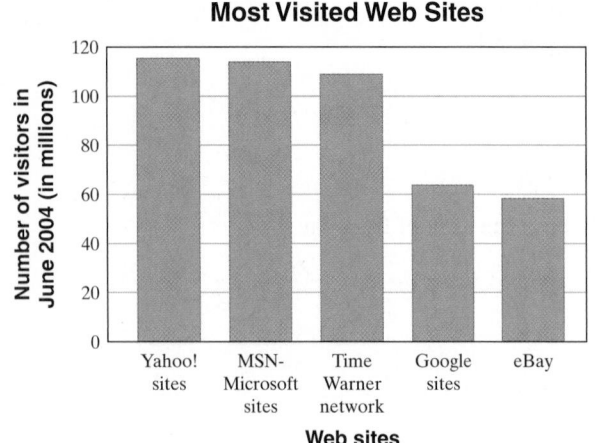

Most Visited Web Sites

91. The total number of Internet users is 940,000,000.

92. The total number of Internet hosts (sites) is 233,000,000.

93. In a recent year, the revenue generated by the Internet was 1.23×10^{12} dollars.

94. The estimated number of e-mail boxes is 1.2×10^{9}.

95. The bar graph above shows the most visited Web sites on the computer. Estimate the height of the tallest bar and the shortest bar. Then write each number in scientific notation.

96. Junk e-mail (SPAM) costs consumers and businesses an estimated $23,000,000,000.

Objective **D** *Evaluate each expression using exponential rules. Write each result in standard notation. See Example 19.*

97. $(1.2 \times 10^{-3})(3 \times 10^{-2})$

98. $(2.5 \times 10^{6})(2 \times 10^{-6})$

99. $(4 \times 10^{-10})(7 \times 10^{-9})$

100. $(5 \times 10^{6})(4 \times 10^{-8})$

101. $\dfrac{8 \times 10^{-1}}{16 \times 10^{5}}$

102. $\dfrac{25 \times 10^{-4}}{5 \times 10^{-9}}$

103. $\dfrac{1.4 \times 10^{-2}}{7 \times 10^{-8}}$

104. $\dfrac{0.4 \times 10^{5}}{0.2 \times 10^{11}}$

105. Although the actual amount varies by season and time of day, the average volume of water that flows over Niagara Falls (the American and Canadian falls combined) each second is 7.5×10^{5} gallons. How much water flows over Niagara Falls in an hour? Write the result in scientific notation. (*Hint:* 1 hour equals 3600 seconds) (*Source:* niagarafallslive.com)

106. A beam of light travels 9.460×10^{12} kilometers per year. How far does light travel in 10,000 years? Write the result in scientific notation.

Review

Simplify each expression by combining any like terms. See Section 8.7.

107. $3x - 5x + 7$

108. $7w + w - 2w$

109. $y - 10 + y$

110. $-6z + 20 - 3z$

111. $7x + 2 - 8x - 6$

112. $10y - 14 - y - 14$

Concept Extensions

Simplify.

113. $(2a^{3})^{3}a^{4} + a^{5}a^{8}$

114. $(2a^{3})^{3}a^{-3} + a^{11}a^{-5}$

Fill in the boxes so that each statement is true. (More than one answer is possible for these exercises.)

115. $x^{\square} = \dfrac{1}{x^{5}}$

116. $7^{\square} = \dfrac{1}{49}$

117. $z^{\square} \cdot z^{\square} = z^{-10}$

118. $(x^{\square})^{\square} = x^{-15}$

119. Which is larger? See the Concept Check in this section.
   a. 9.7×10^{-2} or 1.3×10^{1}
   b. 8.6×10^{5} or 4.4×10^{7}
   c. 6.1×10^{-2} or 5.6×10^{-4}

120. It was stated earlier that for an integer n,
$$x^{-n} = \frac{1}{x^{n}}, \quad x \neq 0$$
Explain why x may not equal 0.

121. Determine whether each statement is true or false.
   a. $5^{-1} < 5^{-2}$
   b. $\left(\dfrac{1}{5}\right)^{-1} < \left(\dfrac{1}{5}\right)^{-2}$
   c. $a^{-1} < a^{-2}$ for all nonzero numbers.

Simplify each expression. Assume that variables represent positive integers.

122. $a^{-4m} \cdot a^{5m}$

123. $(x^{-3s})^{3}$

124. $(3y^{2z})^{3}$

125. $a^{4m+1} \cdot a^{4}$

A Define Term and Coefficient of a Term.

B Define Polynomial, Monomial, Binomial, Trinomial, and Degree.

C Evaluate Polynomials for Given Replacement Values.

D Simplify a Polynomial by Combining Like Terms.

E Simplify a Polynomial in Several Variables.

F Write a Polynomial in Descending Powers of the Variable and with No Missing Powers of the Variable.

12.3 INTRODUCTION TO POLYNOMIALS

Objective **A** Defining Term and Coefficient

In this section, we introduce a special algebraic expression called a polynomial. Let's first review some definitions presented in Section 8.7.

Recall that a term is a number or the product of a number and variables raised to powers. The terms of an expression are separated by plus signs. The terms of the expression $4x^2 + 3x$ are $4x^2$ and $3x$. The terms of the expression $9x^4 - 7x - 1$, or $9x^4 + (-7x) + (-1)$, are $9x^4$, $-7x$, and -1.

Expression	Terms
$4x^2 + 3x$	$4x^2, 3x$
$9x^4 - 7x - 1$	$9x^4, -7x, -1$
$7y^3$	$7y^3$

The **numerical coefficient** of a term, or simply the **coefficient,** is the numerical factor of each term. If no numerical factor appears in the term, then the coefficient is understood to be 1. If the term is a number only, it is called a **constant term** or simply a **constant.**

Term	Coefficient
x^5	1
$3x^2$	3
$-4x$	-4
$-x^2y$	-1
3 (constant)	3

PRACTICE PROBLEM 1

Complete the table for the expression
$-6x^6 + 4x^5 + 7x^3 - 9x^2 - 1.$

Term	Coefficient
$7x^3$	
	-9
$-6x^6$	
	4
-1	

EXAMPLE 1

Complete the table for the expression $7x^5 - 8x^4 + x^2 - 3x + 5.$

Term	Coefficient
x^2	
	-8
$-3x$	
	7
5	

Solution: The completed table is shown below.

Term	Coefficient
x^2	1
$-8x^4$	-8
$-3x$	-3
$7x^5$	7
5	5

▦ **Work Practice Problem 1**

Objective B Defining Polynomial, Monomial, Binomial, Trinomial, and Degree

Now we are ready to define what we mean by a polynomial.

Polynomial

A **polynomial in x** is a finite sum of terms of the form ax^n, where a is a real number and n is a whole number.

For example,

$$x^5 - 3x^3 + 2x^2 - 5x + 1$$

is a polynomial in x. Notice that this polynomial is written in **descending powers** of x because the powers of x decrease from left to right. (Recall that the term 1 can be thought of as $1x^0$.)

On the other hand,

$$x^{-5} + 2x - 3$$

is **not** a polynomial because one of its terms contains a variable with an exponent, -5, that is not a whole number.

Types of Polynomials

A **monomial** is a polynomial with exactly one term.

A **binomial** is a polynomial with exactly two terms.

A **trinomial** is a polynomial with exactly three terms.

The following are examples of monomials, binomials, and trinomials. Each of these examples is also a polynomial.

Polynomials			
Monomials	**Binomials**	**Trinomials**	**More Than Three Terms**
ax^2	$x + y$	$x^2 + 4xy + y^2$	$5x^3 - 6x^2 + 3x - 6$
$-3z$	$3p + 2$	$x^5 + 7x^2 - x$	$-y^5 + y^4 - 3y^3 - y^2 + y$
4	$4x^2 - 7$	$-q^4 + q^3 - 2q$	$x^6 + x^4 - x^3 + 1$

Each term of a polynomial has a degree. The **degree of a term in one variable** is the exponent on the variable.

EXAMPLE 2 Identify the degree of each term of the trinomial $12x^4 - 7x + 3$.

Solution: The term $12x^4$ has degree 4.

The term $-7x$ has degree 1 since $-7x$ is $-7x^1$.

The term 3 has degree 0 since 3 is $3x^0$.

 Work Practice Problem 2

Each polynomial also has a degree.

Degree of a Polynomial

The **degree of a polynomial** is the greatest degree of any term of the polynomial.

PRACTICE PROBLEM 2

Identify the degree of each term of the trinomial $-15x^3 + 2x^2 - 5$.

Answer
2. $3; 2; 0$

PRACTICE PROBLEM 3

Find the degree of each polynomial and tell whether the polynomial is a monomial, binomial, trinomial, or none of these.

a. $-6x + 14$

b. $9x - 3x^6 + 5x^4 + 2$

c. $10x^2 - 6x - 6$

EXAMPLE 3 Find the degree of each polynomial and tell whether the polynomial is a monomial, binomial, trinomial, or none of these.

a. $-2t^2 + 3t + 6$ **b.** $15x - 10$ **c.** $7x + 3x^3 + 2x^2 - 1$

Solution:

a. The degree of the trinomial $-2t^2 + 3t + 6$ is 2, the greatest degree of any of its terms.

b. The degree of the binomial $15x - 10$ or $15x^1 - 10$ is 1.

c. The degree of the polynomial $7x + 3x^3 + 2x^2 - 1$ is 3. The polynomial is neither a monomial, binomial, nor trinomial.

▣ **Work Practice Problem 3**

Objective **C** Evaluating Polynomials

Polynomials have different values depending on the replacement values for the variables. When we find the value of a polynomial for a given replacement value, we are evaluating the polynomial for that value.

PRACTICE PROBLEM 4

Evaluate each polynomial when $x = -1$.

a. $-2x + 10$

b. $6x^2 + 11x - 20$

EXAMPLE 4 Evaluate each polynomial when $x = -2$.

a. $-5x + 6$ **b.** $3x^2 - 2x + 1$

Solution:

a. $-5x + 6 = -5(-2) + 6$ Replace x with -2.

         $= 10 + 6$

         $= 16$

b. $3x^2 - 2x + 1 = 3(-2)^2 - 2(-2) + 1$ Replace x with -2.

                $= 3(4) + 4 + 1$

                $= 12 + 4 + 1$

                $= 17$

▣ **Work Practice Problem 4**

Many physical phenomena can be modeled by polynomials.

PRACTICE PROBLEM 5

Find the height of the object in example 5 when $t = 2$ seconds and $t = 4$ seconds.

EXAMPLE 5 **Finding Free-Fall Time**

The Swiss Re Building, completed in London in 2003, is a unique building. Londoners often refer to it as the "pickle building." The building is 592.1 feet tall. An object is dropped from the highest point of this building. Neglecting air resistance, the height in feet of the object above ground at time t seconds is given by the polynomial $-16t^2 + 592.1$. Find the height of the object when $t = 1$ second, and when $t = 6$ seconds.

Solution: To find each height, we evaluate the polynomial when $t = 1$ and when $t = 6$.

    $-16t^2 + 592.1 = -16(1)^2 + 592.1$ Replace t with 1.

                   $= -16(1) + 592.1$

                   $= -16 + 592.1$

                   $= 576.1$

The height of the object at 1 second is 576.1 feet.

    $-16t^2 + 592.1 = -16(6)^2 + 592.1$ Replace t with 6.

                   $= -16(36) + 592.1$

                   $= -576 + 592.1 = 16.1$

Answers

3. a. binomial, 1,   **b.** none of these, 6,
c. trinomial, 2,   **4. a.** 12,   **b.** −25,
5. 528.1 feet, 336.1 feet

The height of the object at 6 seconds is 16.1 feet.

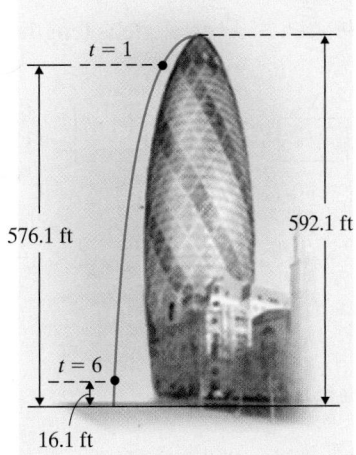

■ Work Practice Problem 5

Objective **D** Simplifying Polynomials by Combining Like Terms

We can simplify polynomials with like terms by combining the like terms. Recall from Section 8.7 that like terms are terms that contain exactly the same variables raised to exactly the same powers.

Like Terms	Unlike Terms
$5x^2, -7x^2$	$3x, 3y$
$y, 2y$	$-2x^2, -5x$
$\frac{1}{2}a^2b, -a^2b$	$6st^2, 4s^2t$

Only like terms can be combined. We combine like terms by applying the distributive property.

EXAMPLES Simplify each polynomial by combining any like terms.

6. $-3x + 7x = (-3 + 7)x = 4x$

7. $11x^2 + 5 + 2x^2 - 7 = 11x^2 + 2x^2 + 5 - 7$
$$= 13x^2 - 2$$

8. $9x^3 + x^3 = 9x^3 + 1x^3$ Write x^3 as $1x^3$.
$$= 10x^3$$

9. $5x^2 + 6x - 9x - 3 = 5x^2 - 3x - 3$ Combine like terms $6x$ and $-9x$.

10. $\frac{2}{5}x^4 + \frac{2}{3}x^3 - x^2 + \frac{1}{10}x^4 - \frac{1}{6}x^3$

$$= \left(\frac{2}{5} + \frac{1}{10}\right)x^4 + \left(\frac{2}{3} - \frac{1}{6}\right)x^3 - x^2$$

$$= \left(\frac{4}{10} + \frac{1}{10}\right)x^4 + \left(\frac{4}{6} - \frac{1}{6}\right)x^3 - x^2$$

$$= \frac{5}{10}x^4 + \frac{3}{6}x^3 - x^2$$

$$= \frac{1}{2}x^4 + \frac{1}{2}x^3 - x^2$$

■ Work Practice Problems 6–10

PRACTICE PROBLEMS 6–10

Simplify each polynomial by combining any like terms.

6. $-6y + 8y$

7. $14y^2 + 3 - 10y^2 - 9$

8. $7x^3 + x^3$

9. $23x^2 - 6x - x - 15$

10. $\frac{2}{7}x^3 - \frac{1}{4}x + 2 - \frac{1}{2}x^3 + \frac{3}{8}x$

Answers

6. $2y$, **7.** $4y^2 - 6$, **8.** $8x^3$,
9. $23x^2 - 7x - 15$,

10. $-\frac{3}{14}x^3 + \frac{1}{8}x + 2$

PRACTICE PROBLEM 11 △

Write a polynomial that describes the total area of the squares and rectangles shown below. Then simplify the polynomial.

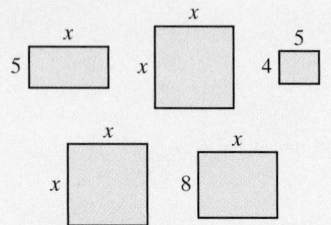

△ **EXAMPLE 11** Write a polynomial that describes the total area of the squares and rectangles shown below. Then simplify the polynomial.

Solution: Recall that the area of a rectangle is length times width.

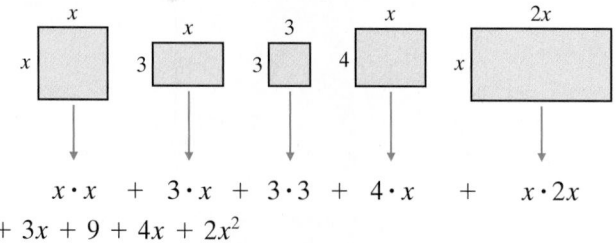

$$\text{Area:} \qquad x \cdot x \;+\; 3 \cdot x \;+\; 3 \cdot 3 \;+\; 4 \cdot x \;+\; x \cdot 2x$$

$$= x^2 + 3x + 9 + 4x + 2x^2$$

$$= 3x^2 + 7x + 9 \qquad \text{Combine like terms.}$$

▣ **Work Practice Problem 11**

Objective 🄴 Simplifying Polynomials Containing Several Variables

A polynomial may contain more than one variable. One example is

$$5x + 3xy^2 - 6x^2y^2 + x^2y - 2y + 1$$

We call this expression a polynomial in several variables.

The **degree of a term** with more than one variable is the sum of the exponents on the variables. The **degree of the polynomial** in several variables is still the greatest degree of the terms of the polynomial.

PRACTICE PROBLEM 12

Identify the degrees of the terms and the degree of the polynomial $-2x^3y^2 + 4 - 8xy + 3x^3y + 5xy^2$.

EXAMPLE 12 Identify the degrees of the terms and the degree of the polynomial $5x + 3xy^2 - 6x^2y^2 + x^2y - 2y + 1$.

Solution: To organize our work, we use a table.

Terms of Polynomial	Degree of Term	Degree of Polynomial
$5x$	1	
$3xy^2$	$1 + 2$ or 3	
$-6x^2y^2$	$2 + 2$ or 4	4 (greatest degree)
x^2y	$2 + 1$ or 3	
$-2y$	1	
1	0	

▣ **Work Practice Problem 12**

To simplify a polynomial containing several variables, we combine any like terms.

PRACTICE PROBLEMS 13–14

Simplify each polynomial by combining any like terms.
13. $11ab - 6a^2 - ba + 8b^2$
14. $7x^2y^2 + 2y^2 - 4y^2x^2 + x^2 - y^2 + 5x^2$

EXAMPLES Simplify each polynomial by combining any like terms.

13. $3xy - 5y^2 + 7yx - 9x^2 = (3 + 7)xy - 5y^2 - 9x^2$

$$= 10xy - 5y^2 - 9x^2$$

14. $9a^2b - 6a^2 + 5b^2 + a^2b - 11a^2 + 2b^2$

$$= 10a^2b - 17a^2 + 7b^2$$

Helpful Hint

This term can be written as $7yx$ or $7xy$.

▣ **Work Practice Problems 13–14**

Answers
11. $2x^2 + 13x + 20$,
12. $5, 0, 2, 4, 3; 5$,
13. $10ab - 6a^2 + 8b^2$,
14. $3x^2y^2 + y^2 + 6x^2$

Objective **F** Inserting "Missing" Terms

To prepare for dividing polynomials in Section 12.7, let's practice writing a polynomial in descending powers of the variable and with no "missing" powers.

Recall from Objective **B** that a polynomial such as

$$x^5 - 3x^3 + 2x^2 - 5x + 1$$

is written in descending powers of x because the powers of x decrease from left to right. Study the decreasing powers of x and notice that there is a "missing" power of x. This missing power is x^4. Writing a polynomial in decreasing powers of the variable helps you immediately determine important features of the polynomial, such as its degree. It is also sometimes helpful to write a polynomial so that there are no "missing" powers of x. For our polynomial above, if we simply insert a term of $0x^4$, which equals 0, we have an equivalent polynomial with no missing powers of x.

$$x^5 - 3x^3 + 2x^2 - 5x + 1 = x^5 + 0x^4 - 3x^3 + 2x^2 - 5x + 1$$

EXAMPLE 15 Write each polynomial in descending powers of the variable with no missing powers.

a. $x^2 - 4$
b. $3m^3 - m + 1$
c. $2x + x^4$

Solution:

a. $x^2 - 4 = x^2 + 0x^1 - 4$ or $x^2 + 0x - 4$ Insert a missing term of $0x^1$ or $0x$.
b. $3m^3 - m + 1 = 3m^3 + 0m^2 - m + 1$ Insert a missing term of $0m^2$.
c. $2x + x^4 = x^4 + 2x$ Write in descending power of variable.
        $= x^4 + 0x^3 + 0x^2 + 2x + 0x^0$ Insert missing terms of $0x^3, 0x^2$, and $0x^0$ (or 0).

■ Work Practice Problem 15

> **Helpful Hint**
>
> Since there is no constant as a last term, we insert a $0x^0$. This $0x^0$ (or 0) is the final power of x in our polynomial.

PRACTICE PROBLEM 15

Write each polynomial in descending powers of the variable with no missing powers.

a. $x^2 + 9$
b. $9m^3 + m^2 - 5$
c. $-3a^3 + a^4$

Answers

15. a. $x^2 + 0x + 9$,
b. $9m^3 + m^2 + 0m - 5$,
c. $a^4 - 3a^3 + 0a^2 + 0a + 0a^0$

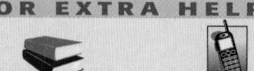

Objective A *Complete each table for each polynomial. See Example 1.*

1. $x^2 - 3x + 5$

Term	Coefficient
x^2	
	-3
5	

2. $2x^3 - x + 4$

Term	Coefficient
	2
$-x$	
4	

3. $-5x^4 + 3.2x^2 + x - 5$

Term	Coefficient
$-5x^4$	
$3.2x^2$	
x	
-5	

4. $9.7x^7 - 3x^5 + x^3 - \dfrac{1}{4}x^2$

Term	Coefficient
$9.7x^7$	
$-3x^5$	
x^3	
$-\dfrac{1}{4}x^2$	

Objective B *Find the degree of each polynomial and determine whether it is a monomial, binomial, trinomial, or none of these. See Examples 2 and 3.*

5. $x + 2$

6. $-6y + 4$

7. $9m^3 - 5m^2 + 4m - 8$

8. $a + 5a^2 + 3a^3 - 4a^4$

9. $12x^4 - x^6 - 12x^2$

10. $7r^2 + 2r - 3r^5$

11. $3z - 5z^4$

12. $5y^6 + 2$

Objective C *Evaluate each polynomial when* **(a)** $x = 0$ *and* **(b)** $x = -1$. *See Examples 4 and 5.*

13. $5x - 6$

14. $2x - 10$

15. $x^2 - 5x - 2$

16. $x^2 + 3x - 4$

17. $-x^3 + 4x^2 - 15$

18. $-2x^3 + 3x^2 - 6$

A rocket is fired upward from the ground with an initial velocity of 200 feet per second. Neglecting air resistance, the height of the rocket at any time t can be described in feet by the polynomial $-16t^2 + 200t$. Find the height of the rocket at the time given in Exercises 19 through 22. See Example 5.

	Time, t (in seconds)	Height $-16t^2 + 200t$
19.	1	
20.	5	
21.	7.6	
22.	10.3	

23. The polynomial $-24x^2 + 336x - 132$ represents the average number of visitors (in thousands) per day to National Park Service areas, where x represents the month of the year. Use this model to predict the average daily attendance at our national parks for the month of July. (*Hint:* July is the seventh month.) (*Source:* Based on data from the National Park Service)

24. The number of wireless telephone subscribers (in millions) x years after 1994 is given by the polynomial $0.56x^2 + 10x + 15.25$ for 1994 through 2004. Use this model to predict the number of wireless telephone subscribers in 2010 ($x = 16$). (*Source:* Based on data from Cellular Telecommunications & Internet Association)

Objective **D** *Simplify each expression by combining like terms. See Examples 6 through 10.*

25. $9x - 20x$

26. $14y - 30y$

27. $14x^3 + 9x^3$

28. $18x^3 + 4x^3$

29. $7x^2 + 3 + 9x^2 - 10$

30. $8x^2 + 4 + 11x^2 - 20$

31. $15x^2 - 3x^2 - 13$

32. $12k^3 - 9k^3 + 11$

33. $8s - 5s + 4s$

34. $5y + 7y - 6y$

35. $0.1y^2 - 1.2y^2 + 6.7 - 1.9$

36. $7.6y + 3.2y^2 - 8y - 2.5y^2$

37. $\dfrac{2}{3}x^4 + 12x^3 + \dfrac{1}{6}x^4 - 19x^3 - 19$

38. $\dfrac{2}{5}x^4 - 23x^2 + \dfrac{1}{15}x^4 + 5x^2 - 5$

39. $\dfrac{3}{20}x^3 + \dfrac{1}{10} - \dfrac{3}{10}x - \dfrac{1}{5} - \dfrac{7}{20}x + 6x^2$

40. $\dfrac{5}{16}x^3 - \dfrac{1}{8} + \dfrac{3}{8}x + \dfrac{1}{4} - \dfrac{9}{16}x - 14x^2$

Objective **E** *Identify the degrees of the terms and the degree of the polynomial. See Example 12.*

41. $9ab - 6a + 5b - 3$

42. $y^4 - 6y^3x + 2x^2y^2 - 5y^2 + 3$

43. $x^3y - 6 + 2x^2y^2 + 5y^3$

44. $2a^2b + 10a^4b - 9ab + 6$

Simplify each polynomial by combining any like terms. See Examples 13 and 14.

45. $3ab - 4a + 6ab - 7a$

46. $-9xy + 7y - xy - 6y$

47. $4x^2 - 6xy + 3y^2 - xy$

48. $3a^2 - 9ab + 4b^2 - 7ab$

49. $5x^2y + 6xy^2 - 5yx^2 + 4 - 9y^2x$

50. $17a^2b - 16ab^2 + 3a^3 + 4ba^3 - b^2a$

51. $14y^3 - 9 + 3a^2b^2 - 10 - 19b^2a^2$

52. $18x^4 + 2x^3y^3 - 1 - 2y^3x^3 - 17x^4$

Objective ⬛**F** *Write each polynomial in descending powers of the variable and with no missing powers. See Example 15.*

53. $7x^2 + 3$

54. $5x^2 - 2$

55. $x^3 - 64$

56. $x^3 - 8$

57. $5y^3 + 2y - 10$

58. $6m^3 - 3m + 4$

59. $8y + 2y^4$

60. $11z + 4z^4$

61. $6x^5 + x^3 - 3x + 15$

62. $9y^5 - y^2 + 2y - 11$

Objective ⬛**D** *Write a polynomial that describes the total area of each set of rectangles and squares shown in Exercises 63 and 64. Then simplify the polynomial. See Example 11.*

△ **63.**

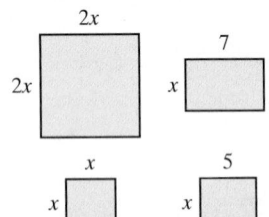

△ **64.**

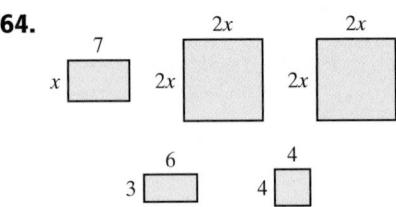

Recall that the perimeter of a figure such as the ones shown in Exercises 65 and 66 is the sum of the lengths of its sides. Write each perimeter as a polynomial. Then simplify the polynomial.

△ **65.**

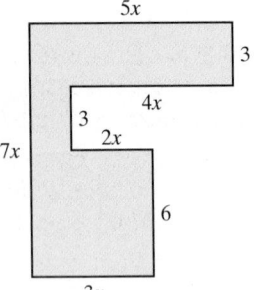

△ **66.**

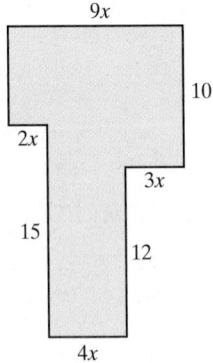

Review

Simplify each expression. See Section 8.7.

67. $4 + 5(2x + 3)$ **68.** $9 - 6(5x + 1)$ **69.** $2(x - 5) + 3(5 - x)$ **70.** $-3(w + 7) + 5(w + 1)$

Concept Extensions

71. Describe how to find the degree of a term.

72. Describe how to find the degree of a polynomial.

73. Explain why xyz is a monomial while $x + y + z$ is a trinomial.

74. Explain why the degree of the term $5y^3$ is 3 and the degree of the polynomial $2y + y + 2y$ is 1.

Simplify, if possible.

75. $x^4 \cdot x^9$

76. $x^4 + x^9$

77. $a \cdot b^3 \cdot a^2 \cdot b^7$

78. $a + b^3 + a^2 + b^7$

79. $(y^5)^4 + (y^2)^{10}$

80. $x^5y^2 + y^2x^5$

Fill in the boxes so that the terms in each expression can be combined. Then simplify. Each exercise has more than one solution.

81. $7x^{\square} + 2x^{\square}$

82. $(3y^2)^{\square} + (4y^3)^{\square}$

83. Explain why the height of the rocket in Exercises 19 through 22 increases and then decreases as time passes.

84. Approximate (to the nearest tenth of a second) how long before the rocket in Exercises 19 through 22 hits the ground.

Simplify each polynomial by combining like terms.

85. $1.85x^2 - 3.76x + 9.25x^2 + 10.76 - 4.21x$

86. $7.75x + 9.16x^2 - 1.27 - 14.58x^2 - 18.34$

 STUDY SKILLS BUILDER

Are You Organized?

Have you ever had trouble finding a completed assignment? When it's time to study for a test, are your notes neat and organized? Have you ever had trouble reading your own mathematics handwriting? (Be honest—I have.)

When any of these things happen, it's time to get organized. Here are a few suggestions:

Write your notes and complete your homework assignment in a notebook with pockets (spiral or ring binder.) Take class notes in this notebook, and then follow the notes with your completed homework assignment. When you receive graded papers or handouts, place them in the notebook pocket so that you will not lose them.

Remember to mark (possibly with an exclamation point) any note(s) that seem extra important to you. Also remember to mark (possibly with a question mark) any notes or homework that you are having trouble with. Don't forget to see your instructor or a math tutor to help you with the concepts or exercises that you are having trouble understanding.

Also, if you are having trouble reading your own handwriting, *slow down* and write your mathematics work clearly!

Exercises

1. Have you been completing your assignments on time?

2. Have you been correcting any exercises you may be having difficulty with?

3. If you are having trouble with a mathematical concept or correcting any homework exercises, have you visited your instructor, a tutor, or your campus math lab?

4. Are you taking lecture notes in your mathematics course? (By the way, these notes should include worked-out examples solved by your instructor.)

5. Is your mathematics course material (handouts, graded papers, lecture notes) organized?

6. If your answer to Exercise 5 is no, take a moment and review your course material. List at least two ways that you might better organize it. Then read the Study Skills Builder on organizing a notebook in Chapter 2.

Objectives

Objective **A** Adding Polynomials

To add polynomials, we use commutative and associative properties and then combine like terms. To see if you are ready to add polynomials, try the Concept Check.

✔**Concept Check** When combining like terms in the expression $5x - 8x^2 - 8x$, which of the following is the proper result?

a. $-11x^2$ **b.** $-3x - 8x^2$ **c.** $-11x$ **d.** $-11x^4$

To Add Polynomials

To add polynomials, combine all like terms.

PRACTICE PROBLEMS 1–2

Add.

1. $(3x^5 - 7x^3 + 2x - 1)$
$+ (3x^3 - 2x)$

2. $(5x^2 - 2x + 1)$
$+ (-6x^2 + x - 1)$

EXAMPLES Add.

1. $(4x^3 - 6x^2 + 2x + 7) + (5x^2 - 2x)$

$= 4x^3 - 6x^2 + 2x + 7 + 5x^2 - 2x$ Remove parentheses.

$= 4x^3 + (-6x^2 + 5x^2) + (2x - 2x) + 7$ Combine like terms.

$= 4x^3 - x^2 + 7$ Simplify.

2. $(-2x^2 + 5x - 1) + (-2x^2 + x + 3)$

$= -2x^2 + 5x - 1 - 2x^2 + x + 3$ Remove parentheses.

$= (-2x^2 - 2x^2) + (5x + 1x) + (-1 + 3)$ Combine like terms.

$= -4x^2 + 6x + 2$ Simplify.

▢ **Work Practice Problems 1–2**

Just as we can add numbers vertically, polynomials can be added vertically if we line up like terms underneath one another.

PRACTICE PROBLEM 3

Add $(9y^2 - 6y + 5)$ and $(4y + 3)$ using a vertical format.

EXAMPLE 3 Add $(7y^3 - 2y^2 + 7)$ and $(6y^2 + 1)$ using a vertical format.

Solution: Vertically line up like terms and add.

$$
\begin{array}{r}
7y^3 - 2y^2 + 7 \\
6y^2 + 1 \\
\hline
7y^3 + 4y^2 + 8
\end{array}
$$

▢ **Work Practice Problem 3**

Objective **B** Subtracting Polynomials

To subtract one polynomial from another, recall the definition of subtraction. To subtract a number, we add its opposite: $a - b = a + (-b)$. To subtract a polynomial, we also add its opposite. Just as $-b$ is the opposite of b, $-(x^2 + 5)$ is the opposite of $(x^2 + 5)$.

Answers

1. $3x^5 - 4x^3 - 1$,   **2.** $-x^2 - x$,

3. $9y^2 - 2y + 8$

◄ Concept Check Answer

To Subtract Polynomials

To subtract two polynomials, change the signs of the terms of the polynomial being subtracted and then add.

EXAMPLE 4 Subtract: $(5x - 3) - (2x - 11)$

Solution: From the definition of subtraction, we have

$$(5x - 3) - (2x - 11) = (5x - 3) + [-(2x - 11)] \quad \text{Add the opposite.}$$
$$= (5x - 3) + (-2x + 11) \quad \text{Apply the distributive property.}$$
$$= 5x - 3 - 2x + 11 \quad \text{Remove parentheses.}$$
$$= 3x + 8 \quad \text{Combine like terms.}$$

■ **Work Practice Problem 4**

EXAMPLE 5 Subtract: $(2x^3 + 8x^2 - 6x) - (2x^3 - x^2 + 1)$

Solution: First, we change the sign of each term of the second polynomial; then we add.

$$(2x^3 + 8x^2 - 6x) - (2x^3 - x^2 + 1)$$
$$= (2x^3 + 8x^2 - 6x) + (-2x^3 + x^2 - 1)$$
$$= 2x^3 + 8x^2 - 6x - 2x^3 + x^2 - 1$$
$$= 2x^3 - 2x^3 + 8x^2 + x^2 - 6x - 1$$
$$= 9x^2 - 6x - 1 \quad \text{Combine like terms.}$$

■ **Work Practice Problem 5**

Just as polynomials can be added vertically, so can they be subtracted vertically.

EXAMPLE 6 Subtract $(5y^2 + 2y - 6)$ from $(-3y^2 - 2y + 11)$ using a vertical format.

Solution: Arrange the polynomials in a vertical format, lining up like terms.

$$\begin{array}{r} -3y^2 - 2y + 11 \\ -(5y^2 + 2y - 6) \end{array} \qquad \begin{array}{r} -3y^2 - 2y + 11 \\ -5y^2 - 2y + 6 \\ \hline -8y^2 - 4y + 17 \end{array}$$

■ **Work Practice Problem 6**

Helpful Hint

Don't forget to change the sign of each term in the polynomial being subtracted.

Objective C Adding and Subtracting Polynomials in One Variable

Let's practice adding and subtracting polynomials in one variable.

EXAMPLE 7 Subtract $(5z - 7)$ from the sum of $(8z + 11)$ and $(9z - 2)$.

Solution: Notice that $(5z - 7)$ is to be subtracted **from** a sum. The translation is

$$[(8z + 11) + (9z - 2)] - (5z - 7)$$
$$= 8z + 11 + 9z - 2 - 5z + 7 \quad \text{Remove grouping symbols.}$$
$$= 8z + 9z - 5z + 11 - 2 + 7 \quad \text{Group like terms.}$$
$$= 12z + 16 \quad \text{Combine like terms.}$$

■ **Work Practice Problem 7**

PRACTICE PROBLEM 4

Subtract:
$(9x + 5) - (4x - 3)$

PRACTICE PROBLEM 5

Subtract:
$(4x^3 - 10x^2 + 1)$
$- (-4x^3 + x^2 - 11)$

PRACTICE PROBLEM 6

Subtract $(6y^2 - 3y + 2)$ from $(2y^2 - 2y + 7)$ using a vertical format.

PRACTICE PROBLEM 7

Subtract $(3x + 1)$ from the sum of $(4x - 3)$ and $(12x - 5)$.

Answers
4. $5x + 8$, **5.** $8x^3 - 11x^2 + 12$,
6. $-4y^2 + y + 5$, **7.** $13x - 9$

Objective D Adding and Subtracting Polynomials in Several Variables

Now that we know how to add or subtract polynomials in one variable, we can also add and subtract polynomials in several variables.

PRACTICE PROBLEMS 8–9

Add or subtract as indicated.

8. $(2a^2 - ab + 6b^2)$
$+ (-3a^2 + ab - 7b^2)$

9. $(5x^2y^2 + 3 - 9x^2y + y^2)$
$- (-x^2y^2 + 7 - 8xy^2 + 2y^2)$

EXAMPLES Add or subtract as indicated.

8. $(3x^2 - 6xy + 5y^2) + (-2x^2 + 8xy - y^2)$
$= 3x^2 - 6xy + 5y^2 - 2x^2 + 8xy - y^2$
$= x^2 + 2xy + 4y^2$ Combine like terms.

9. $(9a^2b^2 + 6ab - 3ab^2) - (5b^2a + 2ab - 3 - 9b^2)$
$= 9a^2b^2 + 6ab - 3ab^2 - 5b^2a - 2ab + 3 + 9b^2$
$= 9a^2b^2 + 4ab - 8ab^2 + 9b^2 + 3$ Combine like terms.

🔲 **Work Practice Problems 8–9**

✔ **Concept Check** If possible, simplify each expression by performing the indicated operation.

a. $2y + y$

b. $2y \cdot y$

c. $-2y - y$

d. $(-2y)(-y)$

e. $2x + y$

Answers

8. $-a^2 - b^2$,

9. $6x^2y^2 - 4 - 9x^2y + 8xy^2 - y^2$

✔ **Concept Check Answers**

a. $3y$, **b.** $2y^2$, **c.** $-3y$, **d.** $2y^2$,
e. cannot be simplified

12.4 EXERCISE SET

Objective A *Add. See Examples 1 and 2.*

1. $(3x + 7) + (9x + 5)$

2. $(-y - 2) + (3y + 5)$

3. $(-7x + 5) + (-3x^2 + 7x + 5)$

4. $(3x - 8) + (4x^2 - 3x + 3)$

5. $(-5x^2 + 3) + (2x^2 + 1)$

6. $(3x^2 + 7) + (3x^2 + 9)$

7. $(-3y^2 - 4y) + (2y^2 + y - 1)$

8. $(7x^2 + 2x - 9) + (-3x^2 + 5)$

9. $(1.2x^3 - 3.4x + 7.9) + (6.7x^3 + 4.4x^2 - 10.9)$

10. $(9.6y^3 + 2.7y^2 - 8.6) + (1.1y^3 - 8.8y + 11.6)$

11. $\left(\dfrac{3}{4}m^2 - \dfrac{2}{5}m + \dfrac{1}{8}\right) + \left(-\dfrac{1}{4}m^2 - \dfrac{3}{10}m + \dfrac{11}{16}\right)$

12. $\left(-\dfrac{4}{7}n^2 + \dfrac{5}{6}m - \dfrac{1}{20}\right) + \left(\dfrac{3}{7}n^2 - \dfrac{5}{12}m - \dfrac{3}{10}\right)$

Add using a vertical format. See Example 3.

13. $3t^2 + 4$
$\underline{5t^2 - 8}$

14. $7x^3 + 3$
$\underline{2x^3 + 1}$

15. $10a^3 - 8a^2 + 4a + 9$
$\underline{5a^3 + 9a^2 - 7a + 7}$

16. $2x^3 - 3x^2 + x - 4$
$\underline{5x^3 + 2x^2 - 3x + 2}$

Objective B *Subtract. See Examples 4 and 5.*

17. $(2x + 5) - (3x - 9)$

18. $(4 + 5a) - (-a - 5)$

19. $(5x^2 + 4) - (-2y^2 + 4)$

20. $(-7y^2 + 5) - (-8y^2 + 12)$

21. $3x - (5x - 9)$

22. $4 - (-y - 4)$

23. $(2x^2 + 3x - 9) - (-4x + 7)$

24. $(-7x^2 + 4x + 7) - (-8x + 2)$

25. $(5x + 8) - (-2x^2 - 6x + 8)$

26. $(-6y^2 + 3y - 4) - (9y^2 - 3y)$

27. $(0.7x^2 + 0.2x - 0.8) - (0.9x^2 + 1.4)$

28. $(-0.3y^2 + 0.6y - 0.3) - (0.5y^2 + 0.3)$

29. $\left(\dfrac{1}{4}z^2 - \dfrac{1}{5}z\right) - \left(-\dfrac{3}{20}z^2 + \dfrac{1}{10}z - \dfrac{7}{20}\right)$

30. $\left(\dfrac{1}{3}x^2 - \dfrac{2}{7}x\right) - \left(\dfrac{4}{21}x^2 + \dfrac{1}{21}x - \dfrac{2}{3}\right)$

Subtract using a vertical format. See Example 6.

31. $4z^2 - 8z + 3$
$-(6z^2 + 8z - 3)$

32. $7a^2 - 9a + 6$
$-(11a^2 - 4a + 2)$

33. $5u^5 - 4u^2 + 3u - 7$
$-(3u^5 + 6u^2 - 8u + 2)$

34. $5x^3 - 4x^2 + 6x - 2$
$-(3x^3 - 2x^2 - x - 4)$

Objectives Ⓐ Ⓑ Ⓒ **Mixed Practice** *Add or subtract as indicated. See Examples 1 through 7.*

35. $(3x + 5) + (2x - 14)$

36. $(2y + 20) + (5y - 30)$

37. $(9x - 1) - (5x + 2)$

38. $(7y + 7) - (y - 6)$

39. $(14y + 12) + (-3y - 5)$

40. $(26y + 17) + (-20y - 10)$

41. $(x^2 + 2x + 1) - (3x^2 - 6x + 2)$

42. $(5y^2 - 3y - 1) - (2y^2 + y + 1)$

43. $(3x^2 + 5x - 8) + (5x^2 + 9x + 12) - (8x^2 - 14)$

44. $(2x^2 + 7x - 9) + (x^2 - x + 10) - (3x^2 - 30)$

45. $(-a^2 + 1) - (a^2 - 3) + (5a^2 - 6a + 7)$

46. $(-m^2 + 3) - (m^2 - 13) + (6m^2 - m + 1)$

Perform each indicated operation. See Examples 3, 6, and 7.

47. Subtract $4x$ from $7x - 3$.

48. Subtract y from $y^2 - 4y + 1$.

49. Add $(4x^2 - 6x + 1)$ and $(3x^2 + 2x + 1)$.

50. Add $(-3x^2 - 5x + 2)$ and $(x^2 - 6x + 9)$.

51. Subtract $(5x + 7)$ from $(7x^2 + 3x + 9)$.

52. Subtract $(5y^2 + 8y + 2)$ from $(7y^2 + 9y - 8)$.

53. Subtract $(4y^2 - 6y - 3)$ from the sum of $(8y^2 + 7)$ and $(6y + 9)$.

54. Subtract $(4x^2 - 2x + 2)$ from the sum of $(x^2 + 7x + 1)$ and $(7x + 5)$.

55. Subtract $(3x^2 - 4)$ from the sum of $(x^2 - 9x + 2)$ and $(2x^2 - 6x + 1)$.

56. Subtract $(y^2 - 9)$ from the sum of $(3y^2 + y + 4)$ and $(2y^2 - 6y - 10)$.

Objective Ⓓ *Add or subtract as indicated. See Examples 8 and 9.*

57. $(9a + 6b - 5) + (-11a - 7b + 6)$

58. $(3x - 2 + 6y) + (7x - 2 - y)$

59. $(4x^2 + y^2 + 3) - (x^2 + y^2 - 2)$

60. $(7a^2 - 3b^2 + 10) - (-2a^2 + b^2 - 12)$

61. $(x^2 + 2xy - y^2) + (5x^2 - 4xy + 20y^2)$

62. $(a^2 - ab + 4b^2) + (6a^2 + 8ab - b^2)$

63. $(11r^2s + 16rs - 3 - 2r^2s^2) - (3sr^2 + 5 - 9r^2s^2)$

64. $(3x^2y - 6xy + x^2y^2 - 5) - (11x^2y^2 - 1 + 5yx^2)$

For Exercises 65 through 68, find the perimeter of each figure.

65.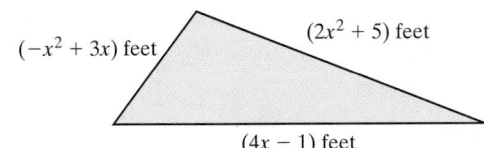

$(-x^2 + 3x)$ feet

$(2x^2 + 5)$ feet

$(4x - 1)$ feet

66.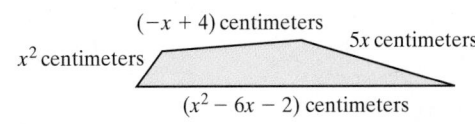

$(-x + 4)$ centimeters

$5x$ centimeters

x^2 centimeters

$(x^2 - 6x - 2)$ centimeters

67.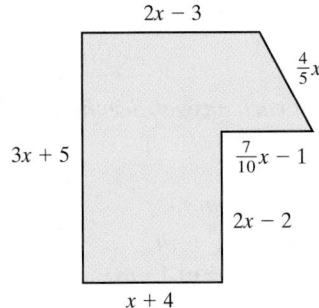

$2x - 3$

$\frac{4}{5}x$

$3x + 5$

$\frac{7}{10}x - 1$

$2x - 2$

$x + 4$

68.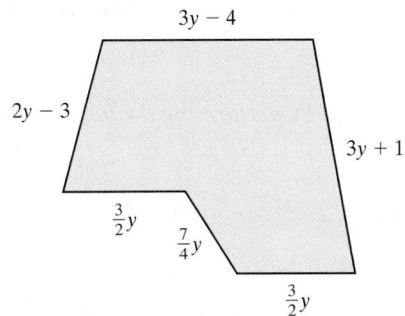

$3y - 4$

$2y - 3$

$3y + 1$

$\frac{3}{2}y$

$\frac{7}{4}y$

$\frac{3}{2}y$

69. A wooden beam is $(4y^2 + 4y + 1)$ meters long. If a piece $(y^2 - 10)$ meters is cut, express the length of the remaining piece of beam as a polynomial in y.

70. A piece of quarter-round molding is $(13x - 7)$ inches long. If a piece $(2x + 2)$ inches is removed, express the length of the remaining piece of molding as a polynomial in x.

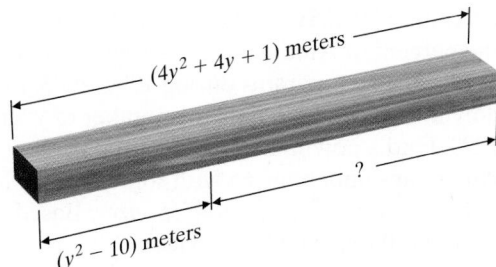

$(4y^2 + 4y + 1)$ meters

?

$(y^2 - 10)$ meters

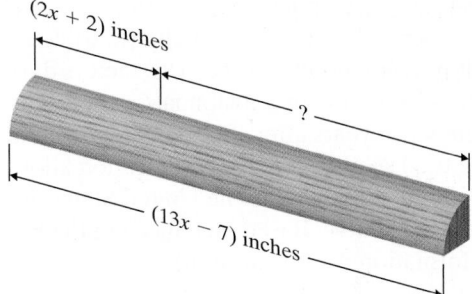

$(2x + 2)$ inches

?

$(13x - 7)$ inches

Perform each indicated operation.

71. $[(1.2x^2 - 3x + 9.1) - (7.8x^2 - 3.1 + 8)] + (1.2x - 6)$

72. $[(7.9y^4 - 6.8y^3 + 3.3y) + (6.1y^3 - 5)] - (4.2y^4 + 1.1y - 1)$

Review

Multiply. See Section 12.1.

73. $3x(2x)$

74. $-7x(x)$

75. $(12x^3)(-x^5)$

76. $6r^3(7r^{10})$

77. $10x^2(20xy^2)$

78. $-z^2y(11zy)$

Concept Extensions

Fill in the squares so that each is a true statement.

79. $3x^{\square} + 4x^2 = 7x^{\square}$

80. $9y^7 + 3y^{\square} = 12y^7$

81. $2x^{\square} + 3x^{\square} - 5x^{\square} + 4x^{\square} = 6x^4 - 2x^3$

82. $3y^{\square} + 7y^{\square} - 2y^{\square} - y^{\square} = 10y^5 - 3y^2$

Match each expression on the left with its simplification on the right. Not all letters on the right must be used and a letter may be used more than once.

83. $10y - 6y^2 - y$

84. $5x + 5x$

85. $(5x - 3) + (5x - 3)$

86. $(15x - 3) - (5x - 3)$

    a. $3y$

    b. $9y - 6y^2$

    c. $10x$

    d. $25x^2$

    e. $10x - 6$

    f. none of these

Simplify each expression by performing the indicated operation. Explain how you arrived at each answer. See the Concept Check in this section.

87. a. $z + 3z$
    b. $z \cdot 3z$
    c. $-z - 3z$
    d. $(-z)(-3z)$

88. a. $x + x$
    b. $x \cdot x$
    c. $-x - x$
    d. $(-x)(-x)$

89. a. $m \cdot m \cdot m$
    b. $m + m + m$
    c. $(-m)(-m)(-m)$
    d. $-m - m - m$

90. The polynomial $0.0005x^2 + 0.0303x + 1.156$ represents the sale of electricity (in trillion kilowatt-hours) in the U.S. residential sector during 1999–2003. The polynomial $0.0215x^2 - 0.1073x + 2.31$ represents the sale of electricity (in trillion kilowatt-hours) in all other U.S. sectors during 1999–2003. In both polynomials, x represents the number of years after 1999. Find a polynomial for the total sales of electricity (in trillion kilowatt hours) to all sectors in the United States during this period. (*Source:* Based on data from the Energy Information Administration)

91. The polynomial $-0.35x^2 + 0.49x + 71.75$ represents the percent of Americans under age 65 covered by private health insurance during 1999–2003. The polynomial $0.025x^2 + 9.65x + 11.83$ represents the percent of Americans under age 65 covered by public health programs during 1999–2003. In both polynomials, x represents the number of years since 1999. Find a polynomial for the total percent of Americans under age 65 with some form of health coverage during this period. (*Source:* Based on data from the Public Health Service)

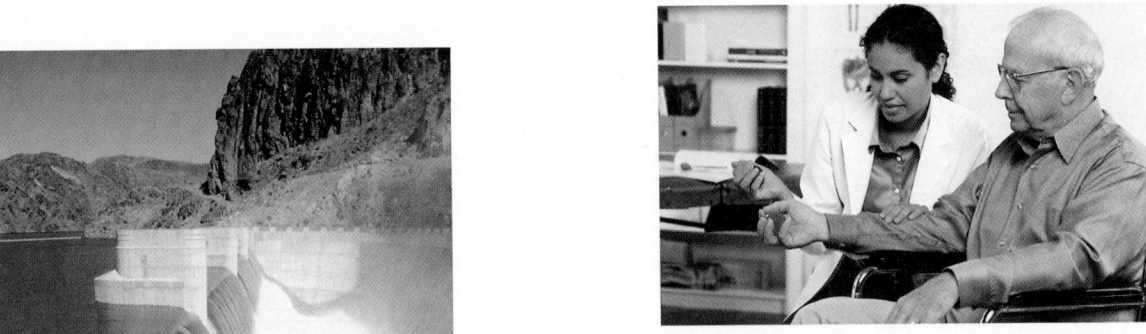

12.5 MULTIPLYING POLYNOMIALS

Objectives

A Multiply Monomials.

B Multiply a Monomial by a Polynomial.

C Multiply Two Polynomials.

D Multiply Polynomials Vertically.

Objective **A** Multiplying Monomials

Recall from Section 12.1 that to multiply two monomials such as $(-5x^3)$ and $(-2x^4)$, we use the associative and commutative properties and regroup. Remember also that to multiply exponential expressions with a common base, we use the product rule for exponents and add exponents.

$$(-5x^3)(-2x^4) = (-5)(-2)(x^3 \cdot x^4) \quad \text{Use the commutative and associative properties.}$$
$$= 10x^7 \quad \text{Multiply.}$$

EXAMPLES Multiply.

1. $6x \cdot 4x = (6 \cdot 4)(x \cdot x)$ Use the commutative and associative properties.
$$= 24x^2 \quad \text{Multiply.}$$

2. $-7x^2 \cdot 2x^5 = (-7 \cdot 2)(x^2 \cdot x^5)$
$$= -14x^7$$

3. $(-12x^5)(-x) = (-12x^5)(-1x)$
$$= (-12)(-1)(x^5 \cdot x)$$
$$= 12x^6$$

▣ **Work Practice Problems 1–3**

✔ **Concept Check** Simplify.

a. $3x \cdot 2x$ **b.** $3x + 2x$

Objective **B** Multiplying Monomials by Polynomials

To multiply a monomial such as $7x$ by a trinomial such as $x^3 + 2x + 5$, we use the distributive property.

EXAMPLES Multiply.

4. $7x(x^2 + 2x + 5) = 7x(x^2) + 7x(2x) + 7x(5)$ Apply the distributive property.
$$= 7x^3 + 14x^2 + 35x \quad \text{Multiply.}$$

5. $5x(2x^3 + 6) = 5x(2x^3) + 5x(6)$ Apply the distributive property.
$$= 10x^4 + 30x \quad \text{Multiply.}$$

6. $-3x^2(5x^2 + 6x - 1)$
$$= (-3x^2)(5x^2) + (-3x^2)(6x) + (-3x^2)(-1) \quad \text{Apply the distributive property.}$$
$$= -15x^4 - 18x^3 + 3x^2 \quad \text{Multiply.}$$

▣ **Work Practice Problems 4–6**

PRACTICE PROBLEMS 1–3

Multiply.
1. $10x \cdot 9x$
2. $8x^3(-11x^7)$
3. $(-5x^4)(-x)$

PRACTICE PROBLEMS 4–6

Multiply.
4. $4x(x^2 + 4x + 3)$
5. $8x(7x^4 + 1)$
6. $-2x^3(3x^2 - x + 2)$

Answers
1. $90x^2$, **2.** $-88x^{10}$, **3.** $5x^5$,
4. $4x^3 + 16x^2 + 12x$, **5.** $56x^5 + 8x$,
6. $-6x^5 + 2x^4 - 4x^3$

✔ **Concept Check Answers**
a. $6x^2$, **b.** $5x$

907

Objective Ⓒ Multiplying Two Polynomials

We also use the distributive property to multiply two binomials.

PRACTICE PROBLEM 7

Multiply:

a. $(x + 5)(x + 10)$
b. $(4x + 5)(3x - 4)$

EXAMPLE 7 Multiply.

a. $(m + 4)(m + 6)$ **b.** $(3x + 2)(2x - 5)$

Solution:

a. $(m + 4)(m + 6) = m(m + 6) + 4(m + 6)$ Use the distributive property.

$\qquad\qquad\qquad\quad = m \cdot m + m \cdot 6 + 4 \cdot m + 4 \cdot 6$ Use the distributive property.

$\qquad\qquad\qquad\quad = m^2 + 6m + 4m + 24$ Multiply.

$\qquad\qquad\qquad\quad = m^2 + 10m + 24$ Combine like terms.

b. $(3x + 2)(2x - 5) = 3x(2x - 5) + 2(2x - 5)$ Use the distributive property.

$\qquad\qquad\qquad\quad = 3x(2x) + 3x(-5) + 2(2x) + 2(-5)$

$\qquad\qquad\qquad\quad = 6x^2 - 15x + 4x - 10$ Multiply.

$\qquad\qquad\qquad\quad = 6x^2 - 11x - 10$ Combine like terms.

⬛ **Work Practice Problem 7**

This idea can be expanded so that we can multiply any two polynomials.

To Multiply Two Polynomials

Multiply each term of the first polynomial by each term of the second polynomial, and then combine like terms.

PRACTICE PROBLEMS 8–9

Multiply.

8. $(3x - 2y)^2$
9. $(x + 3)(2x^2 - 5x + 4)$

EXAMPLES Multiply.

8. $(2x - y)^2$

$\qquad = (2x - y)(2x - y)$ Using the meaning of an exponent, we have 2 factors of $(2x - y)$.

$\qquad = 2x(2x) + 2x(-y) + (-y)(2x) + (-y)(-y)$

$\qquad = 4x^2 - 2xy - 2xy + y^2$ Multiply.

$\qquad = 4x^2 - 4xy + y^2$ Combine like terms.

9. $(t + 2)(3t^2 - 4t + 2)$

$\qquad = t(3t^2) + t(-4t) + t(2) + 2(3t^2) + 2(-4t) + 2(2)$

$\qquad = 3t^3 - 4t^2 + 2t + 6t^2 - 8t + 4$

$\qquad = 3t^3 + 2t^2 - 6t + 4$ Combine like terms.

⬛ **Work Practice Problems 8–9**

✔ **Concept Check** Square where indicated. Simplify if possible.

a. $(4a)^2 + (3b)^2$ **b.** $(4a + 3b)^2$

Objective Ⓓ Multiplying Polynomials Vertically

Another convenient method for multiplying polynomials is to multiply vertically, similar to the way we multiply real numbers. This method is shown in the next examples.

Answers

7. a. $x^2 + 15x + 50$,
b. $12x^2 - x - 20$,
8. $9x^2 - 12xy + 4y^2$,
9. $2x^3 + x^2 - 11x + 12$

✔ **Concept Check Answers**

a. $16a^2 + 9b^2$,   **b.** $16a^2 + 24ab + 9b^2$

EXAMPLE 10 Multiply vertically: $(2y^2 + 5)(y^2 - 3y + 4)$

Solution:

$$
\begin{array}{r}
y^2 - 3y + 4 \\
2y^2 + 5 \\
\hline
5y^2 - 15y + 20 \\
2y^4 - 6y^3 + 8y^2 \\
\hline
2y^4 - 6y^3 + 13y^2 - 15y + 20
\end{array}
$$

Multiply $y^2 - 3y + 4$ by 5

Multiply $y^2 - 3y + 4$ by $2y^2$

Combine like terms.

▣ **Work Practice Problem 10**

EXAMPLE 11 Find the product of $(2x^2 - 3x + 4)$ and $(x^2 + 5x - 2)$ using a vertical format.

Solution: First, we arrange the polynomials in a vertical format. Then we multiply each term of the second polynomial by each term of the first polynomial.

$$
\begin{array}{r}
2x^2 - 3x + 4 \\
x^2 + 5x - 2 \\
\hline
-4x^2 + 6x - 8 \\
10x^3 - 15x^2 + 20x \\
2x^4 - 3x^3 + 4x^2 \\
\hline
2x^4 + 7x^3 - 15x^2 + 26x - 8
\end{array}
$$

Multiply $2x^2 - 3x + 4$ by -2.

Multiply $2x^2 - 3x + 4$ by $5x$.

Multiply $2x^2 - 3x + 4$ by x^2.

Combine like terms.

▣ **Work Practice Problem 11**

PRACTICE PROBLEM 10

Multiply vertically:
$(3y^2 + 1)(y^2 - 4y + 5)$

PRACTICE PROBLEM 11

Find the product of
$(4x^2 - x - 1)$ and
$(3x^2 + 6x - 2)$ using a vertical format.

Answers

10. $3y^4 - 12y^3 + 16y^2 - 4y + 5$,

11. $12x^4 + 21x^3 - 17x^2 - 4x + 2$

Mental Math

Perform the indicated operation, if possible.

1. $x^3 \cdot x^5$

2. $x^2 \cdot x^6$

3. $x^3 + x^5$

4. $x^2 + x^6$

5. $y^4 \cdot y$

6. $y^9 \cdot y$

7. $x^7 \cdot x^7$

8. $x^{11} \cdot x^{11}$

9. $x^7 + x^7$

10. $x^{11} + x^{11}$

12.5 EXERCISE SET

FOR EXTRA HELP

Student Solutions Manual   PH Math/Tutor Center   CD/Video for Review   Math XL MathXL®   MyMathLab MyMathLab

Objective A *Multiply. See Examples 1 through 3.*

1. $8x^2 \cdot 3x$

 2. $6x \cdot 3x^2$

3. $(-x^3)(-x)$

4. $(-x^6)(-x)$

5. $-4n^3 \cdot 7n^7$

6. $9t^6(-3t^5)$

7. $(-3.1x^3)(4x^9)$

8. $(-5.2x^4)(3x^4)$

9. $\left(-\dfrac{1}{3}y^2\right)\left(\dfrac{2}{5}y\right)$

10. $\left(-\dfrac{3}{4}y^7\right)\left(\dfrac{1}{7}y^4\right)$

11. $(2x)(-3x^2)(4x^5)$

12. $(x)(5x^4)(-6x^7)$

Objective B *Multiply. See Examples 4 through 6.*

13. $3x(2x + 5)$

14. $2x(6x + 3)$

15. $7x(x^2 + 2x - 1)$

16. $5y(y^2 + y - 10)$

17. $-2a(a + 4)$

18. $-3a(2a + 7)$

19. $3x(2x^2 - 3x + 4)$

20. $4x(5x^2 - 6x - 10)$

21. $3a^2(4a^3 + 15)$

22. $9x^3(5x^2 + 12)$

23. $-2a^2(3a^2 - 2a + 3)$

24. $-4b^2(3b^3 - 12b^2 - 6)$

25. $3x^2y(2x^3 - x^2y^2 + 8y^3)$

26. $4xy^2(7x^3 + 3x^2y^2 - 9y^3)$

27. $-y(4x^3 - 7x^2y + xy^2 + 3y^3)$

28. $-x(6y^3 - 5xy^2 + x^2y - 5x^3)$

29. $\dfrac{1}{2}x^2(8x^2 - 6x + 1)$

30. $\dfrac{1}{3}y^2(9y^2 - 6y + 1)$

Objective C *Multiply. See Examples 7 through 9.*

31. $(x + 4)(x + 3)$

32. $(x + 2)(x + 9)$

33. $(a + 7)(a - 2)$

34. $(y - 10)(y + 11)$

910

35. $\left(x + \dfrac{2}{3}\right)\left(x - \dfrac{1}{3}\right)$ **36.** $\left(x + \dfrac{3}{5}\right)\left(x - \dfrac{2}{5}\right)$ **37.** $(3x^2 + 1)(4x^2 + 7)$ **38.** $(5x^2 + 2)(6x^2 + 2)$

39. $(4x - 3)(3x - 5)$ **40.** $(8x - 3)(2x - 4)$ **41.** $(1 - 3a)(1 - 4a)$ **42.** $(3 - 2a)(2 - a)$

43. $(2y - 4)^2$ **44.** $(6x - 7)^2$ **45.** $(x - 2)(x^2 - 3x + 7)$ **46.** $(x + 3)(x^2 + 5x - 8)$

47. $(x + 5)(x^3 - 3x + 4)$ **48.** $(a + 2)(a^3 - 3a^2 + 7)$ **49.** $(2a - 3)(5a^2 - 6a + 4)$

50. $(3 + b)(2 - 5b - 3b^2)$ **51.** $(7xy - y)^2$ **52.** $(x^2 - 4)^2$

Objective **D** *Multiply vertically. See Examples 10 and 11.*

53. $(2x - 11)(6x + 1)$ **54.** $(4x - 7)(5x + 1)$ **55.** $(x + 3)(2x^2 + 4x - 1)$

56. $(4x - 5)(8x^2 + 2x - 4)$ **57.** $(x^2 + 5x - 7)(2x^2 - 7x - 9)$ **58.** $(3x^2 - x + 2)(x^2 + 2x + 1)$

Objectives **A** **B** **C** **D** **Mixed Practice** *Multiply. See Examples 1 through 11.*

59. $-1.2y(-7y^6)$ **60.** $-4.2x(-2x^5)$ **61.** $-3x(x^2 + 2x - 8)$ **62.** $-5x(x^2 - 3x + 10)$

63. $(x + 19)(2x + 1)$ **64.** $(3y + 4)(y + 11)$ **65.** $\left(x + \dfrac{1}{7}\right)\left(x - \dfrac{3}{7}\right)$ **66.** $\left(m + \dfrac{2}{9}\right)\left(m - \dfrac{1}{9}\right)$

67. $(3y + 5)^2$ **68.** $(7y + 2)^2$ **69.** $(a + 4)(a^2 - 6a + 6)$ **70.** $(t + 3)(t^2 - 5t + 5)$

Express as the product of polynomials. Then multiply.

△ **71.** Find the area of the rectangle.

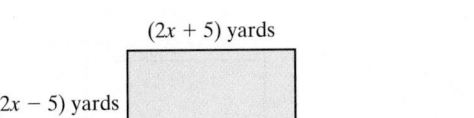

$(2x + 5)$ yards

$(2x - 5)$ yards

△ **72.** Find the area of the square field.

$(x + 4)$ feet

△ **73.** Find the area of the triangle.

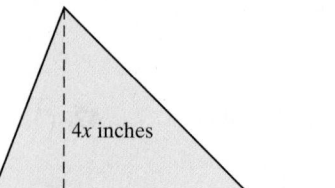

4x inches

(3x − 2) inches

△ **74.** Find the volume of the cube-shaped glass block.

(y − 1) meters

Review

Perform each indicated operation. See Section 12.1.

75. $(5x)^2$ **76.** $(4p)^2$ **77.** $(-3y^3)^2$ **78.** $(-7m^2)^2$

Concept Extensions

79. Perform each indicated operation. Explain the difference between the two expressions.
  a. $(3x + 5) + (3x + 7)$
  b. $(3x + 5)(3x + 7)$

80. Perform each operation. Explain the difference between the two expressions.
  a. $(8x - 3) - (5x - 2)$
  b. $(8x - 3)(5x - 2)$

Mixed Practice *See Sections 12.4 and 12.5. Perform the indicated operations.*

81. $(3x - 1) + (10x - 6)$ **82.** $(2x - 1) + (10x - 7)$ **83.** $(3x - 1)(10x - 6)$

84. $(2x - 1)(10x - 7)$ **85.** $(3x - 1) - (10x - 6)$ **86.** $(2x - 1) - (10x - 7)$

△ **87.** The area of the largest rectangle below is $x(x + 3)$. Find another expression for this area by finding the sum of the areas of the smaller rectangles.

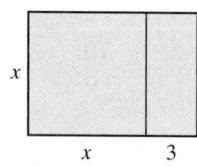

x

x   3

△ **88.** Write an expression for the area of the largest rectangle below in two different ways.

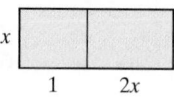

x

1   2x

△ **89.** The area of the figure below is $(x + 2)(x + 3)$. Find another expression for this area by finding the sum of the areas of the smaller rectangles.

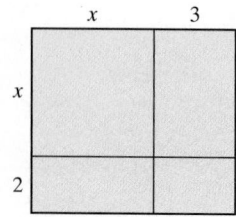

x   3

x

2

△ **90.** Write an expression for the area of the figure below in two different ways

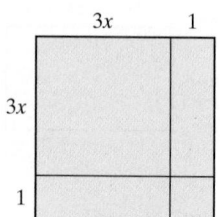

3x   1

3x

1

Simplify. See the Concept Checks in this section.

91. $5a + 6a$

92. $5a \cdot 6a$

Square where indicated. Simplify if possible.

93. $(5x)^2 + (2y)^2$

94. $(5x + 2y)^2$

95. Multiply each of the following polynomials.
  a. $(a + b)(a - b)$
  b. $(2x + 3y)(2x - 3y)$
  c. $(4x + 7)(4x - 7)$
  d. Can you make a general statement about all products of the form $(x + y)(x - y)$?

96. Evaluate each of the following.
  a. $(2 + 3)^2; 2^2 + 3^2$
  b. $(8 + 10)^2; 8^2 + 10^2$
     Does $(a + b)^2 = a^2 + b^2$ no matter what the values of a and b are? Why or why not?

📖 STUDY SKILLS BUILDER

Tips for Studying for an Exam

To prepare for an exam, try the following study techniques:

- Start the study process days before your exam.
- Make sure that you are up-to-date on your assignments.
- If there is a topic that you are unsure of, use one of the many resources that are available to you. For example,
  See your instructor.
  Visit a learning resource center on campus.
  Read the textbook material and examples on the topic.
  View a video on the topic.
- Reread your notes and carefully review the Chapter Highlights at the end of the chapter.
- Work the review exercises at the end of the chapter. Check your answers and correct any mistakes. If you have trouble, use a resource listed above.
- Find a quiet place to take the Chapter Test found at the end of the chapter. Do not use any resources when taking this sample test. This way, you will have a clear indication of how prepared you are for your exam.

Check your answers and make sure that you correct any missed exercises.

- Get lots of rest the night before the exam. It's hard to show how well you know the material if your brain is foggy from lack of sleep.

Good luck and keep a positive attitude.

Let's see how you did on your last exam.

1. How many days before your last exam did you start studying for that exam?

2. Were you up-to-date on your assignments at that time or did you need to catch up on assignments?

3. List the most helpful text supplement (if you used one).

4. List the most helpful campus supplement (if you used one).

5. List your process for preparing for a mathematics test.

6. Was this process helpful? In other words, were you satisfied with your performance on your exam?

7. If not, what changes can you make in your process that will make it more helpful to you?

12.6 SPECIAL PRODUCTS

Objective **A** Using the FOIL Method

In this section, we multiply binomials using special products. First, we introduce a special order for multiplying binomials called the FOIL order or method. This order, or pattern, is a result of the distributive property. We demonstrate by multiplying $(3x + 1)$ by $(2x + 5)$.

The FOIL Method

F stands for the
product of the **First** terms. $(3x + 1)(2x + 5)$

$$(3x)(2x) = 6x^2 \qquad \text{F}$$

O stands for the
product of the **Outer** terms. $(3x + 1)(2x + 5)$

$$(3x)(5) = 15x \qquad \text{O}$$

I stands for the
product of the **Inner** terms. $(3x + 1)(2x + 5)$

$$(1)(2x) = 2x \qquad \text{I}$$

L stands for the
product of the **Last** terms. $(3x + 1)(2x + 5)$

$$(1)(5) = 5 \qquad \text{L}$$

$$\begin{array}{cccc} \text{F} & \text{O} & \text{I} & \text{L} \\ (3x + 1)(2x + 5) = 6x^2 & + 15x & + 2x & + 5 \end{array}$$

$$= 6x^2 + 17x + 5 \qquad \text{Combine like terms.}$$

Let's practice multiplying binomials using the FOIL method.

EXAMPLE 1 Multiply: $(x - 3)(x + 4)$

Solution:

$$\begin{array}{cccc} & \text{F} & \text{O} & \text{I} & \text{L} \\ (x - 3)(x + 4) = & (x)(x) & + (x)(4) & + (-3)(x) & + (-3)(4) \end{array}$$

$$= x^2 + 4x - 3x - 12$$

$$= x^2 + x - 12 \qquad \text{Combine like terms.}$$

Work Practice Problem 1

EXAMPLE 2 Multiply. $(5x - 7)(x - 2)$

Solution:

$$\begin{array}{cccc} & \text{F} & \text{O} & \text{I} & \text{L} \\ (5x - 7)(x - 2) = & 5x(x) & + 5x(-2) & + (-7)(x) & + (-7)(-2) \end{array}$$

$$= 5x^2 - 10x - 7x + 14$$

$$= 5x^2 - 17x + 14 \qquad \text{Combine like terms.}$$

Work Practice Problem 2

PRACTICE PROBLEM 1

Multiply: $(x + 7)(x - 5)$

PRACTICE PROBLEM 2

Multiply: $(6x - 1)(x - 4)$

Helpful Hint

Remember that the FOIL order for multiplying can only be used for the product of 2 binomials.

Answers

1. $x^2 + 2x - 35$,   **2.** $6x^2 - 25x + 4$

EXAMPLE 3 Multiply: $(y^2 + 6)(2y - 1)$

Solution:

$$\overset{\text{F}\quad\text{O}\quad\text{I}\quad\text{L}}{(y^2 + 6)(2y - 1) = 2y^3 - 1y^2 + 12y - 6}$$

Notice in this example that there are no like terms that can be combined, so the product is $2y^3 - y^2 + 12y - 6$.

🔲 **Work Practice Problem 3**

PRACTICE PROBLEM 3

Multiply: $(2y^2 + 3)(y - 4)$

Objective **B** Squaring Binomials

An expression such as $(3y + 1)^2$ is called the square of a binomial. Since $(3y + 1)^2 = (3y + 1)(3y + 1)$, we can use the FOIL method to find this product.

EXAMPLE 4 Multiply: $(3y + 1)^2$

Solution: $(3y + 1)^2 = (3y + 1)(3y + 1)$

$$\overset{\text{F}\qquad\text{O}\qquad\text{I}\qquad\text{L}}{= (3y)(3y) + (3y)(1) + 1(3y) + 1(1)}$$
$$= 9y^2 + 3y + 3y + 1$$
$$= 9y^2 + 6y + 1$$

🔲 **Work Practice Problem 4**

PRACTICE PROBLEM 4

Multiply: $(2x + 9)^2$

Notice the pattern that appears in Example 4.

$(3y + 1)^2 = 9y^2 + 6y + 1$

→ $9y^2$ is the first term of the binomial squared: $(3y)^2 = 9y^2$.

→ $6y$ is 2 times the product of both terms of the binomial: $(2)(3y)(1) = 6y$.

→ 1 is the second term of the binomial squared: $(1)^2 = 1$.

This pattern leads to the formulas below, which can be used when squaring a binomial. We call these **special products.**

Squaring a Binomial

A binomial squared is equal to the square of the first term plus or minus twice the product of both terms plus the square of the second term.

$$(a + b)^2 = a^2 + 2ab + b^2$$
$$(a - b)^2 = a^2 - 2ab + b^2$$

This product can be visualized geometrically.

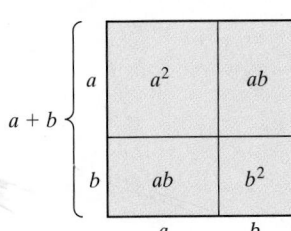

The area of the large square is side · side.
Area $= (a + b)(a + b) = (a + b)^2$
The area of the large square is also the sum of the areas of the smaller rectangles.
Area $= a^2 + ab + ab + b^2 = a^2 + 2ab + b^2$
Thus, $(a + b)^2 = a^2 + 2ab + b^2$.

Answers

3. $2y^3 - 8y^2 + 3y - 12,$
4. $4x^2 + 36x + 81$

PRACTICE PROBLEMS 5–8

Use a special product to square each binomial.

5. $(y + 3)^2$

6. $(r - s)^2$

7. $(6x + 5)^2$

8. $(x^2 - 3y)^2$

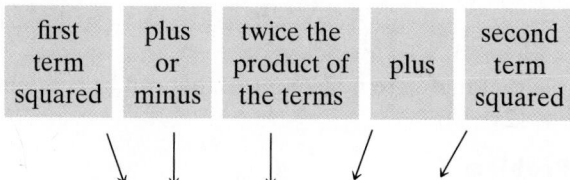 Use a special product to square each binomial.

first term squared	plus or minus	twice the product of the terms	plus	second term squared

5. $(t + 2)^2 = t^2 + 2(t)(2) + 2^2 = t^2 + 4t + 4$

6. $(p - q)^2 = p^2 - 2(p)(q) + q^2 = p^2 - 2pq + q^2$

7. $(2x + 5)^2 = (2x)^2 + 2(2x)(5) + 5^2 = 4x^2 + 20x + 25$

8. $(x^2 - 7y)^2 = (x^2)^2 - 2(x^2)(7y) + (7y)^2 = x^4 - 14x^2y + 49y^2$

Work Practice Problems 5–8

Notice that

$$(a + b)^2 \neq a^2 + b^2 \quad \text{The middle term } 2ab \text{ is missing.}$$
$$(a + b)^2 = (a + b)(a + b) = a^2 + 2ab + b^2$$

Likewise,

$$(a - b)^2 \neq a^2 - b^2$$
$$(a - b)^2 = (a - b)(a - b) = a^2 - 2ab + b^2$$

Objective C Multiplying the Sum and Difference of Two Terms

Another special product is the product of the sum and difference of the same two terms, such as $(x + y)(x - y)$. Finding this product by the FOIL method, we see a pattern emerge.

$$(x + y)(x - y) = x^2 - xy + xy - y^2$$
$$= x^2 - y^2$$

Notice that the two middle terms subtract out. This is because the **O**uter product is the opposite of the **I**nner product. Only the **difference of squares** remains.

Multiplying the Sum and Difference of Two Terms

The product of the sum and difference of two terms is the square of the first term minus the square of the second term.

$$(a + b)(a - b) = a^2 - b^2$$

Answers

5. $y^2 + 6y + 9$, **6.** $r^2 - 2rs + s^2$,
7. $36x^2 + 60x + 25$,
8. $x^4 - 6x^2y + 9y^2$

EXAMPLES Use a special product to multiply.

first term squared	minus	second term squared
↓	↓	↓

9. $(x + 4)(x - 4) = x^2 \quad - \quad 4^2 = x^2 - 16$

10. $(6t + 7)(6t - 7) = (6t)^2 \quad - \quad 7^2 = 36t^2 - 49$

11. $\left(x - \dfrac{1}{4}\right)\left(x + \dfrac{1}{4}\right) = x^2 \quad - \quad \left(\dfrac{1}{4}\right)^2 = x^2 - \dfrac{1}{16}$

12. $(2p - q)(2p + q) = (2p)^2 - q^2 = 4p^2 - q^2$

13. $(3x^2 - 5y)(3x^2 + 5y) = (3x^2)^2 - (5y)^2 = 9x^4 - 25y^2$

▣ **Work Practice Problems 9–13**

✔ **Concept Check** Match each expression on the left to the equivalent expression or expressions in the list on the right.

$(a + b)^2$ **a.** $(a + b)(a + b)$

$(a + b)(a - b)$ **b.** $a^2 - b^2$

                        c. $a^2 + b^2$

                        d. $a^2 - 2ab + b^2$

                        e. $a^2 + 2ab + b^2$

Objective D Using Special Products

Let's now practice using our special products on a variety of multiplication problems. This practice will help us recognize when to apply what special product formula.

EXAMPLES Use a special product to multiply, if possible.

14. $(4x - 9)(4x + 9)$ This is the sum and difference of the same two terms.

     $= (4x)^2 - 9^2 = 16x^2 - 81$

15. $(3y + 2)^2$ This is a binomial squared.

     $= (3y)^2 + 2(3y)(2) + 2^2$

     $= 9y^2 + 12y + 4$

16. $(6a + 1)(a - 7)$ No special product applies.

       F   O   I   L   Use the FOIL method.

     $= 6a \cdot a + 6a(-7) + 1 \cdot a + 1(-7)$

     $= 6a^2 - 42a + a - 7$

     $= 6a^2 - 41a - 7$

17. $\left(4x - \dfrac{1}{11}\right)^2$ This is a binomial squared.

     $= (4x)^2 - 2(4x)\left(\dfrac{1}{11}\right) + \left(\dfrac{1}{11}\right)^2$

     $= 16x^2 - \dfrac{8}{11}x + \dfrac{1}{121}$

▣ **Work Practice Problems 14–17**

Helpful Hint

- When multiplying two binomials, you may always use the FOIL order or method.
- When multiplying any two polynomials, you may always use the distributive property to find the product.

PRACTICE PROBLEMS 9–13

Use a special product to multiply.

9. $(x + 9)(x - 9)$

10. $(5 + 4y)(5 - 4y)$

11. $\left(x - \dfrac{1}{3}\right)\left(x + \dfrac{1}{3}\right)$

12. $(3a - b)(3a + b)$

13. $(2x^2 - 6y)(2x^2 + 6y)$

PRACTICE PROBLEMS 14–17

Use a special product to multiply, if possible.

14. $(7x - 1)^2$

15. $(5y + 3)(2y - 5)$

16. $(2a - 1)(2a + 1)$

17. $\left(5y - \dfrac{1}{9}\right)^2$

Answers

9. $x^2 - 81$, **10.** $25 - 16y^2$,

11. $x^2 - \dfrac{1}{9}$, **12.** $9a^2 - b^2$,

13. $4x^4 - 36y^2$, **14.** $49x^2 - 14x + 1$,

15. $10y^2 - 19y - 15$, **16.** $4a^2 - 1$,

17. $25y^2 - \dfrac{10}{9}y + \dfrac{1}{81}$

✔ **Concept Check Answer**

a or e, b

Objective A *Multiply using the FOIL method. See Examples 1 through 3.*

1. $(x + 3)(x + 4)$

2. $(x + 5)(x + 1)$

3. $(x - 5)(x + 10)$

4. $(y - 12)(y + 4)$

5. $(5x - 6)(x + 2)$

6. $(3y - 5)(2y - 7)$

7. $(y - 6)(4y - 1)$

8. $(2x - 9)(x - 11)$

9. $(2x + 5)(3x - 1)$

10. $(6x + 2)(x - 2)$

11. $(y^2 + 7)(6y + 4)$

12. $(y^2 + 3)(5y + 6)$

13. $\left(x - \dfrac{1}{3}\right)\left(x + \dfrac{2}{3}\right)$

14. $\left(x - \dfrac{2}{5}\right)\left(x + \dfrac{1}{5}\right)$

15. $(0.4 - 3a)(0.2 - 5a)$

16. $(0.3 - 2a)(0.6 - 5a)$

17. $(x + 5y)(2x - y)$

18. $(x + 4y)(3x - y)$

Objective B *Multiply. See Examples 4 through 8.*

19. $(x + 2)^2$

20. $(x + 7)^2$

21. $(2x - 1)^2$

22. $(7x - 3)^2$

23. $(3a - 5)^2$

24. $(5a + 2)^2$

25. $(x^2 + 0.5)^2$

26. $(x^2 + 0.3)^2$

27. $\left(y - \dfrac{2}{7}\right)^2$

28. $\left(y - \dfrac{3}{4}\right)^2$

29. $(2a - 3)^2$

30. $(5b - 4)^2$

31. $(5x + 9)^2$

32. $(6s + 2)^2$

33. $(3x - 7y)^2$

34. $(4s - 2y)^2$

35. $(4m + 5n)^2$

36. $(3n + 5m)^2$

37. $(5x^4 - 3)^2$

38. $(7x^3 - 6)^2$

Objective C *Multiply. See Examples 9 through 13.*

39. $(a - 7)(a + 7)$

40. $(b + 3)(b - 3)$

41. $(x + 6)(x - 6)$

42. $(x - 8)(x + 8)$

43. $(3x - 1)(3x + 1)$

44. $(4x - 5)(4x + 5)$

45. $(x^2 + 5)(x^2 - 5)$

46. $(a^2 + 6)(a^2 - 6)$

47. $(2y^2 - 1)(2y^2 + 1)$ **48.** $(3x^2 + 1)(3x^2 - 1)$ **49.** $(4 - 7x)(4 + 7x)$ **50.** $(8 - 7x)(8 + 7x)$

51. $\left(3x - \dfrac{1}{2}\right)\left(3x + \dfrac{1}{2}\right)$ **52.** $\left(10x + \dfrac{2}{7}\right)\left(10x - \dfrac{2}{7}\right)$ **53.** $(9x + y)(9x - y)$ **54.** $(2x - y)(2x + y)$

55. $(2m + 5n)(2m - 5n)$ **56.** $(5m + 4n)(5m - 4n)$

Objective **D** **Mixed Practice** *Multiply. See Examples 14 through 17.*

57. $(a + 5)(a + 4)$ **58.** $(a + 5)(a + 7)$ **59.** $(a - 7)^2$ **60.** $(b - 2)^2$

61. $(4a + 1)(3a - 1)$ **62.** $(6a + 7)(6a + 5)$ **63.** $(x + 2)(x - 2)$ **64.** $(x - 10)(x + 10)$

65. $(3a + 1)^2$ **66.** $(4a + 2)^2$ **67.** $(x + y)(4x - y)$ **68.** $(3x + 2)(4x - 2)$

69. $\left(a - \dfrac{1}{2}y\right)\left(a + \dfrac{1}{2}y\right)$ **70.** $\left(\dfrac{a}{2} + 4y\right)\left(\dfrac{a}{2} - 4y\right)$ **71.** $(3b + 7)(2b - 5)$ **72.** $(3y - 13)(y - 3)$

73. $(x^2 + 10)(x^2 - 10)$ **74.** $(x^2 + 8)(x^2 - 8)$ **75.** $(4x + 5)(4x - 5)$ **76.** $(3x + 5)(3x - 5)$

77. $(5x - 6y)^2$ **78.** $(4x - 9y)^2$ **79.** $(2r - 3s)(2r + 3s)$ **80.** $(6r - 2x)(6r + 2x)$

Express each as a product of polynomials in x. Then multiply and simplify.

△ **81.** Find the area of the square rug if its side is $(2x + 1)$ feet.

△ **82.** Find the area of the rectangular canvas if its length is $(3x - 2)$ inches and its width is $(x - 4)$ inches.

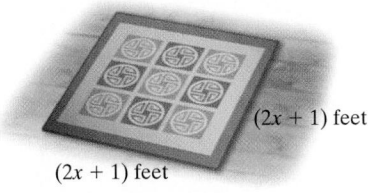

$(2x + 1)$ feet

$(2x + 1)$ feet

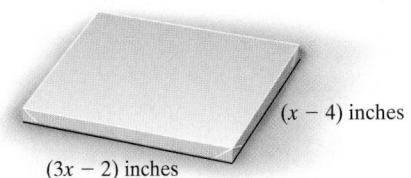

$(x - 4)$ inches

$(3x - 2)$ inches

Review

Simplify each expression. See Sections 12.1 and 12.2.

83. $\dfrac{50b^{10}}{70b^5}$ **84.** $\dfrac{60y^6}{80y^2}$ **85.** $\dfrac{8a^{17}b^5}{-4a^7b^{10}}$ **86.** $\dfrac{-6a^8y}{3a^4y}$ **87.** $\dfrac{2x^4y^{12}}{3x^4y^4}$ **88.** $\dfrac{-48ab^6}{32ab^3}$

Concept Extensions

Match each expression on the left to the equivalent expression on the right. See the Concept Check in this section.

89. $(a - b)^2$

90. $(a - b)(a + b)$

91. $(a + b)^2$

92. $(a + b)^2(a - b)^2$

a. $a^2 - b^2$

b. $a^2 + b^2$

c. $a^2 - 2ab + b^2$

d. $a^2 + 2ab + b^2$

e. none of these

Fill in the squares so that a true statement forms.

93. $(x^\square + 7)(x^\square + 3) = x^4 + 10x^2 + 21$

94. $(5x^\square - 2)^2 = 25x^6 - 20x^3 + 4$

△ **95.** Find the area of the shaded region.

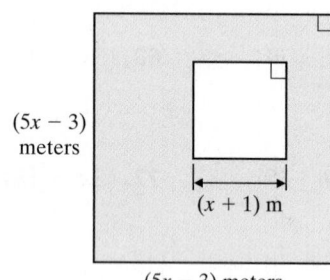

$(5x - 3)$ meters

$(x + 1)$ m

$(5x - 3)$ meters

△ **96.** Find the area of the shaded region.

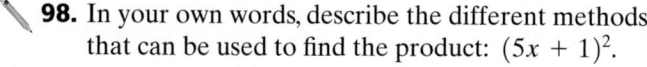

$(3x - 4)$ centimeters

$(3x + 4)$ centimeters

✎ **97.** In your own words, describe the different methods that can be used to find the product: $(2x - 5)(3x + 1)$.

✎ **98.** In your own words, describe the different methods that can be used to find the product: $(5x + 1)^2$.

Exponents and Operations on Polynomials

Perform operations and simplify.

1. $(5x^2)(7x^3)$

2. $(4y^2)(-8y^7)$

3. -4^2

4. $(-4)^2$

5. $(x - 5)(2x + 1)$

6. $(3x - 2)(x + 5)$

7. $(x - 5) + (2x + 1)$

8. $(3x - 2) + (x + 5)$

9. $\dfrac{7x^9 y^{12}}{x^3 y^{10}}$

10. $\dfrac{20a^2 b^8}{14a^2 b^2}$

11. $(12m^7 n^6)^2$

12. $(4y^9 z^{10})^3$

13. $(4y - 3)(4y + 3)$

14. $(7x - 1)(7x + 1)$

15. $(x^{-7} y^5)^9$

16. 8^{-2}

17. $(3^{-1} x^9)^3$

18. $\dfrac{(r^7 s^{-5})^6}{(2r^{-4} s^{-4})^4}$

19. $(7x^2 - 2x + 3) - (5x^2 + 9)$

20. $(10x^2 + 7x - 9) - (4x^2 - 6x + 2)$

Answers

1. _____
2. _____
3. _____
4. _____
5. _____
6. _____
7. _____
8. _____
9. _____
10. _____
11. _____
12. _____
13. _____
14. _____
15. _____
16. _____
17. _____
18. _____
19. _____
20. _____

21. _____

22. _____

23. _____

24. _____

25. _____

26. _____

27. _____

28. _____

29. _____

30. _____

31. _____

32. _____

33. _____

34. _____

35. _____

36. _____

37. _____

38. _____

21. $0.7y^2 - 1.2 + 1.8y^2 - 6y + 1$

22. $7.8x^2 - 6.8x - 3.3 + 0.6x^2 - 0.9$

23. Subtract $y^2 + 2$ from $3y^2 - 6y + 1$

24. $(z^2 + 5) - (3z^2 - 1) + \left(8z^2 + 2z - \dfrac{1}{2}\right)$

25. $(x + 4)^2$

26. $(y - 9)^2$

27. $(x + 4) + (x + 4)$

28. $(y - 9) + (y - 9)$

29. $7x^2 - 6xy + 4(y^2 - xy)$

30. $5a^2 - 3ab + 6(b^2 - a^2)$

31. $(x - 3)(x^2 + 5x - 1)$

32. $(x + 1)(x^2 - 3x - 2)$

33. $(2x - 7)(3x + 10)$

34. $(5x - 1)(4x + 5)$

35. $(2x - 7)(x^2 - 6x + 1)$

36. $(5x - 1)(x^2 + 2x - 3)$

37. $\left(2x + \dfrac{5}{9}\right)\left(2x - \dfrac{5}{9}\right)$

38. $\left(12y + \dfrac{3}{7}\right)\left(12y - \dfrac{3}{7}\right)$

12.7 DIVIDING POLYNOMIALS

Objectives

A Divide a Polynomial by a Monomial.

B Use Long Division to Divide a Polynomial by a Polynomial Other Than a Monomial.

Objective **A** Dividing by a Monomial

To divide a polynomial by a monomial, recall addition of fractions. Fractions that have a common denominator are added by adding the numerators:

$$\frac{a}{c} + \frac{b}{c} = \frac{a + b}{c}$$

If we read this equation from right to left and let a, b, and c be monomials, $c \neq 0$, we have the following.

To Divide a Polynomial by a Monomial

Divide each term of the polynomial by the monomial.

$$\frac{a + b}{c} = \frac{a}{c} + \frac{b}{c}, \quad c \neq 0$$

Throughout this section, we assume that denominators are not 0.

EXAMPLE 1 Divide: $(6m^2 + 2m) \div 2m$

Solution: We begin by writing the quotient in fraction form. Then we divide each term of the polynomial $6m^2 + 2m$ by the monomial $2m$ and use the quotient rule for exponents to simplify.

$$\frac{6m^2 + 2m}{2m} = \frac{6m^2}{2m} + \frac{2m}{2m}$$

$$= 3m + 1 \qquad \text{Simplify.}$$

Check: To check, we multiply.

$$2m(3m + 1) = 2m(3m) + 2m(1) = 6m^2 + 2m$$

The quotient $3m + 1$ checks.

Work Practice Problem 1

✔ **Concept Check** In which of the following is $\frac{x + 5}{5}$ simplified correctly?

a. $\frac{x}{5} + 1$ **b.** x **c.** $x + 1$

EXAMPLE 2 Divide: $\dfrac{9x^5 - 12x^2 + 3x}{3x^2}$

Solution: $\dfrac{9x^5 - 12x^2 + 3x}{3x^2} = \dfrac{9x^5}{3x^2} - \dfrac{12x^2}{3x^2} + \dfrac{3x}{3x^2}$ Divide each term by $3x^2$.

$$= 3x^3 - 4 + \frac{1}{x} \qquad \text{Simplify.}$$

Notice that the quotient is not a polynomial because of the term $\frac{1}{x}$. This expression is called a rational expression—we will study rational expressions in Chapter 14. Although the quotient of two polynomials is not always a polynomial, we may still check by multiplying.

Continued on next page

PRACTICE PROBLEM 1

Divide: $(25x^3 + 5x^2) \div 5x^2$

PRACTICE PROBLEM 2

Divide: $\dfrac{24x^7 + 12x^2 - 4x}{4x^2}$

Answers

1. $5x + 1$,   **2.** $6x^5 + 3 - \dfrac{1}{x}$

✔ **Concept Check Answer**

a

Check: $3x^2\left(3x^3 - 4 + \dfrac{1}{x}\right) = 3x^2(3x^3) - 3x^2(4) + 3x^2\left(\dfrac{1}{x}\right)$

$$= 9x^5 - 12x^2 + 3x$$

▣ **Work Practice Problem 2**

PRACTICE PROBLEM 3

Divide: $\dfrac{12x^3y^3 - 18xy + 6y}{3xy}$

EXAMPLE 3 Divide: $\dfrac{8x^2y^2 - 16xy + 2x}{4xy}$

Solution: $\dfrac{8x^2y^2 - 16xy + 2x}{4xy} = \dfrac{8x^2y^2}{4xy} - \dfrac{16xy}{4xy} + \dfrac{2x}{4xy}$ Divide each term by $4xy$.

$$= 2xy - 4 + \dfrac{1}{2y} \qquad \text{Simplify.}$$

Check: $4xy\left(2xy - 4 + \dfrac{1}{2y}\right) = 4xy(2xy) - 4xy(4) + 4xy\left(\dfrac{1}{2y}\right)$

$$= 8x^2y^2 - 16xy + 2x$$

▣ **Work Practice Problem 3**

Objective Ⓑ Dividing by a Polynomial Other Than a Monomial

To divide a polynomial by a polynomial other than a monomial, we use a process known as long division. Polynomial long division is similar to number long division, so we review long division by dividing 13 into 3660.

$$
\begin{array}{r}
281 \\
13\overline{)3660} \\
\end{array}
$$

$$
\begin{array}{rl}
\underline{26}\!\downarrow & \quad 2 \cdot 13 = 26 \\
106 & \quad \text{Subtract and bring down the next digit in the dividend.} \\
\underline{104}\!\downarrow & \quad 8 \cdot 13 = 104 \\
20 & \quad \text{Subtract and bring down the next digit in the dividend.} \\
\underline{13} & \quad 1 \cdot 13 = 13 \\
7 & \quad \text{Subtract. There are no more digits to bring down, so the remainder is 7.}
\end{array}
$$

Helpful Hint   Recall that 3660 is called the dividend.

The quotient is 281 R 7, which can be written as $281\,\dfrac{7}{13}$ ← remainder / ← divisor

Recall that division can be checked by multiplication. To check this division problem, we see that

$13 \cdot 281 + 7 = 3660$, the dividend.

Now we demonstrate long division of polynomials.

PRACTICE PROBLEM 4

Divide $x^2 + 12x + 35$ by $x + 5$ using long division.

EXAMPLE 4 Divide $x^2 + 7x + 12$ by $x + 3$ using long division.

Solution:

To subtract, change the signs of these terms and add. →

How many times does x divide x^2? $\dfrac{x^2}{x} = x$.

$$
\begin{array}{r}
x \\
x + 3\overline{)x^2 + 7x + 12} \\
\underline{x^2 + 3x}\downarrow \\
4x + 12
\end{array}
$$

Multiply: $x(x + 3)$.

Subtract and bring down the next term.

Answers

3. $4x^2y^2 - 6 + \dfrac{2}{x}$,   **4.** $x + 7$

Now we repeat this process.

$$x + 3\overline{)x^2 + 7x + 12}$$

$x + 4$ How many times does x divide

$4x$? $\dfrac{4x}{x} = 4$.

To subtract, change the signs of these terms and add.

$\dfrac{x^2 + 3x}{}$

$4x + 12$

$\underline{4x + 12}$ Multiply: $4(x + 3)$.

0 Subtract. The remainder is 0.

The quotient is $x + 4$.

Check: We check by multiplying.

divisor	·	quotient	+	remainder	=	dividend

or $\downarrow$ $\downarrow$ $\downarrow$ $\downarrow$

$(x + 3)$ · $(x + 4)$ + 0 = $x^2 + 7x + 12$

The quotient checks.

▣ **Work Practice Problem 4**

EXAMPLE 5 Divide $6x^2 + 10x - 5$ by $3x - 1$ using long division.

Solution:

$$3x - 1\overline{)6x^2 + 10x - 5}$$

$2x + 4$ $\dfrac{6x^2}{3x} = 2x$, so $2x$ is a term of the quotient.

$\underline{6x^2 + 2x}$ Multiply: $2x(3x - 1)$.

$12x - 5$ Subtract and bring down the next term.

$\underline{12x + 4}$ $\dfrac{12x}{3x} = 4$. Multiply: $4(3x - 1)$.

-1 Subtract. The remainder is -1.

Thus $(6x^2 + 10x - 5)$ divided by $(3x - 1)$ is $(2x + 4)$ with a remainder of -1. This can be written as follows.

$$\frac{6x^2 + 10x - 5}{3x - 1} = 2x + 4 + \frac{-1}{3x - 1} \leftarrow \text{remainder} \\ \leftarrow \text{divisor}$$

$$\text{or } 2x + 4 - \frac{1}{3x - 1}$$

Check: To check, we multiply $(3x - 1)(2x + 4)$. Then we add the remainder, -1, to this product.

$$(3x - 1)(2x + 4) + (-1) = (6x^2 + 12x - 2x - 4) - 1$$
$$= 6x^2 + 10x - 5$$

The quotient checks.

▣ **Work Practice Problem 5**

Notice that the division process is continued until the degree of the remainder polynomial is less than the degree of the divisor polynomial.

Recall in Section 12.3 that we practiced writing polynomials in descending order of powers and with no missing terms. For example, $2 - 4x^2$ written in this form is $-4x^2 + 0x + 2$. Writing the dividend and divisor in this form is helpful when dividing polynomials.

PRACTICE PROBLEM 5

Divide: $8x^2 + 2x - 7$ by $2x - 1$

Answer

5. $4x + 3 + \dfrac{-4}{2x - 1}$ or $4x + 3 - \dfrac{4}{2x - 1}$

PRACTICE PROBLEM 6

Divide: $(15 - 2x^2) \div (x - 3)$

EXAMPLE 6 Divide: $(2 - 4x^2) \div (x + 1)$

Solution: We use the rewritten form of $2 - 4x^2$ from the previous page.

$$
\begin{array}{r}
-4x + 4 \\
x + 1 \overline{)-4x^2 + 0x + 2} \\
\underline{-4x^2 - 4x} \\
4x + 2 \\
\underline{4x + 4} \\
-2
\end{array}
$$

$\dfrac{-4x^2}{x} = -4x$, so $-4x$ is a term of the quotient.

Multiply: $-4x(x + 1)$.

Subtract and bring down the next term.

$\dfrac{4x}{x} = 4$. Multiply: $4(x + 1)$.

Remainder.

Thus, $\dfrac{-4x^2 + 0x + 2}{x + 1}$ or $\dfrac{2 - 4x^2}{x + 1} = -4x + 4 + \dfrac{-2}{x + 1}$ or $-4x + 4 - \dfrac{2}{x + 1}$.

Check: To check, see that $(x + 1)(-4x + 4) + (-2) = 2 - 4x^2$.

▨ **Work Practice Problem 6**

PRACTICE PROBLEM 7

Divide: $\dfrac{5 - x + 9x^3}{3x + 2}$

EXAMPLE 7 Divide: $\dfrac{4x^2 + 7 + 8x^3}{2x + 3}$

Solution: Before we begin the division process, we rewrite $4x^2 + 7 + 8x^3$ as $8x^3 + 4x^2 + 0x + 7$. Notice that we have written the polynomial in descending order and have represented the missing x term by $0x$.

$$
\begin{array}{r}
4x^2 - 4x + 6 \\
2x + 3 \overline{)8x^3 + 4x^2 + 0x + 7} \\
\underline{8x^3 + 12x^2} \\
-8x^2 + 0x \\
\underline{-8x^2 - 12x} \\
12x + 7 \\
\underline{12x + 18} \\
-11
\end{array}
$$

Remainder.

Thus, $\dfrac{4x^2 + 7 + 8x^3}{2x + 3} = 4x^2 - 4x + 6 + \dfrac{-11}{2x + 3}$ or $4x^2 - 4x + 6 - \dfrac{11}{2x + 3}$.

▨ **Work Practice Problem 7**

PRACTICE PROBLEM 8

Divide: $x^3 - 1$ by $x - 1$

EXAMPLE 8 Divide $x^3 - 8$ by $x - 2$.

Solution: Notice that the polynomial $x^3 - 8$ is missing an x^2 term and an x term. We'll represent these terms by inserting $0x^2$ and $0x$.

$$
\begin{array}{r}
x^2 + 2x + 4 \\
x - 2 \overline{)x^3 + 0x^2 + 0x - 8} \\
\underline{x^3 - 2x^2} \\
2x^2 + 0x \\
\underline{2x^2 - 4x} \\
4x - 8 \\
\underline{4x - 8} \\
0
\end{array}
$$

Thus, $\dfrac{x^3 - 8}{x - 2} = x^2 + 2x + 4$.

Check: To check, see that $(x^2 + 2x + 4)(x - 2) = x^3 - 8$.

▨ **Work Practice Problem 8**

Answers

6. $-2x - 6 + \dfrac{-3}{x - 3}$

or $-2x - 6 - \dfrac{3}{x - 3}$,

7. $3x^2 - 2x + 1 + \dfrac{3}{3x + 2}$,

8. $x^2 + x + 1$

Mental Math

Simplify each expression.

1. $\dfrac{a^6}{a^4}$ **2.** $\dfrac{y^2}{y}$ **3.** $\dfrac{a^3}{a}$ **4.** $\dfrac{p^8}{p^3}$ **5.** $\dfrac{k^5}{k^2}$ **6.** $\dfrac{k^7}{k^5}$

12.7 EXERCISE SET

FOR EXTRA HELP

Student Solutions Manual PH Math/Tutor Center CD/Video for Review  MathXL®  MyMathLab

Objective A *Perform each division. See Examples 1 through 3.*

1. $\dfrac{12x^4 + 3x^2}{x}$ **2.** $\dfrac{15x^2 - 9x^5}{x}$ **3.** $\dfrac{20x^3 - 30x^2 + 5x + 5}{5}$ **4.** $\dfrac{8x^3 - 4x^2 + 6x + 2}{2}$

5. $\dfrac{15p^3 + 18p^2}{3p}$ **6.** $\dfrac{14m^2 - 27m^3}{7m}$ **7.** $\dfrac{-9x^4 + 18x^5}{6x^5}$ **8.** $\dfrac{6x^5 + 3x^4}{3x^4}$

9. $\dfrac{-9x^5 + 3x^4 - 12}{3x^3}$ **10.** $\dfrac{6a^2 - 4a + 12}{-2a^2}$ **11.** $\dfrac{4x^4 - 6x^3 + 7}{-4x^4}$ **12.** $\dfrac{-12a^3 + 36a - 15}{3a}$

Objective B *Find each quotient using long division. See Examples 4 and 5.*

13. $\dfrac{x^2 + 4x + 3}{x + 3}$ **14.** $\dfrac{x^2 + 7x + 10}{x + 5}$ **15.** $\dfrac{2x^2 + 13x + 15}{x + 5}$ **16.** $\dfrac{3x^2 + 8x + 4}{x + 2}$

17. $\dfrac{2x^2 - 7x + 3}{x - 4}$ **18.** $\dfrac{3x^2 - x - 4}{x - 1}$ **19.** $\dfrac{9a^3 - 3a^2 - 3a + 4}{3a + 2}$ **20.** $\dfrac{4x^3 + 12x^2 + x - 14}{2x + 3}$

21. $\dfrac{8x^2 + 10x + 1}{2x + 1}$ **22.** $\dfrac{3x^2 + 17x + 7}{3x + 2}$ **23.** $\dfrac{2x^3 + 2x^2 - 17x + 8}{x - 2}$ **24.** $\dfrac{4x^3 + 11x^2 - 8x - 10}{x + 3}$

Find each quotient using long division. Don't forget to write the polynomials in descending order and fill in any missing terms. See Examples 6 through 8.

25. $\dfrac{x^2 - 36}{x - 6}$ **26.** $\dfrac{a^2 - 49}{a - 7}$ **27.** $\dfrac{x^3 - 27}{x - 3}$ **28.** $\dfrac{x^3 + 64}{x + 4}$

29. $\dfrac{1 - 3x^2}{x + 2}$ **30.** $\dfrac{7 - 5x^2}{x + 3}$ **31.** $\dfrac{-4b + 4b^2 - 5}{2b - 1}$ **32.** $\dfrac{-3y + 2y^2 - 15}{2y + 5}$

Objectives **A** **B** **Mixed Practice** *Divide. If the divisor contains 2 or more terms, use long division. See Examples 1 through 8.*

33. $\dfrac{a^2b^2 - ab^3}{ab}$

34. $\dfrac{m^3n^2 - mn^4}{mn}$

35. $\dfrac{8x^2 + 6x - 27}{2x - 3}$

36. $\dfrac{18w^2 + 18w - 8}{3w + 4}$

37. $\dfrac{2x^2y + 8x^2y^2 - xy^2}{2xy}$

38. $\dfrac{11x^3y^3 - 33xy + x^2y^2}{11xy}$

 **39.** $\dfrac{2b^3 + 9b^2 + 6b - 4}{b + 4}$

40. $\dfrac{2x^3 + 3x^2 - 3x + 4}{x + 2}$

41. $\dfrac{y^3 + 3y^2 + 4}{y - 2}$

42. $\dfrac{3x^3 + 11x + 12}{x + 4}$

43. $\dfrac{5 - 6x^2}{x - 2}$

44. $\dfrac{3 - 7x^2}{x - 3}$

Divide.

45. $\dfrac{x^5 + x^2}{x^2 + x}$

46. $\dfrac{x^6 - x^4}{x^3 + 1}$

Review

Fill in each blank. See Sections 12.1 and 12.2.

47. $12 = 4 \cdot$ ____

48. $12 = 2 \cdot$ ____

49. $20 = -5 \cdot$ ____

50. $20 = -4 \cdot$ ____

51. $9x^2 = 3x \cdot$ ____

52. $9x^2 = 9x \cdot$ ____

53. $36x^2 = 4x \cdot$ ____

54. $36x^2 = 2x \cdot$ ____

Concept Extensions

Solve.

△ **55.** The perimeter of a square is $(12x^3 + 4x - 16)$ feet. Find the length of its side.

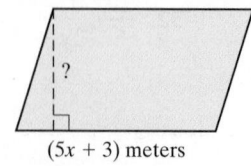

Perimeter is
$(12x^3 + 4x - 16)$ feet

△ **56.** The volume of the swimming pool shown is $(36x^5 - 12x^3 + 6x^2)$ cubic feet. If its height is $2x$ feet and its width is $3x$ feet, find its length.

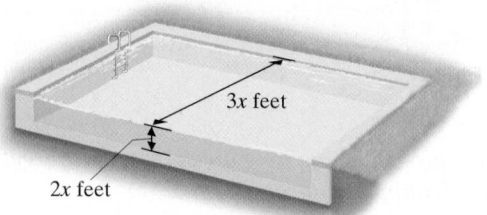

3x feet

2x feet

△ **57.** The area of the parallelogram shown is $(10x^2 + 31x + 15)$ square meters. If its base is $(5x + 3)$ meters, find its height.

?

$(5x + 3)$ meters

△ **58.** The area of the top of the Ping-Pong table shown is $(49x^2 + 70x - 200)$ square inches. If its length is $(7x + 20)$ inches, find its width.

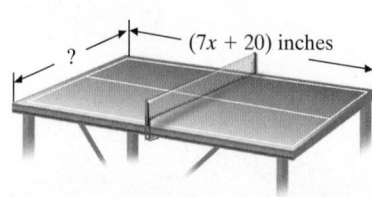

? ⟶ $(7x + 20)$ inches

59. Explain how to check a polynomial long division result when the remainder is 0.

60. Explain how to check a polynomial long division result when the remainder is not 0.

61. In which of the following is $\dfrac{a + 7}{7}$ simplified correctly? See the Concept Check in this section.

a. $a + 1$

b. a

c. $\dfrac{a}{7} + 1$

THE BIGGER PICTURE Simplifying Expressions and Solving Equations and Inequalities

Now we continue our outline from Sections 8.5 and 9.7. Although suggestions are given, this outline should be in your own words. Once you complete this new portion, try the exercises below.

I. Simplifying Expressions

  A. Real Numbers

    1. Add (Section 8.3)

    2. Subtract (Section 8.4)

    3. Multiply or Divide (Section 8.5)

  B. Exponents — $x^7 \cdot x^5 = x^{12}$; $(x^7)^5 = x^{35}$; $\dfrac{x^7}{x^5} = x^2$;

    $x^0 = 1$; $8^{-2} = \dfrac{1}{8^2} = \dfrac{1}{64}$

  C. Polynomials

    1. Add: Combine like terms.

    $(3y^2 + 6y + 7) + (9y^2 - 11y - 15)$

    $= 3y^2 + 6y + 7 + 9y^2 - 11y - 15$

    $= 12y^2 - 5y - 8$

    2. Subtract: Change the sign of the terms of the polynomial being subtracted, then add.

    $(3y^2 + 6y + 7) - (9y^2 - 11y - 15)$

    $= 3y^2 + 6y + 7 - 9y^2 + 11y + 15$

    $= -6y^2 + 17y + 22$

    3. Multiply: Multiply each term of one polynomial by each term of the other polynomial.

    $(x + 5)(2x^2 - 3x + 4)$

    $= x(2x^2 - 3x + 4) + 5(2x^2 - 3x + 4)$

    $= 2x^3 - 3x^2 + 4x + 10x^2 - 15x + 20$

    $= 2x^3 + 7x^2 - 11x + 20$

    4. Divide:

      a. To divide by a monomial, divide each term of the polynomial by the monomial.

      $\dfrac{8x^2 + 2x - 6}{2x} = \dfrac{8x^2}{2x} + \dfrac{2x}{2x} - \dfrac{6}{2x}$

      $= 4x + 1 - \dfrac{3}{x}$

      b. To divide by a polynomial other than a monomial, use long division.

$$x - 6 + \dfrac{40}{2x + 5}$$
$$2x + 5 \overline{)2x^2 - 7x + 10}$$
$$\underline{2x^2 + 5x}$$
$$-12x + 10$$
$$\underline{-12x - 30}$$
$$40$$

II. Solving Equations and Inequalities

  A. Linear Equations (Section 9.3)

  B. Linear Inequalities (Section 9.7)

Simplify the expressions.

1. $-5.7 + (-0.23)$

2. $\dfrac{1}{2} - \dfrac{9}{10}$

3. $(-5x^2y^3)(-x^7y)$

4. $2^{-3}a^{-7}a^3$

5. $(7y^3 - 6y + 2) - (y^3 + 2y^2 + 2)$

6. Subtract $(y^2 + 7)$ from $(9y^2 - 3y)$

7. Multiply: $(x - 3)(4x^2 - x + 7)$

8. Multiply: $(6m - 5)^2$

9. Divide: $\dfrac{20n^2 - 5n + 10}{5n}$

10. Divide: $\dfrac{6x^2 - 20x + 20}{3x - 1}$

Solve the equations or inequalities.

11. $-6x = 3.6$

12. $-6x < 3.6$

13. $6x + 6 \geq 8x + 2$

14. $7y + 3(y - 1) = 4(y + 1) - 3$

CHAPTER 12 Group Activity

Modeling with Polynomials

Materials

Calculator

This activity may be completed by working in groups or individually.

The polynomial model $-13x^2 + 221x + 8476$ gives the average daily total supply of motor gasoline (in thousand barrels per day) in the United States for the period 2000–2003. The polynomial model $-23x^2 + 192x + 7825$ gives the average daily supply of domestically produced motor gasoline (in thousand barrels per day) in the United States for the same period. In both models, x is the number of years after 2000. The other source of motor gasoline in the United States, contributing to the total supply, is imported motor gasoline. (*Source:* Based on data from the Energy Information Administration)

1. Use the given polynomials to complete the following table showing the average daily supply (both total and domestic) over the period 2000–2003 by evaluating each polynomial at the given values of x. Then subtract each value in the fourth column from the corresponding value in the third column. Record the result in the last column, titled "Difference." What do you think these values represent?

Year	x	Average Daily Total Supply (thousand barrels per day)	Average Daily Domestic Supply (thousand barrels per day)	Difference
2000	0			
2001	1			
2002	2			
2003	3			

2. Use the polynomial models to find a new polynomial model representing the average daily supply of imported motor gasoline. Then evaluate your new polynomial model to complete the accompanying table.

Year	x	Average Daily Imported Supply (thousand barrels per day)
2000	0	
2001	1	
2002	2	
2003	3	

3. Compare the values in the last column of the table in question 1 to the values in the last column of the table in question 2. What do you notice? What can you conclude?

4. Make a bar graph of the data in the table in question 2. Describe what you see.

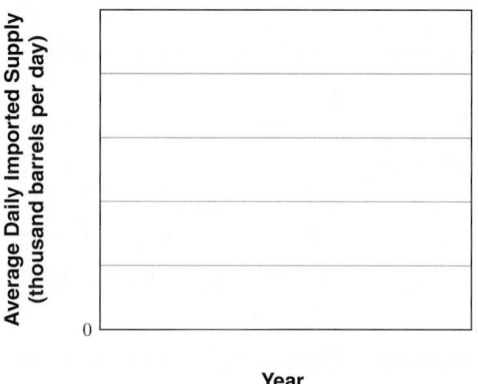

Chapter 12 Vocabulary Check

Fill in each blank with one of the words or phrases listed below.

term   coefficient   monomial   binomial   trinomial

polynomials   degree of a term   degree of a polynomial   FOIL

1. A _____ is a number or the product of a number and variables raised to powers.
2. The _____ method may be used when multiplying two binomials.
3. A polynomial with exactly 3 terms is called a _____.
4. The _____ is the greatest degree of any term of the polynomial.
5. A polynomial with exactly 2 terms is called a _____.
6. The _____ of a term is its numerical factor.
7. The _____ is the sum of the exponents on the variables in the term.
8. A polynomial with exactly 1 term is called a _____.
9. Monomials, binomials, and trinomials are all examples of _____.

Helpful Hint

Are you preparing for your test? Don't forget to take the Chapter 12 Test on page 939. Then check your answers at the back of the text and use the Chapter Test Prep Video CD to see the fully worked-out solutions to any of the exercises you want to review.

12 Chapter Highlights

DEFINITIONS AND CONCEPTS	EXAMPLES
Section 12.1 Exponents	
a^n means the product of n factors, each of which is a.	$3^2 = 3 \cdot 3 = 9$ $(-5)^3 = (-5)(-5)(-5) = -125$ $\left(\frac{1}{2}\right)^4 = \frac{1}{2} \cdot \frac{1}{2} \cdot \frac{1}{2} \cdot \frac{1}{2} = \frac{1}{16}$
Let m and n be integers and no denominators be 0. **Product Rule:** $a^m \cdot a^n = a^{m+n}$ **Power Rule:** $(a^m)^n = a^{mn}$ **Power of a Product Rule:** $(ab)^n = a^n b^n$ **Power of a Quotient Rule:** $\left(\frac{a}{b}\right)^n = \frac{a^n}{b^n}$ **Quotient Rule:** $\frac{a^m}{a^n} = a^{m-n}$ **Zero Exponent:** $a^0 = 1, a \neq 0$	$x^2 \cdot x^7 = x^{2+7} = x^9$ $(5^3)^8 = 5^{3 \cdot 8} = 5^{24}$ $(7y)^4 = 7^4 y^4$ $\left(\frac{x}{8}\right)^3 = \frac{x^3}{8^3}$ $\frac{x^9}{x^4} = x^{9-4} = x^5$ $5^0 = 1; x^0 = 1, x \neq 0$

DEFINITIONS AND CONCEPTS	**EXAMPLES**

Section 12.2   Negative Exponents and Scientific Notation

If $a \neq 0$ and n is an integer, $$a^{-n} = \frac{1}{a^n}$$	$3^{-2} = \frac{1}{3^2} = \frac{1}{9}; \ 5x^{-2} = \frac{5}{x^2}$ Simplify: $\left(\dfrac{x^{-2}y}{x^5}\right)^{-2} = \dfrac{x^4 y^{-2}}{x^{-10}}$ $\qquad\qquad\qquad\quad = x^{4-(-10)}y^{-2}$ $\qquad\qquad\qquad\quad = \dfrac{x^{14}}{y^2}$
A positive number is written in scientific notation if it is written as the product of a number a, where $1 \leq a < 10$, and an integer power r of 10. $$a \times 10^r$$	$1200 = 1.2 \times 10^3$ $0.000000568 = 5.68 \times 10^{-7}$

Section 12.3   Introduction to Polynomials

A **term** is a number or the product of a number and variables raised to powers.	$-5x, \ 7a^2b, \ \dfrac{1}{4}y^4, \ 0.2$
The **numerical coefficient** or **coefficient** of a term is its numerical factor.	**Term** **Coefficient** $7x^2$ 7 y 1 $-a^2b$ -1
A **polynomial** is a finite sum of terms of the form ax^n where a is a real number and n is a whole number.	$5x^3 - 6x^2 + 3x - 6$ (Polynomial)
A **monomial** is a polynomial with exactly 1 term.	$\dfrac{5}{6}y^3$ (Monomial)
A **binomial** is a polynomial with exactly 2 terms.	$-0.2a^2b - 5b^2$ (Binomial)
A **trinomial** is a polynomial with exactly 3 terms.	$3x^2 - 2x + 1$ (Trinomial)
The **degree of a polynomial** is the greatest degree of any term of the polynomial.	**Polynomial** **Degree** $5x^2 - 3x + 2$ 2 $7y + 8y^2z^3 - 12$ $2 + 3 = 5$

Section 12.4   Adding and Subtracting Polynomials

To add polynomials, combine like terms.	Add. $(7x^2 - 3x + 2) + (-5x - 6)$ $\quad = 7x^2 - 3x + 2 - 5x - 6$ $\quad = 7x^2 - 8x - 4$
To subtract two polynomials, change the signs of the terms of the second polynomial, and then add.	Subtract. $(17y^2 - 2y + 1) - (-3y^3 + 5y - 6)$ $\quad = (17y^2 - 2y + 1) + (3y^3 - 5y + 6)$ $\quad = 17y^2 - 2y + 1 + 3y^3 - 5y + 6$ $\quad = 3y^3 + 17y^2 - 7y + 7$

DEFINITIONS AND CONCEPTS	EXAMPLES

Section 12.5   Multiplying Polynomials

To multiply two polynomials, multiply each term of one polynomial by each term of the other polynomial, and then combine like terms.

Multiply.
$$(2x + 1)(5x^2 - 6x + 2)$$
$$= 2x(5x^2 - 6x + 2) + 1(5x^2 - 6x + 2)$$
$$= 10x^3 - 12x^2 + 4x + 5x^2 - 6x + 2$$
$$= 10x^3 - 7x^2 - 2x + 2$$

Section 12.6   Special Products

The **FOIL method** may be used when multiplying two binomials.

Multiply: $(5x - 3)(2x + 3)$

First ⌐Last⌐
$$(5x - 3)(2x + 3)$$
Inner
Outer

$$\text{F} \qquad \text{O} \qquad \text{I} \qquad \text{L}$$
$$= (5x)(2x) + (5x)(3) + (-3)(2x) + (-3)(3)$$
$$= 10x^2 + 15x - 6x - 9$$
$$= 10x^2 + 9x - 9$$

Squaring a Binomial

$$(a + b)^2 = a^2 + 2ab + b^2$$

$$(a - b)^2 = a^2 - 2ab + b^2$$

Square each binomial.

$$(x + 5)^2 = x^2 + 2(x)(5) + 5^2$$
$$= x^2 + 10x + 25$$
$$(3x - 2y)^2 = (3x)^2 - 2(3x)(2y) + (2y)^2$$
$$= 9x^2 - 12xy + 4y^2$$

Multiplying the Sum and Difference of Two Terms

$$(a + b)(a - b) = a^2 - b^2$$

Multiply.

$$(6y + 5)(6y - 5) = (6y)^2 - 5^2$$
$$= 36y^2 - 25$$

Section 12.7   Dividing Polynomials

To divide a polynomial by a monomial,

$$\frac{a + b}{c} = \frac{a}{c} + \frac{b}{c}, c \neq 0$$

Divide.

$$\frac{15x^5 - 10x^3 + 5x^2 - 2x}{5x^2}$$
$$= \frac{15x^5}{5x^2} - \frac{10x^3}{5x^2} + \frac{5x^2}{5x^2} - \frac{2x}{5x^2}$$
$$= 3x^3 - 2x + 1 - \frac{2}{5x}$$

To divide a polynomial by a polynomial other than a monomial, use long division.

$$\begin{array}{r} 5x - 1 + \dfrac{-4}{2x + 3} \\ 2x + 3 \overline{)10x^2 + 13x - 7} \\ \underline{10x^2 + 15x} \\ -2x - 7 \\ \underline{-2x - 3} \\ -4 \end{array}$$

or $5x - 1 - \dfrac{4}{2x + 3}$

Are You Prepared for a Test on Chapter 12?

Below is a list of some *common trouble areas* for students in Chapter 12. After studying for your test—but before taking your test—read these.

- Do you know that a negative exponent does not make the base a negative number? For example,

$$3^{-2} = \frac{1}{3^2} = \frac{1}{9}$$

- Make sure you remember that x has an understood coefficient of 1 and an understood exponent of 1. For example,

$$2x + x = 2x + 1x = 3x; \quad x^5 \cdot x = x^5 \cdot x^1 = x^6$$

- Do you know the difference between $5x^2$ and $(5x)^2$?

$$5x^2 \text{ is } 5 \cdot x^2; \quad (5x)^2 = 5^2 \cdot x^2 \text{ or } 25 \cdot x^2$$

- Can you evaluate $x^2 - x$ when $x = -2$?

$$x^2 - x = (-2)^2 - (-2) = 4 - (-2) = 4 + 2 = 6$$

- Can you subtract $5x^2 + 1$ from $3x^2 - 6$?

$$(3x^2 - 6) - (5x^2 + 1) = 3x^2 - 6 - 5x^2 - 1$$
$$= -2x^2 - 7$$

- Make sure you are familiar with squaring a binomial.

$$(3x - 4)^2 = (3x)^2 - 2(3x)(4) + 4^2$$
$$= 9x^2 - 24x + 16$$

or

$$(3x - 4)^2 = (3x - 4)(3x - 4)$$
$$= 9x^2 - 24x + 16$$

Remember: This is simply a checklist of common trouble areas. For a review of Chapter 12, see the Highlights and Chapter Review.

12 CHAPTER REVIEW

(12.1) *State the base and the exponent for each expression.*

1. 3^2
2. $(-5)^4$
3. -5^4
4. x^6

Evaluate each expression.

5. 8^3
6. $(-6)^2$
7. -6^2
8. $-4^3 - 4^0$
9. $(3b)^0$
10. $\dfrac{8b}{8b}$

Simplify each expression.

11. $y^2 \cdot y^7$
12. $x^9 \cdot x^5$
13. $(2x^5)(-3x^6)$
14. $(-5y^3)(4y^4)$
15. $(x^4)^2$

16. $(y^3)^5$
17. $(3y^6)^4$
18. $(2x^3)^3$
19. $\dfrac{x^9}{x^4}$
20. $\dfrac{z^{12}}{z^5}$

21. $\dfrac{a^5b^4}{ab}$
22. $\dfrac{x^4y^6}{xy}$
23. $\dfrac{12xy^6}{3x^4y^{10}}$
24. $\dfrac{2x^7y^8}{8xy^2}$
25. $5a^7(2a^4)^3$

26. $(2x)^2(9x)$
27. $(-5a)^0 + 7^0 + 8^0$
28. $8x^0 + 9^0$

Simplify the given expression and choose the correct result.

29. $\left(\dfrac{3x^4}{4y}\right)^3$

   a. $\dfrac{27x^{64}}{64y^3}$ **c.** $\dfrac{9x^{12}}{12y^3}$

   b. $\dfrac{27x^{12}}{64y^3}$ **d.** $\dfrac{3x^{12}}{4y^3}$

30. $\left(\dfrac{5a^6}{b^3}\right)^2$

   a. $\dfrac{10a^{12}}{b^6}$ **c.** $\dfrac{25a^{12}}{b^6}$

   b. $\dfrac{25a^{36}}{b^9}$ **d.** $25a^{12}b^6$

(12.2) *Simplify each expression.*

31. 7^{-2} **32.** -7^{-2} **33.** $2x^{-4}$ **34.** $(2x)^{-4}$

35. $\left(\dfrac{1}{5}\right)^{-3}$ **36.** $\left(\dfrac{-2}{3}\right)^{-2}$ **37.** $2^0 + 2^{-4}$ **38.** $6^{-1} - 7^{-1}$

Simplify each expression. Write each answer using positive exponents only.

39. $\dfrac{x^5}{x^{-3}}$ **40.** $\dfrac{z^4}{z^{-4}}$ **41.** $\dfrac{r^{-3}}{r^{-4}}$ **42.** $\dfrac{y^{-2}}{y^{-5}}$

43. $\left(\dfrac{bc^{-2}}{bc^{-3}}\right)^4$ **44.** $\left(\dfrac{x^{-3}y^{-4}}{x^{-2}y^{-5}}\right)^{-3}$ **45.** $\dfrac{x^{-4}y^{-6}}{x^2y^7}$ **46.** $\dfrac{a^5b^{-5}}{a^{-5}b^5}$

Write each number in scientific notation.

47. 0.00027 **48.** 0.8868 **49.** $80,800,000$ **50.** $868,000$

51. In August 2004, the United States imported approximately 112,400,000 kilograms of coffee. Write this number in scientific notation. (*Source:* International Coffee Organization)

52. The approximate diameter of the Milky Way galaxy is 150,000 light years. Write this number in scientific notation. (*Source:* NASA IMAGE/POETRY Education and Public Outreach Program)

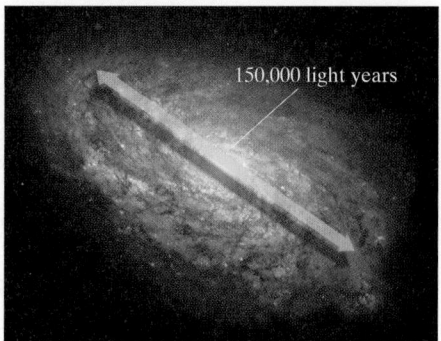

150,000 light years

Write each number in standard form.

53. 8.67×10^5 **54.** 3.86×10^{-3} **55.** 8.6×10^{-4} **56.** 8.936×10^5

57. The volume of the planet Jupiter is 1.43128×10^{15} cubic kilometers. Write this number in standard notation. (*Source:* National Space Science Data Center)

58. An angstrom is a unit of measure, equal to 1×10^{-10} meter, used for measuring wavelengths or the diameters of atoms. Write this number in standard notation. (*Source:* National Institute of Standards and Technology)

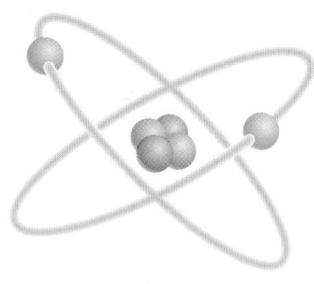

Simplify. Express each result in standard form.

59. $(8 \times 10^4)(2 \times 10^{-7})$

60. $\dfrac{8 \times 10^4}{2 \times 10^{-7}}$

(12.3) *Find the degree of each polynomial.*

61. $y^5 + 7x - 8x^4$

62. $9y^2 + 30y + 25$

63. $-14x^2y - 28x^2y^3 - 42x^2y^2$

64. $6x^2y^2z^2 + 5x^2y^3 - 12xyz$

△ **65.** The surface area of a box with a square base and a height of 5 units is given by the polynomial $2x^2 + 20x$. Fill in the table below by evaluating $2x^2 + 20x$ for the given values of x.

x	1	3	5.1	10
$2x^2 + 20x$				

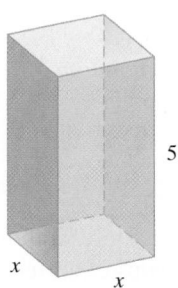

Combine like terms in each expression.

66. $7a^2 - 4a^2 - a^2$

67. $9y + y - 14y$

68. $6a^2 + 4a + 9a^2$

69. $21x^2 + 3x + x^2 + 6$

70. $4a^2b - 3b^2 - 8q^2 - 10a^2b + 7q^2$

71. $2s^{14} + 3s^{13} + 12s^{12} - s^{10}$

(12.4) *Add or subtract as indicated.*

72. $(3x^2 + 2x + 6) + (5x^2 + x)$

73. $(2x^5 + 3x^4 + 4x^3 + 5x^2) + (4x^2 + 7x + 6)$

74. $(-5y^2 + 3) - (2y^2 + 4)$

75. $(2m^7 + 3x^4 + 7m^6) - (8m^7 + 4m^2 + 6x^4)$

76. $(3x^2 - 7xy + 7y^2) - (4x^2 - xy + 9y^2)$

77. Add $(-9x^2 + 6x + 2)$ and $(4x^2 - x - 1)$.

78. Subtract $(4x^2 + 8x - 7)$ from the sum of $(x^2 + 7x + 9)$ and $(x^2 + 4)$.

(12.5) *Multiply each expression.*

79. $6(x + 5)$

80. $9(x - 7)$

81. $4(2a + 7)$

82. $9(6a - 3)$

83. $-7x(x^2 + 5)$

84. $-8y(4y^2 - 6)$

85. $-2(x^3 - 9x^2 + x)$

86. $-3a(a^2b + ab + b^2)$

87. $(3a^3 - 4a + 1)(-2a)$

88. $(6b^3 - 4b + 2)(7b)$

89. $(2x + 2)(x - 7)$

90. $(2x - 5)(3x + 2)$

91. $(4a - 1)(a + 7)$

92. $(6a - 1)(7a + 3)$

93. $(x + 7)(x^3 + 4x - 5)$

94. $(x + 2)(x^5 + x + 1)$

95. $(x^2 + 2x + 4)(x^2 + 2x - 4)$

96. $(x^3 + 4x + 4)(x^3 + 4x - 4)$

97. $(x + 7)^3$

98. $(2x - 5)^3$

(12.6) *Use special products to multiply each of the following.*

99. $(x + 7)^2$

100. $(x - 5)^2$

101. $(3x - 7)^2$

102. $(4x + 2)^2$

103. $(5x - 9)^2$

104. $(5x + 1)(5x - 1)$

105. $(7x + 4)(7x - 4)$

106. $(a + 2b)(a - 2b)$

107. $(2x - 6)(2x + 6)$

108. $(4a^2 - 2b)(4a^2 + 2b)$

Express each as a product of polynomials in x. Then multiply and simplify.

△ **109.** Find the area of the square if its side is $(3x - 1)$ meters.

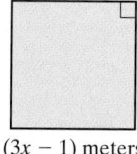

$(3x - 1)$ meters

△ **110.** Find the area of the rectangle.

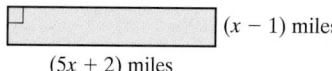
$(x - 1)$ miles
$(5x + 2)$ miles

(12.7) *Divide.*

111. $\dfrac{x^2 + 21x + 49}{7x^2}$

112. $\dfrac{5a^3b - 15ab^2 + 20ab}{-5ab}$

113. $(a^2 - a + 4) \div (a - 2)$

114. $(4x^2 + 20x + 7) \div (x + 5)$

115. $\dfrac{a^3 + a^2 + 2a + 6}{a - 2}$

116. $\dfrac{9b^3 - 18b^2 + 8b - 1}{3b - 2}$

117. $\dfrac{4x^4 - 4x^3 + x^2 + 4x - 3}{2x - 1}$

118. $\dfrac{-10x^2 - x^3 - 21x + 18}{x - 6}$

△ **119.** The area of the rectangle below is $(15x^3 - 3x^2 + 60)$ square feet. If its length is $3x^2$ feet, find its width.

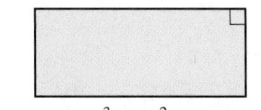

Area is $(15x^3 - 3x^2 + 60)$ sq feet

△ **120.** The perimeter of the equilateral triangle below is $(21a^3b^6 + 3a - 3)$ units. Find the length of a side.

Perimeter is
$(21a^3b^6 + 3a - 3)$ units

Mixed Review

Evaluate.

121. $\left(-\dfrac{1}{2}\right)^3$

Simplify each expression. Write each answer using positive exponents only.

122. $(4xy^2)(x^3y^5)$

123. $\dfrac{18x^9}{27x^3}$

124. $\left(\dfrac{3a^4}{b^2}\right)^3$

125. $(2x^{-4}y^3)^{-4}$

126. $\dfrac{a^{-3}b^6}{9^{-1}a^{-5}b^{-2}}$

Perform the indicated operations and simplify.

127. $(6x + 2) + (5x - 7)$

128. $(-y^2 - 4) + (3y^2 - 6)$

129. $(8y^2 - 3y + 1) - (3y^2 + 2)$

130. $(5x^2 + 2x - 6) - (-x - 4)$

131. $4x(7x^2 + 3)$

132. $(2x + 5)(3x - 2)$

133. $(x - 3)(x^2 + 4x - 6)$

134. $(7x - 2)(4x - 9)$

Use special products to multiply.

135. $(5x + 4)^2$

136. $(6x + 3)(6x - 3)$

Divide.

137. $\dfrac{8a^4 - 2a^3 + 4a - 5}{2a^3}$

138. $\dfrac{x^2 + 2x + 10}{x + 5}$

139. $\dfrac{4x^3 + 8x^2 - 11x + 4}{2x - 3}$

Remember to use the Chapter Test Prep Video CD to see the fully worked-out solutions to any of the exercises you want to review.

Evaluate each expression.

1. 2^5 **2.** $(-3)^4$ **3.** -3^4 **4.** 4^{-3}

Simplify each exponential expression.

5. $(3x^2)(-5x^9)$ **6.** $\dfrac{y^7}{y^2}$ **7.** $\dfrac{r^{-8}}{r^{-3}}$

Simplify each expression. Write the result using only positive exponents.

8. $\left(\dfrac{x^2 y^3}{x^3 y^{-4}}\right)^2$ **9.** $\dfrac{6^2 x^{-4} y^{-1}}{6^3 x^{-3} y^7}$

Express each number in scientific notation.

10. 563,000   **11.** 0.0000863

Write each number in standard form.

12. 1.5×10^{-3} **13.** 6.23×10^4

14. Simplify. Write the answer in standard form.
$(1.2 \times 10^5)(3 \times 10^{-7})$

15. a. Complete the table for the polynomial $4xy^2 + 7xyz + x^3y - 2$.

Term	Numerical Coefficient	Degree of Term
$4xy^2$		
$7xyz$		
x^3y		
-2		

b. What is the degree of the polynomial?

16. Simplify by combining like terms.
$5x^2 + 4x - 7x^2 + 11 + 8x$

Perform each indicated operation.

17. $(8x^3 + 7x^2 + 4x - 7) + (8x^3 - 7x - 6)$

18.
$$\begin{array}{r} 5x^3 + x^2 + 5x - 2 \\ -(8x^3 - 4x^2 + x - 7) \end{array}$$

19. Subtract $(4x + 2)$ from the sum of $(8x^2 + 7x + 5)$ and $(x^3 - 8)$.

Answers

1. _____

2. _____

3. _____

4. _____

5. _____

6. _____

7. _____

8. _____

9. _____

10. _____

11. _____

12. _____

13. _____

14. _____

15. **a.** see table

b. _____

16. _____

17. _____

18. _____

19. _____

20. _____

21. _____

22. _____

23. _____

24. _____

25. _____

26. _____

27. see table _____

28. _____

29. _____

30. _____

31. _____

Multiply. See Exercises 20 through 26.

20. $(3x + 7)(x^2 + 5x + 2)$

21. $3x^2(2x^2 - 3x + 7)$

22. $(x + 7)(3x - 5)$

23. $\left(3x - \dfrac{1}{5}\right)\left(3x + \dfrac{1}{5}\right)$

24. $(4x - 2)^2$

25. $(8x + 3)^2$

26. $(x^2 - 9b)(x^2 + 9b)$

27. The height of the Bank of China in Hong Kong is 1001 feet. Neglecting air resistance, the height of an object dropped from this building at time t seconds is given by the polynomial $-16t^2 + 1001$. Find the height of the object at the given times below.

t	0 seconds	1 second	3 seconds	5 seconds
$-16t^2 + 1001$				

△ **28.** Find the area of the top of the table. Express the area as a product, then multiply and simplify.

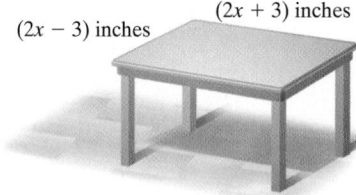

$(2x - 3)$ inches $\quad$ $(2x + 3)$ inches

Divide.

29. $\dfrac{4x^2 + 2xy - 7x}{8xy}$

30. $(x^2 + 7x + 10) \div (x + 5)$

31. $\dfrac{27x^3 - 8}{3x + 2}$

1. Multiply: 0.0531×16

2. Multiply: 0.0531×1000

3. Given the rectangle shown:

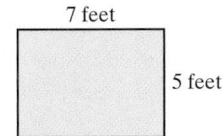

7 feet

5 feet

a. Find the ratio of its width to its length.
b. Find the ratio of its length to its perimeter.

4. Add: $\dfrac{5}{12} + \dfrac{2}{9}$

5. 12% of what number is 0.6?

6. Multiply: $\dfrac{7}{8} \cdot \dfrac{2}{3}$

7. What percent of 12 is 9?

8. Divide: $1\dfrac{4}{5} \div 2\dfrac{3}{10}$

9. Identify each figure as a line, a ray, a line segment, or an angle.

a.
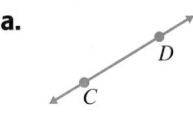
D
C

b.
E F

c.
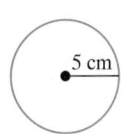
M
N
O

d.
P
T

10. Find the supplement of a 12° angle.

△ **11.** Find the diameter of the circle.

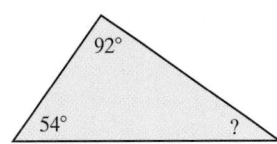
5 cm

12. Find the measure of the unknown angle.

92°
54°
?

△ **13.** Find the perimeter of the room shown below.

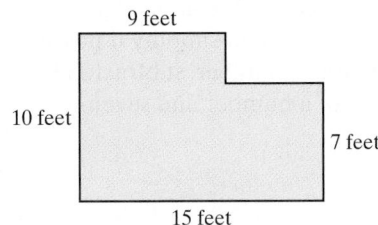
9 feet
10 feet
7 feet
15 feet

△ **14.** Find the area of the room in Exercise 13.

15. Given the set
$\left\{ -2, 0, \dfrac{1}{4}, 112, -3, 11, \sqrt{2} \right\}$, list the
numbers in this set that belong to the set of:

a. Natural numbers
b. Whole numbers
c. Integers
d. Rational numbers
e. Irrational numbers
f. Real numbers

16. Find the absolute value of each number.

a. $|-7.2|$
b. $|0|$
c. $\left| -\dfrac{1}{2} \right|$

1. _____

2. _____

3. a. _____

   b. _____

4. _____

5. _____

6. _____

7. _____

8. _____

9. a. _____

   b. _____

   c. _____

   d. _____

10. _____

11. _____

12. _____

13. _____

14. _____

15. a. _____

   b. _____

   c. _____

   d. _____

   e. _____

   f. _____

16. a. _____

   b. _____

   c. _____

17. _____

18. _____

19. a. _____

 b. _____

 c. _____

 d. _____

 e. _____

20. _____

21. _____

22. _____

23. _____

24. _____

25. _____

26. _____

27. _____

28. _____

29. _____

30. _____

31. _____

32. _____

33. _____

34. see graph

17. Simplify: $\dfrac{3}{2} \cdot \dfrac{1}{2} - \dfrac{1}{2}$

18. Evaluate $\dfrac{2x - 7y}{x^2}$ for $x = 5$ and $y = 1$.

19. Write an algebraic expression that represents each phrase. Let the variable x represent the unknown number.

 a. The sum of a number and 3
 b. The product of 3 and a number
 c. The quotient of 7.3 and a number
 d. 10 decreased by a number
 e. 5 times a number, increased by 7

20. Simplify: $8 + 3(2 \cdot 6 - 1)$

Find each product by using the distributive property to remove parentheses.

21. $-(9x + y - 2z + 6)$

22. $-(-4xy + 6y - 2)$

23. Solve: $6(2a - 1) - (11a + 6) = 7$

24. Solve: $2x + \dfrac{1}{8} = x - \dfrac{3}{8}$

25. Solve: $\dfrac{y}{7} = 20$

26. Solve: $10 = 5j - 2$

27. Solve: $0.25x + 0.10(x - 3) = 1.1$

28. Solve: $\dfrac{7x + 5}{3} = x + 3$

29. Twice the sum of a number and 4 is the same as four times the number decreased by 12. Find the number.

30. Write the phrase as an algebraic expression and simplify if possible. Double a number, subtracted from the sum of a number and seven.

△ **31.** Charles Pecot can afford enough fencing to enclose a rectangular garden with a perimeter of 140 feet. If the width of his garden is to be 30 feet, find the length.

32. Simplify: $\dfrac{4(-3) + (-8)}{5 + (-5)}$

33. The number 120 is 15% of what number?

34. Graph $x < 5$.

Simplify the following expressions. Write each result using positive exponents only.

35. $\left(\dfrac{3a^2}{b}\right)^{-3}$

36. $(5x^7)(-3x^9)$

37. $(5y^3)^{-2}$

38. $(-3)^{-2}$

Simplify each polynomial by combining any like terms.

39. $9x^3 + x^3$

40. $(5y^2 - 6) - (y^2 + 2)$

41. Multiply: $7x(x^2 + 2x + 5)$

42. Multiply $(10x^2 + 3)^2$.

35. _____

36. _____

37. _____

38. _____

39. _____

40. _____

41. _____

42. _____

13

Factoring Polynomials

In Chapter 12, we learned how to multiply polynomials. Now we will deal with an operation that is the reverse process of multiplying–factoring. Factoring is an important algebraic skill because it allows us to write a sum as a product. As we will see in Sections 13.6 and 13.7, factoring can be used to solve equations other than linear equations. In Chapter 14, we will also use factoring to simplify and perform arithmetic operations on rational expressions.

When recently completed, the Taipei 101 building in Taipei, Taiwan became the world's tallest building. At a height of 1671 feet, it is the world's first super tall building to be built in an active earthquake zone. In Exercise 107, Section 13.5, a polynomial expression for the height of an object dropped from Taipei 101 is factored. (*Source:* Council on Tall Buildings and Urban Habitats)

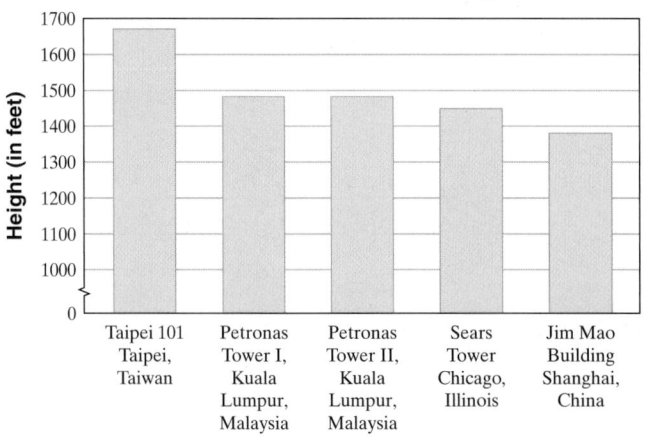

World's Tallest Buildings

13.1 THE GREATEST COMMON FACTOR

Objectives

A Find the Greatest Common Factor of a List of Numbers.

B Find the Greatest Common Factor of a List of Terms.

C Factor Out the Greatest Common Factor from the Terms of a Polynomial.

D Factor by Grouping.

In the product $2 \cdot 3 = 6$, the numbers 2 and 3 are called **factors** of 6 and $2 \cdot 3$ is a **factored form** of 6. This is true of polynomials also. Since $(x + 2)(x + 3) = x^2 + 5x + 6$, then $(x + 2)$ and $(x + 3)$ are factors of $x^2 + 5x + 6$, and $(x + 2)(x + 3)$ is a factored form of the polynomial.

The process of writing a polynomial as a product is called **factoring** the polynomial.

Study the examples below and look for a pattern.

Multiplying: $5(x^2 + 3) = 5x^2 + 15$ $2x(x - 7) = 2x^2 - 14x$

Factoring: $5x^2 + 15 = 5(x^2 + 3)$ $2x^2 - 14x = 2x(x - 7)$

Do you see that factoring is the reverse process of multiplying?

$$x^2 + 5x + 6 = (x + 2)(x + 3)$$

✔ **Concept Check** Multiply: $2(x - 4)$
What do you think the result of factoring $2x - 8$ would be? Why?

Objective **A** Finding the Greatest Common Factor of a List of Numbers

The first step in factoring a polynomial is to see whether the terms of the polynomial have a common factor. If there is one, we can write the polynomial as a product by **factoring out** the common factor. We will usually factor out the *greatest* common factor (GCF).

The GCF of a list of integers is the largest integer that is a factor of all the integers in the list. For example, the GCF of 12 and 20 is 4 because 4 is the largest integer that is a factor of both 12 and 20. With large integers, the GCF may not be easily found by inspection. When this happens, we will write each integer as a product of prime numbers. Recall that a prime number is a whole number other than 1, whose only factors are 1 and itself.

EXAMPLE 1 Find the GCF of each list of numbers.

a. 28 and 40   **b.** 55 and 21   **c.** 15, 18, and 66

Solution:

a. Write each number as a product of primes.

$28 = 2 \cdot 2 \cdot 7 = 2^2 \cdot 7$

$40 = 2 \cdot 2 \cdot 2 \cdot 5 = 2^3 \cdot 5$

There are two common factors, each of which is 2, so the GCF is

$GCF = 2 \cdot 2 = 4$

Continued on next page

PRACTICE PROBLEM 1

Find the GCF of each list of numbers.

a. 45 and 75   **b.** 32 and 33

c. 14, 24, and 60

Answers

1. a. 15,   **b.** 1,   **c.** 2

✔ **Concept Check Answer**

$2x - 8$; The result would be $2(x - 4)$ because factoring is the reverse process of multiplying.

b. $55 = 5 \cdot 11$

$21 = 3 \cdot 7$

There are no common prime factors; thus, the GCF is 1.

c. $15 = 3 \cdot 5$

$18 = 2 \cdot 3 \cdot 3 = 2 \cdot 3^2$

$66 = 2 \cdot 3 \cdot 11$

The only prime factor common to all three numbers is 3, so the GCF is

$\text{GCF} = 3$

■ **Work Practice Problem 1**

Objective **B** Finding the Greatest Common Factor of a List of Terms

The greatest common factor of a list of variables raised to powers is found in a similar way. For example, the GCF of x^2, x^3, and x^5 is x^2 because each term contains a factor of x^2 and no higher power of x is a factor of each term.

$x^2 = x \cdot x$

$x^3 = x \cdot x \cdot x$

$x^5 = x \cdot x \cdot x \cdot x \cdot x$

There are two common factors, each of which is x, so the GCF $= x \cdot x$ or x^2. From this example, we see that **the GCF of a list of common variables raised to powers is the variable raised to the smallest exponent in the list.**

PRACTICE PROBLEM 2

Find the GCF of each list of terms.

a. y^4, y^5, and y^8

b. x and x^{10}

EXAMPLE 2 Find the GCF of each list of terms.

a. x^3, x^7, and x^5

b. y, y^4, and y^7

Solution:

a. The GCF is x^3, since 3 is the smallest exponent to which x is raised.

b. The GCF is y^1 or y, since 1 is the smallest exponent on y.

■ **Work Practice Problem 2**

The **greatest common factor (GCF) of a list of terms** is the product of the GCF of the numerical coefficients and the GCF of the variable factors.

$20x^2y^2 = 2 \cdot 2 \cdot 5 \cdot x \cdot x \cdot y \cdot y$

$6xy^3 = 2 \cdot 3 \cdot x \cdot y \cdot y \cdot y$

$\text{GCF} = 2 \cdot x \cdot y \cdot y = 2xy^2$

Helpful Hint

Remember that the GCF of a list of terms contains the smallest exponent on each common variable.

The GCF of x^5y^6, x^2y^7 and x^3y^4 is x^2y^4. ⎯ Smallest exponent on x. ⎯ Smallest exponent on y.

Answers

2. a. y^4, **b.** x

EXAMPLE 3 Find the greatest common factor of each list of terms.

a. $6x^2$, $10x^3$, and $-8x$
b. $-18y^2$, $-63y^3$, and $27y^4$
c. a^3b^2, a^5b, and a^6b^2

Solution:

a. $6x^2 = 2 \cdot 3 \cdot x^2$
$10x^3 = 2 \cdot 5 \cdot x^3$ $\longrightarrow$ The GCF of x^2, x^3, and x^1 is x^1 or x.
$-8x = -1 \cdot 2 \cdot 2 \cdot 2 \cdot x^1$
GCF $= 2 \cdot x^1$ or $2x$

b. $-18y^2 = -1 \cdot 2 \cdot 3 \cdot 3 \cdot y^2$
$-63y^3 = -1 \cdot 3 \cdot 3 \cdot 7 \cdot y^3$ $\longrightarrow$ The GCF of y^2, y^3, and y^4 is y^2.
$27y^4 = 3 \cdot 3 \cdot 3 \cdot y^4$
GCF $= 3 \cdot 3 \cdot y^2$ or $9y^2$

c. The GCF of a^3, a^5, and a^6 is a^3.
The GCF of b^2, b, and b^2 is b. Thus,
the GCF of a^3b^2, a^5b, and a^6b^2 is a^3b.

 **Work Practice Problem 3**

Objective C Factoring Out the Greatest Common Factor

To factor a polynomial such as $8x + 14$, we first see whether the terms have a greatest common factor other than 1. In this case, they do: The GCF of $8x$ and 14 is 2.

We factor out 2 from each term by writing each term as the product of 2 and the term's remaining factors.

$$8x + 14 = 2 \cdot 4x + 2 \cdot 7$$

Using the distributive property, we can write

$$8x + 14 = 2 \cdot 4x + 2 \cdot 7$$
$$= 2(4x + 7)$$

Thus, a factored form of $8x + 14$ is $2(4x + 7)$. We can check by multiplying:

$$2(4x + 7) = 2 \cdot 4x + 2 \cdot 7 = 8x + 14.$$

> **Helpful Hint**
>
> A factored form of $8x + 14$ is *not*
>
> $$2 \cdot 4x + 2 \cdot 7$$
>
> Although the *terms* have been factored (written as products), the *polynomial* $8x + 14$ has not been factored. A factored form of $8x + 14$ is the *product* $2(4x + 7)$.

✔ **Concept Check** Which of the following is/are factored form(s) of $6t + 18$?

a. 6
b. $6 \cdot t + 6 \cdot 3$
c. $6(t + 3)$
d. $3(t + 6)$

PRACTICE PROBLEM 3

Find the greatest common factor of each list of terms.
a. $6x^2$, $9x^4$, and $-12x^5$
b. $-16y$, $-20y^6$, and $40y^4$
c. a^5b^4, ab^3, and a^3b^2

Answers
3. a. $3x^2$, **b.** $4y$, **c.** ab^2

✔ **Concept Check Answer**
c

PRACTICE PROBLEM 4

Factor each polynomial by factoring out the greatest common factor (GCF).

a. $10y + 25$

b. $x^4 - x^9$

EXAMPLE 4 Factor each polynomial by factoring out the greatest common factor (GCF).

a. $5ab + 10a$ **b.** $y^5 - y^{12}$

Solution:

a. The GCF of terms $5ab$ and $10a$ is $5a$. Thus,

$$5ab + 10a = 5a \cdot b + 5a \cdot 2$$
$$= 5a(b + 2) \qquad \text{Apply the distributive property.}$$

We can check our work by multiplying $5a$ and $(b + 2)$.
$5a(b + 2) = 5a \cdot b + 5a \cdot 2 = 5ab + 10a$, the original polynomial.

b. The GCF of y^5 and y^{12} is y^5. Thus,

$$y^5 - y^{12} = y^5(1) - y^5(y^7)$$
$$= y^5(1 - y^7)$$

Helpful Hint
Don't forget the 1.

▪ **Work Practice Problem 4**

PRACTICE PROBLEM 5

Factor: $-10x^3 + 8x^2 - 2x$

EXAMPLE 5 Factor: $-9a^5 + 18a^2 - 3a$

Solution:

$$-9a^5 + 18a^2 - 3a = 3a(-3a^4) + 3a(6a) + 3a(-1)$$
$$= 3a(-3a^4 + 6a - 1)$$

Helpful Hint
Don't forget the -1.

▪ **Work Practice Problem 5**

In Example 5, we could have chosen to factor out $-3a$ instead of $3a$. If we factor out $-3a$, we have

$$-9a^5 + 18a^2 - 3a = (-3a)(3a^4) + (-3a)(-6a) + (-3a)(1)$$
$$= -3a(3a^4 - 6a + 1)$$

Helpful Hint
Notice the changes in signs when factoring out $-3a$.

PRACTICE PROBLEMS 6-8

Factor.

6. $4x^3 + 12x$

7. $\frac{2}{5}a^5 - \frac{4}{5}a^3 + \frac{1}{5}a^2$

8. $6a^3b + 3a^3b^2 + 9a^2b^4$

EXAMPLES Factor.

6. $6a^4 - 12a = 6a(a^3 - 2)$

7. $\frac{3}{7}x^4 + \frac{1}{7}x^3 - \frac{5}{7}x^2 = \frac{1}{7}x^2(3x^2 + x - 5)$

8. $15p^2q^4 + 20p^3q^5 + 5p^3q^3 = 5p^2q^3(3q + 4pq^2 + p)$

▪ **Work Practice Problems 6-8**

PRACTICE PROBLEM 9

Factor: $7(p + 2) + q(p + 2)$

EXAMPLE 9 Factor: $5(x + 3) + y(x + 3)$

Solution: The binomial $(x + 3)$ is present in both terms and is the greatest common factor. We use the distributive property to factor out $(x + 3)$.

$$5(x + 3) + y(x + 3) = (x + 3)(5 + y)$$

▪ **Work Practice Problem 9**

Answers

4. a. $5(2y + 5)$,   **b.** $x^4(1 - x^5)$,

5. $2x(-5x^2 + 4x - 1)$,

6. $4x(x^2 + 3)$,

7. $\frac{1}{5}a^2(2a^3 - 4a + 1)$,

8. $3a^2b(2a + ab + 3b^3)$,

9. $(p + 2)(7 + q)$

Objective D Factoring by Grouping

Once the GCF is factored out, we can often continue to factor the polynomial, using a variety of techniques. We discuss here a technique called **factoring by grouping.** This technique can be used to factor some polynomials with four terms.

EXAMPLE 10 Factor $xy + 2x + 3y + 6$ by grouping.

Solution: Notice that the first two terms of this polynomial have a common factor of x and the second two terms have a common factor of 3. Because of this, group the first two terms, then the last two terms, and then factor out these common factors.

$$xy + 2x + 3y + 6 = (xy + 2x) + (3y + 6) \quad \text{Group terms.}$$
$$= \underbrace{x(y + 2) + 3(y + 2)}_{} \quad \text{Factor out GCF from each grouping.}$$

Next we factor out the common binomial factor, $(y + 2)$.

$$x(y + 2) + 3(y + 2) = (y + 2)(x + 3)$$

Now the result is a factored form because it is a product. We were able to write the polynomial as a product because of the common binomial factor, $(y + 2)$, that appeared. If this does not happen, try rearranging the terms of the original polynomial.

Check: Multiply $(y + 2)$ by $(x + 3)$.

$$(y + 2)(x + 3) = xy + 2x + 3y + 6,$$

the original polynomial.
Thus, the factored form of $xy + 2x + 3y + 6$ is the product $(y + 2)(x + 3)$.

▢ **Work Practice Problem 10**

You may want to try these steps when factoring by grouping.

To Factor by Grouping

Step 1: Group the terms in two groups so that each group has a common factor.

Step 2: Factor out the GCF from each group.

Step 3: If there is a common binomial factor, factor it out.

Step 4: If not, rearrange the terms and try these steps again.

EXAMPLES Factor by grouping.

11. $15x^3 - 10x^2 + 6x - 4$
$$= (15x^3 - 10x^2) + (6x - 4) \quad \text{Group the terms.}$$
$$= 5x^2(3x - 2) + 2(3x - 2) \quad \text{Factor each group.}$$
$$= (3x - 2)(5x^2 + 2) \quad \text{Factor out the common factor, } (3x - 2).$$

12. $3x^2 + 4xy - 3x - 4y$
$$= (3x^2 + 4xy) + (-3x - 4y)$$
$$= x(3x + 4y) - 1(3x + 4y) \quad \text{Factor each group. A } -1 \text{ is factored from the second pair of terms so that there is a common factor, } (3x + 4y).$$
$$= (3x + 4y)(x - 1) \quad \text{Factor out the common factor, } (3x + 4y).$$

Continued on next page

PRACTICE PROBLEM 10

Factor $ab + 7a + 2b + 14$ by grouping.

Helpful Hint

Notice that this form, $x(y + 2) + 3(y + 2)$, is *not* a factored form of the original polynomial. It is a sum, not a product.

PRACTICE PROBLEMS 11–13

Factor by grouping.
11. $28x^3 - 7x^2 + 12x - 3$
12. $2xy + 5y^2 - 4x - 10y$
13. $3x^2 + 4xy + 3x + 4y$

Answers
10. $(b + 7)(a + 2)$,
11. $(4x - 1)(7x^2 + 3)$,
12. $(2x + 5y)(y - 2)$,
13. $(3x + 4y)(x + 1)$

Notice the factor of 1 is written when $(2a + 5b)$ is factored out.

13. $2a^2 + 5ab + 2a + 5b$

$\quad = (2a^2 + 5ab) + (2a + 5b)$ Factor each group. An understood 1 is written before

$\quad = a(2a + 5b) + 1(2a + 5b)$ $(2a + 5b)$ to help remember that $(2a + 5b)$ is $1(2a + 5b)$.

$\quad = (2a + 5b)(a + 1)$ Factor out the common factor, $(2a + 5b)$.

◼ **Work Practice Problems 11–13**

PRACTICE PROBLEMS 14–16

Factor by grouping.

14. $4x^3 + x - 20x^2 - 5$

15. $3xy - 4 + x - 12y$

16. $2x - 2 + x^3 - 3x^2$

EXAMPLES Factor by grouping.

14. $3x^3 - 2x - 9x^2 + 6$

$\quad = x(3x^2 - 2) - 3(3x^2 - 2)$ Factor each group. A -3 is factored from the second

$\quad = (3x^2 - 2)(x - 3)$ pair of terms so that there is a common factor, $(3x^2 - 2)$. Factor out the common factor, $(3x^2 - 2)$.

15. $3xy + 2 - 3x - 2y$

Notice that the first two terms have no common factor other than 1. However, if we rearrange these terms, a grouping emerges that does lead to a common factor.

$3xy + 2 - 3x - 2y$

$\quad = (3xy - 3x) + (-2y + 2)$

$\quad = 3x(y - 1) - 2(y - 1)$ Factor -2 from the second group.

$\quad = (y - 1)(3x - 2)$ Factor out the common factor, $(y - 1)$.

16. $5x - 10 + x^3 - x^2 = 5(x - 2) + x^2(x - 1)$

There is no common binomial factor that can now be factored out. No matter how we rearrange the terms, no grouping will lead to a common factor. Thus, this polynomial is not factorable by grouping.

◼ **Work Practice Problems 14–16**

Throughout this chapter, we will be factoring polynomials. Even when the instructions do not so state, it is always a good idea to check your answers by multiplying.

Answers

14. $(4x^2 + 1)(x - 5)$,

15. $(3y + 1)(x - 4)$,

16. cannot be factored by grouping

Mental Math

Find the GCF of each pair of integers.

1. 2, 16   **2.** 3, 18   **3.** 6, 7   **4.** 9, 11   **5.** 14, 35   **6.** 33, 55

13.1 EXERCISE SET

FOR EXTRA HELP

Student Solutions Manual   PH Math/Tutor Center   CD/Video for Review   MathXL®   MyMathLab

Objectives **A** **B** **Mixed Practice** *Find the GCF for each list. See Examples 1 through 3.*

1. 32, 36

2. 36, 90

3. 18, 42, 84

4. 30, 75, 135

5. 24, 14, 21

6. 15, 25, 27

7. y^2, y^4, y^7

8. x^3, x^2, x^5

9. z^7, z^9, z^{11}

10. y^8, y^{10}, y^{12}

11. $x^{10}y^2, xy^2, x^3y^3$

12. p^7q, p^8q^2, p^9q^3

13. $14x, 21$

14. $20y, 15$

 **15.** $12y^4, 20y^3$

16. $32x^5, 18x^2$

17. $-10x^2, 15x^3$

18. $-21x^3, 14x$

19. $12x^3, -6x^4, 3x^5$

20. $15y^2, 5y^7, -20y^3$

21. $-18x^2y, 9x^3y^3, 36x^3y$

22. $7x^3y^3, -21x^2y^2, 14xy^4$

23. $20a^6b^2c^8, 50a^7b$

24. $40x^7y^2z, 64x^9y$

Objective **C** *Factor out the GCF from each polynomial. See Examples 4 through 9.*

25. $3a + 6$

26. $18a + 12$

 **27.** $30x - 15$

28. $42x - 7$

29. $x^3 + 5x^2$

30. $y^5 + 6y^4$

31. $6y^4 + 2y^3$

32. $5x^2 + 10x^6$

 **33.** $32xy - 18x^2$

34. $10xy - 15x^2$

35. $4x - 8y + 4$

36. $7x + 21y - 7$

37. $6x^3 - 9x^2 + 12x$

38. $12x^3 + 16x^2 - 8x$

39. $a^7b^6 - a^3b^2 + a^2b^5 - a^2b^2$

40. $x^9y^6 + x^3y^5 - x^4y^3 + x^3y^3$

41. $5x^3y - 15x^2y + 10xy$

42. $14x^3y + 7x^2y - 7xy$

43. $8x^5 + 16x^4 - 20x^3 + 12$

44. $9y^6 - 27y^4 + 18y^2 + 6$

45. $\dfrac{1}{3}x^4 + \dfrac{2}{3}x^3 - \dfrac{4}{3}x^5 + \dfrac{1}{3}x$

46. $\dfrac{2}{5}y^7 - \dfrac{4}{5}y^5 + \dfrac{3}{5}y^2 - \dfrac{2}{5}y$

47. $y(x^2 + 2) + 3(x^2 + 2)$ **48.** $x(y^2 + 1) - 3(y^2 + 1)$ **49.** $z(y + 4) + 3(y + 4)$

50. $8(x + 2) - y(x + 2)$ **51.** $r(z^2 - 6) + (z^2 - 6)$ **52.** $q(b^3 - 5) + (b^3 - 5)$

Factor a −1 from each polynomial. See Example 5.

53. $-x - 7$ **54.** $-y - 3$ **55.** $-2 + z$

56. $-5 + y$ **57.** $3a - b + 2$ **58.** $2y - z - 11$

Objective D *Factor each four-term polynomial by grouping. See Examples 10 through 16.*

59. $x^3 + 2x^2 + 5x + 10$ **60.** $x^3 + 4x^2 + 3x + 12$ **61.** $5x + 15 + xy + 3y$ **62.** $xy + y + 2x + 2$

63. $6x^3 - 4x^2 + 15x - 10$ **64.** $16x^3 - 28x^2 + 12x - 21$ **65.** $5m^3 + 6mn + 5m^2 + 6n$

66. $8w^2 + 7wv + 8w + 7v$ **67.** $2y - 8 + xy - 4x$ **68.** $6x - 42 + xy - 7y$

69. $2x^3 + x^2 + 8x + 4$ **70.** $2x^3 - x^2 - 10x + 5$ **71.** $4x^2 - 8xy - 3x + 6y$

72. $5xy - 15x - 6y + 18$ **73.** $5q^2 - 4pq - 5q + 4p$ **74.** $6m^2 - 5mn - 6m + 5n$

Factor out the GCF from each polynomial. Then factor by grouping.

75. $12x^2y - 42x^2 - 4y + 14$ **76.** $90 + 15y^2 - 18x - 3xy^2$

Review

Multiply. See Section 12.5.

77. $(x + 2)(x + 5)$ **78.** $(y + 3)(y + 6)$ **79.** $(b + 1)(b - 4)$ **80.** $(x - 5)(x + 10)$

Fill in the chart by finding two numbers that have the given product and sum. The first column is filled in for you.

		81.	**82.**	**83.**	**84.**	**85.**	**86.**	**87.**	**88.**
Two Numbers	4, 7								
Their Product	28	12	20	8	16	−10	−9	−24	−36
Their Sum	11	8	9	−9	−10	3	0	−5	−5

Concept Extensions

See the Concept Checks in this section.

89. Which of the following is/are factored form(s) of $8a - 24$?

    a. $8 \cdot a - 24$ **b.** $8(a - 3)$ **c.** $4(2a - 12)$ **d.** $8 \cdot a - 2 \cdot 12$

Which of the following expressions are factored?

90. $(a + 6)(a + 2)$

91. $(x + 5)(x + y)$

92. $5(2y + z) - b(2y + z)$

93. $3x(a + 2b) + 2(a + 2b)$

94. The polynomial $-24x^2 + 336x - 132$ represents the average number of visitors (in thousands) per day to National Park Service areas, where x represents the month of the year. (*Source:* Based on data from National Park Service)

  a. Find the average daily number of visitors to National Park Service areas during the month of August. To do so, let $x = 8$ and evaluate $-24x^2 + 336x - 132$.

  b. Find the average daily number of visitors in May.

  c. Factor the polynomial $-24x^2 + 336x - 132$.

95. The average total daily supply of motor gasoline (in thousands of barrels per day) in the United States for the period 2000–2003 can be approximated by the polynomial $-13x^2 + 221x + 8476$, where x is the number of years after 2000. (*Source:* Based on data from Energy Information Administration)

  a. Find the average daily total supply of motor gasoline in 2001. To do so, let $x = 1$ and evaluate $-13x^2 + 221x + 8476$.

  b. Find the average daily total supply of motor gasoline in 2003.

  c. Factor the polynomial $-13x^2 + 221x + 8476$.

Write an expression for the area of each shaded region. Then write the expression as a factored polynomial.

△ **96.**

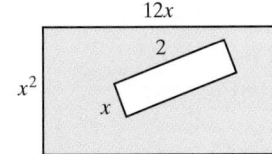

△ **97.**

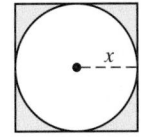

Write an expression for the length of each rectangle. (Hint: Factor the area binomial and recall that Area = width · length.)

△ **98.**

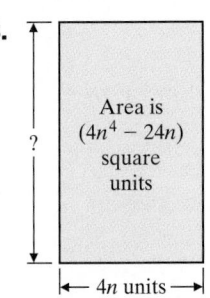

△ **99.**

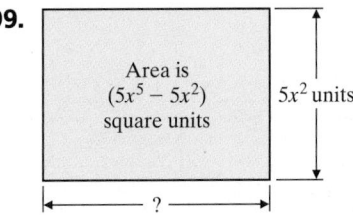

100. Construct a binomial whose greatest common factor is $5a^3$. (*Hint:* Multiply $5a^3$ by a binomial whose terms contain no common factor other than 1. $5a^3(\square + \square)$.)

101. Construct a trinomial whose greatest common factor is $2x^2$. See the hint for Exercise 100.

 102. Explain how you can tell whether a polynomial is written in factored form.

103. Construct a four-term polynomial that can be factored by grouping.

STUDY SKILLS BUILDER

Are You Getting All the Mathematics Help That You Need?

Remember that, in addition to your instructor, there are many places to get help with your mathematics course. For example.

- This text has an accompanying video lesson for every section and worked out solutions to every Chapter Test exercise on video.

- The back of the book contains answers to odd-numbered exercises and selected solutions.

- A student *Solutions Manual* is available that contains worked-out solutions to odd-numbered exercises as well as solutions to every exercise in the Integrated Reviews, Chapter Reviews, Chapter Tests, and Cumulative Reviews.

- Don't forget to check with your instructor for other local resources available to you, such as a tutor center.

Exercises

1. List items you find helpful in the text and all student supplements to this text.

2. List all the campus help that is available to you for this course.

3. List any help (besides the textbook) from Exercises 1 and 2 above that you are using.

4. List any help (besides the textbook) that you feel you should try.

5. Write a goal for yourself that includes trying anything you listed in Exercise 4 during the next week.

13.2

FACTORING TRINOMIALS OF THE FORM $x^2 + bx + c$

Objectives

Objective A Factoring Trinomials of the Form $x^2 + bx + c$

A Factor Trinomials of the Form $x^2 + bx + c$.

B Factor Out the Greatest Common Factor and Then Factor a Trinomial of the Form $x^2 + bx + c$.

In this section, we factor trinomials of the form $x^2 + bx + c$, such as

$$x^2 + 7x + 12, \quad x^2 - 12x + 35, \quad x^2 + 4x - 12, \quad \text{and} \quad r^2 - r - 42$$

Notice that for these trinomials, the coefficient of the squared variable is 1.

Recall that factoring means to write as a product and that factoring and multiplying are reverse processes. Using the FOIL method of multiplying binomials, we have the following.

$$\begin{array}{cccc} \text{F} & \text{O} & \text{I} & \text{L} \end{array}$$
$$(x + 3)(x + 1) = x^2 + 1x + 3x + 3$$
$$= x^2 + 4x + 3$$

Thus, a factored form of $x^2 + 4x + 3$ is $(x + 3)(x + 1)$.

Notice that the product of the first terms of the binomials is $x \cdot x = x^2$, the first term of the trinomial. Also, the product of the last two terms of the binomials is $3 \cdot 1 = 3$, the third term of the trinomial. The sum of these same terms is $3 + 1 = 4$, the coefficient of the middle, x, term of the trinomial.

The product of these numbers is 3.

$$x^2 + 4x + 3 = (x + 3)(x + 1)$$

The sum of these numbers is 4.

Many trinomials, such as the one above, factor into two binomials. To factor $x^2 + 7x + 10$, let's assume that it factors into two binomials and begin by writing two pairs of parentheses. The first term of the trinomial is x^2, so we use x and x as the first terms of the binomial factors.

$$x^2 + 7x + 10 = (x + \square)(x + \square)$$

To determine the last term of each binomial factor, we look for two integers whose product is 10 and whose sum is 7. The integers are 2 and 5. Thus,

$$x^2 + 7x + 10 = (x + 2)(x + 5)$$

Check: To see if we have factored correctly, we multiply.

$$(x + 2)(x + 5) = x^2 + 5x + 2x + 10$$
$$= x^2 + 7x + 10 \qquad \text{Combine like terms.}$$

Helpful Hint

Since multiplication is commutative, the factored form of $x^2 + 7x + 10$ can be written as either $(x + 2)(x + 5)$ or $(x + 5)(x + 2)$.

To Factor a Trinomial of the Form $x^2 + bx + c$

The product of these numbers is c.

$$x^2 + bx + c = (x + \square)(x + \square)$$

The sum of these numbers is b.

PRACTICE PROBLEM 1

Factor: $x^2 + 12x + 20$

EXAMPLE 1 Factor: $x^2 + 7x + 12$

Solution: We begin by writing the first terms of the binomial factors.

$(x + \Box)(x + \Box)$

Next we look for two numbers whose product is 12 and whose sum is 7. Since our numbers must have a positive product and a positive sum, we look at pairs of positive factors of 12 only.

Factors of 12	Sum of Factors
1, 12	13
2, 6	8
3, 4	7

Correct sum, so the numbers are 3 and 4.

Thus, $x^2 + 7x + 12 = (x + 3)(x + 4)$

Check: $(x + 3)(x + 4) = x^2 + 4x + 3x + 12 = x^2 + 7x + 12$.

■ **Work Practice Problem 1**

PRACTICE PROBLEM 2

Factor each trinomial.
a. $x^2 - 23x + 22$
b. $x^2 - 27x + 50$

EXAMPLE 2 Factor: $x^2 - 12x + 35$

Solution: Again, we begin by writing the first terms of the binomials.

$(x + \Box)(x + \Box)$

Now we look for two numbers whose product is 35 and whose sum is -12. Since our numbers must have a positive product and a negative sum, we look at pairs of negative factors of 35 only.

Factors of 35	Sum of Factors
$-1, -35$	-36
$-5, -7$	-12

Correct sum, so the numbers are -5 and -7.

$x^2 - 12x + 35 = (x - 5)(x - 7)$

Check: To check, multiply $(x - 5)(x - 7)$.

■ **Work Practice Problem 2**

PRACTICE PROBLEM 3

Factor: $x^2 + 5x - 36$

EXAMPLE 3 Factor: $x^2 + 4x - 12$

Solution: $x^2 + 4x - 12 = (x + \Box)(x + \Box)$

We look for two numbers whose product is -12 and whose sum is 4. Since our numbers must have a negative product, we look at pairs of factors with opposite signs.

Factors of -12	Sum of Factors
$-1, 12$	11
$1, -12$	-11
$-2, 6$	4
$2, -6$	-4
$-3, 4$	1
$3, -4$	-1

Correct sum, so the numbers are -2 and 6.

$x^2 + 4x - 12 = (x - 2)(x + 6)$

■ **Work Practice Problem 3**

Answers
1. $(x + 10)(x + 2)$,
2. a. $(x - 1)(x - 22)$,
b. $(x - 2)(x - 25)$,
3. $(x + 9)(x - 4)$

EXAMPLE 4 Factor: $r^2 - r - 42$

Solution: Because the variable in this trinomial is r, the first term of each binomial factor is r.

$$r^2 - r - 42 = (r + \square)(r + \square)$$

Now we look for two numbers whose product is -42 and whose sum is -1, the numerical coefficient of r. The numbers are 6 and -7. Therefore,

$$r^2 - r - 42 = (r + 6)(r - 7)$$

■ **Work Practice Problem 4**

PRACTICE PROBLEM 4

Factor each trinomial.
a. $q^2 - 3q - 40$
b. $y^2 + 2y - 48$

EXAMPLE 5 Factor: $a^2 + 2a + 10$

Solution: Look for two numbers whose product is 10 and whose sum is 2. Neither 1 and 10 nor 2 and 5 give the required sum, 2. We conclude that $a^2 + 2a + 10$ is not factorable with integers. A polynomial such as $a^2 + 2a + 10$ is called a **prime polynomial.**

■ **Work Practice Problem 5**

PRACTICE PROBLEM 5

Factor: $x^2 + 6x + 15$

EXAMPLE 6 Factor: $x^2 + 5xy + 6y^2$

Solution: $x^2 + 5xy + 6y^2 = (x + \square)(x + \square)$

Recall that the middle term $5xy$ is the same as $5yx$. Thus, we can see that $5y$ is the "coefficient" of x. We then look for two terms whose product is $6y^2$ and whose sum is $5y$. The terms are $2y$ and $3y$ because $2y \cdot 3y = 6y^2$ and $2y + 3y = 5y$. Therefore,

$$x^2 + 5xy + 6y^2 = (x + 2y)(x + 3y)$$

■ **Work Practice Problem 6**

PRACTICE PROBLEM 6

Factor each trinomial.
a. $x^2 + 9xy + 14y^2$
b. $a^2 - 13ab + 30b^2$

EXAMPLE 7 Factor: $x^4 + 5x^2 + 6$

Solution: As usual, we begin by writing the first terms of the binomials. Since the greatest power of x in this polynomial is x^4, we write

$$(x^2 + \square)(x^2 + \square) \quad \text{since } x^2 \cdot x^2 = x^4$$

Now we look for two factors of 6 whose sum is 5. The numbers are 2 and 3. Thus,

$$x^4 + 5x^2 + 6 = (x^2 + 2)(x^2 + 3)$$

■ **Work Practice Problem 7**

PRACTICE PROBLEM 7

Factor: $x^4 + 8x^2 + 12$

If the terms of a polynomial are not written in descending powers of the variable, you may want to do so before factoring.

EXAMPLE 8 Factor: $40 - 13t + t^2$

Solution: First, we rearrange terms so that the trinomial is written in descending powers of t.

$$40 - 13t + t^2 = t^2 - 13t + 40$$

Next, try to factor.

$$t^2 - 13t + 40 = (t + \square)(t + \square)$$

Now we look for two factors of 40 whose sum is -13. The numbers are -8 and -5. Thus,

$$t^2 - 13t + 40 = (t - 8)(t - 5)$$

■ **Work Practice Problem 8**

PRACTICE PROBLEM 8

Factor: $48 - 14x + x^2$

Answers
4. a. $(q - 8)(q + 5)$,
b. $(y + 8)(y - 6)$,
5. prime polynomial,
6. a. $(x + 2y)(x + 7y)$,
b. $(a - 3b)(a - 10b)$,
7. $(x^2 + 6)(x^2 + 2)$,
8. $(x - 6)(x - 8)$

The following sign patterns may be useful when factoring trinomials.

Helpful Hint

A positive constant in a trinomial tells us to look for two numbers with the same sign. The sign of the coefficient of the middle term tells us whether the signs are both positive or both negative.

both positive | same sign   both negative | same sign

$$x^2 + 10x + 16 = (x + 2)(x + 8) \qquad x^2 - 10x + 16 = (x - 2)(x - 8)$$

A negative constant in a trinomial tells us to look for two numbers with opposite signs.

opposite signs   opposite signs

$$x^2 + 6x - 16 = (x + 8)(x - 2) \qquad x^2 - 6x - 16 = (x - 8)(x + 2)$$

Objective B Factoring Out the Greatest Common Factor

Remember that the first step in factoring any polynomial is to factor out the greatest common factor (if there is one other than 1 or −1).

PRACTICE PROBLEM 9

Factor each trinomial.
a. $4x^2 - 24x + 36$
b. $x^3 + 3x^2 - 4x$

EXAMPLE 9 Factor: $3m^2 - 24m - 60$

Solution: First we factor out the greatest common factor, 3, from each term.

$$3m^2 - 24m - 60 = 3(m^2 - 8m - 20)$$

Now we factor $m^2 - 8m - 20$ by looking for two factors of −20 whose sum is −8. The factors are −10 and 2. Therefore, the complete factored form is

$$3m^2 - 24m - 60 = 3(m + 2)(m - 10)$$

◾ **Work Practice Problem 9**

Helpful Hint

Remember to write the common factor 3 as part of the factored form.

PRACTICE PROBLEM 10

Factor: $5x^5 - 25x^4 - 30x^3$

EXAMPLE 10 Factor: $2x^4 - 26x^3 + 84x^2$

Solution:

$$2x^4 - 26x^3 + 84x^2 = 2x^2(x^2 - 13x + 42) \qquad \text{Factor out common factor, } 2x^2.$$
$$= 2x^2(x - 6)(x - 7) \qquad \text{Factor } x^2 - 13x + 42.$$

◾ **Work Practice Problem 10**

Answers
9. a. $4(x - 3)(x - 3)$,
b. $x(x + 4)(x - 1)$,
10. $5x^3(x + 1)(x - 6)$

Mental Math

Complete each factored form.

1. $x^2 + 9x + 20 = (x + 4)(x \quad)$ **2.** $x^2 + 12x + 35 = (x + 5)(x \quad)$ **3.** $x^2 - 7x + 12 = (x - 4)(x \quad)$

4. $x^2 - 13x + 22 = (x - 2)(x \quad)$ **5.** $x^2 + 4x + 4 = (x + 2)(x \quad)$ **6.** $x^2 + 10x + 24 = (x + 6)(x \quad)$

13.2 EXERCISE SET

FOR EXTRA HELP

Student Solutions Manual   PH Math/Tutor Center   CD/Video for Review   MathXL®   MyMathLab

Objective A *Factor each trinomial completely. If a polynomial can't be factored, write "prime." See Examples 1 through 8.*

1. $x^2 + 7x + 6$ **2.** $x^2 + 6x + 8$ **3.** $y^2 - 10y + 9$ **4.** $y^2 - 12y + 11$

5. $x^2 - 6x + 9$ **6.** $x^2 - 10x + 25$ **7.** $x^2 - 3x - 18$ **8.** $x^2 - x - 30$

9. $x^2 + 3x - 70$ **10.** $x^2 + 4x - 32$ **11.** $x^2 + 5x + 2$ **12.** $x^2 - 7x + 5$

13. $x^2 + 8xy + 15y^2$ **14.** $x^2 + 6xy + 8y^2$ **15.** $a^4 - 2a^2 - 15$ **16.** $y^4 - 3y^2 - 70$

17. $13 + 14m + m^2$ **18.** $17 + 18n + n^2$ **19.** $10t - 24 + t^2$ **20.** $6q - 27 + q^2$

21. $a^2 - 10ab + 16b^2$ **22.** $a^2 - 9ab + 18b^2$

Objectives A B Mixed Practice *Factor each trinomial completely. Some of these trinomials contain a greatest common factor (other than 1). Don't forget to factor out the GCF first. See Examples 1 through 10.*

23. $2z^2 + 20z + 32$ **24.** $3x^2 + 30x + 63$ **25.** $2x^3 - 18x^2 + 40x$ **26.** $3x^3 - 12x^2 - 36x$

27. $x^2 - 3xy - 4y^2$ **28.** $x^2 - 4xy - 77y^2$ **29.** $x^2 + 15x + 36$ **30.** $x^2 + 19x + 60$

31. $x^2 - x - 2$ **32.** $x^2 - 5x - 14$ **33.** $r^2 - 16r + 48$ **34.** $r^2 - 10r + 21$

35. $x^2 + xy - 2y^2$ **36.** $x^2 - xy - 6y^2$ **37.** $3x^2 + 9x - 30$ **38.** $4x^2 - 4x - 48$

39. $3x^2 - 60x + 108$ **40.** $2x^2 - 24x + 70$ **41.** $x^2 - 18x - 144$ **42.** $x^2 + x - 42$

43. $r^2 - 3r + 6$ **44.** $x^2 + 4x - 10$ **45.** $x^2 - 8x + 15$ **46.** $x^2 - 9x + 14$

47. $6x^3 + 54x^2 + 120x$ **48.** $3x^3 + 3x^2 - 126x$ **49.** $4x^2y + 4xy - 12y$ **50.** $3x^2y - 9xy + 45y$

51. $x^2 - 4x - 21$ **52.** $x^2 - 4x - 32$ **53.** $x^2 + 7xy + 10y^2$ **54.** $x^2 - 3xy - 4y^2$

55. $64 + 24t + 2t^2$ **56.** $50 + 20t + 2t^2$ **57.** $x^3 - 2x^2 - 24x$ **58.** $x^3 - 3x^2 - 28x$

59. $2t^5 - 14t^4 + 24t^3$ **60.** $3x^6 + 30x^5 + 72x^4$ **61.** $5x^3y - 25x^2y^2 - 120xy^3$ **62.** $7a^3b - 35a^2b^2 + 42ab^3$

63. $162 - 45m + 3m^2$ **64.** $48 - 20n + 2n^2$ **65.** $-x^2 + 12x - 11$ (Factor out -1 first.)   **66.** $-x^2 + 8x - 7$ (Factor out -1 first.)

67. $\dfrac{1}{2}y^2 - \dfrac{9}{2}y - 11$ (Factor out $\dfrac{1}{2}$ first.)   **68.** $\dfrac{1}{3}y^2 - \dfrac{5}{3}y - 8$ (Factor out $\dfrac{1}{3}$ first.)   **69.** $x^3y^2 + x^2y - 20x$ **70.** $a^2b^3 + ab^2 - 30b$

Review

Multiply. See Section 12.5.

71. $(2x + 1)(x + 5)$ **72.** $(3x + 2)(x + 4)$ **73.** $(5y - 4)(3y - 1)$

74. $(4z - 7)(7z - 1)$ **75.** $(a + 3b)(9a - 4b)$ **76.** $(y - 5x)(6y + 5x)$

Concept Extensions

77. Write a polynomial that factors as $(x - 3)(x + 8)$.

78. To factor $x^2 + 13x + 42$, think of two numbers whose _____ is 42 and whose _____ is 13.

Complete each sentence in your own words.

79. If $x^2 + bx + c$ is factorable and c is negative, then the signs of the last-term factors of the binomials are opposite because . . . .

80. If $x^2 + bx + c$ is factorable and c is positive, then the signs of the last-term factors of the binomials are the same because . . . .

Remember that perimeter means distance around. Write the perimeter of each rectangle as a simplified polynomial. Then factor the polynomial.

△ **81.**

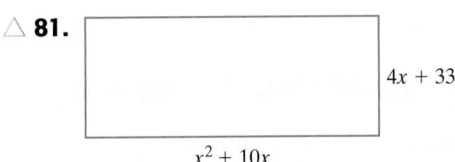

$4x + 33$

$x^2 + 10x$

△ **82.**

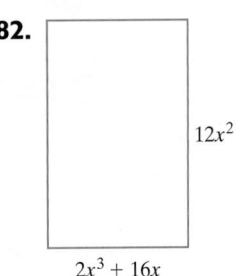

$12x^2$

$2x^3 + 16x$

83. An object is thrown upward from the top of an 80-foot building with an initial velocity of 64 feet per second. The height of the object after t seconds is given by $-16t^2 + 64t + 80$. Factor this polynomial.

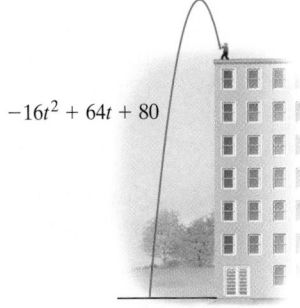

$-16t^2 + 64t + 80$

Factor each trinomial completely.

84. $x^2 + x + \dfrac{1}{4}$

85. $x^2 + \dfrac{1}{2}x + \dfrac{1}{16}$

86. $y^2(x + 1) - 2y(x + 1) - 15(x + 1)$

87. $z^2(x + 1) - 3z(x + 1) - 70(x + 1)$

Find a positive value of c so that each trinomial is factorable.

88. $y^2 - 4y + c$

89. $n^2 - 16n + c$

Find a positive value of b so that each trinomial is factorable.

90. $x^2 + bx + 15$

91. $y^2 + by + 20$

Factor each trinomial. (Hint: Notice that $x^{2n} + 4x^n + 3$ factors as $(x^n + 1)(x^n + 3)$. Remember: $x^n \cdot x^n = x^{n+n}$ or x^{2n}.)

92. $x^{2n} + 5x^n + 6$

93. $x^{2n} + 8x^n - 20$

A Factor Trinomials of the Form
   $ax^2 + bx + c$, where $a \neq 1$.

B Factor Out the GCF before
   Factoring a Trinomial of the Form
   $ax^2 + bx + c$.

13.3 FACTORING TRINOMIALS OF THE FORM $ax^2 + bx + c$

Objective A Factoring Trinomials of the Form $ax^2 + bx + c$

In this section, we factor trinomials of the form $ax^2 + bx + c$, such as

$$3x^2 + 11x + 6, \qquad 8x^2 - 22x + 5, \quad \text{and} \quad 2x^2 + 13x - 7$$

Notice that the coefficient of the squared variable in these trinomials is a number other than 1. We will factor these trinomials using a trial-and-check method based on our work in the last section.

To begin, let's review the relationship between the numerical coefficients of the trinomial and the numerical coefficients of its factored form. For example, since $(2x + 1)(x + 6) = 2x^2 + 13x + 6$,

a factored form of $2x^2 + 13x + 6$ is $(2x + 1)(x + 6)$

Notice that $2x$ and x are factors of $2x^2$, the first term of the trinomial. Also, 6 and 1 are factors of 6, the last term of the trinomial, as shown:

$$2x^2 + 13x + 6 = (2x + 1)(x + 6)$$

Also notice that $13x$, the middle term, is the sum of the following products:

$$2x^2 + 13x + 6 = (2x + 1)(x + 6)$$

$$\begin{aligned}1x \\ +12x \\ \hline 13x \end{aligned} \quad \text{Middle term}$$

Let's use this pattern to factor $5x^2 + 7x + 2$. First, we find factors of $5x^2$. Since all numerical coefficients in this trinomial are positive, we will use factors with positive numerical coefficients only. Thus, the factors of $5x^2$ are $5x$ and x. Let's try these factors as first terms of the binomials. Thus far, we have

$$5x^2 + 7x + 2 = (5x + \square)(x + \square)$$

Next, we need to find positive factors of 2. Positive factors of 2 are 1 and 2. Now we try possible combinations of these factors as second terms of the binomials until we obtain a middle term of $7x$.

$$(5x + 1)(x + 2) = 5x^2 + 11x + 2$$

$$\begin{aligned}1x \\ +10x \\ \hline 11x \end{aligned} \longrightarrow \textbf{Incorrect} \text{ middle term}$$

Let's try switching factors 2 and 1.

$$(5x + 2)(x + 1) = 5x^2 + 7x + 2$$

$$\begin{aligned}2x \\ +5x \\ \hline 7x \end{aligned} \longrightarrow \textbf{Correct} \text{ middle term}$$

Thus a factored form of $5x^2 + 7x + 2$ is $(5x + 2)(x + 1)$. To check, we multiply $(5x + 2)$ and $(x + 1)$. The product is $5x^2 + 7x + 2$.

EXAMPLE 1   Factor: $3x^2 + 11x + 6$

Solution: Since all numerical coefficients are positive, we use factors with positive numerical coefficients. We first find factors of $3x^2$.

Factors of $3x^2$: $3x^2 = 3x \cdot x$

If factorable, the trinomial will be of the form

$3x^2 + 11x + 6 = (3x + \square)(x + \square)$

Next we factor 6.

Factors of 6: $6 = 1 \cdot 6,$ $6 = 2 \cdot 3$

Now we try combinations of factors of 6 until a middle term of $11x$ is obtained. Let's try 1 and 6 first.

$(3x + 1)(x + 6) = 3x^2 + 19x + 6$

$\begin{array}{l} 1x \\ +18x \\ \hline 19x \end{array}$ $\longrightarrow$ **Incorrect** middle term

Now let's next try 6 and 1.

$(3x + 6)(x + 1)$

Before multiplying, notice that the terms of the factor $3x + 6$ have a common factor of 3. The terms of the original trinomial $3x^2 + 11x + 6$ have no common factor other than 1, so the terms of its factors will also contain no common factor other than 1. This means that $(3x + 6)(x + 1)$ is not a factored form.

Next let's try 2 and 3 as last terms.

$(3x + 2)(x + 3) = 3x^2 + 11x + 6$

$\begin{array}{l} 2x \\ +9x \\ \hline 11x \end{array}$ $\longrightarrow$ **Correct** middle term

Thus a factored form of $3x^2 + 11x + 6$ is $(3x + 2)(x + 3)$.

◼ **Work Practice Problem 1**

✔ **Concept Check**   Do the terms of $3x^2 + 29x + 18$ have a common factor? Without multiplying, decide which of the following factored forms could not be a factored form of $3x^2 + 29x + 18$.

a. $(3x + 18)(x + 1)$ **b.** $(3x + 2)(x + 9)$
c. $(3x + 6)(x + 3)$ **d.** $(3x + 9)(x + 2)$

EXAMPLE 2   Factor: $8x^2 - 22x + 5$

Solution: Factors of $8x^2$: $8x^2 = 8x \cdot x,$ $8x^2 = 4x \cdot 2x$

We'll try $8x$ and x.

$8x^2 - 22x + 5 = (8x + \square)(x + \square)$

Since the middle term, $-22x$, has a negative numerical coefficient, we factor 5 into negative factors.

Factors of 5: $5 = -1 \cdot -5$

Continued on next page

PRACTICE PROBLEM 1

Factor each trinomial.
a. $5x^2 + 27x + 10$
b. $4x^2 + 12x + 5$

Helpful Hint

This is true in general: If the terms of a trinomial have no common factor (other than 1), then the terms of each of its binomial factors will contain no common factor (other than 1).

PRACTICE PROBLEM 2

Factor each trinomial.
a. $2x^2 - 11x + 12$
b. $6x^2 - 5x + 1$

Answers
1. a. $(5x + 2)(x + 5),$
b. $(2x + 5)(2x + 1),$
2. a. $(2x - 3)(x - 4),$
b. $(3x - 1)(2x - 1)$

✔ **Concept Check Answer**
no; a, c, d

Let's try -1 and -5.

$$(8x - 1)(x - 5) = 8x^2 - 41x + 5$$

$$\begin{array}{l} -1x \\ + (-40x) \\ \hline -41x \end{array} \longrightarrow \text{Incorrect middle term}$$

Now let's try -5 and -1.

$$(8x - 5)(x - 1) = 8x^2 - 13x + 5$$

$$\begin{array}{l} -5x \\ + (-8x) \\ \hline -13x \end{array} \longrightarrow \text{Incorrect middle term}$$

Don't give up yet! We can still try other factors of $8x^2$. Let's try $4x$ and $2x$ with -1 and -5.

$$(4x - 1)(2x - 5) = 8x^2 - 22x + 5$$

$$\begin{array}{l} -2x \\ + (-20x) \\ \hline -22x \end{array} \longrightarrow \text{Correct middle term}$$

A factored form of $8x^2 - 22x + 5$ is $(4x - 1)(2x - 5)$.

▣ **Work Practice Problem 2**

PRACTICE PROBLEM 3

Factor each trinomial.
a. $3x^2 + 14x - 5$
b. $35x^2 + 4x - 4$

EXAMPLE 3 Factor: $2x^2 + 13x - 7$

Solution: Factors of $2x^2$: $2x^2 = 2x \cdot x$

Factors of -7: $-7 = -1 \cdot 7$, $-7 = 1 \cdot -7$

We try possible combinations of these factors:

$$(2x + 1)(x - 7) = 2x^2 - 13x - 7 \quad \text{Incorrect middle term}$$
$$(2x - 1)(x + 7) = 2x^2 + 13x - 7 \quad \text{Correct middle term}$$

A factored form of $2x^2 + 13x - 7$ is $(2x - 1)(x + 7)$.

▣ **Work Practice Problem 3**

PRACTICE PROBLEM 4

Factor each trinomial.
a. $14x^2 - 3xy - 2y^2$
b. $12a^2 - 16ab - 3b^2$

EXAMPLE 4 Factor: $10x^2 - 13xy - 3y^2$

Solution: Factors of $10x^2$: $10x^2 = 10x \cdot x$, $10x^2 = 2x \cdot 5x$

Factors of $-3y^2$: $-3y^2 = -3y \cdot y$, $-3y^2 = 3y \cdot -y$

We try some combinations of these factors:

$$\begin{array}{cc} & \overset{\text{Correct}}{\downarrow} \quad\quad \overset{\text{Correct}}{\downarrow} \\ (10x - 3y)(x + y) &= 10x^2 + 7xy - 3y^2 \\ (x + 3y)(10x - y) &= 10x^2 + 29xy - 3y^2 \\ (5x + 3y)(2x - y) &= 10x^2 + xy - 3y^2 \\ (2x - 3y)(5x + y) &= 10x^2 - 13xy - 3y^2 \quad \text{Correct middle term} \end{array}$$

A factored form of $10x^2 - 13xy - 3y^2$ is $(2x - 3y)(5x + y)$.

▣ **Work Practice Problem 4**

PRACTICE PROBLEM 5

Factor: $2x^4 - 5x^2 - 7$

Answers

3. a. $(3x - 1)(x + 5)$,
b. $(5x + 2)(7x - 2)$,
4. a. $(7x + 2y)(2x - y)$,
b. $(6a + b)(2a - 3b)$,
5. $(2x^2 - 7)(x^2 + 1)$

EXAMPLE 5 Factor: $3x^4 - 5x^2 - 8$

Solution: Factors of $3x^4$: $3x^4 = 3x^2 \cdot x^2$

Factors of -8: $-8 = -2 \cdot 4, 2 \cdot -4, -1 \cdot 8, 1 \cdot -8$

Try combinations of these factors:

Correct   Correct

$(3x^2 - 2)(x^2 + 4) = 3x^4 + 10x^2 - 8$

$(3x^2 + 4)(x^2 - 2) = 3x^4 - 2x^2 - 8$

$(3x^2 + 8)(x^2 - 1) = 3x^4 + 5x^2 - 8$ **Incorrect** sign on middle term, so switch signs in binomial factors.

$(3x^2 - 8)(x^2 + 1) = 3x^4 - 5x^2 - 8$ **Correct** middle term.

■ **Work Practice Problem 5**

Helpful Hint

Study the last two lines of Example 5. If a factoring attempt gives you a middle term whose numerical coefficient is the opposite of the desired numerical coefficient, try switching the signs of the last terms in the binomials.

Switched signs

$(3x^2 + 8)(x^2 - 1) = 3x^4 + 5x^2 - 8$ Middle term: $+5x$

$(3x^2 - 8)(x^2 + 1) = 3x^4 - 5x^2 - 8$ Middle term: $-5x$

Objective B Factoring Out the Greatest Common Factor

Don't forget that the first step in factoring any polynomial is to look for a common factor to factor out.

EXAMPLE 6   Factor: $24x^4 + 40x^3 + 6x^2$

Solution: Notice that all three terms have a common factor of $2x^2$. Thus we factor out $2x^2$ first.

$24x^4 + 40x^3 + 6x^2 = 2x^2(12x^2 + 20x + 3)$

Next we factor $12x^2 + 20x + 3$.

    Factors of $12x^2$: $12x^2 = 4x \cdot 3x,$ $12x^2 = 12x \cdot x,$ $12x^2 = 6x \cdot 2x$

Since all terms in the trinomial have positive numerical coefficients, we factor 3 using positive factors only.

    Factors of 3: $3 = 1 \cdot 3$

We try some combinations of the factors.

$2x^2(4x + 3)(3x + 1) = 2x^2(12x^2 + 13x + 3)$

$2x^2(12x + 1)(x + 3) = 2x^2(12x^2 + 37x + 3)$

$2x^2(2x + 3)(6x + 1) = 2x^2(12x^2 + 20x + 3)$ **Correct** middle term

A factored form of $24x^4 + 40x^3 + 6x^2$ is $2x^2(2x + 3)(6x + 1)$.

■ **Work Practice Problem 6**

When the term containing the squared variable has a negative coefficient, you may want to first factor out a common factor of -1.

EXAMPLE 7   Factor: $-6x^2 - 13x + 5$

Solution: We begin by factoring out a common factor of -1.

$-6x^2 - 13x + 5 = -1(6x^2 + 13x - 5)$ Factor out -1.

$\qquad\qquad\qquad = -1(3x - 1)(2x + 5)$ Factor $6x^2 + 13x - 5$.

■ **Work Practice Problem 7**

PRACTICE PROBLEM 6

Factor each trinomial.

a. $3x^3 + 17x^2 + 10x$

b. $6xy^2 + 33xy - 18x$

Helpful Hint

Don't forget to include the common factor in the factored form.

PRACTICE PROBLEM 7

Factor: $-5x^2 - 19x + 4$

Answers

6. a. $x(3x + 2)(x + 5),$

b. $3x(2y - 1)(y + 6),$

7. $-1(x + 4)(5x - 1)$

Objective Ⓐ *Complete each factored form. See Examples 1 through 5.*

1. $5x^2 + 22x + 8 = (5x + 2)(\quad)$

2. $2y^2 + 15y + 25 = (2y + 5)(\quad)$

3. $50x^2 + 15x - 2 = (5x + 2)(\quad)$

4. $6y^2 + 11y - 10 = (2y + 5)(\quad)$

5. $20x^2 - 7x - 6 = (5x + 2)(\quad)$

6. $8y^2 - 2y - 55 = (2y + 5)(\quad)$

Factor each trinomial completely. See Examples 1 through 5.

7. $2x^2 + 13x + 15$

8. $3x^2 + 8x + 4$

9. $8y^2 - 17y + 9$

10. $21x^2 - 41x + 10$

11. $2x^2 - 9x - 5$

12. $36r^2 - 5r - 24$

13. $20r^2 + 27r - 8$

14. $3x^2 + 20x - 63$

15. $10x^2 + 17x + 3$

16. $2x^2 + 7x + 5$

17. $x + 3x^2 - 2$

18. $y + 8y^2 - 9$

19. $6x^2 - 13xy + 5y^2$

20. $8x^2 - 14xy + 3y^2$

21. $15m^2 - 16m - 15$

22. $25n^2 - 5n - 6$

23. $-9x + 20 + x^2$

24. $-7x + 12 + x^2$

25. $2x^2 - 7x - 99$

26. $2x^2 + 7x - 72$

27. $-27t + 7t^2 - 4$

28. $-3t + 4t^2 - 7$

29. $3a^2 + 10ab + 3b^2$

30. $2a^2 + 11ab + 5b^2$

31. $49p^2 - 7p - 2$

32. $3r^2 + 10r - 8$

33. $18x^2 - 9x - 14$

34. $42a^2 - 43a + 6$

35. $2m^2 + 17m + 10$

36. $3n^2 + 20n + 5$

37. $24x^2 + 41x + 12$

38. $24x^2 - 49x + 15$

Objectives Ⓐ Ⓑ **Mixed Practice** *Factor each trinomial completely. See Examples 1 through 7.*

39. $12x^3 + 11x^2 + 2x$

40. $8a^3 + 14a^2 + 3a$

41. $21b^2 - 48b - 45$

42. $12x^2 - 14x - 10$

43. $7z + 12z^2 - 12$

44. $16t + 15t^2 - 15$

45. $6x^2y^2 - 2xy^2 - 60y^2$

46. $8x^2y + 34xy - 84y$

47. $4x^2 - 8x - 21$

48. $6x^2 - 11x - 10$

49. $3x^2 - 42x + 63$

50. $5x^2 - 75x + 60$

51. $8x^2 + 6xy - 27y^2$

52. $54a^2 + 39ab - 8b^2$

53. $-x^2 + 2x + 24$

54. $-x^2 + 4x + 21$

55. $4x^3 - 9x^2 - 9x$

56. $6x^3 - 31x^2 + 5x$

57. $24x^2 - 58x + 9$

58. $36x^2 + 55x - 14$

59. $40a^2b + 9ab - 9b$ **60.** $24y^2x + 7yx - 5x$ **61.** $30x^3 + 38x^2 + 12x$ **62.** $6x^3 - 28x^2 + 16x$

63. $6y^3 - 8y^2 - 30y$ **64.** $12x^3 - 34x^2 + 24x$ **65.** $10x^4 + 25x^3y - 15x^2y^2$ **66.** $42x^4 - 99x^3y - 15x^2y^2$

67. $-14x^2 + 39x - 10$ **68.** $-15x^2 + 26x - 8$ **69.** $16p^4 - 40p^3 + 25p^2$ **70.** $9q^4 - 42q^3 + 49q^2$

71. $-2x^2 + 9x + 5$ **72.** $-3x^2 + 8x + 16$ **73.** $-4 + 52x - 48x^2$ **74.** $-5 + 55x - 50x^2$

75. $2t^4 + 3t^2 - 27$ **76.** $4r^4 - 17r^2 - 15$ **77.** $5x^2y^2 + 20xy + 1$ **78.** $3a^2b^2 + 12ab + 1$

79. $6a^5 + 37a^3b^2 + 6ab^4$ **80.** $5m^5 + 26m^3h^2 + 5mh^4$

Review

Multiply. See Section 12.6.

81. $(x - 4)(x + 4)$ **82.** $(2x - 9)(2x + 9)$ **83.** $(x + 2)^2$

84. $(x + 3)^2$ **85.** $(2x - 1)^2$ **86.** $(3x - 5)^2$

Concept Extensions

See the Concept Check in this section.

87. Do the terms of $4x^2 + 19x + 12$ have a common factor (other than 1)?

88. Without multiplying, decide which of the following factored forms is not a factored form of $4x^2 + 19x + 12$.
  a. $(2x + 4)(2x + 3)$ **b.** $(4x + 4)(x + 3)$
  c. $(4x + 3)(x + 4)$ **d.** $(2x + 2)(2x + 6)$

Write the perimeter of each figure as a simplified polynomial. Then factor the polynomial.

89.

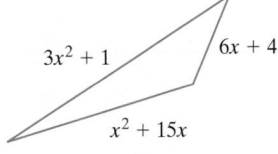

$3x^2 + 1$ $6x + 4$
$x^2 + 15x$

90.

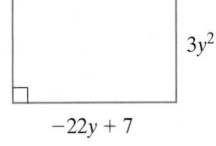

$3y^2$
$-22y + 7$

Factor each trinomial completely.

91. $4x^2 + 2x + \dfrac{1}{4}$

92. $27x^2 + 2x - \dfrac{1}{9}$

93. $4x^2(y - 1)^2 + 10x(y - 1)^2 + 25(y - 1)^2$

94. $3x^2(a + 3)^3 - 28x(a + 3)^3 + 25(a + 3)^3$

Find a positive value of b so that each trinomial is factorable.

95. $3x^2 + bx - 5$

96. $2z^2 + bz - 7$

Find a positive value of c so that each trinomial is factorable.

97. $5x^2 + 7x + c$

98. $3x^2 - 8x + c$

 99. In your own words, describe the steps you will use to factor a trinomial.

STUDY SKILLS BUILDER

Are You Satisfied with Your Performance on a Particular Quiz or Exam?

If not, don't forget to analyze your quiz or exam and look for common errors. Were most of your errors a result of:

- *Carelessness?* Did you turn in your quiz or exam before the allotted time expired? If so, resolve to use the entire time allotted next time. Any extra time can be spent checking your work.

- *Running out of time?* If so, make a point to better manage your time on your next quiz or exam. Try completing any questions that you are unsure of last and delay checking your work until all questions have been answered.

- *Not understanding a concept?* If so, review that concept and correct your work. Try to understand how this happened so that you make sure it doesn't happen before the next quiz or exam.

- *Test conditions?* When studying for a quiz or exam, make sure you place yourself in conditions similar to test conditions. For example, before your next quiz or exam, use a few sheets of blank paper and take a sample test without the aid of your notes or text.

  (See your instructor or use the Chapter Test at the end of each chapter.)

Exercises

1. Have you corrected all your previous quizzes and exams?

2. List any errors you have found common to two or more of your graded papers.

3. Is one of your common errors not understanding a concept? If so, are you making sure you understand all the concepts for the next quiz or exam?

4. Is one of your common errors making careless mistakes? If so, are you now taking all the time allotted to check over your work so that you can minimize the number of careless mistakes?

5. Are you satisfied with your grades thus far on quizzes and tests?

6. If your answer to Exercise 5 is no, are there any more suggestions you can make to your instructor or yourself to help? If so, list them here and share these with your instructor.

A Use the Grouping Method to
Factor Trinomials of the Form
$ax^2 + bx + c$.

Objective **A** Using the Grouping Method

There is an alternative method that can be used to factor trinomials of the form $ax^2 + bx + c, a \neq 1$. This method is called the **grouping method** because it uses factoring by grouping as we learned in Section 13.1.

To see how this method works, recall from Section 13.1 that to factor a trinomial such as $x^2 + 11x + 30$, we find two numbers such that

Product is 30

$$x^2 + 11x + 30$$

Sum is 11.

To factor a trinomial such as $2x^2 + 11x + 12$ by grouping, we use an extension of the method in Section 13.1. Here we look for two numbers such that

Product is $2 \cdot 12 = 24$

$$2x^2 + 11x + 12$$

Sum is 11.

This time, we use the two numbers to write

$$2x^2 + 11x + 12 \text{ as}$$
$$= 2x^2 + \square x + \square x + 12$$

Then we factor by grouping. Since we want a positive product, 24, and a positive sum, 11, we consider pairs of positive factors of 24 only.

Factors of 24	Sum of Factors	
1, 24	25	
2, 12	14	
3, 8	11	**Correct** sum

The factors are 3 and 8. Now we use these factors to write the middle term $11x$ as $3x + 8x$ (or $8x + 3x$). We replace $11x$ with $3x + 8x$ in the original trinomial and then we can factor by grouping.

$$
\begin{aligned}
2x^2 + 11x + 12 &= 2x^2 + 3x + 8x + 12 \\
&= (2x^2 + 3x) + (8x + 12) \quad \text{Group the terms.} \\
&= x(2x + 3) + 4(2x + 3) \quad \text{Factor each group.} \\
&= (2x + 3)(x + 4) \quad \text{Factor out } (2x + 3).
\end{aligned}
$$

In general, we have the following procedure.

To Factor Trinomials by Grouping

Step 1: Factor out a greatest common factor, if there is one other than 1.

Step 2: For the resulting trinomial $ax^2 + bx + c$, find two numbers whose product is $a \cdot c$ and whose sum is b.

Step 3: Write the middle term, bx, using the factors found in Step 2.

Step 4: Factor by grouping.

PRACTICE PROBLEM 1

Factor each trinomial by grouping.

a. $3x^2 + 14x + 8$

b. $12x^2 + 19x + 5$

EXAMPLE 1 Factor $8x^2 - 14x + 5$ by grouping.

Solution:

Step 1: The terms of this trinomial contain no greatest common factor other than 1.

Step 2: This trinomial is of the form $ax^2 + bx + c$ with $a = 8$, $b = -14$, and $c = 5$. Find two numbers whose product is $a \cdot c$ or $8 \cdot 5 = 40$, and whose sum is b or -14.

The numbers are -4 and -10.

Factors of 40	Sum of Factors
$-40, -1$	-41
$-20, -2$	-22
$-10, -4$	-14

Correct sum

Step 3: Write $-14x$ as $-4x - 10x$ so that

$$8x^2 - 14x + 5 = 8x^2 - 4x - 10x + 5$$

Step 4: Factor by grouping.

$$8x^2 - 4x - 10x + 5 = 4x(2x - 1) - 5(2x - 1)$$
$$= (2x - 1)(4x - 5)$$

■ **Work Practice Problem 1**

PRACTICE PROBLEM 2

Factor each trinomial by grouping.

a. $30x^2 - 26x + 4$

b. $6x^2y - 7xy - 5y$

EXAMPLE 2 Factor $6x^2 - 2x - 20$ by grouping.

Solution:

Step 1: First factor out the greatest common factor, 2.

$$6x^2 - 2x - 20 = 2(3x^2 - x - 10)$$

Step 2: Next notice that $a = 3$, $b = -1$, and $c = -10$ in the resulting trinomial. Find two numbers whose product is $a \cdot c$ or $3(-10) = -30$ and whose sum is b, -1. The numbers are -6 and 5.

Step 3: $3x^2 - x - 10 = 3x^2 - 6x + 5x - 10$

Step 4: $3x^2 - 6x + 5x - 10 = 3x(x - 2) + 5(x - 2)$
$$= (x - 2)(3x + 5)$$

The factored form of $6x^2 - 2x - 20 = 2(x - 2)(3x + 5)$.

└ Don't forget to include the common factor of 2.

■ **Work Practice Problem 2**

PRACTICE PROBLEM 3

Factor $12y^5 + 10y^4 - 42y^3$ by grouping.

EXAMPLE 3 Factor $18y^4 + 21y^3 - 60y^2$ by grouping.

Solution:

Step 1: First factor out the greatest common factor, $3y^2$.

$$18y^4 + 21y^3 - 60y^2 = 3y^2(6y^2 + 7y - 20)$$

Step 2: Notice that $a = 6$, $b = 7$, and $c = -20$ in the resulting trinomial. Find two numbers whose product is $a \cdot c$ or $6(-20) = -120$ and whose sum is 7. It may help to factor -120 as a product of primes and -1.

$$-120 = 2 \cdot 2 \cdot 2 \cdot 3 \cdot 5 \cdot (-1)$$

Then choose pairings of factors until you have two pairings whose sum is 7.

$$2 \cdot 2 \cdot 2 \cdot 3 \cdot 5 \cdot (-1) \qquad \text{The numbers are } -8 \text{ and 15.}$$

(with -8 grouped above and 15 below)

Step 3: $6y^2 + 7y - 20 = 6y^2 - 8y + 15y - 20$

Step 4: $6y^2 - 8y + 15y - 20 = 2y(3y - 4) + 5(3y - 4)$
$$= (3y - 4)(2y + 5)$$

The factored form of $18y^4 + 21y^3 - 60y^2$ is $3y^2(3y - 4)(2y + 5)$

└ Don't forget to include the common factor of $3y^2$.

■ **Work Practice Problem 3**

Answers

1. a. $(x + 4)(3x + 2)$,
b. $(4x + 5)(3x + 1)$,
2. a. $2(5x - 1)(3x - 2)$,
b. $y(2x + 1)(3x - 5)$,
3. $2y^3(3y + 7)(2y - 3)$

13.4 EXERCISE SET

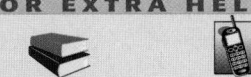

Objective A *Factor each polynomial by grouping. Notice that Step 3 has already been done in these exercises.*
See Examples 1 through 3.

1. $x^2 + 3x + 2x + 6$

2. $x^2 + 5x + 3x + 15$

3. $y^2 + 8y - 2y - 16$

4. $z^2 + 10z - 7z - 70$

5. $8x^2 - 5x - 24x + 15$

6. $4x^2 - 9x - 32x + 72$

7. $5x^4 - 3x^2 + 25x^2 - 15$

8. $2y^4 - 10y^2 + 7y^2 - 35$

Factor each trinomial by grouping. Exercises 9 through 12 are broken into parts to help you get started. See Examples 1 through 3.

9. $6x^2 + 11x + 3$
   a. Find two numbers whose product is $6 \cdot 3 = 18$ and whose sum is 11.
   b. Write $11x$ using the factors from part (a).
   c. Factor by grouping.

10. $8x^2 + 14x + 3$
   a. Find two numbers whose product is $8 \cdot 3 = 24$ and whose sum is 14.
   b. Write $14x$ using the factors from part (a).
   c. Factor by grouping.

11. $15x^2 - 23x + 4$
   a. Find two numbers whose product is $15 \cdot 4 = 60$ and whose sum is -23.
   b. Write $-23x$ using the factors from part (a).
   c. Factor by grouping.

12. $6x^2 - 13x + 5$
   a. Find two numbers whose product is $6 \cdot 5 = 30$ and whose sum is -13.
   b. Write $-13x$ using the factors from part (a).
   c. Factor by grouping.

13. $21y^2 + 17y + 2$

14. $15x^2 + 11x + 2$

15. $7x^2 - 4x - 11$

16. $8x^2 - x - 9$

17. $10x^2 - 9x + 2$

18. $30x^2 - 23x + 3$

19. $2x^2 - 7x + 5$

20. $2x^2 - 7x + 3$

21. $12x + 4x^2 + 9$

22. $20x + 25x^2 + 4$

23. $4x^2 - 8x - 21$

24. $6x^2 - 11x - 10$

25. $10x^2 - 23x + 12$

26. $21x^2 - 13x + 2$

27. $2x^3 + 13x^2 + 15x$

28. $3x^3 + 8x^2 + 4x$

29. $16y^2 - 34y + 18$

30. $4y^2 - 2y - 12$

31. $-13x + 6 + 6x^2$

32. $-25x + 12 + 12x^2$

33. $54a^2 - 9a - 30$

34. $30a^2 + 38a - 20$

35. $20a^3 + 37a^2 + 8a$

36. $10a^3 + 17a^2 + 3a$

37. $12x^3 - 27x^2 - 27x$

38. $30x^3 - 155x^2 + 25x$

39. $3x^2y + 4xy^2 + y^3$

40. $6r^2t + 7rt^2 + t^3$

41. $20z^2 + 7z + 1$

42. $36z^2 + 6z + 1$

43. $24a^2 - 6ab - 30b^2$

44. $30a^2 + 5ab - 25b^2$

45. $15p^4 + 31p^3q + 2p^2q^2$

46. $20s^4 + 61s^3t + 3s^2t^2$

47. $35 + 12x + x^2$

48. $33 + 14x + x^2$

49. $6 - 11x + 5x^2$

50. $5 - 12x + 7x^2$

Review

Multiply. See Section 12.6.

51. $(x - 2)(x + 2)$ **52.** $(y - 5)(y + 5)$ **53.** $(y + 4)(y + 4)$ **54.** $(x + 7)(x + 7)$

55. $(9z + 5)(9z - 5)$ **56.** $(8y + 9)(8y - 9)$ **57.** $(4x - 3)^2$ **58.** $(2z - 1)^2$

Concept Extensions

Write the perimeter of each figure as a simplified polynomial. Then factor the polynomial.

59.

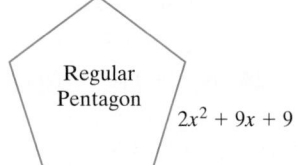

Regular Pentagon $2x^2 + 9x + 9$

60.

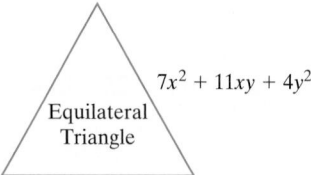

Equilateral Triangle $7x^2 + 11xy + 4y^2$

Factor each polynomial by grouping.

61. $x^{2n} + 2x^n + 3x^n + 6$
    (*Hint:* Don't forget that $x^{2n} = x^n \cdot x^n$.)

62. $x^{2n} + 6x^n + 10x^n + 60$

63. $3x^{2n} + 16x^n - 35$

64. $12x^{2n} - 40x^n + 25$

✎ **65.** In your own words, explain how to factor a trinomial by grouping.

13.5 FACTORING PERFECT SQUARE TRINOMIALS AND THE DIFFERENCE OF TWO SQUARES

Objectives

A Recognize Perfect Square Trinomials.

B Factor Perfect Square Trinomials.

C Factor the Difference of Two Squares.

Objective **A** Recognizing Perfect Square Trinomials

A trinomial that is the square of a binomial is called a **perfect square trinomial.** For example,

$$(x + 3)^2 = (x + 3)(x + 3)$$
$$= x^2 + 6x + 9$$

Thus $x^2 + 6x + 9$ is a perfect square trinomial.

In Chapter 12, we discovered special product formulas for squaring binomials.

$$(a + b)^2 = a^2 + 2ab + b^2 \quad \text{and} \quad (a - b)^2 = a^2 - 2ab + b^2$$

Because multiplication and factoring are reverse processes, we can now use these special products to help us factor perfect square trinomials. If we reverse these equations, we have the following.

Factoring Perfect Square Trinomials

$$a^2 + 2ab + b^2 = (a + b)^2$$

$$a^2 - 2ab + b^2 = (a - b)^2$$

Helpful Hint

Notice that for both given forms of a perfect square trinomial, the last term is positive. This is because the last term is a square.

To use these equations to help us factor, we must first be able to recognize a perfect square trinomial. A trinomial is a perfect square when

1. two terms, a^2 and b^2, are squares and
2. another term is $2 \cdot a \cdot b$ or $-2 \cdot a \cdot b$. That is, this term is twice the product of a and b, or its opposite.

EXAMPLE 1 Decide whether $x^2 + 8x + 16$ is a perfect square trinomial.

Solution:

1. Two terms, x^2 and 16, are squares ($16 = 4^2$).
2. Twice the product of x and 4 is the other term of the trinomial.
   $$2 \cdot x \cdot 4 = 8x$$

Thus, $x^2 + 8x + 16$ is a perfect square trinomial.

 **Work Practice Problem 1**

EXAMPLE 2 Decide whether $4x^2 + 10x + 9$ is a perfect square trinomial.

Solution:

1. Two terms, $4x^2$ and 9, are squares.
   $$4x^2 = (2x)^2 \quad \text{and} \quad 9 = 3^2$$
2. Twice the product of $2x$ and 3 is *not* the other term of the trinomial.
   $$2 \cdot 2x \cdot 3 = 12x, \, not \, 10x$$

The trinomial is *not* a perfect square trinomial.

Work Practice Problem 2

PRACTICE PROBLEM 1

Decide whether each trinomial is a perfect square trinomial.
a. $x^2 + 12x + 36$
b. $x^2 + 20x + 100$

PRACTICE PROBLEM 2

Decide whether each trinomial is a perfect square trinomial.
a. $9x^2 + 20x + 25$
b. $4x^2 + 8x + 11$

Answers
1. a. yes, **b.** yes, **2. a.** no, **b.** no

PRACTICE PROBLEM 3

Decide whether each trinomial is a perfect square trinomial.

a. $25x^2 - 10x + 1$

b. $9x^2 - 42x + 49$

EXAMPLE 3 Decide whether $9x^2 - 12xy + 4y^2$ is a perfect square trinomial.

Solution:

1. Two terms, $9x^2$ and $4y^2$, are squares.

$$9x^2 = (3x)^2 \quad \text{and} \quad 4y^2 = (2y)^2$$

2. Twice the product of $3x$ and $2y$ is the opposite of the other term of the trinomial.

$2 \cdot 3x \cdot 2y = 12xy$, the opposite of $-12xy$

Thus, $9x^2 - 12xy + 4y^2$ is a perfect square trinomial.

▣ **Work Practice Problem 3**

Objective B Factoring Perfect Square Trinomials

Now that we can recognize perfect square trinomials, we are ready to factor them.

PRACTICE PROBLEM 4

Factor: $x^2 + 16x + 64$

EXAMPLE 4 Factor: $x^2 + 12x + 36$

Solution:

$$x^2 + 12x + 36 = x^2 + 2 \cdot x \cdot 6 + 6^2 \quad \text{\small } 36 = 6^2 \text{ and } 12x = 2 \cdot x \cdot 6$$
$$a^2 + 2 \cdot a \cdot b + b^2$$
$$= (x + 6)^2$$
$$(a + b)^2$$

▣ **Work Practice Problem 4**

PRACTICE PROBLEM 5

Factor: $9r^2 + 24rs + 16s^2$

EXAMPLE 5 Factor: $25x^2 + 20xy + 4y^2$

Solution:

$$25x^2 + 20xy + 4y^2 = (5x)^2 + 2 \cdot 5x \cdot 2y + (2y)^2$$
$$= (5x + 2y)^2$$

▣ **Work Practice Problem 5**

PRACTICE PROBLEM 6

Factor: $9n^4 - 6n^2 + 1$

EXAMPLE 6 Factor: $4m^4 - 4m^2 + 1$

Solution:

$$4m^4 - 4m^2 + 1 = (2m^2)^2 - 2 \cdot 2m^2 \cdot 1 + 1^2$$
$$a^2 \quad - 2 \cdot a \cdot b + b^2$$
$$= (2m^2 - 1)^2$$
$$(a \quad - b)^2$$

▣ **Work Practice Problem 6**

PRACTICE PROBLEM 7

Factor: $9x^2 + 15x + 4$

EXAMPLE 7 Factor: $25x^2 + 50x + 9$

Solution: Notice that this trinomial is not a perfect square trinomial.

$$25x^2 = (5x)^2, 9 = 3^2$$

but

$$2 \cdot 5x \cdot 3 = 30x$$

and $30x$ is not the middle term $50x$.

Answers

3. a. yes, **b.** yes, **4.** $(x + 8)^2$,

5. $(3r + 4s)^2$, **6.** $(3n^2 - 1)^2$,

7. $(3x + 1)(3x + 4)$

Although $25x^2 + 50x + 9$ is not a perfect square trinomial, it is factorable. Using techniques we learned in Sections 13.3 or 13.4, we find that

$$25x^2 + 50x + 9 = (5x + 9)(5x + 1)$$

■ **Work Practice Problem 7**

Helpful Hint
A perfect square trinomial can also be factored by the methods found in Sections 13.2 through 13.4.

EXAMPLE 8 Factor: $162x^3 - 144x^2 + 32x$

Solution: Don't forget to first look for a common factor. There is a greatest common factor of $2x$ in this trinomial.

$$\begin{aligned}
162x^3 - 144x^2 + 32x &= 2x(81x^2 - 72x + 16) \\
&= 2x[(9x)^2 - 2 \cdot 9x \cdot 4 + 4^2] \\
&= 2x(9x - 4)^2
\end{aligned}$$

■ **Work Practice Problem 8**

PRACTICE PROBLEM 8

Factor:
a. $8n^2 + 40n + 50$
b. $12x^3 - 84x^2 + 147x$

Objective C Factoring the Difference of Two Squares

In Chapter 12, we discovered another special product, the product of the sum and difference of two terms a and b:

$$(a + b)(a - b) = a^2 - b^2$$

Reversing this equation gives us another factoring pattern, which we use to factor the difference of two squares.

Factoring the Difference of Two Squares

$$a^2 - b^2 = (a + b)(a - b)$$

To use this equation to help us factor, we must first be able to recognize the difference of two squares. A binomial is a difference of two squares if

1. both terms are squares and
2. the signs of the terms are different.

Let's practice using this pattern.

EXAMPLES Factor each binomial.

9. $z^2 - 4 = z^2 - 2^2 = (z + 2)(z - 2)$

$$a^2 - b^2 = (a + b)(a - b)$$

10. $y^2 - 25 = y^2 - 5^2 = (y + 5)(y - 5)$

11. $y^2 - \dfrac{4}{9} = y^2 - \left(\dfrac{2}{3}\right)^2 = \left(y + \dfrac{2}{3}\right)\left(y - \dfrac{2}{3}\right)$

12. $x^2 + 4$

Note that the binomial $x^2 + 4$ is the *sum* of two squares since we can write $x^2 + 4$ as $x^2 + 2^2$. We might try to factor using $(x + 2)(x + 2)$ or $(x - 2)(x - 2)$. But when we multiply to check, we find that neither factoring is correct.

$$(x + 2)(x + 2) = x^2 + 4x + 4$$
$$(x - 2)(x - 2) = x^2 - 4x + 4$$

In both cases, the product is a trinomial, not the required binomial. In fact, $x^2 + 4$ is a prime polynomial.

■ **Work Practice Problems 9–12**

PRACTICE PROBLEMS 9–12

Factor each binomial.
9. $x^2 - 9$ **10.** $a^2 - 16$
11. $c^2 - \dfrac{9}{25}$ **12.** $s^2 + 9$

Helpful Hint
After the greatest common factor has been removed, the *sum* of two squares cannot be factored further using real numbers.

Answers
8. a. $2(2n + 5)^2$, **b.** $3x(2x - 7)^2$,
9. $(x - 3)(x + 3)$,
10. $(a - 4)(a + 4)$,
11. $\left(c - \dfrac{3}{5}\right)\left(c + \dfrac{3}{5}\right)$,
12. prime polynomial

PRACTICE PROBLEMS 13-15

Factor each difference of two squares.

13. $9s^2 - 1$
14. $16x^2 - 49y^2$
15. $p^4 - 81$

EXAMPLES Factor each difference of two squares.

13. $4x^2 - 1 = (2x)^2 - 1^2 = (2x + 1)(2x - 1)$
14. $25a^2 - 9b^2 = (5a)^2 - (3b)^2 = (5a + 3b)(5a - 3b)$
15. $y^4 - 16 = (y^2)^2 - 4^2$
$\qquad = (y^2 + 4)(y^2 - 4)$ Factor the difference of two squares.
$\qquad = (y^2 + 4)(y + 2)(y - 2)$ Factor the difference of two squares.

■ **Work Practice Problems 13-15**

Helpful Hint

1. Don't forget to first see whether there's a greatest common factor (other than 1) that can be factored out.
2. Factor completely. In other words, check to see whether any factors can be factored further (as in Example 15).

PRACTICE PROBLEMS 16-18

Factor each difference of two squares.

16. $9x^3 - 25x$
17. $48x^4 - 3$
18. $-9x^2 + 100$

EXAMPLES Factor each difference of two squares.

16. $4x^3 - 49x = x(4x^2 - 49)$ Factor out the common factor, x.
$\qquad = x[(2x)^2 - 7^2]$
$\qquad = x(2x + 7)(2x - 7)$ Factor the difference of two squares.
17. $162x^4 - 2 = 2(81x^4 - 1)$ Factor out the common factor, 2.
$\qquad = 2(9x^2 + 1)(9x^2 - 1)$ Factor the difference of two squares.
$\qquad = 2(9x^2 + 1)(3x + 1)(3x - 1)$ Factor the difference of two squares.
18. $-49x^2 + 16 = -1(49x^2 - 16)$ Factor out -1.
$\qquad = -1(7x + 4)(7x - 4)$ Factor the difference of two squares.

■ **Work Practice Problems 16-18**

PRACTICE PROBLEM 19

Factor: $121 - m^2$

EXAMPLE 19 Factor: $36 - x^2$.

Solution: This is the difference of two squares. Factor as is or if you like, first write the binomial with variable term first.

Factor as is: $36 - x^2 = 6^2 - x^2 = (6 + x)(6 - x)$.
Rewrite binomial: $36 - x^2 = -x^2 + 36 = -1(x^2 - 36)$
$\qquad\qquad\qquad\qquad\qquad\qquad = -1(x + 6)(x - 6)$.

Both factorizations are correct and are equal. To see this, factor -1 from $(6 - x)$ in the first factorization.

■ **Work Practice Problem 19**

Helpful Hint

When rearranging terms, keep in mind that the sign of a term is in front of the term.

Answers

13. $(3s - 1)(3s + 1)$,
14. $(4x - 7y)(4x + 7y)$,
15. $(p^2 + 9)(p + 3)(p - 3)$,
16. $x(3x - 5)(3x + 5)$,
17. $3(4x^2 + 1)(2x + 1)(2x - 1)$,
18. $-1(3x - 10)(3x + 10)$,
19. $(11 + m)(11 - m)$ or
$-1(m + 11)(m - 11)$

A graphing calculator is a convenient tool for evaluating an expression at a given replacement value. For example, let's evaluate $x^2 - 6x$ when $x = 2$. To do so, store the value 2 in the variable x and then enter and evaluate the algebraic expression.

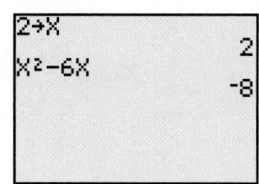

The value of $x^2 - 6x$ when $x = 2$ is -8. You may want to use this method for evaluating expressions as you explore the following.

We can use a graphing calculator to explore factoring patterns numerically. Use your calculator to evaluate

$x^2 - 2x + 1$, $x^2 - 2x - 1$, and $(x - 1)^2$ for each value of x given in the table. What do you observe?

	$x^2 - 2x + 1$	$x^2 - 2x - 1$	$(x - 1)^2$
$x = 5$			
$x = -3$			
$x = 2.7$			
$x = -12.1$			
$x = 0$			

Notice in each case that $x^2 - 2x - 1 \neq (x - 1)^2$. Because for each x in the table the value of $x^2 - 2x + 1$ and the value of $(x - 1)^2$ are the same, we might guess that $x^2 - 2x + 1 = (x - 1)^2$. We can verify our guess algebraically with multiplication:

$(x - 1)(x - 1) = x^2 - x - x + 1 = x^2 - 2x + 1$

Mental Math

Write each number as a square.

1. 1   **2.** 25   **3.** 81   **4.** 64   **5.** 9   **6.** 100

Write each term as a square.

7. $9x^2$ **8.** $16y^2$ **9.** $25a^2$ **10.** $81b^2$ **11.** $36p^4$ **12.** $4q^4$

13.5 EXERCISE SET

FOR EXTRA HELP

 Student Solutions Manual   PH Math/Tutor Center   CD/Video for Review   Math XL / MathXL®   MyMathLab / MyMathLab

Objective A *Determine whether each trinomial is a perfect square trinomial. See Examples 1 through 3.*

1. $x^2 + 16x + 64$ **2.** $x^2 + 22x + 121$ **3.** $y^2 + 5y + 25$ **4.** $y^2 + 4y + 16$

5. $m^2 - 2m + 1$ **6.** $p^2 - 4p + 4$ **7.** $a^2 - 16a + 49$ **8.** $n^2 - 20n + 144$

9. $4x^2 + 12xy + 8y^2$ **10.** $25x^2 + 20xy + 2y^2$ **11.** $25a^2 - 40ab + 16b^2$ **12.** $36a^2 - 12ab + b^2$

Objective B *Factor each trinomial completely. See Examples 4 through 8.*

13. $x^2 + 22x + 121$ **14.** $x^2 + 18x + 81$ **15.** $x^2 - 16x + 64$ **16.** $x^2 - 12x + 36$

17. $16a^2 - 24a + 9$ **18.** $25x^2 - 20x + 4$ **19.** $x^4 + 4x^2 + 4$ **20.** $m^4 + 10m^2 + 25$

21. $2n^2 - 28n + 98$ **22.** $3y^2 - 6y + 3$ **23.** $16y^2 + 40y + 25$ **24.** $9y^2 + 48y + 64$

25. $x^2y^2 - 10xy + 25$ **26.** $4x^2y^2 - 28xy + 49$ **27.** $m^3 + 18m^2 + 81m$ **28.** $y^3 + 12y^2 + 36y$

29. $1 + 6x^2 + x^4$ **30.** $1 + 16x^2 + x^4$ **31.** $9x^2 - 24xy + 16y^2$ **32.** $25x^2 - 60xy + 36y^2$

Objective **C** *Factor each binomial completely. See Examples 9 through 19.*

33. $x^2 - 4$ **34.** $x^2 - 36$ **35.** $81 - p^2$ **36.** $100 - t^2$

37. $-4r^2 + 1$ **38.** $-9t^2 + 1$ **39.** $9x^2 - 16$ **40.** $36y^2 - 25$

41. $16r^2 + 1$ **42.** $49y^2 + 1$ **43.** $-36 + x^2$ **44.** $-1 + y^2$

45. $m^4 - 1$ **46.** $n^4 - 16$ **47.** $x^2 - 169y^2$ **48.** $x^2 - 225y^2$

49. $18r^2 - 8$ **50.** $32t^2 - 50$ **51.** $9xy^2 - 4x$ **52.** $36x^2y - 25y$

53. $16x^4 - 64x^2$ **54.** $25y^4 - 100y^2$ **55.** $xy^3 - 9xyz^2$ **56.** $x^3y - 4xy^3$

57. $36x^2 - 64y^2$ **58.** $225a^2 - 81b^2$ **59.** $144 - 81x^2$ **60.** $12x^2 - 27$

61. $25y^2 - 9$ **62.** $49a^2 - 16$ **63.** $121m^2 - 100n^2$ **64.** $169a^2 - 49b^2$

65. $x^2y^2 - 1$ **66.** $a^2b^2 - 16$ **67.** $x^2 - \dfrac{1}{4}$

68. $y^2 - \dfrac{1}{16}$ **69.** $49 - \dfrac{9}{25}m^2$ **70.** $100 - \dfrac{4}{81}n^2$

Objectives **B** **C** **Mixed Practice** *Factor each binomial or trinomial completely. See Examples 4 through 19.*

71. $81a^2 - 25b^2$ **72.** $49y^2 - 100z^2$ **73.** $x^2 + 14xy + 49y^2$ **74.** $x^2 + 10xy + 25y^2$

75. $32n^4 - 112n^2 + 98$

76. $162a^4 - 72a^2 + 8$

77. $x^6 - 81x^2$

78. $n^9 - n^5$

79. $64p^3q - 81pq^3$

80. $100x^3y - 49xy^3$

Review

Solve each equation. See Section 9.3.

81. $x - 6 = 0$

82. $y + 5 = 0$

83. $2m + 4 = 0$

84. $3x - 9 = 0$

85. $5z - 1 = 0$

86. $4a + 2 = 0$

Concept Extensions

Factor each expression completely.

87. $x^2 - \dfrac{2}{3}x + \dfrac{1}{9}$

88. $x^2 - \dfrac{1}{25}$

89. $(x + 2)^2 - y^2$

90. $(y - 6)^2 - z^2$

91. $a^2(b - 4) - 16(b - 4)$

92. $m^2(n + 8) - 9(n + 8)$

93. $(x^2 + 6x + 9) - 4y^2$ (*Hint:* Factor the trinomial in parentheses first.)

94. $(x^2 + 2x + 1) - 36y^2$

95. $x^{2n} - 100$

96. $x^{2n} - 81$

97. Fill in the blank so that $x^2 +$ _____ $x + 16$ is a perfect square trinomial.

98. Fill in the blank so that $9x^2 +$ _____ $x + 25$ is a perfect square trinomial.

99. Describe a perfect square trinomial.

100. Write a perfect square trinomial that factors as $(x + 3y)^2$.

101. What binomial multiplied by $(x - 6)$ gives the difference of two squares?

102. What binomial multiplied by $(5 + y)$ gives the difference of two squares?

The area of the largest square in the figure is $(a + b)^2$. Use this figure to answer Exercises 103 and 104.

103. Write the area of the largest square as the sum of the areas of the smaller squares and rectangles.

104. What factoring formula from this section is visually represented by this square?

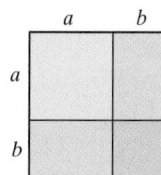

105. An object is dropped from the top of Pittsburgh's USX Towers, which is 841 feet tall. (*Source: World Almanac* research) The height of the object after t seconds is given by the expression $841 - 16t^2$.

  a. Find the height of the object after 2 seconds.

  b. Find the height of the object after 5 seconds.

  c. To the nearest whole second, estimate when the object hits the ground.

  d. Factor $841 - 16t^2$.

841 feet

107. At this writing, the world's tallest building is the Taipei 101 in Taipei, Taiwan, at a height of 1671 feet. (*Source:* Council on Tall Buildings and Urban Habitat) Suppose a worker is suspended 71 feet below the top of the pinnacle atop the building, at a height of 1600 feet above the ground. If the worker accidentally drops a bolt, the height of the bolt after t seconds is given by the expression $1600 - 16t^2$.

  a. Find the height of the bolt after 3 seconds.

  b. Find the height of the bolt after 7 seconds.

  c. To the nearest whole second, estimate when the bolt hits the ground.

  d. Factor $1600 - 16t^2$.

106. A worker on the top of the Aetna Life Building in San Francisco accidentally drops a bolt. The Aetna Life Building is 529 feet tall. (*Source: World Almanac* research) The height of the bolt after t seconds is given by the expression $529 - 16t^2$.

  a. Find the height of the bolt after 1 second.

  b. Find the height of the bolt after 4 seconds.

  c. To the nearest whole second, estimate when the bolt hits the ground.

  d. Factor $529 - 16t^2$.

108. A performer with the Moscow Circus is planning a stunt involving a free fall from the top of the Moscow State University building, which is 784 feet tall. (*Source:* Council on Tall Buildings and Urban Habitat) Neglecting air resistance, the performer's height above gigantic cushions positioned at ground level after t seconds is given by the expression $784 - 16t^2$.

  a. Find the performer's height after 2 seconds.

  b. Find the performer's height after 5 seconds.

  c. To the nearest whole second, estimate when the performer reaches the cushions positioned at ground level.

  d. Factor $784 - 16t^2$.

Choosing a Factoring Strategy

The following steps may be helpful when factoring polynomials.

To Factor a Polynomial

Step 1: Are there any common factors? If so, factor out the GCF.

Step 2: How many terms are in the polynomial?

    a. Two terms: Is it the difference of two squares? $a^2 - b^2 = (a - b)(a + b)$

    b. Three terms: Try one of the following.

      i. Perfect square trinomial: $a^2 + 2ab + b^2 = (a + b)^2$
$$a^2 - 2ab + b^2 = (a - b)^2$$

      ii. If not a perfect square trinomial, factor using the methods presented in Sections 13.2 through 13.4.

    c. Four terms: Try factoring by grouping.

Step 3: See if any factors in the factored polynomial can be factored further.

Step 4: Check by multiplying.

Factor each polynomial completely.

1. $x^2 + x - 12$

2. $x^2 - 10x + 16$

3. $x^2 - x - 6$

4. $x^2 + 2x + 1$

5. $x^2 - 6x + 9$

6. $x^2 + x - 2$

7. $x^2 + x - 6$

8. $x^2 + 7x + 12$

9. $x^2 - 7x + 10$

10. $x^2 - x - 30$

11. $2x^2 - 98$

12. $3x^2 - 75$

13. $x^2 + 3x + 5x + 15$

14. $3y - 21 + xy - 7x$

15. $x^2 + 6x - 16$

16. $x^2 - 3x - 28$

17. $4x^3 + 20x^2 - 56x$

18. $6x^3 - 6x^2 - 120x$

19. $12x^2 + 34x + 24$

20. $8a^2 + 6ab - 5b^2$

21. $4a^2 - b^2$

22. $x^2 - 25y^2$

23. $28 - 13x - 6x^2$

24. $20 - 3x - 2x^2$

25. $4 - 2x + x^2$

26. $a + a^2 - 3$

27. $6y^2 + y - 15$

28. $4x^2 - x - 5$

29. $18x^3 - 63x^2 + 9x$

30. $12a^3 - 24a^2 + 4a$

31. $16a^2 - 56a + 49$

32. $25p^2 - 70p + 49$

33. $14 + 5x - x^2$

34. $3 - 2x - x^2$

35. $3x^4y + 6x^3y - 72x^2y$

36. $2x^3y + 8x^2y^2 - 10xy^3$

Answers

1. _____
2. _____
3. _____
4. _____
5. _____
6. _____
7. _____
8. _____
9. _____
10. _____
11. _____
12. _____
13. _____
14. _____
15. _____
16. _____
17. _____
18. _____
19. _____
20. _____
21. _____
22. _____
23. _____
24. _____
25. _____
26. _____
27. _____
28. _____
29. _____
30. _____
31. _____
32. _____
33. _____
34. _____
35. _____
36. _____

37. _____

38. _____

39. _____

40. _____

41. _____

42. _____

43. _____

44. _____

45. _____

46. _____

47. _____

48. _____

49. _____

50. _____

51. _____

52. _____

53. _____

54. _____

55. _____

56. _____

57. _____

58. _____

59. _____

60. _____

61. _____

62. _____

63. _____

64. _____

65. _____

66. _____

67. _____

68. _____

69. _____

70. _____

71. _____

72. _____

73. _____

74. _____

75. _____

76. _____

37. $12x^3y + 243xy$

38. $6x^3y^2 + 8xy^2$

39. $2xy - 72x^3y$

40. $2x^3 - 18x$

41. $x^3 + 6x^2 - 4x - 24$

42. $x^3 - 2x^2 - 36x + 72$

43. $6a^3 + 10a^2$

44. $4n^2 - 6n$

45. $3x^3 - x^2 + 12x - 4$

46. $x^3 - 2x^2 + 3x - 6$

47. $6x^2 + 18xy + 12y^2$

48. $12x^2 + 46xy - 8y^2$

49. $5(x + y) + x(x + y)$

50. $7(x - y) + y(x - y)$

51. $14t^2 - 9t + 1$

52. $3t^2 - 5t + 1$

53. $-3x^2 - 2x + 5$

54. $-7x^2 - 19x + 6$

55. $1 - 8a - 20a^2$

56. $1 - 7a - 60a^2$

57. $x^4 - 10x^2 + 9$

58. $x^4 - 13x^2 + 36$

59. $x^2 - 23x + 120$

60. $y^2 + 22y + 96$

61. $x^2 - 14x - 48$

62. $16a^2 - 56ab + 49b^2$

63. $25p^2 - 70pq + 49q^2$

64. $7x^2 + 24xy + 9y^2$

65. $-x^2 - x + 30$

66. $-x^2 + 6x - 8$

67. $3rs - s + 12r - 4$

68. $x^3 - 2x^2 + x - 2$

69. $4x^2 - 8xy - 3x + 6y$

70. $4x^2 - 2xy - 7yz + 14xz$

71. $x^2 + 9xy - 36y^2$

72. $3x^2 + 10xy - 8y^2$

73. $x^4 - 14x^2 - 32$

74. $x^4 - 22x^2 - 75$

75. Explain why it makes good sense to factor out the GCF first, before using other methods of factoring.

76. The sum of two squares usually does not factor. Is the sum of two squares $9x^2 + 81y^2$ factorable?

13.6 SOLVING QUADRATIC EQUATIONS BY FACTORING

Objectives

A Solve Quadratic Equations by Factoring.

B Solve Equations with Degree Greater Than 2 by Factoring.

In this section, we introduce a new type of equation—the **quadratic equation.**

Quadratic Equation

A quadratic equation is one that can be written in the form

$$ax^2 + bx + c = 0$$

where a, b, and c are real numbers and $a \neq 0$.

Some examples of quadratic equations are shown below.

$$x^2 - 9x - 22 = 0 \qquad 4x^2 - 28 = -49 \qquad x(2x - 7) = 4$$

The form $ax^2 + bx + c = 0$ is called the **standard form** of a quadratic equation. The quadratic equation $x^2 - 9x - 22 = 0$ is the only equation above that is in standard form.

Quadratic equations model many real-life situations. For example, let's suppose we want to know how long before a person diving from a 144-foot cliff reaches the ocean. The answer to this question is found by solving the quadratic equation $-16t^2 + 144 = 0$. (See Example 1 in section 13.7.)

144 feet

Objective **A** Solving Quadratic Equations by Factoring

Some quadratic equations can be solved by making use of factoring and the **zero factor property.**

Zero Factor Property

If a and b are real numbers and if $ab = 0$, then $a = 0$ or $b = 0$.

In other words, if the product of two numbers is 0, then at least one of the numbers must be 0.

EXAMPLE 1 Solve: $(x - 3)(x + 1) = 0$

Solution: If this equation is to be a true statement, then either the factor $x - 3$ must be 0 or the factor $x + 1$ must be 0. In other words, either

$$x - 3 = 0 \qquad \text{or} \qquad x + 1 = 0$$

If we solve these two linear equations, we have

$$x = 3 \qquad \text{or} \qquad x = -1$$

PRACTICE PROBLEM 1

Solve: $(x - 7)(x + 2) = 0$

Answer

1. 7 and -2

Continued on next page

Thus, 3 and −1 are both solutions of the equation $(x - 3)(x + 1) = 0$. To check, we replace x with 3 in the original equation. Then we replace x with −1 in the original equation.

Check:

$(x - 3)(x + 1) = 0$ $(x - 3)(x + 1) = 0$

$(3 - 3)(3 + 1) \overset{?}{=} 0$ Replace x with 3. $(-1 - 3)(-1 + 1) \overset{?}{=} 0$ Replace x with −1.

$\qquad 0(4) = 0$ True $\qquad (-4)(0) = 0$ True

The solutions are 3 and −1.

▣ **Work Practice Problem 1**

Helpful Hint

The zero factor property says that *if a product is 0, then a factor is 0.*

If $a \cdot b = 0$, then $a = 0$ or $b = 0$.

If $x(x + 5) = 0$, then $x = 0$ or $x + 5 = 0$.

If $(x + 7)(2x - 3) = 0$, then $x + 7 = 0$ or $2x - 3 = 0$.

Use this property only when the product is 0. For example, if $a \cdot b = 8$, we do not know the value of a or b. The values may be $a = 2$, $b = 4$ or $a = 8$, $b = 1$, or any other two numbers whose product is 8.

PRACTICE PROBLEM 2

Solve: $(x - 10)(3x + 1) = 0$

EXAMPLE 2 Solve: $(x - 5)(2x + 7) = 0$

Solution: The product is 0. By the zero factor property, this is true only when a factor is 0. To solve, we set each factor equal to 0 and solve the resulting linear equations.

$(x - 5)(2x + 7) = 0$

$x - 5 = 0$ or $2x + 7 = 0$

$\qquad x = 5 \qquad\qquad 2x = -7$

$\qquad\qquad\qquad\qquad\qquad x = -\dfrac{7}{2}$

Check: Let $x = 5$.

$(x - 5)(2x + 7) = 0$

$(5 - 5)(2 \cdot 5 + 7) \overset{?}{=} 0$ Replace x with 5.

$0 \cdot 17 \overset{?}{=} 0$

$0 = 0$ True

Let $x = -\dfrac{7}{2}$.

$(x - 5)(2x + 7) = 0$

$\left(-\dfrac{7}{2} - 5\right)\left(2\left(-\dfrac{7}{2}\right) + 7\right) \overset{?}{=} 0$ Replace x with $-\dfrac{7}{2}$.

$\left(-\dfrac{17}{2}\right)(-7 + 7) \overset{?}{=} 0$

$\left(-\dfrac{17}{2}\right) \cdot 0 \overset{?}{=} 0$

$0 = 0$ True

The solutions are 5 and $-\dfrac{7}{2}$.

▣ **Work Practice Problem 2**

Answer

2. 10 and $-\dfrac{1}{3}$

EXAMPLE 3 Solve: $x(5x - 2) = 0$

Solution: $x(5x - 2) = 0$

$x = 0$ or $5x - 2 = 0$ Use the zero factor property.

$$5x = 2$$

$$x = \frac{2}{5}$$

Check these solutions in the original equation. The solutions are 0 and $\frac{2}{5}$.

■ **Work Practice Problem 3**

PRACTICE PROBLEM 3
Solve each equation.
a. $y(y + 3) = 0$
b. $x(4x - 3) = 0$

EXAMPLE 4 Solve: $x^2 - 9x - 22 = 0$

Solution: One side of the equation is 0. However, to use the zero factor property, one side of the equation must be 0 *and* the other side must be written as a product (must be factored). Thus, we must first factor this polynomial.

$$x^2 - 9x - 22 = 0$$

$(x - 11)(x + 2) = 0$ Factor.

Now we can apply the zero factor property.

$x - 11 = 0$ or $x + 2 = 0$

$x = 11$ $x = -2$

Check: Let $x = 11$.   Let $x = -2$.

$x^2 - 9x - 22 = 0$	$x^2 - 9x - 22 = 0$
$11^2 - 9 \cdot 11 - 22 \overset{?}{=} 0$	$(-2)^2 - 9(-2) - 22 \overset{?}{=} 0$
$121 - 99 - 22 \overset{?}{=} 0$	$4 + 18 - 22 \overset{?}{=} 0$
$22 - 22 \overset{?}{=} 0$	$22 - 22 \overset{?}{=} 0$
$0 = 0$ True	$0 = 0$ True

The solutions are 11 and -2.

■ **Work Practice Problem 4**

PRACTICE PROBLEM 4
Solve: $x^2 - 3x - 18 = 0$

EXAMPLE 5 Solve: $4x^2 - 28x = -49$

Solution: First we rewrite the equation in standard form so that one side is 0. Then we factor the polynomial.

$$4x^2 - 28x = -49$$

$4x^2 - 28x + 49 = 0$ Write in standard form by adding 49 to both sides.

$(2x - 7)(2x - 7) = 0$ Factor.

Next we use the zero factor property and set each factor equal to 0. Since the factors are the same, the related equations will give the same solution.

$2x - 7 = 0$ or $2x - 7 = 0$ Set each factor equal to 0.

$2x = 7$ $2x = 7$ Solve.

$x = \dfrac{7}{2}$ $x = \dfrac{7}{2}$

Check: Check this solution in the original equation. The solution is $\dfrac{7}{2}$.

■ **Work Practice Problem 5**

PRACTICE PROBLEM 5
Solve: $9x^2 - 24x = -16$

Answers
3. a. 0 and -3,   **b.** 0 and $\frac{3}{4}$,
4. 6 and -3,   **5.** $\frac{4}{3}$

The following steps may be used to solve a quadratic equation by factoring.

To Solve Quadratic Equations by Factoring

Step 1: Write the equation in standard form so that one side of the equation is 0.

Step 2: Factor the quadratic equation completely.

Step 3: Set each factor containing a variable equal to 0.

Step 4: Solve the resulting equations.

Step 5: Check each solution in the original equation.

Since it is not always possible to factor a quadratic polynomial, not all quadratic equations can be solved by factoring. Other methods of solving quadratic equations are presented in Chapter 16.

PRACTICE PROBLEM 6

Solve each equation.
a. $x(x - 4) = 5$
b. $x(3x + 7) = 6$

EXAMPLE 6 Solve: $x(2x - 7) = 4$

Solution: First we write the equation in standard form; then we factor.

$$x(2x - 7) = 4$$
$$2x^2 - 7x = 4 \qquad \text{Multiply.}$$
$$2x^2 - 7x - 4 = 0 \qquad \text{Write in standard form.}$$
$$(2x + 1)(x - 4) = 0 \qquad \text{Factor.}$$
$$2x + 1 = 0 \quad \text{or} \quad x - 4 = 0 \qquad \text{Set each factor equal to zero.}$$
$$2x = -1 \qquad\qquad x = 4 \qquad \text{Solve.}$$
$$x = -\frac{1}{2}$$

Check the solutions in the original equation. The solutions are $-\frac{1}{2}$ and 4.

■ Work Practice Problem 6

Helpful Hint

To solve the equation $x(2x - 7) = 4$, do **not** set each factor equal to 4. Remember that to apply the zero factor property, one side of the equation must be 0 and the other side of the equation must be in factored form.

✔ Concept Check Explain the error and solve the equation correctly.

$$(x - 3)(x + 1) = 5$$
$$x - 3 = 0 \quad \text{or} \quad x + 1 = 0$$
$$x = 3 \quad \text{or} \qquad x = -1$$

Answers
6. a. 5 and −1, **b.** $\frac{2}{3}$ and −3

✔ Concept Check Answer

To use the zero factor property, one side of the equation must be 0, not 5. Correctly, $(x - 3)(x + 1) = 5$, $x^2 - 2x - 3 = 5$, $x^2 - 2x - 8 = 0$, $(x - 4)(x + 2) = 0$, $x - 4 = 0$ or $x + 2 = 0$, $x = 4$ or $x = -2$.

Objective B Solving Equations with Degree Greater Than Two by Factoring

Some equations with degree greater than 2 can be solved by factoring and then using the zero factor property.

EXAMPLE 7 Solve: $3x^3 - 12x = 0$

Solution: To factor the left side of the equation, we begin by factoring out the greatest common factor, $3x$.

$$3x^3 - 12x = 0$$
$$3x(x^2 - 4) = 0 \quad \text{Factor out the GCF, } 3x.$$
$$3x(x + 2)(x - 2) = 0 \quad \text{Factor } x^2 - 4, \text{ a difference of two squares.}$$
$$3x = 0 \quad \text{or} \quad x + 2 = 0 \quad \text{or} \quad x - 2 = 0 \quad \text{Set each factor equal to 0.}$$
$$x = 0 \qquad\qquad x = -2 \qquad\qquad x = 2 \quad \text{Solve.}$$

Thus, the equation $3x^3 - 12x = 0$ has three solutions: 0, −2, and 2.

Check: Replace x with each solution in the original equation.

Let $x = 0$.

$$3(0)^3 - 12(0) \stackrel{?}{=} 0$$
$$0 = 0 \quad \text{True}$$

Let $x = -2$.

$$3(-2)^3 - 12(-2) \stackrel{?}{=} 0$$
$$3(-8) + 24 \stackrel{?}{=} 0$$
$$0 = 0 \quad \text{True}$$

Let $x = 2$.

$$3(2)^3 - 12(2) \stackrel{?}{=} 0$$
$$3(8) - 24 \stackrel{?}{=} 0$$
$$0 = 0 \quad \text{True}$$

The solutions are 0, −2, and 2.

Work Practice Problem 7

EXAMPLE 8 Solve: $(5x - 1)(2x^2 + 15x + 18) = 0$

Solution:

$$(5x - 1)(2x^2 + 15x + 18) = 0$$
$$(5x - 1)(2x + 3)(x + 6) = 0 \quad \text{Factor the trinomial.}$$
$$5x - 1 = 0 \quad \text{or} \quad 2x + 3 = 0 \quad \text{or} \quad x + 6 = 0 \quad \text{Set each factor equal to 0.}$$
$$5x = 1 \qquad\qquad 2x = -3 \qquad\qquad x = -6 \quad \text{Solve.}$$
$$x = \frac{1}{5} \qquad\qquad x = -\frac{3}{2}$$

Check each solution in the original equation. The solutions are $\frac{1}{5}$, $-\frac{3}{2}$, and −6.

Work Practice Problem 8

PRACTICE PROBLEM 7
Solve: $2x^3 - 18x = 0$

PRACTICE PROBLEM 8
Solve:
$(x + 3)(3x^2 - 20x - 7) = 0$

Answers
7. 0, 3, and −3, **8.** $-3, -\frac{1}{3}$, and 7

Mental Math

Solve each equation by inspection.

1. $(a - 3)(a - 7) = 0$

2. $(a - 5)(a - 2) = 0$

3. $(x + 8)(x + 6) = 0$

4. $(x + 2)(x + 3) = 0$

5. $(x + 1)(x - 3) = 0$

6. $(x - 1)(x + 2) = 0$

13.6 EXERCISE SET

Objective A *Solve each equation. See Examples 1 through 3.*

1. $(x - 2)(x + 1) = 0$

2. $(x + 3)(x + 2) = 0$

3. $(x - 6)(x - 7) = 0$

4. $(x + 4)(x - 10) = 0$

5. $(x + 9)(x + 17) = 0$

6. $(x - 11)(x - 1) = 0$

7. $x(x + 6) = 0$

8. $x(x - 7) = 0$

9. $3x(x - 8) = 0$

10. $2x(x + 12) = 0$

11. $(2x + 3)(4x - 5) = 0$

12. $(3x - 2)(5x + 1) = 0$

13. $(2x - 7)(7x + 2) = 0$

14. $(9x + 1)(4x - 3) = 0$

15. $\left(x - \dfrac{1}{2}\right)\left(x + \dfrac{1}{3}\right) = 0$

16. $\left(x + \dfrac{2}{9}\right)\left(x - \dfrac{1}{4}\right) = 0$

17. $(x + 0.2)(x + 1.5) = 0$

18. $(x + 1.7)(x + 2.3) = 0$

Solve. See Examples 4 through 6.

19. $x^2 - 13x + 36 = 0$

20. $x^2 + 2x - 63 = 0$

21. $x^2 + 2x - 8 = 0$

22. $x^2 - 5x + 6 = 0$

23. $x^2 - 7x = 0$

24. $x^2 - 3x = 0$

25. $x^2 + 20x = 0$

26. $x^2 + 15x = 0$

27. $x^2 = 16$

28. $x^2 = 9$

29. $x^2 - 4x = 32$

30. $x^2 - 5x = 24$

31. $(x + 4)(x - 9) = 4x$

32. $(x + 3)(x + 8) = x$

33. $x(3x - 1) = 14$

34. $x(4x - 11) = 3$

35. $3x^2 + 19x - 72 = 0$

36. $36x^2 + x - 21 = 0$

Objectives **A** **B** **Mixed Practice** *Solve each equation. See Examples 1 through 8. (A few exercises are linear equations.)*

37. $4x^3 - x = 0$

38. $4y^3 - 36y = 0$

39. $4(x - 7) = 6$

40. $5(3 - 4x) = 9$

41. $(4x - 3)(16x^2 - 24x + 9) = 0$

42. $(2x + 5)(4x^2 + 20x + 25) = 0$

43. $4y^2 - 1 = 0$

44. $4y^2 - 81 = 0$

45. $(2x + 3)(2x^2 - 5x - 3) = 0$

46. $(2x - 9)(x^2 + 5x - 36) = 0$

47. $x^2 - 15 = -2x$

48. $x^2 - 26 = -11x$

49. $30x^2 - 11x = 30$

50. $12x^2 + 7x - 12 = 0$

51. $5x^2 - 6x - 8 = 0$

52. $9x^2 + 7x = -2$

53. $6y^2 - 22y - 40 = 0$

54. $3x^2 - 6x - 9 = 0$

55. $(y - 2)(y + 3) = 6$

56. $(y - 5)(y - 2) = 28$

57. $x^3 - 12x^2 + 32x = 0$

58. $x^3 - 14x^2 + 49x = 0$

59. $x^2 + 14x + 49 = 0$

60. $x^2 + 22x + 121 = 0$

61. $12y = 8y^2$

62. $9y = 6y^2$

63. $7x^3 - 7x = 0$

64. $3x^3 - 27x = 0$

65. $3x^2 + 8x - 11 = 13 - 6x$

66. $2x^2 + 12x - 1 = 4 + 3x$

67. $3x^2 - 20x = -4x^2 - 7x - 6$

68. $4x^2 - 20x = -5x^2 - 6x - 5$

Review

Perform each indicated operation. Write all results in lowest terms. See Sections 2.4 and 3.3.

69. $\dfrac{3}{5} + \dfrac{4}{9}$

70. $\dfrac{2}{3} + \dfrac{3}{7}$

71. $\dfrac{7}{10} - \dfrac{5}{12}$

72. $\dfrac{5}{9} - \dfrac{5}{12}$

73. $\dfrac{4}{5} \cdot \dfrac{7}{8}$

74. $\dfrac{3}{7} \cdot \dfrac{12}{17}$

Concept Extensions

For Exercises 75 and 76, see the Concept Check in this section.

75. Explain the error and solve correctly:

$$x(x - 2) = 8$$
$$x = 8 \quad \text{or} \quad x - 2 = 8$$
$$x = 10$$

76. Explain the error and solve correctly:

$$(x - 4)(x + 2) = 0$$
$$x = -4 \quad \text{or} \quad x = 2$$

77. Write a quadratic equation that has two solutions, 6 and −1. Leave the polynomial in the equation in factored form.

78. Write a quadratic equation that has two solutions, 0 and −2. Leave the polynomial in the equation in factored form.

79. Write a quadratic equation in standard form that has two solutions, 5 and 7.

80. Write an equation that has three solutions, 0, 1, and 2.

81. A compass is accidentally thrown upward and out of an air balloon at a height of 300 feet. The height, y, of the compass at time x is given by the equation $y = -16x^2 + 20x + 300$.

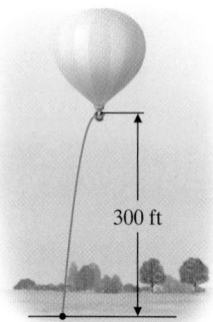

300 ft

a. Find the height of the compass at the given times by filling in the table below.

Time, x (in seconds)	0	1	2	3	4	5	6
Height, y (in feet)							

b. Use the table to determine when the compass strikes the ground.
c. Use the table to approximate the maximum height of the compass.

82. A rocket is fired upward from the ground with an initial velocity of 100 feet per second. The height, y, of the rocket at any time x is given by the equation $y = -16x^2 + 100x$.

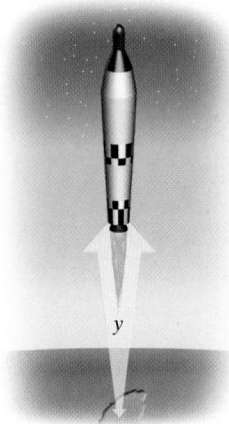

y

a. Find the height of the rocket at the given times by filling in the table below.

Time, x (in seconds)	0	1	2	3	4	5	6	7
Height, y (in feet)								

b. Use the table to determine between what two whole-numbered seconds the rocket strikes the ground.
c. Use the table to approximate the maximum height of the rocket.

Solve each equation.

83. $(x - 3)(3x + 4) = (x + 2)(x - 6)$

84. $(2x - 3)(x + 6) = (x - 9)(x + 2)$

85. $(2x - 3)(x + 8) = (x - 6)(x + 4)$

86. $(x + 6)(x - 6) = (2x - 9)(x + 4)$

THE BIGGER PICTURE   Simplifying Expressions and Solving Equations and Inequalities

Now we continue our outline from Sections 8.5, 9.7, and 12.7. Although suggestions are given, this outline should be in your own words. Once you complete this new portion, try the exercises below.

I. Simplifying Expressions

   A. Real Numbers

     1. Add (Section 8.3)

     2. Subtract (Section 8.4)

     3. Multiply or Divide (Section 8.5)

   B. Exponents (Section 12.2)

   C. Polynomials

     1. Add (Section 12.4)

     2. Subtract (Section 12.4)

     3. Multiply (Section 12.5)

     4. Divide (Section 12.7)

   D. Factoring Polynomials—see the Chapter 13 Integrated Review for steps.

$$3x^4 - 78x^2 + 75$$
$$= 3(x^4 - 26x^2 + 25) \quad \text{Factor out GCF—always first step.}$$

$$= 3(x^2 - 25)(x^2 - 1) \quad \text{Factor trinomial.}$$

$$= 3(x + 5)(x - 5)(x + 1)(x - 1) \quad \text{Factor further—each difference of squares.}$$

II. Solving Equations and Inequalities

   A. Linear Equations (Section 9.3)

   B. Linear Inequalities (Section 9.7)

C. Quadratic & Higher Degree Equations (Solving by Factoring)—highest power on variable is at least 2 when equation is written in standard form (set equal to 0).

$$x^2 + x = 6$$
$$x^2 + x - 6 = 0 \quad \text{Write the equation in standard form (set it equal to 0).}$$
$$(x - 2)(x + 3) = 0 \quad \text{Factor.}$$
$$x = 2 \quad \text{or} \quad x = -3 \quad \text{Set each factor equal to 0 and solve.}$$

Simplify each expression.

1. $-7 + (-27)$

2. $\dfrac{(x^3)^4}{(x^{-2})^5}$

3. $(x^3 - 6x^2 + 2) - (5x^3 - 6)$

4. $\dfrac{3y^3 - 3y^2 + 9}{3y^2}$

Factor each expression.

5. $10x^3 - 250x$

6. $x^2 - 36x + 35$

7. $6xy + 15x - 6y - 15$

8. $5xy^2 - 2xy - 7x$

Solve each equation. Remember to use your outline to determine whether the equation is linear or quadratic and how to proceed with solving.

  9. $(x - 5)(2x + 1) = 0$

10. $5x - 5 = 0$

11. $x(x - 12) = 28$

12. $7(x - 3) + 2(5x + 1) = 14$

A Solve Problems That Can Be
Modeled by Quadratic Equations.

Objective **A** Solving Problems Modeled by Quadratic Equations

Some problems may be modeled by quadratic equations. To solve these problems, we use the same problem-solving steps that were introduced in Section 9.4. When solving these problems, keep in mind that a solution of an equation that models a problem may not be a solution to the problem. For example, a person's age or the length of a rectangle is always a positive number. Thus we discard solutions that do not make sense as solutions of the problem.

PRACTICE PROBLEM 1

Cliff divers also frequent the falls at Waimea Falls Park in Oahu, Hawaii. Here, a diver can jump from a ledge 64 feet up the waterfall into a rocky pool below. Neglecting air resistance, the height of a diver above the pool after t seconds is $h = -16t^2 + 64$. Find how long it takes the diver to reach the pool.

EXAMPLE 1 Finding Free-Fall Time

Since the 1940s, one of the top tourist attractions in Acapulco, Mexico is watching the cliff divers off the La Quebrada. The divers' platform is about 144 feet above the sea. These divers must time their descent just right, since they land in the crashing Pacific, in an inlet that is at most $9\frac{1}{2}$ feet deep. Neglecting air resistance, the height h in feet of a cliff diver above the ocean after t seconds is given by the quadratic equation $h = -16t^2 + 144$.

Find out how long it takes the diver to reach the ocean.

Solution:

1. UNDERSTAND. Read and reread the problem. Then draw a picture of the problem.

   The equation $h = -16t^2 + 144$ models the height of the falling diver at time t. Familiarize yourself with this equation by find the height of the diver at time $t = 1$ second and $t = 2$ seconds.

   When $t = 1$ second, the height of the diver is $h = -16(1)^2 + 144 = 128$ feet.

   When $t = 2$ seconds, the height of the diver is $h = -16(2)^2 + 144 = 80$ feet.

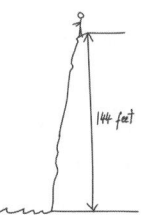

2. TRANSLATE. To find out how long it takes the diver to reach the ocean, we want to know the value of t for which $h = 0$.

$$0 = -16t^2 + 144$$
$$0 = -16(t^2 - 9) \quad \text{Factor out } -16.$$
$$0 = -16(t - 3)(t + 3) \quad \text{Factor completely.}$$
$$t - 3 = 0 \quad \text{or} \quad t + 3 = 0 \quad \text{Set each factor containing a variable equal to 0.}$$
$$t = 3 \quad \text{or} \quad t = -3 \quad \text{Solve.}$$

3. INTERPRET. Since the time t cannot be negative, the proposed solution is 3 seconds.

Check: Verify that the height of the diver when t is 3 seconds is 0.

When $t = 3$ seconds, $h = -16(3)^2 + 144 = -144 + 144 = 0$.

■ **Work Practice Problem 1**

Answer

1. 2 sec

EXAMPLE 2 Finding a Number

The square of a number plus three times the number is 70. Find the number.

Solution:

1. UNDERSTAND. Read and reread the problem. Suppose that the number is 5. The square of 5 is 5^2 or 25. Three times 5 is 15. Then $25 + 15 = 40$, not 70, so the number must be greater than 5. Remember, the purpose of proposing a number, such as 5, is to better understand the problem. Now that we do, we will let x = the number.

2. TRANSLATE.

the square of a number	plus	three times the number	is	70
↓	↓	↓	↓	↓
x^2	$+$	$3x$	$=$	70

3. SOLVE.

$$x^2 + 3x = 70$$
$$x^2 + 3x - 70 = 0 \qquad \text{Subtract 70 from both sides.}$$
$$(x + 10)(x - 7) = 0 \qquad \text{Factor.}$$
$$x + 10 = 0 \quad \text{or} \quad x - 7 = 0 \quad \text{Set each factor equal to 0.}$$
$$x = -10 \qquad\qquad x = 7 \quad \text{Solve.}$$

4. INTERPRET.

Check: The square of -10 is $(-10)^2$, or 100. Three times -10 is $3(-10)$ or -30. Then $100 + (-30) = 70$, the correct sum, so -10 checks.

The square of 7 is 7^2 or 49. Three times 7 is $3(7)$, or 21. Then $49 + 21 = 70$, the correct sum, so 7 checks.

State: There are two numbers. They are -10 and 7.

📕 **Work Practice Problem 2**

⚠ **EXAMPLE 3** Finding the Dimensions of a Sail

The height of a triangular sail is 2 meters less than twice the length of the base. If the sail has an area of 30 square meters, find the length of its base and the height.

Solution:

1. UNDERSTAND. Read and reread the problem. Since we are finding the length of the base and the height, we let

x = the length of the base

Since the height is 2 meters less than twice the length of the base,

$2x - 2$ = the height

An illustration is shown on the next page.

2. TRANSLATE. We are given that the area of the triangle is 30 square meters, so we use the formula for area of a triangle.

area of triangle	$=$	$\frac{1}{2}$	$\cdot$	base	$\cdot$	height
↓		↓		↓		↓
30	$=$	$\frac{1}{2}$	$\cdot$	x	$\cdot$	$(2x - 2)$

Continued on next page

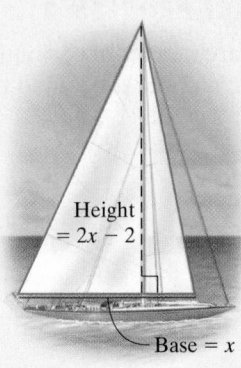

Height = $2x - 2$

Base = x

3. SOLVE. Now we solve the quadratic equation.

$$30 = \frac{1}{2}x(2x - 2)$$

$$30 = x^2 - x \qquad \text{Multiply.}$$

$$0 = x^2 - x - 30 \qquad \text{Write in standard form.}$$

$$0 = (x - 6)(x + 5) \qquad \text{Factor.}$$

$$x - 6 = 0 \quad \text{or} \quad x + 5 = 0 \qquad \text{Set each factor equal to 0.}$$

$$x = 6 \qquad\qquad x = -5$$

4. INTERPRET. Since x represents the length of the base, we discard the solution -5. The base of a triangle cannot be negative. The base is then 6 meters and the height is $2(6) - 2 = 10$ meters.

Check: To check this problem, we recall that

$$\text{area} = \frac{1}{2}\,\text{base} \cdot \text{height or}$$

$$30 \overset{?}{=} \frac{1}{2}(6)(10)$$

$$30 = 30 \qquad \text{True}$$

State: The base of the triangular sail is 6 meters and the height is 10 meters.

▣ **Work Practice Problem 3**

The next examples make use of the **Pythagorean theorem** and consecutive integers. Before we review this theorem, recall that a **right triangle** is a triangle that contains a 90° or right angle. The **hypotenuse** of a right triangle is the side opposite the right angle and is the longest side of the triangle. The **legs** of a right triangle are the other sides of the triangle.

Pythagorean Theorem

In a right triangle, the sum of the squares of the lengths of the two legs is equal to the square of the length of the hypotenuse.

$$(\text{leg})^2 + (\text{leg})^2 = (\text{hypotenuse})^2 \quad \text{or} \quad a^2 + b^2 = c^2$$

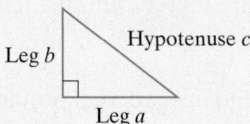

Hypotenuse c

Leg b

Leg a

Study the following diagrams for a review of consecutive integers.

Examples

If x is the first integer, then consecutive integers are
$x, x + 1, x + 2, \ldots$

If x is the first even integer, then consecutive even integers are
$x, x + 2, x + 4, \ldots$

If x is the first odd integer, then consecutive odd integers are
$x, x + 2, x + 4, \ldots$

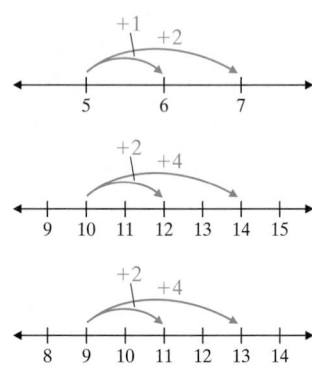

EXAMPLE 4 Finding Consecutive Even Integers

Find two consecutive even integers whose product is 34 more than their sum.

Solution:

1. UNDERSTAND. Read and reread the problem. Let's just choose two consecutive even integers to help us better understand the problem. Let's choose 10 and 12. Their product is $10(12) = 120$ and their sum is $10 + 12 = 22$. The product is $120 - 22$, or 98 greater than the sum. Thus our guess is incorrect, but we have a better understanding of this example.

   Let's let x and $x + 2$ be the consecutive even integers.

2. TRANSLATE.

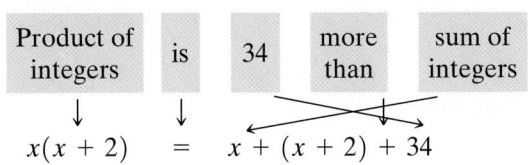

$$x(x + 2) = x + (x + 2) + 34$$

3. SOLVE. Now we solve the equation.

$$x(x + 2) = x + (x + 2) + 34$$
$$x^2 + 2x = x + x + 2 + 34 \qquad \text{Multiply.}$$
$$x^2 + 2x = 2x + 36 \qquad \text{Combine like terms.}$$
$$x^2 - 36 = 0 \qquad \text{Write in standard form.}$$
$$(x + 6)(x - 6) = 0 \qquad \text{Factor.}$$
$$x + 6 = 0 \quad \text{or} \quad x - 6 = 0 \qquad \text{Set each factor equal to 0.}$$
$$x = -6 \qquad\qquad x = 6 \qquad \text{Solve.}$$

4. INTERPRET. If $x = -6$, then $x + 2 = -6 + 2$, or -4.
   If $x = 6$, then $x + 2 = 6 + 2$, or 8.

Check: $-6, -4$ $\qquad\qquad\qquad\qquad$ $6, 8$

$$-6(-4) \stackrel{?}{=} -6 + (-4) + 34 \qquad\qquad 6(8) \stackrel{?}{=} 6 + 8 + 34$$
$$24 \stackrel{?}{=} -10 + 34 \qquad\qquad\qquad 48 \stackrel{?}{=} 14 + 34$$
$$24 = 24 \qquad \text{True} \qquad\qquad 48 = 48 \qquad \text{True}$$

State: The two consecutive even integers are -6 and -4 or 6 and 8.

🔲 **Work Practice Problem 4**

PRACTICE PROBLEM 4

Find two consecutive odd integers whose product is 23 more than their sum.

△ **EXAMPLE 5** Finding the Dimensions of a Triangle

Find the lengths of the sides of a right triangle if the lengths can be expressed as three consecutive even integers.

Solution:

1. UNDERSTAND. Read and reread the problem. Let's suppose that the length of one leg of the right triangle is 4 units. Then the other leg is the next even integer, or 6 units, and the hypotenuse of the triangle is the next even integer, or 8 units. Remember that the hypotenuse is the longest side. Let's see if a triangle with sides of these lengths forms a right triangle. To do this, we check to see whether the Pythagorean theorem holds true.

$$4^2 + 6^2 \stackrel{?}{=} 8^2$$
$$16 + 36 \stackrel{?}{=} 64$$
$$52 = 64 \qquad \text{False}$$

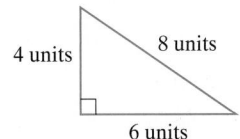

4 units

8 units

6 units

Continued on next page

PRACTICE PROBLEM 5

The length of one leg of a right triangle is 7 meters less than the length of the other leg. The length of the hypotenuse is 13 meters. Find the lengths of the legs.

Answers
4. 5 and 7 or -5 and -3,
5. 5 meters, 12 meters

Our proposed numbers do not check, but we now have a better understanding of the problem.

We let x, $x + 2$, and $x + 4$ be three consecutive even integers. Since these integers represent lengths of the sides of a right triangle, we have the following.

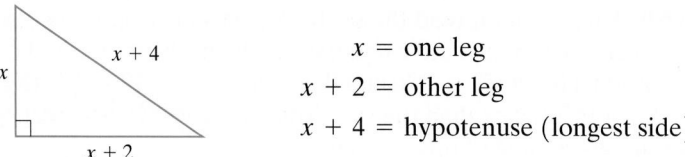

x = one leg

$x + 2$ = other leg

$x + 4$ = hypotenuse (longest side)

2. TRANSLATE. By the Pythagorean theorem, we have that

    $$(\text{leg})^2 + (\text{leg})^2 = (\text{hypotenuse})^2$$
    $$(x)^2 + (x + 2)^2 = (x + 4)^2$$

3. SOLVE. Now we solve the equation.

    $$x^2 + (x + 2)^2 = (x + 4)^2$$

$x^2 + x^2 + 4x + 4 = x^2 + 8x + 16$	Multiply.
$2x^2 + 4x + 4 = x^2 + 8x + 16$	Combine like terms.
$x^2 - 4x - 12 = 0$	Write in standard form.
$(x - 6)(x + 2) = 0$	Factor.
$x - 6 = 0$ or $x + 2 = 0$	Set each factor equal to 0.
$x = 6$ $x = -2$	

4. INTERPRET. We discard $x = -2$ since length cannot be negative. If $x = 6$, then $x + 2 = 8$ and $x + 4 = 10$.

Check: Verify that

$$(\text{leg})^2 + (\text{leg})^2 = (\text{hypotenuse})^2$$
$$6^2 + 8^2 \overset{?}{=} 10^2$$
$$36 + 64 \overset{?}{=} 100$$
$$100 = 100 \qquad \text{True}$$

State: The sides of the right triangle have lengths 6 units, 8 units, and 10 units.

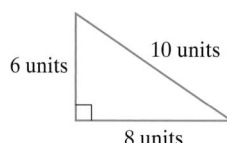

🔲 **Work Practice Problem 5**

13.7 EXERCISE SET

FOR EXTRA HELP

Student Solutions Manual

PH Math/Tutor Center

CD/Video for Review

MathXL
MathXL®

MyMathLab
MyMathLab

Objective A *See Examples 1 through 5 for all exercises. For Exercises 1 through 6, represent each given condition using a single variable, x.*

△ **1.** The length and width of a rectangle whose length is 4 centimeters more than its width

△ **2.** The length and width of a rectangle whose length is twice its width

3. Two consecutive odd integers

4. Two consecutive even integers

△ **5.** The base and height of a triangle whose height is one more than four times its base

△ **6.** The base and height of a trapezoid whose base is three less than five times its height

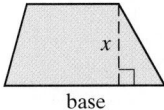

Use the information given to find the dimensions of each figure.

△ **7.**

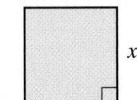

The *area* of the square is 121 square units. Find the length of its sides.

△ **8.**

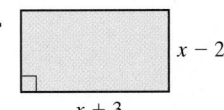

The *area* of the rectangle is 84 square inches. Find its length and width.

△ **9.**

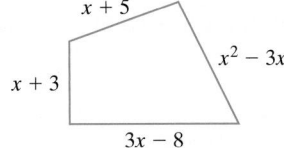

The *perimeter* of the quadrilateral is 120 centimeters. Find the lengths of the sides.

△ **10.**

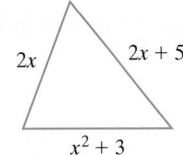

The *perimeter* of the triangle is 85 feet. Find the lengths of its sides.

△ **11.**

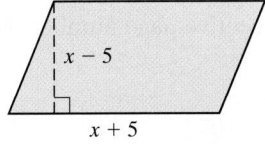

The *area* of the parallelogram is 96 square miles. Find its base and height.

△ **12.**

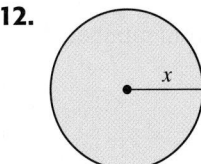

The *area* of the circle is 25π square kilometers. Find its radius.

997

Solve.

13. An object is thrown upward from the top of an 80-foot building with an initial velocity of 64 feet per second. The height h of the object after t seconds is given by the quadratic equation $h = -16t^2 + 64t + 80$. When will the object hit the ground?

14. A hang glider accidentally drops her compass from the top of a 400-foot cliff. The height h of the compass after t seconds is given by the quadratic equation $h = -16t^2 + 400$. When will the compass hit the ground?

15. The width of a rectangle is 7 centimeters less than twice its length. Its area is 30 square centimeters. Find the dimensions of the rectangle.

16. The length of a rectangle is 9 inches more than its width. Its area is 112 square inches. Find the dimensions of the rectangle.

△ *The equation $D = \frac{1}{2}n(n - 3)$ gives the number of diagonals D for a polygon with n sides. For example, a polygon with 6 sides has $D = \frac{1}{2} \cdot 6(6 - 3)$ or $D = 9$ diagonals. (See if you can count all 9 diagonals. Some are shown in the figure.) Use this equation, $D = \frac{1}{2}n(n - 3)$, for Exercises 17 through 20.*

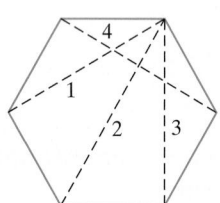

17. Find the number of diagonals for a polygon that has 12 sides.

18. Find the number of diagonals for a polygon that has 15 sides.

19. Find the number of sides n for a polygon that has 35 diagonals.

20. Find the number of sides n for a polygon that has 14 diagonals.

Solve.

21. The sum of a number and its square is 132. Find the number.

22. The sum of a number and its square is 182. Find the number.

23. The product of two consecutive room numbers is 210. Find the room numbers.

24. The product of two consecutive page numbers is 420. Find the page numbers.

25. A ladder is leaning against a building so that the distance from the ground to the top of the ladder is one foot less than the length of the ladder. Find the length of the ladder if the distance from the bottom of the ladder to the building is 5 feet.

26. Use the given figure to find the length of the guy wire.

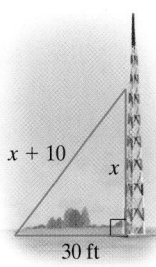

27. If the sides of a square are increased by 3 inches, the area becomes 64 square inches. Find the length of the sides of the original square.

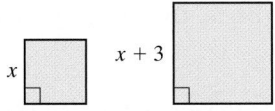

28. If the sides of a square are increased by 5 meters, the area becomes 100 square meters. Find the length of the sides of the original square.

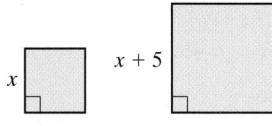

29. One leg of a right triangle is 4 millimeters longer than the smaller leg and the hypotenuse is 8 millimeters longer than the smaller leg. Find the lengths of the sides of the triangle.

30. One leg of a right triangle is 9 centimeters longer than the other leg and the hypotenuse is 45 centimeters. Find the lengths of the legs of the triangle.

31. The length of the base of a triangle is twice its height. If the area of the triangle is 100 square kilometers, find the height.

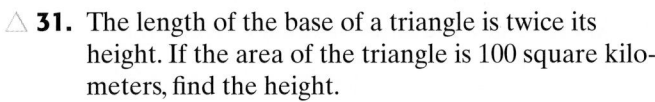

32. The height of a triangle is 2 millimeters less than the base. If the area is 60 square millimeters, find the base.

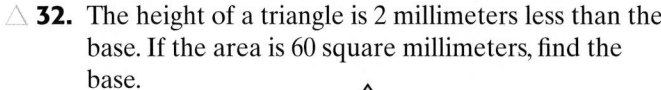

33. Find the length of the shorter leg of a right triangle if the longer leg is 12 feet more than the shorter leg and the hypotenuse is 12 feet less than twice the shorter leg.

34. Find the length of the shorter leg of a right triangle if the longer leg is 10 miles more than the shorter leg and the hypotenuse is 10 miles less than twice the shorter leg.

35. An object is dropped from 39 feet below the tip of the pinnacle atop one of the 1483-foot-tall Petronas Twin Towers in Kuala Lumpur, Malaysia. (*Source:* Council on Tall Buildings and Urban Habitat) The height h of the object after t seconds is given by the equation $h = -16t^2 + 1444$. Find how many seconds pass before the object reaches the ground.

36. An object is dropped from the top of 311 South Wacker Drive, a 961-foot-tall office building in Chicago. (*Source:* Council on Tall Buildings and Urban Habitat) The height h of the object after t seconds is given by the equation $h = -16t^2 + 961$. Find how many seconds pass before the object reaches the ground.

37. At the end of 2 years, P dollars invested at an interest rate r compounded annually increases to an amount, A dollars, given by

$$A = P(1 + r)^2$$

Find the interest rate if $100 increased to $144 in 2 years. Write your answer as a percent.

38. At the end of 2 years, P dollars invested at an interest rate r compounded annually increases to an amount, A dollars, given by

$$A = P(1 + r)^2$$

Find the interest rate if $2000 increased to $2420 in 2 years. Write your answer as a percent.

△ **39.** Find the dimensions of a rectangle whose width is 7 miles less than its length and whose area is 120 square miles.

△ **40.** Find the dimensions of a rectangle whose width is 2 inches less than half its length and whose area is 160 square inches.

41. If the cost, C, for manufacturing x units of a certain product is given by $C = x^2 - 15x + 50$, find the number of units manufactured at a cost of $9500.

42. If a switchboard handles n telephones, the number C of telephone connections it can make simultaneously is given by the equation $C = \dfrac{n(n-1)}{2}$. Find how many telephones are handled by a switchboard making 120 telephone connections simultaneously.

Review

The following double line graph shows a comparison of the amount of land (in thousand acres) occupied by farms in Florida during the years shown with the amount of land occupied by farms in Georgia. Use this graph to answer Exercises 43 through 49. See Section 11.1.

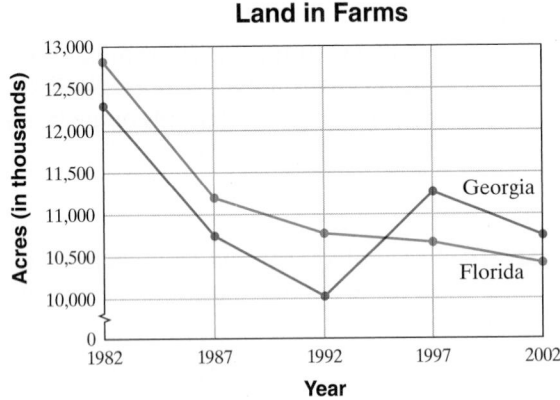

Land in Farms

43. Approximate the amount of land occupied by farms in Georgia in 1997.

44. Approximate the amount of land occupied by farms in Florida in 1997.

45. Approximate the amount of land occupied by farms in Georgia in 1987.

46. Approximate the amount of land occupied by farms in Florida in 1987.

47. Approximate the year that the colored lines in this graph intersect.

48. In your own words, explain the meaning of the point of intersection in the graph.

49. Describe the trends shown in this graph and speculate as to why these trends have occurred.

Concept Extensions

△ **50.** Two boats travel at right angles to each other after leaving the same dock at the same time. One hour later the boats are 17 miles apart. If one boat travels 7 miles per hour faster than the other boat, find the rate of each boat.

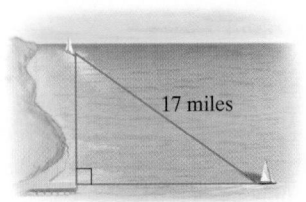

△ **51.** The side of a square equals the width of a rectangle. The length of the rectangle is 6 meters longer than its width. The sum of the areas of the square and the rectangle is 176 square meters. Find the side of the square.

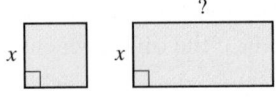

52. The sum of two numbers is 20, and the sum of their squares is 218. Find the numbers.

53. The sum of two numbers is 25, and the sum of their squares is 325. Find the numbers.

△ **54.** According to the International America's Cup Class (IACC) rule, a sailboat competing in the America's Cup match must have a 110-foot-tall mast and a combined mainsail and jib sail area of 3000 square feet. (*Source:* America's Cup Organizing Committee) A design for an IACC-class sailboat calls for the mainsail to be 60% of the combined sail area. If the height of the triangular mainsail is 28 feet more than twice the length of the boom, find the length of the boom and the height of the mainsail.

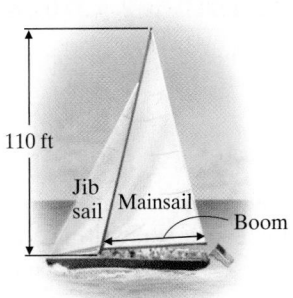

110 ft

Jib sail / Mainsail

Boom

△ **55.** A rectangular pool is surrounded by a walk 4 meters wide. The pool is 6 meters longer than its width. If the total area of the pool and walk is 576 square meters more than the area of the pool, find the dimensions of the pool.

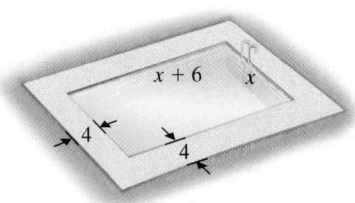

$x + 6$ x

4   4

△ **56.** A rectangular garden is surrounded by a walk of uniform width. The area of the garden is 180 square yards. If the dimensions of the garden plus the walk are 16 yards by 24 yards, find the width of the walk.

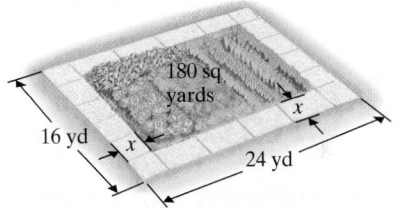

180 sq yards

16 yd x

x

24 yd

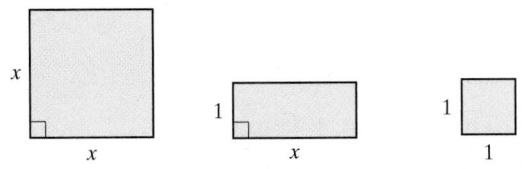

CHAPTER 13 Group Activity

Factoring polynomials can be visualized using areas of rectangles. To see this, let's first find the areas of the following squares and rectangles. (Recall that Area = Length · Width.)

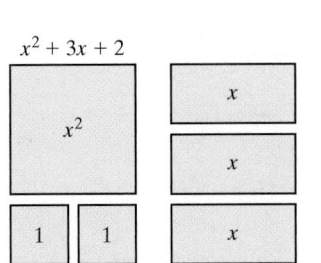

x

x

1

x

1

1

To use these areas to visualize factoring the polynomial $x^2 + 3x + 2$, for example, use the shapes below to form a rectangle. The factored form is found by reading the length and the width of the rectangle as shown below.

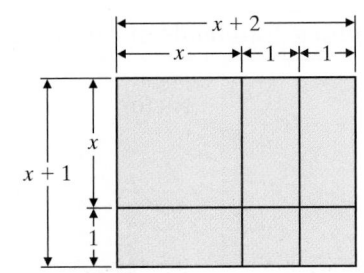

$x^2 + 3x + 2$

x^2

x

x

1   1 x

$x + 2$

x 1 1

x

$x + 1$

1

Thus, $x^2 + 3x + 2 = (x + 2)(x + 1)$.

Try using this method to visualize the factored form of each polynomial below.

Work in a group and use tiles to find the factored form of the polynomials below. (Tiles can be hand made from index cards.)

1. $x^2 + 6x + 5$

2. $x^2 + 5x + 6$

3. $x^2 + 5x + 4$

4. $x^2 + 4x + 3$

5. $x^2 + 6x + 9$

6. $x^2 + 4x + 4$

Chapter 13 Vocabulary Check

Fill in each blank with one of the words or phrases listed below.

factoring   quadratic equation

greatest common factor   perfect square trinomial

1. An equation that can be written in the form $ax^2 + bx + c = 0$ (with a not 0) is called a _____.

2. _____ is the process of writing an expression as a product.

3. The _____ of a list of terms is the product of all common factors.

4. A trinomial that is the square of some binomial is called a _____.

Helpful Hint

Are you preparing for your test? Don't forget to take the Chapter 13 Test on page 1009. Then check your answers at the back of the text and use the Chapter Test Prep Video CD to see the fully worked-out solutions to any of the exercises you want to review.

13 Chapter Highlights

DEFINITIONS AND CONCEPTS	**EXAMPLES**
Section 13.1 The Greatest Common Factor	

Factoring is the process of writing an expression as a product.	Factor: $6 = 2 \cdot 3$ Factor: $x^2 + 5x + 6 = (x + 2)(x + 3)$
The GCF of a list of variable terms contains the smallest exponent on each common variable.	The GCF of z^5, z^3, and z^{10} is z^3.
The GCF of a list of terms is the product of all common factors.	Find the GCF of $8x^2y$, $10x^3y^2$, and $50x^2y^3$. $\quad 8x^2y = 2 \cdot 2 \cdot 2 \cdot x^2 \cdot y$ $\quad 10x^3y^2 = 2 \cdot 5 \cdot x^3 \cdot y^2$ $\quad 50x^2y^3 = 2 \cdot 5 \cdot 5 \cdot x^2 \cdot y^3$ $\quad\quad \text{GCF} = 2 \cdot x^2 \cdot y \quad \text{or} \quad 2x^2y$
TO FACTOR BY GROUPING	Factor: $10ax + 15a - 6xy - 9y$
Step 1. Group the terms in two groups so that each group has a common factor.	**Step 1.** $(10ax + 15a) + (-6xy - 9y)$
Step 2. Factor out the GCF from each group.	**Step 2.** $5a(2x + 3) - 3y(2x + 3)$
Step 3. If there is a common binomial factor, factor it out.	**Step 3.** $(2x + 3)(5a - 3y)$
Step 4. If not, rearrange the terms and try these steps again.	

Section 13.2 Factoring Trinomials of the Form $x^2 + bx + c$	

The product of these numbers is c. $x^2 + bx + c = (x + \square)(x + \square)$ The sum of these numbers is b.	Factor: $x^2 + 7x + 12$ $\quad 3 + 4 = 7 \quad 3 \cdot 4 = 12$ $\quad x^2 + 7x + 12 = (x + 3)(x + 4)$

DEFINITIONS AND CONCEPTS	**EXAMPLES**

Section 13.3 Factoring Trinomials of the Form $ax^2 + bx + c$

To factor $ax^2 + bx + c$, try various combinations of factors of ax^2 and c until a middle term of bx is obtained when checking.

Factor: $3x^2 + 14x - 5$

Factors of $3x^2$: $3x, x$

Factors of -5: $-1, 5$ and $1, -5$.

$$(3x - 1)(x + 5)$$
$$-1x$$
$$+15x$$
$$14x \quad \text{Correct middle term}$$

Section 13.4 Factoring Trinomials of the Form $ax^2 + bx + c$ by Grouping

TO FACTOR $ax^2 + bx + c$ BY GROUPING

Step 1. Find two numbers whose product is $a \cdot c$ and whose sum is b.

Step 2. Rewrite bx, using the factors found in Step 1.

Step 3. Factor by grouping.

Factor: $3x^2 + 14x - 5$

Step 1. Find two numbers whose product is $3 \cdot (-5)$ or -15 and whose sum is 14. They are 15 and -1.

Step 2. $3x^2 + 14x - 5$
$$= 3x^2 + 15x - 1x - 5$$

Step 3. $= 3x(x + 5) - 1(x + 5)$
$$= (x + 5)(3x - 1)$$

Section 13.5 Factoring Perfect Square Trinomials and the Difference of Two Squares

A **perfect square trinomial** is a trinomial that is the square of some binomial.

PERFECT SQUARE TRINOMIAL = SQUARE OF BINOMIAL

$$x^2 + 4x + 4 = (x + 2)^2$$
$$25x^2 - 10x + 1 = (5x - 1)^2$$

Factoring Perfect Square Trinomials

$$a^2 + 2ab + b^2 = (a + b)^2$$
$$a^2 - 2ab + b^2 = (a - b)^2$$

Factor.

$$x^2 + 6x + 9 = x^2 + 2(x \cdot 3) + 3^2 = (x + 3)^2$$
$$4x^2 - 12x + 9 = (2x)^2 - 2(2x \cdot 3) + 3^2$$
$$= (2x - 3)^2$$

Difference of Two Squares

$$a^2 - b^2 = (a + b)(a - b)$$

Factor.

$$x^2 - 9 = x^2 - 3^2 = (x + 3)(x - 3)$$

Section 13.6 Solving Quadratic Equations by Factoring

A **quadratic equation** is an equation that can be written in the form $ax^2 + bx + c = 0$ with a not 0.

The form $ax^2 + bx + c = 0$ is called the **standard form** of a quadratic equation.

Zero Factor Property

If a and b are real numbers and if $ab = 0$, then $a = 0$ or $b = 0$.

Quadratic Equation	**Standard Form**
$x^2 = 16$	$x^2 - 16 = 0$
$y = -2y^2 + 5$	$2y^2 + y - 5 = 0$

If $(x + 3)(x - 1) = 0$, then $x + 3 = 0$ or $x - 1 = 0$.

continued

DEFINITIONS AND CONCEPTS	**EXAMPLES**

Section 13.6 Solving Quadratic Equations by Factoring (*continued*)

TO SOLVE QUADRATIC EQUATIONS BY FACTORING	Solve: $3x^2 = 13x - 4$
Step 1. Write the equation in standard form so that one side of the equation is 0.	**Step 1.** $3x^2 - 13x + 4 = 0$
Step 2. Factor completely.	**Step 2.** $(3x - 1)(x - 4) = 0$
Step 3. Set each factor containing a variable equal to 0.	**Step 3.** $3x - 1 = 0$ or $x - 4 = 0$
Step 4. Solve the resulting equations.	**Step 4.** $3x = 1$ $x = 4$ $x = \dfrac{1}{3}$
Step 5. Check solutions in the original equation.	**Step 5.** Check both $\dfrac{1}{3}$ and 4 in the original equation.

Section 13.7 Quadratic Equations and Problem Solving

PROBLEM-SOLVING STEPS	A garden is in the shape of a rectangle whose length is two feet more than its width. If the area of the garden is 35 square feet, find its dimensions.
1. UNDERSTAND the problem.	**1.** Read and reread the problem. Guess a solution and check your guess. Draw a diagram. Let x be the width of the rectangular garden. Then $x + 2$ is the length. 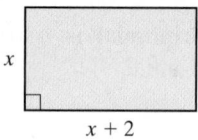
2. TRANSLATE.	**2.** $\begin{array}{ccccc} \text{length} & \cdot & \text{width} & = & \text{area} \\ \downarrow & & \downarrow & & \downarrow \\ (x + 2) & \cdot & x & = & 35 \end{array}$
3. SOLVE.	**3.** $\begin{aligned} (x + 2)x &= 35 \\ x^2 + 2x - 35 &= 0 \\ (x - 5)(x + 7) &= 0 \end{aligned}$ $x - 5 = 0$ or $x + 7 = 0$ $x = 5$ $x = -7$
4. INTERPRET.	**4.** Discard the solution $x = -7$ since x represents width. *Check:* If x is 5 feet, then $x + 2 = 5 + 2 = 7$ feet. The area of a rectangle whose width is 5 feet and whose length is 7 feet is (5 feet)(7 feet) or 35 square feet. *State:* The garden is 5 feet by 7 feet.

Are You Prepared for a Test on Chapter 13?

Below is a list of some *common trouble areas* for students in Chapter 13. After studying for your test—but before taking your test—read these.

- The difference of two squares such as $x^2 - 25$ factors as $x^2 - 25 = (x + 5)(x - 5)$.
- The sum of two squares, for example, $x^2 + 25$, cannot be factored using real numbers.
- Don't forget that the first step to factor any polynomial is to first factor out any common factors.

$$9x^2 - 36 = 9(x^2 - 4) = 9(x + 2)(x - 2)$$

- Can you completely factor $x^4 - 24x^2 - 25$?

$$x^4 - 24x^2 - 25 = (x^2 - 25)(x^2 + 1)$$
$$= (x + 5)(x - 5)(x^2 + 1)$$

- Remember that to use the zero factor property to solve a quadratic equation, one side of the equation must be 0 and the other side must be a factored polynomial.

$$x(x - 2) = 3 \quad \text{Cannot use zero factor property.}$$

$$x^2 - 2x - 3 = 0$$
$$(x - 3)(x + 1) = 0 \quad \text{Now we can use zero factor property.}$$
$$x - 3 = 0 \quad \text{or} \quad x + 1 = 0$$
$$x = 3 \quad \text{or} \quad x = -1$$

Remember: This is simply a sampling of selected topics given to check your understanding. For a review of Chapter 13 in your text, see the material at the end of this chapter.

13 CHAPTER REVIEW

(13.1) *Complete each factoring.*

1. $6x^2 - 15x = 3x(\qquad)$

2. $4x^5 + 2x - 10x^4 = 2x(\qquad)$

Factor out the GCF from each polynomial.

3. $5m + 30$

4. $20x^3 + 12x^2 + 24x$

5. $3x(2x + 3) - 5(2x + 3)$

6. $5x(x + 1) - (x + 1)$

Factor each polynomial by grouping.

7. $3x^2 - 3x + 2x - 2$

8. $6x^2 + 10x - 3x - 5$

9. $3a^2 + 9ab + 3b^2 + ab$

(13.2) *Factor each trinomial.*

10. $x^2 + 6x + 8$

11. $x^2 - 11x + 24$

12. $x^2 + x + 2$

13. $x^2 - 5x - 6$

14. $x^2 + 2x - 8$

15. $x^2 + 4xy - 12y^2$

16. $x^2 + 8xy + 15y^2$

17. $72 - 18x - 2x^2$

18. $32 + 12x - 4x^2$

19. $5y^3 - 50y^2 + 120y$

20. To factor $x^2 + 2x - 48$, think of two numbers whose product is _____ and whose sum is _____.

21. What is the first step to factoring $3x^2 + 15x + 30$?

(13.3) or (13.4) *Factor each trinomial.*

22. $2x^2 + 13x + 6$ **23.** $4x^2 + 4x - 3$ **24.** $6x^2 + 5xy - 4y^2$ **25.** $x^2 - x + 2$

26. $2x^2 - 23x - 39$ **27.** $18x^2 - 9xy - 20y^2$ **28.** $10y^3 + 25y^2 - 60y$

Write the perimeter of each figure as a simplified polynomial. Then factor each polynomial.

△ **29.**

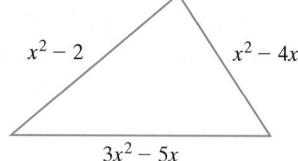

△ **30.**

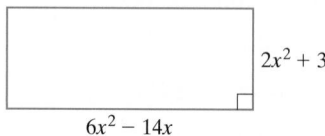

(13.5) *Determine whether each polynomial is a perfect square trinomial.*

31. $x^2 + 6x + 9$ **32.** $x^2 + 8x + 64$ **33.** $9m^2 - 12m + 16$ **34.** $4y^2 - 28y + 49$

Determine whether each binomial is a difference of two squares.

35. $x^2 - 9$ **36.** $x^2 + 16$ **37.** $4x^2 - 25y^2$ **38.** $9a^3 - 1$

Factor each polynomial completely.

39. $x^2 - 81$ **40.** $x^2 + 12x + 36$ **41.** $4x^2 - 9$ **42.** $9t^2 - 25s^2$

43. $16x^2 + y^2$ **44.** $n^2 - 18n + 81$ **45.** $3r^2 + 36r + 108$ **46.** $9y^2 - 42y + 49$

47. $5m^8 - 5m^6$ **48.** $4x^2 - 28xy + 49y^2$ **49.** $3x^2y + 6xy^2 + 3y^3$ **50.** $16x^4 - 1$

(13.6) *Solve each equation.*

51. $(x + 6)(x - 2) = 0$ **52.** $3x(x + 1)(7x - 2) = 0$ **53.** $4(5x + 1)(x + 3) = 0$

54. $x^2 + 8x + 7 = 0$ **55.** $x^2 - 2x - 24 = 0$ **56.** $x^2 + 10x = -25$

57. $x(x - 10) = -16$ **58.** $(3x - 1)(9x^2 + 3x + 1) = 0$ **59.** $56x^2 - 5x - 6 = 0$

60. $m^2 = 6m$

61. $r^2 = 25$

62. Write a quadratic equation that has the two solutions 4 and 5.

(13.7) *Use the given information to choose the correct dimensions.*

△ **63.** The perimeter of a rectangle is 24 inches. The length is twice the width. Find the dimensions of the rectangle.
  a. 5 inches by 7 inches　**b.** 5 inches by 10 inches
  c. 4 inches by 8 inches　**d.** 2 inches by 10 inches

△ **64.** The area of a rectangle is 80 meters. The length is one more than three times the width. Find the dimensions of the rectangle.
  a. 8 meters by 10 meters　**b.** 4 meters by 13 meters
  c. 4 meters by 20 meters　**d.** 5 meters by 16 meters

Use the given information to find the dimensions of each figure.

△ **65.** The *area* of the square is 81 square units. Find the length of a side.

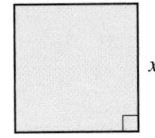

△ **66.** The *perimeter* of the quadrilateral is 47 units. Find the lengths of the sides.

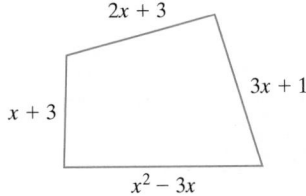

Solve.

△ **67.** A flag for a local organization is in the shape of a rectangle whose length is 15 inches less than twice its width. If the area of the flag is 500 square inches, find its dimensions.

△ **68.** The base of a triangular sail is four times its height. If the area of the triangle is 162 square yards, find the base.

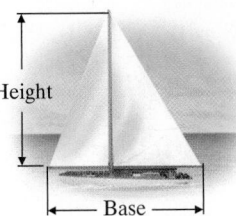

69. Find two consecutive positive integers whose product is 380.

70. A rocket is fired from the ground with an initial velocity of 440 feet per second. Its height h after t seconds is given by the equation $h = -16t^2 + 440t$.

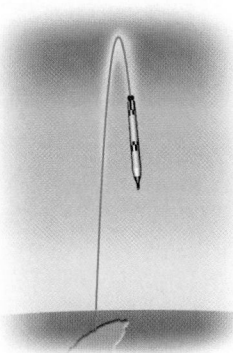

  a. Find how many seconds pass before the rocket reaches a height of 2800 feet. Explain why two answers are obtained.
  b. Find how many seconds pass before the rocket reaches the ground again.

71. An architect's squaring instrument is in the shape of a right triangle. Find the length of the longer leg of the right triangle if the hypotenuse is 8 centimeters longer than the longer leg and the shorter leg is 8 centimeters shorter than the longer leg.

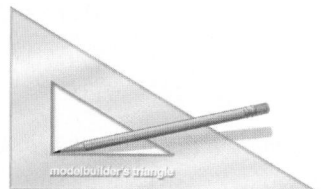

Mixed Review

Factor completely.

72. $6x + 24$

73. $7x - 63$

74. $11x(4x - 3) - 6(4x - 3)$

75. $2x(x - 5) - (x - 5)$

76. $3x^3 - 4x^2 + 6x - 8$

77. $xy + 2x - y - 2$

78. $2x^2 + 2x - 24$

79. $3x^3 - 30x^2 + 27x$

80. $4x^2 - 81$

81. $2x^2 - 18$

82. $16x^2 - 24x + 9$

83. $5x^2 + 20x + 20$

Solve.

84. $2x^2 - x - 28 = 0$

85. $x^2 - 2x = 15$

86. $2x(x + 7)(x + 4) = 0$

87. $x(x - 5) = -6$

88. $x^2 = 16x$

Solve.

89. The perimeter of the following triangle is 48 inches. Find the lengths of its sides.

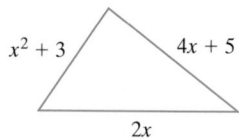

$x^2 + 3$ $4x + 5$

$2x$

90. The width of a rectangle is 4 inches less than its length. Its area is 12 square inches. Find the dimensions of the rectangle.

13 CHAPTER TEST

 Remember to use the Chapter Test Prep Video CD to see the fully worked-out solutions to any of the exercises you want to review.

Factor each polynomial completely. If a polynomial cannot be factored, write "prime."

1. $9x^2 - 3x$

2. $x^2 + 11x + 28$

3. $49 - m^2$

4. $y^2 + 22y + 121$

5. $x^4 - 16$

6. $4(a + 3) - y(a + 3)$

7. $x^2 + 4$

8. $y^2 - 8y - 48$

9. $3a^2 + 3ab - 7a - 7b$

10. $3x^2 - 5x + 2$

11. $180 - 5x^2$

12. $3x^3 - 21x^2 + 30x$

13. $6t^2 - t - 5$

14. $xy^2 - 7y^2 - 4x + 28$

15. $x - x^5$

16. $x^2 + 14xy + 24y^2$

Solve each equation.

17. $(x - 3)(x + 9) = 0$

18. $x^2 + 5x = 14$

19. $x(x + 6) = 7$

20. $3x(2x - 3)(3x + 4) = 0$

21. $5t^3 - 45t = 0$

22. $t^2 - 2t - 15 = 0$

23. $6x^2 = 15x$

1. _____

2. _____

3. _____

4. _____

5. _____

6. _____

7. _____

8. _____

9. _____

10. _____

11. _____

12. _____

13. _____

14. _____

15. _____

16. _____

17. _____

18. _____

19. _____

20. _____

21. _____

22. _____

23. _____

1009

24. _____

Solve.

△ **24.** A deck for a home is in the shape of a triangle. The length of the base of the triangle is 9 feet longer than its height. If the area of the triangle is 68 square feet find the length of the base.

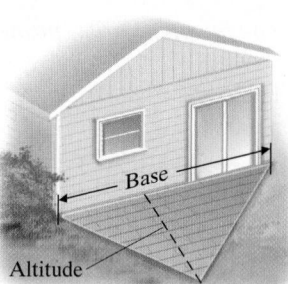

Base

Altitude

△ **25.** The *area* of the rectangle is 54 square units. Find the dimensions of the rectangle.

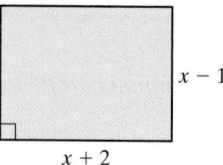

$x - 1$

$x + 2$

25. _____

26. _____

26. An object is dropped from the top of the Woolworth Building on Broadway in New York City. The height h of the object after t seconds is given by the equation

$$h = -16t^2 + 784$$

Find how many seconds pass before the object reaches the ground.

△ **27.** Find the lengths of the sides of a right triangle if the hypotenuse is 10 centimeters longer than the shorter leg and 5 centimeters longer than the longer leg.

27. _____

28. A window washer is suspended 38 feet below the roof of the 1127-foot-tall John Hancock Center in Chicago. (*Source:* Council on Tall Buildings and Urban Habitat) If the window washer drops an object from this height, the object's height h after t seconds is given by the equation $h = -16t^2 + 1089$. Find how many seconds pass before the object reaches the ground.

28. _____

Answers

Perform the indicated operation and simplify.

1. $\dfrac{2}{7} + \dfrac{3}{7}$

2. $\dfrac{26}{30} - \dfrac{7}{30}$

3. $\dfrac{7}{13} + \dfrac{6}{13} + \dfrac{3}{13}$

4. $\dfrac{7}{10} - \dfrac{3}{10} + \dfrac{4}{10}$

5. Find the LCM of 9 and 12.

6. Add: $\dfrac{17}{25} + \dfrac{3}{10}$

7. Write an equivalent fraction with the indicated denominator.

$\dfrac{1}{2} = \dfrac{}{14}$

8. Determine whether these fractions are equivalent.

$\dfrac{10}{55}, \quad \dfrac{6}{33}$

9. Subtract: $\dfrac{10}{11} - \dfrac{2}{3}$

10. Subtract: $17\dfrac{5}{24} - 9\dfrac{5}{9}$

△ 11. Find the area of the triangle.

8 centimeters

14 centimeters

12. Simplify: $\dfrac{\left(4 + \sqrt{4}\right)^2}{\sqrt{100} - \sqrt{64}}$

13. Approximate $\sqrt{32}$ to the nearest thousandth.

14. Divide: $0.1156 \div 0.02$

15. Mel Rose is a 6-foot-tall park ranger who needs to know the height of a particular tree. He measures the shadow of the tree to be 69 feet long when his own shadow is 9 feet long. Find the height of the tree.

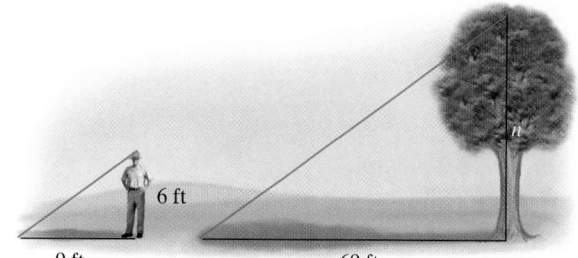

6 ft

9 ft   69 ft

16. What percent of 120 is 28.8?

Answers

1. _____

2. _____

3. _____

4. _____

5. _____

6. _____

7. _____

8. _____

9. _____

10. _____

11. _____

12. _____

13. _____

14. _____

15. _____

16. _____

17. a. _____

b. _____

18. _____

19. a. _____

b. _____

c. _____

20. a. _____

b. _____

21. _____

22. _____

23. _____

24. _____

25. a. _____

b. _____

26. _____

27. _____

28. _____

29. _____

30. _____

31. _____

32. _____

17. The following bar graph shows the number of endangered species in 2001. Use this graph to answer the questions.

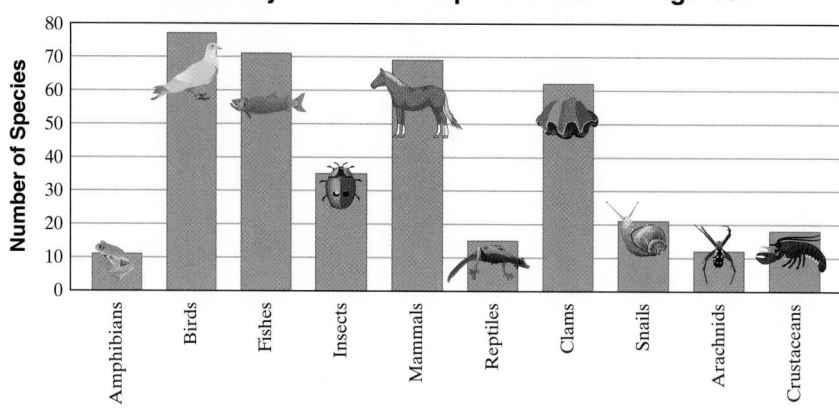

How Many U.S. Animal Species Are Endangered?

Source: U.S. Fish and Wildlife Service

a. Approximate the number of endangered species that are reptiles.
b. Which category has the most endangered species?

18. Find the mean, median, and mode of $1, 7, 8, 10, 11, 11$.

19. Translate each sentence into a mathematical statement.
a. Nine is less than or equal to eleven.
b. Eight is greater than one.
c. Three is not equal to four.

20. Insert $<$ or $>$ in the space to make each statement true.
a. $|-5|$ $|-3|$
b. $|0|$ $|-2|$

21. Decide whether 2 is a solution of $3x + 10 = 8x$.

22. Evaluate $\dfrac{x}{y} + 5x$ if $x = 20$ and $y = 10$.

23. Subtract 8 from -4.

24. Evaluate $\dfrac{x}{y} + 5x$ if $x = -20$ and $y = 10$.

25. If $x = -2$ and $y = -4$, evaluate each expression.
a. $\dfrac{3x}{2y}$
b. $x^3 - y^2$

26. Evaluate $\dfrac{x}{y} + 5x$ if $x = -20$ and $y = -10$.

Solve each equation.

27. $-3x = 33$

28. $\dfrac{x}{-7} = -4$

29. $3(x - 4) = 3x - 12$

30. $-\dfrac{2}{3}x = -22$

31. Solve for l: $V = lwh$

32. Solve for y: $3x + 2y = -7$

Simplify the following expressions. Write each result using positive exponents only.

33. $\dfrac{(x^3)^4 x}{x^7}$

34. 3^{-2}

35. $(y^{-3}z^6)^{-6}$

36. $\dfrac{x^{-3}}{x^{-7}}$

37. $\dfrac{x^{-7}}{(x^4)^3}$

38. $\dfrac{(5a^7)^2}{a^5}$

Use a special product to square each binomial.

39. $(t + 2)^2$

40. $(x - 13)^2$

41. $(x^2 - 7y)^2$

42. $(7x + y)^2$

43. Divide: $\dfrac{8x^2y^2 - 16xy + 2x}{4xy}$

Factor each polynomial.

44. $z^3 + 7z + z^2 + 7$

45. $5(x + 3) + y(x + 3)$

46. $2x^3 + 2x^2 - 84x$

47. $x^4 + 5x^2 + 6$

48. $9xy^2 - 16x$

49. The platform for the cliff divers in Acapulco, Mexico, is about 144 feet above the sea. Neglecting air resistance, the height h in feet of a cliff diver above the ocean after t seconds is given by the quadratic equation $h = -16t^2 + 144$. Find how long it takes the diver to reach the ocean.

50. Solve $x^2 - 13x = -36$.

33. _____

34. _____

35. _____

36. _____

37. _____

38. _____

39. _____

40. _____

41. _____

42. _____

43. _____

44. _____

45. _____

46. _____

47. _____

48. _____

49. _____

50. _____

14

Rational Expressions

In this chapter, we expand our knowledge of algebraic expressions to include algebraic fractions, called *rational expressions*. We explore the operations of addition, subtraction, multiplication, and division using principles similar to the principles for numerical fractions.

American football is one of this nation's most followed sports. It has its roots in English rugby, a game played with the same shaped ball, but where the ball can only advance through running. American college players were the first to add advancing the ball by throwing or kicking it past the opponents. In 1867, both Rutgers and Princeton established a basic set of rules and played the first intercollegiate football game. In 1876, Walter Camp, the coach at Yale, helped establish that teams were to consist of 11 men, standardized the size of the field, and generally instituted the first cohesive set of rules.

In Exercise 87, Section 14.1, you will have the opportunity to calculate a quarterback's rating.

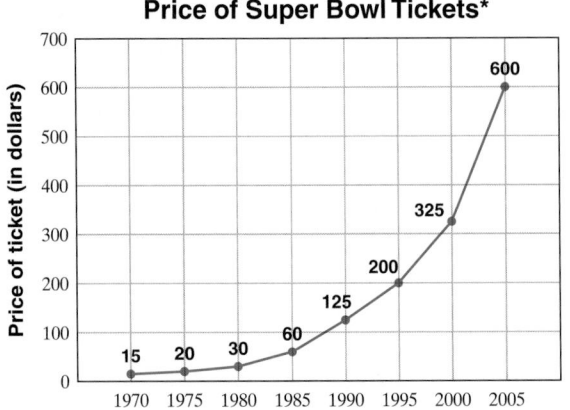

Price of Super Bowl Tickets*

Source: JS Online: Super Bowl Ticket Prices and NFL research
* For years with multiple ticket prices, highest price is shown

14.1 SIMPLIFYING RATIONAL EXPRESSIONS

Objectives

A Find the Value of a Rational Expression Given a Replacement Number.

B Identify Values for Which a Rational Expression Is Undefined.

C Simplify, or Write Rational Expressions in Lowest Terms.

D Write Equivalent Forms of Rational Expressions.

Objective **A** Evaluating Rational Expressions

A rational number is a number that can be written as a quotient of integers. A *rational expression* is also a quotient; it is a quotient of polynomials. Examples are

$$\frac{2}{3}, \quad \frac{3y^3}{8}, \quad \frac{-4p}{p^3 + 2p + 1}, \quad \text{and} \quad \frac{5x^2 - 3x + 2}{3x + 7}$$

Rational Expression

A **rational expression** is an expression that can be written in the form

$$\frac{P}{Q}$$

where P and Q are polynomials and $Q \neq 0$.

Rational expressions have different numerical values depending on what values replace the variables.

EXAMPLE 1 Find the numerical value of $\dfrac{x + 4}{2x - 3}$ for each replacement value.

a. $x = 5$ **b.** $x = -2$

Solution:

a. We replace each x in the expression with 5 and then simplify.

$$\frac{x + 4}{2x - 3} = \frac{5 + 4}{2(5) - 3} = \frac{9}{10 - 3} = \frac{9}{7}$$

b. We replace each x in the expression with -2 and then simplify.

$$\frac{x + 4}{2x - 3} = \frac{-2 + 4}{2(-2) - 3} = \frac{2}{-7} \quad \text{or} \quad -\frac{2}{7}$$

☐ **Work Practice Problem 1**

In the example above, we wrote $\dfrac{2}{-7}$ as $-\dfrac{2}{7}$. For a negative fraction such as $\dfrac{2}{-7}$, recall from Section 8.6 that

$$\frac{2}{-7} = \frac{-2}{7} = -\frac{2}{7}$$

In general, for any fraction,

$$\frac{-a}{b} = \frac{a}{-b} = -\frac{a}{b}, \quad b \neq 0$$

This is also true for rational expressions. For example,

$$\frac{-(x + 2)}{\underbrace{x}} = \frac{x + 2}{-x} = -\frac{x + 2}{x}$$

Notice the parentheses.

PRACTICE PROBLEM 1

Find the value of $\dfrac{x - 3}{5x + 1}$ for each replacement value.

a. $x = 4$

b. $x = -3$

Answers

1. a. $\dfrac{1}{21}$, **b.** $\dfrac{3}{7}$

Objective B Identifying when a Rational Expression Is Undefined

In the definition of rational expression (first "box" in this section), notice that we wrote $Q \neq 0$ for the denominator Q. The denominator of a rational expression must not equal 0 since division by 0 is not defined. (See the Helpful Hint to the left.) This means we must be careful when replacing the variable in a rational expression by a number.

For example, suppose we replace x with 5 in the rational expression $\dfrac{3 + x}{x - 5}$. The expression becomes

$$\frac{3 + x}{x - 5} = \frac{3 + 5}{5 - 5} = \frac{8}{0}$$

But division by 0 is undefined. Therefore, in this expression we can allow x to be any real number *except* 5. **A rational expression is undefined for values that make the denominator 0.** Thus,

---

To find values for which a rational expression is undefined, find values for which the denominator is 0.

EXAMPLE 2 Are there any values for x for which each expression is undefined?

a. $\dfrac{x}{x - 3}$ **b.** $\dfrac{x^2 + 2}{x^2 - 3x + 2}$ **c.** $\dfrac{x^3 - 6x^2 - 10x}{3}$

Solution: To find values for which a rational expression is undefined, we find values that make the denominator 0.

a. The denominator of $\dfrac{x}{x - 3}$ is 0 when $x - 3 = 0$ or when $x = 3$. Thus, when $x = 3$, the expression $\dfrac{x}{x - 3}$ is undefined.

b. We set the denominator equal to 0.

$$x^2 - 3x + 2 = 0$$
$$(x - 2)(x - 1) = 0 \qquad \text{Factor.}$$
$$x - 2 = 0 \quad \text{or} \quad x - 1 = 0 \qquad \text{Set each factor equal to 0.}$$
$$x = 2 \qquad\qquad x = 1 \qquad \text{Solve.}$$

Thus, when $x = 2$ or $x = 1$, the denominator $x^2 - 3x + 2$ is 0. So the rational expression $\dfrac{x^2 + 2}{x^2 - 3x + 2}$ is undefined when $x = 2$ or when $x = 1$.

c. The denominator of $\dfrac{x^3 - 6x^2 - 10x}{3}$ is never 0, so there are no values of x for which this expression is undefined.

Note: Unless otherwise stated, we will now assume that variables in rational expressions are only replaced by values for which the expressions are defined.

■ **Work Practice Problem 2**

Objective C Simplifying Rational Expressions

A fraction is said to be written in lowest terms or simplest form when the numerator and denominator have no common factors other than 1 (or −1). For example, the fraction $\dfrac{7}{10}$ is written in lowest terms since the numerator and denominator have no common factors other than 1 (or −1).

The process of writing a rational expression in lowest terms or simplest form is called **simplifying** a rational expression.

PRACTICE PROBLEM 2

Are there any values for x for which each rational expression is undefined?

a. $\dfrac{x}{x + 8}$

b. $\dfrac{x - 3}{x^2 + 5x + 4}$

c. $\dfrac{x^2 - 3x + 2}{5}$

Answers

2. a. $x = -8$,   **b.** $x = -4, x = -1$,
c. no

Simplifying a rational expression is similar to simplifying a fraction. Recall from Section 2.3 that to simplify a fraction, we essentially "remove factors of 1." Our ability to do this comes from these facts:

- Any nonzero number over itself simplifies to 1 $\left(\dfrac{5}{5} = 1, \dfrac{-7.26}{-7.26} = 1, \text{ or } \dfrac{c}{c} = 1 \text{ as long as } c \text{ is not } 0\right)$, and

- The product of any number and 1 is that number $\left(19 \cdot 1 = 19, -8.9 \cdot 1 = -8.9, \dfrac{a}{b} \cdot 1 = \dfrac{a}{b}\right)$.

In other words, we have the following:

$$\frac{a \cdot c}{b \cdot c} = \frac{a}{b} \cdot \frac{c}{c} = \frac{a}{b}$$

Since $\dfrac{a}{b} \cdot 1 = \dfrac{a}{b}$

Simplify: $\dfrac{15}{20}$

$\dfrac{15}{20} = \dfrac{3 \cdot 5}{2 \cdot 2 \cdot 5}$ Factor the numerator and the denominator.

$= \dfrac{3 \cdot 5}{2 \cdot 2 \cdot 5}$ Look for common factors.

$= \dfrac{3}{2 \cdot 2} \cdot \dfrac{5}{5}$ Common factors in the numerator and denominator form factors of 1.

$= \dfrac{3}{2 \cdot 2} \cdot 1$ Write $\dfrac{5}{5}$ as 1.

$= \dfrac{3}{2 \cdot 2} = \dfrac{3}{4}$ Multiply to remove a factor of 1.

Before we use the same technique to simplify a rational expression, remember that as long as the denominator is not 0, $\dfrac{a^3b}{a^3b} = 1, \dfrac{x + 3}{x + 3} = 1$, and $\dfrac{7x^2 + 5x - 100}{7x^2 + 5x - 100} = 1$.

Simplify: $\dfrac{x^2 - 9}{x^2 + x - 6}$

$\dfrac{x^2 - 9}{x^2 + x - 6} = \dfrac{(x - 3)(x + 3)}{(x - 2)(x + 3)}$ Factor the numerator and the denominator.

$= \dfrac{(x - 3)(x + 3)}{(x - 2)(x + 3)}$ Look for common factors.

$= \dfrac{x - 3}{x - 2} \cdot \dfrac{x + 3}{x + 3}$

$= \dfrac{x - 3}{x - 2} \cdot 1$ Write $\dfrac{x + 3}{x + 3}$ as 1.

$= \dfrac{x - 3}{x - 2}$ Multiply to remove a factor of 1.

Just as for numerical fractions, we can use a shortcut notation. Remember that as long as exact factors in both the numerator and denominator are divided out, we are "removing a factor of 1." We will use the following notation to show this:

$\dfrac{x^2 - 9}{x^2 + x - 6} = \dfrac{(x - 3)(x + 3)}{(x - 2)(x + 3)}$ A factor of 1 is identified by the shading.

$= \dfrac{x - 3}{x - 2}$ Remove a factor of 1.

Thus, the rational expression $\dfrac{x^2 - 9}{x^2 + x - 6}$ has the same value as the rational expression $\dfrac{x - 3}{x - 2}$ for all values of x except 2 and -3. (Remember that when x is 2, the denominator of both rational expressions is 0 and when x is -3, the original rational expression has a denominator of 0.)

As we simplify rational expressions, we will assume that the simplified rational expression is equal to the original rational expression for all real numbers except those for which either denominator is 0. The following steps may be used to simplify rational expressions.

To Simplify a Rational Expression

Step 1: Completely factor the numerator and denominator.

Step 2: Divide out factors common to the numerator and denominator. (This is the same as "removing a factor of 1.")

PRACTICE PROBLEM 3

Simplify: $\dfrac{x^4 + x^3}{5x + 5}$

EXAMPLE 3 Simplify: $\dfrac{5x - 5}{x^3 - x^2}$

Solution: To begin, we factor the numerator and denominator if possible. Then we look for common factors.

$$\frac{5x - 5}{x^3 - x^2} = \frac{5\,(x - 1)}{x^2\,(x - 1)} = \frac{5}{x^2}$$

◻ **Work Practice Problem 3**

PRACTICE PROBLEM 4

Simplify: $\dfrac{x^2 + 11x + 18}{x^2 + x - 2}$

EXAMPLE 4 Simplify: $\dfrac{x^2 + 8x + 7}{x^2 - 4x - 5}$

Solution: We factor the numerator and denominator and then look for common factors.

$$\frac{x^2 + 8x + 7}{x^2 - 4x - 5} = \frac{(x + 7)\,(x + 1)}{(x - 5)\,(x + 1)} = \frac{x + 7}{x - 5}$$

◻ **Work Practice Problem 4**

PRACTICE PROBLEM 5

Simplify: $\dfrac{x^2 + 10x + 25}{x^2 + 5x}$

EXAMPLE 5 Simplify: $\dfrac{x^2 + 4x + 4}{x^2 + 2x}$

Solution: We factor the numerator and denominator and then look for common factors.

$$\frac{x^2 + 4x + 4}{x^2 + 2x} = \frac{(x + 2)\,(x + 2)}{x\,(x + 2)} = \frac{x + 2}{x}$$

◻ **Work Practice Problem 5**

Helpful Hint

When simplifying a rational expression, we look for **common *factors*, not common *terms*.**

$$\frac{x \cdot (x + 2)}{x \cdot x} = \frac{x + 2}{x}$$

Common factors. These can be divided out.

$$\frac{x + 2}{x}$$

Common terms. There is no factor of 1 that can be generated.

Answers

3. $\dfrac{x^3}{5}$, **4.** $\dfrac{x + 9}{x - 1}$, **5.** $\dfrac{x + 5}{x}$

✔**Concept Check** Recall that we can only remove *factors* of 1. Which of the following are *not* true? Explain why.

a. $\dfrac{3-1}{3+5}$ simplifies to $-\dfrac{1}{5}$

b. $\dfrac{2x+10}{2}$ simplifies to $x+5$

c. $\dfrac{37}{72}$ simplifies to $\dfrac{3}{2}$

d. $\dfrac{2x+3}{2}$ simplifies to $x+3$

EXAMPLE 6 Simplify: $\dfrac{x+9}{x^2-81}$

Solution: We factor and then apply the fundamental principle.

$$\frac{x+9}{x^2-81} = \frac{x+9}{(x+9)(x-9)} = \frac{1}{x-9}$$

🖥 **Work Practice Problem 6**

PRACTICE PROBLEM 6

Simplify: $\dfrac{x+5}{x^2-25}$

EXAMPLE 7 Simplify each rational expression.

a. $\dfrac{x+y}{y+x}$

b. $\dfrac{x-y}{y-x}$

Solution:

a. The expression $\dfrac{x+y}{y+x}$ can be simplified by using the commutative property of addition to rewrite the denominator $y+x$ as $x+y$.

$$\frac{x+y}{y+x} = \frac{x+y}{x+y} = 1$$

b. The expression $\dfrac{x-y}{y-x}$ can be simplified by recognizing that $y-x$ and $x-y$ are opposites. In other words, $y-x = -1(x-y)$. We proceed as follows:

$$\frac{x-y}{y-x} = \frac{1\cdot(x-y)}{(-1)(x-y)} = \frac{1}{-1} = -1$$

🖥 **Work Practice Problem 7**

PRACTICE PROBLEM 7

Simplify each rational expression.

a. $\dfrac{x+4}{4+x}$

b. $\dfrac{x-4}{4-x}$

Objective D Writing Equivalent Forms of Rational Expressions

From Example 7a, we have $y+x = x+y$. $y+x$ and $x+y$ are equivalent.
From Example 7b, we have $y-x = -1(x-y)$. $y-x$ and $x-y$ are opposites.

Thus, $\dfrac{x+y}{y+x} = \dfrac{x+y}{x+y} = 1$ and $\dfrac{x-y}{y-x} = \dfrac{x-y}{-1(x-y)} = \dfrac{1}{-1} = -1.$

When performing operations on rational expressions, equivalent forms of answers often result. For this reason, it is very important to be able to recognize equivalent answers.

Answers

6. $\dfrac{1}{x-5}$, **7. a.** 1, **b.** -1

✔ **Concept Check Answer**

a, c, d

PRACTICE PROBLEM 8

List 4 equivalent forms of

$$-\frac{3x + 7}{x - 6}.$$

Helpful Hint

Remember, a negative sign in front of a fraction or rational expression may be moved to the numerator or the denominator, but *not* both.

EXAMPLE 8 List some equivalent forms of

$$-\frac{5x - 1}{x + 9}.$$

Solution: To do so, recall that $-\frac{a}{b} = \frac{-a}{b} = \frac{a}{-b}$. Thus

$$-\frac{5x - 1}{x + 9} = \frac{-(5x - 1)}{x + 9} = \frac{-5x + 1}{x + 9} \quad \text{or} \quad \frac{1 - 5x}{x + 9}$$

Also,

$$-\frac{5x - 1}{x + 9} = \frac{5x - 1}{-(x + 9)} = \frac{5x - 1}{-x - 9} \quad \text{or} \quad \frac{5x - 1}{-9 - x}$$

Thus $-\frac{5x - 1}{x + 9} = \frac{-(5x - 1)}{x + 9} = \frac{-5x + 1}{x + 9} = \frac{5x - 1}{-(x + 9)} = \frac{5x - 1}{-x - 9}$

▣ **Work Practice Problem 8**

Keep in mind that many rational expressions may look different, but in fact be equivalent.

Answer

8. $\dfrac{-(3x + 7)}{x - 6}$; $\dfrac{-3x - 7}{x - 6}$; $\dfrac{3x + 7}{-(x - 6)}$;

$\dfrac{3x + 7}{-x + 6}$

Mental Math

Find any numbers for which each rational expression is undefined. See Example 2.

1. $\dfrac{x+5}{x}$

2. $\dfrac{x^2-5x}{x-3}$

3. $\dfrac{x^2+4x-2}{x(x-1)}$

4. $\dfrac{x+2}{(x-5)(x-6)}$

14.1 EXERCISE SET

Objective A *Find the value of the following expressions when $x = 2$, $y = -2$, and $z = -5$. See Example 1.*

1. $\dfrac{x+5}{x+2}$

2. $\dfrac{x+8}{x+1}$

3. $\dfrac{y^3}{y^2-1}$

4. $\dfrac{z}{z^2-5}$

5. $\dfrac{x^2+8x+2}{x^2-x-6}$

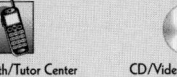 **6.** $\dfrac{x+5}{x^2+4x-8}$

7. The average cost per DVD, in dollars, for a company to produce x DVDs on exercising is given by the formula: $A = \dfrac{3x+400}{x}$, where A is the average cost per DVD, and x is the number of DVDs produced.
  a. Find the cost for producing 1 DVD.
  b. Find the average cost for producing 100 DVDs.
  c. Does the cost per DVD decrease or increase when more DVDs are produced? Explain your answer.

8. For a certain model of fax machine, the manufacturing cost C per machine is given by the equation
$$C = \dfrac{250x+10,000}{x}$$
where x is the number of fax machines manufactured and cost C is in dollars per machine.
  a. Find the cost per fax machine when manufacturing 100 fax machines.
  b. Find the cost per fax machine when manufacturing 1000 fax machines.
  c. Does the cost per machine decrease or increase when more machines are manufactured? Explain why this is so.

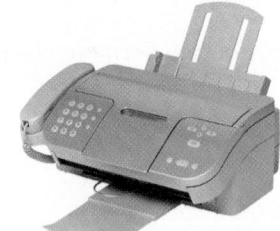

Objective B *Find any numbers for which each rational expression is undefined. See Example 2.*

9. $\dfrac{7}{2x}$

10. $\dfrac{3}{5x}$

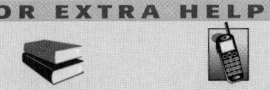 **11.** $\dfrac{x+3}{x+2}$

12. $\dfrac{5x+1}{x-9}$

13. $\dfrac{x-4}{2x-5}$

14. $\dfrac{x+1}{5x-2}$

15. $\dfrac{9x^3+4}{15x^2+30x}$

16. $\dfrac{19x^3+2}{x^2-x}$

17. $\dfrac{x^2-5x-2}{4}$

18. $\dfrac{9y^5+y^3}{9}$

19. $\dfrac{3x^2 + 9}{x^2 - 5x - 6}$

20. $\dfrac{11x^2 + 1}{x^2 - 5x - 14}$

21. $\dfrac{x}{3x^2 + 13x + 14}$

22. $\dfrac{x}{2x^2 + 15x + 27}$

Objective **C** *Simplify each expression. See Examples 3 through 7.*

23. $\dfrac{x + 7}{7 + x}$

24. $\dfrac{y + 9}{9 + y}$

25. $\dfrac{x - 7}{7 - x}$

26. $\dfrac{y - 9}{9 - y}$

27. $\dfrac{2}{8x + 16}$

28. $\dfrac{3}{9x + 6}$

29. $\dfrac{x - 2}{x^2 - 4}$

30. $\dfrac{x + 5}{x^2 - 25}$

31. $\dfrac{2x - 10}{3x - 30}$

32. $\dfrac{3x - 9}{4x - 16}$

33. $\dfrac{-5a - 5b}{a + b}$

34. $\dfrac{-4x - 4y}{x + y}$

35. $\dfrac{7x + 35}{x^2 + 5x}$

36. $\dfrac{9x + 99}{x^2 + 11x}$

37. $\dfrac{x + 5}{x^2 - 4x - 45}$

38. $\dfrac{x - 3}{x^2 - 6x + 9}$

39. $\dfrac{5x^2 + 11x + 2}{x + 2}$

40. $\dfrac{12x^2 + 4x - 1}{2x + 1}$

41. $\dfrac{x^3 + 7x^2}{x^2 + 5x - 14}$

42. $\dfrac{x^4 - 10x^3}{x^2 - 17x + 70}$

43. $\dfrac{14x^2 - 21x}{2x - 3}$

44. $\dfrac{4x^2 + 24x}{x + 6}$

45. $\dfrac{x^2 + 7x + 10}{x^2 - 3x - 10}$

46. $\dfrac{2x^2 + 7x - 4}{x^2 + 3x - 4}$

47. $\dfrac{3x^2 + 7x + 2}{3x^2 + 13x + 4}$

48. $\dfrac{4x^2 - 4x + 1}{2x^2 + 9x - 5}$

49. $\dfrac{2x^2 - 8}{4x - 8}$

50. $\dfrac{5x^2 - 500}{35x + 350}$

51. $\dfrac{4 - x^2}{x - 2}$

52. $\dfrac{49 - y^2}{y - 7}$

53. $\dfrac{x^2 - 1}{x^2 - 2x + 1}$

54. $\dfrac{x^2 - 16}{x^2 - 8x + 16}$

Simplify each expression. Each exercise contains a four-term polynomial that should be factored by grouping.

55. $\dfrac{x^2 + xy + 2x + 2y}{x + 2}$

56. $\dfrac{ab + ac + b^2 + bc}{b + c}$

57. $\dfrac{5x + 15 - xy - 3y}{2x + 6}$

58. $\dfrac{xy - 6x + 2y - 12}{y^2 - 6y}$

59. $\dfrac{2xy + 5x - 2y - 5}{3xy + 4x - 3y - 4}$

60. $\dfrac{2xy + 2x - 3y - 3}{2xy + 4x - 3y - 6}$

Objective **D** *Study Example 8. Then list four equivalent forms for each rational expression.*

61. $-\dfrac{x - 10}{x + 8}$

62. $-\dfrac{x + 11}{x - 4}$

63. $-\dfrac{5y - 3}{y - 12}$

64. $-\dfrac{8y - 1}{y - 15}$

Objectives Ⓒ Ⓓ **Mixed Practice** *Simplify each expression. Then determine whether the given answer is correct. See Examples 3 through 8.*

65. $\dfrac{9 - x^2}{x - 3}$; Answer: $-3 - x$

66. $\dfrac{100 - x^2}{x - 10}$; Answer: $-10 - x$

67. $\dfrac{7 - 34x - 5x^2}{25x^2 - 1}$; Answer: $\dfrac{x + 7}{-5x - 1}$

68. $\dfrac{2 - 15x - 8x^2}{64x^2 - 1}$; Answer: $\dfrac{x + 2}{-8x - 1}$

Review

Perform each indicated operation. See Sections 2.4 and 2.5.

69. $\dfrac{1}{3} \cdot \dfrac{9}{11}$

70. $\dfrac{5}{27} \cdot \dfrac{2}{5}$

71. $\dfrac{1}{3} \div \dfrac{1}{4}$

72. $\dfrac{7}{8} \div \dfrac{1}{2}$

73. $\dfrac{13}{20} \div \dfrac{2}{9}$

74. $\dfrac{8}{15} \div \dfrac{5}{8}$

Concept Extensions

Which of the following are incorrect and why? See the Concept Check in this section.

75. $\dfrac{5a - 15}{5}$ simplifies to $a - 3$

76. $\dfrac{7m - 9}{7}$ simplifies to $m - 9$

77. $\dfrac{1 + 2}{1 + 3}$ simplifies to $\dfrac{2}{3}$

78. $\dfrac{46}{54}$ simplifies to $\dfrac{6}{5}$

79. Explain how to write a fraction in lowest terms.

80. Explain how to write a rational expression in lowest terms.

81. Explain why the denominator of a fraction or a rational expression must not equal 0.

82. Does $\dfrac{(x - 3)(x + 3)}{x - 3}$ have the same value as $x + 3$ for all real numbers? Explain why or why not.

83. The dose of medicine prescribed for a child depends on the child's age A in years and the adult dose D for the medication. Young's Rule is a formula used by pediatricians that gives a child's dose C as

$$C = \dfrac{DA}{A + 12}$$

Suppose that an 8-year-old child needs medication, and the normal adult dose is 1000 mg. What size dose should the child receive?

84. Calculating body-mass index is a way to gauge whether a person should lose weight. Doctors recommend that body-mass index values fall between 19 and 25. The formula for body-mass index B is

$$B = \dfrac{705w}{h^2}$$

where w is weight in pounds and h is height in inches. Should a 148-pound person who is 5 feet 6 inches tall lose weight?

85. A baseball player's slugging percentage S can be calculated with the following formula:

$$S = \frac{h + d + 2t + 3r}{b}, \text{ where } h = \text{number of hits},$$

d = number of doubles, t = number of triples, r = number of home runs, and b = number of at-bats. In 2004, Ichiro Suzuki of the Seattle Mariners led the American League in slugging percentage. During the 2004 season, Suzuki had 704 at-bats, 262 hits, 24 doubles, 5 triples, and 8 home runs. (*Source:* Major League Baseball) Calculate Suzuki's 2004 slugging percentage. Round to the nearest tenth of a percent.

86. A company's gross profit margin P can be computed with the formula $P = \dfrac{R - C}{R}$, where

R = the company's revenue and C = cost of goods sold. For fiscal year 2004, consumer electronics retailer Best Buy had revenues of \$24.5 billion and cost of goods sold of \$18.3 billion. (*Source:* Best Buy Company, Inc.) What was Best Buy's gross profit margin in 2004? Express the answer as a percent, rounded to the nearest tenth of a percent.

87. To calculate a quarterback's rating in football, you may use the formula

$$\left[\frac{20C + 0.5A + Y + 80T - 100I}{A}\right]\left(\frac{25}{6}\right), \text{ where}$$

C = the number of completed passes, A = the number of attempted passes, Y = total yards thrown for passes, T = the number of touchdown passes, and I = the number of interceptions. The New England Patriots were the winners of the Super Bowl in 2005. Their quarterback, Tom Brady, boasted the final season totals of 527 attempts, 317 completions, 3620 yards, 23 touchdown passes, and 12 interceptions. Calculate Brady's quarterback rating for the 2004–2005 season. Round the answer to the nearest tenth. (*Source:* The NFL)

88. Anthropologists and forensic scientists use a measure called the cephalic index to help classify skulls. The cephalic index of a skull with width W and length L from front to back is given by the formula

$$C = \frac{100W}{L}$$

A long skull has an index value less than 75, a medium skull has an index value between 75 and 85, and a broad skull has an index value over 85. Find the cephalic index of a skull that is 5 inches wide and 6.4 inches long. Classify the skull.

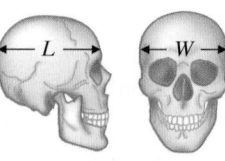

 STUDY SKILLS BUILDER

Is Your Notebook Still Organized?

It's never too late to organize your material in a course. Let's see how you are doing.

1. Are all your graded papers in one place in your math notebook or binder?

2. Flip through the pages of your notebook. Are your notes neat and readable?

3. Are your notes complete with no sections missing?

4. Are important notes marked in some way (like an exclamation point) so that you will know to review them before a quiz or task?

5. Are your assignments complete?

6. Do exercises that have given you trouble have a mark (like a question mark) so that you will remember to talk to your instructor or a tutor about them?

7. Describe your attitude toward this course.

8. List ways your attitude can improve and make a commitment to work on at least one of those during the next week.

14.2 MULTIPLYING AND DIVIDING RATIONAL EXPRESSIONS

Objectives

A Multiply Rational Expressions.

B Divide Rational Expressions.

C Multiply and Divide Rational Expressions.

D Convert between Units of Measure.

Objective **A** Multiplying Rational Expressions

Just as simplifying rational expressions is similar to simplifying number fractions, multiplying and dividing rational expressions is similar to multiplying and dividing number fractions.

Fractions	**Rational Expressions**
Multiply: $\dfrac{3}{5} \cdot \dfrac{10}{11}$	Multiply: $\dfrac{x-3}{x+5} \cdot \dfrac{2x+10}{x^2-9}$

Multiply numerators and then multiply denominators.

$$\frac{3}{5} \cdot \frac{10}{11} = \frac{3 \cdot 10}{5 \cdot 11} \qquad \frac{x-3}{x+5} \cdot \frac{2x+10}{x^2-9} = \frac{(x-3) \cdot (2x+10)}{(x+5) \cdot (x^2-9)}$$

Simplify by factoring numerators and denominators.

$$= \frac{3 \cdot 2 \cdot 5}{5 \cdot 11} \qquad = \frac{(x-3) \cdot 2 (x+5)}{(x+5)(x+3)(x-3)}$$

Apply the fundamental principle.

$$= \frac{3 \cdot 2}{11} \quad \text{or} \quad \frac{6}{11} \qquad = \frac{2}{x+3}$$

Multiplying Rational Expressions

If $\dfrac{P}{Q}$ and $\dfrac{R}{S}$ are rational expressions, then

$$\frac{P}{Q} \cdot \frac{R}{S} = \frac{PR}{QS}$$

To multiply rational expressions, multiply the numerators and then multiply the denominators.

Note: For Sections 14.1 through 14.4, we assume variables in rational expressions have only those replacement values for which the expressions are defined.

EXAMPLE 1 Multiply.

a. $\dfrac{25x}{2} \cdot \dfrac{1}{y^3}$

b. $\dfrac{-7x^2}{5y} \cdot \dfrac{3y^5}{14x^2}$

Solution: To multiply rational expressions, we first multiply the numerators and then multiply the denominators of both expressions. Then we write the product in lowest terms.

a. $\dfrac{25x}{2} \cdot \dfrac{1}{y^3} = \dfrac{25x \cdot 1}{2 \cdot y^3} = \dfrac{25x}{2y^3}$

The expression $\dfrac{25x}{2y^3}$ is in lowest terms.

b. $\dfrac{-7x^2}{5y} \cdot \dfrac{3y^5}{14x^2} = \dfrac{-7x^2 \cdot 3y^5}{5y \cdot 14x^2}$ Multiply.

PRACTICE PROBLEM 1

Multiply.

a. $\dfrac{16y}{3} \cdot \dfrac{1}{x^2}$

b. $\dfrac{-5a^3}{3b^3} \cdot \dfrac{2b^2}{15a}$

Answers

1. **a.** $\dfrac{16y}{3x^2}$,   **b.** $-\dfrac{2a^2}{9b}$

Continued on next page

The expression $\dfrac{-7x^2 \cdot 3y^5}{5y \cdot 14x^2}$ is not in lowest terms, so we factor the numerator and the denominator and apply the fundamental principle.

$$= \frac{-1 \cdot 7 \cdot 3 \cdot x^2 \cdot y \cdot y^4}{5 \cdot 2 \cdot 7 \cdot x^2 \cdot y}$$

$$= -\frac{3y^4}{10}$$

◻ **Work Practice Problem 1**

When multiplying rational expressions, it is usually best to factor each numerator and denominator first. This will help us when we apply the fundamental principle to write the product in lowest terms.

PRACTICE PROBLEM 2

Multiply: $\dfrac{3x + 6}{14} \cdot \dfrac{7x^2}{x^3 + 2x^2}$

EXAMPLE 2 Multiply: $\dfrac{x^2 + x}{3x} \cdot \dfrac{6}{5x + 5}$

Solution:

$$\frac{x^2 + x}{3x} \cdot \frac{6}{5x + 5} = \frac{x(x + 1)}{3x} \cdot \frac{2 \cdot 3}{5(x + 1)} \qquad \text{Factor numerators and denominators.}$$

$$= \frac{x(x + 1) \cdot 2 \cdot 3}{3x \cdot 5(x + 1)} \qquad \text{Multiply.}$$

$$= \frac{2}{5} \qquad \text{Divide out common factors.}$$

◻ **Work Practice Problem 2**

The following steps may be used to multiply rational expressions.

To Multiply Rational Expressions

Step 1: Completely factor numerators and denominators.

Step 2: Multiply numerators and multiply denominators.

Step 3: Simplify or write the product in lowest terms by dividing out common factors.

✔ **Concept Check**   Which of the following is a true statement?

a. $\dfrac{1}{3} \cdot \dfrac{1}{2} = \dfrac{1}{5}$ **b.** $\dfrac{2}{x} \cdot \dfrac{5}{x} = \dfrac{10}{x}$ **c.** $\dfrac{3}{x} \cdot \dfrac{1}{2} = \dfrac{3}{2x}$ **d.** $\dfrac{x}{7} \cdot \dfrac{x + 5}{4} = \dfrac{2x + 5}{28}$

PRACTICE PROBLEM 3

Multiply:

$\dfrac{4x + 8}{7x^2 - 14x} \cdot \dfrac{3x^2 - 5x - 2}{9x^2 - 1}$

EXAMPLE 3 Multiply: $\dfrac{3x + 3}{5x^2 - 5x} \cdot \dfrac{2x^2 + x - 3}{4x^2 - 9}$

Solution:

$$\frac{3x + 3}{5x^2 - 5x} \cdot \frac{2x^2 + x - 3}{4x^2 - 9} = \frac{3(x + 1)}{5x(x - 1)} \cdot \frac{(2x + 3)(x - 1)}{(2x - 3)(2x + 3)} \qquad \text{Factor.}$$

$$= \frac{3(x + 1)(2x + 3)(x - 1)}{5x(x - 1)(2x - 3)(2x + 3)} \qquad \text{Multiply.}$$

$$= \frac{3(x + 1)}{5x(2x - 3)} \qquad \text{Simplify.}$$

◻ **Work Practice Problem 3**

Answers

2. $\dfrac{3}{2}$,   **3.** $\dfrac{4(x + 2)}{7x(3x - 1)}$

✔ **Concept Check Answer**

c

Objective B Dividing Rational Expressions

We can divide by a rational expression in the same way we divide by a number fraction. Recall that to divide by a fraction, we multiply by its reciprocal.

For example, to divide $\frac{3}{2}$ by $\frac{7}{8}$, we multiply $\frac{3}{2}$ by $\frac{8}{7}$.

$$\frac{3}{2} \div \frac{7}{8} = \frac{3}{2} \cdot \frac{8}{7} = \frac{3 \cdot 4 \cdot 2}{2 \cdot 7} = \frac{12}{7}$$

 **Helpful Hint**

Don't forget how to find reciprocals. The reciprocal of $\frac{a}{b}$ is $\frac{b}{a}$, $a \neq 0$, $b \neq 0$.

Dividing Rational Expressions

If $\frac{P}{Q}$ and $\frac{R}{S}$ are rational expressions and $\frac{R}{S}$ is not 0, then

$$\frac{P}{Q} \div \frac{R}{S} = \frac{P}{Q} \cdot \frac{S}{R} = \frac{PS}{QR}$$

To divide two rational expressions, multiply the first rational expression by the reciprocal of the second rational expression.

EXAMPLE 4 Divide: $\frac{3x^3}{40} \div \frac{4x^3}{y^2}$

Solution:

$$\frac{3x^3}{40} \div \frac{4x^3}{y^2} = \frac{3x^3}{40} \cdot \frac{y^2}{4x^3} \qquad \text{Multiply by the reciprocal of } \frac{4x^3}{y^2}.$$

$$= \frac{3 \; x^3 \cdot y^2}{160 \; x^3}$$

$$= \frac{3y^2}{160} \qquad \text{Simplify.}$$

Work Practice Problem 4

PRACTICE PROBLEM 4

Divide: $\frac{7x^2}{6} \div \frac{x}{2y}$

EXAMPLE 5 Divide: $\frac{(x + 2)^2}{10} \div \frac{2x + 4}{5}$

Solution:

$$\frac{(x + 2)^2}{10} \div \frac{2x + 4}{5} = \frac{(x + 2)^2}{10} \cdot \frac{5}{2x + 4} \qquad \text{Multiply by the reciprocal of } \frac{2x + 4}{5}.$$

$$= \frac{(x + 2)(x + 2) \cdot 5}{5 \cdot 2 \cdot 2 \cdot (x + 2)} \qquad \text{Factor and multiply.}$$

$$= \frac{x + 2}{4} \qquad \text{Simplify.}$$

Work Practice Problem 5

PRACTICE PROBLEM 5

Divide: $\frac{(x - 4)^2}{6} \div \frac{3x - 12}{2}$

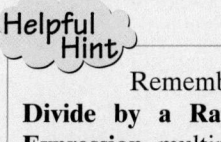 **Helpful Hint**

Remember, **to Divide by a Rational Expression,** multiply by its reciprocal.

Answers

4. $\frac{7xy}{3}$, **5.** $\frac{x - 4}{9}$

PRACTICE PROBLEM 6

Divide: $\dfrac{10x + 4}{x^2 - 4} \div \dfrac{5x^3 + 2x^2}{x + 2}$

EXAMPLE 6 Divide: $\dfrac{6x + 2}{x^2 - 1} \div \dfrac{3x^2 + x}{x - 1}$

Solution:

$$\dfrac{6x + 2}{x^2 - 1} \div \dfrac{3x^2 + x}{x - 1} = \dfrac{6x + 2}{x^2 - 1} \cdot \dfrac{x - 1}{3x^2 + x}$$ Multiply by the reciprocal.

$$= \dfrac{2\,(3x + 1)(x - 1)}{(x + 1)\,(x - 1) \cdot x\,(3x + 1)}$$ Factor and multiply.

$$= \dfrac{2}{x(x + 1)}$$ Simplify.

Work Practice Problem 6

PRACTICE PROBLEM 7

Divide:

$\dfrac{3x^2 - 10x + 8}{7x - 14} \div \dfrac{9x - 12}{21}$

EXAMPLE 7 Divide: $\dfrac{2x^2 - 11x + 5}{5x - 25} \div \dfrac{4x - 2}{10}$

Solution:

$$\dfrac{2x^2 - 11x + 5}{5x - 25} \div \dfrac{4x - 2}{10} = \dfrac{2x^2 - 11x + 5}{5x - 25} \cdot \dfrac{10}{4x - 2}$$ Multiply by the reciprocal.

$$= \dfrac{(2x - 1)(x - 5) \cdot 2 \cdot 5}{5(x - 5) \cdot 2(2x - 1)}$$ Factor and multiply.

$$= \dfrac{1}{1} \quad \text{or} \quad 1$$ Simplify.

Work Practice Problem 7

Objective C Multiplying and Dividing Rational Expressions

Let's make sure that we understand the difference between multiplying and dividing rational expressions.

Rational Expressions	
Multiplication	Multiply the numerators and multiply the denominators.
Division	Multiply by the reciprocal of the divisor.

PRACTICE PROBLEM 8

Multiply or divide as indicated.

a. $\dfrac{x + 3}{x} \cdot \dfrac{7}{x + 3}$

b. $\dfrac{x + 3}{x} \div \dfrac{7}{x + 3}$

c. $\dfrac{3 - x}{x^2 + 6x + 5} \cdot \dfrac{2x + 10}{x^2 - 7x + 12}$

EXAMPLE 8 Multiply or divide as indicated.

a. $\dfrac{x - 4}{5} \cdot \dfrac{x}{x - 4}$

b. $\dfrac{x - 4}{5} \div \dfrac{x}{x - 4}$

c. $\dfrac{x^2 - 4}{2x + 6} \cdot \dfrac{x^2 + 4x + 3}{2 - x}$

Solution:

a. $\dfrac{x - 4}{5} \cdot \dfrac{x}{x - 4} = \dfrac{(x - 4) \cdot x}{5 \cdot (x - 4)} = \dfrac{x}{5}$

b. $\dfrac{x - 4}{5} \div \dfrac{x}{x - 4} = \dfrac{x - 4}{5} \cdot \dfrac{x - 4}{x} = \dfrac{(x - 4)^2}{5x}$

c. $\dfrac{x^2 - 4}{2x + 6} \cdot \dfrac{x^2 + 4x + 3}{2 - x} = \dfrac{(x - 2)(x + 2) \cdot (x + 1)(x + 3)}{2(x + 3) \cdot (2 - x)}$ Factor and multiply.

Answers

6. $\dfrac{2}{x^2(x - 2)}$, 7. 1,

8. a. $\dfrac{7}{x}$, b. $\dfrac{(x + 3)^2}{7x}$,

c. $-\dfrac{2}{(x + 1)(x - 4)}$

Recall from Section 14.1 that $x - 2$ and $2 - x$ are opposites. This means that $\dfrac{x - 2}{2 - x} = -1$. Thus,

$$\frac{(x - 2)\,(x + 2)\cdot(x + 1)\,(x + 3)}{2\,(x + 3)\cdot(2 - x)} = \frac{-1(x + 2)(x + 1)}{2}$$

$$= -\frac{(x + 2)(x + 1)}{2}$$

■ **Work Practice Problem 8**

Objective D Converting between Units of Measure

How many square inches are in 1 square foot?

How many cubic feet are in a cubic yard?

If you have trouble answering these questions, this section will be helpful to you.

Now that we know how to multiply fractions and rational expressions, we can use this knowledge to help us convert between units of measure. To do so, we will use **unit fractions.** A unit fraction is a fraction that equals 1. For example, since 12 in. = 1 ft, we have the unit fractions

$$\frac{12 \text{ in.}}{1 \text{ ft}} = 1 \quad \text{and} \quad \frac{1 \text{ ft}}{12 \text{ in.}} = 1$$

EXAMPLE 9 18 square feet = _____ square yards

Solution: Let's multiply 18 square feet by a unit fraction that has square feet in denominator and square yards in the numerator. From the diagram, you can see that

1 square yard = 9 square feet

Thus,

$$18 \text{ sq ft} = \frac{18 \text{ sq ft}}{1} \cdot 1 = \frac{\overset{2}{\cancel{18 \text{ sq ft}}}}{1} \cdot \frac{1 \text{ sq yd}}{\underset{1}{\cancel{9 \text{ sq ft}}}}$$

$$= \frac{2 \cdot 1}{1 \cdot 1} \text{ sq yd} = 2 \text{ sq yd}$$

Thus, 18 sq ft = 2 sq yd.

Draw a diagram of 18 sq ft to help you see that this is reasonable.

■ **Work Practice Problem 9**

EXAMPLE 10 5.2 square yards = _____ square feet

Solution:

$$5.2 \text{ sq yd} = \frac{5.2 \text{ sq yd}}{1} \cdot 1 = \frac{5.2 \,\cancel{\text{sq yd}}}{1} \cdot \frac{9 \text{ sq ft}}{1 \,\cancel{\text{sq yd}}} \quad \begin{matrix} \leftarrow \text{ Units converting to} \\ \leftarrow \text{ Units given} \end{matrix}$$

$$= \frac{5.2 \cdot 9}{1 \cdot 1} \text{ sq ft}$$

$$= 46.8 \text{ sq ft}$$

Thus, 5.2 sq yd = 46.8 sq ft.

Draw a diagram to see that this is reasonable.

■ **Work Practice Problem 10**

PRACTICE PROBLEM 9

288 square inches = _____ square feet

PRACTICE PROBLEM 10

3.5 square feet = _____ square inches

Answers

9. 2 sq ft, **10.** 504 sq in.

PRACTICE PROBLEM 11

The largest casino in the world is the Foxwoods Resort Casino in Ledyard, CT. The gaming area for this casino is approximately 35,000 *square yards*. Find the size of the gaming area in *square feet*. (*Source:* Foxwoods Resort)

EXAMPLE 11 Converting from Cubic Feet to Cubic Yards

The largest building in the world by volume is The Boeing Company's Everett, Washington, factory complex where Boeing's wide-body jetliners, the 747, 767, and 777, are built. The volume of this factory complex is 472,370,319 cubic feet. Find the volume of this Boeing facility in cubic yards. (*Source:* The Boeing Company)

Solution: There are 27 cubic feet in 1 cubic yard. (See the diagram.)

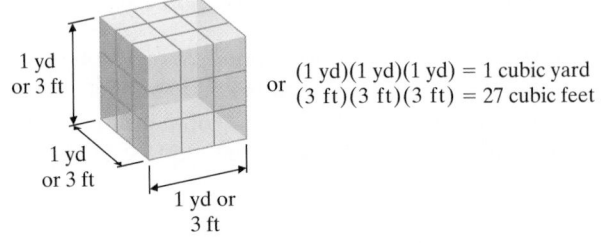

or $\quad \dfrac{(1 \text{ yd})(1 \text{ yd})(1 \text{ yd}) = 1 \text{ cubic yard}}{(3 \text{ ft})(3 \text{ ft})(3 \text{ ft}) = 27 \text{ cubic feet}}$

$$472{,}370{,}319 \text{ cu ft} = 472{,}370{,}319 \; \cancel{\text{cu ft}} \cdot \frac{1 \text{ cu yd}}{27 \; \cancel{\text{cu ft}}}$$

$$= \frac{472{,}370{,}319}{27} \text{ cu yd}$$

$$= 17{,}495{,}197 \text{ cu yd}$$

⬛ **Work Practice Problem 11**

Helpful Hint

When converting among units of measurement, if possible write the unit fraction so that **the numerator contains the units you are converting to** and **the denominator contains the original units.**

$$48 \text{ in.} = \frac{48 \; \cancel{\text{in.}}}{1} \cdot \overbrace{\frac{1 \text{ ft}}{12 \; \cancel{\text{in.}}}}^{\text{Unit fraction}} \quad \begin{array}{l} \leftarrow \text{Units converting to} \\ \leftarrow \text{Original units} \end{array}$$

$$= \frac{48}{12} \text{ ft} = 4 \text{ ft}$$

PRACTICE PROBLEM 12

The cheetah is the fastest land animal, being clocked at about 102.7 feet per second. Convert this to miles per hour. Round to the nearest tenth. (*Source: World Almanac and Book of Facts*)

EXAMPLE 12

At the 2004 Summer Olympics, U.S. athlete Justin Gatlin won the gold medal in the men's 100-meter track event. He ran the distance at an average speed of 33.3 feet per second. Convert this speed to miles per hour. (*Source:* Athens Olympic Committee)

Solution: Recall that 1 mile = 5280 feet and 1 hour = 3600 seconds (60 · 60).

$$33.3 \text{ feet/second} = \frac{33.3 \text{ feet}}{1 \text{ second}} \cdot \overbrace{\frac{3600 \text{ seconds}}{1 \text{ hour}} \cdot \frac{1 \text{ mile}}{5280 \text{ feet}}}^{\text{Unit fractions}}$$

$$= \frac{33.3 \cdot 3600}{5280} \text{ miles/hour}$$

$$\approx 22.7 \text{ miles/hour (rounded to the nearest tenth)}$$

⬛ **Work Practice Problem 12**

Answers

11. 315,000 sq ft,
12. 70.0 miles per hour

Mental Math

Find each product. See Example 1.

1. $\dfrac{2}{y} \cdot \dfrac{x}{3}$ **2.** $\dfrac{3x}{4} \cdot \dfrac{1}{y}$ **3.** $\dfrac{5}{7} \cdot \dfrac{y^2}{x^2}$ **4.** $\dfrac{x^5}{11} \cdot \dfrac{4}{z^3}$ **5.** $\dfrac{9}{x} \cdot \dfrac{x}{5}$ **6.** $\dfrac{y}{7} \cdot \dfrac{3}{y}$

14.2 EXERCISE SET

FOR EXTRA HELP

Student Solutions Manual   PH Math/Tutor Center   CD/Video for Review   Math XL   MathXL®   MyMathLab   MyMathLab

Objective A *Find each product and simplify if possible. See Examples 1 through 3.*

1. $\dfrac{3x}{y^2} \cdot \dfrac{7y}{4x}$

2. $\dfrac{9x^2}{y} \cdot \dfrac{4y}{3x^3}$

 **3.** $\dfrac{8x}{2} \cdot \dfrac{x^5}{4x^2}$

4. $\dfrac{6x^2}{10x^3} \cdot \dfrac{5x}{12}$

5. $-\dfrac{5a^2b}{30a^2b^2} \cdot b^3$

6. $-\dfrac{9x^3y^2}{18xy^5} \cdot y^3$

7. $\dfrac{x}{2x - 14} \cdot \dfrac{x^2 - 7x}{5}$

8. $\dfrac{4x - 24}{20x} \cdot \dfrac{5}{x - 6}$

9. $\dfrac{6x + 6}{5} \cdot \dfrac{10}{36x + 36}$

10. $\dfrac{x^2 + x}{8} \cdot \dfrac{16}{x + 1}$

11. $\dfrac{(m + n)^2}{m - n} \cdot \dfrac{m}{m^2 + mn}$

12. $\dfrac{(m - n)^2}{m + n} \cdot \dfrac{m}{m^2 - mn}$

13. $\dfrac{x^2 - 25}{x^2 - 3x - 10} \cdot \dfrac{x + 2}{x}$

14. $\dfrac{a^2 - 4a + 4}{a^2 - 4} \cdot \dfrac{a + 3}{a - 2}$

15. $\dfrac{x^2 + 6x + 8}{x^2 + x - 20} \cdot \dfrac{x^2 + 2x - 15}{x^2 + 8x + 16}$

16. $\dfrac{x^2 + 9x + 20}{x^2 - 15x + 44} \cdot \dfrac{x^2 - 11x + 28}{x^2 + 12x + 35}$

Objective B *Find each quotient and simplify. See Examples 4 through 7.*

17. $\dfrac{5x^7}{2x^5} \div \dfrac{15x}{4x^3}$

18. $\dfrac{9y^4}{6y} \div \dfrac{y^2}{3}$

19. $\dfrac{8x^2}{y^3} \div \dfrac{4x^2y^3}{6}$

20. $\dfrac{7a^2b}{3ab^2} \div \dfrac{21a^2b^2}{14ab}$

21. $\dfrac{(x - 6)(x + 4)}{4x} \div \dfrac{2x - 12}{8x^2}$

22. $\dfrac{(x + 3)^2}{5} \div \dfrac{5x + 15}{25}$

23. $\dfrac{3x^2}{x^2 - 1} \div \dfrac{x^5}{(x + 1)^2}$

24. $\dfrac{9x^5}{a^2 - b^2} \div \dfrac{27x^2}{3b - 3a}$

25. $\dfrac{m^2 - n^2}{m + n} \div \dfrac{m}{m^2 + nm}$

26. $\dfrac{(m - n)^2}{m + n} \div \dfrac{m^2 - mn}{m}$

 **27.** $\dfrac{x + 2}{7 - x} \div \dfrac{x^2 - 5x + 6}{x^2 - 9x + 14}$

28. $\dfrac{x - 3}{2 - x} \div \dfrac{x^2 + 3x - 18}{x^2 + 2x - 8}$

29. $\dfrac{x^2 + 7x + 10}{x - 1} \div \dfrac{x^2 + 2x - 15}{x - 1}$

30. $\dfrac{x + 1}{(x + 1)(2x + 3)} \div \dfrac{20x + 100}{2x + 3}$

Objective **C** **Mixed Practice** *Multiply or divide as indicated. See Example 8.*

31. $\dfrac{5x - 10}{12} \div \dfrac{4x - 8}{8}$

32. $\dfrac{6x + 6}{5} \div \dfrac{9x + 9}{10}$

33. $\dfrac{x^2 + 5x}{8} \cdot \dfrac{9}{3x + 15}$

34. $\dfrac{3x^2 + 12x}{6} \cdot \dfrac{9}{2x + 8}$

35. $\dfrac{7}{6p^2 + q} \div \dfrac{14}{18p^2 + 3q}$

36. $\dfrac{3x + 6}{20} \div \dfrac{4x + 8}{8}$

37. $\dfrac{3x + 4y}{x^2 + 4xy + 4y^2} \cdot \dfrac{x + 2y}{2}$

38. $\dfrac{x^2 - y^2}{3x^2 + 3xy} \cdot \dfrac{3x^2 + 6x}{3x^2 - 2xy - y^2}$

39. $\dfrac{(x + 2)^2}{x - 2} \div \dfrac{x^2 - 4}{2x - 4}$

40. $\dfrac{x + 3}{x^2 - 9} \div \dfrac{5x + 15}{(x - 3)^2}$

41. $\dfrac{x^2 - 4}{24x} \div \dfrac{2 - x}{6xy}$

42. $\dfrac{3y}{3 - x} \div \dfrac{12xy}{x^2 - 9}$

43. $\dfrac{a^2 + 7a + 12}{a^2 + 5a + 6} \cdot \dfrac{a^2 + 8a + 15}{a^2 + 5a + 4}$

44. $\dfrac{b^2 + 2b - 3}{b^2 + b - 2} \cdot \dfrac{b^2 - 4}{b^2 + 6b + 8}$

45. $\dfrac{5x - 20}{3x^2 + x} \cdot \dfrac{3x^2 + 13x + 4}{x^2 - 16}$

46. $\dfrac{9x + 18}{4x^2 - 3x} \cdot \dfrac{4x^2 - 11x + 6}{x^2 - 4}$

47. $\dfrac{8n^2 - 18}{2n^2 - 5n + 3} \div \dfrac{6n^2 + 7n - 3}{n^2 - 9n + 8}$

48. $\dfrac{36n^2 - 64}{3n^2 - 10n + 8} \div \dfrac{3n^2 - 13n + 12}{n^2 - 5n - 14}$

Objective **D** *Convert as indicated. See Examples 9 through 12.*

49. 10 square feet = _____ square inches.

50. 1008 square inches = _____ square feet.

51. 45 square feet = _____ square yards.

52. 2 square yards = _____ square inches.

53. 3 cubic yards = _____ cubic feet.

54. 2 cubic yards = _____ cubic inches.

55. 50 miles per hour = _____ feet per second (round to the nearest whole).

56. 10 feet per second = _____ miles per hour (round to the nearest tenth).

57. 6.3 square yards = _____ square feet.

58. 3.6 square yards = _____ square feet.

59. The Pentagon, headquarters for the Department of Defense, contains 3,705,793 square feet of office and storage space. Convert this to square yards. Round to the nearest square yard. (*Source:* U.S. Department of Defense)

60. The world's tallest building, Taipei 101 in Taipei, Taiwan, has 427,831 square yards of floor space. Convert this to square feet. (*Source:* Taipei 101)

61. On October 4, 2004, the rocket plane *SpaceShipOne* shot to an altitude of more than 100 km for the second time inside a week to claim the $10 million Ansari X-Prize. At one point in its flight, *SpaceShipOne* was traveling past Mach 1, about 930 miles per hour. Find this speed in feet per second. Round to the nearest whole. (*Source:* Space.com)

62. In 2002, Tim Montgomery of the United States held the current world record for the men's 100-meter track event. In that year, he covered the distance at an average speed of 33.55 feet per second. Convert this speed to miles per hour. Round to the nearest tenth. (*Source:* International Amateur Athletic Association)

Review

Perform each indicated operation. See Section 3.1.

63. $\dfrac{1}{5} + \dfrac{4}{5}$

64. $\dfrac{3}{15} + \dfrac{6}{15}$

65. $\dfrac{9}{9} - \dfrac{19}{9}$

66. $\dfrac{4}{3} - \dfrac{8}{3}$

67. $\dfrac{6}{5} + \left(\dfrac{1}{5} - \dfrac{8}{5}\right)$

68. $-\dfrac{3}{2} + \left(\dfrac{1}{2} - \dfrac{3}{2}\right)$

Concept Extensions

Identify each statement as true or false. If false, correct the multiplication. See the Concept Check in this section.

69. $\dfrac{4}{a} \cdot \dfrac{1}{b} = \dfrac{4}{ab}$

70. $\dfrac{2}{3} \cdot \dfrac{2}{4} = \dfrac{2}{7}$

71. $\dfrac{x}{5} \cdot \dfrac{x + 3}{4} = \dfrac{2x + 3}{20}$

72. $\dfrac{7}{a} \cdot \dfrac{3}{a} = \dfrac{21}{a}$

73. Find the area of the rectangle.

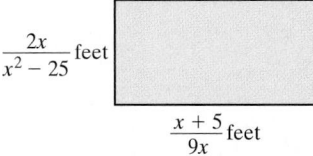

$\dfrac{2x}{x^2 - 25}$ feet

$\dfrac{x + 5}{9x}$ feet

74. Find the area of the square.

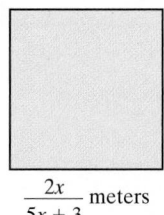

$\dfrac{2x}{5x + 3}$ meters

Multiply or divide as indicated.

75. $\left(\dfrac{x^2 - y^2}{x^2 + y^2} \div \dfrac{x^2 - y^2}{3x}\right) \cdot \dfrac{x^2 + y^2}{6}$

76. $\left(\dfrac{x^2 - 9}{x^2 - 1} \cdot \dfrac{x^2 + 2x + 1}{2x^2 + 9x + 9}\right) \div \dfrac{2x + 3}{1 - x}$

77. $\left(\dfrac{2a + b}{b^2} \cdot \dfrac{3a^2 - 2ab}{ab + 2b^2}\right) \div \dfrac{a^2 - 3ab + 2b^2}{5ab - 10b^2}$

78. $\left(\dfrac{x^2y^2 - xy}{4x - 4y} \div \dfrac{3y - 3x}{8x - 8y}\right) \cdot \dfrac{y - x}{8}$

79. In your own words, explain how you multiply rational expressions.

80. Explain how dividing rational expressions is similar to dividing rational numbers.

81. On November 14, 2004, 1 euro was equivalent to 1.2955 U.S. dollars. If you had wanted to exchange $2000 U.S. for euros on that day for a European vacation, how much would you have received? Round to the nearest hundredth. (*Source:* International Monetary Fund)

82. An environmental technician finds that warm water from an industrial process is being discharged into a nearby pond at a rate of 30 gallons per minute. Plant regulations state that the flow rate should be no more than 0.1 cubic feet per second. Is the flow rate of 30 gallons per minute in violation of the plant regulations? (*Hint:* 1 cubic foot is equivalent to 7.48 gallons.)

Objectives

A Add and Subtract Rational Expressions with Common Denominators.

B Find the Least Common Denominator of a List of Rational Expressions.

C Write a Rational Expression as an Equivalent Expression Whose Denominator Is Given.

14.3 ADDING AND SUBTRACTING RATIONAL EXPRESSIONS WITH THE SAME DENOMINATOR AND LEAST COMMON DENOMINATORS

Objective **A** Adding and Subtracting Rational Expressions with the Same Denominator

Like multiplication and division, addition and subtraction of rational expressions is similar to addition and subtraction of rational numbers. In this section, we add and subtract rational expressions with a common denominator.

$$\text{Add:} \quad \frac{6}{5} + \frac{2}{5} \qquad \Big| \qquad \text{Add:} \quad \frac{9}{x+2} + \frac{3}{x+2}$$

Add the numerators and place the sum over the common denominator.

$$\frac{6}{5} + \frac{2}{5} = \frac{6+2}{5} \qquad \Big| \qquad \frac{9}{x+2} + \frac{3}{x+2} = \frac{9+3}{x+2}$$

$$\qquad\qquad = \frac{8}{5} \quad \text{Simplify.} \qquad \Big| \qquad\qquad\qquad = \frac{12}{x+2} \quad \text{Simplify.}$$

Adding and Subtracting Rational Expressions with Common Denominators

If $\dfrac{P}{R}$ and $\dfrac{Q}{R}$ are rational expressions, then

$$\frac{P}{R} + \frac{Q}{R} = \frac{P+Q}{R} \qquad \text{and} \qquad \frac{P}{R} - \frac{Q}{R} = \frac{P-Q}{R}$$

To add or subtract rational expressions, add or subtract numerators and place the sum or difference over the common denominator.

PRACTICE PROBLEM 1

Add: $\dfrac{8x}{3y} + \dfrac{x}{3y}$

EXAMPLE 1 Add: $\dfrac{5m}{2n} + \dfrac{m}{2n}$

Solution:

$$\frac{5m}{2n} + \frac{m}{2n} = \frac{5m + m}{2n} \qquad \text{Add the numerators.}$$

$$\qquad\qquad = \frac{6m}{2n} \qquad \text{Simplify the numerator by combining like terms.}$$

$$\qquad\qquad = \frac{3m}{n} \qquad \text{Simplify by applying the fundamental principle.}$$

▣ **Work Practice Problem 1**

PRACTICE PROBLEM 2

Subtract: $\dfrac{3x}{3x-7} - \dfrac{7}{3x-7}$

EXAMPLE 2 Subtract: $\dfrac{2y}{2y-7} - \dfrac{7}{2y-7}$

Solution:

$$\frac{2y}{2y-7} - \frac{7}{2y-7} = \boxed{\frac{2y-7}{2y-7}} \qquad \text{Subtract the numerators.}$$

$$\qquad\qquad = \frac{1}{1} \text{ or } 1 \qquad \text{Simplify.}$$

▣ **Work Practice Problem 2**

Answers

1. $\dfrac{3x}{y}$, **2.** 1

1034

EXAMPLE 3 Subtract: $\dfrac{3x^2 + 2x}{x - 1} - \dfrac{10x - 5}{x - 1}$

Solution:

$$\dfrac{3x^2 + 2x}{x - 1} - \dfrac{10x - 5}{x - 1} = \dfrac{3x^2 + 2x - (10x - 5)}{x - 1} \qquad \text{Subtract the numerators. Notice the parentheses.}$$

$$= \dfrac{3x^2 + 2x - 10x + 5}{x - 1} \qquad \text{Use the distributive property.}$$

$$= \dfrac{3x^2 - 8x + 5}{x - 1} \qquad \text{Combine like terms.}$$

$$= \dfrac{(x - 1)(3x - 5)}{x - 1} \qquad \text{Factor.}$$

$$= 3x - 5 \qquad \text{Simplify.}$$

Work Practice Problem 3

PRACTICE PROBLEM 3

Subtract: $\dfrac{2x^2 + 5x}{x + 2} - \dfrac{4x + 6}{x + 2}$

Helpful Hint

Notice how the numerator $10x - 5$ was subtracted in Example 3.

This − sign applies to the entire numerator $10x - 5$.

So parentheses are inserted here to indicate this.

$$\dfrac{3x^2 + 2x}{x - 1} - \dfrac{10x - 5}{x - 1} = \dfrac{3x^2 + 2x - (10x - 5)}{x - 1}$$

Objective B Finding the Least Common Denominator

Recall from Chapter 3 that to add and subtract fractions with different denominators, we first find a least common denominator (LCD). Then we write all fractions as equivalent fractions with the LCD.

For example, suppose we want to add $\dfrac{3}{8}$ and $\dfrac{1}{6}$. To find the LCD of the denominators, factor 8 and 6. Remember, the LCD is the same as the least common multiple LCM. It is the smallest number that is a multiple of 6 and also 8.

$$8 = 2 \cdot 2 \cdot 2$$
$$6 = 2 \cdot 3$$

The LCM is a multiple of 6.

$$LCM = 2 \cdot 2 \cdot 2 \cdot 3 = 24$$

The LCM is a multiple of 8.

In the next section, we will continue and find the sum: $\dfrac{3}{8} + \dfrac{1}{6}$, but for now, let's concentrate on the LCD.

To add or subtract rational expressions with different denominators, we also first find an LCD and then write all rational expressions as equivalent expressions with the LCD. The **least common denominator (LCD) of a list of rational expressions** is a polynomial of least degree whose factors include all the factors of the denominators in the list.

To Find the Least Common Denominator (LCD)

Step 1: Factor each denominator completely.

Step 2: The least common denominator (LCD) is the product of all unique factors found in Step 1, each raised to a power equal to the greatest number of times that the factor appears in any one factored denominator.

Answer

3. $2x - 3$

PRACTICE PROBLEM 4

Find the LCD for each pair.

a. $\dfrac{2}{9}, \dfrac{7}{15}$

b. $\dfrac{5}{6x^3}, \dfrac{11}{8x^5}$

EXAMPLE 4 Find the LCD for each pair.

a. $\dfrac{1}{8}, \dfrac{3}{22}$ **b.** $\dfrac{7}{5x}, \dfrac{6}{15x^2}$

Solution:

a. We start by finding the prime factorization of each denominator.

$$8 = 2^3 \quad \text{and}$$
$$22 = 2 \cdot 11$$

Next we write the product of all the unique factors, each raised to a power equal to the greatest number of times that the factor appears.

The greatest number of times that the factor 2 appears is 3.

The greatest number of times that the factor 11 appears is 1.

$$\text{LCD} = 2^3 \cdot 11^1 = 8 \cdot 11 = 88$$

b. We factor each denominator.

$$5x = 5 \cdot x \quad \text{and}$$
$$15x^2 = 3 \cdot 5 \cdot x^2$$

The greatest number of times that the factor 5 appears is 1.

The greatest number of times that the factor 3 appears is 1.

The greatest number of times that the factor x appears is 2.

$$\text{LCD} = 3^1 \cdot 5^1 \cdot x^2 = 15x^2$$

🔲 **Work Practice Problem 4**

PRACTICE PROBLEM 5

Find the LCD of $\dfrac{3a}{a + 5}$ and $\dfrac{7a}{a - 5}$.

EXAMPLE 5 Find the LCD of $\dfrac{7x}{x + 2}$ and $\dfrac{5x^2}{x - 2}$.

Solution: The denominators $x + 2$ and $x - 2$ are completely factored already. The factor $x + 2$ appears once and the factor $x - 2$ appears once.

$$\text{LCD} = (x + 2)(x - 2)$$

🔲 **Work Practice Problem 5**

PRACTICE PROBLEM 6

Find the LCD of $\dfrac{7x^2}{(x - 4)^2}$ and $\dfrac{5x}{3x - 12}$.

EXAMPLE 6 Find the LCD of $\dfrac{6m^2}{3m + 15}$ and $\dfrac{2}{(m + 5)^2}$.

Solution: We factor each denominator.

$$3m + 15 = 3(m + 5)$$
$$(m + 5)^2 = (m + 5)^2 \quad \text{This denominator is already factored.}$$

The greatest number of times that the factor 3 appears is 1.

The greatest number of times that the factor $m + 5$ appears *in any one denominator* is 2.

$$\text{LCD} = 3(m + 5)^2$$

🔲 **Work Practice Problem 6**

Answers

4. a. 45, **b.** $24x^5$,
5. $(a + 5)(a - 5)$, **6.** $3(x - 4)^2$

✔ Concept Check Answer

b

✔ **Concept Check**   Choose the correct LCD of $\dfrac{x}{(x + 1)^2}$ and $\dfrac{5}{x + 1}$.

a. $x + 1$ **b.** $(x + 1)^2$ **c.** $(x + 1)^3$ **d.** $5x(x + 1)^2$

EXAMPLE 7 Find the LCD of $\dfrac{t - 10}{2t^2 + t - 6}$ and $\dfrac{t + 5}{t^2 + 3t + 2}$.

Solution:

$$2t^2 + t - 6 = (2t - 3)(t + 2)$$
$$t^2 + 3t + 2 = (t + 1)(t + 2)$$
$$\text{LCD} = (2t - 3)(t + 2)(t + 1)$$

⬛ **Work Practice Problem 7**

PRACTICE PROBLEM 7

Find the LCD of $\dfrac{y + 5}{y^2 + 2y - 3}$ and $\dfrac{y + 4}{y^2 - 3y + 2}$.

EXAMPLE 8 Find the LCD of $\dfrac{2}{x - 2}$ and $\dfrac{10}{2 - x}$.

Solution: The denominators $x - 2$ and $2 - x$ are opposites. That is, $2 - x = -1(x - 2)$. We can use either $x - 2$ or $2 - x$ as the LCD.

$$\text{LCD} = x - 2 \quad \text{or} \quad \text{LCD} = 2 - x$$

⬛ **Work Practice Problem 8**

PRACTICE PROBLEM 8

Find the LCD of $\dfrac{6}{x - 4}$ and $\dfrac{9}{4 - x}$.

Objective ⒞ Writing Equivalent Rational Expressions

Next we practice writing a rational expression as an equivalent rational expression with a given denominator. To do this, we multiply by a form of 1. Recall that multiplying an expression by 1 produces an equivalent expression. In other words,

$$\frac{P}{Q} = \frac{P}{Q} \cdot 1 = \frac{P}{Q} \cdot \frac{R}{R} = \frac{PR}{QR}$$

EXAMPLE 9 Write each rational expression as an equivalent rational expression with the given denominator.

a. $\dfrac{4b}{9a} = \dfrac{}{27a^2 b}$ **b.** $\dfrac{7x}{2x + 5} = \dfrac{}{6x + 15}$

Solution:

a. We can ask ourselves: "What do we multiply $9a$ by to get $27a^2 b$?" The answer is $3ab$, since $9a(3ab) = 27a^2 b$. So we multiply by 1 in the form of $\dfrac{3ab}{3ab}$.

$$\frac{4b}{9a} = \frac{4b}{9a} \cdot 1 = \frac{4b}{9a} \cdot \frac{3ab}{3ab}$$
$$= \frac{4b(3ab)}{9a(3ab)} = \frac{12ab^2}{27a^2 b}$$

b. First, factor the denominator on the right.

$$\frac{7x}{2x + 5} = \frac{}{3(2x + 5)}$$

To obtain the denominator on the right from the denominator on the left, we multiply by 1 in the form of $\dfrac{3}{3}$.

$$\frac{7x}{2x + 5} = \frac{7x}{2x + 5} \cdot \frac{3}{3} = \frac{7x \cdot 3}{(2x + 5) \cdot 3} = \frac{21x}{3(2x + 5)}$$

⬛ **Work Practice Problem 9**

PRACTICE PROBLEM 9

Write the rational expression as an equivalent rational expression with the given denominator.

$$\frac{2x}{5y} = \frac{}{20x^2 y^2}$$

Answers

7. $(y + 3)(y - 2)(y - 1)$,

8. $x - 4$ or $4 - x$,

9. $\dfrac{8x^3 y}{20x^2 y^2}$

PRACTICE PROBLEM 10

Write the rational expression as an equivalent rational expression with the given denominator.

$$\frac{3}{x^2 - 25} = \frac{}{(x + 5)(x - 5)(x - 3)}$$

EXAMPLE 10 Write the rational expression as an equivalent rational expression with the given denominator.

$$\frac{5}{x^2 - 4} = \frac{}{(x - 2)(x + 2)(x - 4)}$$

Solution: First we factor the denominator $x^2 - 4$ as $(x - 2)(x + 2)$. If we multiply the original denominator $(x - 2)(x + 2)$ by $x - 4$, the result is the new denominator $(x - 2)(x + 2)(x - 4)$. Thus, we multiply by 1 in the form of $\frac{x - 4}{x - 4}$.

$$\frac{5}{x^2 - 4} = \frac{5}{(x - 2)(x + 2)} = \frac{5}{(x - 2)(x + 2)} \cdot \frac{x - 4}{x - 4}$$

$$= \frac{5(x - 4)}{(x - 2)(x + 2)(x - 4)}$$

$$= \frac{5x - 20}{(x - 2)(x + 2)(x - 4)}$$

■ **Work Practice Problem 10**

Answer

10. $\dfrac{3x - 9}{(x + 5)(x - 5)(x - 3)}$

Mental Math

Perform each indicated operation.

1. $\dfrac{2}{3} + \dfrac{1}{3}$

2. $\dfrac{5}{11} + \dfrac{1}{11}$

3. $\dfrac{3x}{9} + \dfrac{4x}{9}$

4. $\dfrac{3y}{8} + \dfrac{2y}{8}$

5. $\dfrac{8}{9} - \dfrac{7}{9}$

6. $\dfrac{14}{12} - \dfrac{3}{12}$

7. $\dfrac{7y}{5} + \dfrac{10y}{5}$

8. $\dfrac{12x}{7} - \dfrac{4x}{7}$

14.3 EXERCISE SET

Objective A *Add or subtract as indicated. Simplify the result if possible. See Examples 1 through 3.*

1. $\dfrac{a}{13} + \dfrac{9}{13}$

2. $\dfrac{x+1}{7} + \dfrac{6}{7}$

3. $\dfrac{4m}{3n} + \dfrac{5m}{3n}$

4. $\dfrac{3p}{2q} + \dfrac{11p}{2q}$

5. $\dfrac{4m}{m-6} - \dfrac{24}{m-6}$

6. $\dfrac{8y}{y-2} - \dfrac{16}{y-2}$

7. $\dfrac{9}{3+y} + \dfrac{y+1}{3+y}$

8. $\dfrac{9}{y+9} + \dfrac{y-5}{y+9}$

9. $\dfrac{5x^2+4x}{x-1} - \dfrac{6x+3}{x-1}$

10. $\dfrac{x^2+9x}{x+7} - \dfrac{4x+14}{x+7}$

11. $\dfrac{4a}{a^2+2a-15} - \dfrac{12}{a^2+2a-15}$

12. $\dfrac{3y}{y^2+3y-10} - \dfrac{6}{y^2+3y-10}$

13. $\dfrac{2x+3}{x^2-x-30} - \dfrac{x-2}{x^2-x-30}$

14. $\dfrac{3x-1}{x^2+5x-6} - \dfrac{2x-7}{x^2+5x-6}$

Objective B *Find the LCD for each list of rational expressions. See Examples 4 through 8.*

15. $\dfrac{19}{2x}, \quad \dfrac{5}{4x^3}$

16. $\dfrac{17x}{4y^5}, \quad \dfrac{2}{8y}$

17. $\dfrac{9}{8x}, \quad \dfrac{3}{2x+4}$

18. $\dfrac{1}{6y}, \quad \dfrac{3x}{4y+12}$

19. $\dfrac{2}{x+3}, \quad \dfrac{5}{x-2}$

20. $\dfrac{-6}{x-1}, \quad \dfrac{4}{x+5}$

21. $\dfrac{x}{x+6}, \quad \dfrac{10}{3x+18}$

22. $\dfrac{12}{x+5}, \quad \dfrac{x}{4x+20}$

23. $\dfrac{8x^2}{(x-6)^2}, \quad \dfrac{13x}{5x-30}$

24. $\dfrac{9x^2}{7x-14}, \quad \dfrac{6x}{(x-2)^2}$

25. $\dfrac{1}{3x+3}, \dfrac{8}{2x^2+4x+2}$

26. $\dfrac{19x+5}{4x-12}, \quad \dfrac{3}{2x^2-12x+18}$

27. $\dfrac{5}{x-8}, \quad \dfrac{3}{8-x}$

28. $\dfrac{2x+5}{3x-7}, \ \dfrac{5}{7-3x}$

29. $\dfrac{5x+1}{x^2+3x-4}, \ \dfrac{3x}{x^2+2x-3}$

30. $\dfrac{4}{x^2+4x+3}, \ \dfrac{4x-2}{x^2+10x+21}$

31. $\dfrac{2x}{3x^2+4x+1}, \ \dfrac{7}{2x^2-x-1}$

32. $\dfrac{3x}{4x^2+5x+1}, \ \dfrac{5}{3x^2-2x-1}$

33. $\dfrac{1}{x^2-16}, \ \dfrac{x+6}{2x^3-8x^2}$

34. $\dfrac{5}{x^2-25}, \ \dfrac{x+9}{3x^3-15x^2}$

Objective $\boxed{C}$ *Rewrite each rational expression as an equivalent rational expression with the given denominator. See Examples 9 and 10.*

35. $\dfrac{3}{2x}=\dfrac{}{4x^2}$

36. $\dfrac{3}{9y^5}=\dfrac{}{72y^9}$

37. $\dfrac{6}{3a}=\dfrac{}{12ab^2}$

38. $\dfrac{5}{4y^2x}=\dfrac{}{32y^3x^2}$

39. $\dfrac{9}{2x+6}=\dfrac{}{2y(x+3)}$

40. $\dfrac{4x+1}{3x+6}=\dfrac{}{3y(x+2)}$

41. $\dfrac{9a+2}{5a+10}=\dfrac{}{5b(a+2)}$

42. $\dfrac{5+y}{2x^2+10}=\dfrac{}{4(x^2+5)}$

43. $\dfrac{x}{x^3+6x^2+8x}=\dfrac{}{x(x+4)(x+2)(x+1)}$

44. $\dfrac{5x}{x^3+2x^2-3x}=\dfrac{}{x(x-1)(x-5)(x+3)}$

45. $\dfrac{9y-1}{15x^2-30}=\dfrac{}{30x^2-60}$

46. $\dfrac{6m-5}{3x^2-9}=\dfrac{}{12x^2-36}$

Mixed Practice (*Sections 14.2, 14.3*) *Perform the indicated operations.*

47. $\dfrac{5x}{7}+\dfrac{9x}{7}$

48. $\dfrac{5x}{7}\cdot\dfrac{9x}{7}$

49. $\dfrac{x+3}{4}\div\dfrac{2x-1}{4}$

50. $\dfrac{x+3}{4}-\dfrac{2x-1}{4}$

51. $\dfrac{x^2}{x-6}-\dfrac{5x+6}{x-6}$

52. $\dfrac{x^2+5x}{x^2-25}\cdot\dfrac{3x-15}{x^2}$

53. $\dfrac{-2x}{x^3-8x}+\dfrac{3x}{x^3-8x}$

54. $\dfrac{-2x}{x^3-8x}\div\dfrac{3x}{x^3-8x}$

55. $\dfrac{12x-6}{x^2+3x}\cdot\dfrac{4x^2+13x+3}{4x^2-1}$

56. $\dfrac{x^3+7x^2}{3x^3-x^2}\div\dfrac{5x^2+36x+7}{9x^2-1}$

Review

Perform each indicated operation. See Section 3.3.

57. $\dfrac{2}{3} + \dfrac{5}{7}$ **58.** $\dfrac{9}{10} - \dfrac{3}{5}$ **59.** $\dfrac{2}{6} - \dfrac{3}{4}$ **60.** $\dfrac{11}{15} + \dfrac{5}{9}$ **61.** $\dfrac{1}{12} + \dfrac{3}{20}$ **62.** $\dfrac{7}{30} + \dfrac{3}{18}$

Concept Extensions

63. Choose the correct LCD of $\dfrac{11a^3}{4a - 20}$ and $\dfrac{15a^3}{(a - 5)^2}$.
See the Concept Check in this section.
 a. $4a(a - 5)(a + 5)$ **b.** $a - 5$
 c. $(a - 5)^2$ **d.** $4(a - 5)^2$
 e. $(4a - 20)(a - 5)^2$

64. An algebra student approaches you with a problem. He's tried to subtract two rational expressions, but his result does not match the book's. Check to see if the student has made an error. If so, correct his work shown below.

$$\dfrac{2x - 6}{x - 5} - \dfrac{x + 4}{x - 5}$$
$$= \dfrac{2x - 6 - x + 4}{x - 5}$$
$$= \dfrac{x - 2}{x - 5}$$

△ **65.** A square has a side of length $\dfrac{5}{x - 2}$ meters. Express its perimeter as a rational expression.

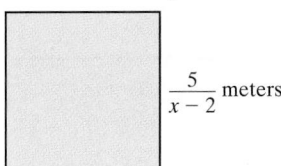
$\dfrac{5}{x - 2}$ meters

△ **66.** A trapezoid has sides of the indicated lengths. Find its perimeter.

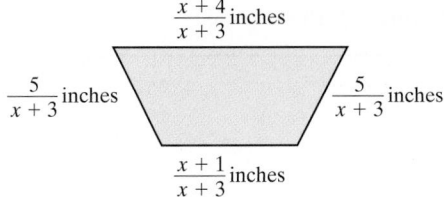
$\dfrac{x + 4}{x + 3}$ inches
$\dfrac{5}{x + 3}$ inches
$\dfrac{5}{x + 3}$ inches
$\dfrac{x + 1}{x + 3}$ inches

67. Write two rational expressions with the same denominator whose sum is $\dfrac{5}{3x - 1}$.

68. Write two rational expressions with the same denominator whose difference is $\dfrac{x - 7}{x^2 + 1}$.

69. You are throwing a barbecue and you want to make sure that you purchase the same number of hot dogs as hot dog buns. Hot dogs come 8 to a package and hot dog buns come 12 to a package. What is the least number of each type of package you should buy?

70. The planet Mercury revolves around the sun in 88 Earth days. It takes Jupiter 4332 Earth days to make one revolution around the Sun. (*Source:* National Space Science Data Center) If the two planets are aligned as shown in the figure, how long will it take for them to align again?

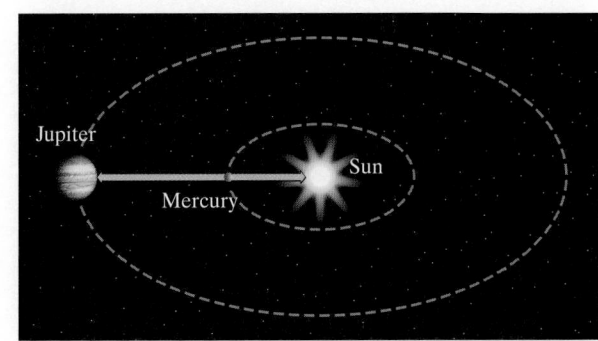

71. Write some instructions to help a friend who is having difficulty finding the LCD of two rational expressions.

72. Explain why the LCD of the rational expressions $\dfrac{7}{x+1}$ and $\dfrac{9x}{(x+1)^2}$ is $(x+1)^2$ and not $(x+1)^3$.

73. In your own words, describe how to add or subtract two rational expressions with the same denominators.

74. Explain the similarities between subtracting $\dfrac{3}{8}$ from $\dfrac{7}{8}$ and subtracting $\dfrac{6}{x+3}$ from $\dfrac{9}{x+3}$.

STUDY SKILLS BUILDER

How Are You Doing?

If you haven't done so yet, take a few moments and think about how you are doing in this course. Are you working toward your goal of successfully completing this course? Is your performance on homework, quizzes, and tests satisfactory? If not, you might want to see your instructor to see if he/she has any suggestions on how you can improve your performance. Reread Section 1.1 for ideas on places to get help with your mathematics course.

Answer the following

1. List any textbook supplements you are using to help you through this course.

2. List any campus resources you are using to help you through this course.

3. Write a short paragraph describing how you are doing in your mathematics course.

4. If improvement is needed, list ways that you can work toward improving your situation as described in Exercise 3.

14.4 ADDING AND SUBTRACTING RATIONAL EXPRESSIONS WITH DIFFERENT DENOMINATORS

Objective

A Add and Subtract Rational Expressions with Different Denominators.

Objective A Adding and Subtracting Rational Expressions with Different Denominators

Let's add $\frac{3}{8}$ and $\frac{1}{6}$. In the previous section, we found the LCD to be 24. Now let's write equivalent fractions with denominators of 24 by multiplying by different forms of 1.

$$\frac{3}{8} = \frac{3}{8} \cdot 1 = \frac{3}{8} \cdot \frac{3}{3} = \frac{3 \cdot 3}{8 \cdot 3} = \frac{9}{24}.$$

$$\frac{1}{6} = \frac{1}{6} \cdot 1 = \frac{1}{6} \cdot \frac{4}{4} = \frac{1 \cdot 4}{6 \cdot 4} = \frac{4}{24}.$$

Now that the denominators are the same, we may add.

$$\frac{3}{8} + \frac{1}{6} = \frac{9}{24} + \frac{4}{24} = \frac{9 + 4}{24} = \frac{13}{24}$$

We add or subtract rational expressions the same way. You may want to use the steps below.

To Add or Subtract Rational Expressions with Different Denominators

Step 1: Find the LCD of the rational expressions.

Step 2: Rewrite each rational expression as an equivalent expression whose denominator is the LCD found in Step 1.

Step 3: Add or subtract numerators and write the sum or difference over the common denominator.

Step 4: Simplify or write the rational expression in lowest terms.

EXAMPLE 1 Perform each indicated operation.

a. $\frac{a}{4} - \frac{2a}{8}$

b. $\frac{3}{10x^2} + \frac{7}{25x}$

Solution:

a. First, we must find the LCD. Since $4 = 2^2$ and $8 = 2^3$, the LCD $= 2^3 = 8$. Next we write each fraction as an equivalent fraction with the denominator 8, and then we subtract.

$$\frac{a}{4} = \frac{a}{4} \cdot 1 = \frac{a}{4} \cdot \frac{2}{2} = \frac{a \cdot 2}{4 \cdot 2} = \frac{2a}{8}$$

$$\frac{a}{4} - \frac{2a}{8} = \frac{a(2)}{4(2)} - \frac{2a}{8} = \frac{2a}{8} - \frac{2a}{8} = \frac{2a - 2a}{8} = \frac{0}{8} = 0$$

Notice that we wrote $\frac{a}{4}$ as the equivalent expression $\frac{2a}{8}$. Multiplying by a form of 1 means we multiply the numerator and the denominator by the same number. Since this is so, we will start using the shorthand notation on the next page.

Continued on next page

PRACTICE PROBLEM 1

Perform each indicated operation.

a. $\frac{y}{5} - \frac{3y}{15}$

b. $\frac{5}{8x} + \frac{11}{10x^2}$

Answers

1. a. 0, **b.** $\frac{25x + 44}{40x^2}$

$$\frac{a}{4} = \frac{a(2)}{4(2)} = \frac{2a}{8}$$

Multiplying the numerator and denominator by 2 is the same as multiplying by $\frac{2}{2}$ or 1.

b. Since $10x^2 = 2 \cdot 5 \cdot x \cdot x$ and $25x = 5 \cdot 5 \cdot x$, the LCD $= 2 \cdot 5^2 \cdot x^2 = 50x^2$. We write each fraction as an equivalent fraction with a denominator of $50x^2$.

$$\frac{3}{10x^2} + \frac{7}{25x} = \frac{3(5)}{10x^2(5)} + \frac{7(2x)}{25x(2x)}$$

$$= \frac{15}{50x^2} + \frac{14x}{50x^2}$$

$$= \frac{15 + 14x}{50x^2} \qquad \text{Add numerators. Write the sum over the common denominator.}$$

▣ **Work Practice Problem 1**

PRACTICE PROBLEM 2

Subtract: $\dfrac{10x}{x^2 - 9} - \dfrac{5}{x + 3}$

EXAMPLE 2 Subtract: $\dfrac{6x}{x^2 - 4} - \dfrac{3}{x + 2}$

Solution: Since $x^2 - 4 = (x + 2)(x - 2)$, the LCD $= (x + 2)(x - 2)$. We write equivalent expressions with the LCD as denominators.

$$\frac{6x}{x^2 - 4} - \frac{3}{x + 2} = \frac{6x}{(x + 2)(x - 2)} - \frac{3(x - 2)}{(x + 2)(x - 2)}$$

$$= \frac{6x - 3(x - 2)}{(x + 2)(x - 2)} \qquad \text{Subtract numerators. Write the difference over the common denominator.}$$

$$= \frac{6x - 3x + 6}{(x + 2)(x - 2)} \qquad \text{Apply the distributive property in the numerator.}$$

$$= \frac{3x + 6}{(x + 2)(x - 2)} \qquad \text{Combine like terms in the numerator.}$$

Next we factor the numerator to see if this rational expression can be simplified.

$$\frac{3x + 6}{(x + 2)(x - 2)} = \frac{3\,(x + 2)}{(x + 2)\,(x - 2)} \qquad \text{Factor.}$$

$$= \frac{3}{x - 2} \qquad \text{Apply the fundamental principle to simplify.}$$

▣ **Work Practice Problem 2**

PRACTICE PROBLEM 3

Add: $\dfrac{5}{7x} + \dfrac{2}{x + 1}$

EXAMPLE 3 Add: $\dfrac{2}{3t} + \dfrac{5}{t + 1}$

Solution: The LCD is $3t(t + 1)$. We write each rational expression as an equivalent rational expression with a denominator of $3t(t + 1)$.

$$\frac{2}{3t} + \frac{5}{t + 1} = \frac{2(t + 1)}{3t(t + 1)} + \frac{5(3t)}{(t + 1)(3t)}$$

$$= \frac{2(t + 1) + 5(3t)}{3t(t + 1)} \qquad \text{Add numerators. Write the sum over the common denominator.}$$

$$= \frac{2t + 2 + 15t}{3t(t + 1)} \qquad \text{Apply the distributive property in the numerator.}$$

$$= \frac{17t + 2}{3t(t + 1)} \qquad \text{Combine like terms in the numerator.}$$

▣ **Work Practice Problem 3**

Answers

2. $\dfrac{5}{x - 3}$,   **3.** $\dfrac{19x + 5}{7x(x + 1)}$

EXAMPLE 4 Subtract: $\dfrac{7}{x-3} - \dfrac{9}{3-x}$

Solution: To find a common denominator, we notice that $x - 3$ and $3 - x$ are opposites. That is, $3 - x = -(x - 3)$. We write the denominator $3 - x$ as $-(x - 3)$ and simplify.

$$\frac{7}{x-3} - \frac{9}{3-x} = \frac{7}{x-3} - \frac{9}{-(x-3)}$$

$$= \frac{7}{x-3} - \frac{-9}{x-3} \qquad \text{Apply } \frac{a}{-b} = \frac{-a}{b}.$$

$$= \frac{7 - (-9)}{x-3} \qquad \text{Subtract numerators. Write the difference over the common denominator.}$$

$$= \frac{16}{x-3}$$

■ **Work Practice Problem 4**

PRACTICE PROBLEM 4

Subtract: $\dfrac{10}{x-6} - \dfrac{15}{6-x}$

EXAMPLE 5 Add: $1 + \dfrac{m}{m+1}$

Solution: Recall that 1 is the same as $\dfrac{1}{1}$. The LCD of $\dfrac{1}{1}$ and $\dfrac{m}{m+1}$ is $m + 1$.

$$1 + \frac{m}{m+1} = \frac{1}{1} + \frac{m}{m+1} \qquad \text{Write 1 as } \frac{1}{1}.$$

$$= \frac{1(m+1)}{1(m+1)} + \frac{m}{m+1} \qquad \text{Multiply both the numerator and the denominator of } \frac{1}{1} \text{ by } m + 1.$$

$$= \frac{m+1+m}{m+1} \qquad \text{Add numerators. Write the sum over the common denominator.}$$

$$= \frac{2m+1}{m+1} \qquad \text{Combine like terms in the numerator.}$$

■ **Work Practice Problem 5**

PRACTICE PROBLEM 5

Add: $2 + \dfrac{x}{x+5}$

EXAMPLE 6 Subtract: $\dfrac{3}{2x^2+x} - \dfrac{2x}{6x+3}$

Solution: First, we factor the denominators.

$$\frac{3}{2x^2+x} - \frac{2x}{6x+3} = \frac{3}{x(2x+1)} - \frac{2x}{3(2x+1)}$$

The LCD is $3x(2x+1)$. We write equivalent expressions with denominators of $3x(2x+1)$.

$$\frac{3}{x(2x+1)} - \frac{2x}{3(2x+1)} = \frac{3(3)}{x(2x+1)(3)} - \frac{2x(x)}{3(2x+1)(x)}$$

$$= \frac{9 - 2x^2}{3x(2x+1)} \qquad \text{Subtract numerators. Write the difference over the common denominator.}$$

■ **Work Practice Problem 6**

PRACTICE PROBLEM 6

Subtract: $\dfrac{4}{3x^2+2x} - \dfrac{3x}{12x+8}$

Answers

4. $\dfrac{25}{x-6}$, **5.** $\dfrac{3x+10}{x+5}$, **6.** $\dfrac{16-3x^2}{4x(3x+2)}$

PRACTICE PROBLEM 7

Add: $\dfrac{6x}{x^2 + 4x + 4} + \dfrac{x}{x^2 - 4}$

EXAMPLE 7 Add: $\dfrac{2x}{x^2 + 2x + 1} + \dfrac{x}{x^2 - 1}$

Solution: First we factor the denominators.

$$\dfrac{2x}{x^2 + 2x + 1} + \dfrac{x}{x^2 - 1}$$

$$= \dfrac{2x}{(x + 1)(x + 1)} + \dfrac{x}{(x + 1)(x - 1)}$$

Rewrite each expression with LCD $(x + 1)(x + 1)(x - 1)$.

$$= \dfrac{2x(x - 1)}{(x + 1)(x + 1)(x - 1)} + \dfrac{x(x + 1)}{(x + 1)(x - 1)(x + 1)}$$

$$= \dfrac{2x(x - 1) + x(x + 1)}{(x + 1)^2(x - 1)} \qquad \text{Add numerators. Write the sum over the common denominator.}$$

$$= \dfrac{2x^2 - 2x + x^2 + x}{(x + 1)^2(x - 1)} \qquad \text{Apply the distributive property in the numerator.}$$

$$= \dfrac{3x^2 - x}{(x + 1)^2(x - 1)} \quad \text{or} \quad \dfrac{x(3x - 1)}{(x + 1)^2(x - 1)}$$

The numerator was factored as a last step to see if the rational expression could be simplified further. Since there are no factors common to the numerator and the denominator, we can't simplify further.

▣ **Work Practice Problem 7**

Answer

7. $\dfrac{x(7x - 10)}{(x + 2)^2(x - 2)}$

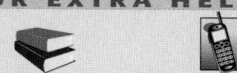

Objective **A** *Perform each indicated operation. Simplify if possible. See Examples 1 through 7.*

1. $\dfrac{4}{2x} + \dfrac{9}{3x}$

2. $\dfrac{15}{7a} + \dfrac{8}{6a}$

3. $\dfrac{15a}{b} + \dfrac{6b}{5}$

4. $\dfrac{4c}{d} - \dfrac{8d}{5}$

5. $\dfrac{3}{x} + \dfrac{5}{2x^2}$

6. $\dfrac{14}{3x^2} + \dfrac{6}{x}$

7. $\dfrac{6}{x+1} + \dfrac{10}{2x+2}$

8. $\dfrac{8}{x+4} - \dfrac{3}{3x+12}$

9. $\dfrac{3}{x+2} - \dfrac{2x}{x^2-4}$

10. $\dfrac{5}{x-4} + \dfrac{4x}{x^2-16}$

11. $\dfrac{3}{4x} + \dfrac{8}{x-2}$

12. $\dfrac{5}{y^2} - \dfrac{y}{2y+1}$

13. $\dfrac{6}{x-3} + \dfrac{8}{3-x}$

14. $\dfrac{15}{y-4} + \dfrac{20}{4-y}$

15. $\dfrac{9}{x-3} + \dfrac{9}{3-x}$

16. $\dfrac{5}{a-7} + \dfrac{5}{7-a}$

17. $\dfrac{-8}{x^2-1} - \dfrac{7}{1-x^2}$

18. $\dfrac{-9}{25x^2-1} + \dfrac{7}{1-25x^2}$

19. $\dfrac{5}{x} + 2$

20. $\dfrac{7}{x^2} - 5x$

21. $\dfrac{5}{x-2} + 6$

22. $\dfrac{6y}{y+5} + 1$

23. $\dfrac{y+2}{y+3} - 2$

24. $\dfrac{7}{2x-3} - 3$

25. $\dfrac{-x+2}{x} - \dfrac{x-6}{4x}$

26. $\dfrac{-y+1}{y} - \dfrac{2y-5}{3y}$

27. $\dfrac{5x}{x+2} - \dfrac{3x-4}{x+2}$

28. $\dfrac{7x}{x-3} - \dfrac{4x+9}{x-3}$

29. $\dfrac{3x^4}{7} - \dfrac{4x^2}{21}$

30. $\dfrac{5x}{6} + \dfrac{11x^2}{2}$

31. $\dfrac{1}{x+3} - \dfrac{1}{(x+3)^2}$

32. $\dfrac{5x}{(x-2)^2} - \dfrac{3}{x-2}$

33. $\dfrac{4}{5b} + \dfrac{1}{b-1}$

34. $\dfrac{1}{y+5} + \dfrac{2}{3y}$

35. $\dfrac{2}{m} + 1$

36. $\dfrac{6}{x} - 1$

37. $\dfrac{2x}{x-7} - \dfrac{x}{x-2}$

38. $\dfrac{9x}{x-10} - \dfrac{x}{x-3}$

39. $\dfrac{6}{1-2x} - \dfrac{4}{2x-1}$

40. $\dfrac{10}{3n-4} - \dfrac{5}{4-3n}$

41. $\dfrac{7}{(x + 1)(x - 1)} + \dfrac{8}{(x + 1)^2}$

42. $\dfrac{5}{(x + 1)(x + 5)} - \dfrac{2}{(x + 5)^2}$

43. $\dfrac{x}{x^2 - 1} - \dfrac{2}{x^2 - 2x + 1}$

44. $\dfrac{x}{x^2 - 4} - \dfrac{5}{x^2 - 4x + 4}$

45. $\dfrac{3a}{2a + 6} - \dfrac{a - 1}{a + 3}$

46. $\dfrac{1}{x + y} - \dfrac{y}{x^2 - y^2}$

47. $\dfrac{y - 1}{2y + 3} + \dfrac{3}{(2y + 3)^2}$

48. $\dfrac{x - 6}{5x + 1} + \dfrac{6}{(5x + 1)^2}$

49. $\dfrac{5}{2 - x} + \dfrac{x}{2x - 4}$

50. $\dfrac{-1}{a - 2} + \dfrac{4}{4 - 2a}$

51. $\dfrac{15}{x^2 + 6x + 9} + \dfrac{2}{x + 3}$

52. $\dfrac{2}{x^2 + 4x + 4} + \dfrac{1}{x + 2}$

53. $\dfrac{13}{x^2 - 5x + 6} - \dfrac{5}{x - 3}$

54. $\dfrac{-7}{y^2 - 3y + 2} - \dfrac{2}{y - 1}$

55. $\dfrac{70}{m^2 - 100} + \dfrac{7}{2(m + 10)}$

56. $\dfrac{27}{y^2 - 81} + \dfrac{3}{2(y + 9)}$

57. $\dfrac{x + 8}{x^2 - 5x - 6} + \dfrac{x + 1}{x^2 - 4x - 5}$

58. $\dfrac{x + 4}{x^2 + 12x + 20} + \dfrac{x + 1}{x^2 + 8x - 20}$

59. $\dfrac{5}{4n^2 - 12n + 8} - \dfrac{3}{3n^2 - 6n}$

60. $\dfrac{6}{5y^2 - 25y + 30} - \dfrac{2}{4y^2 - 8y}$

Mixed Practice (*Sections 14.2, 14.3, 14.4*)   *Perform the indicated operations. Addition, subtraction, multiplication, and division of rational expressions are included here.*

61. $\dfrac{15x}{x + 8} \cdot \dfrac{2x + 16}{3x}$

62. $\dfrac{9z + 5}{15} \cdot \dfrac{5z}{81z^2 - 25}$

63. $\dfrac{8x + 7}{3x + 5} - \dfrac{2x - 3}{3x + 5}$

64. $\dfrac{2z^2}{4z - 1} - \dfrac{z - 2z^2}{4z - 1}$

65. $\dfrac{5a + 10}{18} \div \dfrac{a^2 - 4}{10a}$

66. $\dfrac{9}{x^2 - 1} \div \dfrac{12}{3x + 3}$

67. $\dfrac{5}{x^2 - 3x + 2} + \dfrac{1}{x - 2}$

68. $\dfrac{4}{2x^2 + 5x - 3} + \dfrac{2}{x + 3}$

Review

Solve each linear or quadratic equation. See Sections 9.3 and 13.5.

69. $3x + 5 = 7$

70. $5x - 1 = 8$

71. $2x^2 - x - 1 = 0$

72. $4x^2 - 9 = 0$

73. $4(x + 6) + 3 = -3$

74. $2(3x + 1) + 15 = -7$

Concept Extensions

Perform each indicated operation.

75. $\dfrac{3}{x} - \dfrac{2x}{x^2 - 1} + \dfrac{5}{x + 1}$

76. $\dfrac{5}{x - 2} + \dfrac{7x}{x^2 - 4} - \dfrac{11}{x}$

77. $\dfrac{5}{x^2 - 4} + \dfrac{2}{x^2 - 4x + 4} - \dfrac{3}{x^2 - x - 6}$

78. $\dfrac{8}{x^2 + 6x + 5} - \dfrac{3x}{x^2 + 4x - 5} + \dfrac{2}{x^2 - 1}$

79. $\dfrac{9}{x^2 + 9x + 14} - \dfrac{3x}{x^2 + 10x + 21} + \dfrac{x + 4}{x^2 + 5x + 6}$

80. $\dfrac{x + 10}{x^2 - 3x - 4} - \dfrac{8}{x^2 + 6x + 5} - \dfrac{9}{x^2 + x - 20}$

81. A board of length $\dfrac{3}{x + 4}$ inches was cut into two pieces. If one piece is $\dfrac{1}{x - 4}$ inches, express the length of the other board as a rational expression.

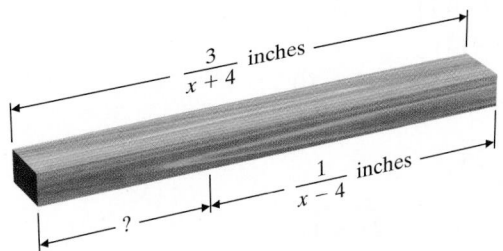

82. The length of a rectangle is $\dfrac{3}{y - 5}$ feet, while its width is $\dfrac{2}{y}$ feet. Find its perimeter and then find its area.

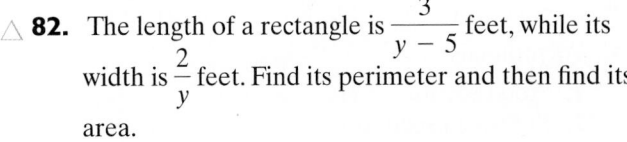

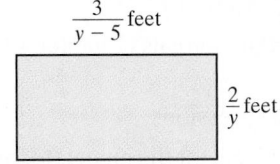

83. In ice hockey, penalty killing percentage is a statistic calculated as $1 - \dfrac{G}{P}$, where G = opponent's power play goals and P = opponent's power play opportunities. Simplify this expression.

84. The dose of medicine prescribed for a child depends on the child's age A in years and the adult dose D for the medication. Two expressions that give a child's dose are Young's Rule, $\dfrac{DA}{A + 12}$, and Cowling's Rule, $\dfrac{D(A + 1)}{24}$. Find an expression for the difference in the doses given by these expressions.

85. Explain when the LCD of the rational expressions in a sum is the product of the denominators.

86. Explain when the LCD is the same as one of the denominators of a rational expression to be added or subtracted.

△ **87.** Two angles are said to be complementary if the sum of their measures is 90°. If one angle measures $\dfrac{40}{x}$ degrees, find the measure of its complement.

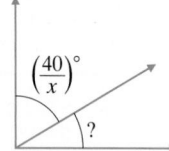

△ **88.** Two angles are said to be supplementary if the sum of their measures is 180°. If one angle measures $\dfrac{x + 2}{x}$ degrees, find the measure of its supplement.

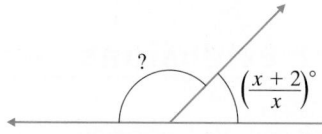

89. In your own words, explain how to add two rational expressions with different denominators.

90. In your own words, explain how to subtract two rational expressions with different denominators.

 THE BIGGER PICTURE   Simplifying Expressions and Solving Equations and Inequalities

Now we continue our outline from Sections 8.5, 9.7, 12.7, and 13.6. Although suggestions are given, this outline should be in your own words. Once you complete this new portion, try the exercises below.

I. Simplifying Expressions

A. Real Numbers

1. Add (Section 8.3)
2. Subtract (Section 8.4)
3. Multiply or Divide (Section 8.5)

B. Exponents (Section 12.2)

C. Polynomials

1. Add (Section 12.4)
2. Subtract (Section 12.4)
3. Multiply (Section 12.5)
4. Divide (Section 12.7)

D. Factoring Polynomials (Chapter 13 Integrated Review)

E. Rational Expressions

1. Simplify: Factor the numerator and denominator. Then divide out factors of 1 by dividing out common factors in the numerator and denominator.
$$\frac{x^2 - 9}{7x^2 - 21x} = \frac{(x + 3)(x - 3)}{7x(x - 3)} = \frac{x + 3}{7x}$$

2. Multiply: Multiply numerators, then multiply denominators.
$$\frac{5z}{2z^2 - 9z - 18} \cdot \frac{22z + 33}{10z}$$
$$= \frac{5 \cdot z}{(2z + 3)(z - 6)} \cdot \frac{11(2z + 3)}{2 \cdot 5 \cdot z} = \frac{11}{2(z - 6)}$$

3. Divide: First fraction times the reciprocal of the second fraction.
$$\frac{14}{x + 5} \div \frac{x + 1}{2} = \frac{14}{x + 5} \cdot \frac{2}{x + 1}$$
$$= \frac{28}{(x + 5)(x + 1)}$$

4. Add or Subtract: Must have same denominator. If not find the LCD and write each fraction as an equivalent fraction with the LCD as denominator.
$$\frac{9}{10} - \frac{x + 1}{x + 5} = \frac{9(x + 5)}{10(x + 5)} - \frac{10(x + 1)}{10(x + 5)}$$
$$= \frac{9x + 45 - 10x - 10}{10(x + 5)}$$
$$= \frac{-x + 35}{10(x + 5)}$$

II. Solving Equations and Inequalities

A. Linear Equations (Section 9.3)

B. Linear Inequalities (Section 9.7)

C. Quadratic & Higher Degree Equations (Section 13.6)

Perform indicated operations and simplify.

1. $-8.6 + (-9.1)$
2. $(-8.6)(-9.1)$
3. $14 - (-14)$
4. $3x^4 - 7 + x^4 - x^2 - 10$
5. $\dfrac{5x^2 - 5}{25x + 25}$
6. $\dfrac{7x}{x^2 + 4x + 3} \div \dfrac{x}{2x + 6}$
7. $\dfrac{2}{9} - \dfrac{5}{6}$
8. $\dfrac{x}{9} - \dfrac{x + 3}{5}$

Factor.

9. $9x^3 - 2x^2 - 11x$
10. $12xy - 21x + 4y - 7$

Solve.

11. $7x - 14 = 5x + 10$
12. $\dfrac{-x + 2}{5} < \dfrac{3}{10}$
13. $1 + 4(x + 4) = 3^2 + x$
14. $x(x - 2) = 24$

14.5 SOLVING EQUATIONS CONTAINING RATIONAL EXPRESSIONS

Objectives

A Solve Equations Containing Rational Expressions.

B Solve Equations Containing Rational Expressions for a Specified Variable.

Objective **A** Solving Equations Containing Rational Expressions

In Chapter 9, we solved equations containing fractions. In this section, we continue the work we began in Chapter 9 by solving equations containing rational expressions. For example,

$$\frac{x}{2} + \frac{8}{3} = \frac{1}{6} \quad \text{and} \quad \frac{4x}{x^2 + x - 30} + \frac{2}{x - 5} = \frac{1}{x + 6}$$

are equations containing rational expressions. To solve equations such as these, we use the multiplication property of equality to clear the equation of fractions by multiplying both sides of the equation by the LCD.

EXAMPLE 1 Solve: $\dfrac{x}{2} + \dfrac{8}{3} = \dfrac{1}{6}$

Solution: The LCD of denominators 2, 3, and 6 is 6, so we multiply both sides of the equation by 6.

$$6\left(\frac{x}{2} + \frac{8}{3}\right) = 6\left(\frac{1}{6}\right)$$

$$6\left(\frac{x}{2}\right) + 6\left(\frac{8}{3}\right) = 6\left(\frac{1}{6}\right) \quad \text{Apply the distributive property.}$$

$$3 \cdot x + 16 = 1 \qquad \text{Multiply and simplify.}$$

$$3x = -15 \qquad \text{Subtract 16 from both sides.}$$

$$x = -5 \qquad \text{Divide both sides by 3.}$$

Check: To check, we replace x with -5 in the original equation.

$$\frac{-5}{2} + \frac{8}{3} \stackrel{?}{=} \frac{1}{6} \qquad \text{Replace } x \text{ with } -5.$$

$$\frac{1}{6} = \frac{1}{6} \qquad \text{True}$$

This number checks, so the solution is -5.

Work Practice Problem 1

EXAMPLE 2 Solve: $\dfrac{t - 4}{2} - \dfrac{t - 3}{9} = \dfrac{5}{18}$

Solution: The LCD of denominators 2, 9, and 18 is 18, so we multiply both sides of the equation by 18.

$$18\left(\frac{t - 4}{2} - \frac{t - 3}{9}\right) = 18\left(\frac{5}{18}\right)$$

$$18\left(\frac{t - 4}{2}\right) - 18\left(\frac{t - 3}{9}\right) = 18\left(\frac{5}{18}\right) \quad \text{Apply the distributive property.}$$

$$9(t - 4) - 2(t - 3) = 5 \qquad \text{Simplify.}$$

$$9t - 36 - 2t + 6 = 5 \qquad \text{Use the distributive property.}$$

$$7t - 30 = 5 \qquad \text{Combine like terms.}$$

$$7t = 35$$

$$t = 5 \qquad \text{Solve for } t.$$

PRACTICE PROBLEM 1

Solve: $\dfrac{x}{4} + \dfrac{4}{5} = \dfrac{1}{20}$

Helpful Hint

Make sure that *each* term is multiplied by the LCD.

PRACTICE PROBLEM 2

Solve: $\dfrac{x + 2}{3} - \dfrac{x - 1}{5} = \dfrac{1}{15}$

Helpful Hint

Multiply *each* term by 18.

Answers

1. $x = -3$, **2.** $x = -6$

Check: $\dfrac{t-4}{2} - \dfrac{t-3}{9} = \dfrac{5}{18}$

$$\dfrac{5-4}{2} - \dfrac{5-3}{9} \stackrel{?}{=} \dfrac{5}{18} \quad \text{Replace } t \text{ with 5.}$$

$$\dfrac{1}{2} - \dfrac{2}{9} \stackrel{?}{=} \dfrac{5}{18} \quad \text{Simplify.}$$

$$\dfrac{5}{18} = \dfrac{5}{18} \quad \text{True}$$

The solution is 5.

■ **Work Practice Problem 2**

Recall from Section 14.1 that a rational expression is defined for all real numbers except those that make the denominator of the expression 0. This means that if an equation contains *rational expressions with variables in the denominator,* we must be certain that the proposed solution does not make the denominator 0. If replacing the variable with the proposed solution makes the denominator 0, the rational expression is undefined and this proposed solution must be rejected.

PRACTICE PROBLEM 3

Solve: $2 + \dfrac{6}{x} = x + 7$

EXAMPLE 3 Solve: $3 - \dfrac{6}{x} = x + 8$

Solution: In this equation, 0 cannot be a solution because if x is 0, the rational expression $\dfrac{6}{x}$ is undefined. The LCD is x, so we multiply both sides of the equation by x.

$$x\left(3 - \dfrac{6}{x}\right) = x(x + 8)$$

Helpful Hint

Multiply *each* term by x.

$$x(3) - x\left(\dfrac{6}{x}\right) = x \cdot x + x \cdot 8 \quad \text{Apply the distributive property.}$$

$$3x - 6 = x^2 + 8x \quad \text{Simplify.}$$

Now we write the quadratic equation in standard form and solve for x.

$$0 = x^2 + 5x + 6$$

$$0 = (x + 3)(x + 2) \qquad \text{Factor.}$$

$$x + 3 = 0 \quad \text{or} \quad x + 2 = 0 \qquad \text{Set each factor equal to 0 and solve.}$$

$$x = -3 \qquad\qquad x = -2$$

Notice that neither -3 nor -2 makes the denominator in the original equation equal to 0.

Check: To check these solutions, we replace x in the original equation by -3, and then by -2.

If $x = -3$:

$$3 - \dfrac{6}{x} = x + 8$$

$$3 - \dfrac{6}{-3} \stackrel{?}{=} -3 + 8$$

$$3 - (-2) \stackrel{?}{=} 5$$

$$5 = 5 \qquad \text{True}$$

If $x = -2$:

$$3 - \dfrac{6}{x} = x + 8$$

$$3 - \dfrac{6}{-2} \stackrel{?}{=} -2 + 8$$

$$3 - (-3) \stackrel{?}{=} 6$$

$$6 = 6 \qquad \text{True}$$

Both -3 and -2 are solutions.

■ **Work Practice Problem 3**

The following steps may be used to solve an equation containing rational expressions.

Answer

3. $x = -6, x = 1$

To Solve an Equation Containing Rational Expressions

Step 1: Multiply both sides of the equation by the LCD of all rational expressions in the equation.

Step 2: Remove any grouping symbols and solve the resulting equation.

Step 3: Check the solution in the original equation.

EXAMPLE 4 Solve: $\dfrac{4x}{x^2 + x - 30} + \dfrac{2}{x - 5} = \dfrac{1}{x + 6}$

Solution: The denominator $x^2 + x - 30$ factors as $(x + 6)(x - 5)$. The LCD is then $(x + 6)(x - 5)$, so we multiply both sides of the equation by this LCD.

$$(x + 6)(x - 5)\left(\frac{4x}{x^2 + x - 30} + \frac{2}{x - 5}\right) = (x + 6)(x - 5)\left(\frac{1}{x + 6}\right) \quad \text{Multiply by the LCD.}$$

$$(x + 6)(x - 5) \cdot \frac{4x}{x^2 + x - 30} + (x + 6)(x - 5) \cdot \frac{2}{x - 5} \quad \text{Apply the distributive property.}$$

$$= (x + 6)(x - 5) \cdot \frac{1}{x + 6}$$

$$4x + 2(x + 6) = x - 5 \quad \text{Simplify.}$$

$$4x + 2x + 12 = x - 5 \quad \text{Apply the distributive property.}$$

$$6x + 12 = x - 5 \quad \text{Combine like terms.}$$

$$5x = -17$$

$$x = -\frac{17}{5} \quad \text{Divide both sides by 5.}$$

Check: Check by replacing x with $-\dfrac{17}{5}$ in the original equation. The solution is $-\dfrac{17}{5}$.

■ **Work Practice Problem 4**

EXAMPLE 5 Solve: $\dfrac{2x}{x - 4} = \dfrac{8}{x - 4} + 1$

Solution: Multiply both sides by the LCD, $x - 4$.

$$(x - 4)\left(\frac{2x}{x - 4}\right) = (x - 4)\left(\frac{8}{x - 4} + 1\right) \quad \text{Multiply by the LCD.}$$

$$(x - 4) \cdot \frac{2x}{x - 4} = (x - 4) \cdot \frac{8}{x - 4} + (x - 4) \cdot 1 \quad \text{Use the distributive property.}$$

$$2x = 8 + (x - 4) \quad \text{Simplify.}$$

$$2x = 4 + x$$

$$x = 4$$

Notice that 4 makes the denominator 0 in the original equation. Therefore, 4 is *not* a solution and this equation has *no solution*.

■ **Work Practice Problem 5**

✔**Concept Check** When can we clear fractions by multiplying through by the LCD?

a. When adding or subtracting rational expressions

b. When solving an equation containing rational expressions

c. Both of these

d. Neither of these

PRACTICE PROBLEM 4

Solve:

$$\frac{2}{x + 3} + \frac{3}{x - 3} = \frac{-2}{x^2 - 9}$$

PRACTICE PROBLEM 5

Solve: $\dfrac{5x}{x - 1} = \dfrac{5}{x - 1} + 3$

Answers

4. $x = -1$, **5.** No solution

✔ Concept Check Answer

b

Helpful Hint

As we can see from Example 5, it is important to check the proposed solution(s) in the original equation.

PRACTICE PROBLEM 6

Solve:

$$x - \frac{6}{x + 3} = \frac{2x}{x + 3} + 2$$

EXAMPLE 6 Solve: $x + \dfrac{14}{x - 2} = \dfrac{7x}{x - 2} + 1$

Solution: Notice the denominators in this equation. We can see that 2 can't be a solution. The LCD is $x - 2$, so we multiply both sides of the equation by $x - 2$.

$$(x - 2)\left(x + \frac{14}{x - 2}\right) = (x - 2)\left(\frac{7x}{x - 2} + 1\right)$$

$$(x - 2)(x) + (x - 2)\left(\frac{14}{x - 2}\right) = (x - 2)\left(\frac{7x}{x - 2}\right) + (x - 2)(1)$$

$$x^2 - 2x + 14 = 7x + x - 2 \quad \text{Simplify.}$$

$$x^2 - 2x + 14 = 8x - 2 \quad \text{Combine like terms.}$$

$$x^2 - 10x + 16 = 0 \quad \begin{array}{l}\text{Write the quadratic equation in}\\ \text{standard form.}\end{array}$$

$$(x - 8)(x - 2) = 0 \quad \text{Factor.}$$

$$x - 8 = 0 \quad \text{or} \quad x - 2 = 0 \quad \text{Set each factor equal to 0.}$$

$$x = 8 \qquad\qquad x = 2 \quad \text{Solve.}$$

As we have already noted, 2 can't be a solution of the original equation. So we need only replace x with 8 in the original equation. We find that 8 is a solution; the only solution is 8.

▢ Work Practice Problem 6

Objective **B** Solving Equations for a Specified Variable

The last example in this section is an equation containing several variables, and we are directed to solve for one of the variables. The steps used in the preceding examples can be applied to solve equations for a specified variable as well.

PRACTICE PROBLEM 7

Solve $\dfrac{1}{a} + \dfrac{1}{b} = \dfrac{1}{x}$ for a.

EXAMPLE 7 Solve $\dfrac{1}{a} + \dfrac{1}{b} = \dfrac{1}{x}$ for x.

Solution: (This type of equation often models a work problem, as we shall see in the next section.) The LCD is abx, so we multiply both sides by abx.

$$abx\left(\frac{1}{a} + \frac{1}{b}\right) = abx\left(\frac{1}{x}\right)$$

$$abx\left(\frac{1}{a}\right) + abx\left(\frac{1}{b}\right) = abx \cdot \frac{1}{x}$$

$$bx + ax = ab \quad \text{Simplify.}$$

$$x(b + a) = ab \quad \text{Factor out } x \text{ from each term on the left side.}$$

$$\frac{x(b + a)}{b + a} = \frac{ab}{b + a} \quad \text{Divide both sides by } b + a.$$

$$x = \frac{ab}{b + a} \quad \text{Simplify.}$$

This equation is now solved for x.

▢ Work Practice Problem 7

Answers

6. $x = 4$, **7.** $a = \dfrac{bx}{b - x}$

Mental Math

Solve each equation for the variable.

1. $\dfrac{x}{5} = 2$

2. $\dfrac{x}{8} = 4$

3. $\dfrac{z}{6} = 6$

4. $\dfrac{y}{7} = 8$

14.5 EXERCISE SET

Objective  **A** *Solve each equation and check each solution. See Examples 1 through 3.*

1. $\dfrac{x}{5} + 3 = 9$

2. $\dfrac{x}{5} - 2 = 9$

3. $\dfrac{x}{2} + \dfrac{5x}{4} = \dfrac{x}{12}$

4. $\dfrac{x}{6} + \dfrac{4x}{3} = \dfrac{x}{18}$

5. $2 - \dfrac{8}{x} = 6$

6. $5 + \dfrac{4}{x} = 1$

7. $2 + \dfrac{10}{x} = x + 5$

8. $6 + \dfrac{5}{y} = y - \dfrac{2}{y}$

9. $\dfrac{a}{5} = \dfrac{a-3}{2}$

10. $\dfrac{b}{5} = \dfrac{b+2}{6}$

11. $\dfrac{x-3}{5} + \dfrac{x-2}{2} = \dfrac{1}{2}$

12. $\dfrac{a+5}{4} + \dfrac{a+5}{2} = \dfrac{a}{8}$

Solve each equation and check each proposed solution. See Examples 4 through 6.

13. $\dfrac{3}{2a-5} = -1$

14. $\dfrac{6}{4-3x} = -3$

15. $\dfrac{4y}{y-4} + 5 = \dfrac{5y}{y-4}$

16. $\dfrac{2a}{a+2} - 5 = \dfrac{7a}{a+2}$

17. $2 + \dfrac{3}{a-3} = \dfrac{a}{a-3}$

18. $\dfrac{2y}{y-2} - \dfrac{4}{y-2} = 4$

19. $\dfrac{1}{x+3} + \dfrac{6}{x^2-9} = 1$

20. $\dfrac{1}{x+2} + \dfrac{4}{x^2-4} = 1$

21. $\dfrac{2y}{y+4} + \dfrac{4}{y+4} = 3$

22. $\dfrac{5y}{y+1} - \dfrac{3}{y+1} = 4$

23. $\dfrac{2x}{x+2} - 2 = \dfrac{x-8}{x-2}$

24. $\dfrac{4y}{y-3} - 3 = \dfrac{3y-1}{y+3}$

Solve each equation. See Examples 1 through 6.

25. $\dfrac{2}{y} + \dfrac{1}{2} = \dfrac{5}{2y}$

26. $\dfrac{6}{3y} + \dfrac{3}{y} = 1$

27. $\dfrac{a}{a-6} = \dfrac{-2}{a-1}$

28. $\dfrac{5}{x-6} = \dfrac{x}{x-2}$

29. $\dfrac{11}{2x} + \dfrac{2}{3} = \dfrac{7}{2x}$

30. $\dfrac{5}{3} - \dfrac{3}{2x} = \dfrac{3}{2}$

31. $\dfrac{2}{x-2} + 1 = \dfrac{x}{x+2}$

32. $1 + \dfrac{3}{x+1} = \dfrac{x}{x-1}$

33. $\dfrac{x+1}{3} - \dfrac{x-1}{6} = \dfrac{1}{6}$

34. $\dfrac{3x}{5} - \dfrac{x-6}{3} = -\dfrac{2}{5}$

35. $\dfrac{t}{t-4} = \dfrac{t+4}{6}$

36. $\dfrac{15}{x+4} = \dfrac{x-4}{x}$

37. $\dfrac{y}{2y + 2} + \dfrac{2y - 16}{4y + 4} = \dfrac{2y - 3}{y + 1}$

38. $\dfrac{1}{x + 2} = \dfrac{4}{x^2 - 4} - \dfrac{1}{x - 2}$

39. $\dfrac{4r - 4}{r^2 + 5r - 14} + \dfrac{2}{r + 7} = \dfrac{1}{r - 2}$

40. $\dfrac{3}{x + 3} = \dfrac{12x + 19}{x^2 + 7x + 12} - \dfrac{5}{x + 4}$

41. $\dfrac{x + 1}{x + 3} = \dfrac{x^2 - 11x}{x^2 + x - 6} - \dfrac{x - 3}{x - 2}$

42. $\dfrac{2t + 3}{t - 1} - \dfrac{2}{t + 3} = \dfrac{5 - 6t}{t^2 + 2t - 3}$

Objective **B** *Solve each equation for the indicated variable. See Example 7.*

43. $R = \dfrac{E}{I}$ for I (Electronics: resistance of a circuit)

44. $T = \dfrac{V}{Q}$ for Q (Water purification: settling time)

45. $T = \dfrac{2U}{B + E}$ for B (Merchandising: stock turnover rate)

46. $i = \dfrac{A}{t + B}$ for t (Hydrology: rainfall intensity)

47. $B = \dfrac{705w}{h^2}$ for w (Health: body-mass index)

△ **48.** $\dfrac{A}{W} = L$ for W (Geometry: area of a rectangle)

49. $N = R + \dfrac{V}{G}$ for G (Urban forestry: tree plantings per year)

50. $C = \dfrac{D(A + 1)}{24}$ for A (Medicine: Cowling's Rule for child's dose)

△ **51.** $\dfrac{C}{\pi r} = 2$ for r (Geometry: circumference of a circle)

52. $W = \dfrac{CE^2}{2}$ for C (Electronics: energy stored in a capacitor)

53. $\dfrac{1}{y} + \dfrac{1}{3} = \dfrac{1}{x}$ for x

54. $\dfrac{1}{5} + \dfrac{2}{y} = \dfrac{1}{x}$ for x

Review

Write each phrase as an expression. See Sections 9.4 and 14.2.

55. The reciprocal of x

56. The reciprocal of $x + 1$

57. The reciprocal of x, added to the reciprocal of 2

58. The reciprocal of x, subtracted from the reciprocal of 5

Answer each question.

59. If a tank is filled in 3 hours, what part of the tank is filled in 1 hour?

60. If a strip of beach is cleaned in 4 hours, what part of the beach is cleaned in 1 hour?

Concept Extensions

Solve each equation.

61. $\dfrac{4}{a^2 + 4a + 3} + \dfrac{2}{a^2 + a - 6} - \dfrac{3}{a^2 - a - 2} = 0$

62. $\dfrac{-4}{a^2 + 2a - 8} + \dfrac{1}{a^2 + 9a + 20} = \dfrac{-4}{a^2 + 3a - 10}$

Recall that two angles are supplementary if the sum of their measures is 180°. Find the measures of the supplementary angles.

△ **63.**

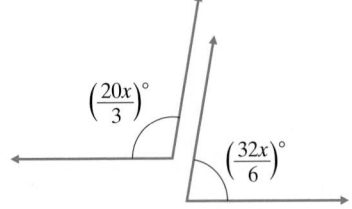

△ **64.**

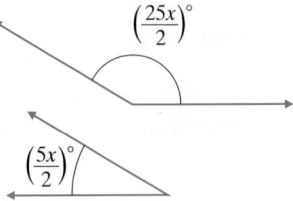

Recall that two angles are complementary if the sum of their measures is 90°. Find the measures of the complementary angles.

△ **65.**

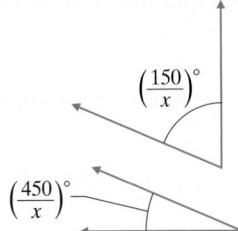

△ **66.**

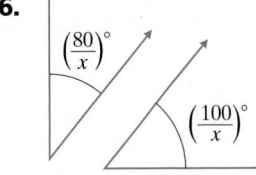

67. When adding the expressions in $\dfrac{3x}{2} + \dfrac{x}{4}$, can you multiply each term by 4? Why or why not?

68. When solving the equation $\dfrac{3x}{2} + \dfrac{x}{4} = 1$, can you multiply both sides of the equation by 4? Why or why not?

Summary on Rational Expressions

It is important to know the difference between performing operations with rational expressions and solving an equation containing rational expressions. Study the examples below.

Performing Operations with Rational Expressions

Adding: $\dfrac{1}{x} + \dfrac{1}{x+5} = \dfrac{1 \cdot (x+5)}{x(x+5)} + \dfrac{1 \cdot x}{x(x+5)} = \dfrac{x+5+x}{x(x+5)} = \dfrac{2x+5}{x(x+5)}$

Subtracting: $\dfrac{3}{x} - \dfrac{5}{x^2 y} = \dfrac{3 \cdot xy}{x \cdot xy} - \dfrac{5}{x^2 y} = \dfrac{3xy - 5}{x^2 y}$

Multiplying: $\dfrac{2}{x} \cdot \dfrac{5}{x-1} = \dfrac{2 \cdot 5}{x(x-1)} = \dfrac{10}{x(x-1)}$

Dividing: $\dfrac{4}{2x+1} \div \dfrac{x-3}{x} = \dfrac{4}{2x+1} \cdot \dfrac{x}{x-3} = \dfrac{4x}{(2x+1)(x-3)}$

Solving an Equation Containing Rational Expressions

To solve an equation containing rational expressions, we clear the equation of fractions by multiplying both sides by the LCD.

$$\frac{3}{x} - \frac{5}{x-1} = \frac{1}{x(x-1)} \qquad \text{Note that } x \text{ can't be 0 or 1.}$$

$$x(x-1)\left(\frac{3}{x}\right) - x(x-1)\left(\frac{5}{x-1}\right) = x(x-1) \cdot \frac{1}{x(x-1)} \qquad \text{Multiply both sides by the LCD.}$$

$$3(x-1) - 5x = 1 \qquad \text{Simplify.}$$

$$3x - 3 - 5x = 1 \qquad \text{Use the distributive property.}$$

$$-2x - 3 = 1 \qquad \text{Combine like terms.}$$

$$-2x = 4 \qquad \text{Add 3 to both sides.}$$

$$x = -2 \qquad \text{Divide both sides by } -2.$$

Don't forget to check to make sure our proposed solution of -2 does not make any denominators 0. If it does, this proposed solution is *not* a solution of the equation. -2 checks and is the solution.

Determine whether each of the following is an equation or an expression. If it is an equation, solve it for its variable. If it is an expression, perform the indicated operation.

1. $\dfrac{1}{x} + \dfrac{2}{3}$

2. $\dfrac{3}{a} + \dfrac{5}{6}$

3. $\dfrac{1}{x} + \dfrac{2}{3} = \dfrac{3}{x}$

4. $\dfrac{3}{a} + \dfrac{5}{6} = 1$

5. $\dfrac{2}{x+1} - \dfrac{1}{x}$

6. $\dfrac{4}{x-3} - \dfrac{1}{x}$

7. $\dfrac{2}{x+1} - \dfrac{1}{x} = 1$

8. $\dfrac{4}{x-3} - \dfrac{1}{x} = \dfrac{6}{x(x-3)}$

9. $\dfrac{15x}{x+8} \cdot \dfrac{2x+16}{3x}$

10. $\dfrac{9z+5}{15} \cdot \dfrac{5z}{81z^2 - 25}$

11. $\dfrac{2x+1}{x-3} + \dfrac{3x+6}{x-3}$

12. $\dfrac{4p-3}{2p+7} + \dfrac{3p+8}{2p+7}$

13. $\dfrac{x+5}{7} = \dfrac{8}{2}$

14. $\dfrac{1}{2} = \dfrac{x+1}{8}$

15. $\dfrac{5a+10}{18} \div \dfrac{a^2-4}{10a}$

16. $\dfrac{9}{x^2-1} \div \dfrac{12}{3x+3}$

17. $\dfrac{x+2}{3x-1} + \dfrac{5}{(3x-1)^2}$

18. $\dfrac{4}{(2x-5)^2} + \dfrac{x+1}{2x-5}$

19. $\dfrac{x-7}{x} - \dfrac{x+2}{5x}$

20. $\dfrac{9}{x^2-4} + \dfrac{2}{x+2} = \dfrac{-1}{x-2}$

21. $\dfrac{3}{x+3} = \dfrac{5}{x^2-9} - \dfrac{2}{x-3}$

22. $\dfrac{10x-9}{x} - \dfrac{x-4}{3x}$

23. Explain the difference between solving an equation such as $\dfrac{x}{2} + \dfrac{3}{4} = \dfrac{x}{4}$ for x and performing an operation such as adding $\dfrac{x}{2} + \dfrac{3}{4}$.

24. When solving an equation such as $\dfrac{y}{4} = \dfrac{y}{2} - \dfrac{1}{4}$, we may multiply all terms by 4. When subtracting two rational expressions such as $\dfrac{y}{2} - \dfrac{1}{4}$, we may not. Explain why.

11. _____

12. _____

13. _____

14. _____

15. _____

16. _____

17. _____

18. _____

19. _____

20. _____

21. _____

22. _____

23. _____

24. _____

14.6 PROBLEM SOLVING WITH RATIONAL EQUATIONS

Objective **A** Solving Problems about Numbers

Let's solve problems that are modeled by rational equations.

PRACTICE PROBLEM 1

The quotient of a number and 2, minus $\frac{1}{3}$, is the quotient of the number and 6. Find the number.

EXAMPLE 1 Finding an Unknown Number

The quotient of a number and 6, minus $\frac{5}{3}$, is the quotient of the number and 2. Find the number.

Solution:

1. UNDERSTAND. Read and reread the problem. Suppose that the unknown number is 2, then we see if the quotient of 2 and 6, or $\frac{2}{6}$, minus $\frac{5}{3}$ is equal to the quotient of 2 and 2, or $\frac{2}{2}$.

$$\frac{2}{6} - \frac{5}{3} = \frac{1}{3} - \frac{5}{3} = -\frac{4}{3}, \text{ not } \frac{2}{2}$$

Don't forget that the purpose of a proposed solution is to better understand the problem.

Let x = the unknown number.

2. TRANSLATE.

In words:	the quotient of x and 6	minus	$\frac{5}{3}$	is	the quotient of x and 2
	↓	↓	↓	↓	↓
Translate:	$\frac{x}{6}$	$-$	$\frac{5}{3}$	$=$	$\frac{x}{2}$

3. SOLVE. Here, we solve the equation $\frac{x}{6} - \frac{5}{3} = \frac{x}{2}$. We begin by multiplying both sides of the equation by the LCD, 6.

$$6\left(\frac{x}{6} - \frac{5}{3}\right) = 6\left(\frac{x}{2}\right)$$

$$6\left(\frac{x}{6}\right) - 6\left(\frac{5}{3}\right) = 6\left(\frac{x}{2}\right) \quad \text{Apply the distributive property.}$$

$$x - 10 = 3x \quad \text{Simplify.}$$

$$-10 = 2x \quad \text{Subtract } x \text{ from both sides.}$$

$$\frac{-10}{2} = \frac{2x}{2} \quad \text{Divide both sides by 2.}$$

$$-5 = x \quad \text{Simplify.}$$

4. INTERPRET.

Check: To check, we verify that "the quotient of -5 and 6 minus $\frac{5}{3}$ is the quotient of -5 and 2," or $-\frac{5}{6} - \frac{5}{3} = -\frac{5}{2}$.

State: The unknown number is -5.

▣ **Work Practice Problem 1**

Answer

1. 1

Objective B Solving Problems about Work

The next example is often called a work problem. Work problems usually involve people or machines doing a certain task.

EXAMPLE 2 Finding Work Rates

Sam Waterton and Frank Schaffer work in a plant that manufactures automobiles. Sam can complete a quality control tour of the plant in 3 hours while his assistant, Frank, needs 7 hours to complete the same job. The regional manager is coming to inspect the plant facilities, so both Sam and Frank are directed to complete a quality control tour together. How long will this take?

Solution:

1. UNDERSTAND. Read and reread the problem. The key idea here is the relationship between the **time** (hours) it takes to complete the job and the **part of the job** completed in 1 unit of time (hour). For example, if the **time** it takes Sam to complete the job is 3 hours, the **part of the job** he can complete in 1 hour is $\frac{1}{3}$. Similarly, Frank can complete $\frac{1}{7}$ of the job in 1 hour.

Let $x =$ the **time** in hours it takes Sam and Frank to complete the job together.

Then $\frac{1}{x} =$ the **part of the job** they complete in 1 hour.

	Hours to Complete Total Job	Part of Job Completed in 1 Hour
Sam	3	$\frac{1}{3}$
Frank	7	$\frac{1}{7}$
Together	x	$\frac{1}{x}$

2. TRANSLATE.

In words:	part of job Sam completed in 1 hour	added to	part of job Frank completed in 1 hour	is equal to	part of job they completed together in 1 hour
	↓	↓	↓	↓	↓
Translate:	$\frac{1}{3}$	$+$	$\frac{1}{7}$	$=$	$\frac{1}{x}$

3. SOLVE. Here, we solve the equation $\frac{1}{3} + \frac{1}{7} = \frac{1}{x}$. We begin by multiplying both sides of the equation by the LCD, $21x$.

$$21x\left(\frac{1}{3}\right) + 21x\left(\frac{1}{7}\right) = 21x\left(\frac{1}{x}\right)$$

$$7x + 3x = 21 \qquad \text{Simplify.}$$

$$10x = 21$$

$$x = \frac{21}{10} \quad \text{or} \quad 2\frac{1}{10} \text{ hours}$$

Continued on next page

PRACTICE PROBLEM 2

Andrew and Timothy Larson volunteer at a local recycling plant. Andrew can sort a batch of recyclables in 2 hours alone while his brother Timothy needs 3 hours to complete the same job. If they work together, how long will it take them to sort one batch?

Answer

2. $1\frac{1}{5}$ hours

4. INTERPRET.

Check: Our proposed solution is $2\frac{1}{10}$ hours. This proposed solution is reasonable since $2\frac{1}{10}$ hours is more than half of Sam's time and less than half of Frank's time. Check this solution in the originally *stated* problem.

State: Sam and Frank can complete the quality control tour in $2\frac{1}{10}$ hours.

▧ **Work Practice Problem 2**

✔ Concept Check Solve $E = mc^2$
a. for m **b.** for c^2.

Objective Ⓒ Solving Problems about Distance

Next we look at a problem solved by the distance formula,

$$d = r \cdot t$$

PRACTICE PROBLEM 3

A car travels 600 miles in the same time that a motorcycle travels 450 miles. If the car's speed is 15 miles per hour more than the motorcycle's, find the speed of the car and the speed of the motorcycle.

EXAMPLE 3 **Finding Speeds of Vehicles**

A car travels 180 miles in the same time that a truck travels 120 miles. If the car's speed is 20 miles per hour faster than the truck's, find the car's speed and the truck's speed.

Solution:

1. **UNDERSTAND.** Read and reread the problem. Suppose that the truck's speed is 45 miles per hour. Then the car's speed is 20 miles per hour more, or 65 miles per hour.

   We are given that the car travels 180 miles in the same time that the truck travels 120 miles. To find the time it takes the car to travel 180 miles, remember that since $d = rt$, we know that $\frac{d}{r} = t$.

Car's Time	Truck's Time

   $$t = \frac{d}{r} = \frac{180}{65} = 2\frac{50}{65} = 2\frac{10}{13} \text{ hours} \qquad t = \frac{d}{r} = \frac{120}{45} = 2\frac{30}{45} = 2\frac{2}{3} \text{ hours}$$

   Since the times are not the same, our proposed solution is not correct. But we have a better understanding of the problem.

   Let $x =$ the speed of the truck.

   Since the car's speed is 20 miles per hour faster than the truck's, then

   $$x + 20 = \text{the speed of the car}$$

Answer

3. car: 60 mph; motorcycle: 45 mph

✔ **Concept Check Answer**

a. $m = \dfrac{E}{c^2}$, **b.** $c^2 = \dfrac{E}{m}$

Use the formula $d = r \cdot t$ or **d**istance = **r**ate · **t**ime. Prepare a chart to organize the information in the problem.

	Distance	=	Rate	·	Time
Truck	120		x		$\dfrac{120}{x}$ ← distance ← rate
Car	180		$x + 20$		$\dfrac{180}{x + 20}$ ← distance ← rate

2. **TRANSLATE.** Since the car and the truck traveled the same amount of time, we have that

In words: car's time = truck's time

Translate: $\dfrac{180}{x + 20} = \dfrac{120}{x}$

3. **Solve.** We begin by multiplying both sides of the equation by the LCD, $x(x + 20)$, or cross multiplying.

$$\frac{180}{x + 20} = \frac{120}{x}$$

$$180x = 120(x + 20)$$

$180x = 120x + 2400$ Use the distributive property.

$60x = 2400$ Subtract $120x$ from both sides.

$x = 40$ Divide both sides by 60.

4. **INTERPRET.** The speed of the truck is 40 miles per hour. The speed of the car must then be $x + 20$ or 60 miles per hour.

Check: Find the time it takes the car to travel 180 miles and the time it takes the truck to travel 120 miles.

Car's Time	*Truck's Time*
$t = \dfrac{d}{r} = \dfrac{180}{60} = 3$ hours	$t = \dfrac{d}{r} = \dfrac{120}{40} = 3$ hours

Since both travel the same amount of time, the proposed solution is correct.

State: The car's speed is 60 miles per hour and the truck's speed is 40 miles per hour.

■ Work Practice Problem 3

Mental Math

Without solving algebraically, select the best choice for each exercise.

1. One person can complete a job in 7 hours. A second person can complete the same job in 5 hours. How long will it take them to complete the job if they work together?
   a. more than 7 hours
   b. between 5 and 7 hours
   c. less than 5 hours

2. One inlet pipe can fill a pond in 30 hours. A second inlet pipe can fill the same pond in 25 hours. How long before the pond is filled if both inlet pipes are on?
   a. less than 25 hours
   b. between 25 and 30 hours
   c. more than 30 hours

14.6 EXERCISE SET

FOR EXTRA HELP

Student Solutions Manual   PH Math/Tutor Center   CD/Video for Review   MathXL®   MyMathLab

Objective A *Solve the following. See Example 1.*

1. Three times the reciprocal of a number equals 9 times the reciprocal of 6. Find the number.

2. Twelve divided by the sum of x and 2 equals the quotient of 4 and the difference of x and 2. Find x.

3. If twice a number added to 3 is divided by the number plus 1, the result is three halves. Find the number.

4. A number added to the product of 6 and the reciprocal of the number equals -5. Find the number.

Objective B *See Example 2.*

5. Smith Engineering found that an experienced surveyor surveys a roadbed in 4 hours. An apprentice surveyor needs 5 hours to survey the same stretch of road. If the two work together, find how long it takes them to complete the job.

6. An experienced bricklayer constructs a small wall in 3 hours. The apprentice completes the job in 6 hours. Find how long it takes if they work together.

7. In 2 minutes, a conveyor belt moves 300 pounds of recyclable aluminum from the delivery truck to a storage area. A smaller belt moves the same quantity of cans the same distance in 6 minutes. If both belts are used, find how long it takes to move the cans to the storage area.

8. Find how long it takes the conveyor belts described in Exercise 23 to move 1200 pounds of cans. (*Hint:* Think of 1200 pounds as four 300-pound jobs.)

Objective C *See Example 3.*

9. A jogger begins her workout by jogging to the park, a distance of 12 miles. She then jogs home at the same speed but along a different route. This return trip is 18 miles and her time is one hour longer. Find her jogging speed. Complete the accompanying chart and use it to find her jogging speed.

	Distance	=	Rate	·	Time
Trip to Park	12				
Return Trip	18				

10. A boat can travel 9 miles upstream in the same amount of time it takes to travel 11 miles downstream. If the current of the river is 3 miles per hour, complete the chart below and use it to find the speed of the boat in still water.

	Distance	=	Rate	·	Time
Upstream	9		$r - 3$		
Downstream	11		$r + 3$		

11. A cyclist rode the first 20-mile portion of his workout at a constant speed. For the 16-mile cooldown portion of his workout, he reduced his speed by 2 miles per hour. Each portion of the workout took the same time. Find the cyclist's speed during the first portion and find his speed during the cooldown portion.

12. A semi-truck travels 300 miles through the flatland in the same amount of time that it travels 180 miles through mountains. The rate of the truck is 20 miles per hour slower in the mountains than in the flatland. Find both the flatland rate and mountain rate.

Objectives **A** **B** **C** **Mixed Practice** *Solve the following. See Examples 1 through 3. (Note: Some exercises may be modeled by equations without rational expressions.)*

13. One-fourth equals the quotient of a number and 8. Find the number.

14. Four times a number added to 5 is divided by 6. The result is $\dfrac{7}{2}$. Find the number.

15. A boater travels 16 miles per hour on the water on a still day. During one particular windy day, he finds that he travels 48 miles with the wind behind him in the same amount of time that he travels 16 miles into the wind. Find the rate of the wind.

16. The current on a portion of the Mississippi River is 3 miles per hour. A barge can go 6 miles upstream in the same amount of time it takes to go 10 miles downstream. Find the speed of the boat in still water.

17. Marcus and Tony work for Lombardo's Pipe and Concrete. Mr. Lombardo is preparing an estimate for a customer. He knows that Marcus lays a slab of concrete in 6 hours. Tony lays the same size slab in 4 hours. If both work on the job and the cost of labor is $45.00 per hour, decide what the labor estimate should be.

18. Mr. Dodson can paint his house by himself in 4 days. His son needs an additional day to complete the job if he works by himself. If they work together, find how long it takes to paint the house.

19. A pilot can travel 400 miles with the wind in the same amount of time as 336 miles against the wind. Find the speed of the wind if the pilot's speed in still air is 230 miles per hour.

20. A fisherman on Pearl River rows 9 miles downstream in the same amount of time he rows 3 miles upstream. If the current is 6 miles per hour, find how long it takes him to cover the 12 miles.

21. Two divided by the difference of a number and 3 minus 4 divided by a number plus 3, equals 8 times the reciprocal of the difference of the number squared and 9. What is the number?

22. If 15 times the reciprocal of a number is added to the ratio of 9 times a number minus 7 and the number plus 2, the result is 9. What is the number?

23. A pilot flies 630 miles with a tail wind of 35 miles per hour. Against the wind, he flies only 455 miles in the same amount of time. Find the rate of the plane in still air.

24. A marketing manager travels 1080 miles in a corporate jet and then an additional 240 miles by car. If the car ride takes one hour longer than the jet ride takes, and if the rate of the jet is 6 times the rate of the car, find the time the manager travels by jet and find the time the manager travels by car.

25. Two hikers are 11 miles apart and walking toward each other. They meet in 2 hours. Find the rate of each hiker if one hiker walks 1.1 mph faster than the other.

26. On a 255-mile trip, Gary Alessandrini traveled at an average speed of 70 mph, got a speeding ticket, and then traveled at 60 mph for the remainder of the trip. If the entire trip took 4.5 hours and the speeding ticket stop took 30 minutes, how long did Gary speed before getting stopped?

27. One custodian cleans a suite of offices in 3 hours. When a second worker is asked to join the regular custodian, the job takes only $1\frac{1}{2}$ hours. How long does it take the second worker to do the same job alone?

28. One person proofreads a copy for a small newspaper in 4 hours. If a second proofreader is also employed, the job can be done in $2\frac{1}{2}$ hours. How long does it take for the second proofreader to do the same job alone?

29. A jet plane traveling at 500 mph overtakes a propeller plane traveling at 200 mph that had a 2-hour head start. How far from the starting point are the planes?

30. How long will it take a bus traveling at 60 miles per hour to overtake a car traveling at 40 mph if the car had a 1.5-hour head start?

31. One pipe fills a storage pool in 20 hours. A second pipe fills the same pool in 15 hours. When a third pipe is added and all three are used to fill the pool, it takes only 6 hours. Find how long it takes the third pipe to do the job.

32. One pump fills a tank 2 times as fast as another pump. If the pumps work together, they fill the tank in 18 minutes. How long does it take for each pump to fill the tank?

33. A car travels 280 miles in the same time that a motorcycle travels 240 miles. If the car's speed is 10 miles per hour more than the motorcycle's, find the speed of the car and the speed of the motorcycle.

34. A bus traveled on a level road for 3 hours at an average speed 20 miles per hour faster than it traveled on a winding road. The time spent on the winding road was 4 hours. Find the average speed on the level road if the entire trip was 305 miles.

35. In 6 hours, an experienced cook prepares enough pies to supply a local restaurant's daily order. Another cook prepares the same number of pies in 7 hours. Together with a third cook, they prepare the pies in 2 hours. Find how long it takes the third cook to prepare the pies alone.

36. Mrs. Smith balances the company books in 8 hours. It takes her assistant 12 hours to do the same job. If they work together, find how long it takes them to balance the books.

37. One pump fills a tank 3 times as fast as another pump. If the pumps work together, they fill the tank in 21 minutes. How long does it take for each pump to fill the tank?

Review

Simplify. Follow the circled steps in the order shown. See Sections 2.5 and 3.1.

38. $\dfrac{\left.\dfrac{3}{4} + \dfrac{1}{4}\right\} \leftarrow \text{①\ Add.}}{\left.\dfrac{3}{8} + \dfrac{13}{8}\right\} \leftarrow \text{②\ Add.}}$

39. $\dfrac{\left.\dfrac{9}{5} + \dfrac{6}{5}\right\} \leftarrow \text{①\ Add.}}{\left.\dfrac{17}{6} + \dfrac{7}{6}\right\} \leftarrow \text{②\ Add.}}$

40. $\dfrac{\left.\dfrac{2}{5} + \dfrac{1}{5}\right\}}{\left.\dfrac{7}{10} + \dfrac{7}{10}\right\}} \begin{array}{l} ①\ \text{Add.} \\ \leftarrow ③\ \text{Divide.} \\ ②\ \text{Add.} \end{array}$

41. $\dfrac{\left.\dfrac{1}{4} + \dfrac{5}{4}\right\}}{\left.\dfrac{3}{8} + \dfrac{7}{8}\right\}} \begin{array}{l} ①\ \text{Add.} \\ \leftarrow ③\ \text{Divide.} \\ ②\ \text{Add.} \end{array}$

Concept Extensions

42. Person A can complete a job in 5 hours, and person B can complete the same job in 3 hours. Without solving algebraically, discuss reasonable and unreasonable answers for how long it would take them to complete the job together.

43. For which of the following equations can we immediately use cross products to solve for x?

a. $\dfrac{2-x}{5} = \dfrac{1+x}{3}$

b. $\dfrac{2}{5} - x = \dfrac{1+x}{3}$

44. For what value of x is $\dfrac{x}{x-1}$ in proportion to $\dfrac{x+1}{x}$? Explain your result.

Solve. See the Concept Check in this section.

Solve $D = RT$

45. for R

46. for T

47. A hyena spots a giraffe 0.5 mile away and begins running toward it. The giraffe starts running away from the hyena just as the hyena begins running toward it. A hyena can run at a speed of 40 mph and a giraffe can run at 32 mph. How long will it take for the hyena to overtake the giraffe? (*Source: The World Almanac and Book of Facts*)

48. The Andretti Green Racing team boasts the proud name of one of the best known Indy car drivers, Mario Andretti. Two of its drivers, Tony Kanaan and Bryan Herta, placed second and fourth, respectively, in the 2004 Indianapolis 500. The track is 2.5 miles long. When traveling at their fastest lap speeds, Herta drove 2.479 miles in the same time that Kanaan completed an entire 2.5-mile lap. Kanaan's fastest lap speed was 1.822 mph faster than Herta's fastest lap speed. Find each driver's fastest lap speed. Round each speed to the nearest tenth. (*Source:* Indy Racing League)

THE BIGGER PICTURE   Simplifying Expressions and Solving Equations and Inequalities

Now we continue our outline from Sections 8.5, 9.7, 12.7, 13.6, and 14.4. Although suggestions are given, this outline should be in your own words. Once you complete this new portion, try the exercises below.

I. Simplifying Expressions

   A. Real Numbers

     1. Add (Section 8.3)

     2. Subtract (Section 8.4)

     3. Multiply or Divide (Section 8.5)

   B. Exponents (Section 12.2)

   C. Polynomials

     1. Add (Section 12.4)

     2. Subtract (Section 12.4)

     3. Multiply (Section 12.5)

     4. Divide (Section 12.7)

   D. Factoring Polynomials (Chapter 13 Integrated Review)

   E. Rational Expressions

     1. Simplify (Section 14.1)

     2. Multiply (Section 14.2)

     3. Divide (Section 14.2)

     4. Add or Subtract (Section 14.4)

II. Solving Equations and Inequalities

   A. Linear Equations (Section 9.3)

   B. Linear Inequalities (Section 9.7)

   C. Quadratic and Higher Degree Equations (Section 13.6)

   D. Equations with Rational Expressions—solving equations with rational expressions

$$\frac{3}{x} - \frac{1}{x-1} = \frac{4}{x-1} \quad \text{Equation with rational expressions.}$$

$$x(x-1) \cdot \frac{3}{x} - x(x-1)\frac{1}{x-1} \quad \text{Multiply through by } x(x-1).$$

$$= x(x-1)\frac{4}{x-1}$$

$$3(x-1) - x \cdot 1 = x \cdot 4 \quad \text{Simplify.}$$

$$3x - 3 - x = 4x \quad \text{Use the distributive property.}$$

$$-3 = 2x \quad \text{Simplify and move variable terms to right side.}$$

$$-\frac{3}{2} = x \quad \text{Divide both sides by 2.}$$

E. Proportions—an equation with two ratios equal. Set cross products equal, then solve.

$$\frac{5}{x} = \frac{9}{2x-3}, \text{ or } 5(2x-3) = 9 \cdot x$$

$$\text{or } 10x - 15 = 9x \text{ or } x = 15$$

Multiply.

1. $(3x-2)(4x^2 - x - 5)$

2. $(2x - y)^2$

Factor.

3. $8y^3 - 20y^5$

4. $9m^2 - 11mn + 2n^2$

Simplify or solve.

If an expression, perform indicated operations and simplify. If an equation or inequality, solve it.

5. $\dfrac{7}{x} = \dfrac{9}{x-10}$

6. $\dfrac{7}{x} + \dfrac{9}{x-10}$

7. $(-3x^5)\left(\dfrac{1}{2}x^7\right)(8x)$

8. $5x - 1 = |-4| + |-5|$

9. $\dfrac{8-12}{12 \div 3 \cdot 2}$

10. $-2(3y - 4) \le 5y - 7 - 7y - 1$

11. $\dfrac{7}{x} + \dfrac{5}{2x+3} = \dfrac{-2}{x}$

12. $\dfrac{(a^{-3}b^2)^{-5}}{ab^4}$

14.7 SIMPLIFYING COMPLEX FRACTIONS

Objectives

A Simplify Complex Fractions Using Method 1.

B Simplify Complex Fractions Using Method 2.

A rational expression whose numerator or denominator or both numerator and denominator contain fractions is called a **complex rational expression** or a **complex fraction.** Some examples are

$$\frac{4}{2-\dfrac{1}{2}} \qquad \frac{\dfrac{3}{2}}{\dfrac{4}{7}-x} \qquad \frac{\dfrac{1}{x+2}}{x+2-\dfrac{1}{x}}$$

← Numerator of complex fraction

← Main fraction bar

← Denominator of complex fraction

Our goal in this section is to write complex fractions in simplest form. A complex fraction is in simplest form when it is in the form $\dfrac{P}{Q}$, where P and Q are polynomials that have no common factors.

Objective A Simplifying Complex Fractions—Method 1

In this section, two methods of simplifying complex fractions are represented. The first method presented uses the fact that the main fraction bar indicates division.

Method 1: To Simplify a Complex Fraction

Step 1: Add or subtract fractions in the numerator or denominator so that the numerator is a single fraction and the denominator is a single fraction.

Step 2: Perform the indicated division by multiplying the numerator of the complex fraction by the reciprocal of the denominator of the complex fraction.

Step 3: Write the rational expression in lowest terms.

EXAMPLE 1 Simplify the complex fraction $\dfrac{\dfrac{5}{8}}{\dfrac{2}{3}}$.

Solution: Since the numerator and denominator of the complex fraction are already single fractions, we proceed to Step 2: perform the indicated division by multiplying the numerator $\dfrac{5}{8}$ by the reciprocal of the denominator $\dfrac{2}{3}$.

$$\frac{\dfrac{5}{8}}{\dfrac{2}{3}} = \frac{5}{8} \div \frac{2}{3} = \frac{5}{8} \cdot \frac{3}{2} = \frac{15}{16}$$

The reciprocal of $\dfrac{2}{3}$ is $\dfrac{3}{2}$.

■ **Work Practice Problem 1**

PRACTICE PROBLEM 1

Simplify the complex fraction $\dfrac{\dfrac{3}{7}}{\dfrac{5}{9}}$.

Answer

1. $\dfrac{27}{35}$

PRACTICE PROBLEM 2

Simplify: $\dfrac{\dfrac{3}{4} - \dfrac{2}{3}}{\dfrac{1}{2} + \dfrac{3}{8}}$

EXAMPLE 2 Simplify: $\dfrac{\dfrac{2}{3} + \dfrac{1}{5}}{\dfrac{2}{3} - \dfrac{2}{9}}$

Solution: We simplify the numerator and denominator of the complex fraction separately. First we add $\dfrac{2}{3}$ and $\dfrac{1}{5}$ to obtain a single fraction in the numerator. Then we subtract $\dfrac{2}{9}$ from $\dfrac{2}{3}$ to obtain a single fraction in the denominator.

$$\dfrac{\dfrac{2}{3} + \dfrac{1}{5}}{\dfrac{2}{3} - \dfrac{2}{9}} = \dfrac{\dfrac{2(5)}{3(5)} + \dfrac{1(3)}{5(3)}}{\dfrac{2(3)}{3(3)} - \dfrac{2}{9}}$$

The LCD of the numerator's fractions is 15.

The LCD of the denominator's fractions is 9.

$$= \dfrac{\dfrac{10}{15} + \dfrac{3}{15}}{\dfrac{6}{9} - \dfrac{2}{9}}$$

Simplify.

$$= \dfrac{\dfrac{13}{15}}{\dfrac{4}{9}}$$

Add the numerator's fractions.

Subtract the denominator's fractions.

Next we perform the indicated division by multiplying the numerator of the complex fraction by the reciprocal of the denominator of the complex fraction.

$$\dfrac{\dfrac{13}{15}}{\dfrac{4}{9}} = \dfrac{13}{15} \cdot \dfrac{9}{4}$$

The reciprocal of $\dfrac{4}{9}$ is $\dfrac{9}{4}$.

$$= \dfrac{13 \cdot 3 \cdot \boxed{3}}{\boxed{3} \cdot 5 \cdot 4} = \dfrac{39}{20}$$

🖱 **Work Practice Problem 2**

PRACTICE PROBLEM 3

Simplify: $\dfrac{\dfrac{2}{5} - \dfrac{1}{x}}{\dfrac{2x}{15} - \dfrac{1}{3}}$

EXAMPLE 3 Simplify: $\dfrac{\dfrac{1}{z} - \dfrac{1}{2}}{\dfrac{1}{3} - \dfrac{z}{6}}$

Solution: Subtract to get a single fraction in the numerator and a single fraction in the denominator of the complex fraction.

$$\dfrac{\dfrac{1}{z} - \dfrac{1}{2}}{\dfrac{1}{3} - \dfrac{z}{6}} = \dfrac{\dfrac{2}{2z} - \dfrac{z}{2z}}{\dfrac{2}{6} - \dfrac{z}{6}}$$

The LCD of the numerator's fractions is $2z$.

The LCD of the denominator's fractions is 6.

$$= \dfrac{\dfrac{2 - z}{2z}}{\dfrac{2 - z}{6}}$$

$$= \dfrac{2 - z}{2z} \cdot \dfrac{6}{2 - z}$$

Multiply by the reciprocal of $\dfrac{2 - z}{6}$.

$$= \dfrac{2 \cdot 3 \cdot \boxed{(2 - z)}}{2 \cdot z \cdot \boxed{(2 - z)}}$$

Factor.

$$= \dfrac{3}{z}$$

Write in lowest terms.

🖱 **Work Practice Problem 3**

Answers

2. $\dfrac{2}{21}$, **3.** $\dfrac{3}{x}$

Objective B Simplifying Complex Fractions—Method 2

Next we study a second method for simplifying complex fractions. In this method, we multiply the numerator and the denominator of the complex fraction by the LCD of all fractions in the complex fraction.

Method 2: To Simplify a Complex Fraction

Step 1: Find the LCD of all the fractions in the complex fraction.

Step 2: Multiply both the numerator and the denominator of the complex fraction by the LCD from Step 1.

Step 3: Perform the indicated operations and write the result in lowest terms.

We use method 2 to rework Example 2.

EXAMPLE 4 Simplify: $\dfrac{\dfrac{2}{3} + \dfrac{1}{5}}{\dfrac{2}{3} - \dfrac{2}{9}}$

Solution: The LCD of $\dfrac{2}{3}, \dfrac{1}{5}, \dfrac{2}{3}$, and $\dfrac{2}{9}$ is 45, so we multiply the numerator and the denominator of the complex fraction by 45. Then we perform the indicated operations, and write in lowest terms.

$$\frac{\dfrac{2}{3} + \dfrac{1}{5}}{\dfrac{2}{3} - \dfrac{2}{9}} = \frac{45\left(\dfrac{2}{3} + \dfrac{1}{5}\right)}{45\left(\dfrac{2}{3} - \dfrac{2}{9}\right)}$$

$$= \frac{45\left(\dfrac{2}{3}\right) + 45\left(\dfrac{1}{5}\right)}{45\left(\dfrac{2}{3}\right) - 45\left(\dfrac{2}{9}\right)} \quad \text{Apply the distributive property.}$$

$$= \frac{30 + 9}{30 - 10} = \frac{39}{20} \quad \text{Simplify.}$$

■ **Work Practice Problem 4**

Helpful Hint

　　The same complex fraction was simplified using two different methods in Examples 2 and 4. Notice that the simplified results are the same.

PRACTICE PROBLEM 4

Use method 2 to simplify the complex fraction in Practice Problem 2:

$$\frac{\dfrac{3}{4} - \dfrac{2}{3}}{\dfrac{1}{2} + \dfrac{3}{8}}$$

Answer

4. $\dfrac{2}{21}$

PRACTICE PROBLEM 5

Simplify: $\dfrac{1 + \dfrac{x}{y}}{\dfrac{2x + 1}{y}}$

EXAMPLE 5 Simplify: $\dfrac{\dfrac{x + 1}{y}}{\dfrac{x}{y} + 2}$

Solution: The LCD of $\dfrac{x + 1}{y}$ and $\dfrac{x}{y}$ is y, so we multiply the numerator and the denominator of the complex fraction by y.

$$\frac{\dfrac{x + 1}{y}}{\dfrac{x}{y} + 2} = \frac{y\left(\dfrac{x + 1}{y}\right)}{y\left(\dfrac{x}{y} + 2\right)}$$

$$= \frac{y\left(\dfrac{x + 1}{y}\right)}{y\left(\dfrac{x}{y}\right) + y \cdot 2} \qquad \text{Apply the distributive property in the denominator.}$$

$$= \frac{x + 1}{x + 2y} \qquad \text{Simplify.}$$

▣ **Work Practice Problem 5**

PRACTICE PROBLEM 6

Simplify: $\dfrac{\dfrac{5}{6y} + \dfrac{y}{x}}{\dfrac{y}{3} - x}$

EXAMPLE 6 Simplify: $\dfrac{\dfrac{x}{y} + \dfrac{3}{2x}}{\dfrac{x}{2} + y}$

Solution: The LCD of $\dfrac{x}{y}, \dfrac{3}{2x}, \dfrac{x}{2}$, and $\dfrac{y}{1}$ is $2xy$, so we multiply both the numerator and the denominator of the complex fraction by $2xy$.

$$\frac{\dfrac{x}{y} + \dfrac{3}{2x}}{\dfrac{x}{2} + y} = \frac{2xy\left(\dfrac{x}{y} + \dfrac{3}{2x}\right)}{2xy\left(\dfrac{x}{2} + y\right)}$$

$$= \frac{2xy\left(\dfrac{x}{y}\right) + 2xy\left(\dfrac{3}{2x}\right)}{2xy\left(\dfrac{x}{2}\right) + 2xy(y)} \qquad \text{Apply the distributive property.}$$

$$= \frac{2x^2 + 3y}{x^2y + 2xy^2}$$

$$\text{or } \frac{2x^2 + 3y}{xy(x + 2y)}$$

▣ **Work Practice Problem 6**

Answers

5. $\dfrac{y + x}{2x + 1}$,

6. $\dfrac{5x + 6y^2}{2xy^2 - 6x^2y}$ or $\dfrac{5x + 6y^2}{2xy(y - 3x)}$

Objectives Ⓐ Ⓑ **Mixed Practice** *Simplify each complex fraction. See Examples 1 through 6.*

1. $\dfrac{\dfrac{1}{2}}{\dfrac{3}{4}}$

2. $\dfrac{\dfrac{1}{8}}{-\dfrac{5}{12}}$

3. $\dfrac{-\dfrac{4x}{9}}{-\dfrac{2x}{3}}$

4. $\dfrac{-\dfrac{6y}{11}}{\dfrac{4y}{9}}$

5. $\dfrac{\dfrac{1+x}{6}}{\dfrac{1+x}{3}}$

6. $\dfrac{\dfrac{6x-3}{5x^2}}{\dfrac{2x-1}{10x}}$

7. $\dfrac{\dfrac{1}{2}+\dfrac{2}{3}}{\dfrac{5}{9}-\dfrac{5}{6}}$

8. $\dfrac{\dfrac{3}{4}-\dfrac{1}{2}}{\dfrac{3}{8}+\dfrac{1}{6}}$

9. $\dfrac{2+\dfrac{7}{10}}{1+\dfrac{3}{5}}$

10. $\dfrac{4-\dfrac{11}{12}}{5+\dfrac{1}{4}}$

11. $\dfrac{\dfrac{1}{3}}{\dfrac{1}{2}-\dfrac{1}{4}}$

12. $\dfrac{\dfrac{7}{10}-\dfrac{3}{5}}{\dfrac{1}{2}}$

13. $\dfrac{-\dfrac{2}{9}}{-\dfrac{14}{3}}$

14. $\dfrac{\dfrac{3}{8}}{\dfrac{4}{15}}$

15. $\dfrac{-\dfrac{5}{12x^2}}{\dfrac{25}{16x^3}}$

16. $\dfrac{\dfrac{7}{8y}}{\dfrac{21}{4y}}$

17. $\dfrac{\dfrac{m}{n}-1}{\dfrac{m}{n}+1}$

18. $\dfrac{\dfrac{x}{2}+2}{\dfrac{x}{2}-2}$

19. $\dfrac{\dfrac{1}{5}-\dfrac{1}{x}}{\dfrac{7}{10}+\dfrac{1}{x^2}}$

20. $\dfrac{\dfrac{1}{y^2}+\dfrac{2}{3}}{\dfrac{1}{y}-\dfrac{5}{6}}$

21. $\dfrac{1+\dfrac{1}{y-2}}{y+\dfrac{1}{y-2}}$

22. $\dfrac{x-\dfrac{1}{2x+1}}{1-\dfrac{x}{2x+1}}$

23. $\dfrac{\dfrac{4y-8}{16}}{\dfrac{6y-12}{4}}$

24. $\dfrac{\dfrac{7y+21}{3}}{\dfrac{3y+9}{8}}$

25. $\dfrac{\dfrac{x}{y}+1}{\dfrac{x}{y}-1}$

26. $\dfrac{\dfrac{3}{5y}+8}{\dfrac{3}{5y}-8}$

27. $\dfrac{1}{2+\dfrac{1}{3}}$

28. $\dfrac{3}{1-\dfrac{4}{3}}$

29. $\dfrac{\dfrac{ax+ab}{x^2-b^2}}{\dfrac{x+b}{x-b}}$

30. $\dfrac{\dfrac{m+2}{m-2}}{\dfrac{2m+4}{m^2-4}}$

31. $\dfrac{\dfrac{-3+y}{4}}{\dfrac{8+y}{28}}$

32. $\dfrac{\dfrac{-x+2}{18}}{\dfrac{8}{9}}$

33. $\dfrac{3+\dfrac{12}{x}}{1-\dfrac{16}{x^2}}$

34. $\dfrac{2+\dfrac{6}{x}}{1-\dfrac{9}{x^2}}$

35. $\dfrac{\dfrac{8}{x+4}+2}{\dfrac{12}{x+4}-2}$

36. $\dfrac{\dfrac{25}{x+5}+5}{\dfrac{3}{x+5}-5}$

37. $\dfrac{\dfrac{s}{r} + \dfrac{r}{s}}{\dfrac{s}{r} - \dfrac{r}{s}}$

38. $\dfrac{\dfrac{2}{x} + \dfrac{x}{2}}{\dfrac{2}{x} - \dfrac{x}{2}}$

39. $\dfrac{\dfrac{6}{x-5} + \dfrac{x}{x-2}}{\dfrac{3}{x-6} - \dfrac{2}{x-5}}$

40. $\dfrac{\dfrac{4}{x} + \dfrac{x}{x+1}}{\dfrac{1}{2x} + \dfrac{1}{x+6}}$

Review

Use the bar graph below to answer Exercises 41 through 44. See Section 7.1.

Women's Tennis Career Prize Money Leaders

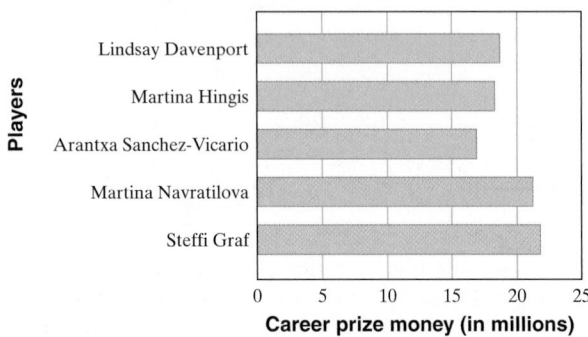

Career prize money (in millions)

Source: Sanex WTA Tour Media Information System

41. Which women's tennis player has earned the most prize money in her career?

42. Estimate how much more prize money Lindsay Davenport has earned over her career than Arantxa Sanchez-Vicario.

43. Which of the players shown have earned over $20 million in prize money over their careers?

44. During her career, through July 4, 2004, Martina Navratilova has won 347 singles and doubles tournaments. Assuming her prize money was earned only for tournament titles, how much prize money did she earn per tournament title, on average?

Concept Extensions

45. Explain how to simplify a complex fraction using method 1.

46. Explain how to simplify a complex fraction using method 2.

To find the average of two numbers, we find their sum and divide by 2. For example, the average of 65 and 81 is found by simplifying $\dfrac{65 + 81}{2}$. This simplifies to $\dfrac{146}{2} = 73$.

47. Find the average of $\dfrac{1}{3}$ and $\dfrac{3}{4}$.

48. Write the average of $\dfrac{3}{n}$ and $\dfrac{5}{n^2}$ as a simplified rational expression.

49. In electronics, when two resistors R_1 (read R sub 1) and R_2 (read R sub 2) are connected in parallel, the total resistance is given by the complex fraction

$$\dfrac{1}{\dfrac{1}{R_1} + \dfrac{1}{R_2}}.$$

Simplify this expression.

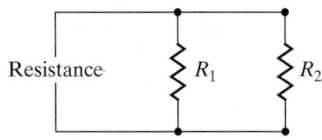

50. Astronomers occasionally need to know the day of the week a particular date fell on. The complex fraction

$$\dfrac{J + \dfrac{3}{2}}{7}$$

where J is the *Julian day number,* is used to make this calculation. Simplify this expression.

Simplify each of the following. First, write each expression with positive exponents. Then simplify the complex fraction. The first step has been completed for Exercise 51.

51. $\dfrac{x^{-1} + 2^{-1}}{x^{-2} - 4^{-1}} = \dfrac{\dfrac{1}{x} + \dfrac{1}{2}}{\dfrac{1}{x^2} - \dfrac{1}{4}}$

52. $\dfrac{3^{-1} - x^{-1}}{9^{-1} - x^{-2}}$

53. $\dfrac{y^{-2}}{1 - y^{-2}}$

54. $\dfrac{4 + x^{-1}}{3 + x^{-1}}$

55. If the distance formula $d = r \cdot t$ is solved for t, then $t = \dfrac{d}{r}$. Use this formula to find t if distance d is $\dfrac{20x}{3}$ miles and rate r is $\dfrac{5x}{9}$ miles per hour. Write t in simplified form.

△ **56.** If the formula for area of a rectangle, $A = l \cdot w$, is solved for w, then $w = \dfrac{A}{l}$. Use this formula to find w if area A is $\dfrac{4x - 2}{3}$ square meters and length l is $\dfrac{6x - 3}{5}$ meters. Write w in simplified form.

CHAPTER 14   Group Activity

Fast-Growing Careers

According to U.S. Bureau of Labor Statistics projections, the careers listed below will have the largest job growth in the next decade.

Occupation	Employment (number in thousands)		
	2002	2012	Change
1 Registered nurses	2284	2908	+623
2 Postsecondary teachers	1581	2184	+603
3 Retail salespersons	4076	4672	+596
4 Customer service representatives	1894	2354	+460
5 Combined food preparation and serving workers, including fast food	1990	2444	+454
6 Cashiers, except gaming	3432	3886	+454
7 Janitors and cleaners, except maids and housekeeping cleaners	2267	2681	+414
8 General and operations managers	2049	2425	+376
9 Waiters and waitresses	2097	2464	+367
10 Nursing aides, orderlies, and attendants	1375	1718	+343

What do all of these in-demand occupations have in common? They all require a knowledge of math! For some careers, like nurses, postsecondary teachers, and salespersons, the ways math is used on the job may be obvious. For other occupations, the use of math may not be quite as obvious. However, tasks common to many jobs, such as filling in a time sheet or a medication log, writing up an expense report, planning a budget, figuring a bill, ordering supplies, and even making a work schedule, all require math.

Activity

Suppose that your college placement office is planning to publish an occupational handbook on math in popular occupations. Choose one of the occupations from the given list that interests you. Research the occupation. Then write a brief entry for the occupational handbook that describes how a person in that career would use math in his or her job. Include an example if possible.

Chapter 14 Vocabulary Check

Fill in each blank with one of the words or phrases listed below.

| rational expression | complex fraction | proportion |
| cross products | ratio | rate |

1. A _____ is the quotient of two numbers.

2. $\dfrac{x}{2} = \dfrac{7}{16}$ is an example of a _____.

3. If $\dfrac{a}{b} = \dfrac{c}{d}$, the *ad* and *bc* are called _____.

4. A _____ is an expression that can be written in the form $\dfrac{P}{Q}$, where P and Q are polynomials and Q is not 0.

5. In a _____, the numerator or denominator or both may contain fractions.

6. A _____ is a special type of ratio where different measurements are used.

> **Helpful Hint**
>
>  Are you preparing for your test? Don't forget to take the Chapter 14 Test on page 1084. Then check your answers at the back of the text and use the Chapter Test Prep Video CD to see the fully worked-out solutions to any of the exercises you want to review.

14 Chapter Highlights

DEFINITIONS AND CONCEPTS	EXAMPLES
Section 14.1 Simplifying Rational Expressions	
A **rational expression** is an expression that can be written in the form $\dfrac{P}{Q}$, where P and Q are polynomials and Q does not equal 0.	$\dfrac{7y^3}{4}, \dfrac{x^2 + 6x + 1}{x - 3}, \dfrac{-5}{s^3 + 8}$
To find values for which a rational expression is undefined, find values for which the denominator is 0.	Find any values for which the expression $\dfrac{5y}{y^2 - 4y + 3}$ is undefined. $$y^2 - 4y + 3 = 0 \quad \text{Set the denominator equal to 0.}$$ $$(y - 3)(y - 1) = 0 \quad \text{Factor.}$$ $$y - 3 = 0 \quad \text{or} \quad y - 1 = 0 \quad \text{Set each factor equal to 0.}$$ $$y = 3 \qquad\qquad y = 1 \quad \text{Solve.}$$ The expression is undefined when y is 3 and when y is 1.
TO SIMPLIFY A RATIONAL EXPRESSION **Step 1.** Factor the numerator and denominator. **Step 2.** Divide out factors common to the numerator and denominator. (This is the same as removing a factor of 1.)	Simplify: $\dfrac{4x + 20}{x^2 - 25}$ $$\dfrac{4x + 20}{x^2 - 25} = \dfrac{4\,(x + 5)}{(x + 5)\,(x - 5)} = \dfrac{4}{x - 5}$$

DEFINITIONS AND CONCEPTS	**EXAMPLES**

Section 14.2 Multiplying and Dividing Rational Expressions

TO MULTIPLY RATIONAL EXPRESSIONS

Step 1. Factor numerators and denominators.

Step 2. Multiply numerators and multiply denominators.

Step 3. Write the product in lowest terms.

$$\frac{P}{Q} \cdot \frac{R}{S} = \frac{PR}{QS}$$

Multiply: $\dfrac{4x + 4}{2x - 3} \cdot \dfrac{2x^2 + x - 6}{x^2 - 1}$

$$\frac{4x + 4}{2x - 3} \cdot \frac{2x^2 + x - 6}{x^2 - 1}$$

$$= \frac{4(x + 1)}{2x - 3} \cdot \frac{(2x - 3)(x + 2)}{(x + 1)(x - 1)}$$

$$= \frac{4\,(x + 1)(2x - 3)\,(x + 2)}{(2x - 3)(x + 1)\,(x - 1)}$$

$$= \frac{4(x + 2)}{x - 1}$$

To divide by a rational expression, multiply by the reciprocal.

$$\frac{P}{Q} \div \frac{R}{S} = \frac{P}{Q} \cdot \frac{S}{R} = \frac{PS}{QR}$$

Divide: $\dfrac{15x + 5}{3x^2 - 14x - 5} \div \dfrac{15}{3x - 12}$

$$\frac{15x + 5}{3x^2 - 14x - 5} \div \frac{15}{3x - 12}$$

$$= \frac{5(3x + 1)}{(3x + 1)\,(x - 5)} \cdot \frac{3\,(x - 4)}{3 \cdot 5}$$

$$= \frac{x - 4}{x - 5}$$

Section 14.3 Adding and Subtracting Rational Expressions with the Same Denominator and Least Common Denominators

To add or subtract rational expressions with the same denominator, add or subtract numerators, and place the sum or difference over the common denominator.

$$\frac{P}{R} + \frac{Q}{R} = \frac{P + Q}{R}$$

$$\frac{P}{R} - \frac{Q}{R} = \frac{P - Q}{R}$$

Perform each indicated operation.

$$\frac{5}{x + 1} + \frac{x}{x + 1} = \frac{5 + x}{x + 1}$$

$$\frac{2y + 7}{y^2 - 9} - \frac{y + 4}{y^2 - 9}$$

$$= \frac{(2y + 7) - (y + 4)}{y^2 - 9}$$

$$= \frac{2y + 7 - y - 4}{y^2 - 9}$$

$$= \frac{y + 3}{(y + 3)\,(y - 3)}$$

$$= \frac{1}{y - 3}$$

TO FIND THE LEAST COMMON DENOMINATOR (LCD)

Step 1. Factor the denominators.

Step 2. The LCD is the product of all unique factors, each raised to a power equal to the greatest number of times that it appears in any one factored denominator.

Find the LCD for

$$\frac{7x}{x^2 + 10x + 25} \quad \text{and} \quad \frac{11}{3x^2 + 15x}$$

$$x^2 + 10x + 25 = (x + 5)(x + 5)$$

$$3x^2 + 15x = 3x(x + 5)$$

$$\text{LCD} = 3x(x + 5)(x + 5) \text{ or}$$

$$3x(x + 5)^2$$

DEFINITIONS AND CONCEPTS	**EXAMPLES**

Section 14.4   Adding and Subtracting Rational Expressions with Different Denominators

To Add or Subtract Rational Expressions with Different Denominators

Step 1. Find the LCD.

Step 2. Rewrite each rational expression as an equivalent expression whose denominator is the LCD.

Step 3. Add or subtract numerators and place the sum or difference over the common denominator.

Step 4. Write the result in lowest terms.

Perform the indicated operation.

$$\frac{9x + 3}{x^2 - 9} - \frac{5}{x - 3}$$

$$= \frac{9x + 3}{(x + 3)(x - 3)} - \frac{5}{x - 3}$$

LCD is $(x + 3)(x - 3)$.

$$= \frac{9x + 3}{(x + 3)(x - 3)} - \frac{5(x + 3)}{(x - 3)(x + 3)}$$

$$= \frac{9x + 3 - 5(x + 3)}{(x + 3)(x - 3)}$$

$$= \frac{9x + 3 - 5x - 15}{(x + 3)(x - 3)}$$

$$= \frac{4x - 12}{(x + 3)(x - 3)}$$

$$= \frac{4(x - 3)}{(x + 3)(x - 3)} = \frac{4}{x + 3}$$

Section 14.5   Solving Equations Containing Rational Expressions

To Solve an Equation Containing Rational Expressions

Step 1. Multiply both sides of the equation by the LCD of all rational expressions in the equation.

Step 2. Remove any grouping symbols and solve the resulting equation.

Step 3. Check the solution in the original equation.

Solve: $\dfrac{5x}{x + 2} + 3 = \dfrac{4x - 6}{x + 2}$ The LCD is $x + 2$.

$$(x + 2)\left(\frac{5x}{x + 2} + 3\right) = (x + 2)\left(\frac{4x - 6}{x + 2}\right)$$

$$(x + 2)\left(\frac{5x}{x + 2}\right) + (x + 2)(3) = (x + 2)\left(\frac{4x - 6}{x + 2}\right)$$

$$5x + 3x + 6 = 4x - 6$$

$$4x = -12$$

$$x = -3$$

The solution checks; the solution is -3.

DEFINITIONS AND CONCEPTS	**EXAMPLES**

Section 14.6   Problem Solving with Rational Equations

PROBLEM-SOLVING STEPS

1. UNDERSTAND. Read and reread the problem.

A small plane and a car leave Kansas City, Missouri, and head for Minneapolis, Minnesota, a distance of 450 miles. The speed of the plane is 3 times the speed of the car, and the plane arrives 6 hours ahead of the car. Find the speed of the car.

Let x = the speed of the car.
Then $3x$ = the speed of the plane.

	Distance	**=** **Rate**	**· Time**
Car	450	x	$\dfrac{450}{x} \left(\dfrac{\text{distance}}{\text{rate}}\right)$
Plane	450	$3x$	$\dfrac{450}{3x} \left(\dfrac{\text{distance}}{\text{rate}}\right)$

2. TRANSLATE.

In words: $\boxed{\text{plane's time}}$ + $\boxed{\text{6 hours}}$ = $\boxed{\text{car's time}}$

Translate: $\dfrac{450}{3x}$ + 6 = $\dfrac{450}{x}$

3. SOLVE.

$$\frac{450}{3x} + 6 = \frac{450}{x}$$

$$3x\left(\frac{450}{3x}\right) + 3x(6) = 3x\left(\frac{450}{x}\right)$$

$$450 + 18x = 1350$$

$$18x = 900$$

$$x = 50$$

4. INTERPRET.

Check this solution in the originally stated problem. **State** the conclusion: The speed of the car is 50 miles per hour.

DEFINITIONS AND CONCEPTS	EXAMPLES

Section 14.7   Simplifying Complex Fractions

METHOD 1: TO SIMPLIFY A COMPLEX FRACTION

Step 1. Add or subtract fractions in the numerator and the denominator of the complex fraction.

Step 2. Perform the indicated division.

Step 3. Write the result in lowest terms.

Simplify:

$$\frac{\dfrac{1}{x}+2}{\dfrac{1}{x}-\dfrac{1}{y}} = \frac{\dfrac{1}{x}+\dfrac{2x}{x}}{\dfrac{y}{xy}-\dfrac{x}{xy}}$$

$$= \frac{\dfrac{1+2x}{x}}{\dfrac{y-x}{xy}}$$

$$= \frac{1+2x}{x}\cdot\frac{x\ y}{y-x}$$

$$= \frac{y(1+2x)}{y-x}$$

METHOD 2: TO SIMPLIFY A COMPLEX FRACTION

Step 1. Find the LCD of all fractions in the complex fraction.

Step 2. Multiply the numerator and the denominator of the complex fraction by the LCD.

Step 3. Perform the indicated operations and write the result in lowest terms.

$$\frac{\dfrac{1}{x}+2}{\dfrac{1}{x}-\dfrac{1}{y}} = \frac{xy\left(\dfrac{1}{x}+2\right)}{xy\left(\dfrac{1}{x}-\dfrac{1}{y}\right)}$$

$$= \frac{xy\left(\dfrac{1}{x}\right)+xy(2)}{xy\left(\dfrac{1}{x}\right)-xy\left(\dfrac{1}{y}\right)}$$

$$= \frac{y+2xy}{y-x} \quad \text{or} \quad \frac{y(1+2x)}{y-x}$$

STUDY SKILLS BUILDER

Are You Prepared for a Test on Chapter 14?

Below I have listed *a common trouble* area for students in Chapter 14. After studying for your test, but before taking your test, read this.

Do you know the differences between how to perform operations such as $\dfrac{4}{x}+\dfrac{2}{3}$ or $\dfrac{4}{x}\div\dfrac{2}{x}$ and how to solve an equation such as $\dfrac{4}{x}+\dfrac{2}{3}=1$?

$$\frac{4}{x}+\frac{2}{3}=\frac{4\cdot 3}{x\cdot 3}+\frac{2\cdot x}{3\cdot x}$$
Addition—write each expression as an equivalent expression with the same LCD denominator.

$$=\frac{12}{3x}+\frac{2x}{3x}=\frac{12+2x}{3x} \quad \text{or} \quad \frac{2(6+x)}{3x}\text{, the sum.}$$

$$\frac{4}{x}\div\frac{2}{x}=\frac{4}{x}\cdot\frac{x}{2}=\frac{4\cdot x}{x\cdot 2}=\frac{4}{2}=2\text{, the quotient.}$$
Division—multiply the first rational expression by the reciprocal of the second.

$$\frac{4}{x}+\frac{2}{3}=1$$ Equation to be solved.

$$3x\left(\frac{4}{x}+\frac{2}{3}\right)=3x\cdot 1$$ Multiply both sides of the equation by the LCD, $3x$.

$$3x\left(\frac{4}{x}\right)+3x\left(\frac{2}{3}\right)=3x\cdot 1$$ Use the distributive property.

$$12+2x=3x$$ Multiply and simplify.

$$12=x$$ Subtract $2x$ from both sides.

The solution is 12.

For more examples and exercises, see the Chapter 14 Integrated Review.

14 CHAPTER REVIEW

(14.1) *Find any real number for which each rational expression is undefined.*

1. $\dfrac{x + 5}{x^2 - 4}$

2. $\dfrac{5x + 9}{4x^2 - 4x - 15}$

Find the value of each rational expression when $x = 5$, $y = 7$, and $z = -2$.

3. $\dfrac{2 - z}{z + 5}$

4. $\dfrac{x^2 + xy - y^2}{x + y}$

Simplify each rational expression.

5. $\dfrac{2x + 6}{x^2 + 3x}$

6. $\dfrac{3x - 12}{x^2 - 4x}$

7. $\dfrac{x + 2}{x^2 - 3x - 10}$

8. $\dfrac{x + 4}{x^2 + 5x + 4}$

9. $\dfrac{x^3 - 4x}{x^2 + 3x + 2}$

10. $\dfrac{5x^2 - 125}{x^2 + 2x - 15}$

11. $\dfrac{x^2 - x - 6}{x^2 - 3x - 10}$

12. $\dfrac{x^2 - 2x}{x^2 + 2x - 8}$

Simplify each expression. First, factor the four-term polynomials by grouping.

13. $\dfrac{x^2 + xa + xb + ab}{x^2 - xc + bx - bc}$

14. $\dfrac{x^2 + 5x - 2x - 10}{x^2 - 3x - 2x + 6}$

(14.2) *Perform each indicated operation and simplify.*

15. $\dfrac{15x^3y^2}{z} \cdot \dfrac{z}{5xy^3}$

16. $\dfrac{-y^3}{8} \cdot \dfrac{9x^2}{y^3}$

17. $\dfrac{x^2 - 9}{x^2 - 4} \cdot \dfrac{x - 2}{x + 3}$

18. $\dfrac{2x + 5}{x - 6} \cdot \dfrac{2x}{-x + 6}$

19. $\dfrac{x^2 - 5x - 24}{x^2 - x - 12} \div \dfrac{x^2 - 10x + 16}{x^2 + x - 6}$

20. $\dfrac{4x + 4y}{xy^2} \div \dfrac{3x + 3y}{x^2y}$

21. $\dfrac{x^2 + x - 42}{x - 3} \cdot \dfrac{(x - 3)^2}{x + 7}$

22. $\dfrac{2a + 2b}{3} \cdot \dfrac{a - b}{a^2 - b^2}$

23. $\dfrac{2x^2 - 9x + 9}{8x - 12} \div \dfrac{x^2 - 3x}{2x}$

24. $\dfrac{x^2 - y^2}{x^2 + xy} \div \dfrac{3x^2 - 2xy - y^2}{3x^2 + 6x}$

(14.3) *Perform each indicated operation and simplify.*

25. $\dfrac{x}{x^2 + 9x + 14} + \dfrac{7}{x^2 + 9x + 14}$

26. $\dfrac{x}{x^2 + 2x - 15} + \dfrac{5}{x^2 + 2x - 15}$

27. $\dfrac{4x - 5}{3x^2} - \dfrac{2x + 5}{3x^2}$

28. $\dfrac{9x + 7}{6x^2} - \dfrac{3x + 4}{6x^2}$

Find the LCD of each pair of rational expressions.

29. $\dfrac{x + 4}{2x}, \dfrac{3}{7x}$

30. $\dfrac{x - 2}{x^2 - 5x - 24}, \dfrac{3}{x^2 + 11x + 24}$

Rewrite each rational expression as an equivalent expression whose denominator is the given polynomial.

31. $\dfrac{5}{7x} = \dfrac{}{14x^3 y}$

32. $\dfrac{9}{4y} = \dfrac{}{16y^3 x}$

33. $\dfrac{x + 2}{x^2 + 11x + 18} = \dfrac{}{(x + 2)(x - 5)(x + 9)}$

34. $\dfrac{3x - 5}{x^2 + 4x + 4} = \dfrac{}{(x + 2)^2 (x + 3)}$

(14.4) *Perform each indicated operation and simplify.*

35. $\dfrac{4}{5x^2} - \dfrac{6}{y}$

36. $\dfrac{2}{x - 3} - \dfrac{4}{x - 1}$

37. $\dfrac{4}{x + 3} - 2$

38. $\dfrac{3}{x^2 + 2x - 8} + \dfrac{2}{x^2 - 3x + 2}$

39. $\dfrac{2x - 5}{6x + 9} - \dfrac{4}{2x^2 + 3x}$

40. $\dfrac{x - 1}{x^2 - 2x + 1} - \dfrac{x + 1}{x - 1}$

(14.5) *Solve each equation.*

41. $\dfrac{n}{10} = 9 - \dfrac{n}{5}$

42. $\dfrac{2}{x + 1} - \dfrac{1}{x - 2} = -\dfrac{1}{2}$

43. $\dfrac{y}{2y + 2} + \dfrac{2y - 16}{4y + 4} = \dfrac{y - 3}{y + 1}$

44. $\dfrac{2}{x - 3} - \dfrac{4}{x + 3} = \dfrac{8}{x^2 - 9}$

45. $\dfrac{x - 3}{x + 1} - \dfrac{x - 6}{x + 5} = 0$

46. $x + 5 = \dfrac{6}{x}$

(14.6) *Solve.*

47. Five times the reciprocal of a number equals the sum of $\dfrac{3}{2}$ the reciprocal of the number and $\dfrac{7}{6}$. What is the number?

48. The reciprocal of a number equals the reciprocal of the difference of 4 and the number. Find the number.

49. A car travels 90 miles in the same time that a car traveling 10 miles per hour slower travels 60 miles. Find the speed of each car.

50. The current in a bayou near Lafayette, Louisiana, is 4 miles per hour. A paddle boat travels 48 miles upstream in the same amount of time it takes to travel 72 miles downstream. Find the speed of the boat in still water.

51. When Mark and Maria manicure Mr. Stergeon's lawn, it takes them 5 hours. If Mark works alone, it takes 7 hours. Find how long it takes Maria alone.

52. It takes pipe A 20 days to fill a fish pond. Pipe B takes 15 days. Find how long it takes both pipes together to fill the pond.

(14.7) *Simplify each complex fraction.*

53. $\dfrac{\dfrac{5x}{27}}{-\dfrac{10xy}{21}}$

54. $\dfrac{\dfrac{3}{5} + \dfrac{2}{7}}{\dfrac{1}{5} + \dfrac{5}{6}}$

55. $\dfrac{3 - \dfrac{1}{y}}{2 - \dfrac{1}{y}}$

56. $\dfrac{\dfrac{6}{x + 2} + 4}{\dfrac{8}{x + 2} - 4}$

Mixed Review

Simplify each rational expression.

57. $\dfrac{4x + 12}{8x^2 + 24x}$

58. $\dfrac{x^3 - 6x^2 + 9x}{x^2 + 4x - 21}$

Perform the indicated operations and simplify.

59. $\dfrac{x^2 + 9x + 20}{x^2 - 25} \cdot \dfrac{x^2 - 9x + 20}{x^2 + 8x + 16}$

60. $\dfrac{x^2 - x - 72}{x^2 - x - 30} \div \dfrac{x^2 + 6x - 27}{x^2 - 9x + 18}$

61. $\dfrac{x}{x^2 - 36} + \dfrac{6}{x^2 - 36}$

62. $\dfrac{5x - 1}{4x} - \dfrac{3x - 2}{4x}$

63. $\dfrac{4}{3x^2 + 8x - 3} + \dfrac{2}{3x^2 - 7x + 2}$

64. $\dfrac{3x}{x^2 + 9x + 14} - \dfrac{6x}{x^2 + 4x - 21}$

Solve.

65. $\dfrac{4}{a - 1} + 2 = \dfrac{3}{a - 1}$

66. $\dfrac{x}{x + 3} + 4 = \dfrac{x}{x + 3}$

Solve.

67. The quotient of twice a number and three, minus one-sixth is the quotient of the number and two. Find the number.

68. Mr. Crocker can paint his shed by himself in three days. His son will need an additional day to complete the job if he works alone. If they work together, find how long it takes to paint the house.

Simplify each complex fraction.

69. $\dfrac{\dfrac{1}{4}}{\dfrac{1}{3} + \dfrac{1}{2}}$

70. $\dfrac{4 + \dfrac{2}{x}}{6 + \dfrac{3}{x}}$

CHAPTER TEST

 Remember to use the Chapter Test Prep Video CD to see the fully worked-out solutions to any of the exercises you want to review.

1. Find any real numbers for which the following expression is undefined.

$$\frac{x + 5}{x^2 + 4x + 3}$$

2. For a certain computer desk, the average manufacturing cost C per desk (in dollars) is

$$C = \frac{100x + 3000}{x}$$

where x is the number of desks manufactured.
   a. Find the average cost per desk when manufacturing 200 computer desks.
   b. Find the average cost per desk when manufacturing 1000 computer desks.

Simplify each rational expression.

3. $\dfrac{3x - 6}{5x - 10}$

4. $\dfrac{x + 6}{x^2 + 12x + 36}$

5. $\dfrac{7 - x}{x - 7}$

6. $\dfrac{y - x}{x^2 - y^2}$

7. $\dfrac{2m^3 - 2m^2 - 12m}{m^2 - 5m + 6}$

8. $\dfrac{ay + 3a + 2y + 6}{ay + 3a + 5y + 15}$

Perform each indicated operation and simplify if possible.

9. $\dfrac{x^2 - 13x + 42}{x^2 + 10x + 21} \div \dfrac{x^2 - 4}{x^2 + x - 6}$

10. $\dfrac{3}{x - 1} \cdot (5x - 5)$

11. $\dfrac{y^2 - 5y + 6}{2y + 4} \cdot \dfrac{y + 2}{2y - 6}$

12. $\dfrac{5}{2x + 5} - \dfrac{6}{2x + 5}$

13. $\dfrac{5a}{a^2 - a - 6} - \dfrac{2}{a - 3}$

14. $\dfrac{6}{x^2 - 1} + \dfrac{3}{x + 1}$

15. $\dfrac{x^2 - 9}{x^2 - 3x} \div \dfrac{x^2 + 4x + 1}{2x + 10}$

16. $\dfrac{x + 2}{x^2 + 11x + 18} + \dfrac{5}{x^2 - 3x - 10}$

17. $\dfrac{4y}{y^2 + 6y + 5} - \dfrac{3}{y^2 + 5y + 4}$

1. _____

2. a. _____

   b. _____

3. _____

4. _____

5. _____

6. _____

7. _____

8. _____

9. _____

10. _____

11. _____

12. _____

13. _____

14. _____

15. _____

16. _____

17. _____

Solve each equation.

18. $\dfrac{4}{y} - \dfrac{5}{3} = \dfrac{-1}{5}$

19. $\dfrac{5}{y+1} = \dfrac{4}{y+2}$

20. $\dfrac{a}{a-3} = \dfrac{3}{a-3} - \dfrac{3}{2}$

21. $\dfrac{10}{x^2-25} = \dfrac{3}{x+5} + \dfrac{1}{x-5}$

22. $x - \dfrac{14}{x-1} = 4 - \dfrac{2x}{x-1}$

Simplify each complex fraction.

23. $\dfrac{\dfrac{5x^2}{yz^2}}{\dfrac{10x}{z^3}}$

24. $\dfrac{\dfrac{b}{a} - \dfrac{a}{b}}{\dfrac{1}{b} + \dfrac{1}{a}}$

25. $\dfrac{5 - \dfrac{1}{y^2}}{\dfrac{1}{y} + \dfrac{2}{y^2}}$

26. One number plus five times its reciprocal is equal to six. Find the number.

27. A pleasure boat traveling down the Red River takes the same time to go 14 miles upstream as it takes to go 16 miles downstream. If the current of the river is 2 miles per hour, find the speed of the boat in still water.

28. An inlet pipe can fill a tank in 12 hours. A second pipe can fill the tank in 15 hours. If both pipes are used, find how long it takes to fill the tank?

18. _____

19. _____

20. _____

21. _____

22. _____

23. _____

24. _____

25. _____

26. _____

27. _____

28. _____

Answers

1. _____

2. _____

3. _____

4. _____

5. _____

6. _____

7. _____

8. _____

9. _____

10. _____

11. _____

12. _____

13. _____

14. _____

15. _____

16. _____

△ **1.** Find the area of the parallelogram:

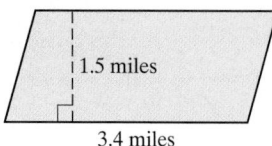

1.5 miles

3.4 miles

△ **2.** Find the area of the circle. Give an exact area, then use 3.14 for π to approximate the area.

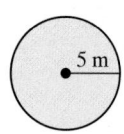

5 m

△ **3.** Approximate the volume of a ball of radius 3 inches. Use the approximation $\frac{22}{7}$ for π. Give an exact answer and an approximate answer.

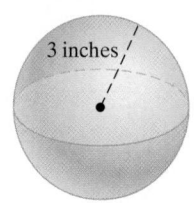

3 inches

△ **4.** Find the volume of the box.

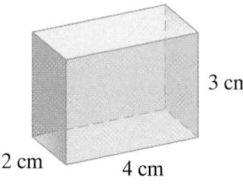

3 cm

2 cm   4 cm

5. Find the median of the list of numbers: $25, 54, 56, 57, 60, 71, 98$

6. Find the mean or average of $36, 25, 18,$ and 19.

7. If a die is rolled, find the probability of rolling a 3 or a 4.

8. Subtract: $-9 - (-4.1)$

Simplify each expression.

9. $\left(\dfrac{m}{n}\right)^7$

10. $\dfrac{a^7 b^{10}}{ab^{15}}$

11. Subtract: $(2x^3 + 8x^2 - 6x) - (2x^3 - x^2 + 1)$

12. Add: $\left(5x^2 + 6x + \dfrac{1}{2}\right) + \left(x^2 - \dfrac{4}{3}x - \dfrac{10}{21}\right)$

13. Solve: $x(2x - 7) = 4$

14. Solve: $x(2x - 7) = 0$

15. Subtract: $\dfrac{2y}{2y - 7} - \dfrac{7}{2y - 7}$

16. Add: $\dfrac{2}{x - 6} + \dfrac{3}{x + 1}$

17. Write each sentence as an equation. Let x represent the unknown number.
  a. The quotient of 15 and a number is 4.
  b. Three subtracted from 12 is a number.
  c. 17 added to four times a number is 21.

18. Write each sentence as an equation. Let x represent the unknown number.
  a. The difference of 12 and a number is -45.
  b. The product of 12 and a number is -45.
  c. A number less 10 is twice the number.

19. Find the sums.
  a. $3 + (-7) + (-8)$
  b. $[7 + (-10)] + [-2 + (-4)]$

20. Find the differences.
  a. $28 - 6 - 30$
  b. $7 - 2 - 22$

For Exercises 21 through 24, name the property illustrated by each true statement.

21. $3(x + y) = 3 \cdot x + 3 \cdot y$

22. $3 + y = y + 3$

23. $(x + 7) + 9 = x + (7 + 9)$

24. $(x \cdot 7) \cdot 9 = x \cdot (7 \cdot 9)$

25. Solve: $3 - x = 7$

26. Solve: $7x - 6 = 6x - 6$

27. A 10-foot board is to be cut into two pieces so that the longer piece is 4 times the shorter. Find the length of each piece.

28. Find two consecutive even integers whose sum is 382.

29. Solve: $y = mx + b$ for x.

30. Solve: $3x - 2y = 6$ for y.

31. Factor: $25x^2 + 20xy + 4y^2$

32. Factor: $x^2 - 4$

17. a. _____
    b. _____
    c. _____
18. a. _____
    b. _____
    c. _____
19. a. _____
    b. _____
20. a. _____
    b. _____
21. _____
22. _____
23. _____
24. _____
25. _____
26. _____
27. _____
28. _____
29. _____
30. _____
31. _____
32. _____

33. _____

34. _____

35. _____

36. _____

37. _____

38. _____

39. _____

40. _____

41. _____

42. _____

43. _____

44. _____

33. Solve: $x^2 - 9x - 22 = 0$

34. Solve: $3x^2 + 5x = 2$

35. Multiply: $\dfrac{x^2 + x}{3x} \cdot \dfrac{6}{5x + 5}$

36. Simplify: $\dfrac{2x^2 - 50}{4x^4 - 20x^3}$

37. Subtract: $\dfrac{3x^2 + 2x}{x - 1} - \dfrac{10x - 5}{x - 1}$

38. Factor: $7x^6 - 7x^5 + 7x^4$

39. Subtract: $\dfrac{6x}{x^2 - 4} - \dfrac{3}{x + 2}$

40. Factor: $4x^2 + 12x + 9$

41. Solve: $\dfrac{t - 4}{2} - \dfrac{t - 3}{9} = \dfrac{5}{18}$

42. Multiply: $\dfrac{6x^2 - 18x}{3x^2 - 2x} \cdot \dfrac{15x - 10}{x^2 - 9}$

43. Sam Waterton and Frank Schaffer work in a plant that manufactures automobiles. Sam can complete a quality control tour of the plant in 3 hours while his assistant, Frank, needs 7 hours to complete the same job. The regional manager is coming to inspect the plant facilities, so both Sam and Frank are directed to complete a quality control tour together. How long will this take?

44. Simplify: $\dfrac{\dfrac{m}{3} + \dfrac{n}{6}}{\dfrac{m + n}{12}}$

B Tables

B.1 TABLE OF SQUARES AND SQUARE ROOTS

		Squares and Square Roots			
n	n^2	$\sqrt{n}$	n	n^2	$\sqrt{n}$
1	1	1.000	51	2601	7.141
2	4	1.414	52	2704	7.211
3	9	1.732	53	2809	7.280
4	16	2.000	54	2916	7.348
5	25	2.236	55	3025	7.416
6	36	2.449	56	3136	7.483
7	49	2.646	57	3249	7.550
8	64	2.828	58	3364	7.616
9	81	3.000	59	3481	7.681
10	100	3.162	60	3600	7.746
11	121	3.317	61	3721	7.810
12	144	3.464	62	3844	7.874
13	169	3.606	63	3969	7.937
14	196	3.742	64	4096	8.000
15	225	3.873	65	4225	8.062
16	256	4.000	66	4356	8.124
17	289	4.123	67	4489	8.185
18	324	4.243	68	4624	8.246
19	361	4.359	69	4761	8.307
20	400	4.472	70	4900	8.367
21	441	4.583	71	5041	8.426
22	484	4.690	72	5184	8.485
23	529	4.796	73	5329	8.544
24	576	4.899	74	5476	8.602
25	625	5.000	75	5625	8.660
26	676	5.099	76	5776	8.718
27	729	5.196	77	5929	8.775
28	784	5.292	78	6084	8.832
29	841	5.385	79	6241	8.888
30	900	5.477	80	6400	8.944
31	961	5.568	81	6561	9.000
32	1024	5.657	82	6724	9.055
33	1089	5.745	83	6889	9.110
34	1156	5.831	84	7056	9.165
35	1225	5.916	85	7225	9.220
36	1296	6.000	86	7396	9.274
37	1369	6.083	87	7569	9.327
38	1444	6.164	88	7744	9.381
39	1521	6.245	89	7921	9.434
40	1600	6.325	90	8100	9.487
41	1681	6.403	91	8281	9.539
42	1764	6.481	92	8464	9.592
43	1849	6.557	93	8649	9.644
44	1936	6.633	94	8836	9.695
45	2025	6.708	95	9025	9.747
46	2116	6.782	96	9216	9.798
47	2209	6.856	97	9409	9.849
48	2304	6.928	98	9604	9.899
49	2401	7.000	99	9801	9.950
50	2500	7.071	100	10,000	10.000

Percent, Decimal, and Fraction Equivalents		
Percent	**Decimal**	**Fraction**
1%	0.01	$\frac{1}{100}$
5%	0.05	$\frac{1}{20}$
10%	0.1	$\frac{1}{10}$
12.5% or $12\frac{1}{2}$%	0.125	$\frac{1}{8}$
$16.\overline{6}$% or $16\frac{2}{3}$%	$0.1\overline{6}$	$\frac{1}{6}$
20%	0.2	$\frac{1}{5}$
25%	0.25	$\frac{1}{4}$
30%	0.3	$\frac{3}{10}$
$33.\overline{3}$% or $33\frac{1}{3}$%	$0.\overline{3}$	$\frac{1}{3}$
37.5% or $37\frac{1}{2}$%	0.375	$\frac{3}{8}$
40%	0.4	$\frac{2}{5}$
50%	0.5	$\frac{1}{2}$
60%	0.6	$\frac{3}{5}$
62.5% or $62\frac{1}{2}$%	0.625	$\frac{5}{8}$
$66.\overline{6}$% or $66\frac{2}{3}$%	$0.\overline{6}$	$\frac{2}{3}$
70%	0.7	$\frac{7}{10}$
75%	0.75	$\frac{3}{4}$
80%	0.8	$\frac{4}{5}$
$83.\overline{3}$% or $83\frac{1}{3}$%	$08.\overline{3}$	$\frac{5}{6}$
87.5% or $87\frac{1}{2}$%	0.875	$\frac{7}{8}$
90%	0.9	$\frac{9}{10}$
100%	1.0	1
110%	1.1	$1\frac{1}{10}$
125%	1.25	$1\frac{1}{4}$
$133.\overline{3}$% or $133\frac{1}{3}$%	$1.\overline{3}$	$1\frac{1}{3}$
150%	1.5	$1\frac{1}{2}$
$166.\overline{6}$% or $166\frac{2}{3}$%	$1.\overline{6}$	$1\frac{2}{3}$
175%	1.75	$1\frac{3}{4}$
200%	2.0	2

B.3 COMPOUND INTEREST

Compounded Annually

	5%	6%	7%	8%	9%	10%	11%	12%	13%	14%	15%	16%	17%	18%
1 year	1.05000	1.06000	1.07000	1.08000	1.09000	1.10000	1.11000	1.12000	1.13000	1.14000	1.15000	1.16000	1.17000	1.18000
5 years	1.27628	1.33823	1.40255	1.46933	1.53862	1.61051	1.68506	1.76234	1.84244	1.92541	2.01136	2.10034	2.19245	2.28776
10 years	1.62889	1.79085	1.96715	2.15892	2.36736	2.59374	2.83942	3.10585	3.39457	3.70722	4.04556	4.41144	4.80683	5.23384
15 years	2.07893	2.39656	2.75903	3.17217	3.64248	4.17725	4.78459	5.47357	6.25427	7.13794	8.13706	9.26552	10.53872	11.97375
20 years	2.65330	3.20714	3.86968	4.66096	5.60441	6.72750	8.06231	9.64629	11.52309	13.74349	16.36654	19.46076	23.10560	27.39303

Compounded Semiannually

	5%	6%	7%	8%	9%	10%	11%	12%	13%	14%	15%	16%	17%	18%
1 year	1.05063	1.06090	1.07123	1.08160	1.09203	1.10250	1.11303	1.12360	1.13423	1.14490	1.15563	1.16640	1.17723	1.18810
5 years	1.28008	1.34392	1.41060	1.48024	1.55297	1.62889	1.70814	1.79085	1.87714	1.96715	2.06103	2.15892	2.26098	2.36736
10 years	1.63862	1.80611	1.98979	2.19112	2.41171	2.65330	2.91776	3.20714	3.52365	3.86968	4.24785	4.66096	5.11205	5.60441
15 years	2.09757	2.42726	2.80679	3.24340	3.74532	4.32194	4.98395	5.74349	6.61437	7.61226	8.75496	10.06266	11.55825	13.26768
20 years	2.68506	3.26204	3.95926	4.80102	5.81636	7.03999	8.51331	10.28572	12.41607	14.97446	18.04424	21.72452	26.13302	31.40942

Compounded Quarterly

	5%	6%	7%	8%	9%	10%	11%	12%	13%	14%	15%	16%	17%	18%
1 year	1.05095	1.06136	1.07186	1.08243	1.09308	1.10381	1.11462	1.12551	1.13648	1.14752	1.15865	1.16986	1.18115	1.19252
5 years	1.28204	1.34686	1.41478	1.48595	1.56051	1.63862	1.72043	1.80611	1.89584	1.98979	2.08815	2.19112	2.29891	2.41171
10 years	1.64362	1.81402	2.00160	2.20804	2.43519	2.68506	2.95987	3.26204	3.59420	3.95926	4.36038	4.80102	5.28497	5.81636
15 years	2.10718	2.44322	2.83182	3.28103	3.80013	4.39979	5.09225	5.89160	6.81402	7.87809	9.10513	10.51963	12.14965	14.02741
20 years	2.70148	3.29066	4.00639	4.87544	5.93015	7.20957	8.76085	10.64089	12.91828	15.67574	19.01290	23.04980	27.93091	33.83010

Compounded Daily

	5%	6%	7%	8%	9%	10%	11%	12%	13%	14%	15%	16%	17%	18%
1 year	1.05127	1.06183	1.07250	1.08328	1.09416	1.10516	1.11626	1.12747	1.13880	1.15024	1.16180	1.17347	1.18526	1.19716
5 years	1.28400	1.34983	1.41902	1.49176	1.56823	1.64861	1.73311	1.82194	1.91532	2.01348	2.11667	2.22515	2.33918	2.45906
10 years	1.64866	1.82203	2.01362	2.22535	2.45933	2.71791	3.00367	3.31946	3.66845	4.05411	4.48031	4.95130	5.47178	6.04696
15 years	2.11689	2.45942	2.85736	3.31968	3.85678	4.48077	5.20569	6.04786	7.02625	8.16288	9.48335	11.01738	12.79950	14.86983
20 years	2.71810	3.31979	4.05466	4.95216	6.04831	7.38703	9.02202	11.01883	13.45751	16.43582	20.07316	24.51533	29.94039	36.56577

C

The Bigger Picture

C.1 OPERATIONS ON SETS OF NUMBERS AND SOLVING EQUATIONS

I. Some Operations on Sets of Numbers

  A. Whole Numbers

    1. Add or Subtract:
(Sec. 1.3 and 1.4)

$$\begin{array}{r} 14 \\ +\ 39 \\ \hline 53 \end{array} \qquad \begin{array}{r} 300 \\ -\ 27 \\ \hline 273 \end{array}$$

    2. Multiply or Divide:
(Sec. 1.6 and 1.7)

$$\begin{array}{r} 238 \\ \times\ 47 \\ \hline 1666 \\ 9520 \\ \hline 11{,}186 \end{array} \qquad \begin{array}{r} 127\ \text{R2} \\ 7\overline{)891} \\ -7 \\ \hline 19 \\ -14 \\ \hline 51 \\ -49 \\ \hline 2 \end{array}$$

    3. Exponent:
(Sec. 1.9)

$$3^4 = \overbrace{3 \cdot 3 \cdot 3 \cdot 3}^{4 \text{ factors of } 3} = 81$$

    4. Square Root: (Sec. 1.9)

$$\sqrt{25} = 5 \ because \ 5 \cdot 5 = 25 \text{ and } 5 \text{ is a positive number.}$$

    5. Order of Operations: (Sec. 1.9)

$$\begin{aligned} 24 \div 3 \cdot 2 - (2 + 8) &= 24 \div 3 \cdot 2 - (10) &&\text{Parentheses.} \\ &= 8 \cdot 2 - 10 &&\text{Multiply or divide from left to right.} \\ &= 16 - 10 &&\text{Multiply or divide from left to right.} \\ &= 6 &&\text{Add or subtract from left to right.} \end{aligned}$$

  B. Fractions

    1. Simplify: (Sec. 2.3) Factor the numerator and denominator. Then divide out factors of 1 by dividing out common factors in the numerator and denominator.

Simplify: $\dfrac{20}{35} = \dfrac{4 \cdot 5}{4 \cdot 7} = \dfrac{5}{7}$

    2. Multiply: (Sec. 2.4) Numerator times numerator over denominator times denominator.

$$\frac{5}{9} \cdot \frac{2}{7} = \frac{10}{63}$$

    3. Divide: (Sec. 2.5) First fraction times the reciprocal of the second fraction.

$$\frac{2}{11} \div \frac{3}{4} = \frac{2}{11} \cdot \frac{4}{3} = \frac{8}{33}$$

4. Add or Subtract: (Sec. 3.3) Must have same denominators. If not, find the LCD, and write each fraction as an equivalent fraction with the LCD as denominator.

$$\frac{2}{5} + \frac{1}{15} = \frac{2}{5} \cdot \frac{3}{3} + \frac{1}{15} = \frac{6}{15} + \frac{1}{15} = \frac{7}{15}$$

C. Decimals

1. Add or Subtract: (Sec. 4.3) Line up decimal points.

$$\begin{array}{r} 1.27 \\ + \ 0.6 \\ \hline 1.87 \end{array}$$

2. Multiply: (Sec. 4.4)

$$\begin{array}{r} 2.56 \quad \text{2 decimal places} \\ \times \ 3.2 \quad \text{1 decimal place} \\ \hline 512 \quad 2 + 1 = 3 \\ 768 \\ \hline 8.192 \quad \text{3 decimal places} \end{array}$$

3. Divide: (Sec. 4.5)

$$8)\overline{5.6}^{\,.7} \qquad 0.6)\overline{0.786}^{\,1.31}$$

II. Solving Equations

A. Proportions: (Sec. 5.1) Set cross products equal to each other. Then solve.

$$\frac{14}{3} = \frac{2}{n}, \text{ or } 14 \cdot n = 3 \cdot 2, \text{ or } 14 \cdot n = 6, \text{ or } n = \frac{6}{14} = \frac{3}{7}$$

B. Percent Problems

1. Solved by Equations: (Sec. 5.4) Remember that "of" means multiplication and "is" means equals.

"12% of some number is 6" translates to

$$12\% \cdot n = 6 \text{ or } 0.12 \cdot n = 6 \text{ or } n = \frac{6}{0.12} \text{ or } n = 50$$

2. Solved by Proportions: (Sec. 5.5) Remember that percent, p, is identified by % or percent, base, b, usually appears after "of" and amount, a, is the part compared to the whole.

"12% of some number is 6" translates to

$$\frac{6}{b} = \frac{12}{100} \text{ or } 6 \cdot 100 = b \cdot 12 \text{ or } \frac{600}{12} = b \text{ or } 50 = b$$

C.2 SIMPLIFYING EXPRESSIONS AND SOLVING EQUATIONS AND INEQUALITIES

I. Simplifying Expressions

A. Real Numbers

1. Add: (Sec. 8.3)

$$-1.7 + (-0.21) = -1.91 \quad \text{Adding like signs.}$$
Add absolute values. Attach common sign.

$$-7 + 3 = -4 \quad \text{Adding different signs.}$$
Subtract absolute values. Attach the sign of the number with the larger absolute value.

2. Subtract: Add the first number to the opposite of the second number. (Sec. 8.4)

$$17 - 25 = 17 + (-25) = -8$$

3. Multiply or divide: Multiply or divide the two numbers as usual. If the signs are the same, the answer is positive. If the signs are different, the answer is negative. (Sec. 8.5)

$$-10 \cdot 3 = -30, \qquad -81 \div (-3) = 27$$

B. Exponents (Sec. 12.2)

$$x^7 \cdot x^5 = x^{12}; \ (x^7)^5 = x^{35}; \ \frac{x^7}{x^5} = x^2; \ x^0 = 1; \ 8^{-2} = \frac{1}{8^2} = \frac{1}{64}$$

C. Polynomials

1. Add: Combine like terms. (Sec. 12.4)

$$(3y^2 + 6y + 7) + (9y^2 - 11y - 15) = 3y^2 + 6y + 7 + 9y^2 - 11y - 15$$
$$= 12y^2 - 5y - 8$$

2. Subtract: Change the sign of the terms of the polynomial being subtracted, then add. (Sec. 12.4)

$$(3y^2 + 6y + 7) - (9y^2 - 11y - 15) = 3y^2 + 6y + 7 - 9y^2 + 11y + 15$$
$$= -6y^2 + 17y + 22$$

3. Multiply: Multiply each term of one polynomial by each term of the other polynomial. (Sec. 12.5)

$$(x + 5)(2x^2 - 3x + 4) = x(2x^2 - 3x + 4) + 5(2x^2 - 3x + 4)$$
$$= 2x^3 - 3x^2 + 4x + 10x^2 - 15x + 20$$
$$= 2x^3 + 7x^2 - 11x + 20$$

4. Divide: (Sec. 12.7)

a. To divide by a monomial, divide each term of the polynomial by the monomial.

$$\frac{8x^2 + 2x - 6}{2x} = \frac{8x^2}{2x} + \frac{2x}{2x} - \frac{6}{2x} = 4x + 1 - \frac{3}{x}$$

b. To divide by a polynomial other than a monomial, use long division.

$$
\begin{array}{r}
x - 6 + \dfrac{40}{2x + 5} \\[4pt]
2x + 5\overline{)2x^2 - 7x + 10} \\
\underline{2x^2 + 5x} \\
-12x + 10 \\
\underline{-12x - 30} \\
40
\end{array}
$$

D. Factoring Polynomials

See the Chapter 13 Integrated Review for steps.

$$
\begin{aligned}
3x^4 - 78x^2 + 75 &= 3(x^4 - 26x^2 + 25) \quad \text{Factor out GCF—always first step.} \\
&= 3(x^2 - 25)(x^2 - 1) \quad \text{Factor trinomial.} \\
&= 3(x + 5)(x - 5)(x + 1)(x - 1) \quad \text{Factor further—each} \\
&\qquad\qquad\qquad\qquad\qquad\qquad\qquad \text{difference of squares.}
\end{aligned}
$$

E. Rational Expressions

1. **Simplify:** Factor the numerator and denominator. Then divide out factors of 1 by dividing out common factors in the numerator and denominator. (Sec. 14.1)

$$
\frac{x^2 - 9}{7x^2 - 21x} = \frac{(x + 3)(x - 3)}{7x(x - 3)} = \frac{x + 3}{7x}
$$

2. **Multiply:** Multiply numerators, then multiply denominators. (Sec. 14.2)

$$
\frac{5z}{2z^2 - 9z - 18} \cdot \frac{22z + 33}{10z} = \frac{5 \cdot z}{(2z + 3)(z - 6)} \cdot \frac{11(2z + 3)}{2 \cdot 5 \cdot z} = \frac{11}{2(z - 6)}
$$

3. **Divide:** First fraction times the reciprocal of the second fraction. (Sec. 14.2)

$$
\frac{14}{x + 5} \div \frac{x + 1}{2} = \frac{14}{x + 5} \cdot \frac{2}{x + 1} = \frac{28}{(x + 5)(x + 1)}
$$

4. **Add or subtract:** Must have same denominator. If not, find the LCD and write each fraction as an equivalent fraction with the LCD as denominator. (Sec. 14.4)

$$
\begin{aligned}
\frac{9}{10} - \frac{x + 1}{x + 5} &= \frac{9(x + 5)}{10(x + 5)} - \frac{10(x + 1)}{10(x + 5)} \\
&= \frac{9x + 45 - 10x - 10}{10(x + 5)} = \frac{-x + 35}{10(x + 5)}
\end{aligned}
$$

F. Radicals

1. **Simplify square roots:** If possible, factor the radicand so that one factor is a perfect square. Then use the product rule and simplify. (Sec. 15.2)

$$
\sqrt{75} = \sqrt{25 \cdot 3} = \sqrt{25} \cdot \sqrt{3} = 5\sqrt{3}
$$

2. **Add or subtract:** Only like radicals (same index and radicand) can be added or subtracted. (Sec. 15.3)

$$
8\sqrt{10} - \sqrt{40} + \sqrt{5} = 8\sqrt{10} - 2\sqrt{10} + \sqrt{5} = 6\sqrt{10} + \sqrt{5}
$$

3. **Multiply or divide:** $\sqrt{a} \cdot \sqrt{b} = \sqrt{ab}; \dfrac{\sqrt{a}}{\sqrt{b}} = \sqrt{\dfrac{a}{b}}$. (Sec. 15.4)

$$
\sqrt{11} \cdot \sqrt{3} = \sqrt{33}; \frac{\sqrt{140}}{\sqrt{7}} = \sqrt{\frac{140}{7}} = \sqrt{20} = \sqrt{4 \cdot 5} = 2\sqrt{5}
$$

4. **Rationalizing the denominator:** (Sec. 15.4)
   a. If denominator is one term,

   $$\frac{5}{\sqrt{11}} = \frac{5 \cdot \sqrt{11}}{\sqrt{11} \cdot \sqrt{11}} = \frac{5\sqrt{11}}{11}$$

   b. If denominator is two terms, multiply by 1 in the form of $\dfrac{\text{conjugate of denominator}}{\text{conjugate of denominator}}$.

   $$\frac{13}{3 + \sqrt{2}} = \frac{13}{3 + \sqrt{2}} \cdot \frac{3 - \sqrt{2}}{3 - \sqrt{2}} = \frac{13(3 - \sqrt{2})}{9 - 2} = \frac{13(3 - \sqrt{2})}{7}$$

II. Solving Equations and Inequalities

A. Linear Equations: Power on variable is 1 and there are no variables in denominator. (Sec. 9.3)

$$7(x - 3) = 4x + 6 \quad \text{Linear equation. (If fractions, multiply by LCD.)}$$
$$7x - 21 = 4x + 6 \quad \text{Use the distributive property.}$$
$$7x = 4x + 27 \quad \text{Add 21 to both sides.}$$
$$3x = 27 \quad \text{Subtract } 4x \text{ from both sides.}$$
$$x = 9 \quad \text{Divide both sides by 3.}$$

B. Linear Inequalities: Same as linear equation except if you multiply or divide by a negative number, then reverse direction of inequality. (Sec. 9.7)

$$-4x + 11 \le -1 \quad \text{Linear inequality.}$$
$$-4x \le -12 \quad \text{Subtract 11 from both sides.}$$
$$\frac{-4x}{-4} \ge \frac{-12}{-4} \quad \text{Divide both sides by } -4 \text{ and reverse the direction of the inequality symbol.}$$
$$x \ge 3 \quad \text{Simplify.}$$

C. Quadratic and Higher Degree Equations: Solve: first write the equation in standard form (one side is 0.)

1. If the polynomial on one side factors, solve by factoring. (Sec. 16.1)
2. If the polynomial does not factor, solve by the quadratic formula. (Sec. 16.3)

By factoring:	By quadratic formula:
$x^2 + x = 6$	$x^2 + x = 5$
$x^2 + x - 6 = 0$	$x^2 + x - 5 = 0$
$(x - 2)(x + 3) = 0$	$a = 1, b = 1, c = -5$
$x - 2 = 0$ or $x + 3 = 0$	$x = \dfrac{-1 \pm \sqrt{1^2 - 4(1)(-5)}}{2 \cdot 1}$
$x = 2$ or $x = -3$	$x = \dfrac{-1 \pm \sqrt{21}}{2}$

D. Equations with Rational Expressions: Make sure the proposed solution does not make the denominator 0. (Sec. 14.5)

$$\frac{3}{x} - \frac{1}{x-1} = \frac{4}{x-1}$$ Equation with rational expressions.

$$x(x-1) \cdot \frac{3}{x} - x(x-1) \cdot \frac{1}{x-1} = x(x-1) \cdot \frac{4}{x-1}$$ Multiply through by $x(x-1)$.

$$3(x-1) - x \cdot 1 = x \cdot 4$$ Simplify.

$$3x - 3 - x = 4x$$ Use the distributive property.

$$-3 = 2x$$ Simplify and move variable terms to right side.

$$-\frac{3}{2} = x$$ Divide both sides by 2.

E. Proportions: An equation with two ratios equal. Set cross products equal, then solve. Make sure the proposed solution does not make the denominator 0. (Sec. 14.6)

$$\frac{5}{x} = \frac{9}{2x-3}$$

$$5(2x-3) = 9 \cdot x$$ Set cross products equal.

$$10x - 15 = 9x$$ Multiply.

$$x = 15$$ Write equation with variable terms on one side and constants on the other.

F. Equations with Radicals: To solve, isolate a radical, then square both sides. You may have to repeat this. Check possible solution in the original equation. (Sec. 15.5)

$$\sqrt{x+49} + 7 = x$$

$$\sqrt{x+49} = x - 7$$ Subtract 7 from both sides.

$$x + 49 = x^2 - 14x + 49$$ Square both sides.

$$0 = x^2 - 15x$$ Set terms equal to 0.

$$0 = x(x-15)$$ Factor.

$$\cancel{x = 0} \text{ or } x = 15$$ Set each factor equal to 0 and solve.

D Further Geometric Topics

A Define U.S. Units of Length and Convert from One Unit to Another.

B Use Mixed Units of Length.

C Perform Arithmetic Operations on U.S. Units of Length.

D Define Metric Units of Length and Convert from One Unit to Another.

E Perform Arithmetic Operations on Metric Units of Length.

D.1 LENGTH: U.S. AND METRIC SYSTEMS

Objective **A** Defining and Converting U.S. System Units of Length

In the United States, two systems of measurement are commonly used. They are the **United States (U.S.), or English, measurement system** and the **metric system.** The U.S. measurement system is familiar to most Americans. Units such as feet, miles, ounces, and gallons are used. However, the metric system is also commonly used in fields such as medicine, sports, international marketing, and certain physical sciences. We are accustomed to buying 2-liter bottles of soft drinks, watching televised coverage of the 100-meter dash at the Olympic Games, or taking a 200-milligram dose of pain reliever.

The U.S. system of measurement uses the **inch, foot, yard,** and **mile** to measure **length.** The following is a summary of equivalencies between units of length:

U.S. Units of Length

$$12 \text{ inches (in.)} = 1 \text{ foot (ft)}$$
$$3 \text{ feet} = 1 \text{ yard (yd)}$$
$$36 \text{ inches} = 1 \text{ yard}$$
$$5280 \text{ feet} = 1 \text{ mile (mi)}$$

To convert from one unit of length to another, we will use **unit fractions.** We define a unit fraction to be a fraction that is equivalent to 1. Examples of unit fractions are as follows:

Unit Fractions

$$\frac{12 \text{ in.}}{1 \text{ ft}} = 1 \text{ or } \frac{1 \text{ ft}}{12 \text{ in.}} = 1 \text{ (since 12 in.} = 1 \text{ ft)}$$

$$\frac{3 \text{ ft}}{1 \text{ yd}} = 1 \text{ or } \frac{1 \text{ yd}}{3 \text{ ft}} = 1 \text{ (since 3 ft} = 1 \text{ yd)}$$

$$\frac{5280 \text{ ft}}{1 \text{ mi}} = 1 \text{ or } \frac{1 \text{ mi}}{5280 \text{ ft}} = 1 \text{ (since 5280 ft} = 1 \text{ mi)}$$

Remember that multiplying a number by 1 does not change the value of the number.

EXAMPLE 1 Convert 8 feet to inches.

Solution: We multiply 8 feet by a unit fraction that uses the equality 12 inches = 1 foot. The unit fraction should be in the form $\dfrac{\text{units to convert to}}{\text{original units}}$ or in this case $\dfrac{12 \text{ inches}}{1 \text{ foot}}$. We do this so that like units divide out, as shown.

$$8 \text{ ft} = \frac{8 \text{ ft}}{1} \cdot 1 \qquad \text{Multiply by 1 in the form of } \frac{12 \text{ in.}}{1 \text{ ft}}.$$
$$= \frac{8 \ \cancel{\text{ft}}}{1} \cdot \frac{12 \text{ in.}}{1 \ \cancel{\text{ft}}}$$
$$= 8 \cdot 12 \text{ in.}$$
$$= 96 \text{ in.} \qquad \text{Multiply.}$$

Thus, 8 ft = 96 in., as shown in the diagram:

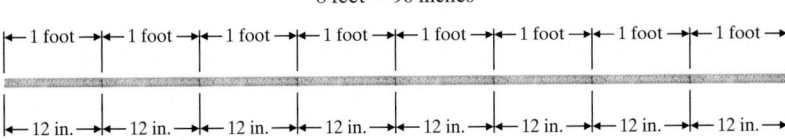

8 feet = 96 inches

Work Practice Problem 1

PRACTICE PROBLEM 1

Convert 5 feet to inches.

EXAMPLE 2 Convert 7 feet to yards.

Solution: We multiply by a unit fraction that compares 1 yard to 3 feet.

$$7 \text{ ft} = \frac{7 \text{ ft}}{1} \cdot 1$$
$$= \frac{7 \ \cancel{\text{ft}}}{1} \cdot \frac{1 \text{ yd}}{3 \ \cancel{\text{ft}}} \qquad \begin{array}{l} \leftarrow \text{ Units to convert to} \\ \leftarrow \text{ Original units} \end{array}$$
$$= \frac{7}{3} \text{ yd}$$
$$= 2\frac{1}{3} \text{ yd} \qquad \text{Divide.}$$

Thus, 7 ft = $2\frac{1}{3}$ yd, as shown in the diagram.

7 feet = $2\frac{1}{3}$ yards

Work Practice Problem 2

PRACTICE PROBLEM 2

Convert 7 yards to feet.

Answers

1. 60 in., **2.** 21 ft

PRACTICE PROBLEM 3

Suppose the bill in the photo measures 18 inches. Convert 18 inches to feet, using decimals.

EXAMPLE 3 Finding Length of Pelican's Bill

The Australian pelican has the longest bill, measuring from 13 to 18.5 inches long. The pelican in the photo has a 15-inch bill. Convert 15 inches to feet, using decimals.

Solution:

$$15 \text{ in.} = \frac{15 \text{ in.}}{1} \cdot \frac{1 \text{ ft}}{12 \text{ in.}} \quad \leftarrow \text{ Units to convert to} \\ \leftarrow \text{ Original units}$$

$$= \frac{15}{12} \text{ ft}$$

$$= \frac{5}{4} \text{ ft} \qquad \text{Simplify } \frac{15}{12}.$$

$$= 1.25 \text{ ft} \qquad \text{Divide.}$$

Thus, 15 in. = 1.25 ft, as shown in the diagram.

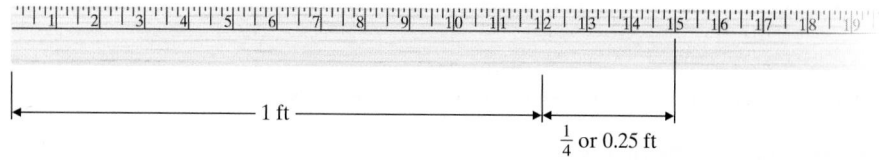

15 inches = 1.25 ft

1 ft $\frac{1}{4}$ or 0.25 ft

⬛ **Work Practice Problem 3**

When converting from one unit to another, select a unit fraction with the properties below:

$$\frac{\text{units you are converting to}}{\text{original units}}$$

By using this unit fraction, the original units will divide out, as wanted.

Objective B Using Mixed U.S. System Units of Length

Sometimes it is more meaningful to express a measurement of length with mixed units such as 1 ft and 5 in. We usually condense this and write 1 ft 5 in.

In Example 2, we found that 7 feet was the same as $2\frac{1}{3}$ yards. The measurement can also be written as a mixture of yards and feet. That is,

$$7 \text{ ft} = \underline{\quad} \text{ yd} \underline{\quad} \text{ ft}$$

Because 3 ft = 1 yd, we divide 3 into 7 to see how many whole yards are in 7 feet. The quotient is the number of yards, and the remainder is the number of feet.

$$\begin{array}{r} 2 \text{ yd } 1 \text{ ft} \\ 3\overline{)7} \\ -6 \\ \hline 1 \end{array}$$

Thus, 7 ft = 2 yd 1 ft, as seen in the diagram:

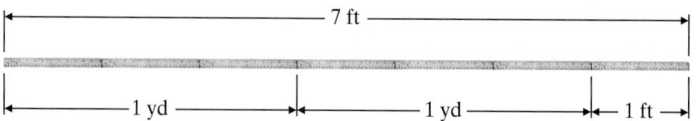

7 ft

1 yd   1 yd   1 ft

EXAMPLE 4 Convert: 134 in. = _____ ft _____ in.

Solution: Because 12 in. = 1 ft, we divide 12 into 134. The quotient is the number of feet. The remainder is the number of inches. To see why we divide 12 into 134, notice that

$$134 \text{ in.} = \frac{134 \text{ in.}}{1} \cdot \frac{1 \text{ ft}}{12 \text{ in.}} = \frac{134}{12} \text{ ft}$$

$$\begin{array}{r} 11 \text{ ft } 2 \text{ in.} \\ 12\overline{)134} \\ -12 \\ \overline{14} \\ -12 \\ \overline{2} \end{array}$$

Thus, 134 in. = 11 ft 2 in.

▣ **Work Practice Problem 4**

EXAMPLE 5 Convert 3 feet 7 inches to inches.

Solution: First, we convert 3 feet to inches. Then we add 7 inches.

$$3 \text{ ft} = \frac{3 \text{ ft}}{1} \cdot \frac{12 \text{ in.}}{1 \text{ ft}} = 36 \text{ in.}$$

Then

$$3 \text{ ft } 7 \text{ in.} = 36 \text{ in.} + 7 \text{ in.} = 43 \text{ in.}$$

▣ **Work Practice Problem 5**

Objective C Performing Operations on U.S. System Units of Length

Finding sums or differences of measurements often involves converting units, as shown in the next example. Just remember that, as usual, only like units can be added or subtracted.

EXAMPLE 6 Add 3 ft 2 in. and 5 ft 11 in.

Solution: To add, we line up the similar units.

$$\begin{array}{r} 3 \text{ ft } 2 \text{ in.} \\ + 5 \text{ ft } 11 \text{ in.} \\ \hline 8 \text{ ft } 13 \text{ in.} \end{array}$$

Since 13 inches is the same as 1 ft 1 in., we have

$$8 \text{ ft } 13 \text{ in.} = 8 \text{ ft} + 1 \text{ ft } 1 \text{ in.}$$
$$= 9 \text{ ft } 1 \text{ in.}$$

▣ **Work Practice Problem 6**

✔ *Concept Check* How could you estimate the following sum?

$$\begin{array}{r} 7 \text{ yd } 4 \text{ in.} \\ + 3 \text{ yd } 27 \text{ in.} \end{array}$$

PRACTICE PROBLEM 4

Convert:
68 in. = _____ ft _____ in.

PRACTICE PROBLEM 5

Convert 5 yards 2 feet to feet.

PRACTICE PROBLEM 6

Add 4 ft 8 in. to 8 ft 11 in.

Answers
4. 5 ft 8 in., **5.** 17 ft, **6.** 13 ft 7 in.

✔ **Concept Check Answer**
round each to the nearest yard:
7 yd + 4 yd = 11 yd

PRACTICE PROBLEM 7

A carpenter cuts 1 ft 9 in. from a board of length 5 ft 8 in. Find the remaining length of the board.

EXAMPLE 7 Finding the Length of a Piece of Rope

A rope of length 6 yd 1 ft has 2 yd 2 ft cut from one end. Find the length of the remaining rope.

Solution: Subtract 2 yd 2 ft from 6 yd 1 ft.

$$\begin{aligned} \text{beginning length} &\rightarrow & 6 \text{ yd } 1 \text{ ft} \\ - \quad \text{amount cut} &\rightarrow & -2 \text{ yd } 2 \text{ ft} \\ \hline \text{remaining length} \end{aligned}$$

We cannot subtract 2 ft from 1 ft, so we borrow 1 yd from the 6 yd. One yard is converted to 3 ft and combined with the 1 ft already there.

Borrow 1 yd = 3 ft

5 yd + (1 yd) (3 ft)

$$\begin{aligned} 6 \text{ yd } 1 \text{ ft} &= & 5 \text{ yd } 4 \text{ ft} \\ -2 \text{ yd } 2 \text{ ft} &= & -2 \text{ yd } 2 \text{ ft} \\ \hline & & 3 \text{ yd } 2 \text{ ft} \end{aligned}$$

The remaining rope is 3 yd 2 ft long.

■ **Work Practice Problem 7**

Objective D Defining and Converting Metric System Units of Length

The basic unit of length in the metric system is the **meter.** A meter is slightly longer than a yard. It is approximately 39.37 inches long. Recall that a yard is 36 inches long.

1 yard = 36 inches

1 meter ≈ 39.37 inches

All units of length in the metric system are based on the meter. The following is a summary of the prefixes used in the metric system. Also shown are equivalencies between units of length. Like the decimal system, the metric system uses powers of 10 to define units.

Metric Unit of Length
1 **kilo**meter (km) = 1000 meters (m)
1 **hecto**meter (hm) = 100 m
1 **deka**meter (dam) = 10 m
1 **meter (m)** = 1 m
1 **deci**meter (dm) = 1/10 m or 0.1 m
1 **centi**meter (cm) = 1/100 m or 0.01 m
1 **milli**meter (mm) = 1/1000 m or 0.001 m

The figure below will help you with decimeters, centimeters, and millimeters.

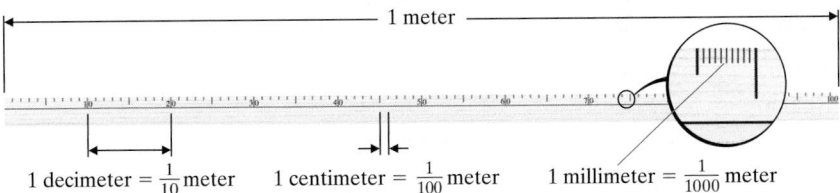

1 decimeter $= \frac{1}{10}$ meter   1 centimeter $= \frac{1}{100}$ meter   1 millimeter $= \frac{1}{1000}$ meter

Helpful Hint

Study the figure above for other equivalencies between metric units of length.

10 decimeters = 1 meter   10 millimeters = 1 centimeter

100 centimeters = 1 meter   10 centimeters = 1 decimeter

1000 millimeters = 1 meter

These same prefixes are used in the metric system for mass and capacity. The most commonly used measurements of length in the metric system are the **meter, millimeter, centimeter,** and **kilometer.**

Being comfortable with the metric units of length means gaining a "feeling" for metric lengths, just as you have a "feeling" for the length of an inch, a foot, and a mile. To help you accomplish this, study the following examples:

A millimeter is about the thickness of a large paper clip.

A centimeter is about the width of a large paper clip.

A meter is slightly longer than a yard.

A kilometer is about two-thirds of a mile.

The length of this book is approximately 27.5 centimeters.

The width of this book is approximately 21.5 centimeters.

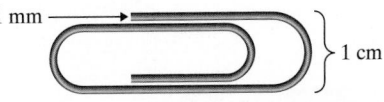

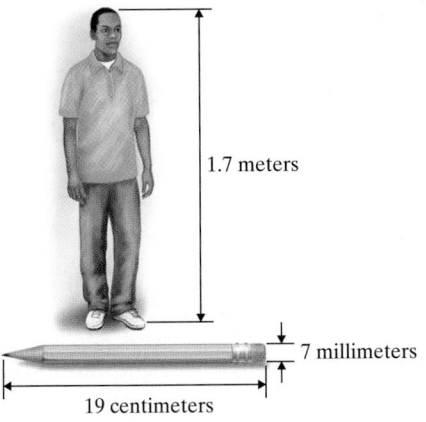

As with the U.S. system of measurement, unit fractions may be used to convert from one unit of length to another. For example, let's convert 1200 meters to kilometers. To do so, we will multiply by 1 in the form of the unit fraction

$$\frac{1 \text{ km}}{1000 \text{ m}}$$ ← Units to convert to
← Original units

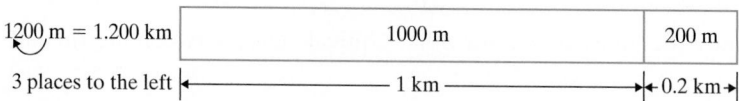

$$1200 \text{ m} = \frac{1200 \text{ m}}{1} \cdot 1 = \frac{1200 \text{ m}}{1} \cdot \frac{1 \text{ km}}{1000 \text{ m}} = \frac{1200 \text{ km}}{1000} = 1.2 \text{ km}$$

Thus, 1200 m = 1.2 km as shown in the diagram.

1200 m = 1.200 km	1000 m	200 m
3 places to the left	← 1 km →	← 0.2 km →

The metric system does, however, have a distinct advantage over the U.S. system of measurement: The ease of converting from one unit of length to another. Since all units of length are powers of 10 of the meter, converting from one unit of length to another is as simple as moving the decimal point. Listing units of length in order from largest to smallest helps to keep track of how many places to move the decimal point when converting.

Let's again convert 1200 meters to kilometers. This time, to convert from meters to kilometers, we move along the chart shown 3 units to the left, from meters to kilometers. This means that we move the decimal point 3 places to the left.

km hm dam **m** dm cm mm
3 units to the left

PRACTICE PROBLEM 8

Convert 2.5 m to millimeters.

EXAMPLE 8 Convert 2.3 m to centimeters.

Solution: First we will convert by using a unit fraction.

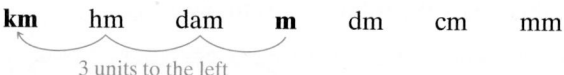

$$2.3 \text{ m} = \frac{2.3 \text{ m}}{1} \cdot \frac{100 \text{ cm}}{1 \text{ m}} = 230 \text{ cm}$$

Now we will convert by listing the units of length in order from left to right and moving from meters to centimeters.

km hm dam m dm cm mm
2 units to the right

2.30 m = 230. cm
2 places to the right

With either method, we get 230 cm.

🖳 **Work Practice Problem 8**

PRACTICE PROBLEM 9

Convert 3500 m to kilometers.

EXAMPLE 9 Convert 450,000 mm to meters.

Solution: We list the units of length in order from left to right and move from millimeters to meters.

km hm dam m dm cm mm
3 units to the left

450,000 mm = 450.000 m or 450 m

🖳 **Work Practice Problem 9**

Answers
8. 2500 mm, **9.** 3.5 km

✔Concept Check What is wrong with the following conversion of 150 cm to meters?

150.00 cm = 15,000 m

Objective E Performing Operations on Metric System Units of Length

To add, subtract, multiply, or divide with metric measurements of length, we write all numbers using the same unit of length and then add, subtract, multiply, or divide as with decimals.

EXAMPLE 10 Subtract 430 m from 1.3 km.

Solution: First we convert both measurements to kilometers or both to meters.

$$430 \text{ m} = 0.43 \text{ km} \quad\quad \text{or} \quad\quad 1.3 \text{ km} = 1300 \text{ m}$$

$$\begin{array}{r} 1.30 \text{ km} \\ -\ 0.43 \text{ km} \\ \hline 0.87 \text{ km} \end{array} \quad\quad\quad \begin{array}{r} 1300 \text{ m} \\ -\ 430 \text{ m} \\ \hline 870 \text{ m} \end{array}$$

The difference is 0.87 km or 870 m.

▣ **Work Practice Problem 10**

PRACTICE PROBLEM 10

Subtract 640 m from 2.1 km.

Answer
10. 1.46 km or 1460 m

✔ Concept Check Answer
decimal should be moved to the left: 1.5 m

Mental Math

Convert as indicated.

1. 12 inches to feet

2. 6 feet to yards

3. 24 inches to feet

4. 36 inches to feet

5. 36 inches to yards

6. 2 yards to inches

Determine whether the measurement in each statement is reasonable.

7. The screen of a home television set has a 30-meter diagonal.

8. A window measures 1 meter by 0.5 meter.

9. A drinking glass is made of glass 2 millimeters thick.

10. A paper clip is 4 kilometers long.

11. The distance across the Colorado River is 50 kilometers.

12. A model's hair is 30 centimeters long.

D.1 EXERCISE SET

FOR EXTRA HELP

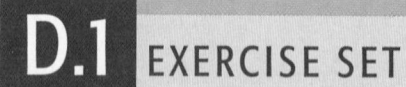 Student Solutions Manual  PH Math/Tutor Center  CD/Video for Review Math XL MathXL®  MyMathLab MyMathLab

Objective **A** *Convert each measurement as indicated. See Examples 1 through 3.*

1. 60 in. to feet

2. 84 in. to feet

3. 12 yd to feet

4. 18 yd to feet

5. 42,240 ft to miles

6. 36,960 ft to miles

7. 102 in. to feet

8. 150 in. to feet

9. 10 ft to yards

10. 25 ft to yards

11. 6.4 mi to feet

12. 3.8 mi to feet

13. 162 in. to yd (Write answer as a decimal.)

14. 7216 yd to mi (Write answer as a decimal.)

15. 3 in. to ft (Write answer as a decimal.)

16. 129 in. to ft (Write answer as a decimal.)

Objective **B** *Convert each measurement as indicated. See Examples 4 and 5.*

17. 40 ft = _____ yd _____ ft

18. 100 ft = _____ yd _____ ft

19. 41 in. = _____ ft _____ in.

20. 75 in. = _____ ft _____ in.

21. 10,000 ft = _____ mi _____ ft

22. 25,000 ft = _____ mi _____ ft

23. 5 ft 2 in. = _____ in.

24. 4 ft 11 in. = _____ in.

25. 7 yd 2 ft = _____ ft

26. 7 yd 1 ft = _____ ft

27. 2 yd 1 ft = _____ in.

28. 1 yd 2 ft = _____ in.

Objective **C** *Perform each indicated operation. Simplify the result if possible. See Examples 6 and 7.*

29. 5 ft 8 in. + 6 ft 7 in.

30. 9 ft 10 in. + 8 ft 4 in.

31. 12 yd 2 ft + 9 yd 2 ft

32. 16 yd 2 ft + 8 yd 1 ft

33. 24 ft 8 in. − 16 ft 3 in.

34. 15 ft 5 in. − 8 ft 2 in.

35. 16 ft 3 in. − 10 ft 9 in.

36. 14 ft 8 in. − 3 ft 11 in.

37. 6 ft 8 in. ÷ 2

38. 26 ft 10 in. ÷ 2

39. 12 yd 2 ft × 4

40. 15 yd 1 ft × 8

Objective **D** *Convert as indicated. See Examples 8 and 9.*

41. 40 m to centimeters

42. 18 m to centimeters

43. 40 mm to centimeters

44. 18 mm to centimeters

45. 300 m to kilometers

46. 400 m to kilometers

47. 1400 mm to meters

48. 6400 mm to meters

49. 1500 cm to meters

50. 6400 cm to meters

51. 0.42 km to centimeters

52. 0.95 km to centimeters

53. 7 km to meters

54. 5 km to meters

55. 8.3 cm to millimeters

56. 4.6 cm to millimeters

57. 20.1 mm to decimeters

58. 140.2 mm to decimeters

59. 0.04 m to millimeters

60. 0.2 m to millimeters

Objective **E** *Perform each indicated operation. See Example 10.*

61. 8.6 m + 0.34 m

62. 14.1 cm + 3.96 cm

63. 2.9 m + 40 mm

64. 30 cm + 8.9 m

65. 24.8 mm − 1.19 cm

66. 45.3 m − 2.16 dam

67. 15 km − 2360 m

68. 14 cm − 15 mm

69. 18.3 m × 3

70. 14.1 m × 4

71. 6.2 km ÷ 4

72. 9.6 m ÷ 5

Objectives **A C D E** **Mixed Practice** *Solve. Remember to insert units when writing your answers. For Exercises 73 through 82, complete the charts.*

		Yards	Feet	Inches
73.	Crysler Building in New York City		1046	
74.	4-story building			792
75.	Python length		35	
76.	Ostrich height			108

Complete the chart.

		Meters	Millimeters	Kilometers	Centimeters
77.	Length of elephant	5			
78.	Height of grizzly bear	3			
79.	Tennis ball diameter				6.5
80.	Golf ball diameter				4.6
81.	Distance from London to Paris			342	
82.	Distance from Houston to Dallas			396	

83. The National Zoo maintains a small patch of bamboo, which it grows as a food supply for its pandas. Two weeks ago, the bamboo was 6 ft 10 in. tall. Since then, the bamboo has grown 3 ft 8 in. How tall is the bamboo now?

84. While exploring in the Marianas Trench, a submarine probe was lowered to a point 1 mile 1400 feet below the ocean's surface. Later it was lowered an additional 1 mile 4000 feet below this point. How far is the probe below the surface of the Pacific?

85. The length of one of the Statue of Liberty's hands is 16 ft 5 in. One of the Statue's eyes is 2 ft 6 in. across. How much longer is a hand than the width of an eye? (*Source:* National Park Service)

86. The width of the Statue of Liberty's head from ear to ear is 10 ft. The height of the Statue's head from chin to cranium is 17 ft 3 in. How much taller is the Statue's head than its width? (*Source:* National Park Service)

87. A 3.4-m rope is attached to a 5.8-m rope. However, when the ropes are tied, 8 cm of length is lost to form the knot. What is the length of the tied ropes?

88. A 2.15-m-long sash cord has become frayed at both ends so that 1 cm is trimmed from each end. How long is the remaining cord?

89. The ice on a pond is 5.33 cm thick. For safe skating, the owner of the pond insists that it must be 80 mm thick. How much thicker must the ice be before skating is allowed?

90. The sediment on the bottom of the Towamencin Creek is normally 14 cm thick, but the recent flood washed away 22 mm of sediment. How thick is it now?

91. The Amana Corporation stacks up its microwave ovens in a distribution warehouse. Each stack is 1 ft 9 in. wide. How far from the wall would 9 of these stacks extend?

92. The highway commission is installing concrete sound barriers along a highway. Each barrier is 1 yd 2 ft long. Find the total length of 25 barriers placed end to end.

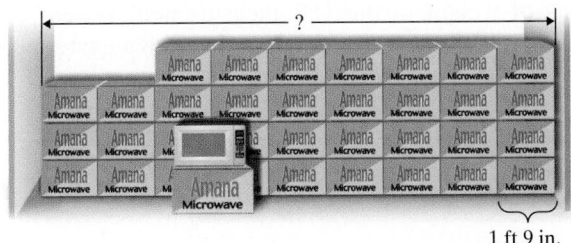

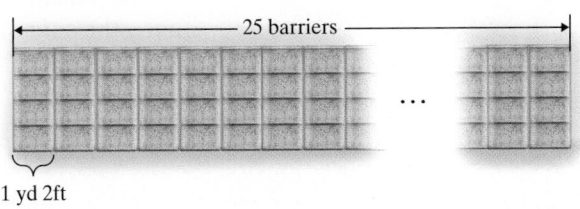

93. A logging firm needs to cut a 67-m-long redwood log into 20 equal pieces before loading it onto a truck for shipment. How long will each piece be?

94. An 18.3-m-tall flagpole is mounted on a 65-cm-high pedestal. How far is the top of the flagpole from the ground?

Estimate each sum or difference. See the Concept Check in this section.

95.   5 yd 2 in.
      + 7 yd 30 in.

96.   45 ft 1 in.
      − 10 ft 11 in.

97. Using a unit other than the foot, write a length that is equivalent to 4 feet. (*Hint:* There are many possibilities.)

98. Using a unit other than the meter, write a length that is equivalent to 7 meters. (*Hint:* There are many possibilities.)

99. To convert from meters to centimeters, the decimal point is moved two places to the right. Explain how this relates to the fact that the prefix *centi* means $\frac{1}{100}$.

100. Explain why conversions in the metric system are easier to make than conversions in the U.S. system of measurement.

Ⓐ Define U.S. Units of Weight and Convert from One Unit to Another.

Ⓑ Perform Arithmetic Operations on Units of Weight.

Ⓒ Define Metric Units of Mass and Convert from One Unit to Another.

Ⓓ Perform Arithmetic Operations on Units of Mass.

D.2 WEIGHT AND MASS: U.S. AND METRIC SYSTEMS

Objective Ⓐ Defining and Converting U.S. System Units of Weight

Whenever we talk about how heavy an object is, we are concerned with the object's **weight.** We discuss weight when we refer to a 12-ounce box of Rice Krispies, a 15-pound tabby cat, or a barge hauling 24 tons of garbage.

| 12 ounces | 15 pounds | 24 tons of garbage |

The most common units of weight in the U.S. measurement system are the **ounce,** the **pound,** and the **ton.** The following is a summary of equivalencies between units of weight:

U.S. Units of Weight	Unit Fractions
16 ounces (oz) = 1 pound (lb)	$\dfrac{16 \text{ oz}}{1 \text{ lb}} = \dfrac{1 \text{ lb}}{16 \text{ oz}} = 1$
2000 pounds = 1 ton	$\dfrac{2000 \text{ lb}}{1 \text{ ton}} = \dfrac{1 \text{ ton}}{2000 \text{ lb}} = 1$

✔ **Concept Check** If you were describing the weight of a fully-loaded semi-trailer, which type of unit would you use: ounce, pound, or ton? Why?

Unit fractions that equal 1 are used to convert between units of weight in the U.S. system. When converting using unit fractions, recall that the numerator of a unit fraction should contain the units we are converting to and the denominator should contain the original units.

EXAMPLE 1 Convert 9000 pounds to tons.

Solution: We multiply 9000 lb by a unit fraction that uses the equality

2000 pounds = 1 ton.

Remember, the unit fraction should be $\dfrac{\text{units to convert to}}{\text{original units}}$ or $\dfrac{1 \text{ ton}}{2000 \text{ lb}}$.

PRACTICE PROBLEM 1

Convert 4500 pounds to tons.

Answer

1. $2\dfrac{1}{4}$ tons

✔ **Concept Check Answer**

ton

$$9000 \text{ lb} = \frac{9000 \text{ lb}}{1} \cdot 1 = \frac{9000 \text{ lb}}{1} \cdot \frac{1 \text{ ton}}{2000 \text{ lb}} = \frac{9000 \text{ tons}}{2000} = \frac{9}{2} \text{ tons or } 4\frac{1}{2} \text{ tons}$$

2000 lb   2000 lb   2000 lb   2000 lb   1000 lb

9000 lb =
$4\frac{1}{2}$ tons

1 ton   1 ton   1 ton   1 ton $\frac{1}{2}$ ton

▣ **Work Practice Problem 1**

EXAMPLE 2 Convert 3 pounds to ounces.

Solution: We multiply by the unit fraction $\frac{16 \text{ oz}}{1 \text{ lb}}$ to convert from pounds to ounces.

$$3 \text{ lb} = \frac{3 \text{ lb}}{1} \cdot 1 = \frac{3 \text{ lb}}{1} \cdot \frac{16 \text{ oz}}{1 \text{ lb}} = 3 \cdot 16 \text{ oz} = 48 \text{ oz}$$

1 pound   1 pound   1 pound

3 lb = 48 oz

16 ounces   16 ounces   16 ounces

▣ **Work Practice Problem 2**

As with length, it is sometimes useful to simplify a measurement of weight by writing it in terms of mixed units.

EXAMPLE 3 Convert: 33 ounces = _____ lb _____ oz

Solution: Because 16 oz = 1 lb, divide 16 into 33 to see how many pounds are in 33 ounces. The quotient is the number of pounds, and the remainder is the number of ounces. To see why we divide 16 into 33, notice that

$$33 \text{ oz} = 33 \text{ oz} \cdot \frac{1 \text{ lb}}{16 \text{ oz}} = \frac{33}{16} \text{ lb}$$

$$\begin{array}{r} 2 \text{ lb } 1 \text{ oz} \\ 16\overline{)33} \\ -32 \\ \hline 1 \end{array}$$

Thus, 33 ounces is the same as 2 lb 1 oz.

16 ounces   16 ounces   1 ounce

   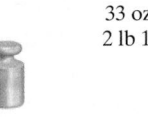

33 oz =
2 lb 1 oz

1 pound   1 pound   1 ounce

▣ **Work Practice Problem 3**

PRACTICE PROBLEM 2
Convert 56 ounces to pounds.

PRACTICE PROBLEM 3
Convert:
45 ounces = _____ lb _____ oz

Answers
2. $3\frac{1}{2}$ lb,   **3.** 2 lb 13 oz

Objective B Performing Operations on U.S. System Units of Weight

Performing arithmetic operations on units of weight works the same way as performing arithmetic operations on units of length.

PRACTICE PROBLEM 4

Subtract 5 tons 1200 lb from 8 tons 100 lb.

EXAMPLE 4 Subtract 3 tons 1350 lb from 8 tons 1000 lb.

Solution: To subtract, we line up similar units.

$$
\begin{array}{r}
8 \text{ tons } 1000 \text{ lb} \\
- 3 \text{ tons } 1350 \text{ lb} \\
\end{array}
$$

Since we cannot subtract 1350 lb from 1000 lb, we borrow 1 ton from the 8 tons. To do so, we write 1 ton as 2000 lb and combine it with the 1000 lb.

$$
\underbrace{7 \text{ tons } + \overbrace{1 \text{ ton}}\ 2000 \text{ lb}}
$$

$$
\begin{array}{rcr}
\cancel{8} \text{ tons } 1000 \text{ lb} & = & 7 \text{ tons } 3000 \text{ lb} \\
- 3 \text{ tons } 1350 \text{ lb} & = & - 3 \text{ tons } 1350 \text{ lb} \\
\hline
& & 4 \text{ tons } 1650 \text{ lb} \\
\end{array}
$$

To check, see that the sum of 4 tons 1650 lb and 3 tons 1350 lb is 8 tons 1000 lb.

■ Work Practice Problem 4

PRACTICE PROBLEM 5

A 5-lb 14-oz batch of cookies is packed into a 6-oz container before it is mailed. Find the total weight.

EXAMPLE 5 Finding the Weight of a Child

Bryan weighed 8 lb 8 oz at birth. By the time he was 1 year old, he had gained 11 lb 14 oz. Find his weight at age 1 year.

Solution:

$$
\begin{array}{lcl}
\text{birth weight} & \rightarrow & 8 \text{ lb } \ 8 \text{ oz} \\
+ \text{ weight gained} & \rightarrow & + 11 \text{ lb } 14 \text{ oz} \\
\hline
\text{total weight} & \rightarrow & 19 \text{ lb } 22 \text{ oz} \\
\end{array}
$$

Since 22 oz equals 1 lb 6 oz,

$$
\begin{array}{l}
19 \text{ lb } 22 \text{ oz } = 19 \text{ lb } + \ 1 \text{ lb } 6 \text{ oz} \\
\qquad\qquad\quad\ = 20 \text{ lb } 6 \text{ oz} \\
\end{array}
$$

Bryan weighed 20 lb 6 oz on his first birthday.

■ Work Practice Problem 5

Objective C Defining and Converting Metric System Units of Mass

In scientific and technical areas, a careful distinction is made between **weight** and **mass**. **Weight** is really a measure of the pull of gravity. The farther from Earth an object gets, the less it weighs. However, **mass** is a measure of the amount of substance in the object and does not change. Astronauts orbiting Earth weigh much less than they weigh on Earth, but they have the same mass in orbit as they do on Earth. Here on Earth weight and mass are the same, so either term may be used.

Answers
4. 2 tons 900 lb, **5.** 6 lb 4 oz

The basic unit of mass in the metric system is the **gram.** It is defined as the mass of water contained in a cube 1 centimeter (cm) on each side.

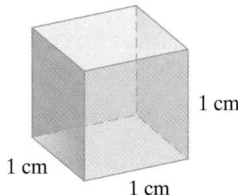

The following examples may help you get a feeling for metric masses:

A tablet contains 200 milligrams of ibuprofen.

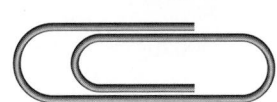

A large paper clip weighs approximately 1 gram.

A box of crackers weighs 453 grams.

A kilogram is slightly over 2 pounds. An adult woman may weigh 60 kilograms.

The prefixes for units of mass in the metric system are the same as for units of length, as shown in the following table:

Metric Unit of Mass
1 **kilo**gram (kg) = 1000 grams (g)
1 **hecto**gram (hg) = 100 g
1 **deka**gram (dag) = 10 g
1 gram (g) = 1 g
1 **deci**gram (dg) = 1/10 g or 0.1 g
1 **centi**gram (cg) = 1/100 g or 0.01 g
1 **milli**gram (mg) = 1/1000 g or 0.001 g

✔ Concept Check   True or false? A decigram is larger than a dekagram. Explain.

The **milligram,** the **gram,** and the **kilogram** are the three most commonly used units of mass in the metric system.

✔ **Concept Check Answer**
false

As with lengths, all units of mass are powers of 10 of the gram, so converting from one unit of mass to another involves moving only the decimal point. To convert from one unit of mass to another in the metric system, list the units of mass in order from largest to smallest.

Let's convert 4300 milligrams to grams. To convert from milligrams to grams, we move along the table 3 units to the left.

kg   hg   dag   **g**   dg   cg   **mg**

3 units to the left

This means that we move the decimal point 3 places to the left to convert from milligrams to grams.

$$4300 \text{ mg} = 4.3 \text{ g}$$

Don't forget, the same conversion can be done with unit fractions.

$$4300 \text{ mg} = \frac{4300 \text{ mg}}{1} \cdot 1 = \frac{4300 \text{ mg}}{1} \cdot \frac{0.001 \text{ g}}{1 \text{ mg}}$$
$$= 4300 \cdot 0.001 \text{ g}$$
$$= 4.3 \text{ g} \quad \text{To multiply by 0.001, move the decimal point 3 places to the left.}$$

To see that this is reasonable, study the diagram:

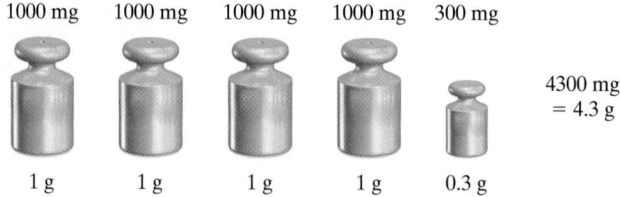

Thus, 4300 mg = 4.3 g

PRACTICE PROBLEM 6

Convert 3.41 g to milligrams.

EXAMPLE 6 Convert 3.2 kg to grams.

Solution: First we convert by using a unit fraction.

Unit fraction

$$3.2 \text{ kg} = 3.2 \text{ kg} \cdot 1 = 3.2 \text{ kg} \cdot \frac{1000 \text{ g}}{1 \text{ kg}} = 3200 \text{ g}$$

Now let's list the units of mass in order from left to right and move from kilograms to grams.

kg   hg   dag   g   dg   cg   mg

3 units to the right

$$3.200 \text{ kg} = 3200. \text{ g}$$

3 places to the right

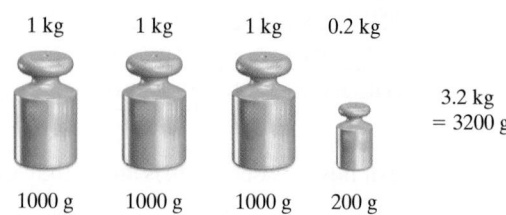

Work Practice Problem 6

Answer

6. 3410 mg

EXAMPLE 7 Convert 2.35 cg to grams.

Solution: We list the units of mass in a chart and move from centigrams to grams.

kg   hg   dag   g   dg   cg   mg

2 units to the left

02.35 cg = 0.0235 g

2 places to the left

■ **Work Practice Problem 7**

Objective D Performing Operations on Metric System Units of Mass

Arithmetic operations can be performed with metric units of mass just as we performed operations with metric units of length. We convert each number to the same unit of mass and add, subtract, multiply, or divide as with decimals.

EXAMPLE 8 Subtract 5.4 dg from 1.6 g.

Solution: We convert both numbers to decigrams or to grams before subtracting.

$$5.4 \text{ dg} = 0.54 \text{ g} \qquad \text{or} \qquad 1.6 \text{ g} = 16 \text{ dg}$$

$$\begin{array}{r} 1.60 \text{ g} \\ -\ 0.54 \text{ g} \\ \hline 1.06 \text{ g} \end{array} \qquad \begin{array}{r} 16.0 \text{ dg} \\ -\ 5.4 \text{ dg} \\ \hline 10.6 \text{ dg} \end{array}$$

The difference is 1.06 g or 10.6 dg.

■ **Work Practice Problem 8**

PRACTICE PROBLEM 7
Convert 56.2 cg to grams.

PRACTICE PROBLEM 8
Subtract 3.1 dg from 2.5 g.

Answers
7. 0.562 g, **8.** 2.19 g or 21.9 dg

Mental Math

Convert.

1. 16 ounces to pounds   **2.** 32 ounces to pounds   **3.** 1 ton to pounds   **4.** 3 tons to pounds

5. 1 pound to ounces   **6.** 3 pounds to ounces   **7.** 2000 pounds to tons   **8.** 4000 pounds to tons

Determine whether the measurement in each statement is reasonable.

9. The doctor prescribed a pill containing 2 kg of medication.

10. A full-grown cat weighs approximately 15 g.

11. A bag of flour weighs 4.5 kg.

12. A staple weighs 15 mg.

13. A professor weighs less than 150 g.

14. A car weighs 2000 mg.

D.2 EXERCISE SET

FOR EXTRA HELP

Student Solutions Manual   PH Math/Tutor Center   CD/Video for Review   MathXL®   MyMathLab

Objective A *Convert as indicated. See Examples 1 through 3.*

1. 2 pounds to ounces   **2.** 5 pounds to ounces   **3.** 5 tons to pounds   **4.** 7 tons to pounds

5. 12,000 pounds to tons   **6.** 32,000 pounds to tons    **7.** 60 ounces to pounds   **8.** 90 ounces to pounds

9. 3500 pounds to tons   **10.** 11,000 pounds to tons   **11.** 16.25 pounds to ounces   **12.** 14.5 pounds to ounces

 **13.** 4.9 tons to pounds   **14.** 8.3 tons to pounds   **15.** $4\frac{3}{4}$ pounds to ounces   **16.** $9\frac{1}{8}$ pounds to ounces

17. 2950 pounds to the nearest tenth of a ton   **18.** 51 ounces to the nearest tenth of a pound

19. $\frac{4}{5}$ oz to pounds   **20.** $\frac{1}{4}$ oz to pounds

1272

21. $5\frac{3}{4}$ lb to ounces

22. $2\frac{1}{4}$ lb to ounces

23. 10 lb 1 oz to ounces

24. 7 lb 6 oz to ounces

25. 89 oz to _____ lb _____ oz

26. 100 oz = _____ lb _____ oz

Objective B *Perform each indicated operation. See Examples 4 and 5.*

27. 34 lb 12 oz + 18 lb 14 oz

28. 6 lb 10 oz + 10 lb 8 oz

29. 6 tons 1540 lb + 2 tons 850 lb

30. 2 tons 1575 lb + 1 ton 480 lb

31. 5 tons 1050 lb − 2 tons 875 lb

32. 4 tons 850 lb − 1 ton 260 lb

33. 12 lb 4 oz − 3 lb 9 oz

34. 45 lb 6 oz − 26 lb 10 oz

35. 5 lb 3 oz × 6

36. 2 lb 5 oz × 5

37. 6 tons 1500 lb ÷ 5

38. 5 tons 400 lb ÷ 4

Objective C *Convert as indicated. See Examples 6 and 7.*

39. 500 g to kilograms

40. 650 g to kilograms

41. 4 g to milligrams

42. 9 g to milligrams

43. 25 kg to grams

44. 18 kg to grams

45. 48 mg to grams

46. 112 mg to grams

47. 6.3 g to kilograms

48. 4.9 g to kilograms

49. 15.14 g to milligrams

50. 16.23 g to milligrams

51. 4.01 kg to grams

52. 3.16 kg to grams

53. 35 hg to centigrams

54. 4.26 cg to dekagrams

Objective D *Perform each indicated operation. See Example 8.*

55. 3.8 mg + 9.7 mg

56. 41.6 g + 9.8 g

57. 205 mg + 5.61 g

58. 2.1 g + 153 mg

59. 9 g − 7150 mg

60. 4 kg − 2410 g

61. 1.61 kg − 250 g

62. 6.13 g − 418 mg

63. 5.2 kg × 2.6   **64.** 4.8 kg × 9.3   **65.** 17 kg ÷ 8   **66.** 8.25 g ÷ 6

Objectives Ⓐ Ⓑ Ⓒ Ⓓ **Mixed Practice** *Solve. Remember to insert units when writing your answers.*

	Object	Tons	Pounds	Ounces
67.	Statue of Liberty—weight of copper sheeting	100		
68.	Statue of Liberty—weight of steel	125		
69.	A 12-inch cube of osmium (heaviest metal)		1,345	
70.	A 12-inch cube of lithium (lightest metal)		32	

	Object	Grams	Kilograms	Milligrams	Centigrams
71.	Capsule of Amoxicillin (Antibiotic)			500	
72.	Tablet of Topamax (Epilepsy and Migraine uses)			25	
73.	A six-year-old boy		21		
74.	A golf ball	45			

75. A can of 7-Up weighs 336 grams. Find the weight in kilograms of 24 cans.

76. Guy Green normally weighs 73 kg, but he lost 2800 grams after being sick with the flu. Find Guy's new weight.

77. Sudafed is a decongestant that comes in two strengths. Regular strength contains 60 mg of medication. Extra strength contains 0.09 g of medication. How much extra medication is in the extra-strength tablet?

78. A small can of Planters sunflower seeds weighs 177 g. If each can contains 6 servings, find the weight of one serving.

79. Doris Johnson has two open containers of Uncle Ben's rice. If she combines 1 lb 10 oz from one container with 3 lb 14 oz from the other container, how much total rice does she have?

80. Dru Mizel maintains the records of the amount of coal delivered to his department in the steel mill. In January, 3 tons 1500 lb were delivered. In February, 2 tons 1200 lb were delivered. Find the total amount delivered in these two months.

81. Carla Hamtini was amazed when she grew a 28 lb 10 oz zucchini in her garden, but later she learned that the heaviest zucchini ever grown weighed 64 lb 8 oz in Llanharry, Wales, by B. Lavery in 1990. How far below the record weight was Carla's zucchini? (*Source: The Guinness Book of Records*)

82. The heaviest baby born in good health weighed an incredible 22 lb 8 oz. He was born in Italy in September, 1955. How much heavier is this than a 7 lb 12 oz baby? (*Source: The Guinness Book of Records*)

83. Tim Caucutt's doctor recommends that Tim limit his daily intake of sodium to 0.6 gram. A one-ounce serving of Cheerios with $\frac{1}{2}$ cup of fortified skim milk contains 350 mg of sodium. How much more sodium can Tim have after he eats a bowl of Cheerios for breakfast, assuming he intends to follow the doctor's orders?

84. A large bottle of Hire's Root Beer weighs 1900 grams. If a carton contains 6 large bottles of root beer, find the weight in kilograms of 5 cartons.

85. Three milligrams of preservatives are added to a 0.5-kg box of dried fruit. How many milligrams of preservatives are in 3 cartons of dried fruit if each carton contains 16 boxes?

86. One box of Swiss Miss Cocoa Mix weighs 0.385 kg, but 39 grams of this weight is the packaging. Find the actual weight of the cocoa in 8 boxes.

87. A carton of 12 boxes of Quaker Oats Oatmeal weighs 6.432 kg. Each box includes 26 grams of packaging material. What is the actual weight of the oatmeal in the carton?

88. The supermarket prepares hamburger in 85-gram market packages. When Leo Gonzalas gets home, he divides the package in half before refrigerating the meat. How much will each package weigh?

89. The Shop 'n Bag supermarket chain ships hamburger meat by placing 10 packages of hamburger in a box, with each package weighing 3 lb 4 oz. How much will 4 boxes of hamburger weigh?

90. The Quaker Oats Company ships its 1-lb 2-oz boxes of oatmeal in cartons containing 12 boxes of oatmeal. How much will 3 such cartons weigh?

91. A carton of Del Monte Pineapple weighs 55 lb 4 oz, but 2 lb 8 oz of this weight is due to packaging. Subtract the weight of the packaging to find the actual weight of the pineapple in 4 cartons.

92. The Hormel Corporation ships cartons of canned ham weighing 43 lb 2 oz each. Of this weight, 3 lb 4 oz is due to packaging. Find the actual weight of the ham found in 3 cartons.

93. A package of Trailway's Gorp, a high-energy hiking trail mix, contains 0.3 kg of nuts, 0.15 kg of chocolate bits, and 400 grams of raisins. Find the total weight of the package.

94. The manufacturer of Anacin wants to reduce the caffeine content of its aspirin by $\frac{1}{4}$. Currently, each regular tablet contains 32 mg of caffeine. How much caffeine should be removed from each tablet?

95. Use a unit other than centigram and write a mass that is equivalent to 25 centigrams. (*Hint:* There are many possibilities.)

96. Use a unit other than pound and write a weight that is equivalent to 4000 pounds. (*Hint:* There are many possibilities.)

True or False? See the Concept Check in the section.

97. A kilogram is larger than a gram.

98. A decigram is larger than a milligram.

99. Why is the decimal point moved to the right when grams are converted to milligrams?

100. To change 8 pounds to ounces, multiply by 16. Why is this the correct procedure?

A Define U.S. Units of Capacity and Convert from One Unit to Another.

B Perform Arithmetic Operations on U.S. Units of Capacity.

C Define Metric Units of Capacity and Convert from One Unit to Another.

D Perform Arithmetic Operations on Metric Units of Capacity.

D.3 CAPACITY: U.S. AND METRIC SYSTEMS

Objective **A** Defining and Converting U.S. System Units of Capacity

Units of **capacity** are generally used to measure liquids. The number of gallons of gasoline needed to fill a gas tank in a car, the number of cups of water needed in a bread recipe, and the number of quarts of milk sold each day at a supermarket are all examples of using units of capacity. The following summary shows equivalencies between units of capacity:

U.S. Units of Capacity

$$8 \text{ fluid ounces (fl oz)} = 1 \text{ cup (c)}$$
$$2 \text{ cups} = 1 \text{ pint (pt)}$$
$$2 \text{ pints} = 1 \text{ quart (qt)}$$
$$4 \text{ quarts} = 1 \text{ gallon (gal)}$$

Just as with units of length and weight, we can form unit fractions to convert between different units of capacity. For instance,

$$\frac{2 \text{ c}}{1 \text{ pt}} = \frac{1 \text{ pt}}{2 \text{ c}} = 1 \quad \text{and} \quad \frac{2 \text{ pt}}{1 \text{ qt}} = \frac{1 \text{ qt}}{2 \text{ pt}} = 1$$

PRACTICE PROBLEM 1

Convert 43 pints to quarts.

EXAMPLE 1 Convert 9 quarts to gallons.

Solution: We multiply by the unit fraction $\dfrac{1 \text{ gal}}{4 \text{ qt}}$.

$$9 \text{ qt} = \frac{9 \text{ qt}}{1} \cdot 1$$

$$= \frac{9 \text{ qt}}{1} \cdot \frac{1 \text{ gal}}{4 \text{ qt}}$$

$$= \frac{9 \text{ gal}}{4}$$

$$= 2\frac{1}{4} \text{ gal}$$

Thus, 9 quarts is the same as $2\dfrac{1}{4}$ gallons, as shown in the diagram:

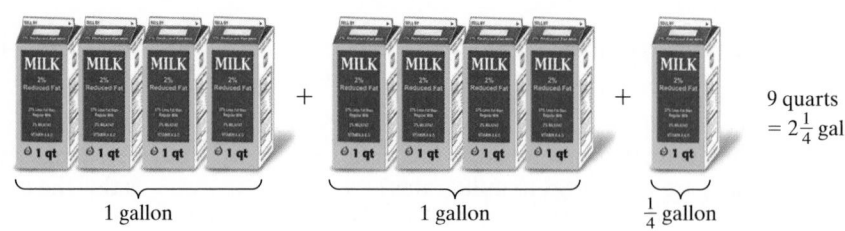

1 gallon   1 gallon $\frac{1}{4}$ gallon

9 quarts $= 2\frac{1}{4}$ gal

▣ **Work Practice Problem 1**

Answer

1. $21\dfrac{1}{2}$ qt

EXAMPLE 2 Convert 14 cups to quarts.

Solution: Our equivalency table contains no direct conversion from cups to quarts. However, from this table we know that

$$1 \text{ qt} = 2 \text{ pt} = \frac{2 \text{ pt}}{1} \cdot 1 = \frac{2 \text{ pt}}{1} \cdot \frac{2 \text{ c}}{1 \text{ pt}} = 4 \text{ c}$$

so 1 qt = 4 c. Now we have the unit fraction $\dfrac{1 \text{ qt}}{4 \text{ c}}$. Thus,

$$14 \text{ c} = \frac{14 \text{ c}}{1} \cdot 1 = \frac{14 \cancel{c}}{1} \cdot \frac{1 \text{ qt}}{4 \cancel{c}} = \frac{14 \text{ qt}}{4} = \frac{7}{2} \text{ qt} \quad \text{or} \quad 3\frac{1}{2} \text{ qt}$$

$\underbrace{\qquad\qquad}_{1 \text{ quart}} + \underbrace{\qquad\qquad}_{1 \text{ quart}} + \underbrace{\qquad\qquad}_{1 \text{ quart}} + \underbrace{\qquad}_{\frac{1}{2} \text{ quart}}$ 14 cups $= 3\frac{1}{2}$ qt

◼ **Work Practice Problem 2**

✔ **Concept Check** If 50 cups are converted to quarts, will the equivalent number of quarts be less than or greater than 50? Explain.

Objective B Performing Operations on U.S. System Units of Capacity

As is true of units of length and weight, units of capacity can be added, subtracted, multiplied, and divided.

EXAMPLE 3 Subtract 3 qt from 4 gal 2 qt.

Solution: To subtract, we line up similar units.

```
    4 gal 2 qt
  −       3 qt
```

We cannot subtract 3 qt from 2 qt. We need to borrow 1 gallon from the 4 gallons, convert it to 4 quarts, and then combine it with the 2 quarts.

$\underbrace{3 \text{ gal} + \overset{\frown}{(1 \text{ gal})}}{} \;\; 4 \text{ qt}$

```
    4 gal 2 qt    =     3 gal 6 qt
  −       3 qt    =   −       3 qt
                        3 gal 3 qt
```

To check, see that the sum of 3 gal 3 qt and 3 qt is 4 gal 2 qt.

◼ **Work Practice Problem 3**

EXAMPLE 4 Finding the Amount of Water in an Aquarium

An aquarium contains 6 gal 3 qt of water. If 2 gal 2 qt of water is added, what is the total amount of water in the aquarium?

Solution:
```
   beginning water   →     6 gal 3 qt
 +     water added   →   + 2 gal 2 qt
       total water   →     8 gal 5 qt
```

Continued on next page

PRACTICE PROBLEM 2

Convert 26 quarts to cups.

PRACTICE PROBLEM 3

Subtract 2 qt from 1 gal 1 qt.

PRACTICE PROBLEM 4

A large oil drum contains 15 gal 3 qt of oil. How much will be in the drum if an additional 4 gal 3 qt of oil is poured into it?

Answers
2. 104 c, **3.** 3 qt, **4.** 20 gal 2 qt

✔ **Concept Check Answer**
less than 50

Since 5 qt = 1 gal 1 qt, we have

$$= \overbrace{8 \text{ gal}}^{8\text{ gal}} + \overbrace{1 \text{ gal } 1 \text{ qt}}^{5\text{ qt}}$$
$$= 9 \text{ gal } 1 \text{ qt}$$

The total amount of water is 9 gal 1 qt.

▣ Work Practice Problem 4

Objective ⓒ Defining and Converting Metric System Units of Capacity

Thus far, we know that the basic unit of length in the metric system is the meter and that the basic unit of mass in the metric system is the gram. What is the basic unit of capacity? The **liter.** By definition, a **liter** is the capacity or volume of a cube measuring 10 centimeters on each side.

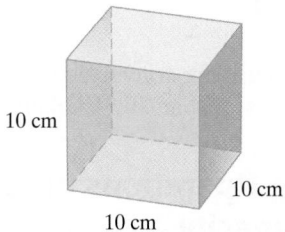

10 cm

10 cm

10 cm

The following examples may help you get a feeling for metric capacities:

One liter of liquid is slightly more than one quart.

1 quart   1 liter

Many soft drinks are packaged in 2-liter bottles.

The metric system was designed to be a consistent system. Once again, the prefixes for metric units of capacity are the same as for metric units of length and mass, as summarized in the following table:

Metric Unit of Capacity
1 **kilo**liter (kl) = 1000 liters (L)
1 **hecto**liter (hl) = 100 L
1 **deka**liter (dal) = 10 L
1 liter (L) = 1 L
1 **deci**liter (dl) = 1/10 L or 0.1 L
1 **centi**liter (cl) = 1/100 L or 0.01 L
1 **milli**liter (ml) = 1/1000 L or 0.001 L

The **milliliter** and the **liter** are the two most commonly used metric units of capacity.

Converting from one unit of capacity to another involves multiplying by powers of 10 or moving the decimal point to the left or to the right. Listing units of capacity in order from largest to smallest helps to keep track of how many places to move the decimal point when converting.

Let's convert 2.6 liters to milliliters. To convert from liters to milliliters, we move along the chart 3 units to the right.

kl   hl   dal   **L**   dl   cl   **ml**

3 units to the right

This means that we move the decimal point 3 places to the right to convert from liters to milliliters.

2.600 L = 2600. ml

This same conversion can be done with unit fractions.

$$2.6 \text{ L} = \frac{2.6 \text{ L}}{1} \cdot 1$$

$$= \frac{2.6 \cancel{\text{L}}}{1} \cdot \frac{1000 \text{ ml}}{1 \cancel{\text{L}}}$$

$$= 2.6 \cdot 1000 \text{ ml}$$

$$= 2600 \text{ ml} \quad \text{To multiply by 1000, move the decimal point 3 places to the right.}$$

To visualize the result, study the diagram below:

MILK 2% Reduced Fat ○1L   MILK 2% Reduced Fat ○1L   MILK 2% Reduced Fat ○0.6L   2.6 L

1000 ml   1000 ml   600 ml = 2600 ml

Thus, 2.6 L = 2600 ml.

EXAMPLE 5 Convert 3210 ml to liters.

Solution: Let's use the unit fraction method first.

Unit fraction

$$3210 \text{ ml} = \frac{3210 \text{ ml}}{1} \cdot 1 = 3210 \cancel{\text{ml}} \cdot \frac{1 \text{ L}}{1000 \cancel{\text{ml}}} = 3.21 \text{ L}$$

Now let's list the unit measures in order from left to right and move from milliliters to liters.

kl   hl   dal   L   dl   cl   ml

3 units to the left

3210 ml = 3.210 L, the same results as before and
3 places to the left   shown below in the diagram.

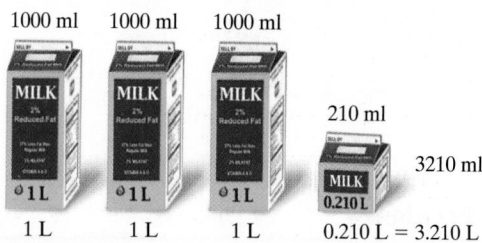

1000 ml   1000 ml   1000 ml

MILK 2% Reduced Fat ○1L   MILK 2% Reduced Fat ○1L   MILK 2% Reduced Fat ○1L   210 ml

MILK 0.210 L   3210 ml

1 L   1 L   1 L   0.210 L = 3.210 L

Work Practice Problem 5

PRACTICE PROBLEM 5

Convert 2100 ml to liters.

Answer

5. 2.1 L

PRACTICE PROBLEM 6

Convert 2.13 dal to liters.

EXAMPLE 6 Convert 0.185 dl to milliliters.

Solution: We list the unit measures in order from left to right and move from deciliters to milliliters.

kl   hl   dal   L   dl   cl   ml

2 units to the right

$0.185 \text{ dl} = 18.5 \text{ ml}$

2 places to the right

Work Practice Problem 6

Objective D Performing Operations on Metric System Units of Capacity

As was true for length and weight, arithmetic operations involving metric units of capacity can also be performed. Make sure that the metric units of capacity are the same before adding, subtracting, multiplying, or dividing.

PRACTICE PROBLEM 7

Add 1250 ml to 2.9 L.

EXAMPLE 7 Add 2400 ml to 8.9 L.

Solution: We must convert both to liters or both to milliliters before adding the capacities together.

$2400 \text{ ml} = 2.4 \text{ L}$ or $8.9 \text{ L} = 8900 \text{ ml}$

$\begin{array}{r} 2.4 \text{ L} \\ + \ 8.9 \text{ L} \\ \hline 11.3 \text{ L} \end{array}$ $\begin{array}{r} 2400 \text{ ml} \\ + \ 8900 \text{ ml} \\ \hline 11{,}300 \text{ ml} \end{array}$

The total is 11.3 L or 11,300 ml. They both represent the same capacity.

Work Practice Problem 7

✔ **Concept Check** How could you estimate the following operation? Subtract 950 ml from 7.5 L.

PRACTICE PROBLEM 8

If 28.6 L of water can be pumped every minute, how much water can be pumped in 85 minutes?

EXAMPLE 8 Finding the Amount of Medication a Person Has Received

A patient hooked up to an IV unit in the hospital is to receive 12.5 ml of medication every hour. How much medication does the patient receive in 3.5 hours?

Solution: We multiply 12.5 ml by 3.5.

$\begin{array}{rl} \text{medication per hour} \rightarrow & 12.5 \text{ ml} \\ \times \quad \text{hours} \rightarrow & \times \ 3.5 \\ \hline & 625 \\ & 3750 \\ \hline & 43.75 \text{ ml} \end{array}$

The patient receives 43.75 ml of medication.

Work Practice Problem 8

Answers
6. 21.3 L,   **7.** 4150 ml or 4.15 L,
8. 2431 L

✔ **Concept Check Answer**
950 ml = 0.95 L; round 0.95 to 1;
7.5 − 1 = 6.5 L

Mental Math

Convert as indicated.

1. 2 c to pints

2. 4 c to pints

3. 4 qt to gallons

4. 8 qt to gallons

5. 2 pt to quarts

6. 6 pt to quarts

7. 8 fl oz to cups

8. 24 fl oz to cups

9. 1 pt to cups

10. 3 pt to cups

11. 1 gal to quarts

12. 2 gal to quarts

Determine whether the measurement in each statement is reasonable.

13. Clair took a dose of 2 L of cough medicine to cure her cough.

14. John drank 250 ml of milk for lunch.

15. Jeannie likes to relax in a tub filled with 3000 ml of hot water.

16. Sarah pumped 20 L of gasoline into her car yesterday.

D.3 EXERCISE SET

FOR EXTRA HELP

Student Solutions Manual · PH Math/Tutor Center · CD/Video for Review · MathXL® · MyMathLab

Objective **A** *Convert each measurement as indicated. See Examples 1 and 2.*

1. 32 fluid ounces to cups

2. 16 quarts to gallons

3. 8 quarts to pints

4. 9 pints to quarts

5. 10 quarts to gallons

6. 15 cups to pints

 **7.** 80 fluid ounces to pints

8. 18 pints to gallons

9. 2 quarts to cups

10. 3 pints to fluid ounces

11. 120 fluid ounces to quarts

12. 20 cups to gallons

13. 6 gallons to fluid ounces

14. 5 quarts to cups

15. $4\frac{1}{2}$ pints to cups

16. $6\frac{1}{2}$ gallons to quarts

17. 5 gal 3 qt to quarts   **18.** 4 gal 1 qt to quarts   **19.** $\frac{1}{2}$ cup to pint   **20.** $\frac{1}{2}$ pint to quarts

21. 58 qt = _____ gal _____ qt

22. 70 qt = _____ gal _____ qt

23. 39 pt = _____ gal _____ qt _____ pt

24. 29 pt = _____ gal _____ qt _____ pt

25. $2\frac{3}{4}$ gallons to pints

26. $3\frac{1}{4}$ quarts to cups

Objective B *Perform each indicated operation. See Examples 3 and 4.*

27. 4 gal 3 qt + 5 gal 2 qt   **28.** 2 gal 3 qt + 8 gal 3 qt   **29.** 1 c 5 fl oz + 2 c 7 fl oz

30. 2 c 3 fl oz + 2 c 6 fl oz   **31.** 3 gal − 1 gal 3 qt   **32.** 2 pt − 1 pt 1 c

33. 3 gal 1 qt − 1 qt 1 pt   **34.** 3 qt 1 c − 1 c 4 fl oz   **35.** 1 pt 1 c × 3

36. 1 qt 1 pt × 2   **37.** 8 gal 2 qt × 2   **38.** 6 gal 1 pt × 2

39. 9 gal 2 qt ÷ 2   **40.** 5 gal 6 fl oz ÷ 2

Objective C *Convert as indicated. See Examples 5 and 6.*

41. 5 L to milliliters   **42.** 8 L to milliliters   **43.** 4500 ml to liters   **44.** 3100 ml to liters

45. 3.2 L to centiliters   **46.** 1.7 L to centiliters   **47.** 410 L to kiloliters   **48.** 250 L to kiloliters

49. 64 ml to liters   **50.** 39 ml to liters   **51.** 0.16 kl to liters   **52.** 0.48 kl to liters

53. 3.6 L to milliliters   **54.** 1.9 L to milliliters   **55.** 0.16 L to kiloliters   **56.** 0.127 L to kiloliters

Objective D *Perform each indicated operation. See Examples 7 and 8.*

57. 2.9 L + 19.6 L

58. 18.5 L + 4.6 L

59. 2700 ml + 1.8 L

60. 4.6 L + 1600 ml

61. 8.6 L − 190 ml

62. 4.8 L − 283 ml

63. 11,400 ml − 0.8 L

64. 6850 ml − 0.3 L

65. 480 ml × 8

66. 290 ml × 6

67. 81.2 L ÷ 0.5

68. 5.4 L ÷ 3.6

Objectives A B C D **Mixed Practice** *Solve. Remember to insert units when writing your answers.*

	Capacity	Cups	Gallons	Quarts	Pints
69.	An average-size bath of water		21		
70.	A dairy cow's daily milk yield				38
71.	Your kidneys filter about this amount of blood every minute	4			
72.	The amount of water needed in a punch recipe	2			

73. Many diet experts advise individuals to drink 64 ounces of water each day. How many quarts of water is this?

74. A recipe for walnut fudge cake calls for $1\frac{1}{4}$ cups of water. How many fluid ounces is this?

75. Margie Phitts added 354 ml of Prestone dry gas to the 18.6 L of gasoline in her car's tank. Find the total amount of gasoline in the tank.

76. Chris Peckaitis wishes to share a 2-L bottle of Coca Cola equally with 7 of his friends. How much will each person get?

77. Can 5 pt 1 c of fruit punch and 2 pt 1 c of ginger ale be poured into a 1-gal container without it overflowing?

78. Three cups of prepared Jell-O are poured into 6 dessert dishes. How many fluid ounces of Jell-O are in each dish?

Solve. See the Concept Checks in the section.

79. If 70 pints are converted to gallons, will the equivalent number of gallons be less than or greater than 70? Explain why.

80. If 30 gallons are converted to quarts, will the equivalent number of quarts be less than or greater than 30? Explain why.

81. Explain how to estimate the following operation: Add 986 ml to 6.9 L.

82. Find the number of fluid ounces in 1 gallon.

A cubic centimeter (cc) is the amount of space that a volume of 1 mL occupies. Because of this, we will say that 1 cc = 1 mL.

A common syringe is one with a capacity of 3 cc. Use the diagram and give the measurement indicated by each arrow.

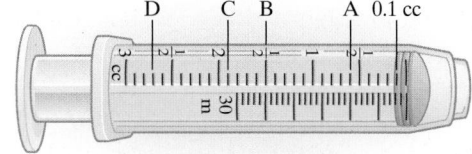

83. A

84. B

85. C

86. D

D.4 REVIEW OF SURFACE AREA

A convex solid is a set of points, S, not all in one plane, such that for any two points A and B in S, all points between A and B are also in S. In this Appendix; we will find the volume and surface area of special types of solids called polyhedrons. A solid formed by the intersection of a finite number of planes is called a **polyhedron.** The box below is an example of a polyhedron.

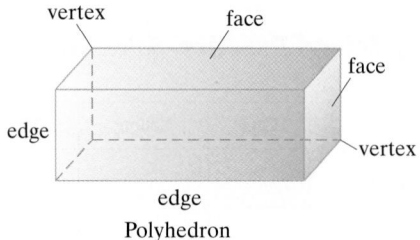

Polyhedron

Each of the plane regions of the polyhedron is called a **face** of the polyhedron. If the intersection of two faces is a line segment, this line segment is an **edge** of the polyhedron. The intersections of the edges are the **vertices** of the polyhedron.

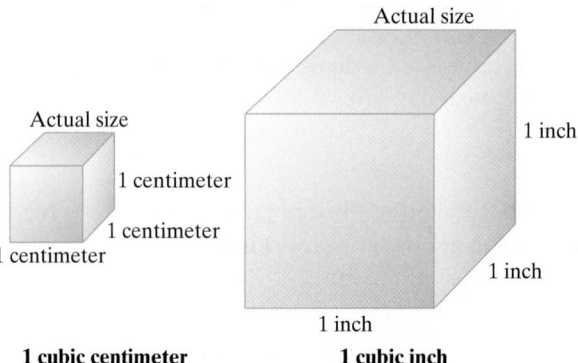

1 cubic centimeter　　　**1 cubic inch**

The **surface area** of a polyhedron is the sum of the areas of the faces of the polyhedron. For example, each face of the cube to the left above has an area of 1 square centimeter. Since there are 6 faces of the cube, the sum of the areas of the faces is 6 square centimeters. Surface area can be used to describe the amount of material needed to cover a solid. Surface area is measured in square units.

Formulas for finding the surface areas, SA, of some common solids are given next. (Volume is given as a review.)

Volume and Surface Area Formulas of Common Solids

Solid	Formulas
RECTANGULAR SOLID height width length	$V = lwh$ $SA = 2lh + 2wh + 2lw$ where h = height, w = width, l = length
CUBE side side side	$V = s^3$ $SA = 6s^2$ where s = side
SPHERE radius	$V = \dfrac{4}{3}\pi r^3$ $SA = 4\pi r^2$ where r = radius
CIRCULAR CYLINDER height radius	$V = \pi r^2 h$ $SA = 2\pi rh + 2\pi r^2$ where h = height, r = radius
CONE height radius	$V = \dfrac{1}{3}\pi r^2 h$ $SA = \pi r\sqrt{r^2 + h^2} + \pi r^2$ where h = height, r = radius
SQUARE-BASED PYRAMID height side	$V = \dfrac{1}{3}s^2 h$ $SA = B + \dfrac{1}{2}pl$ where B = area of base; p = perimeter of base, h = height, s = side, l = slant height

> **Helpful Hint**
>
> Volume is measured in cubic units. Surface area is measured in square units.

EXAMPLE 1 Find the volume and surface area of a rectangular box that is 12 inches long, 6 inches wide, and 3 inches high.

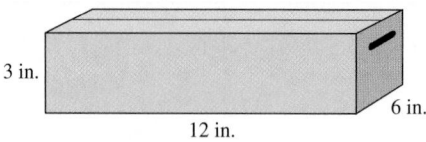

3 in.

12 in.

6 in.

Solution: Let $h = 3$ in., $l = 12$ in., and $w = 6$ in.

$V = lwh$

$V = 12 \text{ inches} \cdot 6 \text{ inches} \cdot 3 \text{ inches} = 216 \text{ cubic inches}$

The volume of the rectangular box is 216 cubic inches.

$SA = 2lh + 2wh + 2lw$

$\quad = 2(12 \text{ in.})(3 \text{ in.}) + 2(6 \text{ in.})(3 \text{ in.}) + 2(12 \text{ in.})(6 \text{ in.})$

$\quad = 72 \text{ sq in.} + 36 \text{ sq in.} + 144 \text{ sq in.}$

$\quad = 252 \text{ sq in.}$

The surface area of rectangular box is 252 square inches.

EXAMPLE 2 Find the surface area of a ball that has a radius of 2 inches. Give the exact surface area and then use the approximation $\frac{22}{7}$ for π.

Solution:

$SA = 4\pi r^2$ Formula for surface area.

$SA = 4 \cdot \pi (2 \text{ in.})^2$ Let $r = 2$ inches.

$\quad = 16\pi \text{ sq in.}$ Simplify.

$\quad \approx 16 \cdot \frac{22}{7} \text{ sq in.}$ Approximate π with $\frac{22}{7}$.

$\quad = \frac{352}{7}$ or $50\frac{2}{7} \text{ sq in.}$

The surface area of the sphere is exactly 16π square inches or approximately $50\frac{2}{7}$ square inches.

D.4 EXERCISE SET

FOR EXTRA HELP

 Student Solutions Manual

 PH Math/Tutor Center

 CD/Video for Review

Math XL
MathXL®

MyMathLab
MyMathLab

Find the volume and surface area of each solid. See Examples 1 and 2. For formulas that contain π, give an exact answer and then approximate using $\frac{22}{7}$ for π.

1.

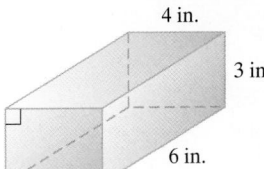

4 in.
3 in.
6 in.

2.

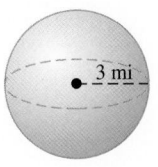

3 mi

3.

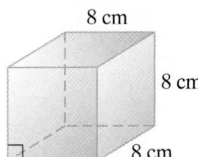

8 cm
8 cm
8 cm

4.

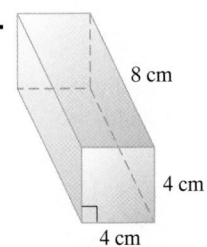

8 cm
4 cm
4 cm

5. (For surface area, use 3.14 for π.)

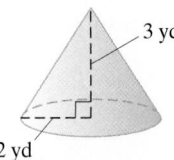

3 yd
2 yd

6.

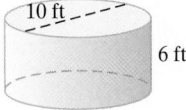

10 ft
6 ft

7.

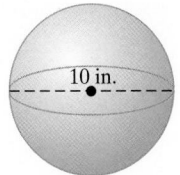

10 in.

8. Find the volume only.

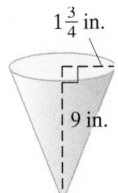

$1\frac{3}{4}$ in.
9 in.

9.

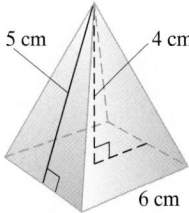

5 cm
4 cm
6 cm

10.

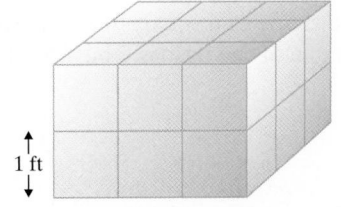

1 ft

1287

Solve.

11. Find the volume of a cube with edges of $1\frac{1}{3}$ inches.

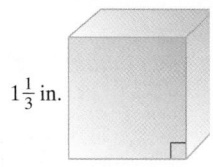

$1\frac{1}{3}$ in.

12. A water storage tank is in the shape of a cone with the pointed end down. If the radius is 14 ft and the depth of the tank is 15 ft, approximate the volume of the tank in cubic feet. Use $\frac{22}{7}$ for π.

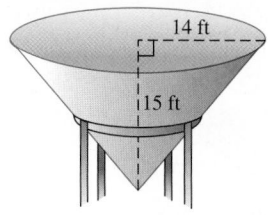

14 ft

15 ft

13. Find the surface area of a rectangular box 2 ft by 1.4 ft by 3 ft.

14. Find the surface area of a box in the shape of a cube that is 5 ft on each side.

15. Find the volume of a pyramid with a square base 5 in. on a side and a height of 1.3 in.

16. Approximate to the nearest hundredth the volume of a sphere with a radius of 2 cm. Use 3.14 for π.

17. A paperweight is in the shape of a square-based pyramid 20 cm tall. If an edge of the base is 12 cm, find the volume of the paperweight.

18. A bird bath is made in the shape of a hemisphere (half-sphere). If its radius is 10 in., approximate the volume. Use $\frac{22}{7}$ for π.

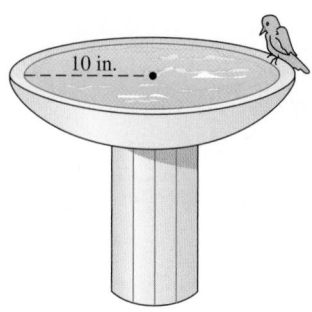

10 in.

19. Find the exact surface area of a sphere with a radius of 7 in.

20. A tank is in the shape of a cylinder 8 ft tall and 3 ft in radius. Find the exact surface area of the tank.

21. Find the volume of a rectangular block of ice 2 ft by $2\frac{1}{2}$ ft by $1\frac{1}{2}$ ft.

22. Find the capacity (volume in cubic feet) of a rectangular ice chest with inside measurements of 3 ft by $1\frac{1}{2}$ ft by $1\frac{3}{4}$ ft.

23. An ice cream cone with a 4-cm diameter and 3-cm depth is filled exactly level with the top of the cone. Approximate how much ice cream (in cubic centimeters) is in the cone. Use $\frac{22}{7}$ for π.

24. A child's toy is in the shape of a square-based pyramid 10 in. tall. If an edge of the base is 7 in., find the volume of the toy.

ANSWERS TO SELECTED EXERCISES

CHAPTER 1 The Whole Numbers

Exercise Set 1.2 1. tens **3.** thousands **5.** hundred-thousands **7.** millions **9.** five hundred forty-two
11. seven thousand, eight hundred ninety-six **13.** twenty-six thousand, nine hundred ninety **15.** one million, six hundred twenty thousand
17. fifty-three million, five hundred twenty thousand, one hundred seventy **19.** sixty-four thousand, four hundred eighty-two
21. one thousand, six hundred seventy-nine **23.** thirteen million, six hundred thousand **25.** twelve thousand, six hundred sixty-two
27. two hundred two thousand, seven hundred **29.** 6587 **31.** 29,900 **33.** 16,504,019 **35.** 3,000,014 **37.** 220 **39.** 440,276
41. 70,251,710 **43.** 1815 **45.** 755 **47.** 400 + 6 **49.** 5000 + 200 + 90 **51.** 60,000 + 2000 + 400 + 7 **53.** 30,000 + 600 + 80
55. 30,000,000 + 9,000,000 + 600,000 + 80,000 **57.** 5532; five thousand, five hundred thirty-two **59.** 5000 + 400 + 90 + 2
61. Mt. Washington **63.** Golden retriever **65.** Labrador retriever; one hundred forty-four thousand, nine hundred thirty-four
67. 25 pounds **69.** 7632 **71.** no; one hundred five **73.** answers may vary **75.** Canton

Calculator Explorations 1. 134 **3.** 340 **5.** 2834

Mental Math 1. 16 **3.** 9000 **5.** 1620

Exercise Set 1.3 1. 36 **3.** 292 **5.** 49 **7.** 5399 **9.** 117 **11.** 512 **13.** 209,078 **15.** 25 **17.** 62 **19.** 212 **21.** 94
23. 910 **25.** 8273 **27.** 11,926 **29.** 1884 **31.** 16,717 **33.** 1110 **35.** 8999 **37.** 35,901 **39.** 632,389 **41.** 42 in. **43.** 25 ft
45. 24 in. **47.** 8 yd **49.** 29 in. **51.** 2093 **53.** 266 **55.** 544 **57.** 3452 **59.** 6684 ft **61.** 340 ft **63.** 291,147 motorcycles
65. 2425 ft **67.** 13,255 mi **69.** 124 ft **71.** 767,312 **73.** 8867 **75.** California **77.** 366 stores **79.** Florida and Georgia
81. answers may vary **83.** answers may vary **85.** 40 ft **87.** 1,044,473,765 **89.** correct **91.** incorrect; 933

Calculator Explorations 1. 770 **3.** 109 **5.** 8978

Mental Math 1. 7 **3.** 5 **5.** 0 **7.** 400 **9.** 500

Exercise Set 1.4 1. 44 **3.** 265 **5.** 135 **7.** 2254 **9.** 5545 **11.** 600 **13.** 25 **15.** 45 **17.** 146 **19.** 288 **21.** 168
23. 106 **25.** 447 **27.** 5723 **29.** 504 **31.** 89 **33.** 79 **35.** 39,914 **37.** 32,711 **39.** 5041 **41.** 31,213 **43.** 4 **45.** 20
47. 7 **49.** 72 **51.** 88 **53.** 264 pages **55.** 4 million sq km **57.** 6065 ft **59.** 23 points **61.** $409 **63.** 358 mi **65.** $389
67. 3,044,452 people **69.** 19,036 cocker spaniels **71.** 5920 sq ft **73.** Hartsfield Atlanta International **75.** 32 million
77. General Motors Corp., Time Warner, Procter & Gamble Co. **79.** $1112 million or $1,112,000,000 **81.** 1034 **83.** 9 **85.** 8515
87. 22,876 **89.** minuend: 48; subtrahend: 1 **91.** minuend: 70; subtrahend: 7 **93.** Jo; by 271 votes **95.** incorrect; 685 **97.** correct
99. 5269 − 2385 = 2884 **101.** answers may vary **103.** no; 1089 more pages

Exercise Set 1.5 1. 630 **3.** 640 **5.** 1800 **7.** 400 **9.** 51,000 **11.** 43,000 **13.** 248,700 **15.** 36,000 **17.** 100,000
19. 60,000,000 **21.** 5280; 5300; 5000 **23.** 9440; 9400; 9000 **25.** 14,880; 14,900; 15,000 **27.** 380,000 **29.** 10,800 **31.** 70,000,000,000
33. 2,500,000 **35.** 159,000,000; 7,000,000 **37.** 130 **39.** 380 **41.** 5500 **43.** 300 **45.** 8500 **47.** correct **49.** incorrect
51. correct **53.** $3100 **55.** 80 mi **57.** 6000 ft **59.** 1,400,000 people **61.** 14,000,000 votes **63.** 52,000 children
65. $3,430,000,000; $3,400,000,000; $3,000,000,000 **67.** $2,234,000,000; $2,200,000,000; $2,000,000,000 **69.** 4618, for example
71. a. 8550 **b.** 8649 **73.** answers may vary **75.** 140 m

Calculator Explorations 1. 3456 **3.** 15,322 **5.** 272,291

Mental Math 1. 24 **3.** 0 **5.** 0 **7.** 87

Exercise Set 1.6 1. 4·3 + 4·9 **3.** 2·4 + 2·6 **5.** 10·11 + 10·7 **7.** 252 **9.** 1872 **11.** 1662 **13.** 5310 **15.** 1372
17. 10,857 **19.** 11,326 **21.** 24,800 **23.** 0 **25.** 5900 **27.** 59,232 **29.** 142,506 **31.** 1,821,204 **33.** 3,949,935 **35.** 64,790
37. 800 **39.** 11,000 **41.** 74,060 **43.** 24,000 **45.** 45,000 **47.** 3,280,000 **49.** 240,000 **51.** 300,000 **53.** c **55.** c
57. 63 sq m **59.** 390 sq ft **61.** 770 **63.** 5400 **65.** 4480 **67.** 375 cal **69.** $1890 **71. a.** 192 cans **b.** 96 cans
73. 900 sq ft **75.** 56,000 sq ft **77.** 5828 pixels **79.** 1500 characters **81.** 1280 cal **83.** 71,343 mi
85. $10, $50; $10, $100; $12, $24; $12, $24; $228 **87.** 21,700,000 qt **89.** 134 **91.** 1008 **93.** 24 **95.** 12
97. 5·3 or 3·5 **99. a.** 7 + 7 + 7 + 7 or 4 + 4 + 4 + 4 + 4 + 4 + 4 **b.** answers may vary

101.
$$
\begin{array}{r}
203 \\
\times\ \ \ 14 \\
\hline
812 \\
2030 \\
\hline
2842
\end{array}
$$
103. 2; 9 **105.** answers may vary **107.** 506 windows

Calculator Explorations 1. 53 **3.** 62 **5.** 261 **7.** 0

Mental Math 1. 5 **3.** 9 **5.** 0 **7.** 9 **9.** 1 **11.** 5 **13.** undefined **15.** 7 **17.** 0 **19.** 8

Exercise Set 1.7 1. 26 **3.** 37 **5.** 338 **7.** undefined **9.** 8 **11.** 25 **13.** 65 R 4 **15.** 225 R 4 **17.** 37 R 1 **19.** 265 R 5
21. 49 **23.** 13 **25.** 97 R 40 **27.** 206 R 10 **29.** 506 **31.** 202 R 7 **33.** 45 **35.** 98 R 100 **37.** 202 R 15 **39.** 579 R 72
41. 19 **43.** 513 R 1 **45.** 2082 R 26 **47.** 5030 **49.** 21 R 1 **51.** 2 R 30 **53.** 20 R 2 **55.** 58 students **57.** $252,000

59. 415 bushels **61.** 105 lane dividers **63.** yes, she needs 176 ft; she has 9 ft left over **65.** 27 touchdowns **67.** 1760 yd **69.** 26
71. 498 **73.** 79 **75.** 16° **77.** 8862 **79.** 29,210 **81.** 589 **83.** undefined **85.** 7 R 15 **87.** d **89.** a **91.** $3,376,500,000
93. increase; answers may vary **95.** no; answers may vary **97.** answers may vary

The Bigger Picture 1. 118 **2.** 28 **3.** 3285 **4.** 89 R 11 **5.** 0 **6.** 0 **7.** 19 **8.** undefined **9.** 64 **10.** 1844

Integrated Review 1. 148 **2.** 6555 **3.** 1620 **4.** 562 **5.** 79 **6.** undefined **7.** 9 **8.** 1 **9.** 0 **10.** 0 **11.** 0 **12.** 3
13. 2433 **14.** 9826 **15.** 213 R 3 **16.** 79,317 **17.** 27 **18.** 9 **19.** 138 **20.** 276 **21.** 1099 R 2 **22.** 111 R 1 **23.** 663 R 6
24. 1076 R 60 **25.** 1024 **26.** 9899 **27.** 30,603 **28.** 47,500 **29.** 65 **30.** 456 **31.** 7 R 1 **32.** 49 **33.** 86 **34.** 22
35. 8630; 8600; 9000 **36.** 1550; 1600; 2000 **37.** 10,900; 10,909; 11,000 **38.** 432,200; 432,200; 432,000 **39.** perimeter: 20 ft; area: 25 sq ft
40. perimeter: 42 in.; area: 98 sq in. **41.** 26 mi **42.** 26 m **43.** 24 **44.** 124 **45.** Lake Pontchartrain; 2175 ft **46.** $5904

Exercise Set 1.8 1. 49 **3.** 237 **5.** 42 **7.** 600 **9. a.** 400 ft **b.** 9600 sq ft **11.** $15,500 **13.** 168 hr **15.** 5758 **17.** 129 yr
19. 312 billion bricks **21.** 719 towns **23.** $21 **25.** 55 cal **27.** 24 **29.** $33,506,850 **31.** 38,034,000 students **33.** 3987 mi
35. 13 paychecks **37.** $239 **39.** $1045 **41.** b will be cheaper by $3 **43.** IBM Corporation **45.** 2113 patents **47.** 99 patents
49. 2433 **51.** $14,754 **53.** 16,800 mg **55. a.** 3750 sq ft **b.** 375 sq ft **c.** 3375 sq ft
57. $240 **59.** answers may vary

Calculator Explorations 1. 729 **3.** 1024 **5.** 2048 **7.** 2526 **9.** 4295 **11.** 8

Exercise Set 1.9 1. 3^4 **3.** 7^8 **5.** 12^3 **7.** $6^2 \cdot 5^3$ **9.** $9^3 \cdot 8$ **11.** $3 \cdot 2^5$ **13.** $3 \cdot 2^2 \cdot 5^3$ **15.** 49 **17.** 125 **19.** 64 **21.** 1
23. 7 **25.** 243 **27.** 256 **29.** 64 **31.** 81 **33.** 729 **35.** 100 **37.** 20 **39.** 729 **41.** 48 **43.** 54 **45.** 3 **47.** 8
49. 12 **51.** 4 **53.** 21 **55.** 11 **57.** 4 **59.** 17 **61.** 46 **63.** 10 **65.** 126 **67.** 105 **69.** 2 **71.** 35 **73.** 4
75. undefined **77.** 30 **79.** 52 **81.** 44 **83.** 12 **85.** 21 **87.** 24 **89.** 28 **91.** 3 **93.** 25 **95.** 23 **97.** 13
99. 400 sq mi **101.** 64 sq cm **103.** false **105.** false **107.** $(2 + 3) \cdot 6 - 2$ **109.** $24 \div (3 \cdot 2) + 2 \cdot 5$ **111.** 1260 ft
113. 6,384,814 **115.** answers may vary; $(20 - 10) \cdot 5 \div 25 + 3$

The Bigger Picture 1. 64 **2.** 48 **3.** 9 **4.** 15 **5.** 22 **6.** 50 **7.** 688 **8.** 2160 **9.** 10 R 46 **10.** 27

Chapter 1 Vocabulary Check 1. whole numbers **2.** perimeter **3.** place value **4.** exponent **5.** area **6.** square root
7. digits **8.** sum **9.** divisor **10.** dividend **11.** quotient **12.** factor **13.** product **14.** minuend **15.** subtrahend
16. difference **17.** addend

Chapter 1 Review 1. hundreds **2.** ten-millions **3.** five thousand, four hundred eighty
4. forty-six million, two hundred thousand, one hundred twenty **5.** $6000 + 200 + 70 + 9$
6. $400,000,000 + 3,000,000 + 200,000 + 20,000 + 5000$ **7.** 59,800 **8.** 6,304,000,000 **9.** 1,630,553 **10.** 2,968,528
11. San Antonio, TX **12.** New York, NY **13.** 63 **14.** 67 **15.** 48 **16.** 77 **17.** 956 **18.** 840 **19.** 7950 **20.** 7250
21. 4211 **22.** 1967 **23.** 1326 **24.** 886 **25.** 27,346 **26.** 39,300 **27.** 8032 mi **28.** $197,699 **29.** 276 ft **30.** 66 km
31. 14 **32.** 34 **33.** 65 **34.** 304 **35.** 3914 **36.** 7908 **37.** 17,897 **38.** 34,658 **39.** 531,341 **40.** 76,704 **41.** 397 pages
42. $25,626 **43.** May **44.** August **45.** $110 **46.** $240 **47.** 90 **48.** 50 **49.** 470 **50.** 500 **51.** 4800 **52.** 58,000
53. 50,000,000 **54.** 800,000 **55.** 73,000,000 **56.** 571,000 **57.** 7400 **58.** 4100 **59.** 2500 mi **60.** 2,500,000 **61.** 1911
62. 1396 **63.** 1410 **64.** 2898 **65.** 800 **66.** 900 **67.** 3696 **68.** 1694 **69.** 0 **70.** 0 **71.** 16,994 **72.** 8954
73. 113,634 **74.** 44,763 **75.** 411,426 **76.** 636,314 **77.** 375,000 **78.** 108,000 **79.** 12,000 **80.** 35,000 **81.** 5,100,000
82. 7,600,000 **83.** 1150 **84.** 4920 **85.** 108 **86.** 112 **87.** 24 g **88.** $4,897,341 **89.** 60 sq mi **90.** 500 sq cm **91.** 3
92. 4 **93.** 6 **94.** 7 **95.** 5 R 2 **96.** 4 R 2 **97.** undefined **98.** 0 **99.** 1 **100.** 10 **101.** undefined **102.** 0
103. 33 R 2 **104.** 19 R 7 **105.** 24 R 2 **106.** 35 R 15 **107.** 506 R 10 **108.** 907 R 40 **109.** 2793 R 140 **110.** 2012 R 60
111. 18 R 2 **112.** 21 R 2 **113.** 458 ft **114.** 13 mi **115.** 51 **116.** 59 **117.** 27 boxes **118.** $192 **119.** 7 billion **120.** 75¢
121. $898 **122.** 23,150 sq ft **123.** 49 **124.** 125 **125.** 45 **126.** 400 **127.** 13 **128.** 10 **129.** 15 **130.** 7 **131.** 12
132. 9 **133.** 42 **134.** 33 **135.** 9 **136.** 2 **137.** 1 **138.** 0 **139.** 6 **140.** 29 **141.** 40 **142.** 72 **143.** 5
144. 7 **145.** 49 sq m **146.** 9 sq in. **147.** 307 **148.** 682 **149.** 2160 **150.** 2516 **151.** 901 **152.** 1411 **153.** 458 R 8
154. 237 R 1 **155.** 70,848 **156.** 95,832 **157.** 1644 **158.** 8481 **159.** 740 **160.** 258,000 **161.** 2000 **162.** 40,000
163. thirty-six thousand, nine hundred eleven **164.** one hundred fifty-four thousand, eight hundred sixty-three **165.** 70,943 **166.** 43,401
167. 64 **168.** 125 **169.** 12 **170.** 10 **171.** 12 **172.** 1 **173.** 2 **174.** 6 **175.** 4 **176.** 24 **177.** 24 **178.** 14
179. $59,452,000 **180.** $582,140,000 **181.** 53 full boxes with 18 left over **182.** $86

Chapter 1 Test 1. eighty-two thousand, four hundred twenty-six **2.** 402,550 **3.** 141 **4.** 113 **5.** 14,880 **6.** 766 R 42 **7.** 200
8. 10 **9.** 0 **10.** undefined **11.** 33 **12.** 21 **13.** 8 **14.** 36 **15.** 5,698,000 **16.** 11,200,000 **17.** 52,000 **18.** 13,700
19. 1600 **20.** 92 **21.** 122 **22.** 1605 **23.** 7 R 2 **24.** $17 **25.** $126 **26.** 360 cal **27.** $7905 **28.** 20 cm; 25 sq cm
29. 60 yd; 200 sq yd

CHAPTER 2 Multiplying and Dividing Fractions

Mental Math 1. numerator: 1; denominator: 2; proper **3.** numerator: 10; denominator: 3; improper
5. numerator: 15; denominator: 15; improper

Exercise Set 2.1 1. 1 **3.** undefined **5.** 13 **7.** 0 **9.** undefined **11.** 16 **13.** $\frac{5}{6}$ **15.** $\frac{7}{12}$ **17.** $\frac{3}{7}$ **19.** $\frac{4}{9}$ **21.** $\frac{1}{6}$

23. $\frac{5}{8}$ **25.** **27.** **29.** **31.**

33. $\frac{42}{131}$ **35. a.** 89 **b.** $\frac{89}{131}$ **37.** $\frac{8}{43}$ **39.** $\frac{27}{70}$ of the hard drive **41.** $\frac{11}{31}$ of the month **43.** $\frac{10}{31}$ of the class

45. a. $\frac{33}{50}$ of the states **b.** 17 states **c.** $\frac{17}{50}$ of the states **47. a.** $\frac{21}{50}$ **b.** 29 **c.** $\frac{29}{50}$ **49. a.** $\frac{11}{4}$ **b.** $2\frac{3}{4}$ **51. a.** $\frac{23}{6}$ **b.** $3\frac{5}{6}$

53. a. $\frac{4}{3}$ **b.** $1\frac{1}{3}$ **55. a.** $\frac{11}{2}$ **b.** $5\frac{1}{2}$ **57.** $\frac{7}{3}$ **59.** $\frac{18}{5}$ **61.** $\frac{53}{8}$ **63.** $\frac{41}{15}$ **65.** $\frac{83}{7}$ **67.** $\frac{84}{13}$ **69.** $\frac{109}{24}$ **71.** $\frac{211}{12}$ **73.** $\frac{187}{20}$

75. $\frac{265}{107}$ **77.** $\frac{500}{3}$ **79.** $3\frac{2}{5}$ **81.** $4\frac{5}{8}$ **83.** $3\frac{2}{15}$ **85.** $2\frac{4}{21}$ **87.** 33 **89.** 15 **91.** $66\frac{2}{3}$ **93.** $10\frac{17}{23}$ **95.** $17\frac{13}{18}$

97. $1\frac{7}{175}$ **99.** $6\frac{65}{112}$ **101.** 9 **103.** 125 **105.** 7^5 **107.** $2^3 \cdot 3$ **109.** answers may vary **111.** $\frac{2}{3}$

113. ⬤ ⬤ ⬤ ⬤ ◯ ◯ ◯ ◯ ◯ **115.** $\frac{6253}{8851}$ of the restaurants **117.** $\frac{1651}{2285}$ of the affiliates

Exercise Set 2.2 **1.** 1, 2, 4, 8 **3.** 1, 5, 25 **5.** 1, 2, 4 **7.** 1, 2, 3, 6, 9, 18 **9.** 1, 29 **11.** 1, 2, 4, 5, 8, 10, 16, 20, 40, 80 **13.** 1, 2, 3, 4, 6, 12
15. 1, 2, 17, 34 **17.** prime **19.** composite **21.** prime **23.** composite **25.** prime **27.** composite **29.** prime **31.** composite
33. composite **35.** 2^5 **37.** $3 \cdot 5$ **39.** $2^3 \cdot 5$ **41.** $2^2 \cdot 3^2$ **43.** $3 \cdot 13$ **45.** $2^2 \cdot 3 \cdot 5$ **47.** $2 \cdot 5 \cdot 11$ **49.** $5 \cdot 17$ **51.** 2^7
53. $2 \cdot 7 \cdot 11$ **55.** $2^2 \cdot 3 \cdot 5^2$ **57.** $2^4 \cdot 3 \cdot 5$ **59.** $2^2 \cdot 3^2 \cdot 23$ **61.** $2 \cdot 3^2 \cdot 7^2$ **63.** $7^2 \cdot 13$ **65.** $3 \cdot 11$ **67.** $2 \cdot 7^2$ **69.** prime

71. $3^3 \cdot 17$ **73.** prime **75.** $2^2 \cdot 5^2 \cdot 7$ **77.** 4300 **79.** 4,286,340 **81.** 10,000,000 **83.** $\frac{19}{130}$ **85.** $2^2 \cdot 3^5 \cdot 5 \cdot 7$ **87.** answers may vary
89. answers may vary

Calculator Explorations **1.** $\frac{4}{7}$ **3.** $\frac{20}{27}$ **5.** $\frac{15}{8}$ **7.** $\frac{9}{2}$

Exercise Set 2.3 **1.** $\frac{1}{4}$ **3.** $\frac{2}{21}$ **5.** $\frac{7}{8}$ **7.** $\frac{2}{3}$ **9.** $\frac{7}{10}$ **11.** $\frac{7}{9}$ **13.** $\frac{3}{5}$ **15.** $\frac{27}{64}$ **17.** $\frac{5}{8}$ **19.** $\frac{5}{8}$ **21.** $\frac{14}{17}$ **23.** $\frac{3}{2}$ or $1\frac{1}{2}$

25. $\frac{3}{4}$ **27.** $\frac{5}{14}$ **29.** $\frac{3}{14}$ **31.** $\frac{11}{17}$ **33.** $\frac{3}{14}$ **35.** $\frac{7}{8}$ **37.** $\frac{3}{5}$ **39.** 14 **41.** equivalent **43.** not equivalent **45.** equivalent

47. equivalent **49.** not equivalent **51.** not equivalent **53.** $\frac{1}{4}$ of a shift **55.** $\frac{1}{2}$ mi **57. a.** $\frac{3}{10}$ **b.** 35 states **c.** $\frac{7}{10}$

59. $\frac{5}{12}$ of the wall **61. a.** 22 **b.** $\frac{11}{25}$ **63.** 364 **65.** 2322 **67.** 2520 **69.** answers may vary **71.** $\frac{3}{5}$ **73.** $\frac{9}{25}$ **75.** $\frac{1}{25}$

77. $\frac{3}{20}$ **79.** $\frac{2}{25}$ **81.** answers may vary

Integrated Review **1.** $\frac{3}{6}$ **2.** $\frac{7}{4}$ or $1\frac{3}{4}$ **3.** $\frac{73}{85}$ **4.** ▦▦▦▦▦▦▦▦□□□□ **5.** 1 **6.** 17

7. 0 **8.** undefined **9.** $\frac{25}{8}$ **10.** $\frac{28}{5}$ **11.** $\frac{69}{7}$ **12.** $\frac{141}{7}$ **13.** $2\frac{6}{7}$ **14.** 5 **15.** $4\frac{7}{8}$ **16.** $8\frac{10}{11}$ **17.** 1, 5, 7, 35

18. 1, 2, 4, 5, 8, 10, 20, 40 **19.** composite **20.** prime **21.** $5 \cdot 13$ **22.** $2 \cdot 5 \cdot 7$ **23.** $2^5 \cdot 3$ **24.** $2^2 \cdot 3 \cdot 11$ **25.** $2^2 \cdot 3^2 \cdot 7$ **26.** prime

27. $3^2 \cdot 5 \cdot 7$ **28.** $3^2 \cdot 7^2$ **29.** $2 \cdot 11 \cdot 13$ **30.** prime **31.** $\frac{1}{7}$ **32.** $\frac{6}{5}$ or $1\frac{1}{5}$ **33.** $\frac{9}{19}$ **34.** $\frac{21}{55}$ **35.** $\frac{14}{15}$ **36.** $\frac{9}{10}$ **37.** $\frac{2}{5}$ **38.** $\frac{3}{8}$

39. $\frac{11}{14}$ **40.** $\frac{7}{11}$ **41.** not equivalent **42.** equivalent **43. a.** $\frac{1}{25}$ **b.** 48 **c.** $\frac{24}{25}$ **44. a.** $\frac{55}{92}$ **b.** 185 **c.** $\frac{37}{92}$

Mental Math **1.** 8 **3.** 6 **5.** 8 **7.** 20

Exercise Set 2.4 **1.** $\frac{2}{15}$ **3.** $\frac{6}{35}$ **5.** $\frac{9}{80}$ **7.** $\frac{5}{28}$ **9.** $\frac{12}{5}$ or $2\frac{2}{5}$ **11.** $\frac{1}{70}$ **13.** 0 **15.** $\frac{1}{110}$ **17.** $\frac{18}{55}$ **19.** $\frac{27}{80}$ **21.** $\frac{1}{56}$

23. $\frac{2}{105}$ **25.** 0 **27.** $\frac{1}{90}$ **29.** 3 **31.** $\frac{5}{2}$ or $2\frac{1}{2}$ **33.** $\frac{1}{5}$ **35.** $\frac{5}{3}$ or $1\frac{2}{3}$ **37.** $\frac{2}{3}$ **39.** Exact: $\frac{77}{10}$ or $7\frac{7}{10}$; Estimate: 8

41. Exact: $\frac{836}{35}$ or $23\frac{31}{35}$; Estimate: 24 **43.** $\frac{25}{2}$ or $21\frac{1}{2}$ **45.** 15 **47.** 6 **49.** $\frac{45}{4}$ or $11\frac{1}{4}$ **51.** $\frac{49}{3}$ or $16\frac{1}{3}$ **53.** $\frac{1}{30}$ **55.** 0

57. $\frac{16}{5}$ or $3\frac{1}{5}$ **59.** $\frac{7}{2}$ or $3\frac{1}{2}$ **61.** $\frac{1}{8}$ **63.** $\frac{1}{56}$ **65.** $\frac{55}{3}$ or $18\frac{1}{3}$ **67.** 0 **69.** $\frac{208}{7}$ or $29\frac{5}{7}$ **71.** 50 **73.** 20 **75.** $\frac{3}{2}$ or $1\frac{1}{2}$ in.

77. 868 mi **79.** $\frac{17}{2}$ or $8\frac{1}{2}$ in. **81.** $\frac{3}{16}$ in. **83.** 600 cal **85.** $1838 **87.** $\frac{39}{2}$ or $19\frac{1}{2}$ in. **89.** $3\frac{367}{625}$ sq in. **91.** $\frac{1}{14}$ sq ft

93. $\frac{7}{2}$ or $3\frac{1}{2}$ sq yd **95.** 3840 mi **97.** 2400 mi **99.** 206 **101.** 56 R 12 **103.** answers may vary

105. Incorrect; $3\frac{2}{3} \cdot 1\frac{1}{7} = \frac{11}{3} \cdot \frac{8}{7} = \frac{11 \cdot 8}{3 \cdot 7} = \frac{88}{21} = 4\frac{4}{21}$ **107.** c **109.** d **111.** 15,660,000 Americans

Exercise Set 2.5 **1.** $\frac{7}{4}$ **3.** 11 **5.** $\frac{1}{15}$ **7.** $\frac{7}{12}$ **9.** $\frac{4}{5}$ **11.** $\frac{16}{9}$ or $1\frac{7}{9}$ **13.** $\frac{18}{35}$ **15.** $\frac{3}{4}$ **17.** $\frac{1}{100}$ **19.** $\frac{1}{3}$ **21.** $\frac{5}{3}$ or $1\frac{2}{3}$

23. $\frac{35}{36}$ **25.** $\frac{14}{37}$ **27.** $\frac{8}{45}$ **29.** 1 **31.** undefined **33.** 0 **35.** $\frac{7}{10}$ **37.** $\frac{1}{6}$ **39.** $\frac{40}{3}$ or $13\frac{1}{3}$ **41.** 5 **43.** $\frac{5}{28}$

45. $\frac{36}{35}$ or $1\frac{1}{35}$ **47.** $\frac{26}{51}$ **49.** 0 **51.** $\frac{17}{13}$ or $1\frac{4}{13}$ **53.** $\frac{35}{18}$ or $1\frac{17}{18}$ **55.** $\frac{19}{30}$ **57.** $\frac{1}{6}$ **59.** $\frac{121}{60}$ or $2\frac{1}{60}$ **61.** 96 **63.** $\frac{3}{4}$

65. undefined **67.** $\frac{11}{119}$ **69.** $\frac{35}{11}$ or $3\frac{2}{11}$ **71.** $\frac{9}{5}$ or $1\frac{4}{5}$ **73.** $\frac{5}{6}$ Tbsp **75.** $3\frac{3}{16}$ miles **77.** $\frac{19}{30}$ in. **79.** 14 lb **81.** $4\frac{2}{3}$ m

83. $\frac{8}{35}$ **85.** $\frac{17}{6}$ or $2\frac{5}{6}$ **87.** $\frac{16}{15}$ or $1\frac{1}{15}$ **89.** $\frac{121}{400}$ **91.** 201 **93.** 196 **95.** 1569

97. Incorrect; to divide mixed numbers, first write each mixed number as an improper fraction. **99.** c **101.** d **103.** 5 **105.** 640

The Bigger Picture **1.** $\frac{16}{27}$ **2.** $\frac{3}{4}$ **3.** $1\frac{1}{3}$ **4.** $2\frac{2}{5}$ **5.** 8 **6.** 72 **7.** $\frac{1}{24}$ **8.** 40 **9.** 35 **10.** 24

Vocabulary Check **1.** reciprocals **2.** composite number **3.** equivalent **4.** improper fraction **5.** prime number **6.** simplest form **7.** proper fraction **8.** mixed number **9.** numerator; denominator **10.** prime factorization **11.** undefined **12.** 0

Chapter 2 Review **1.** proper **2.** improper **3.** proper **4.** mixed number **5.** $\frac{2}{6}$ **6.** $\frac{4}{7}$ **7.** $\frac{7}{3}$ **8.** $\frac{13}{4}$ **9.** $\frac{11}{12}$

10. a. 108 **b.** $\frac{108}{131}$ **11.** $3\frac{3}{4}$ **12.** $45\frac{5}{6}$ **13.** 3 **14.** 5 **15.** $\frac{6}{5}$ **16.** $\frac{22}{21}$ **17.** $\frac{26}{9}$ **18.** $\frac{47}{12}$ **19.** composite **20.** prime

21. 1, 2, 3, 6, 7, 14, 21, 42 **22.** 1, 2, 4, 5, 10, 20 **23.** $2^2 \cdot 17$ **24.** $2 \cdot 3^2 \cdot 5$ **25.** $5 \cdot 157$ **26.** $3 \cdot 5 \cdot 17$ **27.** $\frac{3}{7}$ **28.** $\frac{5}{9}$ **29.** $\frac{1}{3}$

30. $\frac{1}{2}$ **31.** $\frac{29}{32}$ **32.** $\frac{18}{23}$ **33.** 8 **34.** 6 **35.** no **36.** no **37.** no **38.** yes **39.** $\frac{3}{10}$ **40.** $\frac{5}{14}$ **41.** 9 **42.** $\frac{1}{2}$

43. $\frac{35}{8}$ or $4\frac{3}{8}$ **44.** $\frac{5}{2}$ or $2\frac{1}{2}$ **45.** $\frac{5}{3}$ or $1\frac{2}{3}$ **46.** $\frac{49}{3}$ or $16\frac{1}{3}$ **47.** Exact: $\frac{26}{5}$ or $5\frac{1}{5}$; Estimate: 6 **48.** Exact: $\frac{60}{11}$ or $5\frac{5}{11}$; Estimate: 8

49. $\frac{99}{4}$ or $24\frac{3}{4}$ **50.** $\frac{1}{6}$ **51.** $\frac{110}{3}$ or $36\frac{2}{3}$ g **52.** $\frac{135}{4}$ or $33\frac{3}{4}$ in. **53.** $\frac{119}{80}$ or $1\frac{39}{80}$ sq in. **54.** $\frac{275}{8}$ or $34\frac{3}{8}$ sq m **55.** $\frac{1}{7}$ **56.** 8

57. $\frac{23}{14}$ **58.** $\frac{5}{17}$ **59.** 2 **60.** $\frac{15}{4}$ or $3\frac{3}{4}$ **61.** $\frac{5}{6}$ **62.** $\frac{8}{3}$ or $2\frac{2}{3}$ **63.** $\frac{21}{4}$ or $5\frac{1}{4}$ **64.** $\frac{121}{46}$ or $2\frac{29}{46}$ **65.** 22 mi **66.** $\frac{21}{20}$ or $1\frac{1}{20}$ mi

67. proper **68.** improper **69.** mixed number **70.** improper **71.** $31\frac{1}{4}$ **72.** 6 **73.** $\frac{95}{17}$ **74.** $\frac{47}{6}$ **75.** composite **76.** prime

77. $2^2 \cdot 3^2 \cdot 5$ **78.** $2 \cdot 7^2$ **79.** $\frac{9}{10}$ **80.** $\frac{5}{7}$ **81.** $\frac{14}{15}$ **82.** $\frac{3}{5}$ **83.** $\frac{7}{12}$ **84.** $\frac{1}{4}$ **85.** 9 **86.** $\frac{27}{2}$ or $13\frac{1}{2}$ **87.** Exact: 10; Estimate: 8

88. Exact: $\frac{51}{4}$ or $12\frac{3}{4}$; Estimate: 12 **89.** $\frac{7}{3}$ or $2\frac{1}{3}$ **90.** $\frac{32}{5}$ or $6\frac{2}{5}$ **91.** $\frac{81}{2}$ or $40\frac{1}{2}$ sq ft **92.** $\frac{47}{61}$ in.

Chapter 2 Test **1.** $\frac{7}{16}$ **2.** $\frac{13}{5}$ **3.** $\frac{23}{3}$ **4.** $\frac{39}{11}$ **5.** $4\frac{3}{5}$ **6.** $18\frac{3}{4}$ **7.** $\frac{4}{35}$ **8.** $\frac{3}{5}$ **9.** not equivalent **10.** equivalent

11. $2^2 \cdot 3 \cdot 7$ **12.** $3^2 \cdot 5 \cdot 11$ **13.** $\frac{4}{3}$ or $1\frac{1}{3}$ **14.** $\frac{4}{3}$ or $1\frac{1}{3}$ **15.** $\frac{1}{4}$ **16.** $\frac{16}{45}$ **17.** 16 **18.** $\frac{9}{2}$ or $4\frac{1}{2}$ **19.** $\frac{4}{11}$ **20.** 9 **21.** $\frac{64}{3}$ or $21\frac{1}{3}$

22. $\frac{45}{2}$ or $22\frac{1}{2}$ **23.** $\frac{18}{5}$ or $3\frac{3}{5}$ **24.** $\frac{20}{3}$ or $6\frac{2}{3}$ **25.** $\frac{34}{27}$ or $1\frac{7}{27}$ sq mi **26.** 24 mi **27.** $\frac{16,000}{3}$ or $5333\frac{1}{3}$ sq yd **28.** $90 per share

Cumulative Review **1.** ten-thousands (Sec. 1.2, Ex. 1) **2.** two thousand thirty-six (Sec. 1.2) **3.** 805 (Sec. 1.2, Ex. 9) **4.** 31 (Sec. 1.3)
5. 184,046 (Sec. 1.3, Ex. 2) **6.** 39 (Sec. 1.7) **7.** 13 in. (Sec. 1.3, Ex. 5) **8.** 17 (Sec. 1.4) **9.** $96,351 (Sec. 1.3, Ex. 7) **10.** 5 (Sec. 1.9)
11. 7321 (Sec. 1.4, Ex. 2) **12.** 64 (Sec. 1.9) **13. a.** R **b.** 44 (Sec. 1.3, Ex. 8) **14.** 25 R 5 (Sec. 1.7) **15.** 570 (Sec. 1.5, Ex. 1)
16. 2400 (Sec. 1.5) **17.** 1800 (Sec. 1.5, Ex. 5) **18.** 300 (Sec. 1.5) **19. a.** 6 **b.** 0 **c.** 45 **d.** 0 (Sec. 1.6, Ex. 1) **20.** 20 (Sec. 1.9)
21. a. $3 \cdot 4 + 3 \cdot 5$ **b.** $10 \cdot 6 + 10 \cdot 8$ **c.** $2 \cdot 7 + 2 \cdot 3$ (Sec. 1.6, Ex. 2) **22.** 180 (Sec. 1.6) **23. a.** 0 **b.** 0 **c.** 0 **d.** undefined (Sec. 1.7, Ex. 3)
24. 154 sq mi (Sec. 1.6) **25.** 208 (Sec. 1.7, Ex. 5) **26.** 4014 (Sec. 1.4) **27.** 7 boxes (Sec. 1.7, Ex. 11) **28.** 63 (Sec. 1.6)
29. 40 ft (Sec. 1.8, Ex. 5) **30.** 16 (Sec. 1.3) **31.** 4^3 (Sec. 1.9, Ex. 1) **32.** 7^4 (Sec. 1.9) **33.** $6^3 \cdot 8^5$ (Sec. 1.9, Ex. 4) **34.** $2^2 \cdot 3^4$ (Sec. 1.9)
35. 7 (Sec. 1.9, Ex. 12) **36.** 0 (Sec. 1.9) **37.** $\frac{2}{5}$ (Sec. 2.1, Ex. 7) **38.** $2^2 \cdot 3 \cdot 13$ (Sec. 2.2) **39. a.** $\frac{38}{9}$ **b.** $\frac{19}{11}$ (Sec. 2.1, Ex. 17)

40. $\frac{39}{5}$ (Sec. 2.1) **41.** 1, 2, 4, 5, 10, 20 (Sec. 2.2, Ex. 1) **42.** yes (Sec. 2.3) **43.** $\frac{7}{11}$ (Sec. 2.3, Ex. 2) **44.** $\frac{2}{3}$ (Sec. 2.3)

45. $\frac{35}{12}$ or $2\frac{11}{12}$ (Sec. 2.4, Ex. 8) **46.** $\frac{8}{3}$ or $2\frac{2}{3}$ (Sec. 2.4) **47.** $\frac{3}{1}$ or 3 (Sec. 2.5, Ex. 3) **48.** $\frac{1}{9}$ (Sec. 2.5) **49.** $\frac{5}{12}$ (Sec. 2.5, Ex. 6)

50. $\frac{11}{56}$ (Sec. 2.5)

CHAPTER 3   Adding and Subtracting Fractions

Mental Math   **1.** unlike   **3.** like   **5.** like   **7.** unlike

Exercise Set 3.1   **1.** $\frac{3}{7}$ **3.** $\frac{1}{5}$ **5.** $\frac{2}{3}$ **7.** $\frac{7}{20}$ **9.** $\frac{1}{2}$ **11.** $\frac{13}{11}$ or $1\frac{2}{11}$ **13.** $\frac{7}{13}$ **15.** $\frac{2}{3}$ **17.** $\frac{6}{11}$ **19.** $\frac{3}{5}$ **21.** 1   **23.** $\frac{3}{4}$

25. $\frac{5}{6}$ **27.** $\frac{4}{5}$ **29.** $\frac{19}{33}$ **31.** $\frac{13}{21}$ **33.** $\frac{9}{10}$ **35.** 0   **37.** $\frac{3}{4}$ **39.** 1 in.   **41.** 2 m   **43.** $\frac{3}{2}$ or $1\frac{1}{2}$ h   **45.** $\frac{7}{25}$ **47.** $\frac{1}{50}$

49. $\frac{7}{10}$ of a mi   **51.** $\frac{3}{4}$ **53.** $\frac{21}{50}$ **55.** $2\cdot5$ **57.** 2^3 **59.** $5\cdot11$ **61.** $\frac{5}{8}$ **63.** $\frac{8}{11}$ **65.** $\frac{2}{7}+\frac{9}{7}=\frac{11}{7}$ **67.** answers may vary

69. 1; answers may vary

Exercise Set 3.2   **1.** 12   **3.** 45   **5.** 36   **7.** 72   **9.** 126   **11.** 75   **13.** 24   **15.** 42   **17.** 216   **19.** 150   **21.** 68   **23.** 588
25. 900   **27.** 1800   **29.** 363   **31.** 60   **33.** 20   **35.** 14   **37.** 10   **39.** 15   **41.** 30   **43.** 21   **45.** 30   **47.** 36   **49.** 90

51. 56   **53.** $\frac{1}{2}$ **55.** $\frac{2}{5}$ **57.** $\frac{4}{9}$ **59.** 1   **61.** 814   **63.** answers may vary   **65.** a, b, and d

Calculator Explorations   **1.** $\frac{37}{80}$ **3.** $\frac{95}{72}$ **5.** $\frac{394}{323}$

Exercise Set 3.3   **1.** $\frac{5}{6}$ **3.** $\frac{5}{6}$ **5.** $\frac{8}{33}$ **7.** $\frac{9}{14}$ **9.** $\frac{3}{5}$ **11.** $\frac{13}{25}$ **13.** $\frac{53}{60}$ **15.** $\frac{1}{6}$ **17.** $\frac{67}{99}$ **19.** $\frac{98}{143}$ **21.** $\frac{13}{27}$ **23.** $\frac{75}{56}$ or $1\frac{19}{56}$

25. $\frac{16}{11}$ or $1\frac{5}{11}$ **27.** $\frac{19}{12}$ or $1\frac{7}{12}$ **29.** $\frac{11}{16}$ **31.** $\frac{17}{42}$ **33.** $\frac{33}{56}$ **35.** $\frac{4}{33}$ **37.** $\frac{1}{35}$ **39.** $\frac{11}{36}$ **41.** $\frac{1}{20}$ **43.** $\frac{1}{84}$ **45.** $\frac{9}{1000}$ **47.** $\frac{17}{99}$

49. $\frac{19}{36}$ **51.** $\frac{1}{5}$ **53.** $\frac{69}{280}$ **55.** $\frac{14}{9}$ or $1\frac{5}{9}$ **57.** $\frac{34}{15}$ or $2\frac{4}{15}$ cm   **59.** $\frac{17}{10}$ or $1\frac{7}{10}$ m   **61.** $\frac{61}{264}$ mi   **63.** $\frac{11}{8}$ or $1\frac{3}{8}$ in.

65. $\frac{49}{100}$ of students   **67.** $\frac{77}{100}$ of Americans   **69.** $\frac{19}{25}$ **71.** 5   **73.** $\frac{16}{29}$ **75.** $\frac{19}{3}$ or $6\frac{1}{3}$ **77.** $\frac{3}{5}+\frac{4}{5}=\frac{7}{5}$ or $1\frac{2}{5}$ **79.** $\frac{1}{60}$

81. $\frac{49}{44}$ or $1\frac{5}{44}$ **83.** answers may vary

Integrated Review   **1.** 30   **2.** 21   **3.** 14   **4.** 25   **5.** 100   **6.** 90   **7.** $\frac{9}{24}$ **8.** $\frac{28}{36}$ **9.** $\frac{10}{40}$ **10.** $\frac{12}{30}$ **11.** $\frac{55}{75}$ **12.** $\frac{40}{48}$

13. $\frac{1}{2}$ **14.** $\frac{2}{5}$ **15.** $\frac{7}{12}$ **16.** $\frac{13}{15}$ **17.** $\frac{3}{4}$ **18.** $\frac{2}{15}$ **19.** $\frac{17}{45}$ **20.** $\frac{19}{50}$ **21.** $\frac{37}{40}$ **22.** $\frac{11}{36}$ **23.** 0   **24.** $\frac{1}{17}$ **25.** $\frac{5}{33}$ **26.** $\frac{1}{42}$

27. $\frac{5}{18}$ **28.** $\frac{5}{13}$ **29.** $\frac{11}{18}$ **30.** $\frac{37}{50}$ **31.** $\frac{47}{30}$ or $1\frac{17}{30}$ **32.** $\frac{7}{30}$ **33.** $\frac{3}{5}$ **34.** $\frac{27}{20}$ or $1\frac{7}{20}$ **35.** $\frac{279}{350}$ **36.** $\frac{309}{350}$ **37.** $\frac{98}{5}$ or $19\frac{3}{5}$

38. $\frac{9}{250}$ **39.** $\frac{31}{3}$ or $10\frac{1}{3}$ **40.** $\frac{93}{64}$ or $1\frac{29}{64}$ **41.** $\frac{49}{54}$ **42.** $\frac{83}{48}$ or $1\frac{35}{48}$ **43.** $\frac{390}{101}$ or $3\frac{87}{101}$ **44.** $\frac{145}{72}$ or $2\frac{1}{72}$ **45.** $\frac{106}{135}$ **46.** $\frac{67}{224}$

Mental Math   **1.** a   **3.** b

Exercise Set 3.4   **1.** Exact: $6\frac{4}{5}$; Estimate: 7   **3.** Exact: $13\frac{11}{14}$; Estimate: 14   **5.** Exact: $17\frac{7}{25}$; Estimate: 17   **7.** $7\frac{5}{8}$ **9.** $7\frac{5}{24}$

11. $20\frac{1}{15}$ **13.** 19   **15.** $56\frac{53}{270}$ **17.** $13\frac{13}{24}$ **19.** $47\frac{53}{84}$ **21.** Exact: $2\frac{3}{5}$; Estimate: 3   **23.** Exact: $7\frac{5}{14}$; Estimate: 7

25. Exact: $\frac{24}{25}$; Estimate: 1   **27.** $2\frac{7}{15}$ **29.** $5\frac{11}{14}$ **31.** $23\frac{31}{72}$ **33.** $1\frac{4}{5}$ **35.** $1\frac{13}{15}$ **37.** $3\frac{5}{9}$ **39.** $15\frac{3}{4}$ **41.** $28\frac{7}{12}$ **43.** $15\frac{7}{8}$

45. 8   **47.** $17\frac{11}{12}$ **49.** $\frac{1}{16}$ in.   **51.** no; she will be $\frac{1}{12}$ of a foot short   **53.** $7\frac{13}{20}$ in.   **55.** $10\frac{1}{4}$ hr   **57.** $2\frac{3}{8}$ hr   **59.** $92\frac{99}{100}$ m

61. $352\frac{1}{3}$ yd   **63.** $9\frac{7}{12}$ min   **65.** $1\frac{4}{5}$ min   **67.** 7 mi   **69.** $21\frac{5}{24}$ m   **71.** 8   **73.** 25   **75.** 4   **77.** 167   **79.** 4   **81.** $9\frac{5}{8}$

83. a, b, c   **85.** answers may vary   **87.** Supreme is heavier by $\frac{1}{8}$ lb

The Bigger Picture   **1.** $\frac{5}{17}$ **2.** $\frac{4}{5}$ **3.** $\frac{29}{30}$ **4.** $\frac{1}{24}$ **5.** $1\frac{33}{40}$ **6.** $\frac{27}{64}$ **7.** $12\frac{3}{7}$ **8.** $9\frac{13}{24}$ **9.** $\frac{16}{33}$ **10.** $\frac{34}{27}$ or $1\frac{7}{27}$

Exercise Set 3.5   **1.** >   **3.** <   **5.** <   **7.** >   **9.** >   **11.** <   **13.** >   **15.** <   **17.** $\frac{1}{16}$ **19.** $\frac{8}{125}$ **21.** $\frac{64}{343}$ **23.** $\frac{4}{81}$

25. $\frac{1}{6}$ **27.** $\frac{18}{125}$ **29.** $\frac{11}{15}$ **31.** $\frac{3}{35}$ **33.** $\frac{5}{9}$ **35.** $\frac{994}{99}$ or $10\frac{4}{99}$ **37.** $\frac{1}{12}$ **39.** $\frac{9}{11}$ **41.** 0   **43.** 0   **45.** $\frac{2}{5}$ **47.** $\frac{2}{77}$ **49.** $\frac{17}{60}$

51. $\frac{5}{8}$ **53.** $\frac{1}{2}$ **55.** $\frac{29}{10}$ or $2\frac{9}{10}$ **57.** $\frac{27}{32}$ **59.** $\frac{1}{81}$ **61.** $\frac{5}{6}$ **63.** $\frac{3}{5}$ **65.** $\frac{1}{2}$ **67.** $\frac{19}{7}$ or $2\frac{5}{7}$ **69.** $\frac{9}{64}$ **71.** $\frac{3}{4}$ **73.** $\frac{13}{60}$

75. $\frac{88}{100}, \frac{90}{100}, \frac{96}{100}, \frac{92}{100}, \frac{68}{100}, \frac{91}{100}, \frac{80}{100}, \frac{82}{100}, \frac{89}{100}, \frac{70}{100}$ **77.** Japan **79.** $\frac{91}{100}$ **81.** A **83.** M **85.** S **87.** D **89.** M **91.** A
93. no; answers may vary **95.** subtraction, multiplication, addition, division **97.** division, multiplication, subtraction, addition
99. standard mail **101.** savings account

Exercise Set 3.6 1. $11 + 2 = 13$ **3.** $6\overline{)20}$ 3 R 2 **5.** $35 - 8 = 27$ **7.** $68 + 7 = 75$ **9.** $21 \cdot 9 = 189$ **11.** $3\frac{1}{3}$ c **13.** $12\frac{1}{2}$ in.

15. $21\frac{1}{2}$ mi per gal **17.** $1\frac{1}{2}$ yr **19.** $9\frac{2}{5}$ in. **21.** no; $\frac{1}{4}$ yd **23.** 5 pieces **25.** $\frac{9}{8}$ or $1\frac{1}{8}$ in. **27.** $3\frac{3}{4}$ c **29.** $11\frac{1}{4}$ sq in. **31.** $1\frac{2}{3}$ min

33. $5\frac{11}{25}$ cu in. **35.** 67 sheets **37. a.** yes **b.** 1 ft left over **39.** $2\frac{15}{16}$ lb **41.** area: $\frac{9}{128}$ sq in.; perimeter: $1\frac{1}{8}$ in.

43. area: $\frac{25}{81}$ sq m; perimeter: $2\frac{2}{9}$ m **45.** $4\frac{3}{4}$ ft **47.** $\frac{5}{26}$ ft **49.** 3 **51.** 81 **53.** 4 **55.** 30 **57.** 35

59. no; no; answers may vary **61.** $26\frac{8}{9}$ ft **63.** 10 apples **65.** $485\frac{1}{3}$ cu ft

Vocabulary Check 1. like **2.** least common multiple **3.** equivalent **4.** mixed number **5.** > **6.** <
7. least common denominator

Chapter 3 Review 1. $\frac{10}{11}$ **2.** $\frac{3}{25}$ **3.** $\frac{2}{3}$ **4.** $\frac{1}{7}$ **5.** $\frac{3}{5}$ **6.** $\frac{3}{5}$ **7.** 1 **8.** 1 **9.** $\frac{19}{25}$ **10.** $\frac{16}{21}$ **11.** $\frac{3}{4}$ of his homework

12. $\frac{3}{2}$ or $1\frac{1}{2}$ mi **13.** 55 **14.** 60 **15.** 120 **16.** 80 **17.** 252 **18.** 72 **19.** $\frac{56}{64}$ **20.** $\frac{20}{30}$ **21.** $\frac{21}{33}$ **22.** $\frac{20}{26}$

23. $\frac{16}{60}$ **24.** $\frac{25}{60}$ **25.** $\frac{11}{18}$ **26.** $\frac{7}{15}$ **27.** $\frac{7}{26}$ **28.** $\frac{17}{36}$ **29.** $\frac{41}{42}$ **30.** $\frac{43}{72}$ **31.** $\frac{13}{45}$ **32.** $\frac{39}{70}$ **33.** $2\frac{1}{9}$ m **34.** $1\frac{1}{2}$ ft

35. $\frac{1}{4}$ of a yd **36.** $\frac{7}{10}$ has been cleaned **37.** $45\frac{16}{21}$ **38.** 60 **39.** $32\frac{13}{22}$ **40.** $3\frac{19}{60}$ **41.** $111\frac{5}{18}$ **42.** $20\frac{7}{24}$ **43.** $5\frac{16}{35}$

44. $3\frac{4}{55}$ **45.** $7\frac{4}{5}$ in. **46.** $11\frac{1}{6}$ ft **47.** 5 ft **48.** $\frac{1}{40}$ oz **49.** < **50.** > **51.** < **52.** > **53.** >

54. > **55.** $\frac{9}{49}$ **56.** $\frac{64}{125}$ **57.** $\frac{9}{400}$ **58.** $\frac{9}{100}$ **59.** $\frac{8}{13}$ **60.** 2 **61.** $\frac{81}{196}$ **62.** $\frac{1}{7}$ **63.** $\frac{13}{18}$ **64.** $\frac{11}{15}$ **65.** $\frac{1}{27}$

66. $\frac{18}{5}$ or $3\frac{3}{5}$ **67.** $\frac{45}{28}$ or $1\frac{17}{28}$ **68.** $\frac{5}{6}$ **69.** $\frac{99}{56}$ or $1\frac{43}{56}$ **70.** $\frac{29}{110}$ **71.** $\frac{29}{54}$ **72.** $\frac{37}{60}$ **73.** 21 moons **74.** $15\frac{5}{8}$ acres

75. each measurement is $4\frac{1}{4}$ in. **76.** $\frac{7}{10}$ yd **77.** perimeter: $1\frac{6}{11}$ mi; area: $\frac{3}{22}$ sq mi **78.** perimeter: $2\frac{1}{3}$ m; area: $\frac{5}{16}$ sq m **79.** 90

80. 60 **81.** 40 **82.** 63 **83.** $\frac{1}{6}$ **84.** $\frac{1}{5}$ **85.** $\frac{11}{12}$ **86.** $\frac{27}{55}$ **87.** $13\frac{5}{12}$ **88.** $12\frac{3}{8}$ **89.** $3\frac{16}{35}$ **90.** $8\frac{1}{21}$ **91.** $\frac{11}{25}$ **92.** $\frac{1}{8}$

93. $\frac{1}{144}$ **94.** $\frac{64}{27}$ **95.** $\frac{5}{17}$ **96.** $\frac{1}{12}$ **97.** < **98.** > **99.** $\frac{1}{2}$ hr **100.** $6\frac{7}{20}$ lb **101.** $44\frac{1}{2}$ yd **102.** $2\frac{2}{15}$ ft

103. $7\frac{1}{2}$ tablespoons **104.** $\frac{3}{8}$ of a gallon

Chapter 3 Test 1. 60 **2.** 72 **3.** < **4.** < **5.** $\frac{8}{9}$ **6.** $\frac{2}{5}$ **7.** $\frac{13}{10}$ or $1\frac{3}{10}$ **8.** $\frac{8}{21}$ **9.** $\frac{13}{24}$ **10.** $\frac{1}{7}$ **11.** $\frac{67}{60}$ or $1\frac{7}{60}$ **12.** $\frac{7}{50}$

13. $\frac{3}{2}$ or $1\frac{1}{2}$ **14.** $14\frac{1}{40}$ **15.** $30\frac{13}{45}$ **16.** $1\frac{7}{24}$ **17.** $16\frac{8}{11}$ **18.** $\frac{5}{3}$ or $1\frac{2}{3}$ **19.** $\frac{16}{81}$ **20.** $\frac{9}{16}$ **21.** $\frac{153}{200}$ **22.** $\frac{3}{8}$ **23.** $\frac{11}{12}$

24. $3\frac{3}{4}$ ft **25.** $7\frac{5}{6}$ gal **26.** $\frac{23}{50}$ **27.** $\frac{13}{50}$ **28.** $2820 **29.** perimeter: $3\frac{1}{3}$ ft; area: $\frac{2}{3}$ sq ft **30.** $1\frac{2}{3}$ in.

Cumulative Review 1. eighty-five (Sec. 1.2, Ex. 4) **2.** one hundred seven (Sec. 1.2) **3.** one hundred twenty-six (Sec. 1.2, Ex. 5)
4. five thousand, twenty-six (Sec. 1.2) **5.** 159 (Sec. 1.3, Ex. 1) **6.** 19 in. (Sec. 1.3) **7.** 514 (Sec. 1.4, Ex. 3) **8.** 121 R 1 (Sec. 1.7)
9. 278,000 (Sec. 1.5, Ex. 2) **10.** 1, 2, 3, 5, 6, 10, 15, 30 (Sec. 2.2) **11.** 20,296 (Sec. 1.6, Ex. 4) **12.** 0 (Sec. 1.6)
13. a. 8 **b.** 11 **c.** 1 **d.** 1 **e.** 10 **f.** 1 (Sec. 1.7, Ex. 2) **14.** 25 (Sec. 1.7) **15.** 1038 mi (Sec. 1.8, Ex. 1) **16.** 11 (Sec. 1.9)

17. 64 (Sec. 1.9, Ex. 5) **18.** 125 (Sec. 1.9) **19.** 32 (Sec. 1.9, Ex. 7) **20.** 1000 (Sec. 1.9) **21.** $\frac{4}{3}$ or $1\frac{1}{3}$ (Sec. 2.1, Ex. 15)

22. $\frac{11}{4}$ or $2\frac{3}{4}$ (Sec. 2.1) **23.** $\frac{5}{2}$ or $2\frac{1}{2}$ (Sec. 2.1, Ex. 16) **24.** $\frac{14}{3}$ or $4\frac{2}{3}$ (Sec. 2.1) **25.** 3, 11, 17 are prime; 9, 26 are composite; (Sec. 2.2, Ex. 2)

26. 5 (Sec. 1.9) **27.** $2^2 \cdot 3^2 \cdot 5$ (Sec. 2.2, Ex. 4) **28.** 62 (Sec. 1.4) **29.** $\frac{36}{13}$ or $2\frac{10}{13}$ (Sec. 2.3, Ex. 5) **30.** $\frac{79}{8}$ (Sec. 2.1)

31. equivalent (Sec. 2.3, Ex. 8)   **32.** > (Sec. 3.5)   **33.** $\frac{10}{33}$ (Sec. 2.4, Ex. 1)   **34.** $\frac{3}{2}$ or $1\frac{1}{2}$ (Sec. 2.4)   **35.** $\frac{1}{8}$ (Sec. 2.4, Ex. 2)   **36.** 37 (Sec. 2.4)

37. $\frac{11}{51}$ (Sec. 2.5, Ex. 9)   **38.** $\frac{25}{19}$ or $1\frac{6}{19}$ (Sec. 2.5)   **39.** $\frac{51}{23}$ or $2\frac{5}{23}$ (Sec. 2.5, Ex. 10)   **40.** 16 (Sec. 3.1)   **41.** $\frac{5}{8}$ (Sec. 3.1, Ex. 2)

42. $\frac{1}{5}$ (Sec. 3.1)   **43.** 24 (Sec. 3.2, Ex. 1)   **44.** 35 (Sec. 3.2)   **45.** 2 (Sec. 3.3, Ex. 4)   **46.** $\frac{25}{81}$ (Sec. 3.5)   **47.** $4\frac{1}{3}$ (Sec. 3.4, Ex. 4)

48. $\frac{11}{100}$ (Sec. 3.3)   **49.** $\frac{6}{13}$ (Sec. 3.5, Ex. 11)   **50.** $\frac{8}{175}$ (Sec. 3.5)

CHAPTER 4   Decimals

Mental Math   1. tens   **3.** tenths

Exercise Set 4.1   1. six and fifty-two hundredths   **3.** sixteen and twenty-three hundredths   **5.** two hundred five thousandths
7. one hundred sixty-seven and nine thousandths   **9.** two hundred and five thousandths   **11.** one hundred five and six tenths
13. thirty-one and four hundredths   **15.** one and eight tenths   **17.** thirty-two and nine tenths
19. R. W. Financial; 321.42; Three hundred twenty-one and 42/100   **21.** Bell South; 59.68; Fifty-nine and 68/100   **23.** 6.5   **25.** 9.08
27. 705.625   **29.** 0.0064   **31.** 32.52   **33.** 15.8   **35.** $\frac{3}{10}$ **37.** $\frac{27}{100}$ **39.** $\frac{4}{5}$ **41.** $\frac{3}{20}$ **43.** $5\frac{47}{100}$ **45.** $\frac{6}{125}$ **47.** $7\frac{1}{125}$
49. $15\frac{401}{500}$ **51.** $\frac{601}{2000}$ **53.** $487\frac{8}{25}$ **55.** 0.6   **57.** 0.45   **59.** 3.7   **61.** 0.268   **63.** 0.09   **65.** 4.026   **67.** 0.028   **69.** 56.3
71. 0.43; forty-three hundredths   **73.** $0.8; \frac{8}{10}$ or $\frac{4}{5}$ **75.** seventy-seven thousandths; $\frac{77}{1000}$ **77.** 47,260   **79.** 47,000
81. answers may vary   **83.** twenty-six million, eight hundred forty-nine thousand, five hundred seventy-six hundred-billionths   **85.** 17.268

Exercise Set 4.2   1. <   **3.** >   **5.** <   **7.** =   **9.** <   **11.** >   **13.** 0.006, 0.0061, 0.06   **15.** 0.03, 0.042, 0.36   **17.** 1.01, 1.09, 1.1, 1.16
19. 20.905, 21.001, 21.03, 21.12   **21.** 0.6   **23.** 0.23   **25.** 0.594   **27.** 98,210   **29.** 12.3   **31.** 17.67   **33.** 0.5   **35.** 0.130
37. 3830   **39.** $0.07   **41.** $42,650   **43.** $27   **45.** $0.20   **47.** 2.2 cm   **49.** 2.41 hr   **51.** $48.00   **53.** 24.623 hr   **55.** 2.8 min
57. 5766   **59.** 71   **61.** 243   **63.** b   **65.** a   **67.** 228.040; $228\frac{1}{25}$; Parker Bohn III
69. 228.040, 226.130, 225.370, 224.940, 222.730, 222.008, 2221.546, 220.930   **71.** answers may vary   **73.** answers may vary   **75.** 0.0612; 0.0586

Calculator Explorations   1. 328.742   **3.** 5.2414   **5.** 865.392

Mental Math   1. 0.5   **3.** 1.26   **5.** 8.9   **7.** 0.6

Exercise Set 4.3   1. 3.5   **3.** 6.83   **5.** 0.094   **7.** 622.012   **9.** 583.09   **11.** Exact: 465.56; Estimate:
$$\begin{array}{r} 230 \\ +\ 230 \\ \hline 460 \end{array}$$

13. Exact: 115.123; Estimate:
$$\begin{array}{r} 100 \\ 6 \\ +\ \ 9 \\ \hline 115 \end{array}$$
15. 27.0578   **17.** 56.432   **19.** 6.5   **21.** 15.3   **23.** 598.23   **25.** Exact: 1.83; Estimate: $6 - 4 = 2$

27. 861.6   **29.** 376.89   **31.** Exact: 876.6; Estimate:
$$\begin{array}{r} 1000 \\ -\ 100 \\ \hline 900 \end{array}$$
33. 194.4   **35.** 2.9988   **37.** 16.3   **39.** 88.028   **41.** 84.072

43. 243.17   **45.** 56.83   **47.** 3.16   **49.** $454.71   **51.** $0.14   **53.** 28.56 m   **55.** 11.2 in.   **57.** $7.52   **59.** 4.1 lb
61. 285.8 mph   **63.** 763.035 mph   **65.** $3.4 billion   **67.** 240.8 in.   **69.** 67.44 ft   **71.** $0.122   **73.** 715.05 hr
75. Switzerland   **77.** 8.1 lb
79.

Country	Pounds of Chocolate per Person
Switzerland	22.0
Norway	16.0
Germany	15.8
United Kingdom	14.5
Belgium	13.9

81. 138   **83.** 960   **85.** $\frac{1}{125}$ **87.** $\frac{5}{12}$ **89.** 6.08 in.   **91.** $1.20
93. 1 nickel, 1 dime, and 2 pennies; 3 nickels and 2 pennies; 1 dime and 7 pennies
95. answers may vary   **97.** 0.777 mi

Mental Math   1. 4   **3.** 4   **5.** 5

Exercise Set 4.4   1. 0.12   **3.** 0.6   **5.** 1.3   **7.** Exact: 22.26; Estimate: $5 \times 4 = 20$ **9.** 0.4032   **11.** Exact: 8.23854; Estimate:
$$\begin{array}{r} 1 \\ \times\ 8 \\ \hline 8 \end{array}$$

13. 11.2746   **15.** 84.97593   **17.** 65   **19.** 0.65   **21.** 0.072   **23.** 709.3   **25.** 6046   **27.** 0.03762   **29.** 0.0492   **31.** 12.3

33. 1.29 **35.** 0.096 **37.** 0.5623 **39.** 43.274 **41.** 5,500,000,000 **43.** 49,800,000 **45.** 353,000 **47.** $8\pi \approx 25.12$ m
49. $10\pi \approx 31.4$ cm **51.** $18.2\pi \approx 57.148$ yd **53.** 24.8 g **55.** $4550 **57.** 250π ft ≈ 785 ft **59.** 135π m ≈ 423.9 m
61. 64.9605 in. **63.** $555.20 **65. a.** 62.8 m and 125.6 m **b.** yes **67.** 7.2 sq in. **69.** 26 **71.** 36 **73.** 8 **75.** 9 **77.** 3.64
79. 3.56 **81.** 0.1105 **83.** 3,831,600 mi **85.** answers may vary **87.** answers may vary

Integrated Review—Operations on Decimals **1.** 2.57 **2.** 4.05 **3.** 8.9 **4.** 3.5 **5.** 0.16 **6.** 0.24 **7.** 11.06 **8.** 9.72 **9.** 4.8
10. 6.09 **11.** 75.56 **12.** 289.12 **13.** 25.026 **14.** 44.125 **15.** 82.7 **16.** 273.9 **17.** 280 **18.** 1600 **19.** 224.938
20. 145.079 **21.** 6 **22.** 6.2 **23.** 27.6092 **24.** 145.6312 **25.** 5.4 **26.** 17.74 **27.** 414.44 **28.** 1295.03 **29.** 116.81
30. 18.79 **31.** 156.2 **32.** 25.62 **33.** 5.62 **34.** 304.876 **35.** 114.66 **36.** 119.86 **37.** 0.000432 **38.** 0.000075 **39.** 0.0672
40. 0.0275 **41.** 862 **42.** 0.0293 **43.** 200 mi

Calculator Explorations **1.** not reasonable **3.** reasonable

Mental Math **1.** 5.9 **3.** 0 **5.** 1 **7.** undefined

Exercise Set 4.5 **1.** 4.6 **3.** 0.094 **5.** 300 **7.** 5.8 **9.** Exact: 6.6; Estimate: $6\overline{)36}$ **11.** 0.413 **13.** 0.045 **15.** 7 **17.** 4.8

19. 2100 **21.** 30 **23.** 7000 **25.** Exact: 9.8; Estimate: $7\overline{)70}$ **27.** 9.6 **29.** 45 **31.** 54.592 **33.** 0.0055 **35.** 179 **37.** 23.87

39. 113.1 **41.** 0.54982 **43.** 2.687 **45.** 0.0129 **47.** 12.6 **49.** 1.31 **51.** 12.225 **53.** 0.045625 **55.** 24 mo **57.** $3641.30
59. 202.1 lb **61.** 5.1 m **63.** 11.4 boxes **65.** 24 tsp **67.** 8 days **69.** 133.8 mph **71.** 20.45 points **73.** 2.45 **75.** 0.66

77. 80.52 **79.** 14.7 **81.** 930.7 **83.** 571 **85.** 92.06 **87.** 144.4 **89.** $\frac{9}{10}$ **91.** $\frac{1}{20}$ **93.** 4.26 **95.** 1.578 **97.** 26.66

99. 904.29 **101.** c **103.** b **105.** 85.5 **107.** 14.345 million, or 14,345,000 CDs **109.** 45.2 cm **111.** answers may vary
113. 65.2–82.6 knots

The Bigger Picture **1.** 22.172 **2.** 3.951 **3.** 9133.2 **4.** 6.8 **5.** 1.404 **6.** 8.66 **7.** 0.051 **8.** 2.14 **9.** $\frac{2}{15}$ **10.** $\frac{16}{75}$

Exercise Set 4.6 **1.** 0.2 **3.** 0.68 **5.** 0.75 **7.** 0.08 **9.** 1.2 **11.** $0.91\overline{6}$ **13.** 0.425 **15.** 0.45 **17.** $0.\overline{3}$ **19.** 0.4375 **21.** $0.\overline{63}$
23. 5.85 **25.** 0.624 **27.** 0.33 **29.** 0.44 **31.** 0.6 **33.** 0.68 **35.** 0.62 **37.** 0.71 **39.** < **41.** = **43.** < **45.** <

47. < **49.** > **51.** < **53.** < **55.** 0.32, 0.34, 0.35 **57.** 0.49, 0.491, 0.498 **59.** 0.73, $\frac{3}{4}$, 0.78 **61.** 0.412, 0.453, $\frac{4}{7}$

63. 5.23, $\frac{42}{8}$, 5.34 **65.** $\frac{17}{8}$, 2.37, $\frac{12}{5}$ **67.** 25.65 sq in. **69.** 9.36 sq cm **71.** 0.248 sq yd **73.** 8 **75.** 72 **77.** $\frac{1}{81}$ **79.** $\frac{9}{25}$ **81.** $\frac{5}{2}$

83. = 1 **85.** > 1 **87.** <1 **89.** 0.192 **91.** 6000 stations **93.** answers may vary **95.** answers may vary **97.** 47.25
99. 3.37 **101.** 0.45

Chapter 4 Vocabulary Check **1.** decimal **2.** numerator; denominator **3.** vertically **4.** and **5.** sum

Chapter 4 Review **1.** tenths **2.** hundred-thousandths **3.** forty-five hundredths **4.** three hundred forty-five hundred-thousandths
5. one hundred nine and twenty-three hundredths **6.** forty-six and seven thousandths **7.** 2.15 **8.** 503.102 **9.** $\frac{4}{25}$ **10.** $12\frac{23}{1000}$

11. $1\frac{9}{2000}$ **12.** $25\frac{1}{4}$ **13.** 0.9 **14.** 0.25 **15.** 0.045 **16.** 26.1 **17.** > **18.** = **19.** 0.92, 8.09, 8.6 **20.** 0.09, 0.091, 0.1

21. 0.6 **22.** 0.94 **23.** $0.26 **24.** $12.46 **25.** 13.491 **26.** $10\frac{3}{4}$ **27.** 9.52 **28.** 2.7 **29.** 7.28 **30.** 26.007 **31.** 459.7
32. 100.278 **33.** 65.02 **34.** 189.98 **35.** 52.6 mi **36.** $2.44 **37.** 22.2 in. **38.** 38.9 ft **39.** 18.5 **40.** 54.6 **41.** 72
42. 9345 **43.** 9.246 **44.** 3406.446 **45.** 14π m, 43.96 m **46.** 63.8 mi **47.** 887,000,000 **48.** 600,000 **49.** 0.0877 **50.** 15.825
51. 70 **52.** 0.21 **53.** 8.059 **54.** 30.4 **55.** 0.0267 **56.** 9.3 **57.** 7.3 m **58.** 45 mo **59.** 16.94 **60.** 3.89 **61.** 129
62. 0.81 **63.** 55 **64.** 7.26 **65.** 0.8 **66.** 0.923 **67.** $2.\overline{3}$ or 2.333 **68.** $0.21\overline{6}$ or 0.217 **69.** = **70.** < **71.** <

72. 0.837, 0.839, $\frac{17}{20}$ **73.** 0.42, $\frac{3}{7}$, 0.43 **74.** $\frac{19}{12}$, 1.63, $\frac{18}{11}$ **75.** 6.9 sq ft **76.** 5.46 sq in. **77.** two hundred and thirty-two ten-thousandths

78. 16,025.014 **79.** $\frac{231}{100,000}$ **80.** 0.75, $\frac{6}{7}$, $\frac{8}{9}$ **81.** 0.07 **82.** 0.1125 **83.** 51.057 **84.** > **85.** < **86.** < **87.** 42.90
88. 16.349 **89.** $123.00 **90.** $3646.00 **91.** 1.7 **92.** 2.49 **93.** 320.312 **94.** 148.74236 **95.** 8.128 **96.** 7.245 **97.** 4900
98. 23.904 **99.** 9600 sq ft **100.** yes **101.** 0.1024 **102.** 3.6

Chapter 4 Test **1.** forty-five and ninety-two thousandths **2.** 3000.059 **3.** 34.9 **4.** 0.862 **5.** < **6.** $\frac{4}{9}$, 0.445, 0.454 **7.** $\frac{69}{200}$
8. $24\frac{73}{100}$ **9.** 0.65 **10.** $5.\overline{8}$ or 5.889 **11.** 0.941 **12.** 17.583 **13.** 11.4 **14.** 43.86 **15.** 56 **16.** 0.07755 **17.** 6.673
18. 12,690 **19.** 4.73 **20.** 0.363 **21.** 6.2 **22.** 4,583,000,000 **23.** 2.31 sq mi **24.** 18π mi, 56.52 mi **25. a.** 9904 sq ft **b.** 198.08 oz
26. 54 mi

Cumulative Review **1.** one hundred six million, fifty-two thousand, four hundred forty-seven (Sec. 1.2, Ex. 7) **2.** 276,004 (Sec. 1.2)
3. $96,361 (Sec 1.3, Ex. 7) **4.** 288 (Sec. 1.6) **5.** 726 (Sec. 1.4, Ex. 4) **6.** 200 (Sec. 1.9) **7.** 2300 (Sec. 1.5, Ex. 4) **8.** 84 (Sec. 1.9)
9. 57,600 megabytes (Sec. 1.6, Ex. 11) **10.** perimeter: 28 ft; area: 49 sq ft (Sec. 1.3, 1.6) **11.** 401 R 2 (Sec. 1.7, Ex. 8) **12.** $\frac{21}{8}$ (Sec. 2.1)
13. 47 (Sec. 1.9, Ex. 15) **14.** $12\frac{4}{5}$ (Sec. 2.1) **15.** numerator: 3; denominator: 7 (Sec. 2.1, Ex. 1) **16.** 9 (Sec. 1.9) **17.** $\frac{1}{10}$ (Sec. 2.3, Ex. 6)

18. 17 (Sec. 1.9)   **19.** $\frac{15}{1}$ or 15 (Sec. 2.4, Ex. 9)   **20.** 13 (Sec. 1.9)   **21.** $\frac{63}{16}$ (Sec. 2.5, Ex. 5)   **22.** 128 (Sec. 1.7)

23. $\frac{15}{4}$ or $3\frac{3}{4}$ (Sec. 2.4, Ex. 10)   **24.** $9 (Sec. 1.7)   **25.** $\frac{3}{20}$ (Sec. 2.5, Ex. 8)   **26.** $\frac{27}{20}$ or $1\frac{7}{20}$ (Sec. 2.5)   **27.** $\frac{7}{9}$ (Sec. 3.1, Ex. 4)

28. $\frac{2}{5}$ (Sec. 3.1)   **29.** $\frac{1}{4}$ (Sec. 3.1, Ex. 5)   **30.** $\frac{2}{5}$ (Sec. 3.1)   **31.** $\frac{15}{20}$ (Sec. 3.2, Ex. 8)   **32.** $\frac{35}{45}$ (Sec. 3.2)   **33.** $\frac{13}{30}$ (Sec. 3.3, Ex. 2)

34. $\frac{1}{90}$ (Sec. 3.3)   **35.** $4\frac{7}{40}$ lb (Sec. 3.4, Ex. 7)   **36.** $27\frac{3}{4}$ lb (Sec. 2.4)   **37.** $\frac{1}{16}$ (Sec. 3.5, Ex. 3)   **38.** $\frac{49}{121}$ (Sec. 3.5)

39. $\frac{3}{256}$ (Sec. 3.5, Ex. 5)   **40.** $\frac{2}{81}$ (Sec. 3.5)   **41.** $\frac{43}{100}$ (Sec. 4.1, Ex. 8)   **42.** 0.75 (Sec. 4.1)   **43.** > (Sec. 4.2, Ex. 1)   **44.** 5.06 (Sec. 4.1)

45. 11.568 (Sec. 4.3, Ex. 4)   **46.** 75.329 (Sec. 4.3)   **47.** 2370.2 (Sec. 4.4, Ex. 6)   **48.** 0.119 (Sec. 4.4)   **49.** 768.05 (Sec. 4.4, Ex. 9)

50. 8.9 (Sec. 4.5)

CHAPTER 5   Percent

Exercise Set 5.1   1. $\frac{23}{10}$ **3.** $\frac{3\frac{3}{4}}{1\frac{2}{3}}$ **5.** $\frac{2}{3}$ **7.** $\frac{77}{100}$ **9.** $\frac{5}{12}$ **11.** $\frac{8}{25}$ **13.** $\frac{12}{7}$ **15.** $\frac{16}{23}$ **17.** $\frac{2}{5}$ **19.** $\frac{17}{40}$ **21.** $\frac{5}{4}$ **23.** $\frac{1}{3}$

25. $\frac{1\text{ shrub}}{3\text{ ft}}$ **27.** $\frac{3\text{ returns}}{20\text{ sales}}$ **29.** $\frac{2\text{ phone lines}}{9\text{ employees}}$ **31.** $\frac{9\text{ gal}}{2\text{ acres}}$ **33.** $\frac{3\text{ flight attendants}}{100\text{ passengers}}$ **35.** $\frac{71\text{ cal}}{2\text{ fl oz}}$ **37.** 110 cal/oz

39. 90 wingbeats/sec   **41.** false   **43.** true   **45.** $\frac{1.8}{2} = \frac{4.5}{5}$; true   **47.** $\frac{\frac{2}{3}}{\frac{1}{5}} = \frac{\frac{2}{5}}{\frac{1}{9}}$; false   **49.** 3   **51.** 9   **53.** 4   **55.** 3.2

57. 0.0025   **59.** 1   **61.** $\frac{3}{4}$ **63.** $\frac{35}{18}$ **65.** 165 min   **67.** 23 ft   **69.** 450 km   **71.** 56 mi   **73.** 112 ft; 11-in. difference

75. 6 people   **77. a.** 2062.5 mg   **b.** no   **79. a.** 0.1 gal   **b.** 13 fl oz   **81.** $2^2 \cdot 5$ **83.** $2^3 \cdot 5^2$ **85.** 2^5 **87.** 0.8 ml   **89.** 1.25 ml

91. no; answers may vary   **93.** answers may vary   **95.** 1400

The Bigger Picture   1. $\frac{1}{4}$ **2.** $\frac{7}{200}$ **3.** $\frac{7}{2}$ or $3\frac{1}{2}$ **4.** $\frac{9}{20}$ **5.** 7.62   **6.** 0.152   **7.** 8   **8.** $\frac{5}{2}$ or $2\frac{1}{2}$ **9.** 0.004   **10.** $\frac{35}{12}$ or $2\frac{11}{12}$

Exercise Set 5.2   1. 81%   **3. a.** 75%   **b.** 25%   **5.** 9%   **7.** chocolate chip; 52%   **9.** 0.48   **11.** 0.06   **13.** 1.00 or 1   **15.** 0.613
17. 0.028   **19.** 0.006   **21.** 3.00 or 3   **23.** 0.3258   **25.** 0.67   **27.** 0.212   **29.** 0.057   **31.** 98%   **33.** 310%   **35.** 2900%
37. 0.3%   **39.** 22%   **41.** 530%   **43.** 5.6%   **45.** 33.28%   **47.** 300%   **49.** 70%   **51.** 10%   **53.** 38%   **55.** 9.3%   **57.** 0.25
59. 0.65   **61.** 0.9   **63.** b, d   **65.** 4%   **67.** network systems and data communication analysts   **69.** 0.49   **71.** answers may vary

Mental Math   1. 13%   **3.** 87%   **5.** 1%

Exercise Set 5.3   1. $\frac{3}{25}$ **3.** $\frac{1}{25}$ **5.** $\frac{9}{200}$ **7.** $\frac{7}{4}$ or $1\frac{3}{4}$ **9.** $\frac{73}{100}$ **11.** $\frac{1}{8}$ **13.** $\frac{1}{16}$ **15.** $\frac{3}{50}$ **17.** $\frac{31}{300}$ **19.** $\frac{179}{800}$ **21.** 75%

23. 70%   **25.** 40%   **27.** 59%   **29.** 34%   **31.** $37\frac{1}{2}$%   **33.** $31\frac{1}{4}$%   **35.** 160%   **37.** $77\frac{7}{9}$%   **39.** 65%   **41.** 250%

43. 190%   **45.** 63.64%   **47.** 26.67%   **49.** 14.29%   **51.** 91.67%   **53.** 0.35, $\frac{7}{20}$; 20%, 0.2; 50%, $\frac{1}{2}$; 0.7, $\frac{7}{10}$; 37.5%, 0.375

55. 0.4, $\frac{2}{5}$; $23\frac{1}{2}$%, $\frac{47}{200}$; 80%, 0.8; 0.3333, $\frac{1}{3}$; 87.5%, 0.875; 0.075, $\frac{3}{40}$ **57.** 2, 2; 280%, $2\frac{4}{5}$; 7.05, $7\frac{1}{20}$; 454%, 4.54   **59.** 0.148; $\frac{37}{250}$

61. 0.23; $\frac{23}{100}$ **63.** 27.4%   **65.** 0.0875   **67.** 24%   **69.** 0.004; $\frac{1}{250}$ **71.** 0.12; $\frac{3}{25}$ **73.** 0.071; $\frac{71}{1000}$ **75.** $n = 15$ **77.** $n = 10$
79. $n = 12$ **81. a.** 52.9%   **b.** 52.86%   **83.** 107.8%   **85.** 65.79%   **87.** 77%   **89.** 75%   **91.** 80%   **93.** greater
95. answers may vary   **97.** 0.266; 26.6%   **99.** 1.155; 115.5%

Mental Math   1. percent: 42%; base: 50; amount: 21   **3.** percent: 125%; base: 86; amount: 107.5

Exercise Set 5.4   1. $15\% \cdot 72 = n$ **3.** $30\% \cdot n = 80$ **5.** $1.9 = 40\% \cdot n$ **7.** $n \cdot 90 = 20$ **9.** $n = 9\% \cdot 43$ **11.** 3.5   **13.** 7.28
15. 600   **17.** 10   **19.** 110%   **21.** 32%   **23.** 1   **25.** 45   **27.** 500   **29.** 400%   **31.** 25.2   **33.** 45%   **35.** 35
37. 0.624   **39.** 0.5%   **41.** 145   **43.** 63%   **45.** $n = 30$ **47.** $n = 3\frac{7}{11}$ **49.** $\frac{17}{12} = \frac{n}{20}$ **51.** $\frac{8}{9} = \frac{14}{n}$ **53.** c   **55.** b

57. some number equals thirty-three and one-third percent of twenty-four   **59.** a   **61.** c   **63.** a   **65.** a   **67.** answers may vary
69. 686.625   **71.** 12,285

The Bigger Picture   1. $\frac{19}{45}$ **2.** 63   **3.** 0.021   **4.** 8   **5.** 48   **6.** 1.6   **7.** 250%   **8.** 45.6 or $45\frac{3}{5}$ **9.** 28%   **10.** 180

Mental Math   1. amount: 12.6; base: 42; percent: 30   **3.** amount: 102; base: 510; percent: 20

Exercise Set 5.5 **1.** $\dfrac{a}{65} = \dfrac{32}{100}$ **3.** $\dfrac{a}{130} = \dfrac{19}{100}$ **5.** $\dfrac{2.3}{b} = \dfrac{58}{100}$ **7.** $\dfrac{75}{b} = \dfrac{40}{100}$ **9.** $\dfrac{70}{200} = \dfrac{p}{100}$ **11.** 5.5 **13.** 18.9 **15.** 400 **17.** 10 **19.** 125% **21.** 28% **23.** 29 **25.** 1.92 **27.** 1000 **29.** 210% **31.** 55.18 **33.** 45% **35.** 85 **37.** 0.864 **39.** 0.6% **41.** 140 **43.** 113% **45.** $\dfrac{7}{8}$ **47.** $3\dfrac{2}{15}$ **49.** 0.7 **51.** 2.19 **53.** answers may vary **55.** yes **57.** answers may vary **59.** 12,011.2 **61.** 7270.6

The Bigger Picture **1.** $\dfrac{19}{45}$ **2.** 63 **3.** 0.021 **4.** 8 **5.** 48 **6.** 1.6 **7.** 250% **8.** $45\dfrac{3}{5}$ or 45.6 **9.** 28% **10.** 180

Integrated Review **1.** 12% **2.** 68% **3.** 12.5% **4.** 250% **5.** 520% **6.** 800% **7.** 6% **8.** 44% **9.** 750% **10.** 325% **11.** 3% **12.** 5% **13.** 0.65 **14.** 0.31 **15.** 0.08 **16.** 0.07 **17.** 1.42 **18.** 4 **19.** 0.029 **20.** 0.066 **21.** 0.03; $\dfrac{3}{100}$ **22.** 0.05; $\dfrac{1}{20}$ **23.** 0.0525; $\dfrac{21}{400}$ **24.** 0.1275; $\dfrac{51}{400}$ **25.** 0.38; $\dfrac{19}{50}$ **26.** 0.45; $\dfrac{9}{20}$ **27.** 0.123; $\dfrac{37}{300}$ **28.** 0.167; $\dfrac{1}{6}$ **29.** 8.4 **30.** 100 **31.** 250 **32.** 120% **33.** 28% **34.** 76 **35.** 11 **36.** 130% **37.** 86% **38.** 37.8 **39.** 150 **40.** 62

Exercise Set 5.6 **1.** 1600 bolts **3.** $662.40 **5.** 15% **7.** 295 components **9.** 13.6% **11.** 100, 102 dental hygienists **13.** 50% **15.** 29.2% **17.** 496 chairs; 5704 chairs **19.** $136 **21.** $867.87; $20,153.87 **23.** 93,870 physician assistants **25.** 28 million; 63 million **27.** 10; 25% **29.** 102; 120% **31.** 2; 25% **33.** 120; 75% **35.** 44% **37.** 21.5% **39.** 1.3% **41.** 153.4% **43.** 893.8% **45.** 81.3% **47.** 300% **49.** 21.6% **51.** 4.56 **53.** 11.18 **55.** 58.54 **57.** The increased number is double the original number. **59. a.** percent increase = $\dfrac{30}{150}$ = 20% **b.** percent decrease = $\dfrac{30}{180}$ = $16\dfrac{2}{3}$% **c.** False; the percents are different.

Exercise Set 5.7 **1.** $7.50 **3.** $858.93 **5.** 9.5% **7. a.** $120 **b.** $130.20 **9.** $1917 **11.** $11,500 **13.** 6% **15.** $112.35 **17.** $49,474.24 **19.** 14% **21.** $1888.50 **23.** $85,500 **25.** $6.80; $61.20 **27.** $48.25; $48.25 **29.** $75.25; $139.75 **31.** $3255; $18,445 **33.** $45; $255 **35.** $52.74; $638.74 **37.** $4.51; $86.51 **39.** $7074 **41.** 8% **43.** 1200 **45.** 132 **47.** 16 **49.** d **51.** $4.00; $6.00; $8.00 **53.** $7.20; $10.80; $14.40 **55.** A discount of 60% is better; answers may vary **57.** $26,838.45

Calculator Explorations **1.** 1.56051 **3.** 8.06231 **5.** $634.49

Exercise Set 5.8 **1.** $32 **3.** $73.60 **5.** $750 **7.** $33.75 **9.** $700 **11.** $78,125 **13.** $5562.50 **15.** $12,580 **17.** $46,815.40 **19.** $2327.15 **21.** $58,163.60 **23.** $240.75 **25.** $938.66 **27.** $971.90 **29.** $260.31 **31.** $637.26 **33.** 32 yd **35.** 35 m **37.** answers may vary **39.** answers may vary

Chapter 5 Vocabulary Check **1.** ratio **2.** proportion **3.** rate **4.** cross products **5.** equal **6.** not equal **7.** of **8.** is **9.** percent **10.** compound interest **11.** $\dfrac{\text{amount}}{\text{base}}$ **12.** 100% **13.** 0.01 **14.** $\dfrac{1}{100}$

Chapter 5 Review **1.** $\dfrac{23}{37}$ **2.** $\dfrac{5}{4}$ **3.** $\dfrac{11}{13}$ **4.** $\dfrac{17}{35}$ **5. a.** 6 **b.** $\dfrac{3}{10}$ **6. a.** 3 **b.** $\dfrac{3}{20}$ **7.** $\dfrac{3 \text{ professors}}{10 \text{ assistants}}$ **8.** $\dfrac{5 \text{ pages}}{2 \text{ min}}$ **9.** 52 mi/hr **10.** 15 ft/sec **11.** no **12.** yes **13.** 15 **14.** 32.5 **15.** 60 **16.** 0.94 **17.** no **18.** 79 gal **19.** $54,600 **20.** $1023.50 **21.** 37% **22.** 77% **23.** 0.83 **24.** 0.75 **25.** 0.005 **26.** 0.007 **27.** 2.00 or 2 **28.** 4.00 or 4 **29.** 0.2625 **30.** 0.8534 **31.** 260% **32.** 5.5% **33.** 35% **34.** 102% **35.** 71% **36.** 65% **37.** 400% **38.** 900% **39.** $\dfrac{1}{100}$ **40.** $\dfrac{1}{10}$ **41.** $\dfrac{1}{4}$ **42.** $\dfrac{17}{200}$ **43.** $\dfrac{51}{500}$ **44.** $\dfrac{1}{6}$ **45.** $\dfrac{1}{3}$ **46.** $1\dfrac{1}{10}$ **47.** 20% **48.** 70% **49.** $83\dfrac{1}{3}$% **50.** $166\dfrac{2}{3}$% **51.** 125% **52.** 60% **53.** 6.25% **54.** 62.5% **55.** 100,000 **56.** 8000 **57.** 23% **58.** 114.5 **59.** 3000 **60.** 150% **61.** 418 **62.** 300 **63.** 64.8 **64.** 180% **65.** 110% **66.** 165 **67.** 66% **68.** 16% **69.** 20.9% **70.** 106.25% **71.** $206,400 **72.** $13.23 **73.** $263.75 **74.** $1.15 **75.** $5000 **76.** $300.38 **77.** discount: $900; sale price: $2100 **78.** discount: $9; sale price: $81 **79.** $160 **80.** $325 **81.** $30,104.64 **82.** $17,506.56 **83.** $80.61 **84.** $32,830.10 **85.** 1.6 **86.** 84 **87.** 0.038 **88.** 0.245 **89.** 0.009 **90.** 54% **91.** 9520% **92.** 30% **93.** $\dfrac{47}{100}$ **94.** $\dfrac{8}{125}$ **95.** $\dfrac{7}{125}$ **96.** $37\dfrac{1}{2}$% **97.** $15\dfrac{5}{13}$% **98.** 120% **99.** 268.75 **100.** 110% **101.** 708.48 **102.** 134% **103.** 300% **104.** 38.4 **105.** 560 **106.** 325% **107.** 26% **108.** $6786.50 **109.** $617.70 **110.** $3.45 **111.** 12.5% **112.** $1491 **113.** $11,687.50

Chapter 5 Test **1.** $\dfrac{15}{2}$ **2.** $\dfrac{43}{50}$ **3.** $\dfrac{2}{3}$ in./hr **4.** 9 inches/sec **5.** $4\dfrac{4}{11}$ **6.** 8 **7.** $53\dfrac{1}{3}$ g **8.** 4266 adults **9.** 0.85 **10.** 5 **11.** 0.008 **12.** 5.6% **13.** 610% **14.** 39% **15.** $\dfrac{6}{5}$ **16.** $\dfrac{77}{200}$ **17.** $\dfrac{1}{500}$ **18.** 55% **19.** 37.5% **20.** $155\dfrac{5}{9}$% **21.** 33.6 **22.** 1250 **23.** 75% **24.** 38.4 lb **25.** $56,750 **26.** $358.43 **27.** 5% **28.** discount: $18; sale price: $102 **29.** $395 **30.** 1% **31.** $647.50 **32.** $2005.64 **33.** $427

Cumulative Review **1.** 206 cases; 12 cans; yes (Sec. 1.8, Ex. 2) **2.** 31,084 (Sec. 1.6) **3. a.** $4\dfrac{2}{7}$ **b.** $1\dfrac{1}{15}$ **c.** 14 (Sec. 2.1, Ex. 18) **4. a.** $\dfrac{19}{7}$ **b.** $\dfrac{101}{10}$ **c.** $\dfrac{43}{8}$ (Sec. 2.1) **5.** $2 \cdot 2 \cdot 2 \cdot 3$ or $2^3 \cdot 3$ (Sec. 2.2, Ex. 7) **6.** 119 sq mi (Sec. 1.6) **7.** $\dfrac{10}{27}$ (Sec. 2.3, Ex. 3) **8.** 44 (Sec. 1.7) **9.** $\dfrac{23}{56}$ (Sec. 2.4, Ex. 4) **10.** 76,500 (Sec. 1.5) **11.** $\dfrac{8}{11}$ (Sec. 2.5, Ex. 2) **12.** $\dfrac{15}{4}$ or $3\dfrac{3}{4}$ (Sec. 2.1) **13.** $\dfrac{4}{5}$ in. (Sec. 3.1, Ex. 6) **14.** 50 (Sec. 1.9) **15.** 60 (Sec. 3.2, Ex. 4) **16.** $\dfrac{1}{3}$ (Sec. 3.1) **17.** $\dfrac{2}{3}$ (Sec. 3.3, Ex. 1) **18.** 340 (Sec. 2.4) **19.** $3\dfrac{5}{14}$ (Sec. 3.4, Ex. 5) **20.** 33 (Sec. 1.9)

21. $\frac{7}{16}$ (Sec. 3.5, Ex. 6)   **22.** $33\frac{27}{40}$ (Sec. 3.4)   **23.** $\frac{2}{33}$ (Sec. 3.5, Ex. 8)   **24.** $6\frac{3}{8}$ (Sec. 3.5)   **25.** 0.8 (Sec. 4.1, Ex. 13)   **26.** 0.09 (Sec. 4.1)
27. 8.7 (Sec. 4.1, Ex. 14)   **28.** 0.0048 (Sec. 4.1)   **29.** $2.18 (Sec. 4.2, Ex. 7)   **30.** 27.94 (Sec. 4.3)   **31.** 829.6561 (Sec. 4.3, Ex. 2)
32. 1248.3 (Sec. 4.4)   **33.** 18.408 (Sec. 4.4, Ex. 1)   **34.** 76,300 (Sec. 4.4)   **35.** 0.7861 (Sec. 4.5, Ex. 8)   **36.** 1.276 (Sec. 4.5)
37. 0.012 (Sec. 4.5, Ex. 9)   **38.** 50.65 (Sec. 4.5)   **39.** 7.236 (Sec. 4.5, Ex. 11)   **40.** 0.191 (Sec. 4.5)   **41.** 0.25 (Sec. 4.6, Ex. 1)
42. $0.\overline{5} \approx 0.556$ (Sec. 4.6)   **43.** $n = 25\% \cdot 0.008$ (Sec. 5.4, Ex. 3)   **44.** 37.5% or $37\frac{1}{2}\%$ (Sec. 5.3)

CHAPTER 6   Geometry

Exercise Set 6.1   **1.** line; line YZ or $\overleftrightarrow{YZ}$ **3.** line segment; line segment LM or $\overline{LM}$ **5.** line segment; line segment PQ or $\overline{PQ}$
7. ray; ray UW or $\overrightarrow{UW}$ **9.** 90°   **11.** 0°; 90°   **13.** straight   **15.** right   **17.** obtuse   **19.** right   **21.** 73°   **23.** 163°   **25.** 32°
27. 75°   **29.** $\angle MNP$ and $\angle RNO$; $\angle PNQ$ and $\angle QNR$ **31.** $\angle SPT$ and $\angle TPQ$; $\angle SPR$ and $\angle RPQ$; $\angle SPT$ and $\angle SPR$; $\angle TPQ$ and $\angle QPR$
33. 32°   **35.** 132°   **37.** $m\angle x = 35°$; $m\angle y = 145°$; $m\angle z = 145°$ **39.** $m\angle x = 77°$; $m\angle y = 103°$; $m\angle z = 77°$
41. $m\angle x = 100°$; $m\angle y = 80°$; $m\angle z = 100°$ **43.** $m\angle x = 134°$; $m\angle y = 46°$; $m\angle z = 134°$ **45.** $\angle ABC$ or $\angle CBA$ **47.** $\angle DBE$ or $\angle EBD$
49. 15°   **51.** 50°   **53.** 65°   **55.** 95°   **57.** $\frac{9}{8}$ or $1\frac{1}{8}$ **59.** $\frac{7}{32}$ **61.** $\frac{5}{6}$ **63.** $\frac{4}{3}$ or $1\frac{1}{3}$ **65.** 54.8°   **67.** false   **69.** true
71. $m\angle a = 60°$; $m\angle b = 50°$; $m\angle c = 110°$; $m\angle d = 70°$; $m\angle e = 120°$ **73.** 45°, 45°

Exercise Set 6.2   **1.** pentagon   **3.** hexagon   **5.** quadrilateral   **7.** pentagon   **9.** equilateral   **11.** scalene; right   **13.** isosceles
15. 25°   **17.** 13°   **19.** 40°   **21.** diameter   **23.** rectangle   **25.** parallelogram   **27.** hypotenuse   **29.** 14 m   **31.** 14.5 cm
33. 40.6 cm   **35.** 36 in.   **37.** cylinder   **39.** rectangular solid   **41.** cone   **43.** cube   **45.** rectangular solid   **47.** sphere
49. pyramid   **51.** 14.8 in.   **53.** 13 mi   **55.** 72,368 mi   **57.** 108   **59.** 12.56   **61.** true   **63.** true   **65.** false
67. yes; answers may vary   **69.** answers may vary

Exercise Set 6.3   **1.** 64 ft   **3.** 120 cm   **5.** 21 in.   **7.** 48 ft   **9.** 12 in.   **11.** 105 cm   **13.** 21 ft   **15.** 60 ft   **17.** 346 yd   **19.** 22 ft
21. $66   **23.** 36 in.   **25.** 28 in.   **27.** $24.08   **29.** 96 m   **31.** 66 ft   **33.** 128 mi   **35.** 17π cm; 53.38 cm   **37.** 16π mi; 50.24 mi
39. 26π m; 81.64 m   **41.** $31\frac{3}{7}$ ft ≈ 31.43 ft   **43.** 12,560 ft   **45.** 30.7 mi   **47.** $14\pi \approx 43.96$ cm   **49.** 40 mm   **51.** 84 ft   **53.** 23
55. 1   **57.** 10   **59.** 216   **61.** perimeter   **63.** area   **65.** area   **67.** perimeter   **69. a.** width: 30 yd; length: 40 yd   **b.** 140 yd
71. b   **73. a.** 62.8 m; 125.6 m   **b.** yes   **75.** $44 + 10\pi \approx 75.4$ m   **77.** 6 ft   **79.** 27.4 m

Exercise Set 6.4   **1.** 7 sq m   **3.** $9\frac{3}{4}$ sq yd   **5.** 15 sq yd   **7.** 2.25π sq in. ≈ 7.065 sq in.   **9.** 17.64 sq ft   **11.** 28 sq m   **13.** 22 sq yd
15. $36\frac{3}{4}$ sq ft   **17.** $22\frac{1}{2}$ sq in.   **19.** 25 sq cm   **21.** 86 sq mi   **23.** 24 sq cm   **25.** 36π sq in. $\approx 113\frac{1}{7}$ sq in.   **27.** 168 sq ft
29. 113,625 sq ft   **31.** $4\pi \approx 12.56$ sq ft   **33.** 128 sq in.; $\frac{8}{9}$ sq ft   **35.** 510 sq in.   **37.** 168 sq ft   **39.** 9200 sq ft   **41.** 381 sq ft
43. 14π in. ≈ 43.96 in.   **45.** 25 ft   **47.** $12\frac{3}{4}$ ft   **49.** 12-in. pizza   **51.** $1\frac{1}{3}$ sq ft; 192 sq ft   **53.** 7.74 sq in.   **55.** $1296\pi \approx 4069.404$ sq in.
57. 298.5 sq m   **59.** no; answers may vary

Exercise Set 6.5   **1.** 72 cu in.   **3.** 512 cu cm   **5.** $12\frac{4}{7}$ cu yd   **7.** $523\frac{17}{21}$ cu in.   **9.** $28\frac{2}{7}$ cu in.   **11.** 75 cu cm   **13.** $2\frac{10}{27}$ cu in.
15. 8.4 cu ft   **17.** $10\frac{5}{6}$ cu in.   **19.** 960 cu cm   **21.** $\frac{1372}{3}\pi$ cu in. or $457\frac{1}{3}\pi$ cu in.   **23.** $7\frac{1}{2}$ cu ft   **25.** $12\frac{4}{7}$ cu cm
27. 36π cu in. ≈ 113.04 cu in.   **29.** 25   **31.** 9   **33.** 5   **35.** 20   **37. a.** width: 40 yd; length: 60 yd   **b.** 2400 sq yd   **39.** 2,583,283 cu m
41. 2,583,669 cu m   **43.** 26,696.5 cu ft   **45.** answers may vary

Integrated Review   **1.** 153°; 63°   **2.** $m\angle x = 75°$; $m\angle y = 105°$; $m\angle z = 75°$ **3.** $m\angle x = 128°$; $m\angle y = 52°$; $m\angle z = 128°$ **4.** $m\angle x = 52°$
5. 4.6 in.   **6.** $4\frac{1}{4}$ in.   **7.** 20 m; 25 sq m   **8.** 12 ft; 6 sq ft   **9.** 10π cm ≈ 31.4 cm; 25π sq cm ≈ 78.5 sq cm   **10.** 32 mi; 44 sq mi
11. 54 cm; 143 sq cm   **12.** 62 ft; 238 sq ft   **13.** 64 cu in.   **14.** 30.6 cu ft   **15.** 400 cu cm   **16.** $4\frac{1}{2}\pi$ cm mi $\approx 14\frac{1}{7}$ cu mi

Calculator Explorations   **1.** 32   **3.** 3.873   **5.** 9.849

Exercise Set 6.6   **1.** 2   **3.** 8   **5.** $\frac{1}{9}$ **7.** $\frac{4}{8} = \frac{1}{2}$ **9.** 1.732   **11.** 3.873   **13.** 6.856   **15.** 5.099   **17.** 16   **19.** 3.742   **21.** $\frac{7}{12}$
23. 8.426   **25.** 13 in.   **27.** 6.633 cm   **29.** 52.802 m   **31.** 117 mm   **33.** 5   **35.** 12   **37.** 17.205   **39.** 44.822   **41.** 42.426
43. 1.732   **45.** 8.5   **47.** 141.42 yd   **49.** 25.0 ft   **51.** 340 ft   **53.** $n = 4$ **55.** $n = 45$ **57.** $n = 6$ **59.** 6, 7   **61.** 10, 11
63. answers may vary   **65.** no

Mental Math   **1.** $\angle A$ and $\angle D$, $\angle B$ and $\angle E$, $\angle C$ and $\angle F$, $\frac{a}{d} = \frac{b}{e} = \frac{c}{f}$

Exercise Set 6.7   **1.** congruent   **3.** not congruent   **5.** congruent   **7.** congruent   **9.** $\frac{2}{1}$ **11.** $\frac{3}{2}$ **13.** 4.5   **15.** 6   **17.** 5
19. 13.5   **21.** 17.5   **23.** 8   **25.** 21.25   **27.** 10   **29.** 500 ft   **31.** 60 ft   **33.** 14.4 ft   **35.** 200 ft, 300 ft, 425 ft   **37.** 17.5   **39.** 81
41. $3\frac{8}{9}$ in.; no   **43.** 32.7

Chapter 6 Vocabulary Check   **1.** right triangle; hypotenuse; legs   **2.** line segment   **3.** complementary   **4.** line   **5.** perimeter
6. angle; vertex   **7.** congruent   **8.** area   **9.** ray   **10.** square root   **11.** transversal   **12.** straight   **13.** volume   **14.** vertical
15. adjacent   **16.** obtuse   **17.** right   **18.** acute   **19.** supplementary   **20.** similar

Chapter 6 Review   **1.** right   **2.** straight   **3.** acute   **4.** obtuse   **5.** $65°$ **6.** $75°$ **7.** $58°$ **8.** $98°$ **9.** $90°$ **10.** $25°$
11. $\angle a$ and $\angle b$; $\angle b$ and $\angle c$; $\angle c$ and $\angle d$; $\angle d$ and $\angle a$ **12.** $\angle x$ and $\angle w$; $\angle y$ and $\angle z$ **13.** $m\angle x = 100°$; $m\angle y = 80°$; $m\angle z = 80°$
14. $m\angle x = 155°$; $m\angle y = 155°$; $m\angle z = 25°$ **15.** $m\angle x = 53°$; $m\angle y = 53°$; $m\angle z = 127°$ **16.** $m\angle x = 42°$; $m\angle y = 42°$; $m\angle z = 138°$
17. $103°$ **18.** $60°$ **19.** $60°$ **20.** $65°$ **21.** $4\frac{2}{10}$ m or $4\frac{1}{5}$ m   **22.** 7 ft   **23.** 9.5 m   **24.** $15\frac{1}{5}$ cm   **25.** cube   **26.** cylinder
27. pyramid   **28.** rectangular solid   **29.** 18 in.   **30.** 2.35 m   **31.** pentagon   **32.** hexagon   **33.** equilateral   **34.** isosceles, right
35. 89 m   **36.** 30.6 cm   **37.** 36 m   **38.** 90 ft   **39.** 32 ft   **40.** 440 ft   **41.** 5.338 in.   **42.** 31.4 yd   **43.** 240 sq ft   **44.** 140 sq m
45. 600 sq cm   **46.** 189 sq yd   **47.** 49π sq ft ≈ 153.86 sq ft   **48.** 82.81 sq m   **49.** 119 sq in.   **50.** 1248 sq cm   **51.** 144 sq m
52. 432 sq ft   **53.** 130 sq ft   **54.** $15\frac{5}{8}$ cu in.   **55.** 84 cu ft   **56.** $20,000\pi$ cu cm $\approx 62,800$ cu cm   **57.** $\frac{1}{6}\pi$ cu km $\approx \frac{11}{21}$ cu km
58. $2\frac{2}{3}$ cu ft   **59.** 307.72 cu in.   **60.** $7\frac{1}{2}$ cu ft   **61.** 0.5π cu ft or $\frac{1}{2}\pi$ cu ft   **62.** 8   **63.** 12   **64.** $\frac{2}{5}$ **65.** $\frac{1}{10}$ **66.** 13   **67.** 29
68. 10.7   **69.** 93   **70.** 127.3 ft   **71.** 88.2 ft   **72.** $37\frac{1}{2}$ **73.** $13\frac{1}{3}$ **74.** 17.4   **75.** approximately 33 ft   **76.** $x = \frac{5}{6}$ in.; $y = 2\frac{1}{6}$ in.
77. $108°$ **78.** $89°$ **79.** $82°$ **80.** $78°$ **81.** $95°$ **82.** $57°$ **83.** 13 m   **84.** 12.6 in.   **85.** 22 dm   **86.** 27.3 in.   **87.** 194 ft
88. 1624 sq m   **89.** 9π sq m ≈ 28.26 sq m   **90.** $346\frac{1}{2}$ cu in.   **91.** 140 cubic in.   **92.** 1260 cu ft   **93.** 28.728 cu ft   **94.** 1   **95.** 6
96. $\frac{4}{9}$ **97.** 86.6   **98.** 20.8   **99.** 48.1   **100.** 19.7   **101.** 12   **102.** $6\frac{1}{2}$

Chapter 6 Test   **1.** $12°$ **2.** $56°$ **3.** $57°$ **4.** $m\angle x = 118°$; $m\angle y = 62°$; $m\angle z = 118°$ **5.** $m\angle x = 73°$; $m\angle y = 73°$; $m\angle z = 73°$
6. 6.2 m   **7.** $10\frac{1}{4}$ in.   **8.** $26°$ **9.** circumference $= 18\pi \approx 56.52$ in.; area $= 81\pi \approx 254.34$ sq in.
10. perimeter $= 24.6$ yd; area $= 37.1$ sq yd   **11.** perimeter $= 68$ in.; area $= 185$ sq in.   **12.** $62\frac{6}{7}$ cu in.   **13.** 30 cu ft   **14.** 7   **15.** 8.888
16. $\frac{8}{10} = \frac{4}{5}$ **17.** 16 in.   **18.** 18 cu ft   **19.** 62 ft; \$115.94   **20.** 5.66 cm   **21.** 198.08 oz   **22.** 7.5   **23.** approximately 69 ft

Cumulative Review   **1.** nineteen and five thousand twenty-three ten-thousandths (Sec. 4.1, Ex. 3)   **2.** $\frac{53}{66}$ (Sec. 3.3)   **3.** 736.2 (Sec. 4.2, Ex. 5)
4. 700 (Sec. 4.2)   **5.** 47.06 (Sec. 4.3, Ex. 3)   **6.** $\frac{20}{11}$ or $1\frac{9}{11}$ (Sec. 2.5)   **7.** 76.8 (Sec. 4.4, Ex. 5)   **8.** $\frac{7}{66}$ (Sec. 2.4)
9. 76,300 (Sec. 4.4, Ex. 7)   **10.** $\frac{23}{2}$ or $11\frac{1}{2}$ (Sec. 2.4)   **11.** 38.6 (Sec. 4.5, Ex. 1)   **12.** 0.567 (Sec. 4.5)   **13.** 3.7 (Sec. 4.5, Ex. 12)
14. $\frac{3}{5}$ or 0.6 (Sec. 4.5)   **15.** $>$ (Sec. 4.6, Ex. 7)   **16.** $<$ (Sec. 3.5)   **17.** 225,000 (Sec. 1.6, Ex. 8)   **18.** $\frac{16}{45}$ (Sec. 3.3)
19. 140,000 (Sec. 1.6, Ex. 9)   **20.** $\frac{35}{2}$ or $17\frac{1}{2}$ (Sec. 5.1)   **21.** 17% (Sec. 5.2, Ex. 1)   **22.** 68% (Sec. 5.2)   **23.** $\frac{19}{1000}$ (Sec. 5.3, Ex. 2)
24. $\frac{13}{50}$ (Sec. 5.3)   **25.** $\frac{5}{4}$ or $1\frac{1}{4}$ (Sec. 5.3, Ex. 3)   **26.** $5\frac{3}{5}$ (Sec. 5.3)   **27.** 255 (Sec. 5.4, Ex. 8)   **28.** 15% (Sec. 5.4 or 5.5)
29. 52 (Sec. 5.5, Ex. 9)   **30.** $\frac{5}{9}$ (Sec. 6.6)   **31.** 775 freshmen (Sec. 5.6, Ex. 2)   **32.** \$2.25/sq ft (Sec. 4.5)   **33.** \$1710 (Sec. 5.7, Ex. 3)
34. 35 exercises (Sec. 5.1)   **35.** 7 (Sec. 1.9, Ex. 12)   **36.** 70,052 (Sec. 1.2)   **37.** 8.33% (Sec. 5.3, Ex. 9)   **38.** 12.5% (Sec. 5.3)
39. $50°$ (Sec. 6.2, Ex. 1)   **40.** 33 m (Sec. 6.3)   **41.** 28 in. (Sec. 6.3, Ex. 1)   **42.** 45 sq in. (Sec. 6.4)   **43.** $\frac{2}{5}$ (Sec. 6.6, Ex. 3)   **44.** $\frac{3}{4}$ (Sec. 6.6)
45. $\frac{12}{17}$ (Sec. 6.7, Ex. 2)   **46.** $14\frac{1}{6}$ (Sec. 6.7)

CHAPTER 7   Statistics and Probability

Exercise Set 7.1   **1.** 2004   **3.** 4000 cars   **5.** 10,500 cars   **7. a.** 2000, 2001, 2005   **b.** 250 fewer cars in 2000, 750 fewer cars in 2001, 500
fewer cars in 2005   **9.** 1999, 2002   **11.** 22.5 oz   **13.** 1998, 2001, 2004   **15.** 3 oz/wk   **17.** $5\frac{2}{3}$ symbols   **19.** April
21. 19 deaths   **23.** February, March, April, May, June   **25.** 18.5 million or 18,500,000   **27.** Tokyo: 34 million or 34,000,000
29. New York: 21.7 million or 21,700,000   **31.** 14 million or 14,000,000   **33.** 15 adults   **35.** 61 adults   **37.** 24 adults
39. 12 adults   **41.** $\frac{9}{100}$ **43.** 45–54   **45.** 21 million householders   **47.** 44 million householders

49. answers may vary   **51.** |; 1   **53.** ⊮⊮|||; 8   **55.** ⊮⊮|; 6   **57.** ⊮⊮|; 6   **59.** ||; 2   **61.**

63. 2.7 goals   **65.** 1982   **67.** decrease   **69.** 1990   **71.** 3.6   **73.** 6.2
75. 25%   **77.** 34%   **79.** 83°F   **81.** Sunday; 68°F   **83.** Tuesday: 13°F
85. answers may vary

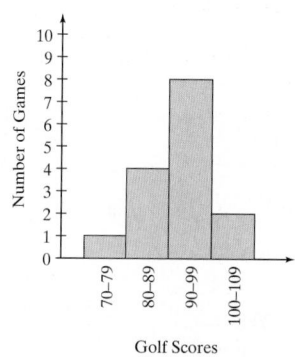

Exercise Set 7.2   **1.** parent or guardian's home   **3.** $\frac{9}{35}$ **5.** $\frac{9}{16}$ **7.** Asia   **9.** 37%   **11.** 17,100,000 sq mi   **13.** 2,850,000 sq mi

15. 55%   **17.** nonfiction   **19.** 31,400 books   **21.** 27,632 books   **23.** 25,120 books   **25.**   **27.** $2^2 \times 5$

29. $2^3 \times 5$ **31.** 5×17 **33.** answers may vary   **35.** 129,600,002 sq km

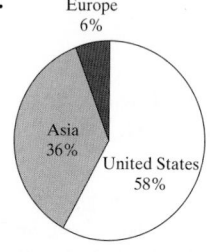

37. 55,542,858 sq km   **39.** true

Integrated Review   **1.** 69 lb   **2.** 78 lb   **3.** 10 lb   **4.** 2001 and 2002   **5.** Oroville Dam; 755 ft   **6.** New Bullards Bar Dam; 635 ft
7. 15 ft   **8.** 4 dams   **9.** Thursday and Saturday; 100°F   **10.** Monday; 82°F   **11.** Sunday, Monday, and Tuesday
12. Wednesday, Thursday, Friday, and Saturday   **13.** 70 qt containers   **14.** 52 qt containers   **15.** 2 qt containers   **16.** 6 qt containers
17. ||; 2   **18.** |; 1   **19.** |||; 3   **20.** ⊮⊮|; 6   **21.** ⊮⊮; 5   **22.**

Mental Math   **1.** 4   **3.** 3

Exercise Set 7.3   **1.** mean: 29; median: 28; no mode   **3.** mean: 8.1; median: 8.2; mode: 8.2   **5.** mean: 0.6; median: 0.6; mode: 0.2 and 0.6
7. mean: 370.9; median: 313.5; no mode   **9.** 1416 ft   **11.** 1332 ft   **13.** answers may vary   **15.** 2.79   **17.** 3.46   **19.** 6.8   **21.** 6.9

23. 85.5   **25.** 73   **27.** 70 and 71   **29.** 9 rates   **31.** $\frac{1}{3}$ **33.** $\frac{3}{5}$ **35.** $\frac{11}{15}$ **37.** 35, 35, 37, 43

Mental Math   **1.** $\frac{1}{2}$ **3.** $\frac{1}{2}$

Exercise Set 7.4   **1.**

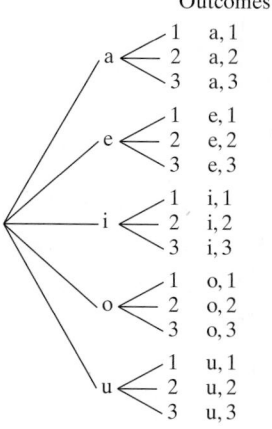

15 outcomes

3.

Outcomes

Red   Red
Blue   Blue
Yellow   Yellow

3 outcomes

5.

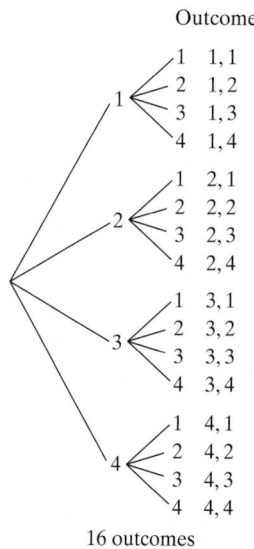

16 outcomes

7.

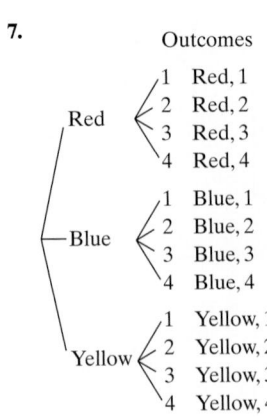

12 outcomes

9.

Outcomes

8 outcomes

11. $\frac{1}{6}$ **13.** $\frac{1}{3}$ **15.** $\frac{1}{2}$ **17.** $\frac{5}{6}$ **19.** $\frac{1}{3}$ **21.** 1 **23.** $\frac{2}{3}$

25. $\frac{1}{7}$ **27.** $\frac{2}{7}$ **29.** $\frac{2}{7}$ **31.** $\frac{19}{100}$ **33.** $\frac{1}{20}$ **35.** $\frac{5}{6}$ **37.** $\frac{1}{6}$

39. $\frac{20}{3}$ or $6\frac{2}{3}$ **41.** $\frac{1}{52}$ **43.** $\frac{1}{13}$ **45.** $\frac{1}{4}$ **47.** $\frac{1}{2}$ **49.** $\frac{1}{12}$ **51.** 0

53. answers may vary

Chapter 7 Vocabulary Check **1.** bar **2.** mean **3.** outcomes **4.** pictograph **5.** mode **6.** line **7.** median **8.** tree diagram
9. experiment **10.** circle **11.** probability **12.** histogram; class interval; class frequency

Chapter 7 Review **1.** 475,000 **2.** 175,000 **3.** 650,000 **4.** 375,000 **5.** Midwest, South, and West **6.** Northeast **7.** 7.5%
8. 2003 **9.** 1980, 1990, 2000, 2003 **10.** answers may vary **11.** $2,100,000 **12.** $1,200,000
13. 1991 and 1992, 2000 and 2001, 2001 and 2002 **14.** 1999 and 2000 **15.** 1990, 1991, 1992, 1993, 1994 **16.** 4 employees **17.** 1 employee
18. 9 employees **19.** 18 employees **20.** ⾡⾡; 5 **21.** ⵏ; 3 **22.** ⵏⵏ; 4 **23.**   **24.** mortgage payment

25. utilities **26.** $1225 **27.** $700 **28.** $\frac{39}{160}$ **29.** $\frac{7}{40}$ **30.** $\frac{5}{7}$

31. 20 states **32.** 11 states **33.** 1 state **34.** 29 states

35. mean: 17.8; median: 14; no mode **36.** mean: 58.1; median: 60; mode: 45 and 86

37. mean: $24,500; median: $20,000; mode: $20,000

38. mean: 447.3; median: 420; mode: 400 **39.** 3.25 **40.** 2.57

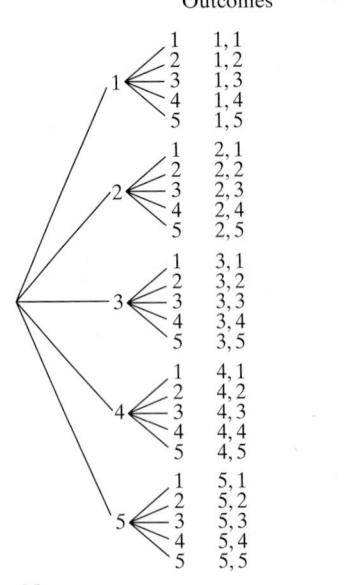

41.

Outcomes

10 outcomes

42.

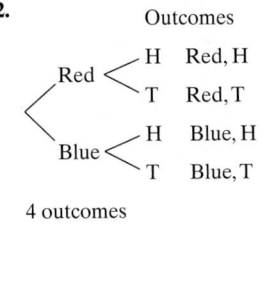

Outcomes

4 outcomes

43.

Outcomes

25 outcomes

44.

Outcomes

4 outcomes

45.

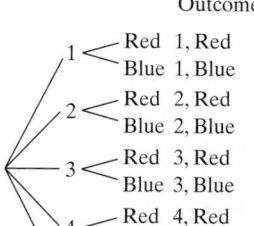

Outcomes

1 — Red 1, Red / Blue 1, Blue
2 — Red 2, Red / Blue 2, Blue
3 — Red 3, Red / Blue 3, Blue
4 — Red 4, Red / Blue 4, Blue
5 — Red 5, Red / Blue 5, Blue

10 outcomes

46. $\frac{1}{6}$ **47.** $\frac{1}{6}$ **48.** $\frac{1}{5}$ **49.** $\frac{1}{5}$ **50.** $\frac{3}{5}$ **51.** $\frac{2}{5}$ **52.** $\frac{1}{2}$ **53.** $\frac{1}{2}$

54. mean: 74.4; median: 73; mode: none **55.** mean: 48.8; median: 32; mode: none
56. mean: $454; median: $463.5; mode: $500 **57.** mean: $619.17; median: $647.5; mode: $327
58. $\frac{1}{4}$ **59.** $\frac{3}{8}$ **60.** $\frac{1}{4}$ **61.** $\frac{1}{8}$

Chapter 7 Test **1.** $225 **2.** 3rd week; $350 **3.** $1100 **4.** June, August, September **5.** February; 3 cm **6.** March and November

7.

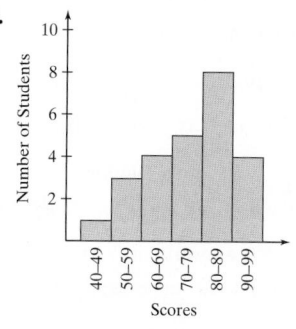

Countries with the Highest Newspaper Circulations

(bar graph: Average Daily Circulation (in millions) vs Country: Japan, U.S., China, India, Germany, Russia, U.K.)

8. 1.5% **9.** 1990, 1991, 2000 **10.** 1994–1995, 1995–1996, 1998–1999, 1999–2000, 2002–2003

11. $\frac{17}{40}$ **12.** $\frac{31}{22}$ **13.** 40,920,000 people **14.** 21,120,000 people **15.** 9 students

16. 11 students **17.**

Class Interval (Scores)	Tally	Class Frequency (Number of Students)
40–49	I	1
50–59	III	3
60–69	IIII	4
70–79	IHL	5
80–89	IHL III	8
90–99	IIII	4

18.

(histogram: Number of Students vs Scores 40–49, 50–59, 60–69, 70–79, 80–89, 90–99)

19. mean: 38.4; median: 42; no mode **20.** mean: 12.625; median: 12.5; mode: 12 and 16

21. 3.07 **22.**

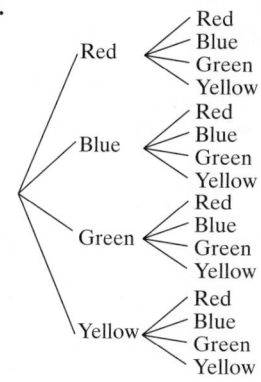

Red — Red, Blue, Green, Yellow
Blue — Red, Blue, Green, Yellow
Green — Red, Blue, Green, Yellow
Yellow — Red, Blue, Green, Yellow

16 outcomes

23.

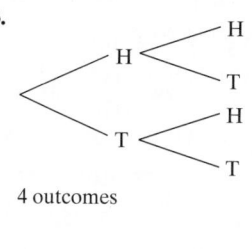

H — H, T
T — H, T

4 outcomes

24. $\frac{1}{10}$ **25.** $\frac{1}{5}$

Cumulative Review **1.** 28 (Sec. 1.9, Ex. 14) **2.** 12 (Sec. 1.9) **3.** $\frac{5}{18}$ (Sec. 2.3, Ex. 4) **4.** $\frac{7}{40}$ (Sec. 3.3) **5.** $8\frac{3}{10}$ (Sec. 3.4, Ex. 3)

6. $\frac{34}{3}$ or $11\frac{1}{3}$ (Sec. 2.4) **7.** 8.4 sq ft (Sec. 4.6, Ex. 10) **8.** 10 m (Sec. 6.3) **9. a.** 3 **b.** 5 **c.** 0 **d.** 7 (Sec. 1.4, Ex. 1)

10. a. 0 **b.** 20 **c.** 0 **d.** 20 (Sec. 1.6) **11.** 249,000 (Sec. 1.5, Ex. 3) **12.** 249,000 (Sec. 1.5) **13. a.** 200 **b.** 1230 (Sec. 1.6, Ex. 3)

14. 373 R 24 (Sec. 1.7) **15.** $6171 (Sec. 1.8, Ex. 3) **16.** 16,591 ft (Sec. 1.8) **17.** $3 \cdot 3 \cdot 5$ or $3^2 \cdot 5$ (Sec. 2.2, Ex. 3) **18.** 8 (Sec 1.9)

19. 0.046 (Sec. 5.2, Ex. 4) **20.** 0.0029 (Sec. 5.2) **21.** 1.9 (Sec. 5.2, Ex. 5) **22.** 4.52 (Sec. 5.2) **23.** $\frac{2}{5}$ (Sec. 5.3, Ex. 1)

24. $\frac{27}{100}$ (Sec. 5.3) **25.** $\frac{1}{3}$ (Sec. 5.3, Ex. 4) **26.** $\frac{107}{175}$ (Sec. 5.3) **27.** $5 = n \cdot 20$; (Sec. 5.4, Ex. 1) **28.** $\frac{5}{20} = \frac{p}{100}$ (Sec. 5.5)

29. sales tax: $6.41; total price: $91.91 (Sec. 5.7, Ex. 1) **30.** $1610 (Sec. 5.7) **31.** $2400 (Sec. 5.8, Ex. 3) **32.** 33.75 (Sec. 4.5)

33. 42° (Sec. 6.1, Ex. 4) **34.** 132° (Sec. 6.1) **35.** $\frac{1}{6}$ (Sec. 6.6, Ex. 2) **36.** $\frac{1}{5}$ (Sec. 6.6) **37.** 14, 77 (Sec. 7.3, Ex. 5) **38.** 56 (Sec. 7.3)

39. $\frac{1}{4}$ (Sec. 7.4, Ex. 3) **40.** $\frac{3}{5}$ (Sec. 7.4)

CHAPTER 8 Real Numbers and Introduction to Algebra

Exercise Set 8.1 **1.** < **3.** > **5.** = **7.** < **9.** $32 < 212$ **11.** $30 \le 45$ **13.** true **15.** false **17.** true **19.** false
21. $20 \le 25$ **23.** $6 > 0$ **25.** $-12 < -10$ **27.** $7 < 11$ **29.** $5 \ge 4$ **31.** $15 \ne -2$ **33.** $14{,}494; -282$ **35.** $-43{,}413$
37. $475; -195$ **39.** **41.** **43.**

45. whole, integers, rational, real **47.** integers, rational, real **49.** natural, whole, integers, rational, real **51.** rational, real **53.** false
55. true **57.** false **59.** false **61.** 8.9 **63.** 20 **65.** $\dfrac{9}{2}$ **67.** $\dfrac{12}{13}$ **69.** > **71.** = **73.** < **75.** < **77.** 109 **79.** 8
81. $762 < 1548$ **83.** went down by 261 or -261 **85.** $-0.04 > -26.7$ **87.** sun **89.** sun **91.** answers may vary

Calculator Explorations **1.** 125 **3.** 59,049 **5.** 30 **7.** 9857 **9.** 2376

Exercise Set 8.2 **1.** 243 **3.** 27 **5.** 1 **7.** 5 **9.** 49 **11.** $\dfrac{16}{81}$ **13.** $\dfrac{1}{125}$ **15.** 1.44 **17.** 0.343 **19.** 5^2 sq m **21.** 17
23. 20 **25.** 12 **27.** 21 **29.** 45 **31.** 0 **33.** $\dfrac{2}{7}$ **35.** 30 **37.** 2 **39.** $\dfrac{7}{18}$ **41.** $\dfrac{27}{10}$ **43.** $\dfrac{7}{5}$ **45.** 32 **47.** $\dfrac{23}{27}$ **49.** 9
51. 1 **53.** 1 **55.** 11 **57.** 8 **59.** 45 **61.** 15 **63.** $\dfrac{1}{4}$ **65.** 6 **67.** solution **69.** not a solution **71.** not a solution
73. solution **75.** not a solution **77.** solution **79.** $x + 15$ **81.** $x - 5$ **83.** $\dfrac{x}{4}$ **85.** $3x + 22$ **87.** $1 + 2 = 9 \div 3$
89. $3 \ne 4 \div 2$ **91.** $5 + x = 20$ **93.** $7.6x = 17$ **95.** $13 - 3x = 13$ **97.** 35 **99.** 360 **101.** no **103. a.** 64 **b.** 43 **c.** 19 **d.** 22
105. 14 in., 12 sq in.; 14 in., 6 sq in.; 14 in., 10 sq in. **107.** $(20 - 4) \cdot 4 \div 2$ **109.** answers may vary **111. a.** expression **b.** equation
c. equation **d.** expression **e.** expression **113.** answers may vary

Exercise Set 8.3 **1.** 3 **3.** -14 **5.** 1 **7.** -12 **9.** -5 **11.** -12 **13.** -4 **15.** 7 **17.** -2 **19.** 0 **21.** -19 **23.** 31
25. -47 **27.** -2.1 **29.** 38 **31.** -13.1 **33.** $\dfrac{1}{4}$ **35.** $-\dfrac{3}{16}$ **37.** $-\dfrac{13}{10}$ **39.** -8 **41.** -8 **43.** -59 **45.** -9 **47.** 5
49. 11 **51.** -18 **53.** 19 **55.** -7 **57.** -26 **59.** -6 **61.** 2 **63.** 0 **65.** -6 **67.** -2 **69.** 7 **71.** 7.9 **73.** $5z$
75. $\dfrac{2}{3}$ **77.** $107°$F **79.** -95 m **81.** -3.36 points **83.** -8 **85.** $-\$356$ million **87.** 72.01 **89.** 141 **91.** answers may vary
93. July **95.** October **97.** $4.7°$F **99.** negative **101.** positive **103.** answers may vary **105.** answers may vary

Exercise Set 8.4 **1.** -10 **3.** -5 **5.** 19 **7.** 11 **9.** -8 **11.** -11 **13.** 37 **15.** 5 **17.** -71 **19.** 0 **21.** $\dfrac{2}{11}$
23. -6.4 **25.** 4.1 **27.** $-\dfrac{1}{6}$ **29.** $-\dfrac{11}{12}$ **31.** 8.92 **33.** -8.92 **35.** 13 **37.** -5 **39.** -1 **41.** -23 **43.** -26 **45.** -24
47. 3 **49.** -45 **51.** -4 **53.** 13 **55.** 6 **57.** 9 **59.** -9 **61.** $\dfrac{7}{5}$ **63.** -7 **65.** 21 **67.** $\dfrac{1}{4}$ **69.** not a solution
71. not a solution **73.** solution **75.** $100°$ **77.** lost 23 yd **79.** -569 or 569 B.C. **81.** $30°$ **83.** -308 ft **85.** 19,852 ft **87.** $130°$
89. 0 **91.** $\dfrac{10}{13}$ **93.** $-4.4°, 2.6°, 12°, 23.5°, 15.3°, 3.9°, -0.3°, -6.3°, -18.2°, -15.7°, -10.3°$ **95.** October **97.** answers may vary
99. true; answers may vary **101.** true; answers may vary **103.** negative, -2.6466 **105.** sometimes positive and sometimes negative

Integrated Review **1.** negative **2.** negative **3.** positive **4.** 0 **5.** positive **6.** 0 **7.** positive **8.** positive **9.** $-\dfrac{1}{7}; \dfrac{1}{7}$
10. $\dfrac{12}{5}; \dfrac{12}{5}$ **11.** $3; 3$ **12.** $-\dfrac{9}{11}; \dfrac{9}{11}$ **13.** -42 **14.** 10 **15.** 2 **16.** -18 **17.** -7 **18.** -39 **19.** -2 **20.** -9 **21.** -3.4
22. -9.8 **23.** $-\dfrac{25}{28}$ **24.** $-\dfrac{5}{24}$ **25.** -4 **26.** -24 **27.** 6 **28.** 20 **29.** 6 **30.** 61 **31.** -6 **32.** -16 **33.** -19
34. -13 **35.** -4 **36.** -1 **37.** $\dfrac{13}{20}$ **38.** $-\dfrac{29}{40}$ **39.** 4 **40.** 9 **41.** -1 **42.** -3 **43.** 8 **44.** 10 **45.** 47 **46.** $\dfrac{2}{3}$

Calculator Explorations **1.** 38 **3.** -441 **5.** 490 **7.** 54,499 **9.** 15,625

Mental Math **1.** positive **3.** negative **5.** positive

Exercise Set 8.5 **1.** -24 **3.** -2 **5.** 50 **7.** -45 **9.** $\dfrac{3}{10}$ **11.** -7 **13.** -15 **15.** 0 **17.** 16 **19.** -16 **21.** $\dfrac{9}{16}$
23. -0.49 **25.** $\dfrac{3}{2}$ **27.** $-\dfrac{1}{14}$ **29.** $-\dfrac{11}{3}$ **31.** $\dfrac{1}{0.2}$ **33.** -9 **35.** -4 **37.** 0 **39.** undefined **41.** $-\dfrac{18}{7}$ **43.** 160 **45.** 64
47. $-\dfrac{8}{27}$ **49.** 3 **51.** -15 **53.** -125 **55.** -0.008 **57.** $\dfrac{2}{3}$ **59.** $\dfrac{20}{27}$ **61.** 0.84 **63.** -40 **65.** 81 **67.** -1 **69.** -121
71. -1 **73.** -19 **75.** 90 **77.** -84 **79.** -5 **81.** $-\dfrac{9}{2}$ **83.** 18 **85.** 17 **87.** -20 **89.** 16 **91.** 2 **93.** $-\dfrac{34}{7}$ **95.** 0
97. $\dfrac{6}{5}$ **99.** $\dfrac{3}{2}$ **101.** $-\dfrac{5}{38}$ **103.** 3 **105.** -1 **107.** undefined **109.** $-\dfrac{22}{9}$ **111.** solution **113.** not a solution **115.** solution
117. 32 in. **119.** 30 ft **121.** true **123.** false **125.** $-162°$F **127.** answers may vary **129.** $1, -1$ **131.** $\dfrac{0}{5} - 7 = -7$
133. $-8(-5) + (-1) = 39$

The Bigger Picture **1.** -5 **2.** -14 **3.** $-\dfrac{26}{35}$ **4.** 8 **5.** 49 **6.** -49 **7.** -21 **8.** undefined **9.** 0 **10.** -12 **11.** -16.6 **12.** $\dfrac{1}{6}$ **13.** -79 **14.** $\dfrac{10}{13}$ **15.** 50 **16.** -12

Exercise Set 8.6 **1.** $16 + x$ **3.** $y \cdot (-4)$ **5.** yx **7.** $13 + 2x$ **9.** $x \cdot (yz)$ **11.** $(2 + a) + b$ **13.** $(4a) \cdot b$ **15.** $a + (b + c)$ **17.** $17 + b$ **19.** $24y$ **21.** y **23.** $26 + a$ **25.** $-72x$ **27.** s **29.** $-\dfrac{5}{2}x$ **31.** $4x + 4y$ **33.** $9x - 54$ **35.** $6x + 10$ **37.** $28x - 21$ **39.** $18 + 3x$ **41.** $-2y + 2z$ **43.** $-y - \dfrac{5}{3}$ **45.** $5x + 20m + 10$ **47.** $8m - 4n$ **49.** $-5x - 2$ **51.** $-r + 6 + 7p$ **53.** $3x + 4$ **55.** $-x + 3y$ **57.** $6r + 8$ **59.** $-36x - 70$ **61.** $-1.6x - 2.5$ **63.** $4(1 + y)$ **65.** $11(x + y)$ **67.** $-1(5 + x)$ **69.** $30(a + b)$ **71.** commutative property of multiplication **73.** associative property of addition **75.** commutative property of addition **77.** associative property of multiplication **79.** identity element for addition **81.** distributive property **83.** multiplicative inverse property **85.** identity element for multiplication **87.** 4050 **89.** 45 **91.** $-8; \dfrac{1}{8}$ **93.** $-x; \dfrac{1}{x}$ **95.** $2x; -2x$ **97.** false **99.** no **101.** yes **103.** yes **105.** yes **107. a.** commutative property of addition **b.** commutative property of addition **c.** associative property of addition **109.** answers may vary **111.** answers may vary

Mental Math **1.** -7 **3.** 1 **5.** 17 **7.** like **9.** unlike **11.** like

Exercise Set 8.7 **1.** $15y$ **3.** $13w$ **5.** $-7b - 9$ **7.** $-m - 6$ **9.** -8 **11.** $7.2x - 5.2$ **13.** $k - 6$ **15.** $-15x + 18$ **17.** $4x - 3$ **19.** $5x^2$ **21.** -11 **23.** $1.3x + 3.5$ **25.** $5y + 20$ **27.** $-2x - 4$ **29.** $-10x + 15y - 30$ **31.** $-3x + 2y - 1$ **33.** $7d - 11$ **35.** 16 **37.** $x + 5$ **39.** $x + 2$ **41.** $2k + 10$ **43.** $-3x + 5$ **45.** $2x + 14$ **47.** $3y + \dfrac{5}{6}$ **49.** $-22 + 24x$ **51.** $0.9m + 1$ **53.** $10 - 6x - 9y$ **55.** $-x - 38$ **57.** $5x - 7$ **59.** $10x - 3$ **61.** $-4x - 9$ **63.** $-4m - 3$ **65.** $2x - 4$ **67.** $\dfrac{3}{4}x + 12$ **69.** $12x - 2$ **71.** $8x + 48$ **73.** $x - 10$ **75.** 2 **77.** -23 **79.** -25 **81.** balanced **83.** balanced **85.** answers may vary **87.** $(18x - 2)$ ft **89.** $(15x + 23)$ in. **91.** answers may vary

Chapter 8 Vocabulary Check **1.** inequality symbols **2.** equation **3.** absolute value **4.** variable **5.** opposites **6.** numerator **7.** solution **8.** reciprocals **9.** base; exponent **10.** numerical coefficient **11.** denominator **12.** grouping symbols **13.** term **14.** like terms **15.** unlike terms

Chapter 8 Review **1.** $<$ **2.** $>$ **3.** $>$ **4.** $>$ **5.** $<$ **6.** $>$ **7.** $=$ **8.** $=$ **9.** $>$ **10.** $<$ **11.** $4 \geq -3$ **12.** $6 \neq 5$ **13.** $0.03 < 0.3$ **14.** $400 < 155$ **15. a.** $1, 3$ **b.** $0, 1, 3$ **c.** $-6, 0, 1, 3$ **d.** $-6, 0, 1, 1\frac{1}{2}, 3, 9.62$ **e.** π **f.** all numbers in set **16. a.** $2, 5$ **b.** $2, 5$ **c.** $-3, 2, 5$ **d.** $-3, -1.6, 2, 5, \frac{11}{2}, 15.1$ **e.** $\sqrt{5}, 2\pi$ **f.** all numbers in set **17.** Friday **18.** Wednesday **19.** c **20.** b **21.** 37 **22.** 41 **23.** $\dfrac{18}{7}$ **24.** 80 **25.** $20 - 12 = 2 \cdot 4$ **26.** $\dfrac{9}{2} > -5$ **27.** 18 **28.** 108 **29.** 5 **30.** 24 **31.** $63°$ **32.** solution **33.** not a solution **34.** 9 **35.** $-\dfrac{2}{3}$ **36.** -2 **37.** 7 **38.** -11 **39.** -17 **40.** $-\dfrac{3}{16}$ **41.** -5 **42.** -13.9 **43.** 3.9 **44.** -14 **45.** -11.5 **46.** 5 **47.** -11 **48.** -19 **49.** 4 **50.** a **51.** a **52.** $\$51$ **53.** $-\dfrac{1}{6}$ **54.** $\dfrac{5}{3}$ **55.** -48 **56.** 28 **57.** 3 **58.** -14 **59.** -36 **60.** 0 **61.** undefined **62.** $-\dfrac{1}{2}$ **63.** commutative property of addition **64.** multiplicative identity property **65.** distributive property **66.** additive inverse property **67.** associative property of addition **68.** commutative property of multiplication **69.** distributive property **70.** associative property of multiplication **71.** multiplicative inverse property **72.** additive identity property **73.** commutative property of addition **74.** distributive property **75.** $6x$ **76.** $-11.8z$ **77.** $4x - 2$ **78.** $2y + 3$ **79.** $3n - 18$ **80.** $4w - 6$ **81.** $-6x + 7$ **82.** $-0.4y + 2.3$ **83.** $3x - 7$ **84.** $5x + 5.6$ **85.** $<$ **86.** $>$ **87.** -15.3 **88.** -6 **89.** -80 **90.** -5 **91.** $-\dfrac{1}{4}$ **92.** 0.15 **93.** 16 **94.** 16 **95.** -5 **96.** 9 **97.** $-\dfrac{5}{6}$ **98.** undefined **99.** $16x - 41$ **100.** $18x - 12$

Chapter 8 Test **1.** $|-7| > 5$ **2.** $(9 + 5) \geq 4$ **3.** -5 **4.** -11 **5.** -14 **6.** -39 **7.** 12 **8.** -2 **9.** undefined **10.** -8 **11.** $-\dfrac{1}{3}$ **12.** $4\dfrac{5}{8}$ **13.** $\dfrac{51}{40}$ **14.** -32 **15.** -48 **16.** 3 **17.** 0 **18.** $>$ **19.** $>$ **20.** $>$ **21.** $=$ **22. a.** $1, 7$ **b.** $0, 1, 7$ **c.** $-5, -1, 0, 1, 7$ **d.** $-5, -1, \frac{1}{4}, 0, 1, 7, 11.6$ **e.** $\sqrt{7}, 3\pi$ **f.** $-5, -1, \frac{1}{4}, 0, 1, 7, 11.6, \sqrt{7}, 3\pi$ **23.** 40 **24.** 12 **25.** 22 **26.** -1 **27.** associative property of addition **28.** commutative property of multiplication **29.** distributive property **30.** multiplicative inverse **31.** 9 **32.** -3 **33.** second down **34.** yes **35.** $17°$ **36.** loss of $\$420$ **37.** $y - 10$ **38.** $5.9x + 1.2$ **39.** $-2x + 10$ **40.** $-15y + 1$

Cumulative Review **1.** 2010 (Sec. 1.3, Ex. 4) **2.** 1531 (Sec. 1.4) **3.** $3 \cdot 3 \cdot 3 \cdot 5 \cdot 7$ or $3^3 \cdot 5 \cdot 7$ (Sec. 2.2, Ex. 5) **4.** 153 sq in. (Sec. 1.6) **5.** 33 (Sec. 3.2, Ex. 7) **6.** $\dfrac{10}{63}$ (Sec. 3.3) **7.** $5\dfrac{1}{15}$ (Sec. 3.4, Ex. 2) **8.** $10\dfrac{1}{3}$ (Sec. 2.4) **9.** $\dfrac{1}{8}$ (Sec. 4.1, Ex. 10) **10.** $1\dfrac{1}{5}$ (Sec. 4.6) **11.** $105\dfrac{83}{1000}$ (Sec. 4.1, Ex. 12) **12.** $\dfrac{8}{27}$ (Sec. 3.5) **13.** $<$ (Sec. 4.2, Ex. 2) **14.** 25 (Sec. 1.9) **15.** 67.69 (Sec. 4.3, Ex. 6)

16. 139.231 (Sec. 4.3)   **17.** 4.21 (Sec. 4.4, Ex. 8)   **18.** 186,040 (Sec. 4.4)   **19.** 0.0092 (Sec. 4.4, Ex. 10)   **20.** 5.8 (Sec. 4.5)

21. 7.53 (Sec. 4.5, Ex. 2)   **22.** $\frac{21}{20}$ or $1\frac{1}{20}$ (Sec. 3.3)   **23.** 2.1875 (Sec. 4.6, Ex. 4)   **24.** 7.3 (Sec. 4.2)   **25.** $0.\overline{6}$ (Sec. 4.6, Ex. 2)

26. 2.16 (Sec. 4.5)   **27.** 0.23 (Sec. 5.2, Ex. 3)   **28.** 87.5% or $87\frac{1}{2}$% (Sec. 5.3)   **29.** 8.33% (Sec. 5.3, Ex. 9)   **30.** 24% (Sec. 5.4 or 5.5)

31. 14 (Sec. 5.4, Ex. 7)   **32.** $\frac{23}{100}$ (Sec. 5.3)   **33.** $\frac{75}{30} = \frac{p}{100}$ (Sec. 5.5, Ex. 5)   **34.** -4.5 (Sec. 4.3)   **35.** 18% (Sec. 5.6, Ex. 6)

36. -0.9 (Sec 4.3)   **37.** discount: $16.25; sale price: $48.75 (Sec. 5.7, Ex. 5)   **38.** 94 (Sec 5.4 or 5.5)   **39.** $120 (Sec. 5.8, Ex. 1)
40. 15% (Sec. 5.6)

CHAPTER 9   Equations, Inequalities, and Problem Solving

Mental Math   1. 2   **3.** 12   **5.** 17

Exercise Set 9.1   1. 3   **3.** -2 **5.** -14 **7.** 0.5   **9.** $\frac{1}{4}$ **11.** $\frac{5}{12}$ **13.** -3 **15.** -9 **17.** -10 **19.** 2   **21.** -7 **23.** -1

25. -9 **27.** -12 **29.** $-\frac{1}{2}$ **31.** 11   **33.** 21   **35.** 25   **37.** -3 **39.** -0.7 **41.** 11   **43.** 13   **45.** -30 **47.** -0.4 **49.** -7

51. $-\frac{1}{3}$ **53.** -17.9 **55.** $(10 - x)$ ft   **57.** $(180 - x)°$ **59.** $n - 28,000$ **61.** $7x$ sq mi   **63.** $\frac{8}{5}$ **65.** $\frac{1}{2}$ **67.** -9 **69.** x

71. y **73.** x **75.** answers may vary   **77.** 4   **79.** answers may vary   **81.** $(173 - 3x)°$ **83.** answers may vary   **85.** $x = -145.478$

Mental Math   1. 9   **3.** 2   **5.** -5

Exercise Set 9.2   1. 4   **3.** 0   **5.** 12   **7.** -12 **9.** 3   **11.** 2   **13.** 0   **15.** 6.3   **17.** 10   **19.** -20 **21.** 0   **23.** -9 **25.** 1

27. -30 **29.** 3   **31.** $\frac{10}{9}$ **33.** -1 **35.** -4 **37.** $-\frac{1}{2}$ **39.** 0   **41.** 4   **43.** $-\frac{1}{14}$ **45.** 0.21   **47.** 5   **49.** 6   **51.** -5.5

53. -5 **55.** 0   **57.** -3 **59.** $-\frac{9}{28}$ **61.** $\frac{14}{3}$ **63.** -9 **65.** -2 **67.** $\frac{11}{2}$ **69.** $-\frac{1}{4}$ **71.** $\frac{9}{10}$ **73.** $-\frac{17}{20}$ **75.** -16

77. $2x + 2$ **79.** $2x + 2$ **81.** $5x + 20$ **83.** $7x - 12$ **85.** $12z + 44$ **87.** 1   **89.** -48 **91.** answers may vary
93. answers may vary   **95.** 2

Calculator Explorations   1. solution   **3.** not a solution   **5.** solution

Exercise Set 9.3   1. -6 **3.** 3   **5.** 1   **7.** $\frac{3}{2}$ **9.** 0   **11.** 1   **13.** 4   **15.** -4 **17.** -3 **19.** 2   **21.** 50   **23.** 1   **25.** $\frac{7}{3}$

27. 0.2   **29.** all real numbers   **31.** no solution   **33.** no solution   **35.** all real numbers   **37.** 18   **39.** $\frac{19}{9}$ **41.** $\frac{14}{3}$ **43.** 13

45. 4   **47.** all real numbers   **49.** $-\frac{3}{5}$ **51.** -5 **53.** 10   **55.** no solution   **57.** 3   **59.** -17 **61.** $(6x - 8)$ m   **63.** $-8 - x$

65. $-3 + 2x$ **67.** $9(x + 20)$ **69. a.** all real numbers   **b.** answers may vary   **c.** answers may vary   **71.** a   **73.** b   **75.** c
77. answers may vary   **79. a.** $x + x + x + 2x + 2x = 28$ **b.** $x = 4$ **c.** $x = 4$ cm; $2x = 8$ cm   **81.** answers may vary   **83.** 15.3
85. -0.2

Integrated Review   1. 6   **2.** -17 **3.** 12   **4.** -26 **5.** -3 **6.** -1 **7.** $\frac{27}{2}$ **8.** $\frac{25}{2}$ **9.** 8   **10.** -64 **11.** 2

12. -3 **13.** 5   **14.** -1 **15.** 2   **16.** 2   **17.** -2 **18.** -2 **19.** $-\frac{5}{6}$ **20.** $\frac{1}{6}$ **21.** 1   **22.** 6   **23.** 4   **24.** 1   **25.** $\frac{9}{5}$

26. $-\frac{6}{5}$ **27.** all real numbers   **28.** all real numbers   **29.** 0   **30.** -1.6 **31.** $\frac{4}{19}$ **32.** $-\frac{5}{19}$ **33.** $\frac{7}{2}$ **34.** $-\frac{1}{4}$ **35.** no solution

36. no solution   **37.** $\frac{7}{6}$ **38.** $\frac{1}{15}$

Exercise Set 9.4   1. -25 **3.** $-\frac{3}{4}$ **5.** 234, 235   **7.** Belgium: 32; France: 33; Spain: 34   **9.** 3 in.; 6 in.; 16 in.   **11.** 1st piece: 5 in.;
2nd piece: 10 in.; 3rd piece: 25 in.   **13.** Governor of California: $175,000;   Governor of Florida: $124,575   **15.** 172 mi   **17.** 25 mi
19. 1st angle: 37.5°; 2nd angle: 37.5°; 3rd angle: 105°   **21.** A: 60°; B: 120°; C: 120°; D: 60°   **23.** 5 ft, 12 ft   **25.** 1997: 15.1 million prescriptions;
2001: 20.6 million prescriptions   **27.** 45°, 135°   **29.** 58°, 60°, 62°   **31.** 1   **33.** 280 mi   **35.** Johnson: 4932; Kenseth: 5022
37. Montana: 56 counties; California: 58 counties   **39.** Neptune: 8 moons; Uranus: 21 moons; Saturn: 18 moons   **41.** -16
43. Sahara: 3,500,000 sq mi; Gobi: 500,000 sq mi   **45.** Korea: 9, Italy: 10, France: 11   **47.** Brown: 66,362; Randall: 53,074   **49.** Illinois
51. Texas: $29.4 million; Florida: $27.2 million   **53.** answers may vary   **55.** 34   **57.** 225π **59.** 15 ft by 24 ft
61. 720 blinks per hour; 11,520 blinks per day; 4,204,800 blinks per year   **63.** answers may vary   **65.** answers may vary

Exercise Set 9.5   1. $h = 3$ **3.** $h = 3$ **5.** $h = 20$ **7.** $c = 12$ **9.** $r = 2.5$ **11.** $h = \frac{f}{5g}$ **13.** $w = \frac{V}{lh}$ **15.** $y = 7 - 3x$

17. $R = \frac{A - P}{PT}$ **19.** $A = \frac{3V}{h}$ **21.** $a = P - b - c$ **23.** $h = \frac{S - 2\pi r^2}{2\pi r}$ **25. a.** area: 103.5 sq ft; perimeter: 41 ft   **b.** baseboard: perimeter;
carpet: area   **27. a.** area: 480 sq in.; perimeter: 120 in.   **b.** frame: perimeter; glass: area   **29.** 70 ft   **31.** $-10°$C   **33.** 6.25 hr
35. length: 78 ft; width: 52 ft   **37.** 18 ft, 36 ft, 48 ft   **39.** 137.5 mi   **41.** 96 piranhas   **43.** 2 bags   **45.** one 16-in. pizza   **47.** 4.65 min
49. 13 in.   **51.** 2.25 hr   **53.** 12,090 ft   **55.** 50°C   **57.** 515,509.5 cu in.   **59.** 449 cu in.   **61.** 333°F   **63.** 0.32   **65.** 2.00 or 2

67. 17%   **69.** 720%   **71.** $V = G(N - R)$ **73.** multiplies the volume by 8   **75.** $-40°$ **77.** $\frac{\triangle - \square}{\blacksquare}$ **79.** 44.3 sec
81. $P = 3{,}200{,}000$ **83.** $V = 113.1$

Mental Math   1. no   **3.** yes

Exercise Set 9.6   1. 11.2   **3.** 55%   **5.** 180   **7.** 4%   **9.** 9990   **11.** discount: $1480; new price: $17,020   **13.** $46.58   **15.** 73%
17. 30%   **19.** $104   **21.** $42,500   **23.** 2 gal   **25.** 7 lb   **27.** 4.6   **29.** 50   **31.** 30%   **33.** 71%   **35.** 176,118
37. 5462; 60%; 27%; 6%   **39.** 75% increase   **41.** $3900   **43.** 300%   **45.** mark-up: $0.11; new price: $2.31   **47.** 400 oz   **49.** 51.7%
51. 120 employees   **53.** decrease: $64; sale price: $192   **55.** 854 thousand Scoville units   **57.** 361   **59.** 400 oz   **61.** >   **63.** =
65. >   **67.** no; answers may vary   **69.** 9.6%   **71.** 26.9%; yes   **73.** 17.1%

Mental Math   1. $x > 2$ **3.** $x \geq 8$ **5.** -5 **7.** 4.1

Exercise Set 9.7   1.   **3.**   **5.**   **7.**   **9.**

11.   **13.** $\{x \mid x \geq -5\}$ **15.** $\{y \mid y < 9\}$ **17.** $\{x \mid x > -3\}$

19. $\{x \mid x \leq 1\}$ **21.** $\{x \mid x < -3\}$ **23.** $\{x \mid x \geq -2\}$ **25.** $\{x \mid x < 0\}$

27. $\left\{y \mid y \geq -\dfrac{8}{3}\right\}$ **29.** $\{y \mid y > 3\}$ **31.** $\{x \mid x > -15\}$ **33.** $\{x \mid x \geq -11\}$ **35.** $\left\{x \mid x > \dfrac{1}{4}\right\}$

37. $\{y \mid y \geq -12\}$ **39.** $\{z \mid z < 0\}$ **41.** $\{x \mid x > -3\}$ **43.** $\left\{x \mid x \geq -\dfrac{2}{3}\right\}$ **45.** $\{x \mid x \leq -2\}$ **47.** $\{x \mid x > -13\}$ **49.** $\{x \mid x \leq -8\}$

51. $\{x \mid x > 4\}$ **53.** $\left\{x \mid x \leq \dfrac{5}{4}\right\}$ **55.** $\left\{x \mid x > \dfrac{8}{3}\right\}$ **57.** $\{x \mid x \geq 0\}$ **59.** all numbers greater than -10 **61.** 35 cm   **63.** 193

65. 86 people   **67.** 35 min   **69.** 81   **71.** 1   **73.** $\dfrac{49}{64}$ **75.** about 120   **77.** 2003 and 2004   **79.** 2001   **81.** >   **83.** ≥
85. when multiplying or dividing by a negative number   **87.** final exam score ≥ 78.5

The Bigger Picture   1. -3 **2.** $\{x \mid x < -3\}$ **3.** $\dfrac{2}{9}$ **4.** $-\dfrac{1}{4}$ **5.** $\{x \mid x \geq -15\}$ **6.** no solution   **7.** 7   **8.** $\{x \mid x < 37\}$
9. all real numbers   **10.** $\dfrac{41}{29}$

Chapter 9 Vocabulary Check   1. linear equation in one variable   **2.** equivalent equations   **3.** formula   **4.** linear inequality in one variable
5. all real numbers   **6.** no solution   **7.** the same   **8.** reversed

Chapter 9 Review   1. 4   **2.** -3 **3.** 6   **4.** -6 **5.** 0   **6.** -9 **7.** -23 **8.** 28   **9.** b   **10.** a   **11.** b   **12.** c   **13.** -12
14. 4   **15.** 0   **16.** -7 **17.** 0.75   **18.** -3 **19.** -6 **20.** -1 **21.** -1 **22.** $\dfrac{3}{2}$ **23.** $-\dfrac{1}{5}$ **24.** 7   **25.** $3x + 3$
26. $2x + 6$ **27.** -4 **28.** -4 **29.** 2   **30.** -3 **31.** no solution   **32.** no solution   **33.** $\dfrac{3}{4}$ **34.** $-\dfrac{8}{9}$ **35.** 20   **36.** $-\dfrac{6}{23}$
37. $\dfrac{23}{7}$ **38.** $-\dfrac{2}{5}$ **39.** 102   **40.** 0.25   **41.** 6665.5 in.   **42.** short piece: 4 ft; long piece: 8 ft   **43.** Kellogg: 35 plants; Keebler: 18 plants
44. $-39, -38, -37$ **45.** 3   **46.** -4 **47.** $w = 9$ **48.** $h = 4$ **49.** $m = \dfrac{y - b}{x}$ **50.** $s = \dfrac{r + 5}{vt}$ **51.** $x = \dfrac{2y - 7}{5}$
52. $y = \dfrac{2 + 3x}{6}$ **53.** $\pi = \dfrac{C}{D}$ **54.** $\pi = \dfrac{C}{2r}$ **55.** 15 m   **56.** 18 ft by 12 ft   **57.** 1 hr and 20 min   **58.** 40°C   **59.** 20%
60. 70%   **61.** 110   **62.** 1280   **63.** mark-up: $209; new price: $2109   **64.** 50,844   **65.** 40% solution: 10 gal; 10% solution: 20 gal
66. 1.45% increase   **67.** 18%   **68.** swerving into another lane   **69.** 966 customers   **70.** no; answers may vary   **71.**
72.   **73.** $\{x \mid x \leq 1\}$ **74.** $\{x \mid x > -5\}$ **75.** $\{x \mid x \leq 10\}$ **76.** $\{x \mid x < -4\}$ **77.** $\{x \mid x < -4\}$
78. $\{x \mid x \leq 4\}$ **79.** $\{y \mid y > 9\}$ **80.** $\{y \mid y \geq -15\}$ **81.** $\left\{x \mid x < \dfrac{7}{4}\right\}$ **82.** $\left\{x \mid x \leq \dfrac{19}{3}\right\}$ **83.** at least $2500
84. score must be less than 83   **85.** $x = 4$ **86.** $y = -14$ **87.** $a = -\dfrac{3}{2}$ **88.** $x = 21$ **89.** all real numbers   **90.** no solution
91. -13 **92.** shorter piece: 4 in.; longer piece: 19 in.   **93.** $h = \dfrac{3v}{A}$ **94.** 22.1   **95.** 160   **96.** 20%   **97.** $\{x \mid x > 9\}$
98. $\{x \mid x > -4\}$ **99.** $\{x \mid x \leq 0\}$

Chapter 9 Test   1. -5 **2.** 8   **3.** $\dfrac{7}{10}$ **4.** 0   **5.** 27   **6.** $-\dfrac{19}{6}$ **7.** 3   **8.** $\dfrac{3}{11}$ **9.** 0.25   **10.** $\dfrac{25}{7}$ **11.** no solution   **12.** 21

13. 7 gal   **14.** $x = 6$ **15.** $h = \dfrac{V}{\pi r^2}$ **16.** $y = \dfrac{3x - 10}{4}$ **17.** $\{x \mid x < -2\}$ **18.** $\{x \mid x < 4\}$ **19.** $\{x \mid x \leq -8\}$ **20.** $\{x \mid x \geq 11\}$

21. $\left\{x \mid x > \dfrac{2}{5}\right\}$ **22.** 29%   **23.** 552   **24.** 40%   **25.** New York: 1077; Indiana: 427

Cumulative Review   1. True (Sec. 8.1, Ex. 3)   **2.** False (Sec. 8.1)   **3.** True (Sec. 8.1, Ex. 4)   **4.** True (Sec. 8.1)   **5.** False (Sec. 8.1, Ex. 5)
6. True (Sec. 8.1)   **7.** True (Sec. 8.1, Ex. 6)   **8.** True (Sec. 8.1)   **9.** $7\dfrac{17}{24}$ (Sec. 3.4, Ex. 1)   **10. a.** $\dfrac{7}{10}$ **b.** $\dfrac{13}{24}$ (Sec. 3.3)   **11.** $\dfrac{8}{3}$ (Sec. 8.2, Ex. 6)
12. 33 (Sec. 8.2)   **13.** -19 (Sec. 8.3, Ex. 6)   **14.** -10 (Sec. 8.3)   **15.** 8 (Sec. 8.3, Ex. 7)   **16.** 10 (Sec. 8.3)   **17.** -0.3 (Sec. 8.3, Ex. 8)
18. 0 (Sec. 8.3)   **19. a.** -12 **b.** -3 (Sec. 8.4, Ex. 7)   **20. a.** 5   **b.** $\dfrac{2}{3}$ **c.** a **d.** -3 (Sec. 8.4)   **21. a.** 0   **b.** -24 **c.** 45   **d.** 54 (Sec. 8.5, Ex. 7)

22. a. -11.1 **b.** $-\dfrac{1}{5}$ **c.** $\dfrac{3}{4}$ (Sec. 8.4)   **23. a.** -6 **b.** 7   **c.** -5 (Sec. 8.5, Ex. 10)   **24. a.** -0.36 **b.** $\dfrac{6}{17}$ (Sec. 8.5)   **25.** $15 - 10z$ (Sec. 8.6, Ex. 8)

26. $2x^3 - 6x^2 + 8x$ (Sec. 8.6)   **27.** $12x + 38$ (Sec. 8.6, Ex. 12)   **28.** $2x + 8$ (Sec. 8.6)   **29. a.** unlike   **b.** like   **c.** like   **d.** like (Sec. 8.7, Ex. 2)

30. a. -4 **b.** 9   **c.** $\dfrac{10}{63}$ (Sec. 8.5)   **31.** $-2x - 1$ (Sec. 8.7, Ex. 15)   **32.** $-15x - 2$ (Sec. 8.7)   **33.** 17 (Sec. 9.1, Ex. 1)   **34.** $-\dfrac{1}{6}$ (Sec. 9.1)

35. -10 (Sec. 9.2, Ex. 7)   **36.** 3 (Sec. 9.3)   **37.** 0 (Sec. 9.3, Ex. 4)   **38.** 72 (Sec. 9.2)   **39.** Republicans: 223; Democrats: 208 (Sec. 9.4, Ex. 4)

40. 5 (Sec. 9.3)   **41.** 79.2 yr (Sec. 9.5, Ex. 1)   **42.** 6 (Sec. 9.4)   **43.** 87.5% (Sec. 9.6, Ex. 1)   **44.** $\dfrac{C}{2\pi} = r$ (Sec. 9.5)   **45.** $-\dfrac{9}{10}$ (Sec. 9.2, Ex. 10)

46. $\{x \mid x > 5\}$ (Sec. 9.7)   **47.** 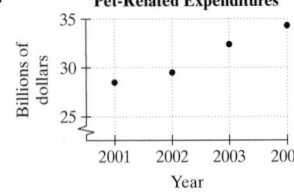 (Sec. 9.7, Ex. 2)   **48.** $\{x \mid x \le -10\}$ (Sec. 9.7)   **49.** $\{x \mid x \ge 1\}$ (Sec. 9.7, Ex. 9)

50. $\{x \mid x \le -3\}$ (Sec. 9.7)

CHAPTER 10 Graphing Equations and Inequalities

Mental Math   **1.** answers may vary; Ex. $(5, 5), (7, 3)$

Exercise Set 10.1   **1.**

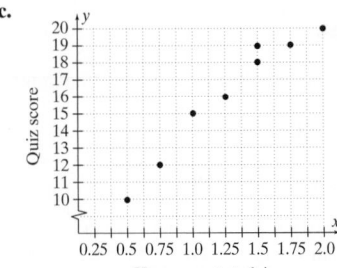

$(1, 5)$ and $(3.7, 2.2)$ are in quadrant I, $\left(-1, 4\dfrac{1}{2}\right)$ is in quadrant II, $(-5, -2)$ is in quadrant III, $(2, -4)$ and $\left(\dfrac{1}{2}, -3\right)$ are in quadrant IV, $(-3, 0)$ lies on the x-axis, $(0, -1)$ lies on the y-axis

3. $(0, 0)$ **5.** $(3, 2)$ **7.** $(-2, -2)$ **9.** $(2, -1)$ **11.** $(0, -3)$ **13.** $(1, 3)$ **15.** $(-3, -1)$

17. a. $(2001, 28.5), (2002, 29.5), (2003, 32.4), (2004, 34.3)$ **b.** In the year 2004, \$34.3 billion was spent on pet-related expenditures.
c.

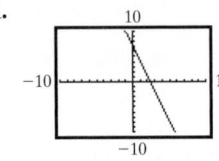

Pet-Related Expenditures

d. Pet-related expenditures increased every year.

19. a. $(0.50, 10), (0.75, 12), (1.00, 15), (1.25, 16), (1.50, 18), (1.50, 19), (1.75, 19), (2.00, 20)$ **b.** When Minh studied 1.25 hours, her quiz score was 16.
c.

(graph: Quiz score vs Hours spent studying)

d. answers may vary   **21.** $(-4, -2), (4, 0)$ **23.** $(-8, -5), (16, 1)$

25. $0; 7; -\dfrac{2}{7}$ **27.** $2; 2; 5$ **29.** $0; -3; 2$ **31.** $2; 6; 3$ **33.** $-12; 5; -6$ **35.** $\dfrac{5}{7}; \dfrac{5}{2}; -1$

37. $0; -5; -2$ **39.** $2; 1; -6$

(two coordinate graphs showing points $(-5, 1), (0, 0), (10, -2)$ and $(-3, 1), (0, 2), (-6, 0)$)

41. a. $13{,}000; 21{,}000; 29{,}000$ **b.** 45 desks
43. a. $10.6; 5.8; 1$ **b.** 2002   **45.** $y = 5 - x$
47. $y = \dfrac{5 - 2x}{4}$ **49.** $y = -2x$ **51.** false
53. true   **55.** negative; negative
57. positive; negative   **59.** $0; 0$ **61.** y
63. no; answers may vary   **65.** answers may vary
67. $(4, -7)$ **69.** 26 units
71. \$25 million, \$26 million, \$25 million, \$27 million
73. answers may vary

Calculator Explorations   **1.**

(graphing calculator screen, window -10 to 10)

3.

(graphing calculator screen, window -10 to 10)

5.

(graphing calculator screen, window -10 to 10)

Exercise Set 10.2   **1.** $6; -2; 5$ **3.** $-4; 0; 4$ **5.** $0; 2; -1$ **7.** $3; -1; -5$

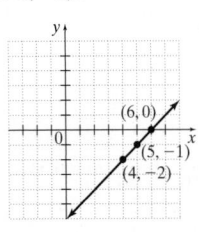 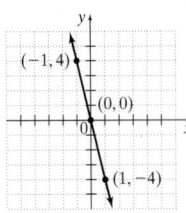 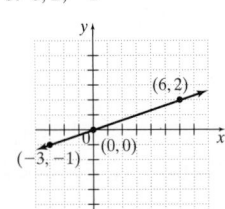 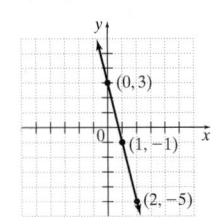

9. 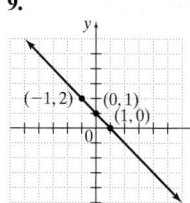 **11.** 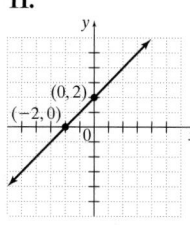 **13.** 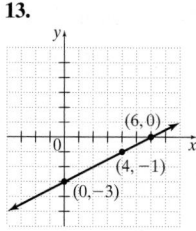 **15.** 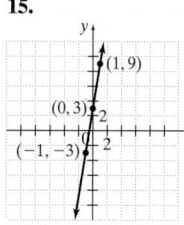 **17.** 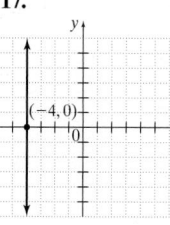 **19.**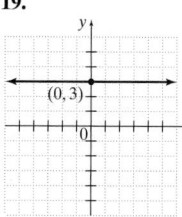

21. 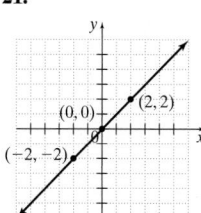 **23.** 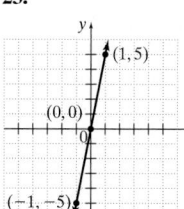 **25.** 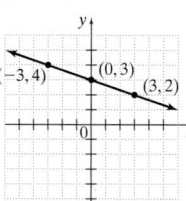 **27.** 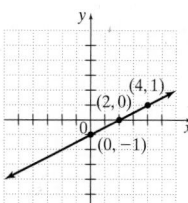 **29.** 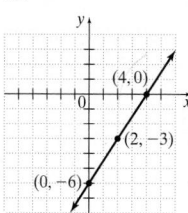 **31.**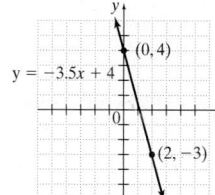

33. a. 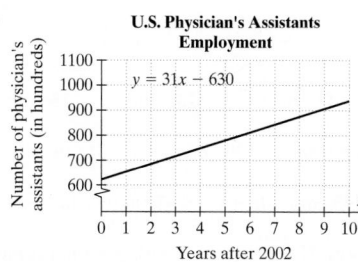 **b.** yes; answers may vary   **35. a.** 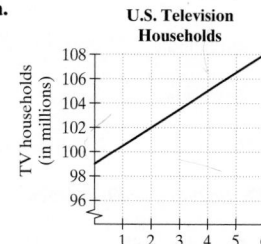 **b.** $(5, 106.5)$
c. In 2004, there were 106.5 million households in the United States with at least one television.

37. $(4, -1)$ **39.** $3; -3$ **41.** $0; 0$ **43.** 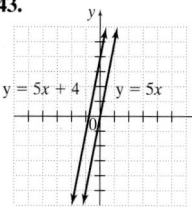   **45.** 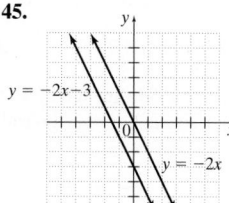   **47.** $0; 1; 1; 4; 4$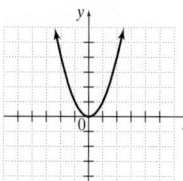

49. $x + y = 12$; 9 cm   **51.** yes; answers may vary

Calculator Explorations   **1.** 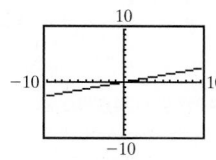   **5.**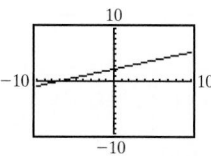

Mental Math   **1.** false   **3.** true   **5.** false

Exercise Set 10.3   **1.** $(-1, 0); (0, 1)$ **3.** $(-2, 0); (2, 0); (0, -2)$ **5.** $(-2, 0); (1, 0); (3, 0); (0, 3)$ **7.** $(-1, 0); (1, 0); (0, 1); (0, -2)$

9. 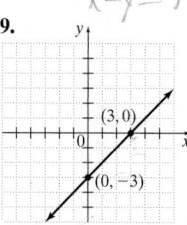 **11.** 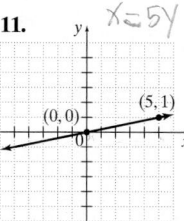 **13.** 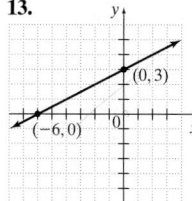 **15.** 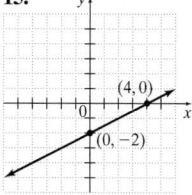 **17.** 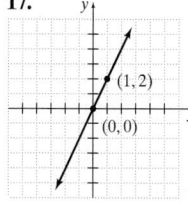 **19.**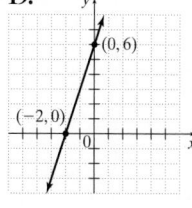

21. 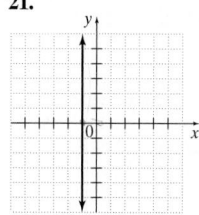 **23.** 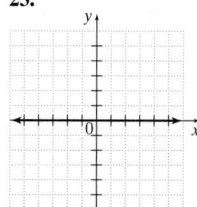 **25.** 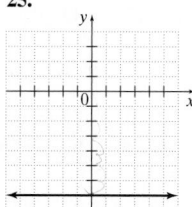 **27.** 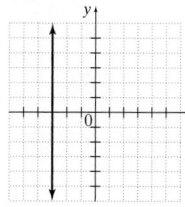 **29.** 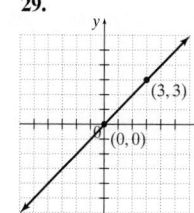 **31.**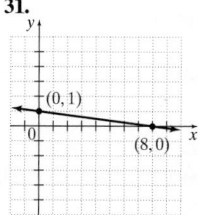

33. 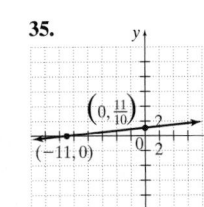   **35.** 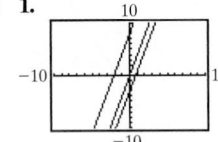   **37.** 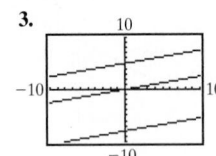   **39.** 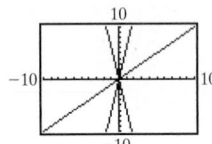   **41.** 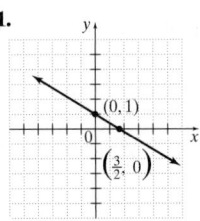   **43.**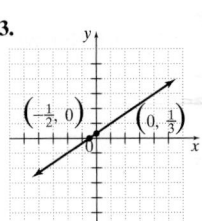

45. $\dfrac{3}{2}$ **47.** 6   **49.** $-\dfrac{6}{5}$ **51.** c   **53.** a   **55.** infinite   **57.** 0   **59.** answers may vary

61. a. $(0, 200)$; no chairs and 200 desks are manufactured.   **b.** $(400, 0)$; 400 chairs and no desks are manufactured.   **c.** 300 chairs   **63.** $y = -4$
65. a. $(0, 919)$ **b.** In 1999, the number of stores was 919.

Calculator Explorations   1. 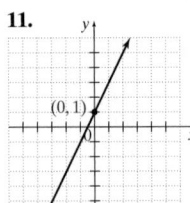   **3.**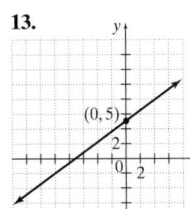

Mental Math   1. negative   **3.** undefined   **5.** upward   **7.** horizontal

Exercise Set 10.4   1. $m = -1$ **3.** $m = -\dfrac{1}{4}$ **5.** $m = 0$ **7.** undefined slope   **9.** $m = -\dfrac{4}{3}$ **11.** $m = \dfrac{5}{2}$ **13.** line 1   **15.** line 2

17. $m = 5$ **19.** $m = -0.3$ **21.** $m = -2$ **23.** undefined slope   **25.** $m = \dfrac{2}{3}$ **27.** undefined slope   **29.** $m = \dfrac{1}{2}$ **31.** $m = 0$

33. $m = -\dfrac{3}{4}$ **35.** $m = 4$ **37.** neither   **39.** neither   **41.** parallel   **43.** perpendicular   **45. a.** 1   **b.** -1 **47. a.** $\dfrac{9}{11}$ **b.** $-\dfrac{11}{9}$

49. $\dfrac{3}{5}$ **51.** 12.5%   **53.** 40%   **55.** 79%   **57.** $m = 3$; Every 1 year, there are/should be 3 million more U.S. households with personal computers.

59. $m = 0.42$; It costs $0.42 per 1 mile to own and operate a compact car.   **61.** $y = 2x - 14$ **63.** $y = -6x - 11$ **65.** d   **67.** b   **69.** e

71. $m = \dfrac{1}{2}$ **73.** answers may vary   **75.** 28.5   **77.** 1994 and 2000; 28.1 miles per gallon   **79.** from 2000 to 2001   **81.** $x = 20$

83. a. $(1993, 10{,}359)$; $(2003, 15{,}139)$ **b.** 478   **c.** For the years 1993 through 2003, the number of kidney transplants increased at a rate of 478 per year.
85. Opposite sides are parallel since their slopes are equal, so the figure is a parallelogram.   **87.** 2.0625   **89.** -1.6 **91.** the line becomes steeper

Calculator Explorations   1. 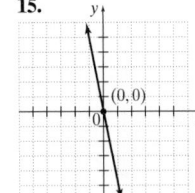   **3.**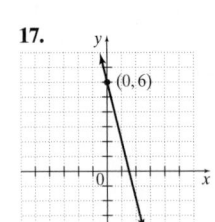

Mental Math   1. $m = 2$; $(0, -1)$ **3.** $m = 1$; $\left(0, \dfrac{1}{3}\right)$ **5.** $m = \dfrac{5}{7}$; $(0, -4)$ **7.** $m = 3$; answers may vary, Ex. $(4, 8)$ **9.** $m = -2$; answers

may vary, Ex. $(10, -3)$ **11.** $m = \dfrac{2}{5}$; answers may vary, Ex. $(-1, 0)$

Exercise Set 10.5   1. $y = 5x + 3$ **3.** $y = -4x - \dfrac{1}{6}$ **5.** $y = \dfrac{2}{3}x$ **7.** $y = -8$ **9.** $y = -\dfrac{1}{5}x + \dfrac{1}{9}$

11. 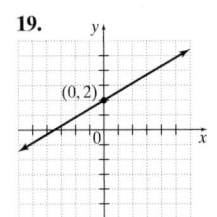   **13.**   **15.**   **17.**   **19.**   **21.**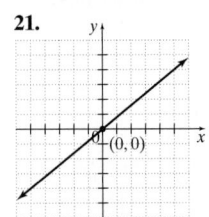

23. $-6x + y = -10$ **25.** $8x + y = -13$ **27.** $3x - 2y = 27$ **29.** $x + 2y = -3$ **31.** $2x - y = 4$ **33.** $8x - y = -11$

35. $4x - 3y = -1$ **37.** $8x + 13y = 0$ **39.** $y = -\dfrac{1}{2} + \dfrac{5}{3}$ **41.** $y = -x + 17$ **43.** $x = -\dfrac{3}{4}$ **45.** $y = x + 16$ **47.** $y = -5x + 7$

49. $y = 7$ **51.** $y = \dfrac{3}{2}x$ **53.** $y = -3$ **55.** $y = -\dfrac{4}{7}x - \dfrac{18}{7}$ **57. a.** $s = 32t$ **b.** 128 ft/sec

59. a. $y = 16{,}000x + 22{,}000$ **b.** 102,000 vehicles   **61. a.** $y = -333x + 7032$ **b.** 4368 cinema sites
63. a. $(0, 1509)$; $(6, 1456)$ **b.** $y = -8.8x + 1509$ **c.** 1491 daily newspapers   **65. a.** $S = -1000p + 13{,}000$ **b.** 9500 Fun Noodles   **67.** -1
69. 5   **71.** b   **73.** d   **75.** $3x - y = -5$ **77. a.** $3x - y = -5$ **b.** $x + 3y = 5$

Integrated Review   **1.** $m = 2$ **2.** $m = 0$ **3.** $m = -\dfrac{2}{3}$ **4.** slope is undefined

5. 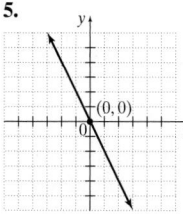   **6.** 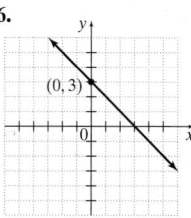   **7.** 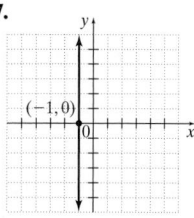   **8.**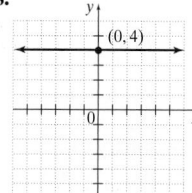

9. 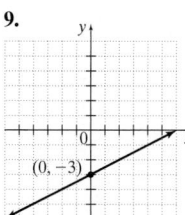   **10.** 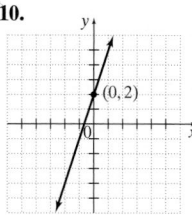   **11.** 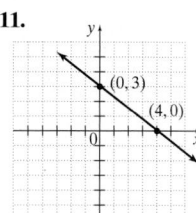   **12.**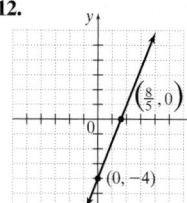

13. $m = 3$ **14.** $m = -6$ **15.** $m = -\dfrac{7}{2}$ **16.** $m = 2$ **17.** undefined slope   **18.** $m = 0$ **19.** $y = 2x - \dfrac{1}{3}$ **20.** $y = -4x - 1$

21. $-x + y = -2$ **22.** neither   **23.** perpendicular   **24. a.** $(1998, 1639); (2002, 2135)$ **b.** 124   **c.** For the years 1998 through 2002, the amount of yogurt produced increased at a rate of 124 million pounds per year.

Exercise Set 10.6   **1.** $\{-7, 0, 2, 10\}; \{-7, 0, 4, 10\}$ **3.** $\{0, 1, 5\}; \{-2\}$ **5.** yes   **7.** no   **9.** no   **11.** yes   **13.** yes   **15.** no
17. 9:30 P.M.   **19.** January 1 and December 1   **21.** yes; it passes the vertical line test   **23.** \$4.75 per hour   **25.** 2005
27. yes; answers may vary   **29.** $-9, -5, 1$ **31.** $6, 2, 11$ **33.** $-6, 0, 9$ **35.** $2, 0, 3$ **37.** $5, 0, -20$ **39.** $5, 3, 35$ **41.** $(3, 6)$ **43.** -1
45. -1 **47.** $-1, 5$ **49.** $x < 1$ **51.** $x \geq -3$ **53.** $\dfrac{19}{14}$ m or $1\dfrac{5}{14}$ m   **55.** $f(-5) = 12$ **57.** answers may vary   **59.** $f(x) = x + 7$
61. a. 190.4 mg   **b.** 380.8 mg

Mental Math   **1.** yes   **3.** yes   **5.** yes   **7.** no

Exercise Set 10.7   **1.** no; no   **3.** yes; no   **5.** no; yes   **7.** 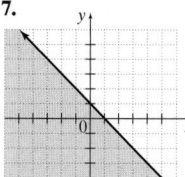   **9.** 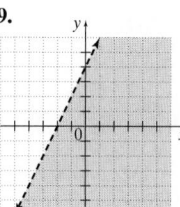   **11.**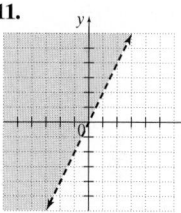

13. 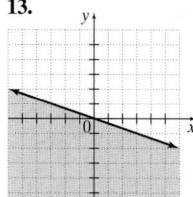   **15.** 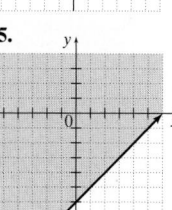   **17.** 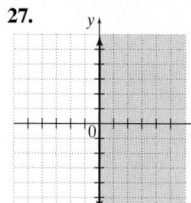   **19.** 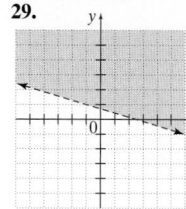   **21.**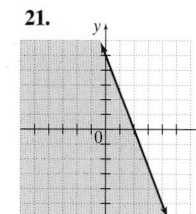

23. 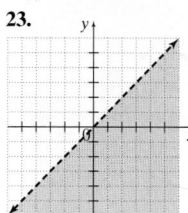   **25.**   **27.** 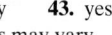   **29.** 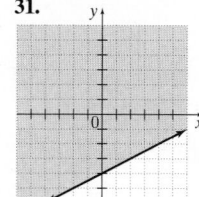   **31.**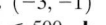

33. $(-2, 1)$ **35.** $(-3, -1)$ **37.** a   **39.** b   **41.** answers may vary   **43.** yes   **45.** yes
47. a. $30x + 0.15y \leq 500$ **b.**   **c.** answers may vary

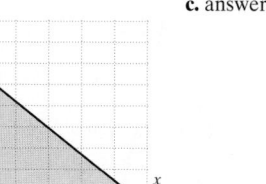

Mental Math   **1.** direct   **3.** inverse   **5.** inverse   **7.** direct

Exercise Set 10.8   **1.** $y = \frac{1}{2}x$ **3.** $y = 6x$ **5.** $y = 3x$ **7.** $y = \frac{2}{3}x$ **9.** $y = \frac{7}{x}$ **11.** $y = \frac{0.5}{x}$ **13.** $y = kx$ **15.** $h = \frac{k}{t}$

17. $z = kx^2$ **19.** $y = \frac{k}{z^3}$ **21.** $x = \frac{k}{\sqrt{y}}$ **23.** $y = 40$ **25.** $y = 3$ **27.** $z = 54$ **29.** $a = \frac{4}{9}$ **31.** \$62.50   **33.** \$6   **35.** $5\frac{1}{3}$ in.

37. 179.1 lb   **39.** 1600 feet   **41.** $2y = 16$ **43.** $-4x = 0.5$ **45.** multiplied by 3   **47.** it is doubled

Chapter 10 Vocabulary Check   **1.** solution   **2.** y-axis   **3.** linear   **4.** x-intercept   **5.** standard   **6.** y-intercept   **7.** function
8. slope-intercept   **9.** domain   **10.** range   **11.** relation   **12.** point-slope   **13.** y **14.** x-axis   **15.** x **16.** slope   **17.** direct
18. inverse

Chapter 10 Review   **1–6.**   **7.** $(7, 44)$ **8.** $\left(-\frac{13}{3}, -8\right)$ **9.** $-3; 1; 9$ **10.** $5; 5; 5$ **11.** $0; 10; -10$

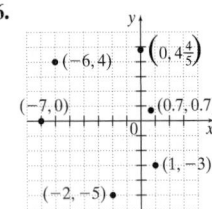

12. a. $2005; 2500; 7000$ **b.** 886 compact disc holders

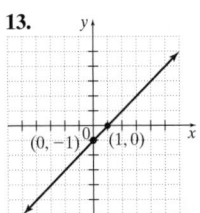   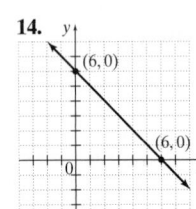   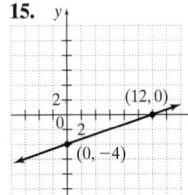   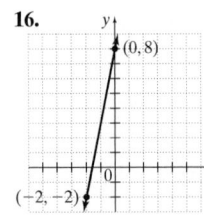   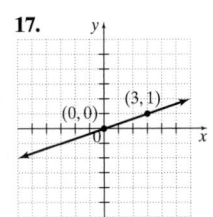 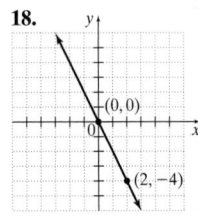

19. $(4, 0); (0, -2)$ **20.** $(-2, 0); (2, 0); (0, 2); (0, -2)$ **21.**   **22.**   **23.** $(12, 0), (0, -4)$

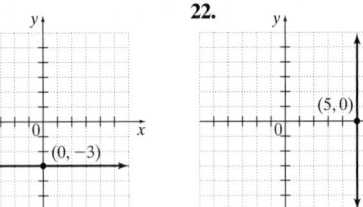

24. $(-2, 0), (0, 8)$ **25.** $m = -\frac{3}{4}$ **26.** $m = \frac{1}{5}$ **27.** d   **28.** b   **29.** c   **30.** a   **31.** $\frac{3}{4}$ **32.** $\frac{5}{3}$ **33.** 4   **34.** -1 **35.** 3

36. $\frac{1}{2}$ **37.** 0   **38.** undefined slope   **39.** perpendicular   **40.** parallel   **41.** neither

42. $m = 1.24$; Every 1 year, 1.24 million more persons have a bachelor's degree or higher.   **43.** $m = 27$; Every 1 year, 27 million more people go

on vacations.   **44.** $m = -3; (0, 7)$ **45.** $m = \frac{1}{6}; \left(0, \frac{1}{6}\right)$ **46.** $y = -5x + \frac{1}{2}$ **47.** $y = \frac{2}{3}x + 6$ **48.** d   **49.** c   **50.** a   **51.** b

52. $-4x + y = -8$ **53.** $3x + y = -5$ **54.** $-3x + 5y = 17$ **55.** $x + 3y = 6$ **56.** $y = -14x + 21$ **57.** $y = -\frac{1}{2}x + 4$ **58.** no

59. yes   **60.** yes   **61.** yes   **62.** no   **63.** yes   **64. a.** 6   **b.** 10   **c.** 5

65.   **66.**   **67.**   **68.**   **69.**   **70.**

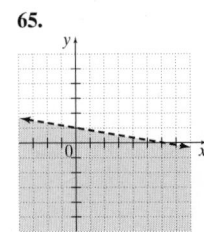   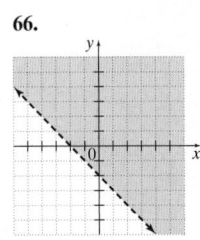   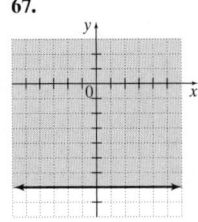   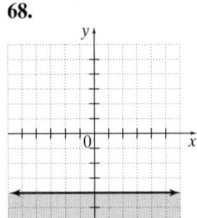   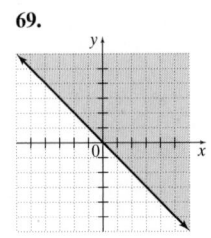 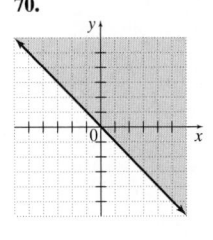

71. $y = 110$ **72.** $y = \frac{1}{2}$ **73.** $y = \frac{100}{27}$ **74.** $y = 700$ **75.** \$3960   **76.** $4\frac{4}{5}$ in.   **77.** $7; -1; -3$ **78.** $0; -3; -2$ **79.** $(3, 0); (0, -2)$

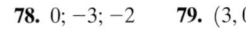

80. $(-2, 0); (0, 10)$ **81.**   **82.**   **83.**   **84.**

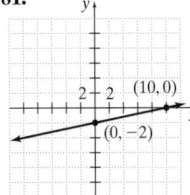   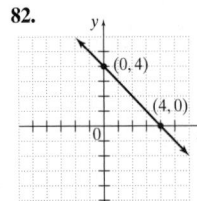   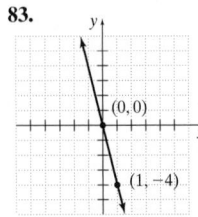 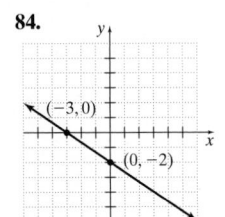

85. 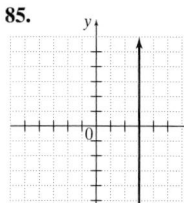 **86.** 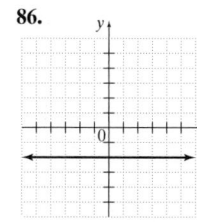 **87.** -1 **88.** $\dfrac{11}{7}$ **89.** 2 **90.** $-\dfrac{1}{3}$ **91.** $m = \dfrac{2}{3}; (0, -5)$

92. $m = -6; (0, 2)$ **93.** $5x + y = 8$ **94.** $3x - y = -6$ **95.** $4x + y = -3$

96. $5x + y = 16$

Chapter 10 Test **1.** $(1, 1)$ **2.** $(-4, 17)$ **3.** $m = \dfrac{2}{5}$ **4.** $m = 0$ **5.** $m = -1$ **6.** $m = -7$ **7.** $m = 3$ **8.** undefined slope

9. 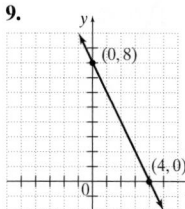 **10.** 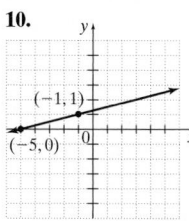 **11.** 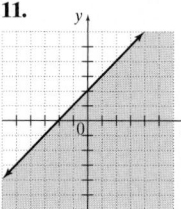 **12.** 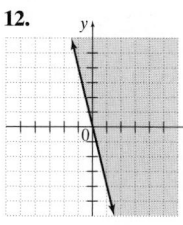 **13.** 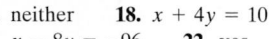 **14.**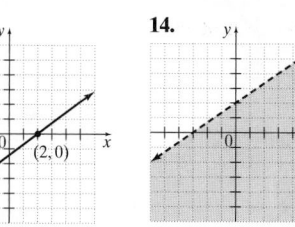

15. 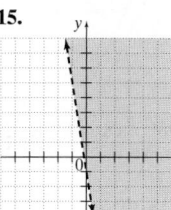 **16.** 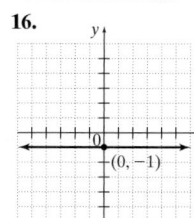 **17.** neither **18.** $x + 4y = 10$ **19.** $7x + 6y = 0$ **20.** $8x + y = 11$

21. $x - 8y = -96$ **22.** yes **23.** no **24.** yes **25.** yes

26. a. -8 **b.** -3.6 **c.** -4 **27. a.** 0 **b.** 0 **c.** 60 **28.** $x + 2y = 21; x = 5$ m

29. a. $(2000, 69.3); (2001, 70.0); (2002, 69.9); (2003, 70.1); (2004, 70.3); (2005, 70.5)$

b.

Basic Cable TV Subscribers

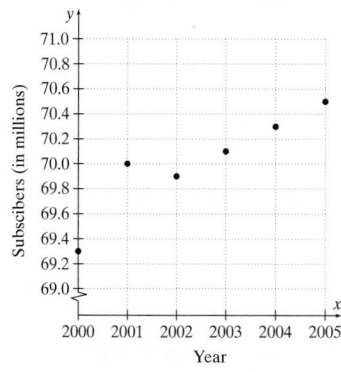

30. $m = 50$; Every 1 year, 50 million more movie tickets are sold. **31.** 28 **32.** $\dfrac{8}{9}$

Cumulative Review **1.** $78{,}875$ (Sec. 1.6, Ex. 5) **2.** $\dfrac{25}{44}$ (Sec. 2.4) **3.** $\dfrac{4}{5}$ (Sec. 2.5, Ex. 7) **4.** 236 (Sec. 1.7) **5.** $\dfrac{17}{21}$ (Sec. 3.3, Ex. 3)

6. $1\dfrac{11}{14}$ (Sec. 3.4) **7.** 48.26 (Sec. 4.1, Ex. 6) **8.** 0.08 (Sec. 4.1) **9.** 6.095 (Sec. 4.1, Ex. 7) **10.** $56{,}321$ (Sec. 1.6)

11. 3.432 (Sec. 4.3, Ex. 5) **12.** 13.5 (Sec. 4.5) **13.** 28.4405 (Sec. 4.5, Ex. 13) **14.** 20 (Sec. 1.9) **15.** 46% (Sec. 5.2, Ex. 2)

16. 80% (Sec. 5.2) **17.** 27 (Sec. 8.2, Ex. 2) **18.** $\dfrac{25}{7}$ (Sec. 3.3) **19.** 51 (Sec. 8.2, Ex. 5) **20.** 23 (Sec. 8.2) **21.** $30{,}384$ feet (Sec. 8.4, Ex. 10)

22. $0.8x - 36$ (Sec. 8.7) **23.** $2x + 6$ (Sec. 8.7, Ex. 16) **24.** $-15\left(x + \dfrac{2}{3}\right)$ (Sec. 8.7) **25.** $(x - 4) \div 7$ (Sec. 8.7, Ex. 17) **26.** $\dfrac{-9}{2x}$ (Sec. 8.7)

27. $5 + (x + 1) = 6 + x$ (Sec. 8.7, Ex. 18) **28.** $-86 - x$ (Sec. 8.7) **29.** 6 (Sec. 9.2, Ex. 1) **30.** -24 (Sec. 9.2) **31.**

$\{x \mid x < -2\}$ (Sec. 9.7, Ex. 6)

32. $\left\{x \mid x \le \dfrac{8}{3}\right\}$ (Sec. 9.7) **33. a.** $(0, 12)$ **b.** $(2, 6)$ **c.** $(-1, 15)$ (Sec. 10.1, Ex. 3) **34.** $0; 5; -2$ (Sec. 10.1)

35. 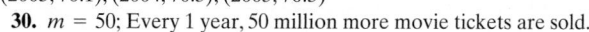 (Sec. 10.2, Ex. 1) **36.** $\dfrac{1}{5}$ (Sec. 10.4) **37.** $\dfrac{2}{3}$ (Sec. 10.4, Ex. 3) **38.** undefined slope (Sec. 10.4) **39.** $y = -2x + 3$ (Sec. 10.5, Ex. 4)

40. $m = \dfrac{2}{5}$, y-intercept: $(0, -2)$ (Sec. 10.5) **41. a.** $1; (2, 1)$ **b.** $1; (-2, 1)$ **c.** $-3; (0, -3)$ (Sec. 10.6, Ex. 6)

42. $3x - 2y = 0$ (Sec. 10.5)

CHAPTER 11   Systems of Equations

Calculator Explorations   **1.** $(0.37, 0.23)$ **3.** $(0.03, -1.89)$

Mental Math   **1.** 1 solution, $(-1, 3)$ **3.** infinite number of solutions   **5.** no solution   **7.** 1 solution, $(3, 2)$

Exercise Set 11.1   **1. a.** no   **b.** yes   **3. a.** yes   **b.** no   **5. a.** yes   **b.** yes   **7. a.** no   **b.** no

9. 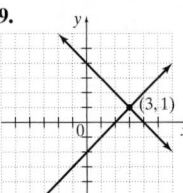   **11.** 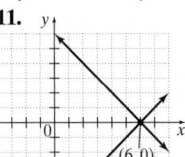   **13.** 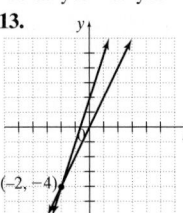   **15.**   **17.**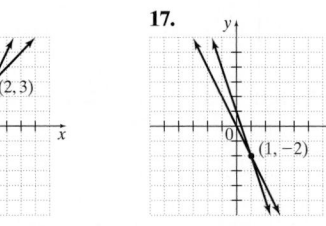

19. 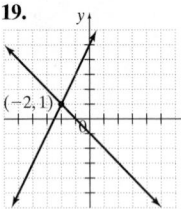   **21.** no solution 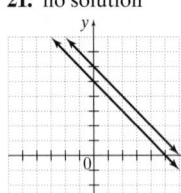   **23.** 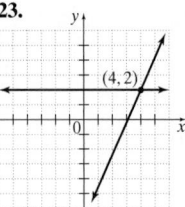   **25.** 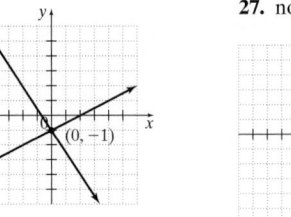   **27.** no solution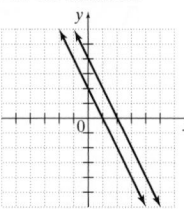

29. infinite number of solutions 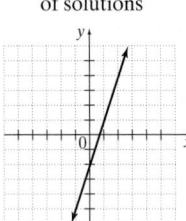   **31.** 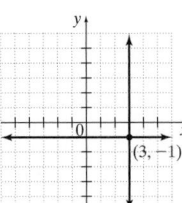   **33.** 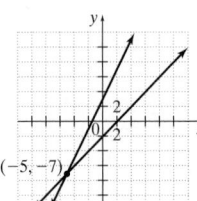   **35.** 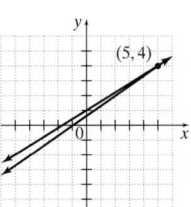   **37.** infinite number of solutions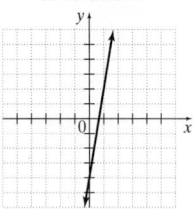

39. $x = 2$ **41.** $y = -\dfrac{2}{5}$ **43.** $a = 2$ **45.** answers may vary   **47.** answers may vary   **49.** 1984, 1988   **51.** 2003

53. answers may vary   **55.** answers may vary   **57.** answers may vary

Exercise Set 11.2   **1.** $(2, 1)$ **3.** $(-3, 9)$ **5.** $(2, 7)$ **7.** $\left(-\dfrac{1}{5}, \dfrac{43}{5}\right)$ **9.** $(2, -1)$ **11.** $(-2, 4)$ **13.** $(4, 2)$ **15.** $(-2, -1)$

17. no solution   **19.** $(3, -1)$ **21.** $(3, 5)$ **23.** $\left(\dfrac{2}{3}, -\dfrac{1}{3}\right)$ **25.** $(-1, -4)$ **27.** $(-6, 2)$ **29.** $(2, 1)$ **31.** no solution

33. infinite number of solutions   **35.** $\left(\dfrac{1}{2}, 2\right)$ **37.** $-6x - 4y = -12$ **39.** $-12x + 3y = 9$ **41.** $5n$ **43.** $-15b$ **45.** $(1, -3)$

47. answers may vary   **49.** no; answers may vary   **51.** c; answers may vary   **53.** $(-2.6, 1.3)$ **55.** $(3.28, 2.1)$ **57. a.** $(9, 17)$

b. In $1973 + 9 = 1982$, the percent of households that used fuel oil and electricity for heat was the same, 17%.   **c.**

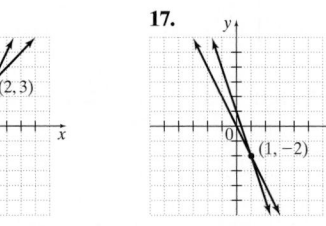

Heating Homes in America

Exercise Set 11.3   **1.** $(1, 2)$ **3.** $(2, -3)$ **5.** $(-2, -5)$ **7.** $(5, -2)$ **9.** $(-7, 5)$ **11.** $(6, 0)$ **13.** no solution

15. infinite number of solutions   **17.** $\left(2, -\dfrac{1}{2}\right)$ **19.** $(-2, 0)$ **21.** $(1, -1)$ **23.** infinite number of solutions   **25.** $\left(\dfrac{12}{11}, -\dfrac{4}{11}\right)$ **27.** $\left(\dfrac{3}{2}, 3\right)$

29. infinite number of solutions   **31.** $(1, 6)$ **33.** $\left(-\dfrac{1}{2}, -2\right)$ **35.** infinite number of solutions   **37.** $\left(-\dfrac{2}{3}, \dfrac{2}{5}\right)$ **39.** $(2, 4)$ **41.** $(-0.5, 2.5)$

43. $2x + 6 = x - 3$ **45.** $20 - 3x = 2$ **47.** $4(x + 6) = 2x$ **49.** $2; 6x - 2y = -24$ **51.** b; answers may vary   **53.** answers may vary
55. a. $b = 15$ **b.** any real number except 15   **57.** $(-8.9, 10.6)$ **59. a.** $(8, 536)$ or $(8, 537)$ **b.** In 2010 $(2002 + 8)$, the number of medical assistant jobs equals the number of computer software engineer jobs.   **c.** 536 thousand or 537 thousand

Integrated Review   **1.** $(2, 5)$ **2.** $(4, 2)$ **3.** $(5, -2)$ **4.** $(6, -14)$ **5.** $(-3, 2)$ **6.** $(-4, 3)$ **7.** $(0, 3)$ **8.** $(-2, 4)$ **9.** $(5, 7)$

10. $(-3, -23)$ **11.** $\left(\dfrac{1}{3}, 1\right)$ **12.** $\left(-\dfrac{1}{4}, 2\right)$ **13.** no solution   **14.** infinite number of solutions   **15.** $(0.5, 3.5)$ **16.** $(-0.75, 1.25)$

17. infinite number of solutions   **18.** no solution   **19.** $(7, -3)$ **20.** $(-1, -3)$ **21.** answers may vary   **22.** answers may vary

Exercise Set 11.4　**1.** c　　**3.** b　　**5.** a　　**7.** $\begin{cases} x + y = 15 \\ x - y = 7 \end{cases}$　**9.** $\begin{cases} x + y = 6500 \\ x = y + 800 \end{cases}$　**11.** 33 and 50　　**13.** 14 and −3

15. Jackson: 634 points; Leslie: 598 points　　**17.** child's ticket: $18; adult's ticket: $29　　**19.** quarters: 53; nickels: 27
21. McDonald's: $31.50; The Ohio Art Company: $6.50　　**23.** daily fee: $32; mileage charge: $0.25 per mi

25. distance downstream = distance upstream = 18 mi; time downstream: 2 hr; time upstream: $4\frac{1}{2}$ hr; still water: 6.5 mph; current: 2.5 mph

27. still air: 455 mph; wind: 65 mph　　**29.** $4\frac{1}{2}$ hr　　**31.** 12% solution: $7\frac{1}{2}$ oz; 4% solution: $4\frac{1}{2}$ oz　　**33.** $4.95 beans: 113 lb; $2.65 beans: 87 lb

35. 60°, 30°　　**37.** 20°, 70°　　**39.** number sold at $9.50: 23; number sold at $7.50: 67　　**41.** $2\frac{1}{4}$ mph and $2\frac{3}{4}$ mph　　**43.** 30%: 50 gal; 60%: 100 gal

45. length: 42 in.; width: 30 in.　　**47.** 16　　**49.** 36　　**51.** 100　　**53.** a　　**55.** width: 9 ft; length: 15 ft

Chapter 11 Vocabulary Check　**1.** dependent　　**2.** system of linear equations　　**3.** consistent　　**4.** solution　　**5.** addition; substitution
6. inconsistent　　**7.** independent

Chapter 11 Review　**1. a.** no　**b.** yes　　**2. a.** yes　**b.** no　　**3. a.** no　**b.** no　　**4. a.** no　**b.** yes

5. 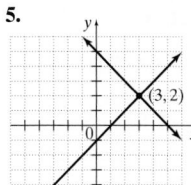　**6.** 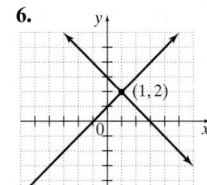　**7.** 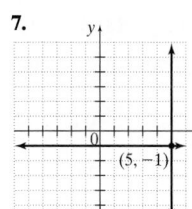　**8.** 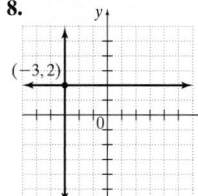　**9.**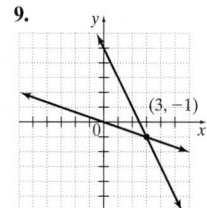

10. 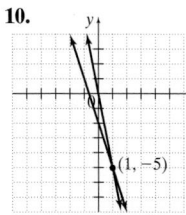　**11.** no solution　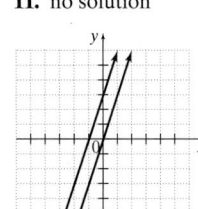　**12.** infinite number of solutions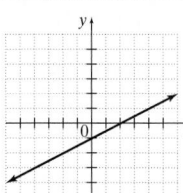

13. (−1, 4)　　**14.** (2, −1)　　**15.** (3, −2)
16. (2, 5)　　**17.** infinite number of solutions
18. infinite number of solutions　　**19.** no solution
20. no solution　　**21.** (−6, 2)　　**22.** (4, −1)
23. (3, 7)　　**24.** (−2, 4)　　**25.** infinite number of solutions
26. infinite number of solutions　　**27.** (8, −6)

28. $\left(-\frac{3}{2}, \frac{15}{2} \right)$　　**29.** −6 and 22

30. orchestra: 255 seats; balcony: 105 seats　　**31.** current of river: 3.2 mph; speed in still water: 21.1 mph

32. 6% solution: $12\frac{1}{2}$ cc; 14% solution: $37\frac{1}{2}$ cc　　**33.** egg: $0.40; strip of bacon: $0.65　　**34.** jogging: 0.86 hr; walking: 2.14 hr

35. 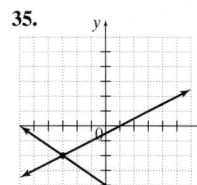　**36.** infinite number of solutions　**37.** (3, 2)　　**38.** (7, 1)　　**39.** $\left(1\frac{1}{2}, -3 \right)$

40. no solution　　**41.** infinite number of solutions　　**42.** (8, 11)　　**43.** (−5, 2)
44. (16, −4)　　**45.** infinite number of solutions　　**46.** no solution　　**47.** 4 and 8
48. −5 and 13　　**49.** 24 nickels and 41 dimes　　**50.** 13¢ stamps: 17; 22¢ stamps: 9

Chapter 11 Test　**1.** false　　**2.** false　　**3.** true　　**4.** false　　**5.** no　　**6.** yes

7. 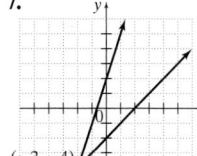　**8.** 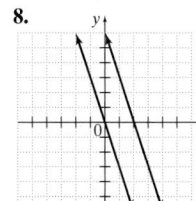　**9.** (−4, 1)　　**10.** $\left(\frac{1}{2}, -2 \right)$　　**11.** (20, 8)　　**12.** no solution　　**13.** (4, −5)　　**14.** (7, 2)

15. (5, −2)　　**16.** infinite number of solutions　　**17.** (−5, 3)　　**18.** $\left(\frac{47}{5}, \frac{48}{5} \right)$

19. 78, 46　　**20.** 120 cc　　**21.** Texas: 226 thousand; Missouri: 110 thousand
22. 3 mph; 6 mph　　**23.** 1999　　**24.** 1991–1999

Cumulative Review　**1.** $\frac{6}{5}$ (Sec. 2.4, Ex. 5)　　**2.** $\frac{123}{8}$ or $15\frac{3}{8}$ (Sec. 2.4)　　**3.** $\frac{2}{5}$ (Sec. 2.4, Ex. 6)　　**4.** $\frac{5}{54}$ (Sec. 2.4)　　**5.** 25.454 (Sec. 4.3, Ex. 1)

6. 681.24 (Sec. 4.3)　　**7.** 0.0849 (Sec. 4.4, Ex. 2)　　**8.** 0.375 (Sec. 4.1)　　**9.** 0.125 (Sec. 4.5, Ex. 3)　　**10.** $\frac{79}{10}$ (Sec. 4.1)　　**11.** 3.7 (Sec. 4.5, Ex. 12)

12. 3 (Sec. 5.1)　　**13.** $\frac{4}{9}, \frac{9}{20}$, 0.456 (Sec. 4.6, Ex. 9)　　**14.** 140 m/sec (Sec. 5.1)　　**15. a.** −6　**b.** 6.3 (Sec. 8.4, Ex. 6)　　**16. a.** 25　**b.** 32 (Sec. 8.2)

17. $\frac{1}{22}$ (Sec. 8.5, Ex. 9a)　　**18.** −22 (Sec. 8.3)　　**19.** $\frac{16}{3}$ (Sec. 8.5, Ex. 9b)　　**20.** $-\frac{3}{16}$ (Sec. 8.3)　　**21.** $-\frac{1}{10}$ (Sec. 8.5, Ex. 9c)　　**22.** 10 (Sec. 8.3)

23. $-\frac{13}{9}$ (Sec. 8.5, Ex. 9d)　　**24.** $\frac{9}{13}$ (Sec. 8.3)　　**25.** $\frac{1}{1.7}$ (Sec. 8.5, Ex. 9e)　　**26.** −1.7 (Sec. 8.3)　　**27. a.** 5　**b.** 8 − x (Sec. 9.1, Ex. 8)

28. -5 (Sec. 9.1) **29.** no solution (Sec. 9.3, Ex. 6) **30.** no solution (Sec. 9.3) **31.** 12 (Sec. 9.3, Ex. 3) **32.** 40 (Sec. 9.3)

33. $\left\{ x \mid x > \dfrac{13}{7} \right\}$ ←———∘———→ $\frac{13}{7}$ (Sec. 9.7, Ex. 8) **34.** $b = P - a - c$ (Sec. 9.5) **35.** $m = 0$ (Sec. 10.4, Ex. 5)

36. undefined slope (Sec. 10.4) **37.** $-x + 5y = 23$ (Sec. 10.5, Ex. 5) **38.** $y = -5x - 7$ (Sec. 10.5)

39. domain: $\{-1, 0, 3\}$; range: $\{-2, 0, 2, 3\}$ (Sec. 10.6, Ex. 1) **40.** -6; 14 (Sec. 10.6) **41.** It is a solution (Sec. 11.1, Ex. 1)

42. a. yes **b.** no **c.** no (Sec. 11.1) **43.** $\left(6, \dfrac{1}{2} \right)$ (Sec. 11.2, Ex. 3) **44.** $(-2, -4)$ (Sec. 11.2) **45.** $\left(-\dfrac{15}{7}, -\dfrac{5}{7} \right)$ (Sec. 11.3, Ex. 6)

46. $\left(-\dfrac{44}{3}, -\dfrac{7}{3} \right)$ (Sec. 11.3) **47.** 29 and 8 (Sec. 11.4, Ex. 1) **48. a.** no **b.** yes **c.** no (Sec. 10.6)

CHAPTER 12   Exponents and Polynomials

Mental Math 1. base: 3; exponent: 2 **3.** base: -3; exponent: 6 **5.** base: 4; exponent: 2 **7.** base: 5; exponent: 1; base: 3; exponent: 4
9. base: 5; exponent: 1; base: x; exponent: 2

Exercise Set 12.1 1. 49 **3.** -5 **5.** -16 **7.** 16 **9.** $\dfrac{1}{27}$ **11.** 112 **13.** 4 **15.** 135 **17.** 150 **19.** $\dfrac{80}{7}$ **21.** x^7

23. $(-3)^{12}$ **25.** $15y^5$ **27.** $x^{19}y^6$ **29.** $-72m^3n^8$ **31.** $-24z^{20}$ **33.** $20x^5$ sq ft **35.** x^{36} **37.** p^8q^8 **39.** $8a^{15}$ **41.** $x^{10}y^{15}$

43. $49a^4b^{10}c^2$ **45.** $\dfrac{r^9}{s^9}$ **47.** $\dfrac{m^9p^9}{n^9}$ **49.** $\dfrac{4x^2z^2}{y^{10}}$ **51.** $64z^{10}$ sq dm **53.** $27y^{12}$ cu ft **55.** x^2 **57.** -64 **59.** p^6q^5 **61.** $\dfrac{y^3}{2}$

63. 1 **65.** 1 **67.** -7 **69.** 2 **71.** -81 **73.** $\dfrac{1}{64}$ **75.** b^6 **77.** a^9 **79.** $-16x^7$ **81.** $a^{11}b^{20}$ **83.** $26m^9n^7$ **85.** z^{40}

87. $64a^3b^3$ **89.** $36x^2y^2z^6$ **91.** z^8 **93.** $3x$ **95.** 1 **97.** $81x^2y^2$ **99.** 40 **101.** $\dfrac{y^{15}}{8x^{12}}$ **103.** $2x^2y$ **105.** -2 **107.** 5

109. -7 **111.** c **113.** e **115.** answers may vary **117.** answers may vary **119.** 343 cu m **121.** volume
123. answers may vary **125.** answers may vary **127.** x^{9a} **129.** a^{5b} **131.** x^{5a}

Calculator Explorations 1. 5.31 EE 3 **3.** 6.6 EE -9 **5.** 1.5×10^{13} **7.** 8.15×10^{19}

Mental Math 1. $\dfrac{5}{x^2}$ **3.** y^6 **5.** $4y^3$

Exercise Set 12.2 1. $\dfrac{1}{64}$ **3.** $\dfrac{7}{x^3}$ **5.** -64 **7.** $\dfrac{5}{6}$ **9.** p^3 **11.** $\dfrac{q^4}{p^5}$ **13.** $\dfrac{1}{x^3}$ **15.** z^3 **17.** $\dfrac{4}{9}$ **19.** $\dfrac{1}{9}$ **21.** $-p^4$ **23.** -2

25. x^4 **27.** p^4 **29.** m^{11} **31.** r^6 **33.** $\dfrac{1}{x^{15}y^9}$ **35.** $\dfrac{1}{x^4}$ **37.** $\dfrac{1}{a^2}$ **39.** $4k^3$ **41.** $3m$ **43.** $-\dfrac{4a^5}{b}$ **45.** $-\dfrac{6}{7y^2}$ **47.** $\dfrac{27a^6}{b^{12}}$

49. $\dfrac{a^{30}}{b^{12}}$ **51.** $\dfrac{1}{x^{10}y^6}$ **53.** $\dfrac{z^2}{4}$ **55.** $\dfrac{x^{11}}{81}$ **57.** $\dfrac{49a^4}{b^6}$ **59.** $-\dfrac{3m^7}{n^4}$ **61.** $a^{24}b^8$ **63.** 200 **65.** x^9y^{19} **67.** $-\dfrac{y^8}{8x^2}$ **69.** $\dfrac{25b^{33}}{a^{16}}$

71. $\dfrac{27}{z^3x^6}$ cu in. **73.** 7.8×10^4 **75.** 1.67×10^{-6} **77.** 6.35×10^{-3} **79.** 1.16×10^6 **81.** 1.36×10^4 **83.** 0.0000000008673
85. 0.033 **87.** 20,320 **89.** 700,000,000 **91.** 9.4×10^8 **93.** 1,230,000,000,000
95. Yahoo!: 115,000,000: 1.15×10^8; eBay: 58,000,000; 5.8×10^7 **97.** 0.000036 **99.** 0.0000000000000000028 **101.** 0.0000005
103. 200,000 **105.** 2.7×10^9 gal **107.** $-2x + 7$ **109.** $2y - 10$ **111.** $-x - 4$ **113.** $9a^{13}$ **115.** -5 **117.** answers may vary

119. a. 1.3×10^1 **b.** 4.4×10^7 **c.** 6.1×10^{-2} **121. a.** false **b.** true **c.** false **123.** $\dfrac{1}{x^{9s}}$ **125.** a^{4m+5}

Exercise Set 12.3 1. 1; $-3x$; 5 **3.** -5; 3.2; 1; -5 **5.** 1; binomial **7.** 3; none of these **9.** 6; trinomial **11.** 4; binomial
13. a. -6 **b.** -11 **15. a.** -2 **b.** 4 **17. a.** -15 **b.** -10 **19.** 184 ft **21.** 595.84 ft **23.** 1044 thousand, or 1,044,000 visitors

25. $-11x$ **27.** $23x^3$ **29.** $16x^2 - 7$ **31.** $12x^2 - 13$ **33.** $7s$ **35.** $-1.1y^2 + 4.8$ **37.** $\dfrac{5}{6}x^4 - 7x^3 - 19$

39. $\dfrac{3}{20}x^3 + 6x^2 - \dfrac{13}{20}x - \dfrac{1}{10}$ **41.** 2, 1, 1, 0; 2 **43.** 4, 0, 4, 3; 4 **45.** $9ab - 11a$ **47.** $4x^2 - 7xy + 3y^2$ **49.** $-3xy^2 + 4$

51. $14y^3 - 19 - 16a^2b^2$ **53.** $7x^2 + 0x + 3$ **55.** $x^3 + 0x^2 + 0x - 64$ **57.** $5y^3 + 0y^2 + 2y - 10$
59. $2y^4 + 0y^3 + 0y^2 + 8y + 0y^0$ or $2y^4 + 0y^3 + 0y^2 + 8y + 0$ **61.** $6x^5 + 0x^4 + x^3 + 0x^2 - 3x + 15$ **63.** $4x^2 + 7x + x^2 + 5x$; $5x^2 + 12x$
65. $5x + 3 + 4x + 3 + 2x + 6 + 3x + 7x$; $21x + 12$ **67.** $10x + 19$ **69.** $-x + 5$ **71.** answers may vary **73.** answers may vary
75. x^{13} **77.** a^3b^{10} **79.** $2y^{20}$ **81.** answers may vary **83.** answers may vary **85.** $11.1x^2 - 7.97x + 10.76$

Exercise Set 12.4 1. $12x + 12$ **3.** $-3x^2 + 10$ **5.** $-3x^2 + 4$ **7.** $-y^2 - 3y - 1$ **9.** $7.9x^3 + 4.4x^2 - 3.4x - 3$ **11.** $\dfrac{1}{2}m^2 - \dfrac{7}{10}m + \dfrac{13}{16}$

13. $8t^2 - 4$ **15.** $15a^3 + a^2 - 3a + 16$ **17.** $-x + 14$ **19.** $5x^2 + 2y^2$ **21.** $-2x + 9$ **23.** $2x^2 + 7x - 16$ **25.** $2x^2 + 11x$

27. $-0.2x^2 + 0.2x - 2.2$ **29.** $\dfrac{2}{5}z^2 - \dfrac{3}{10}z + \dfrac{7}{20}$ **31.** $-2z^2 - 16z + 6$ **33.** $2u^5 - 10u^2 + 11u - 9$ **35.** $5x - 9$ **37.** $4x - 3$

39. $11y + 7$ **41.** $-2x^2 + 8x - 1$ **43.** $14x + 18$ **45.** $3a^2 - 6a + 11$ **47.** $3x - 3$ **49.** $7x^2 - 4x + 2$ **51.** $7x^2 - 2x + 2$
53. $4y^2 + 12y + 19$ **55.** $-15x + 7$ **57.** $-2a - b + 1$ **59.** $3x^2 + 5$ **61.** $6x^2 - 2xy + 19y^2$ **63.** $8r^2s + 16rs - 8 + 7r^2s^2$

65. $(x^2 + 7x + 4)$ ft   **67.** $\left(\dfrac{19}{2}x + 3\right)$ units   **69.** $(3y^2 + 4y + 11)$ m   **71.** $-6.6x^2 - 1.8x - 1.8$ **73.** $6x^2$ **75.** $-12x^8$
77. $200x^3y^2$ **79.** $2; 2$ **81.** $4; 3; 3; 4$ **83.** b   **85.** e   **87. a.** $4z$ **b.** $3z^2$ **c.** $-4z$ **d.** $3z^2$; answers may vary
89. a. m^3 **b.** $3m$ **c.** $-m^3$ **d.** $-3m$; answers may vary   **91.** $-0.325x^2 + 10.14x + 83.58$

Mental Math   1. x^8 **3.** cannot simplify   **5.** y^5 **7.** x^{14} **9.** $2x^7$

Exercise Set 12.5   1. $24x^3$ **3.** x^4 **5.** $-28n^{10}$ **7.** $-12.4x^{12}$ **9.** $-\dfrac{2}{15}y^3$ **11.** $-24x^8$ **13.** $6x^2 + 15x$ **15.** $7x^3 + 14x^2 - 7x$
17. $-2a^2 - 8a$ **19.** $6x^3 - 9x^2 + 12x$ **21.** $12a^5 + 45a^2$ **23.** $-6a^4 + 4a^3 - 6a^2$ **25.** $6x^5y - 3x^4y^3 + 24x^2y^4$
27. $-4x^3y + 7x^2y^2 - xy^3 - 3y^4$ **29.** $4x^4 - 3x^3 + \dfrac{1}{2}x^2$ **31.** $x^2 + 7x + 12$ **33.** $a^2 + 5a - 14$ **35.** $x^2 + \dfrac{1}{3}x - \dfrac{2}{9}$
37. $12x^4 + 25x^2 + 7$ **39.** $12x^2 - 29x + 15$ **41.** $1 - 7a + 12a^2$ **43.** $4y^2 - 16y + 16$ **45.** $x^3 - 5x^2 + 13x - 14$
47. $x^4 + 5x^3 - 3x^2 - 11x + 20$ **49.** $10a^3 - 27a^2 + 26a - 12$ **51.** $49x^2y^2 - 14xy + y^2$ **53.** $12x^2 - 64x - 11$
55. $2x^3 + 10x^2 + 11x - 3$ **57.** $2x^4 + 3x^3 - 58x^2 + 4x + 63$ **59.** $8.4y^7$ **61.** $-3x^3 - 6x^2 + 24x$ **63.** $2x^2 + 39x + 19$
65. $x^2 - \dfrac{2}{7}x - \dfrac{3}{49}$ **67.** $9y^2 + 30y + 25$ **69.** $a^3 - 2a^2 - 18a + 24$ **71.** $(4x^2 - 25)$ sq yd   **73.** $(6x^2 - 4x)$ sq in.   **75.** $25x^2$
77. $9y^6$ **79. a.** $6x + 12$ **b.** $9x^2 + 36x + 35$; answers may vary   **81.** $13x - 7$ **83.** $30x^2 - 28x + 6$ **85.** $-7x + 5$
87. $x^2 + 3x$ **89.** $x^2 + 5x + 6$ **91.** $11a$ **93.** $25x^2 + 4y^2$ **95. a.** $a^2 - b^2$ **b.** $4x^2 - 9y^2$ **c.** $16x^2 - 49$ **d.** answers may vary

Exercise Set 12.6   1. $x^2 + 7x + 12$ **3.** $x^2 + 5x - 50$ **5.** $5x^2 + 4x - 12$ **7.** $4y^2 - 25y + 6$ **9.** $6x^2 + 13x - 5$
11. $6y^3 + 4y^2 + 42y + 28$ **13.** $x^2 + \dfrac{1}{3}x - \dfrac{2}{9}$ **15.** $0.08 - 2.6a + 15a^2$ **17.** $2x^2 + 9xy - 5y^2$ **19.** $x^2 + 4x + 4$ **21.** $4x^2 - 4x + 1$
23. $9a^2 - 30a + 25$ **25.** $x^4 + x^2 + 0.25$ **27.** $y^2 - \dfrac{4}{7}y + \dfrac{4}{49}$ **29.** $4a^2 - 12a + 9$ **31.** $25x^2 + 90x + 81$ **33.** $9x^2 - 42xy + 49y^2$
35. $16m^2 + 40mn + 25n^2$ **37.** $25x^8 - 15x^4 + 9$ **39.** $a^2 - 49$ **41.** $x^2 - 36$ **43.** $9x^2 - 1$ **45.** $x^4 - 25$ **47.** $4y^4 - 1$
49. $16 - 49x^2$ **51.** $9x^2 - \dfrac{1}{4}$ **53.** $81x^2 - y^2$ **55.** $4m^2 - 25n^2$ **57.** $a^2 + 9a + 20$ **59.** $a^2 - 14a + 49$ **61.** $12a^2 - a - 1$
63. $x^2 - 4$ **65.** $9a^2 + 6a + 1$ **67.** $4x^2 + 3xy - y^2$ **69.** $a^2 - \dfrac{1}{4}y^2$ **71.** $6b^2 - b - 35$ **73.** $x^4 - 100$ **75.** $16x^2 - 25$
77. $25x^2 - 60xy + 36y^2$ **79.** $4r^2 - 9s^2$ **81.** $(4x^2 + 4x + 1)$ sq ft   **83.** $\dfrac{5b^5}{7}$ **85.** $-\dfrac{2a^{10}}{b^5}$ **87.** $\dfrac{2y^8}{3}$ **89.** c   **91.** d   **93.** 2
95. $(24x^2 - 32x + 8)$ sq m   **97.** answers may vary

Integrated Review   1. $35x^5$ **2.** $-32y^9$ **3.** -16 **4.** 16   **5.** $2x^2 - 9x - 5$ **6.** $3x^2 + 13x - 10$ **7.** $3x - 4$ **8.** $4x + 3$
9. $7x^6y^2$ **10.** $\dfrac{10b^6}{7}$ **11.** $144m^{14}n^{12}$ **12.** $64y^{27}z^{30}$ **13.** $16y^2 - 9$ **14.** $49x^2 - 1$ **15.** $\dfrac{y^{45}}{x^{63}}$ **16.** $\dfrac{1}{64}$ **17.** $\dfrac{x^{27}}{27}$ **18.** $\dfrac{r^{58}}{16s^{14}}$
19. $2x^2 - 2x - 6$ **20.** $6x^2 + 13x - 11$ **21.** $2.5y^2 - 6y - 0.2$ **22.** $8.4x^2 - 6.8x - 4.2$ **23.** $2y^2 - 6y - 1$ **24.** $6z^2 + 2z + \dfrac{11}{2}$
25. $x^2 + 8x + 16$ **26.** $y^2 - 18y + 81$ **27.** $2x + 8$ **28.** $2y - 18$ **29.** $7x^2 - 10xy + 4y^2$ **30.** $-a^2 - 3ab + 6b^2$
31. $x^3 + 2x^2 - 16x + 3$ **32.** $x^3 - 2x^2 - 5x - 2$ **33.** $6x^2 - x - 70$ **34.** $20x^2 + 21x - 5$ **35.** $2x^3 - 19x^2 + 44x - 7$
36. $5x^3 + 9x^2 - 17x + 3$ **37.** $4x^2 - \dfrac{25}{81}$ **38.** $144y^2 - \dfrac{9}{49}$

Mental Math   1. a^2 **3.** a^2 **5.** k^3

Exercise Set 12.7   1. $12x^3 + 3x$ **3.** $4x^3 - 6x^2 + x + 1$ **5.** $5p^2 + 6p$ **7.** $-\dfrac{3}{2x} + 3$ **9.** $-3x^2 + x - \dfrac{4}{x^3}$ **11.** $-1 + \dfrac{3}{2x} - \dfrac{7}{4x^4}$
13. $x + 1$ **15.** $2x + 3$ **17.** $2x + 1 + \dfrac{7}{x - 4}$ **19.** $3a^2 - 3a + 1 + \dfrac{2}{3a + 2}$ **21.** $4x + 3 - \dfrac{2}{2x + 1}$ **23.** $2x^2 + 6x - 5 - \dfrac{2}{x - 2}$
25. $x + 6$ **27.** $x^2 + 3x + 9$ **29.** $-3x + 6 - \dfrac{11}{x + 2}$ **31.** $2b - 1 - \dfrac{6}{2b - 1}$ **33.** $ab - b^2$ **35.** $4x + 9$ **37.** $x + 4xy - \dfrac{y}{2}$
39. $2b^2 + b + 2 - \dfrac{12}{b + 4}$ **41.** $y^2 + 5y + 10 + \dfrac{24}{y - 2}$ **43.** $-6x - 12 - \dfrac{19}{x - 2}$ **45.** $x^3 - x^2 + x$ **47.** 3   **49.** -4 **51.** $3x$
53. $9x$ **55.** $(3x^3 + x - 4)$ ft   **57.** $(2x + 5)$ m   **59.** answers may vary   **61.** c

The Bigger Picture   1. -5.93 **2.** $-\dfrac{2}{5}$ **3.** $5x^9y^4$ **4.** $\dfrac{1}{8a^4}$ **5.** $6y^3 - 2y^2 - 6y$ **6.** $8y^2 - 3y - 7$ **7.** $4x^3 - 13x^2 + 10x - 21$
8. $36m^2 - 60m + 25$ **9.** $4n - 1 + \dfrac{2}{n}$ **10.** $2x - 6 + \dfrac{14}{3x - 1}$ **11.** -0.6 **12.** $\{x \mid x > 0.6\}$ **13.** $\{x \mid x \le 2\}$ **14.** $\dfrac{2}{3}$

Vocabulary Check   1. term   **2.** FOIL   **3.** trinomial   **4.** degree of polynomial   **5.** binomial   **6.** coefficient   **7.** degree of a term
8. monomial   **9.** polynomials

Chapter 12 Review   1. base: 3; exponent: 2   **2.** base: -5; exponent: 4   **3.** base: 5; exponent: 4   **4.** base: x; exponent: 6   **5.** 512
6. 36   **7.** -36 **8.** -65 **9.** 1   **10.** 1   **11.** y^9 **12.** x^{14} **13.** $-6x^{11}$ **14.** $-20y^7$ **15.** x^8 **16.** y^{15} **17.** $81y^{24}$ **18.** $8x^9$
19. x^5 **20.** z^7 **21.** a^4b^3 **22.** x^3y^5 **23.** $\dfrac{4}{x^3y^4}$ **24.** $\dfrac{x^6y^6}{4}$ **25.** $40a^{19}$ **26.** $36x^3$ **27.** 3   **28.** 9   **29.** b   **30.** c   **31.** $\dfrac{1}{49}$

32. $-\dfrac{1}{49}$ **33.** $\dfrac{2}{x^4}$ **34.** $\dfrac{1}{16x^4}$ **35.** 125 **36.** $\dfrac{9}{4}$ **37.** $\dfrac{17}{16}$ **38.** $\dfrac{1}{42}$ **39.** x^8 **40.** z^8 **41.** r **42.** y^3 **43.** c^4 **44.** $\dfrac{x^3}{y^3}$

45. $\dfrac{1}{x^6 y^{13}}$ **46.** $\dfrac{a^{10}}{b^{10}}$ **47.** 2.7×10^{-4} **48.** 8.868×10^{-1} **49.** 8.08×10^7 **50.** -8.68×10^5 **51.** 1.124×10^8 **52.** 1.5×10^5

53. $867{,}000$ **54.** 0.00386 **55.** 0.00086 **56.** $893{,}600$ **57.** $1{,}431{,}280{,}000{,}000{,}000$ cu km   **58.** 0.0000000001 m   **59.** 0.016
60. $400{,}000{,}000{,}000$ **61.** 5 **62.** 2 **63.** 5 **64.** 6 **65.** $22; 78; 154.02; 400$ **66.** $2a^2$ **67.** $-4y$ **68.** $15a^2 + 4a$
69. $22x^2 + 3x + 6$ **70.** $-6a^2b - 3b^2 - q^2$ **71.** cannot be combined   **72.** $8x^2 + 3x + 6$ **73.** $2x^5 + 3x^4 + 4x^3 + 9x^2 + 7x + 6$
74. $-7y^2 - 1$ **75.** $-6m^7 - 3x^4 + 7m^6 - 4m^2$ **76.** $-x^2 - 6xy - 2y^2$ **77.** $-5x^2 + 5x + 1$ **78.** $-2x^2 - x + 20$ **79.** $6x + 30$
80. $9x - 63$ **81.** $8a + 28$ **82.** $54a - 27$ **83.** $-7x^3 - 35x$ **84.** $-32y^3 + 48y$ **85.** $-2x^3 + 18x^2 - 2x$ **86.** $-3a^3b - 3a^2b - 3ab^2$
87. $-6a^4 + 8a^2 - 2a$ **88.** $42b^4 - 28b^2 + 14b$ **89.** $2x^2 - 12x - 14$ **90.** $6x^2 - 11x - 10$ **91.** $4a^2 + 27a - 7$ **92.** $42a^2 + 11a - 3$
93. $x^4 + 7x^3 + 4x^2 + 23x - 35$ **94.** $x^6 + 2x^5 + x^2 + 3x + 2$ **95.** $x^4 + 4x^3 + 4x^2 - 16$ **96.** $x^6 + 8x^4 + 16x^2 - 16$
97. $x^3 + 21x^2 + 147x + 343$ **98.** $8x^3 - 60x^2 + 150x - 125$ **99.** $x^2 + 14x + 49$ **100.** $x^2 - 10x + 25$ **101.** $9x^2 - 42x + 49$
102. $16x^2 + 16x + 4$ **103.** $25x^2 - 90x + 81$ **104.** $25x^2 - 1$ **105.** $49x^2 - 16$ **106.** $a^2 - 4b^2$ **107.** $4x^2 - 36$ **108.** $16a^4 - 4b^2$

109. $(9x^2 - 6x + 1)$ sq m   **110.** $(5x^2 - 3x - 2)$ sq mi   **111.** $\dfrac{1}{7} + \dfrac{3}{x} + \dfrac{7}{x^2}$ **112.** $-a^2 + 3b - 4$ **113.** $a + 1 + \dfrac{6}{a - 2}$

114. $4x + \dfrac{7}{x + 5}$ **115.** $a^2 + 3a + 8 + \dfrac{22}{a - 2}$ **116.** $3b^2 - 4b - \dfrac{1}{3b - 2}$ **117.** $2x^3 - x^2 + 2 - \dfrac{1}{2x - 1}$

118. $-x^2 - 16x - 117 - \dfrac{684}{x - 6}$ **119.** $\left(5x - 1 + \dfrac{20}{x^2}\right)$ ft   **120.** $(7a^3b^6 + a - 1)$ units   **121.** $-\dfrac{1}{8}$ **122.** $4x^4y^7$ **123.** $\dfrac{2x^6}{3}$

124. $\dfrac{27a^{12}}{b^6}$ **125.** $\dfrac{x^{16}}{16y^{12}}$ **126.** $9a^2b^8$ **127.** $11x - 5$ **128.** $2y^2 - 10$ **129.** $5y^2 - 3y - 1$ **130.** $5x^2 + 3x - 2$ **131.** $28x^3 + 12x$

132. $6x^2 + 11x - 10$ **133.** $x^3 + x^2 - 18x + 18$ **134.** $28x^2 - 71x + 18$ **135.** $25x^2 + 40x + 16$ **136.** $36x^2 - 9$

137. $4a - 1 + \dfrac{2}{a^2} - \dfrac{5}{2a^3}$ **138.** $x - 3 + \dfrac{25}{x + 5}$ **139.** $2x^2 + 7x + 5 + \dfrac{19}{2x - 3}$

Chapter 12 Test   **1.** 32 **2.** 81 **3.** -81 **4.** $\dfrac{1}{64}$ **5.** $-15x^{11}$ **6.** y^5 **7.** $\dfrac{1}{r^5}$ **8.** $\dfrac{y^{14}}{x^2}$ **9.** $\dfrac{1}{6xy^8}$ **10.** 5.63×10^5

11. 8.63×10^{-5} **12.** 0.0015 **13.** $62{,}300$ **14.** 0.036 **15. a.** $4, 3; 7, 3; 1, 4; -2, 0$ **b.** 4 **16.** $-2x^2 + 12x + 11$

17. $16x^3 + 7x^2 - 3x - 13$ **18.** $-3x^3 + 5x^2 + 4x + 5$ **19.** $x^3 + 8x^2 + 3x - 5$ **20.** $3x^3 + 22x^2 + 41x + 14$ **21.** $6x^4 - 9x^3 + 21x^2$

22. $3x^2 + 16x - 35$ **23.** $9x^2 - \dfrac{1}{25}$ **24.** $16x^2 - 16x + 4$ **25.** $64x^2 + 48x + 9$ **26.** $x^4 - 81b^2$ **27.** 1001 ft; 985 ft; 857 ft; 601 ft

28. $(4x^2 - 9)$ sq in.   **29.** $\dfrac{x}{2y} + \dfrac{1}{4} - \dfrac{7}{8y}$ **30.** $x + 2$ **31.** $9x^2 - 6x + 4 - \dfrac{16}{3x + 2}$

Cumulative Review   **1.** 0.8496 (Sec. 4.4, Ex. 3)   **2.** 53.1 (Sec. 4.4)   **3. a.** $\dfrac{5}{7}$ **b.** $\dfrac{7}{24}$ (Sec. 5.1, Ex. 5)   **4.** $\dfrac{23}{36}$ (Sec. 3.3)   **5.** 5 (Sec. 5.4, Ex. 9)

6. $\dfrac{7}{12}$ (Sec. 2.4)   **7.** 75% (Sec. 5.4, Ex. 11)   **8.** $\dfrac{18}{23}$ (Sec. 2.5)   **9. a.** line   **b.** line segment   **c.** angle   **d.** ray (Sec. 6.1, Ex. 1)

10. $168°$ (Sec. 6.1)   **11.** 10 cm (Sec. 6.2 Ex. 3)   **12.** $34°$ (Sec. 6.2)   **13.** 50 ft (Sec. 6.3, Ex. 6)   **14.** 132 sq ft (Sec. 6.4)

15. a. $11, 112$ **b.** $0, 11, 112$ **c.** $-3, -2, 0, 11, 112$ **d.** $-3, -2, 0, \dfrac{1}{4}, 11, 112$ **e.** $\sqrt{2}$ **f.** $-2, 0, \dfrac{1}{4}, 112, -3, 11, \sqrt{2}$ (Sec. 8.1, Ex. 11)

16. a. 7.2 **b.** 0 **c.** $\dfrac{1}{2}$ (Sec. 8.1)   **17.** $\dfrac{1}{4}$ (Sec. 8.2, Ex. 4)   **18.** $\dfrac{3}{25}$ (Sec. 8.2)   **19. a.** $x + 3$ **b.** $3x$ **c.** $7.3 \div x$ or $\dfrac{7.3}{x}$ **d.** $10 - x$

e. $5x + 7$ (Sec. 8.2, Ex. 8)   **20.** 41 (Sec. 8.2)   **21.** $-9x - y + 2z - 6$ (Sec. 8.7, Ex. 10)   **22.** $4xy - 6y + 2$ (Sec. 8.7)   **23.** $a = 19$ (Sec. 9.1, Ex. 6)

24. $x = -\dfrac{1}{2}$ (Sec. 9.1)   **25.** $y = 140$ (Sec. 9.2, Ex. 4)   **26.** $x = \dfrac{12}{5}$ (Sec. 9.2)   **27.** $x = 4$ (Sec. 9.3, Ex. 5)   **28.** $x = 1$ (Sec. 9.3)

29. 10 (Sec. 9.4, Ex. 1)   **30.** $(x + 7) - 2x$ or $-x - 7$ (Sec. 9.1)   **31.** 40 feet (Sec. 9.5, Ex. 2)   **32.** undefined (Sec. 8.5)   **33.** 800 (Sec. 9.6, Ex. 2)

34. ⟵———○———⟶ (Sec. 9.7) 5 **35.** $\dfrac{b^3}{27a^6}$ (Sec. 12.2, Ex. 10)   **36.** $-15x^{16}$ (Sec. 12.2)   **37.** $\dfrac{1}{25y^6}$ (Sec. 12.2, Ex. 14)   **38.** $\dfrac{1}{9}$ (Sec. 12.2)

39. $10x^3$ (Sec. 12.3, Ex. 8)   **40.** $4y^2 - 8$ (Sec. 12.3)   **41.** $7x^3 + 14x^2 + 35x$ (Sec. 12.5, Ex. 4)   **42.** $100x^4 + 60x^2 + 9$ (Sec. 12.5)

CHAPTER 13   Factoring Polynomials

Mental Math   **1.** 2 **3.** 1 **5.** 7

Exercise Set 13.1   **1.** 4 **3.** 6 **5.** 1 **7.** y^2 **9.** z^7 **11.** xy^2 **13.** 7 **15.** $4y^3$ **17.** $5x^2$ **19.** $3x^3$ **21.** $9x^2y$ **23.** $10a^6b$
25. $3(a + 2)$ **27.** $15(2x - 1)$ **29.** $x^2(x + 5)$ **31.** $2y^3(3y + 1)$ **33.** $2x(16y - 9x)$ **35.** $4(x - 2y + 1)$ **37.** $3x(2x^2 - 3x + 4)$
39. $a^2b^2(a^5b^4 - a + b^3 - 1)$ **41.** $5xy(x^2 - 3x + 2)$ **43.** $4(2x^5 + 4x^4 - 5x^3 + 3)$ **45.** $\dfrac{1}{3}x(x^3 + 2x^2 - 4x^4 + 1)$ **47.** $(x^2 + 2)(y + 3)$
49. $(y + 4)(z + 3)$ **51.** $(z^2 - 6)(r + 1)$ **53.** $-1(x + 7)$ **55.** $-1(2 - z)$ **57.** $-1(-3a + b - 2)$ **59.** $(x + 2)(x^2 + 5)$

61. $(x + 3)(5 + y)$ **63.** $(3x - 2)(2x^2 + 5)$ **65.** $(5m^2 + 6n)(m + 1)$ **67.** $(y - 4)(2 + x)$ **69.** $(2x + 1)(x^2 + 4)$
71. $(x - 2y)(4x - 3)$ **73.** $(5q - 4p)(q - 1)$ **75.** $2(2y - 7)(3x^2 - 1)$ **77.** $x^2 + 7x + 10$ **79.** $b^2 - 3b - 4$ **81.** $2, 6$
83. $-1, -8$ **85.** $-2, 5$ **87.** $-8, 3$ **89.** b **91.** factored **93.** not factored **95. a.** 8684 thousand barrels per day
b. 9022 thousand barrels per day **c.** $-13(x^2 - 17x - 652)$ or $13(-x^2 + 17x + 652)$ **97.** $4x^2 - \pi x^2; x^2(4 - \pi)$ **99.** $(x^3 - 1)$ units
101. answers may vary **103.** answers may vary

Mental Math 1. $+5$ **3.** -3 **5.** $+2$

Exercise Set 13.2 1. $(x + 6)(x + 1)$ **3.** $(y - 9)(y - 1)$ **5.** $(x - 3)(x - 3)$ or $(x - 3)^2$ **7.** $(x - 6)(x + 3)$ **9.** $(x + 10)(x - 7)$
11. prime **13.** $(x + 5y)(x + 3y)$ **15.** $(a^2 - 5)(a^2 + 3)$ **17.** $(m + 13)(m + 1)$ **19.** $(t - 2)(t + 12)$ **21.** $(a - 2b)(a - 8b)$
23. $2(z + 8)(z + 2)$ **25.** $2x(x - 5)(x - 4)$ **27.** $(x - 4y)(x + y)$ **29.** $(x + 12)(x + 3)$ **31.** $(x - 2)(x + 1)$ **33.** $(r - 12)(r - 4)$
35. $(x + 2y)(x - y)$ **37.** $3(x + 5)(x - 2)$ **39.** $3(x - 18)(x - 2)$ **41.** $(x - 24)(x + 6)$ **43.** prime **45.** $(x - 5)(x - 3)$
47. $6x(x + 4)(x + 5)$ **49.** $4y(x^2 + x - 3)$ **51.** $(x - 7)(x + 3)$ **53.** $(x + 5y)(x + 2y)$ **55.** $2(t + 8)(t + 4)$ **57.** $x(x - 6)(x + 4)$
59. $2t^3(t - 4)(t - 3)$ **61.** $5xy(x - 8y)(x + 3y)$ **63.** $3(m - 9)(m - 6)$ **65.** $-1(x - 11)(x - 1)$ **67.** $\frac{1}{2}(y - 11)(y + 2)$
69. $x(xy - 4)(xy + 5)$ **71.** $2x^2 + 11x + 5$ **73.** $15y^2 - 17y + 4$ **75.** $9a^2 + 23ab - 12b^2$ **77.** $x^2 + 5x - 24$ **79.** answers may vary
81. $2x^2 + 28x + 66; 2(x + 3)(x + 11)$ **83.** $-16(t - 5)(t + 1)$ **85.** $\left(x + \frac{1}{4}\right)\left(x + \frac{1}{4}\right)$ or $\left(x + \frac{1}{4}\right)^2$ **87.** $(x + 1)(z - 10)(z + 7)$
89. $15; 28; 39; 48; 55; 60; 63; 64$ **91.** $9; 12; 21$ **93.** $(x^n + 10)(x^n - 2)$

Exercise Set 13.3 1. $x + 4$ **3.** $10x - 1$ **5.** $4x - 3$ **7.** $(2x + 3)(x + 5)$ **9.** $(y - 1)(8y - 9)$ **11.** $(2x + 1)(x - 5)$
13. $(4r - 1)(5r + 8)$ **15.** $(5x + 1)(2x + 3)$ **17.** $(3x - 2)(x + 1)$ **19.** $(3x - 5y)(2x - y)$ **21.** $(3m - 5)(5m + 3)$
23. $(x - 4)(x - 5)$ **25.** $(2x + 11)(x - 9)$ **27.** $(7t + 1)(t - 4)$ **29.** $(3a + b)(a + 3b)$ **31.** $(7p + 1)(7p - 2)$
33. $(6x - 7)(3x + 2)$ **35.** prime **37.** $(8x + 3)(3x + 4)$ **39.** $x(3x + 2)(4x + 1)$ **41.** $3(7b + 5)(b - 3)$ **43.** $(3z + 4)(4z - 3)$
45. $2y^2(3x - 10)(x + 3)$ **47.** $(2x - 7)(2x + 3)$ **49.** $3(x^2 - 14x + 21)$ **51.** $(4x + 9y)(2x - 3y)$ **53.** $-1(x - 6)(x + 4)$
55. $x(4x + 3)(x - 3)$ **57.** $(4x - 9)(6x - 1)$ **59.** $b(8a - 3)(5a + 3)$ **61.** $2x(3x + 2)(5x + 3)$ **63.** $2y(3y + 5)(y - 3)$
65. $5x^2(2x - y)(x + 3y)$ **67.** $-1(2x - 5)(7x - 2)$ **69.** $p^2(4p - 5)(4p - 5)$ or $p^2(4p - 5)^2$ **71.** $-1(2x + 1)(x - 5)$
73. $-4(12x - 1)(x - 1)$ **75.** $(2t^2 + 9)(t^2 - 3)$ **77.** prime **79.** $a(6a^2 + b^2)(a^2 + 6b^2)$ **81.** $x^2 - 16$ **83.** $x^2 + 4x + 4$
85. $4x^2 + 4x + 1$ **87.** no **89.** $4x^2 + 21x + 5; (4x + 1)(x + 5)$ **91.** $\left(2x + \frac{1}{2}\right)\left(2x + \frac{1}{2}\right)$ or $\left(2x + \frac{1}{2}\right)^2$
93. $(y - 1)^2(4x^2 + 10x + 25)$ **95.** $2; 14$ **97.** 2 **99.** answers may vary

Exercise Set 13.4 1. $(x + 3)(x + 2)$ **3.** $(y + 8)(y - 2)$ **5.** $(8x - 5)(x - 3)$ **7.** $(5x^2 - 3)(x^2 + 5)$ **9. a.** 9.2 **b.** $9x + 2x$
c. $(2x + 3)(3x + 1)$ **11. a.** $-20, -3$ **b.** $-20x - 3x$ **c.** $(3x - 4)(5x - 1)$ **13.** $(3y + 2)(7y + 1)$ **15.** $(7x - 11)(x + 1)$
17. $(5x - 2)(2x - 1)$ **19.** $(2x - 5)(x - 1)$ **21.** $(2x + 3)(2x + 3)$ or $(2x + 3)^2$ **23.** $(2x + 3)(2x - 7)$ **25.** $(5x - 4)(2x - 3)$
27. $x(2x + 3)(x + 5)$ **29.** $2(8y - 9)(y - 1)$ **31.** $(2x - 3)(3x - 2)$ **33.** $3(3a + 2)(6a - 5)$ **35.** $a(4a + 1)(5a + 8)$
37. $3x(4x + 3)(x - 3)$ **39.** $y(3x + y)(x + y)$ **41.** prime **43.** $6(a + b)(4a - 5b)$ **45.** $p^2(15p + q)(p + 2q)$
47. $(7 + x)(5 + x)$ or $(x + 7)(x + 5)$ **49.** $(6 - 5x)(1 - x)$ or $(5x - 6)(x - 1)$ **51.** $x^2 - 4$ **53.** $y^2 + 8y + 16$ **55.** $81z^2 - 25$
57. $16x^2 - 24x + 9$ **59.** $10x^2 + 45x + 45; 5(2x + 3)(x + 3)$ **61.** $(x^n + 2)(x^n + 3)$ **63.** $(3x^n - 5)(x^n + 7)$ **65.** answers may vary

Calculator Explorations

	$x^2 - 2x + 1$	$x^2 - 2x - 1$	$(x - 1)^2$
$x = 5$	16	14	16
$x = -3$	16	14	16
$x = 2.7$	2.89	0.89	2.89
$x = -12.1$	171.61	169.61	171.61
$x = 0$	1	-1	1

Mental Math 1. 1^2 **3.** 9^2 **5.** 3^2 **7.** $(3x)^2$ **9.** $(5a)^2$ **11.** $(6p^2)^2$

Exercise Set 13.5 1. yes **3.** no **5.** yes **7.** no **9.** no **11.** yes **13.** $(x + 11)^2$ **15.** $(x - 8)^2$ **17.** $(4a - 3)^2$
19. $(x^2 + 2)^2$ **21.** $2(n - 7)^2$ **23.** $(4y + 5)^2$ **25.** $(xy - 5)^2$ **27.** $m(m + 9)^2$ **29.** prime **31.** $(3x - 4y)^2$
33. $(x + 2)(x - 2)$ **35.** $(9 + p)(9 - p)$ or $-1(p + 9)(p - 9)$ **37.** $-1(2r + 1)(2r - 1)$ **39.** $(3x + 4)(3x - 4)$ **41.** prime
43. $(-6 + x)(6 + x)$ or $-1(6 + x)(6 - x)$ **45.** $(m^2 + 1)(m + 1)(m - 1)$ **47.** $(x + 13y)(x - 13y)$ **49.** $2(3r + 2)(3r - 2)$
51. $x(3y + 2)(3y - 2)$ **53.** $16x^2(x + 2)(x - 2)$ **55.** $xy(y - 3z)(y + 3z)$ **57.** $4(3x - 4y)(3x + 4y)$ **59.** $9(4 - 3x)(4 + 3x)$
61. $(5y - 3)(5y + 3)$ **63.** $(11m + 10n)(11m - 10n)$ **65.** $(xy - 1)(xy + 1)$ **67.** $\left(x - \frac{1}{2}\right)\left(x + \frac{1}{2}\right)$ **69.** $\left(7 - \frac{3}{5}m\right)\left(7 + \frac{3}{5}m\right)$
71. $(9a + 5b)(9a - 5b)$ **73.** $(x + 7y)^2$ **75.** $2(4n^2 - 7)^2$ **77.** $x^2(x^2 + 9)(x + 3)(x - 3)$ **79.** $pq(8p + 9q)(8p - 9q)$
81. $x = 6$ **83.** $m = -2$ **85.** $z = \frac{1}{5}$ **87.** $\left(x - \frac{1}{3}\right)^2$ **89.** $(x + 2 + y)(x + 2 - y)$ **91.** $(b - 4)(a + 4)(a - 4)$
93. $(x + 3 + 2y)(x + 3 - 2y)$ **95.** $(x^n + 10)(x^n - 10)$ **97.** 8 **99.** answers may vary **101.** $(x + 6)$ **103.** $a^2 + 2ab + b^2$
105. a. 777 ft **b.** 441 ft **c.** 7 sec **d.** $(29 + 4t)(29 - 4t)$ **107. a.** 1456 feet **b.** 816 feet **c.** 10 seconds **d.** $16(10 + t)(10 - t)$

Integrated Review   1. $(x - 3)(x + 4)$ **2.** $(x - 8)(x - 2)$ **3.** $(x + 2)(x - 3)$ **4.** $(x + 1)^2$ **5.** $(x - 3)^2$ **6.** $(x + 2)(x - 1)$
7. $(x + 3)(x - 2)$ **8.** $(x + 3)(x + 4)$ **9.** $(x - 5)(x - 2)$ **10.** $(x - 6)(x + 5)$ **11.** $2(x - 7)(x + 7)$ **12.** $3(x - 5)(x + 5)$
13. $(x + 3)(x + 5)$ **14.** $(y - 7)(3 + x)$ **15.** $(x + 8)(x - 2)$ **16.** $(x - 7)(x + 4)$ **17.** $4x(x + 7)(x - 2)$ **18.** $6x(x - 5)(x + 4)$
19. $2(3x + 4)(2x + 3)$ **20.** $(2a - b)(4a + 5b)$ **21.** $(2a + b)(2a - b)$ **22.** $(x + 5y)(x - 5y)$ **23.** $(4 - 3x)(7 + 2x)$
24. $(5 - 2x)(4 + x)$ **25.** prime   **26.** prime   **27.** $(3y + 5)(2y - 3)$ **28.** $(4x - 5)(x + 1)$ **29.** $9x(2x^2 - 7x + 1)$
30. $4a(3a^2 - 6a + 1)$ **31.** $(4a - 7)^2$ **32.** $(5p - 7)^2$ **33.** $(7 - x)(2 + x)$ **34.** $(3 + x)(1 - x)$ **35.** $3x^2y(x + 6)(x - 4)$
36. $2xy(x + 5y)(x - y)$ **37.** $3xy(4x^2 + 81)$ **38.** $2xy^2(3x^2 + 4)$ **39.** $2xy(1 + 6x)(1 - 6x)$ **40.** $2x(x - 3)(x + 3)$
41. $(x + 6)(x + 2)(x - 2)$ **42.** $(x - 2)(x + 6)(x - 6)$ **43.** $2a^2(3a + 5)$ **44.** $2n(2n - 3)$ **45.** $(3x - 1)(x^2 + 4)$
46. $(x - 2)(x^2 + 3)$ **47.** $6(x + 2y)(x + y)$ **48.** $2(x + 4y)(6x - y)$ **49.** $(x + y)(5 + x)$ **50.** $(x - y)(7 + y)$
51. $(7t - 1)(2t - 1)$ **52.** prime   **53.** $-1(3x + 5)(x - 1)$ **54.** $-1(7x - 2)(x + 3)$ **55.** $(1 - 10a)(1 + 2a)$ **56.** $(1 + 5a)(1 - 12a)$
57. $(x + 3)(x - 3)(x - 1)(x + 1)$ **58.** $(x + 3)(x - 3)(x + 2)(x - 2)$ **59.** $(x - 15)(x - 8)$ **60.** $(y + 16)(y + 6)$ **61.** prime
62. $(4a - 7b)^2$ **63.** $(5p - 7q)^2$ **64.** $(7x + 3y)(3 + 3y)$ **65.** $-1(x - 5)(x + 6)$ **66.** $-1(x - 2)(x - 4)$ **67.** $(3r - 1)(s + 4)$
68. $(x - 2)(x^2 + 1)$ **69.** $(x - 2y)(4x - 3)$ **70.** $(2x - y)(2x + 7z)$ **71.** $(x + 12y)(x - 3y)$ **72.** $(3x - 2y)(x + 4y)$
73. $(x^2 + 2)(x + 4)(x - 4)$ **74.** $(x^2 + 3)(x + 5)(x - 5)$ **75.** answers may vary   **76.** yes; $9(x^2 + 9y^2)$

Mental Math   1. $3, 7$ **3.** $-8, -6$ **5.** $-1, 3$

Exercise Set 13.6   1. $2, -1$ **3.** $6, 7$ **5.** $-9, -17$ **7.** $0, -6$ **9.** $0, 8$ **11.** $-\dfrac{3}{2}, \dfrac{5}{4}$ **13.** $\dfrac{7}{2}, -\dfrac{2}{7}$ **15.** $\dfrac{1}{2}, -\dfrac{1}{3}$ **17.** $-0.2, -1.5$

19. $9, 4$ **21.** $-4, 2$ **23.** $0, 7$ **25.** $0, -20$ **27.** $4, -4$ **29.** $8, -4$ **31.** $-3, 12$ **33.** $\dfrac{7}{3}, -2$ **35.** $\dfrac{8}{3}, -9$ **37.** $0, -\dfrac{1}{2}, \dfrac{1}{2}$ **39.** $\dfrac{17}{2}$

41. $\dfrac{3}{4}$ **43.** $-\dfrac{1}{2}, \dfrac{1}{2}$ **45.** $-\dfrac{3}{2}, -\dfrac{1}{2}, 3$ **47.** $-5, 3$ **49.** $-\dfrac{5}{6}, \dfrac{6}{5}$ **51.** $2, -\dfrac{4}{5}$ **53.** $-\dfrac{4}{3}, 5$ **55.** $-4, 3$ **57.** $0, 8, 4$

59. -7 **61.** $0, \dfrac{3}{2}$ **63.** $0, 1, -1$ **65.** $-6, \dfrac{4}{3}$ **67.** $\dfrac{6}{7}, 1$ **69.** $\dfrac{47}{45}$ **71.** $\dfrac{17}{60}$ **73.** $\dfrac{7}{10}$

75. didn't write equation in standard form; should be $x = 4$ or $x = -2$ **77.** answers may vary, for example, $(x - 6)(x + 1) = 0$

79. answers may vary, for example, $x^2 - 12x + 35 = 0$ **81. a.** $300; 304; 276; 216; 124; 0; -156$ **b.** 5 sec   **c.** 304 ft   **83.** $0, \dfrac{1}{2}$ **85.** $0, -15$

The Bigger Picture   1. -34 **2.** x^{22} **3.** $-4x^3 - 6x^2 + 8$ **4.** $y - 1 + \dfrac{3}{y^2}$ **5.** $10x(x + 5)(x - 5)$ **6.** $(x - 1)(x - 35)$

7. $3(2y + 5)(x - 1)$ **8.** $x(5y - 7)(y + 1)$ **9.** $5, -\dfrac{1}{2}$ **10.** 1 **11.** $-2, 14$ **12.** $\dfrac{33}{17}$

Exercise Set 13.7   1. width: x; length: $x + 4$ **3.** x and $x + 2$ if x is an odd integer   **5.** base: x; height: $4x + 1$ **7.** 11 units
9. 15 cm, 13 cm, 22 cm, 70 cm   **11.** base: 16 mi; height: 6 mi   **13.** 5 sec   **15.** width: 5 cm; length: 6 cm   **17.** 54 diagonals
19. 10 sides   **21.** -12 or 11   **23.** 14, 15   **25.** 13 feet   **27.** 5 in.   **29.** 12 mm, 16 mm, 20 mm   **31.** 10 km   **33.** 36 ft   **35.** 9.5 sec
37. 20%   **39.** length: 15 mi; width: 8 mi   **41.** 105 units   **43.** 11,250 thousand acres   **45.** 10,750 thousand acres   **47.** 1995
49. answers may vary   **51.** 8 m   **53.** 10 and 15   **55.** width of pool: 29 m; length of pool: 35 m

Chapter 13 Vocabulary Check   1. quadratic equation   **2.** factoring   **3.** greatest common factor   **4.** perfect square trinomial

Chapter 13 Review   1. $2x - 5$ **2.** $2x^4 + 1 - 5x^3$ **3.** $5(m + 6)$ **4.** $4x(5x^2 + 3x + 6)$ **5.** $(2x + 3)(3x - 5)$ **6.** $(x + 1)(5x - 1)$
7. $(x - 1)(3x + 2)$ **8.** $(3x + 5)(2x - 1)$ **9.** $(a + 3b)(3a + b)$ **10.** $(x + 4)(x + 2)$ **11.** $(x - 8)(x - 3)$ **12.** prime
13. $(x - 6)(x + 1)$ **14.** $(x + 4)(x - 2)$ **15.** $(x + 6y)(x - 2y)$ **16.** $(x + 5y)(x + 3y)$ **17.** $2(3 - x)(12 + x)$
18. $4(8 + 3x - x^2)$ **19.** $5y(y - 6)(y - 4)$ **20.** $-48, 2$ **21.** factor out the GCF, 3   **22.** $(2x + 1)(x + 6)$ **23.** $(2x + 3)(2x - 1)$
24. $(3x + 4y)(2x - y)$ **25.** prime   **26.** $(2x + 3)(x - 13)$ **27.** $(6x + 5y)(3x - 4y)$ **28.** $5y(2y - 3)(y + 4)$
29. $5x^2 - 9x - 2; (5x + 1)(x - 2)$ **30.** $16x^2 - 28x + 6; 2(4x - 1)(2x - 3)$ **31.** yes   **32.** no   **33.** no   **34.** yes   **35.** yes
36. no   **37.** yes   **38.** no   **39.** $(x + 9)(x - 9)$ **40.** $(x + 6)^2$ **41.** $(2x + 3)(2x - 3)$ **42.** $(3t + 5s)(3t - 5s)$ **43.** prime
44. $(n - 9)^2$ **45.** $3(r + 6)^2$ **46.** $(3y - 7)^2$ **47.** $5m^6(m + 1)(m - 1)$ **48.** $(2x - 7y)^2$ **49.** $3y(x + y)^2$

50. $(4x^2 + 1)(2x + 1)(2x - 1)$ **51.** $-6, 2$ **52.** $0, -1, \dfrac{2}{7}$ **53.** $-\dfrac{1}{5}, -3$ **54.** $-7, -1$ **55.** $-4, 6$ **56.** -5 **57.** $2, 8$ **58.** $\dfrac{1}{3}$

59. $-\dfrac{2}{7}, \dfrac{3}{8}$ **60.** $0, 6$ **61.** $5, -5$ **62.** $x^2 - 9x + 20 = 0$ **63.** c   **64.** d   **65.** 9 units   **66.** 8 units, 13 units, 16 units, 10 units
67. width: 20 in.; length: 25 in.   **68.** 36 yd   **69.** 19 and 20   **70. a.** 17.5 sec and 10 sec; answers may vary   **b.** 27.5 sec   **71.** 32 cm
72. $6(x + 4)$ **73.** $7(x - 9)$ **74.** $(4x - 3)(11x - 6)$ **75.** $(x - 5)(2x - 1)$ **76.** $(3x - 4)(x^2 + 2)$ **77.** $(y + 2)(x - 1)$
78. $2(x + 4)(x - 3)$ **79.** $3x(x - 9)(x - 1)$ **80.** $(2x + 9)(2x - 9)$ **81.** $2(x + 3)(x - 3)$ **82.** $(4x - 3)^2$ **83.** $5(x + 2)^2$

84. $-\dfrac{7}{2}, 4$ **85.** $-3, 5$ **86.** $0, -7, -4$ **87.** $3, 2$ **88.** $0, 16$ **89.** 19 in.; 8 in.; 21 in.   **90.** length: 6 in.; width: 2 in.

Chapter 13 Test   1. $3x(3x - 1)$ **2.** $(x + 7)(x + 4)$ **3.** $(7 + m)(7 - m)$ **4.** $(y + 11)^2$ **5.** $(x^2 + 4)(x + 2)(x - 2)$
6. $(a + 3)(4 - y)$ **7.** prime   **8.** $(y - 12)(y + 4)$ **9.** $(a + b)(3a - 7)$ **10.** $(3x - 2)(x - 1)$ **11.** $5(6 + x)(6 - x)$
12. $3x(x - 5)(x - 2)$ **13.** $(6t + 5)(t - 1)$ **14.** $(x - 7)(y - 2)(y + 2)$ **15.** $x(1 + x^2)(1 + x)(1 - x)$ **16.** $(x + 12y)(x + 2y)$

17. $3, -9$ **18.** $-7, 2$ **19.** $-7, 1$ **20.** $0, \dfrac{3}{2}, -\dfrac{4}{3}$ **21.** $0, 3, -3$ **22.** $-3, 5$ **23.** $0, \dfrac{5}{2}$ **24.** 17 ft   **25.** width: 6 units; length: 9 units

26. 7 sec   **27.** hypotenuse: 25 cm; legs: 15 cm, 20 cm   **28.** 8.25 Sec

Cumulative Review   1. $\dfrac{5}{7}$ (Sec. 3.1, Ex. 1)   **2.** $\dfrac{19}{30}$ (Sec. 3.1)   **3.** $\dfrac{16}{13}$ or $1\dfrac{3}{13}$ (Sec. 3.1, Ex. 3)   **4.** $\dfrac{4}{5}$ (Sec. 3.1)   **5.** 36 (Sec. 3.2, Ex. 2)

6. $\dfrac{49}{50}$ (Sec. 3.3)   **7.** $\dfrac{7}{14}$ (Sec. 3.2, Ex. 9)   **8.** yes (Sec. 3.5)   **9.** $\dfrac{8}{33}$ (Sec. 3.3, Ex. 6)   **10.** $7\dfrac{47}{72}$ (Sec. 3.4)   **11.** 56 sq cm (Sec. 6.4, Ex. 1)

12. 18 (Sec. 6.6)   **13.** 5.657 (Sec. 6.6, Ex. 5)   **14.** 5.78 (Sec. 4.5)   **15.** 46 ft (Sec. 6.7, Ex. 4)   **16.** 24% (Sec. 5.4)

17. a. 15 reptile species   **b.** birds (Sec. 7.1, Ex. 2)   **18.** mean: 8; median: 9; mode: 11 (Sec. 7.3)

19. a. $9 \leq 11$ **b.** $8 > 1$ **c.** $3 \neq 4$ (Sec. 8.1, Ex. 7)   **20. a.** $>$ **b.** $<$ (Sec. 8.1)   **21.** solution (Sec. 8.2, Ex. 8)   **22.** 102 (Sec. 8.2)

23. -12 (Sec. 8.4, Ex. 5)   **24.** -102 (Sec. 8.4)   **25. a.** $\frac{3}{4}$ **b.** -24 (Sec. 8.5, Ex. 16)   **26.** -98 (Sec. 8.5)

27. -11 (Sec. 9.3, Ex. 3)   **28.** 28 (Sec. 9.2)   **29.** every real number (Sec. 9.3, Ex. 7)   **30.** 33 (Sec. 9.2)   **31.** $l = \frac{V}{wh}$ (Sec. 9.5, Ex. 5)

32. $y = \frac{-3x - 7}{2}$ or $y = -\frac{3}{2}x - \frac{7}{2}$ (Sec. 9.5)   **33.** x^6 (Sec. 12.2, Ex. 9)   **34.** $\frac{1}{9}$ (Sec. 12.2)   **35.** $\frac{y^{18}}{z^{36}}$ (Sec. 12.2, Ex. 11)   **36.** x^4 (Sec. 12.2)

37. $\frac{1}{x^{19}}$ (Sec. 12.2, Ex. 13)   **38.** $25a^9$ (Sec. 12.2)   **39.** $t^2 + 4t + 4$ (Sec. 12.6, Ex. 5)   **40.** $x^2 - 26x + 169$ (Sec. 12.6)

41. $x^4 - 14x^2y + 49y^2$ (Sec. 12.6, Ex. 8)   **42.** $49x^2 + 14xy + y^2$ (Sec. 12.6)   **43.** $2xy - 4 + \frac{1}{2y}$ (Sec. 12.7, Ex. 3)   **44.** $(z^2 + 7)(z + 1)$ (Sec. 13.1)

45. $(x + 3)(5 + y)$ (Sec. 13.1, Ex. 9)   **46.** $2x(x + 7)(x - 6)$ (Sec. 13.2)   **47.** $(x^2 + 2)(x^2 + 3)$ (Sec. 13.2, Ex. 7)

48. $x(3y + 4)(3y - 4)$ (Sec. 13.5)   **49.** 3 sec (Sec. 13.7, Ex. 1)   **50.** 9, 4 (Sec. 13.6)

CHAPTER 14   Rational Expressions

Mental Math   1. $x = 0$ **3.** $x = 0, x = 1$

Exercise Set 14.1   1. $\frac{7}{4}$ **3.** $-\frac{8}{3}$ **5.** $-\frac{11}{2}$ **7. a.** \$403   **b.** \$7   **c.** decrease; answers may vary   **9.** $x = 0$ **11.** $x = -2$ **13.** $x = \frac{5}{2}$

15. $x = 0, x = -2$ **17.** none   **19.** $x = 6, x = -1$ **21.** $x = -2, x = -\frac{7}{3}$ **23.** 1   **25.** -1 **27.** $\frac{1}{4(x + 2)}$ **29.** $\frac{1}{x + 2}$

31. can't simplify   **33.** -5 **35.** $\frac{7}{x}$ **37.** $\frac{1}{x - 9}$ **39.** $5x + 1$ **41.** $\frac{x^2}{x - 2}$ **43.** $7x$ **45.** $\frac{x + 5}{x - 5}$ **47.** $\frac{x + 2}{x + 4}$ **49.** $\frac{x + 2}{2}$

51. $-(x + 2)$ **53.** $\frac{x + 1}{x - 1}$ **55.** $x + y$ **57.** $\frac{5 - y}{2}$ **59.** $\frac{2y + 5}{3y + 4}$ **61.** $\frac{-(x - 10)}{x + 8}; \frac{-x + 10}{x + 8}; \frac{x - 10}{-(x + 8)}; \frac{x - 10}{-x - 8}$

63. $\frac{-(5y - 3)}{y - 12}; \frac{-5y + 3}{y - 12}; \frac{5y - 3}{-(y - 12)}; \frac{5y - 3}{-y + 12}$ **65.** correct   **67.** correct   **69.** $\frac{3}{11}$ **71.** $\frac{4}{3}$ **73.** $\frac{117}{40}$ **75.** correct

77. incorrect; $\frac{1 + 2}{1 + 3} = \frac{3}{4}$ **79.** answers may vary   **81.** answers may vary   **83.** 400 mg   **85.** 45.5%   **87.** 85.9

Mental Math   1. $\frac{2x}{3y}$ **3.** $\frac{5y^2}{7x^2}$ **5.** $\frac{9}{5}$

Exercise Set 14.2   1. $\frac{21}{4y}$ **3.** x^4 **5.** $-\frac{b^2}{6}$ **7.** $\frac{x^2}{10}$ **9.** $\frac{1}{3}$ **11.** $\frac{m + n}{m - n}$ **13.** $\frac{x + 5}{x}$ **15.** $\frac{(x + 2)(x - 3)}{(x - 4)(x + 4)}$ **17.** $\frac{2x^4}{3}$ **19.** $\frac{12}{y^6}$

21. $x(x + 4)$ **23.** $\frac{3(x + 1)}{x^3(x - 1)}$ **25.** $m^2 - n^2$ **27.** $-\frac{x + 2}{x - 3}$ **29.** $\frac{x + 2}{x - 3}$ **31.** $\frac{5}{6}$ **33.** $\frac{3x}{8}$ **35.** $\frac{3}{2}$ **37.** $\frac{3x + 4y}{2(x + 2y)}$

39. $\frac{2(x + 2)}{x - 2}$ **41.** $-\frac{y(x + 2)}{4}$ **43.** $\frac{(a + 5)(a + 3)}{(a + 2)(a + 1)}$ **45.** $\frac{5}{x}$ **47.** $\frac{2(n - 8)}{3n - 1}$ **49.** 1440   **51.** 5   **53.** 81   **55.** 73   **57.** 56.7

59. 411,755 sq yd   **61.** 1364 feet per second   **63.** 1   **65.** $-\frac{10}{9}$ **67.** $-\frac{1}{5}$ **69.** true   **71.** false; $\frac{x^2 + 3x}{20}$ **73.** $\frac{2}{9(x - 5)}$ sq ft

75. $\frac{x}{2}$ **77.** $\frac{5a(2a + b)(3a - 2b)}{b^2(a - b)(a + 2b)}$ **79.** answers may vary   **81.** 1543.81 euros

Mental Math   1. 1   **3.** $\frac{7x}{9}$ **5.** $\frac{1}{9}$ **7.** $\frac{17y}{5}$

Exercise Set 14.3   1. $\frac{a + 9}{13}$ **3.** $\frac{3m}{n}$ **5.** 4   **7.** $\frac{y + 10}{3 + y}$ **9.** $5x + 3$ **11.** $\frac{4}{a + 5}$ **13.** $\frac{1}{x - 6}$ **15.** $4x^3$ **17.** $8x(x + 2)$

19. $(x + 3)(x - 2)$ **21.** $3(x + 6)$ **23.** $5(x - 6)^2$ **25.** $6(x + 1)^2$ **27.** $x - 8$ or $8 - x$ **29.** $(x - 1)(x + 4)(x + 3)$

31. $(3x + 1)(x + 1)(x - 1)(2x + 1)$ **33.** $2x^2(x + 4)(x - 4)$ **35.** $\frac{6x}{4x^2}$ **37.** $\frac{24b^2}{12ab^2}$ **39.** $\frac{9y}{2y(x + 3)}$ **41.** $\frac{9ab + 2b}{5b(a + 2)}$

43. $\frac{x^2 + x}{x(x + 4)(x + 2)(x + 1)}$ **45.** $\frac{18y - 2}{30x^2 - 60}$ **47.** $2x$ **49.** $\frac{x + 3}{2x - 1}$ **51.** $x + 1$ **53.** $\frac{1}{x^2 - 8}$ **55.** $\frac{6(4x + 1)}{x(2x + 1)}$ **57.** $\frac{29}{21}$

59. $-\frac{5}{12}$ **61.** $\frac{7}{30}$ **63.** d   **65.** $\frac{20}{x - 2}$ m   **67.** answers may vary   **69.** 3 packages hot dogs and 2 packages buns

71. answers may vary   **73.** answers may vary

Exercise Set 14.4   1. $\frac{5}{x}$ **3.** $\frac{75a + 6b^2}{5b}$ **5.** $\frac{6x + 5}{2x^2}$ **7.** $\frac{11}{x + 1}$ **9.** $\frac{x - 6}{(x - 2)(x + 2)}$ **11.** $\frac{35x - 6}{4x(x - 2)}$ **13.** $-\frac{2}{x - 3}$ **15.** 0

17. $-\frac{1}{x^2 - 1}$ **19.** $\frac{5 + 2x}{x}$ **21.** $\frac{6x - 7}{x - 2}$ **23.** $-\frac{y + 4}{y + 3}$ **25.** $\frac{-5x + 14}{4x}$ or $-\frac{5x - 14}{4x}$ **27.** 2   **29.** $\frac{9x^4 - 4x^2}{21}$ **31.** $\frac{x + 2}{(x + 3)^2}$

33. $\dfrac{9b-4}{5b(b-1)}$ **35.** $\dfrac{2+m}{m}$ **37.** $\dfrac{x^2+3x}{(x-7)(x-2)}$ or $\dfrac{x(x+3)}{(x-7)(x-2)}$ **39.** $\dfrac{10}{1-2x}$ **41.** $\dfrac{15x-1}{(x+1)^2(x-1)}$ **43.** $\dfrac{x^2-3x-2}{(x-1)^2(x+1)}$

45. $\dfrac{a+2}{2(a+3)}$ **47.** $\dfrac{y(2y+1)}{(2y+3)^2}$ **49.** $\dfrac{x-10}{2(x-2)}$ **51.** $\dfrac{2x+21}{(x+3)^2}$ **53.** $\dfrac{-5x+23}{(x-2)(x-3)}$ **55.** $\dfrac{7}{2(m-10)}$

57. $\dfrac{2x^2-2x-46}{(x+1)(x-6)(x-5)}$ **59.** $\dfrac{n+4}{4n(n-1)(n-2)}$ **61.** 10 **63.** 2 **65.** $\dfrac{25a}{9(a-2)}$ **67.** $\dfrac{x+4}{(x-2)(x-1)}$ **69.** $x=\dfrac{2}{3}$

71. $x=-\dfrac{1}{2}, x=1$ **73.** $x=-\dfrac{15}{2}$ **75.** $\dfrac{6x^2-5x-3}{x(x+1)(x-1)}$ **77.** $\dfrac{4x^2-15x+6}{(x-2)^2(x+2)(x-3)}$ **79.** $\dfrac{-2x^2+14x+55}{(x+2)(x+7)(x+3)}$

81. $\dfrac{2x-16}{(x+4)(x-4)}$ in. **83.** $\dfrac{P-G}{P}$ **85.** answers may vary **87.** $\left(\dfrac{90x-40}{x}\right)^{\circ}$ **89.** answers may vary

The Bigger Picture **1.** -17.7 **2.** 78.26 **3.** 28 **4.** $4x^4-x^2-17$ **5.** $\dfrac{x-1}{5}$ **6.** $\dfrac{14}{x+1}$ **7.** $-\dfrac{11}{18}$ **8.** $\dfrac{-4x-27}{45}$ or $-\dfrac{4x+27}{45}$

9. $x(9x-11)(x+1)$ **10.** $(4y-7)(3x+1)$ **11.** 12 **12.** $\left\{x\,|\,x>\dfrac{1}{2}\right\}$ **13.** $-\dfrac{8}{3}$ **14.** $-4,6$

Mental Math **1.** 10 **3.** 36

Exercise Set 14.5 **1.** 30 **3.** 0 **5.** -2 **7.** $-5,2$ **9.** 5 **11.** 3 **13.** 1 **15.** 5 **17.** no solution **19.** 4 **21.** -8

23. $6,-4$ **25.** 1 **27.** $3,-4$ **29.** -3 **31.** 0 **33.** -2 **35.** $8,-2$ **37.** no solution **39.** 3 **41.** $-11,1$ **43.** $I=\dfrac{E}{R}$

45. $B=\dfrac{2U-TE}{T}$ **47.** $W=\dfrac{Bh^2}{705}$ **49.** $G=\dfrac{V}{N-R}$ **51.** $r=\dfrac{C}{2\pi}$ **53.** $x=\dfrac{3y}{3+y}$ **55.** $\dfrac{1}{x}$ **57.** $\dfrac{1}{x}+\dfrac{1}{2}$ **59.** $\dfrac{1}{3}$ **61.** 5

63. $100°,80°$ **65.** $22.5°,67.5°$ **67.** no; multiplying both terms in the expression by 4 changes the value of the original expression.

Integrated Review **1.** expression; $\dfrac{3+2x}{3x}$ **2.** expression; $\dfrac{18+5a}{6a}$ **3.** equation; 3 **4.** equation; 18 **5.** expression; $\dfrac{x-1}{x(x+1)}$

6. expression; $\dfrac{3(x+1)}{x(x-3)}$ **7.** equation; no solution **8.** equation; 1 **9.** expression; 10 **10.** expression; $\dfrac{z}{3(9z-5)}$

11. expression; $\dfrac{5x+7}{x-3}$ **12.** expression; $\dfrac{7p+5}{2p+7}$ **13.** equation; 23 **14.** equation; 3 **15.** expression; $\dfrac{25a}{9(a-2)}$

16. expression; $\dfrac{9}{4(x-1)}$ **17.** expression; $\dfrac{3x^2+5x+3}{(3x-1)^2}$ **18.** expression; $\dfrac{2x^2-3x-1}{(2x-5)^2}$ **19.** expression; $\dfrac{4x-37}{5x}$ **20.** equation; $-\dfrac{7}{3}$

21. equation; $\dfrac{8}{5}$ **22.** expression; $\dfrac{29x-23}{3x}$ **23.** answers may vary **24.** answers may vary

Mental Math **1.** c

Exercise Set 14.6 **1.** 2 **3.** -3 **5.** $2\dfrac{2}{9}$ hr **7.** $1\dfrac{1}{2}$ min

9. trip to park rate: r; to park time: $\dfrac{12}{r}$; return trip rate: r; return time: $\dfrac{18}{r}=\dfrac{12}{r}+1$; $r=6$ mph

11. 1st portion: 10 mph; cooldown: 8 mph **13.** 2 **15.** 8 mph **17.** $108.00 **19.** 20 mph **21.** 5 **23.** 217 mph

25. 2.2 mph; 3.3 mph **27.** 3 hr **29.** $666\dfrac{2}{3}$ mi **31.** 20 hr **33.** car: 70 mph; motorcycle: 60 mph **35.** $5\dfrac{1}{4}$ hr

37. first pump: 28 min; second pump: 84 min **39.** $\dfrac{3}{4}$ **41.** $\dfrac{6}{5}$ **43.** a **45.** $R=\dfrac{D}{T}$ **47.** 3.75 min

The Bigger Picture **1.** $12x^3-11x^2-13x+10$ **2.** $4x^2-4xy+y^2$ **3.** $4y^3(2-5y^2)$ **4.** $(9m-2n)(m-n)$ **5.** -35

6. $\dfrac{16x-70}{x(x-10)}$ or $\dfrac{2(8x-35)}{x(x-10)}$ **7.** $-12x^{13}$ **8.** 2 **9.** $-\dfrac{1}{2}$ **10.** $\{y\,|\,y\geq 4\}$ **11.** $-\dfrac{27}{23}$ **12.** $\dfrac{a^{14}}{b^{14}}$

Exercise Set 14.7 **1.** $\dfrac{2}{3}$ **3.** $\dfrac{2}{3}$ **5.** $\dfrac{1}{2}$ **7.** $-\dfrac{21}{5}$ **9.** $\dfrac{27}{16}$ **11.** $\dfrac{4}{3}$ **13.** $\dfrac{1}{21}$ **15.** $-\dfrac{4x}{15}$ **17.** $\dfrac{m-n}{m+n}$ **19.** $\dfrac{2x(x-5)}{7x^2+10}$ **21.** $\dfrac{1}{y-1}$

23. $\dfrac{1}{6}$ **25.** $\dfrac{x+y}{x-y}$ **27.** $\dfrac{3}{7}$ **29.** $\dfrac{a}{x+b}$ **31.** $\dfrac{7(y-3)}{8+y}$ **33.** $\dfrac{3x}{x-4}$ **35.** $-\dfrac{x+8}{x-2}$ **37.** $\dfrac{s^2+r^2}{s^2-r^2}$ **39.** $\dfrac{(x-6)(x+4)}{x-2}$ **41.** Steffi Graf

43. Martina Navratilova and Steffi Graf **45.** answers may vary **47.** $\dfrac{13}{24}$ **49.** $\dfrac{R_1R_2}{R_2+R_1}$ **51.** $\dfrac{2x}{2-x}$ **53.** $\dfrac{1}{y^2-1}$ **55.** 12 hr

Chapter 14 Vocabulary Check **1.** ratio **2.** proportion **3.** cross products **4.** rational expression **5.** complex fraction **6.** rate

Chapter 14 Review **1.** $x=2, x=-2$ **2.** $x=\dfrac{5}{2}, x=-\dfrac{3}{2}$ **3.** $\dfrac{4}{3}$ **4.** $\dfrac{11}{12}$ **5.** $\dfrac{2}{x}$ **6.** $\dfrac{3}{x}$ **7.** $\dfrac{1}{x-5}$ **8.** $\dfrac{1}{x+1}$ **9.** $\dfrac{x(x-2)}{x+1}$

10. $\dfrac{5(x-5)}{x-3}$ **11.** $\dfrac{x-3}{x-5}$ **12.** $\dfrac{x}{x+4}$ **13.** $\dfrac{x+a}{x-c}$ **14.** $\dfrac{x+5}{x-3}$ **15.** $\dfrac{3x^2}{y}$ **16.** $-\dfrac{9x^2}{8}$ **17.** $\dfrac{x-3}{x+2}$ **18.** $\dfrac{-2x(2x+5)}{(x-6)^2}$

19. $\dfrac{x+3}{x-4}$ **20.** $\dfrac{4x}{3y}$ **21.** $(x-6)(x-3)$ **22.** $\dfrac{2}{3}$ **23.** $\dfrac{1}{2}$ **24.** $\dfrac{3(x+2)}{3x+y}$ **25.** $\dfrac{1}{x+2}$ **26.** $\dfrac{1}{x-3}$ **27.** $\dfrac{2x-10}{3x^2}$ **28.** $\dfrac{2x+1}{2x^2}$

29. $14x$ **30.** $(x-8)(x+8)(x+3)$ **31.** $\dfrac{10x^2y}{14x^3y}$ **32.** $\dfrac{36y^2x}{16y^3x}$ **33.** $\dfrac{x^2-3x-10}{(x+2)(x-5)(x+9)}$ **34.** $\dfrac{3x^2+4x-15}{(x+2)^2(x+3)}$ **35.** $\dfrac{4y-30x^2}{5x^2y}$

36. $\dfrac{-2x+10}{(x-3)(x-1)}$ **37.** $\dfrac{-2x-2}{x+3}$ **38.** $\dfrac{5x+5}{(x+4)(x-2)(x-1)}$ **39.** $\dfrac{x-4}{3x}$ **40.** $-\dfrac{x}{x-1}$ **41.** 30   **42.** 3, -4 **43.** no solution

44. 5   **45.** $\dfrac{9}{7}$ **46.** $-6,1$ **47.** 3   **48.** 2   **49.** fast car speed: 30 mph; slow car speed: 20 mph   **50.** 20 mph   **51.** $17\dfrac{1}{2}$ hr

52. $8\dfrac{4}{7}$ days   **53.** $-\dfrac{7}{18y}$ **54.** $\dfrac{6}{7}$ **55.** $\dfrac{3y-1}{2y-1}$ **56.** $-\dfrac{7+2x}{2x}$ **57.** $\dfrac{1}{2x}$ **58.** $\dfrac{x(x-3)}{x+7}$ **59.** $\dfrac{x-4}{x+4}$ **60.** $\dfrac{(x-9)(x+8)}{(x+5)(x+9)}$

61. $\dfrac{1}{x-6}$ **62.** $\dfrac{2x+1}{4x}$ **63.** $\dfrac{2}{(x+3)(x-2)}$ **64.** $-\dfrac{3x}{(x+2)(x-3)}$ **65.** $\dfrac{1}{2}$ **66.** no solution   **67.** 1   **68.** $1\dfrac{5}{7}$ days

69. $\dfrac{3}{10}$ **70.** $\dfrac{2}{3}$

Chapter 14 Test   1. $x=-1, x=-3$ **2. a.** \$115   **b.** \$103   **3.** $\dfrac{3}{5}$ **4.** $\dfrac{1}{x+6}$ **5.** -1 **6.** $-\dfrac{1}{x+y}$ **7.** $\dfrac{2m(m+2)}{m-2}$ **8.** $\dfrac{a+2}{a+5}$

9. $\dfrac{(x-6)(x-7)}{(x+7)(x+2)}$ **10.** 15   **11.** $\dfrac{y-2}{4}$ **12.** $-\dfrac{1}{2x+5}$ **13.** $\dfrac{3a-4}{(a-3)(a+2)}$ **14.** $\dfrac{3}{x-1}$ **15.** $\dfrac{2(x+3)(x+5)}{x(x^2+4x+1)}$

16. $\dfrac{x^2+2x+35}{(x+9)(x+2)(x-5)}$ **17.** $\dfrac{4y^2+13y-15}{(y+5)(y+1)(y+4)}$ **18.** $\dfrac{30}{11}$ **19.** -6 **20.** no solution   **21.** no solution   **22.** $-2,5$

23. $\dfrac{xz}{2y}$ **24.** $b-a$ **25.** $\dfrac{5y^2-1}{y+2}$ **26.** $x=1$ and $x=5$ **27.** 30 mph   **28.** $6\dfrac{2}{3}$ hr

Cumulative Review   1. 5.1 sq mi (Sec. 6.4, Ex. 2)   **2.** $25\pi \approx 78.5$ sq m (Sec. 6.4)   **3.** $36\pi \approx 113\dfrac{1}{7}$ cu in. (Sec. 6.5, Ex. 2)

4. 24 cu cm (Sec. 6.5)   **5.** 57 (Sec. 7.3, Ex. 3)   **6.** 24.5 (Sec. 7.3)   **7.** $\dfrac{1}{3}$ (Sec. 7.4, Ex. 4)   **8.** -4.9 (Sec. 7.4)   **9.** $\dfrac{m^7}{n^7}, n \neq 0$ (Sec. 12.1, Ex. 22)

10. $\dfrac{a^6}{b^5}, b \neq 0$ (Sec. 12.1)   **11.** $9x^2-6x-1$ (Sec. 12.4, Ex. 5)   **12.** $6x^2-\dfrac{14}{3}x+\dfrac{1}{42}$ (Sec. 12.4)   **13.** $-\dfrac{1}{2},4$ (Sec. 13.6, Ex. 6)

14. $0, \dfrac{7}{2}$ (Sec. 13.6)   **15.** 1 (Sec. 14.3, Ex. 2)   **16.** $\dfrac{5x-16}{(x-6)(x+1)}$ (Sec. 14.3)   **17. a.** $\dfrac{15}{x}=4$ **b.** $12-3=x$ **c.** $4x+17=21$ (Sec. 8.2, Ex. 10)

18. a. $12-x=-45$ **b.** $12x=-45$ **c.** $x-10=2x$ (Sec. 8.2)   **19. a.** -12 **b.** -9 (Sec. 8.3, Ex. 12)   **20. a.** -8 **b.** -17 (Sec. 8.3)

21. distributive property (Sec. 8.6, Ex. 15)   **22.** commutative property of addition (Sec. 8.6)   **23.** associative property of addition (Sec. 8.6, Ex. 16)

24. associative property of multiplication (Sec. 8.6)   **25.** $x=-4$ (Sec. 9.1, Ex. 7)   **26.** 0 (Sec. 9.1)

27. shorter piece, 2 ft; longer piece, 8 ft (Sec. 9.4, Ex. 3)   **28.** 190, 192 (Sec. 9.4)   **29.** $\dfrac{y-b}{m}=x$ (Sec. 9.5, Ex. 6)   **30.** $x=\dfrac{2y+6}{3}$ (Sec. 9.5)

31. $(5x+2y)^2$ (Sec. 13.5, Ex. 5)   **32.** $(x+2)(x-2)$ (Sec. 13.5)   **33.** $x=11, x=-2$ (Sec. 13.6, Ex. 4)   **34.** $-2, \dfrac{1}{3}$ (Sec. 13.6)

35. $\dfrac{2}{5}$ (Sec. 14.2, Ex. 2)   **36.** $\dfrac{x+5}{2x^3}$ (Sec. 14.1)   **37.** $3x-5$ (Sec. 14.3, Ex. 3)   **38.** $7x^4(x^2-x+1)$ (Sec. 13.1)   **39.** $\dfrac{3}{x-2}$ (Sec. 14.4, Ex. 2)

40. $(2x+3)^2$ (Sec. 13.5)   **41.** $t=5$ (Sec. 14.5, Ex. 2)   **42.** $\dfrac{30}{x+3}$ (Sec. 14.2)   **43.** $2\dfrac{1}{10}$ hr (Sec. 14.6, Ex. 6)

44. $\dfrac{4m+2n}{m+n}$ or $\dfrac{2(2m+n)}{m+n}$ (Sec. 14.7)

CHAPTER 15 Roots and Radicals

Calculator Explorations   1. 2.449   **3.** 3.317   **5.** 9.055   **7.** 3.420   **9.** 2.115   **11.** 1.783

Exercise Set 15.1   1. 4   **3.** $\dfrac{1}{5}$ **5.** -10 **7.** not a real number   **9.** -11 **11.** $\dfrac{3}{5}$ **13.** 30   **15.** 12   **17.** $\dfrac{1}{10}$ **19.** 0.5   **21.** 5

23. -4 **25.** -2 **27.** $\dfrac{1}{2}$ **29.** -5 **31.** 2   **33.** 9   **35.** not a real number   **37.** $-\dfrac{3}{4}$ **39.** -5 **41.** 1   **43.** 2.646   **45.** 6.083

47. 11.662   **49.** $\sqrt{2} \approx 1.41$; 126.90 ft   **51.** m **53.** x^2 **55.** $3x^4$ **57.** $9x$ **59.** ab^2 **61.** $4a^3b^2$ **63.** a^2b^6 **65.** $-2xy^9$

67. $25 \cdot 2$ **69.** $16 \cdot 2$ or $4 \cdot 8$ **71.** $4 \cdot 7$ **73.** $9 \cdot 3$ **75.** a, b   **77.** 7 mi   **79.** 3.01 in.   **81.** 3   **83.** 10   **85.** $T=6.1$ seconds

87. answers may vary   **89.** 1; 1.7; 2; 3   **91.** $(2, 0)$ **93.** $(-4, 0)$

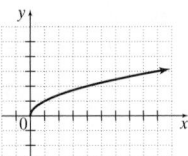

Mental Math   1. 6   **3.** x **5.** 0   **7.** $5x^2$

Exercise Set 15.2   1. $2\sqrt{5}$ **3.** $5\sqrt{2}$ **5.** $\sqrt{33}$ **7.** $7\sqrt{2}$ **9.** $2\sqrt{15}$ **11.** $6\sqrt{5}$ **13.** $2\sqrt{13}$ **15.** 15   **17.** $21\sqrt{7}$ **19.** $-15\sqrt{3}$

21. $\dfrac{2\sqrt{2}}{5}$ **23.** $\dfrac{3\sqrt{3}}{11}$ **25.** $\dfrac{3}{2}$ **27.** $\dfrac{5\sqrt{5}}{3}$ **29.** $\dfrac{\sqrt{11}}{6}$ **31.** $-\dfrac{\sqrt{3}}{4}$ **33.** $x^3\sqrt{x}$ **35.** $x^6\sqrt{x}$ **37.** $6a\sqrt{a}$ **39.** $4x^2\sqrt{6}$ **41.** $\dfrac{2\sqrt{3}}{m}$

43. $\dfrac{3\sqrt{x}}{y^5}$ **45.** $\dfrac{2\sqrt{22}}{x^6}$ **47.** 16   **49.** $\dfrac{6}{11}$ **51.** $5\sqrt{7}$ **53.** $\dfrac{2\sqrt{5}}{3}$ **55.** $2m^3\sqrt{6m}$ **57.** $\dfrac{y\sqrt{23y}}{2x^3}$ **59.** $2\sqrt[3]{3}$ **61.** $5\sqrt[3]{2}$ **63.** $\dfrac{\sqrt[3]{5}}{4}$

65. $\dfrac{\sqrt[3]{23}}{2}$ **67.** $\dfrac{\sqrt[3]{15}}{4}$ **69.** $2\sqrt[3]{10}$ **71.** $14x$ **73.** $2x^2 - 7x - 15$ **75.** 0   **77.** $x^3y\sqrt{y}$ **79.** $7x^2y^2\sqrt{2x}$ **81.** $-2x^2$ **83.** $2\sqrt[3]{10}$ in.

85. answers may vary   **87.** $2\sqrt{5}$ in.   **89.** 2.25 in.   **91.** \$1700   **93.** 1.7 sq m

Mental Math   1. $8\sqrt{2}$ **3.** $7\sqrt{x}$ **5.** $3\sqrt{7}$

Exercise Set 15.3   1. $-4\sqrt{3}$ **3.** $9\sqrt{6} - 5$ **5.** $\sqrt{5} + \sqrt{2}$ **7.** $7\sqrt{3} - \sqrt{2}$ **9.** $-5\sqrt{2} - 6$ **11.** $5\sqrt{3}$ **13.** $9\sqrt{5}$

15. $4\sqrt{6} + \sqrt{5}$ **17.** $x + \sqrt{x}$ **19.** 0   **21.** $\dfrac{4\sqrt{5}}{9}$ **23.** $\dfrac{3\sqrt{3}}{8}$ **25.** $7\sqrt{5}$ **27.** $9\sqrt{3}$ **29.** $\sqrt{5} + \sqrt{15}$ **31.** $x\sqrt{x}$

33. $5\sqrt{2} + 12$ **35.** $8\sqrt{2} - 5$ **37.** $2\sqrt{5}$ **39.** $-\sqrt{35}$ **41.** $6 - 3\sqrt{3}$ **43.** $11\sqrt{x}$ **45.** $12x - 11\sqrt{x}$ **47.** $x\sqrt{3x} + 3x\sqrt{x}$

49. $8x\sqrt{2} + 2x$ **51.** $2x^2\sqrt{10} - x^2\sqrt{5}$ **53.** $7\sqrt[3]{9} - \sqrt[3]{25}$ **55.** $-5\sqrt[3]{2} - 6$ **57.** $5\sqrt[3]{3}$ **59.** $4x + 4x\sqrt[3]{2}$ **61.** $x\sqrt[3]{5}$ **63.** $10y^2\sqrt[3]{y}$

65. $x^2 + 12x + 36$ **67.** $4x^2 - 4x + 1$ **69.** answers may vary   **71.** $8\sqrt{5}$ in.   **73.** $\left(48 + \dfrac{9\sqrt{3}}{2}\right)$ sq ft   **75.** yes; $7\sqrt{2}$

77. no   **79.** yes; $3\sqrt{7}$ **81.** $\dfrac{83x\sqrt{x}}{20}$

Mental Math   1. $\sqrt{22}$ **3.** $\sqrt{6}$ **5.** $\sqrt{10y}$

Exercise Set 15.4   1. 4   **3.** $5\sqrt{2}$ **5.** 6   **7.** $2x$ **9.** 20   **11.** $36x$ **13.** $3x^3\sqrt{2}$ **15.** $4xy\sqrt{y}$ **17.** $\sqrt{30} + \sqrt{42}$

19. $2\sqrt{5} + 5\sqrt{2}$ **21.** $y\sqrt{7} - 14\sqrt{y}$ **23.** -33 **25.** $\sqrt{6} - \sqrt{15} + \sqrt{10} - 5$ **27.** $16 - 11\sqrt{11}$ **29.** $x - 36$

31. $x - 14\sqrt{x} + 49$ **33.** $6y + 2\sqrt{6y} + 1$ **35.** 4   **37.** $\sqrt{7}$ **39.** $3\sqrt{2}$ **41.** $5y^2$ **43.** $5\sqrt{3}$ **45.** $2y\sqrt{6}$ **47.** $2xy\sqrt{3y}$

49. $\dfrac{\sqrt{15}}{5}$ **51.** $\dfrac{7\sqrt{2}}{2}$ **53.** $\dfrac{\sqrt{6y}}{6y}$ **55.** $\dfrac{\sqrt{10}}{6}$ **57.** $\dfrac{\sqrt{3x}}{x}$ **59.** $\dfrac{\sqrt{2}}{4}$ **61.** $\dfrac{\sqrt{30}}{15}$ **63.** $\dfrac{\sqrt{15}}{10}$ **65.** $\dfrac{3\sqrt{2x}}{2}$ **67.** $\dfrac{8y\sqrt{5}}{5}$

69. $\dfrac{\sqrt{3xy}}{6x}$ **71.** $3\sqrt{2} - 3$ **73.** $-8 - 4\sqrt{5}$ **75.** $5 + \sqrt{30} + \sqrt{6} + \sqrt{5}$ **77.** $\sqrt{6} + \sqrt{3} + \sqrt{2} + 1$ **79.** $\dfrac{10 - 5\sqrt{x}}{4 - x}$

81. $\dfrac{3\sqrt{x} + 12}{x - 16}$ **83.** $x = 44$ **85.** $z = 2$ **87.** $x = 3$ **89.** $130\sqrt{3}$ sq m   **91.** $\dfrac{\sqrt{A\pi}}{\pi}$ **93.** true   **95.** false   **97.** false

99. answers may vary   **101.** answers may vary   **103.** $\dfrac{2}{\sqrt{6} - \sqrt{2} - \sqrt{3} + 1}$

Integrated Review   1. 6   **2.** $4\sqrt{3}$ **3.** x^2 **4.** $y^3\sqrt{y}$ **5.** $4x$ **6.** $3x^5\sqrt{2x}$ **7.** 2   **8.** 3   **9.** -3 **10.** not a real number

11. $\dfrac{\sqrt{11}}{3}$ **12.** $\dfrac{\sqrt[3]{7}}{4}$ **13.** -4 **14.** -5 **15.** $\dfrac{3}{7}$ **16.** $\dfrac{1}{8}$ **17.** a^4b **18.** x^5y^{10} **19.** $5m^3$ **20.** $3n^8$ **21.** $6\sqrt{7}$ **22.** $3\sqrt{2}$

23. cannot be simplified   **24.** $\sqrt{x} + 3x$ **25.** $\sqrt{30}$ **26.** 3   **27.** 28   **28.** 45   **29.** $\sqrt{33} + \sqrt{3}$ **30.** $3\sqrt{2} - 2\sqrt{6}$ **31.** $4y$

32. $3x^2\sqrt{5}$ **33.** $x - 3\sqrt{x} - 10$ **34.** $11 + 6\sqrt{2}$ **35.** 2   **36.** $\sqrt{3}$ **37.** $2x^2\sqrt{3}$ **38.** $ab^2\sqrt{15a}$ **39.** $\dfrac{\sqrt{6}}{6}$ **40.** $\dfrac{x\sqrt{5}}{10}$

41. $\dfrac{4\sqrt{6} - 4}{5}$ **42.** $\dfrac{\sqrt{2x} + 5\sqrt{2} + \sqrt{x} + 5}{x - 25}$

Exercise Set 15.5   1. 81   **3.** -1 **5.** 49   **7.** no solution   **9.** 4   **11.** 2   **13.** 2   **15.** 9   **17.** -3 **19.** $-1, -2$

21. no solution   **23.** $0, -3$ **25.** 16   **27.** 25   **29.** 1   **31.** 5   **33.** -2 **35.** no solution   **37.** 2   **39.** 36   **41.** no solution

43. $\dfrac{3}{2}$ **45.** 16   **47.** 3   **49.** 12   **51.** $3, 1$ **53.** -1 **55.** $3x - 8 = 19; x = 9$ **57.** $2(2x + x) = 24$; length $= 8$ in.   **59.** $4, 7$

61. answers may vary   **63. a.** $3.2, 10, 31.6$ **b.** no   **65.** 7.30   **67.** 0.76

The Bigger Picture

1. $2\sqrt{14}$ **2.** $\dfrac{2x^2\sqrt{5x}}{7}$ **3.** $-15x^5y^{11}$ **4.** $\dfrac{\sqrt{110}}{11}$ **5.** $2(\sqrt{5}+1)$ or $2\sqrt{5}+2$ **6.** $5x^2-19$ **7.** -1 **8.** $-\dfrac{5}{2}$

9. $\left\{y\mid y\geq-\dfrac{4}{11}\right\}$ **10.** $6,-7$ **11.** $\dfrac{28}{3}$ **12.** 2

Exercise Set 15.6   **1.** $\sqrt{13}$; 3.61   **3.** $3\sqrt{3}$; 5.20   **5.** 25   **7.** $\sqrt{22}$; 4.69   **9.** $3\sqrt{17}$; 12.37   **11.** $\sqrt{41}$; 6.40   **13.** $4\sqrt{2}$; 5.66
15. $3\sqrt{10}$; 9.49   **17.** 20.6 ft   **19.** 11.7 ft   **21.** 24 cu ft   **23.** 54 mph   **25.** 27 mph   **27.** 59.1 km   **29.** 60.2 km   **31.** $3,-3$
33. $10,-10$ **35.** $8,-8$ **37.** $y=2\sqrt{10}$; $x=2\sqrt{10}-4$ **39.** 201 miles   **41.** answers may vary

Chapter 15 Vocabulary Check   **1.** like radicals   **2.** index; radicand; radical   **3.** conjugate   **4.** principal square root
5. rationalizing the denominator

Chapter 15 Review   **1.** 9   **2.** -7 **3.** 3   **4.** 3   **5.** $-\dfrac{3}{8}$ **6.** $\dfrac{2}{3}$ **7.** 2   **8.** -2 **9.** c   **10.** a, c   **11.** x^6 **12.** x^4 **13.** $3y$
14. $5x^2$ **15.** $2\sqrt{10}$ **16.** $2\sqrt{6}$ **17.** $3\sqrt{6}$ **18.** $2\sqrt{22}$ **19.** $x^2\sqrt{x}$ **20.** $y^3\sqrt{y}$ **21.** $2x\sqrt{5}$ **22.** $5y^2\sqrt{2}$ **23.** $3\sqrt[3]{2}$
24. $2\sqrt[3]{11}$ **25.** $\dfrac{3\sqrt{2}}{5}$ **26.** $\dfrac{5\sqrt{3}}{8}$ **27.** $-\dfrac{5\sqrt{2}}{3}$ **28.** $-\dfrac{2\sqrt{3}}{7}$ **29.** $\dfrac{\sqrt{11}}{x}$ **30.** $\dfrac{\sqrt{7}}{y^2}$ **31.** $\dfrac{y^2\sqrt{y}}{10}$ **32.** $\dfrac{x\sqrt{x}}{9}$ **33.** $-3\sqrt{2}$
34. $-5\sqrt{3}$ **35.** $4\sqrt{5}+4\sqrt{6}$ **36.** $-2\sqrt{7}+2\sqrt{2}$ **37.** $5\sqrt{7}+2\sqrt{14}$ **38.** $9\sqrt{3}-4$ **39.** $\dfrac{\sqrt{5}}{6}$ **40.** $\dfrac{9\sqrt{11}}{20}$ **41.** $10-x\sqrt{5}$
42. $2\sqrt{2x}-\sqrt{3x}$ **43.** $3\sqrt{2}$ **44.** $5\sqrt{3}$ **45.** $\sqrt{10}-\sqrt{14}$ **46.** $\sqrt{55}+\sqrt{15}$ **47.** $3\sqrt{2}-5\sqrt{3}+2\sqrt{6}-10$ **48.** $2-2\sqrt{5}$
49. $x-4\sqrt{x}+4$ **50.** $y+8\sqrt{y}+16$ **51.** 3   **52.** 2   **53.** $2\sqrt{5}$ **54.** $4\sqrt{2}$ **55.** $x\sqrt{15x}$ **56.** $3x^2\sqrt{2}$ **57.** $\dfrac{\sqrt{22}}{11}$
58. $\dfrac{\sqrt{39}}{13}$ **59.** $\dfrac{\sqrt{30}}{6}$ **60.** $\dfrac{\sqrt{70}}{10}$ **61.** $\dfrac{\sqrt{5x}}{5x}$ **62.** $\dfrac{5\sqrt{3y}}{3y}$ **63.** $\dfrac{\sqrt{3x}}{x}$ **64.** $\dfrac{\sqrt{6y}}{y}$ **65.** $3\sqrt{5}+6$ **66.** $8\sqrt{10}+24$
67. $\dfrac{\sqrt{6}+\sqrt{2}+\sqrt{3}+1}{2}$ **68.** $\sqrt{15}-2\sqrt{3}-2\sqrt{5}+4$ **69.** $\dfrac{10\sqrt{x}-50}{x-25}$ **70.** $\dfrac{8\sqrt{x}+8}{x-1}$ **71.** 18   **72.** 13   **73.** 25
74. no solution   **75.** 12   **76.** 5   **77.** 1   **78.** 9   **79.** $2\sqrt{14}$; 7.48   **80.** $\sqrt{117}$; 10.82   **81.** $4\sqrt{34}$ ft; 23.33 ft
82. $5\sqrt{3}$ in.; 8.66 in.   **83.** 2.4 in.   **84.** 144π sq in.   **85.** 12   **86.** -4 **87.** $4x^8$ **88.** $2x^{12}$ **89.** $3x^3\sqrt{2x}$ **90.** $4y^3\sqrt{3}$
91. $\dfrac{y^2}{9}$ **92.** $\dfrac{x^4\sqrt{x}}{3}$ **93.** $7\sqrt{3}$ **94.** $5\sqrt{7}-3$ **95.** $-\dfrac{\sqrt{3}}{4}$ **96.** $4x\sqrt{5x}$ **97.** $7\sqrt{2}$ **98.** $3\sqrt{3}-\sqrt{6}$
99. $\sqrt{10}-\sqrt{2}+4\sqrt{5}-4$ **100.** $x+6\sqrt{x}+9$ **101.** $2\sqrt{6}$ **102.** $2x$ **103.** $\dfrac{\sqrt{14}}{7}$ **104.** $\dfrac{3\sqrt{2x}}{2x}$ **105.** $\dfrac{3\sqrt{x}+18}{x-36}$
106. $\dfrac{\sqrt{35}-3\sqrt{7}-5\sqrt{5}+15}{-4}$ **107.** 1   **108.** 13   **109.** 14   **110.** 9   **111.** $\sqrt{58}$; 7.62   **112.** $4\sqrt{2}$ in.; 5.66 in.

Chapter 15 Test   **1.** 4   **2.** 5   **3.** 3   **4.** $\dfrac{3}{4}$ **5.** not a real number   **6.** x^5 **7.** $3\sqrt{6}$ **8.** $2\sqrt{23}$ **9.** $y^3\sqrt{y}$ **10.** $2x^4\sqrt{6}$ **11.** 3
12. $2\sqrt[3]{2}$ **13.** $\dfrac{\sqrt{5}}{4}$ **14.** $\dfrac{y\sqrt{y}}{5}$ **15.** $-2\sqrt{13}$ **16.** $\sqrt{2}+2\sqrt{3}$ **17.** $\dfrac{7\sqrt{3}}{10}$ **18.** $7\sqrt{2}$ **19.** $2\sqrt{3}-\sqrt{10}$ **20.** $x-\sqrt{x}-6$
21. $\sqrt{5}$ **22.** $2x\sqrt{5x}$ **23.** $\dfrac{\sqrt{6}}{3}$ **24.** $\dfrac{8\sqrt{5y}}{5y}$ **25.** $4\sqrt{6}-8$ **26.** $\dfrac{3+\sqrt{x}}{9-x}$ **27.** 9   **28.** 5   **29.** 9   **30.** $4\sqrt{5}$ in.   **31.** 2.19 m

Cumulative Review   **1.** $\dfrac{1}{6}$ of an hour (Sec. 3.3, Ex. 9)   **2.** 27 (Sec. 3.5)   **3.** $7\dfrac{17}{24}$ (Sec. 3.4, Ex. 1)   **4.** $\dfrac{16}{27}$ (Sec. 3.3)   **5.** $>$ (Sec. 3.5, Ex. 1)
6. 14,000,000 (Sec. 1.6)   **7.** one and three tenths (Sec. 4.1, Ex. 1)   **8.** 0.075 (Sec. 4.1)   **9.** 736.2 (Sec. 4.2, Ex. 5)   **10.** 736.24 (Sec. 4.2)

11. 28 (Sec. 8.5, Ex. 3)   **12.** -46.8 (Sec. 8.5)   **13.** $-\dfrac{8}{21}$ (Sec. 8.5, Ex. 4)   **14.** -18 (Sec. 8.5)   **15.** 2 (Sec. 9.3, Ex. 1)   **16.** 15 (Sec. 9.3)

17. a. 17%   **b.** 21%   **c.** 43 American travelers (Sec. 9.6, Ex. 3)   **18. a.** $\dfrac{3}{2}$ **b.** 9 (Sec. 8.2)   **19. a.** 102,000   **b.** 0.007358   **c.** 84,000,000
d. 0.00003007 (Sec. 12.2, Ex. 18)   **20. a.** 7.2×10^6 **b.** 3.08×10^{-4} (Sec. 12.2)   **21.** $6x^2-11x-10$ (Sec. 12.5, Ex. 7b)
22. $49x^2+14x+1$ (Sec. 12.5)   **23.** $(y+2)(x+3)$ (Sec. 13.1, Ex. 10)   **24.** $(y^2+5)(x-1)$ (Sec. 13.1)   **25.** $(3x+2)(x+3)$ (Sec. 13.3, Ex. 1)

26. $3(x+2)(x+3)$ (Sec. 13.2)   **27. a.** $x=3$ **b.** $x=2, x=1$ **c.** none (Sec. 14.1, Ex. 2)   **28.** $\dfrac{2x+1}{x-3}$ (Sec. 14.1)   **29.** $-\dfrac{17}{5}$ (Sec. 14.5, Ex. 4)

30. $y=-2x+4$ (Sec. 10.5)   **31.** (Sec. 10.3, Ex. 7)   **32.** (Sec. 10.1)   **33.** $y=\dfrac{1}{4}x-3$ (Sec. 10.5, Ex. 1)

x	y
0	6
4	-2
3	0

34. $y = -\frac{1}{2}x + \frac{11}{2}$; (Sec. 10.5)   **35.** $(3, 1)$; (Sec. 11.3, Ex. 5)   **36.** $\left(\frac{2}{3}, \frac{1}{2}\right)$; (Sec. 11.3)   **37.** Alfredo: 3.25 mph; Louisa: 4.25 mph; (Sec. 11.4, Ex. 3)

38. 20 mph, 35 mph; (Sec. 11.4)   **39.** $3\sqrt{6}$; (Sec. 15.2, Ex. 1)   **40.** $3\sqrt{7}$; (Sec. 15.2)   **41.** $10\sqrt{2}$; (Sec. 15.2, Ex. 3)   **42.** $10\sqrt{5}$; (Sec. 15.2)

43. $4\sqrt{3}$; (Sec. 15.3, Ex. 6)   **44.** $x - 25$; (Sec. 15.4)   **45.** $2x - 4x^2\sqrt{x}$; (Sec. 15.3, Ex. 8)   **46.** $10 + 4\sqrt{6}$; (Sec. 15.4)

47. $\frac{2\sqrt{7}}{7}$; (Sec. 15.4, Ex. 10)   **48.** $3x$; (Sec. 14.7)   **49.** $\frac{1}{2}$; (Sec. 15.5, Ex. 2)   **50.** $\frac{5}{2}$; (Sec. 15.5)

CHAPTER 16 Quadratic Equations

Exercise Set 16.1   **1.** ± 7 **3.** $-5, 3$ **5.** ± 4 **7.** ± 3 **9.** $-5, -2$ **11.** ± 8 **13.** $\pm\sqrt{21}$ **15.** $\pm\frac{1}{5}$ **17.** no real solution

19. $\pm\frac{\sqrt{39}}{3}$ **21.** $\pm\frac{2\sqrt{7}}{7}$ **23.** $\pm\sqrt{2}$ **25.** $12, -2$ **27.** $-2 \pm \sqrt{7}$ **29.** $1, 0$ **31.** $-2 \pm \sqrt{10}$ **33.** $\frac{8}{3}, -4$ **35.** no real solution

37. $\frac{11 \pm 5\sqrt{2}}{2}$ **39.** $\frac{7 \pm 4\sqrt{2}}{3}$ **41.** $\pm\sqrt{2}$ **43.** $-6 \pm 2\sqrt{6}$ **45.** $\pm\sqrt{10}$ **47.** $\frac{1 \pm \sqrt{5}}{4}$ **49.** $\pm 2\sqrt{3}$

51. $\frac{-8 \pm 3\sqrt{5}}{-3}$ or $\frac{8 \pm 3\sqrt{5}}{3}$ **53.** 2.3 sec   **55.** 4.6 seconds   **57.** $2\sqrt{5}$ in. ≈ 4.47 in.   **59.** 177 meters   **61.** $(x + 3)^2$ **63.** $(x - 2)^2$

65. answers may vary   **67.** $2, -6$ **69.** $r = 6$ in.   **71.** ± 1.33 **73.** $x = 7$, which is 2006

Mental Math   **1.** 16   **3.** 100   **5.** 49

Exercise Set 16.2   **1.** $-6, -2$ **3.** $-1 \pm 2\sqrt{2}$ **5.** $0, 6$ **7.** $\frac{-5 \pm \sqrt{53}}{2}$ **9.** $1 \pm \sqrt{2}$ **11.** $-1, -4$ **13.** $-2, 4$ **15.** no real solution

17. $\frac{3 \pm \sqrt{19}}{2}$ **19.** $-2 \pm \frac{\sqrt{6}}{2}$ **21.** $-3 \pm \sqrt{34}$ **23.** $\frac{3 \pm \sqrt{21}}{2}$ **25.** $\frac{1}{2}, 1$ **27.** $-6, 3$ **29.** no real solution   **31.** $2, -6$ **33.** $-\frac{1}{2}$

35. -1 **37.** $3 + 2\sqrt{5}$ **39.** $\frac{1 - 3\sqrt{2}}{2}$ **41.** answers may vary   **43. a.** $-3 \pm \sqrt{11}$ **b.** answers may vary   **45.** $k = 8$ or $k = -8$

47. 8 years, or 2009   **49.** $-6, -2$ **51.** $\approx -0.68, 3.68$

Mental Math   **1.** $a = 2, b = 5, c = 3$ **3.** $a = 10, b = -13, c = -2$ **5.** $a = 1, b = 0, c = -6$

Exercise Set 16.3   **1.** $x = 2, 1$ **3.** $k = \frac{-7 \pm \sqrt{37}}{6}$ **5.** $x = \pm\frac{\sqrt{3}}{2}$ **7.** no real solution   **9.** $y = 10, -3$ **11.** $x = \pm\sqrt{5}$

13. $m = -3, 4$ **15.** $x = -2 \pm \sqrt{7}$ **17.** $x = \frac{-9 \pm \sqrt{129}}{12}$ **19.** $p = \frac{4 \pm \sqrt{2}}{7}$ **21.** $x = 3 \pm \sqrt{7}$ **23.** $x = \frac{3 \pm \sqrt{3}}{2}$

25. $x = \frac{1}{3}, -1$ **27.** $y = \frac{3 \pm \sqrt{13}}{4}$ **29.** $y = \frac{1}{5}, -\frac{3}{4}$ **31.** no real solution   **33.** $m = 1 \pm \sqrt{2}$ **35.** no real solution

37. $p = -\frac{1}{2}, -\frac{3}{4}$ **39.** $x = \frac{7 \pm \sqrt{129}}{20}$ **41.** $x = \frac{11 \pm \sqrt{129}}{4}$ **43.** $z = \frac{1 \pm \sqrt{2}}{5}$ **45.** $\pm\sqrt{7}$; $-2.6, 2.6$ **47.** $-3 \pm 2\sqrt{2}$; $-5.8, -0.2$

49. $\frac{9 \pm \sqrt{97}}{2}$; $9.4, -0.4$ **51.** $\frac{1 \pm \sqrt{7}}{3}$; $1.2, -0.5$ **53.**   **55.**   **57.** c   **59.** b

61. 10.3 ft by 4.9 ft   **63.** $x = \frac{-3\sqrt{2} \pm \sqrt{38}}{2}$ **65.** answers may vary   **67.** $-0.9, 0.2$ **69.** 8.1 sec   **71.** 2008

The Bigger Picture   **1.** -1.8 **2.** -5 **3.** -9 **4.** $10x + 2$ **5.** $\frac{1}{4}x^2 - 25$ **6.** $3x + 1 - \frac{4}{x}$ **7.** $\frac{x + 2}{x - 4}$ **8.** $\frac{x^2 + 8x - 50}{(x - 10)(x + 3)}$

9. $5\sqrt{2}$ **10.** $b\sqrt{10a}$ **11.** $\frac{\sqrt{6}}{3}$ **12.** $\frac{x + 3}{7}$ **13.** $\frac{-3 \pm \sqrt{29}}{2}$ **14.** 6   **15.** $\{x \mid x \geq -2.8\}$ **16.** $\frac{1}{2}, -8$ **17.** 7   **18.** 27

Integrated Review   **1.** $x = 2, \frac{1}{5}$ **2.** $x = \frac{2}{5}, -3$ **3.** $x = 1 \pm \sqrt{2}$ **4.** $x = 3 \pm \sqrt{2}$ **5.** $a = \pm 2\sqrt{5}$ **6.** $a = \pm 6\sqrt{2}$

7. no real solution   **8.** no real solution   **9.** $x = 2$ **10.** $x = 3$ **11.** $p = 3$ **12.** $p = \frac{7}{2}$ **13.** $y = \pm 2$ **14.** $y = \pm 3$

15. $x = 1, 2$ **16.** $x = -3, -4$ **17.** $z = 0, -5$ **18.** $z = \frac{8}{3}, 0$ **19.** $x = \frac{3 \pm \sqrt{7}}{5}$ **20.** $x = \frac{3 \pm \sqrt{5}}{2}$ **21.** $m = \frac{3}{2}, -1$

22. $m = \frac{2}{5}, -2$ **23.** $x = \frac{5 \pm \sqrt{105}}{20}$ **24.** $x = \frac{-1 \pm \sqrt{3}}{4}$ **25.** $x = 5, \frac{7}{4}$ **26.** $x = 1, \frac{7}{9}$ **27.** $x = \frac{7 \pm 3\sqrt{2}}{5}$ **28.** $x = \frac{5 \pm 5\sqrt{3}}{4}$

29. $z = \dfrac{7 \pm \sqrt{193}}{6}$ **30.** $z = \dfrac{-7 \pm \sqrt{193}}{12}$ **31.** $x = 11, -10$ **32.** $x = 7, -8$ **33.** $x = 4, -\dfrac{2}{3}$ **34.** $x = 2, -\dfrac{4}{5}$ **35.** $x = 0.5, 0.1$

36. $x = 0.3, -0.2$ **37.** $x = \dfrac{11 \pm \sqrt{41}}{20}$ **38.** $x = \dfrac{11 \pm \sqrt{41}}{40}$ **39.** $z = \dfrac{4 \pm \sqrt{10}}{2}$ **40.** $z = \dfrac{5 \pm \sqrt{185}}{4}$ **41.** answers may vary

Calculator Explorations   **1.** $x = -0.41, 7.41$ **3.** $x = 0.91, 2.38$ **5.** $x = -0.39, 0.84$

Exercise Set 16.4   **1.** 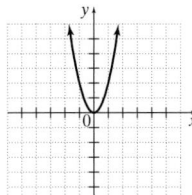   **3.** 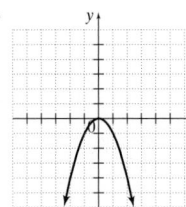   **5.** 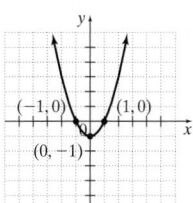   **7.**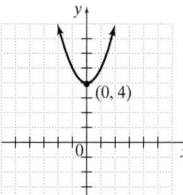

9. 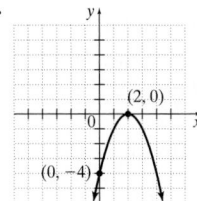   **11.** 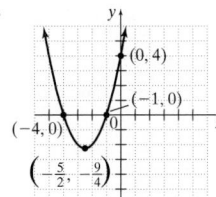   **13.** 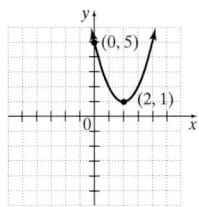   **15.** 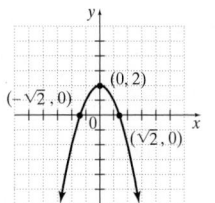   **17.**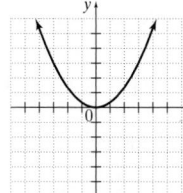

19. 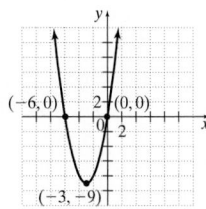   **21.** 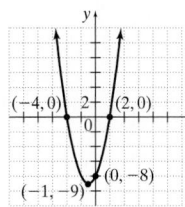   **23.** 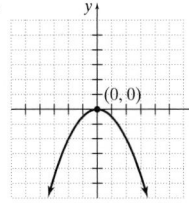   **25.** 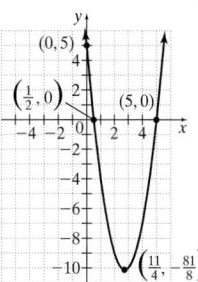   **27.**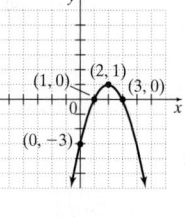

29. $\dfrac{5}{14}$ **31.** $\dfrac{x}{2}$ **33.** $\dfrac{2x^2}{x-1}$ **35.** $-4b$ **37. a.** 256 ft   **b.** $t = 4$ sec   **c.** $t = 8$ sec   **39.** A   **41.** D   **43.** F

Exercise Set 16.5   **1.** 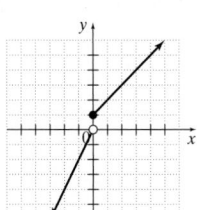 $(-\infty, -3)$ **3.** $[0.3, \infty)$ **5.** $[-7, \infty)$

7. $(-2, 5)$ **9.** $(-1, 5]$ **11.** domain: $[0, \infty)$; range: $(-\infty, \infty)$ **13.** domain: $(-\infty, \infty)$; range: $[0, \infty)$

15. domain: $(-\infty, \infty)$; range: $(-\infty, -3] \cup [3, \infty)$ **17.** domain: $[1, 7]$; range: $[1, 7]$ **19.** domain: $\{-2\}$; range: $(-\infty, \infty)$

21. domain: $(-\infty, \infty)$; range: $(-\infty, 3]$ **23.** domain: $(-\infty, \infty)$; range: $(-\infty, 3]$ **25.** domain: $[2, \infty)$; range: $[3, \infty)$

27. 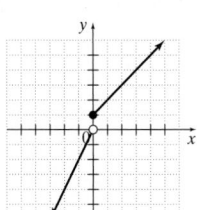   **29.** 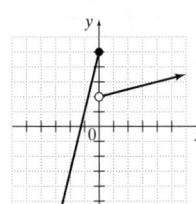   **31.** 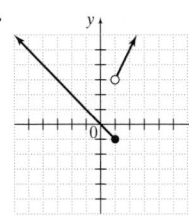   **33.**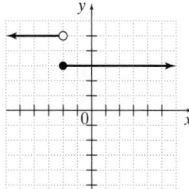

35. 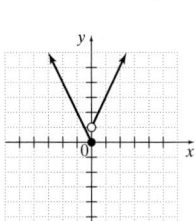   domain: $(-\infty, \infty)$; range: $[0, \infty)$ **37.** 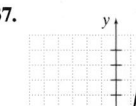   domain: $(-\infty, \infty)$; range: $(-\infty, 5)$

39. 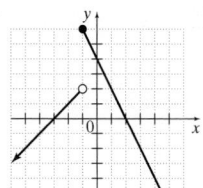 domain: $(-\infty, \infty)$; range: $(-\infty, 6]$ **41.** 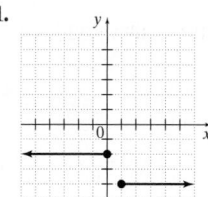 domain: $(-\infty, 0] \cup [1, \infty)$; range: $\{-4, -2\}$

43. A **45.** D **47.** answers may vary **49.**

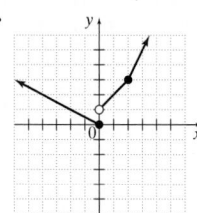

Chapter 16 Vocabulary Check **1.** square root **2.** vertex **3.** completing the square **4.** quadratic **5.** range **6.** domain

Chapter 16 Review **1.** $x = \pm 11$ **2.** $y = \pm 10$ **3.** $m = -\frac{1}{3}, 2$ **4.** $m = \frac{5}{7}, -1$ **5.** $x = \pm 6$ **6.** $x = \pm 9$ **7.** $k = \pm 5\sqrt{2}$

8. $k = \pm 3\sqrt{5}$ **9.** $x = 4, 18$ **10.** $x = 7, -13$ **11.** $p = \frac{-5 \pm \sqrt{41}}{4}$ **12.** $p = \frac{-7 \pm \sqrt{37}}{3}$ **13.** 2.5 sec **14.** 40.6 sec

15. $x = 1, 8$ **16.** $x = -10, 2$ **17.** $x = -2 \pm \sqrt{5}$ **18.** $x = 4 \pm \sqrt{19}$ **19.** $x = 3 \pm \sqrt{2}$ **20.** $x = -3 \pm \sqrt{2}$ **21.** $y = \frac{1}{2}, -1$

22. $y = \frac{-3 \pm \sqrt{13}}{2}$ **23.** $x = -\frac{5}{3}$ **24.** $x = \frac{9}{4}$ **25.** $x = \pm\sqrt{5}$ **26.** $\pm\sqrt{3}$ **27.** $x = 5 \pm 3\sqrt{2}$ **28.** $x = -2 \pm \sqrt{11}$

29. $x = \frac{-1 \pm \sqrt{13}}{6}$ **30.** $x = \frac{-3 \pm \sqrt{13}}{2}$ **31.** no real solution **32.** no real solution **33.** 0.4, −0.8 **34.** 0.3, −3.3 **35.** 2007 **36.** 2007

37. 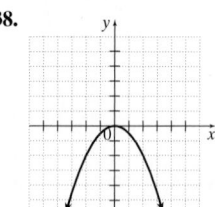 **38.** 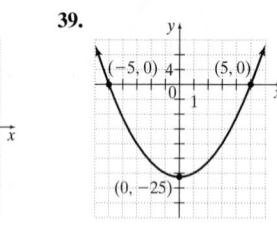 **39.** 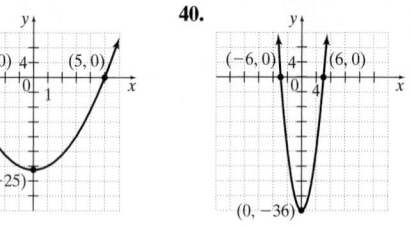 **40.** 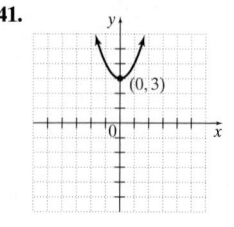 **41.**

42. 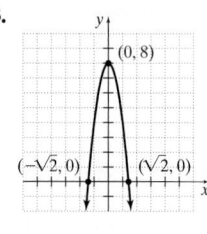 **43.** 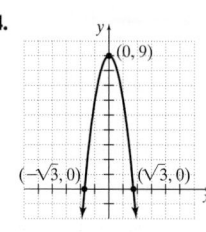 **44.** 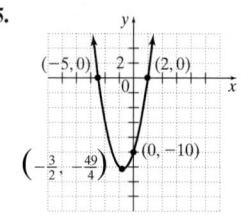 **45.** **46.**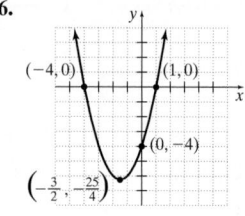

47. 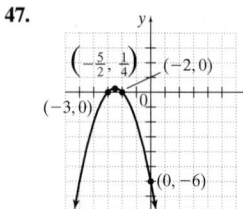 **48.** 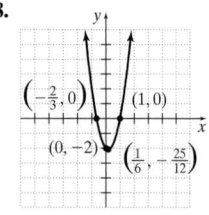 **49.** 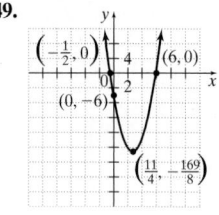 **50.** 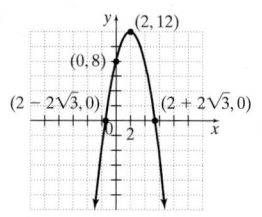 **51.** A **52.** D

53. B **54.** C **55.** one real solution **56.** two real solutions **57.** no real solution **58.** two real solutions

59. domain: $\{2\}$; range: $(-\infty, \infty)$ **60.** domain: $(-\infty, \infty)$; range: $(-\infty, \infty)$ **61.** domain: $[-4, 4]$; range: $[-1, 5]$

62. domain: $(-\infty, \infty)$; range: $\{-5\}$ **63.** 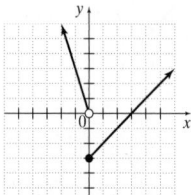 **64.** 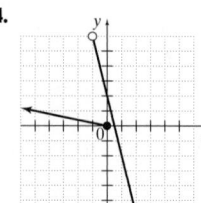 **65.** $x = \pm 7$

66. $x = \pm 5\sqrt{3}$ **67.** $x = 15, -1$ **68.** $x = -2 \pm \sqrt{10}$ **69.** $x = \dfrac{2}{3}, -1$ **70.** $x = \dfrac{1 \pm \sqrt{33}}{8}$ **71.** $x = \dfrac{3 \pm \sqrt{41}}{8}$

72. $x = \dfrac{-1 \pm \sqrt{41}}{10}$ **73.** $x = -\dfrac{3}{2}$ **74.** no real solution

75. 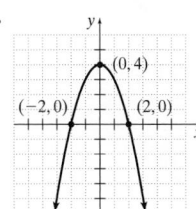   **76.** 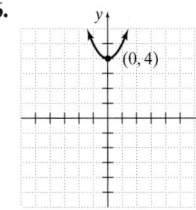   **77.** 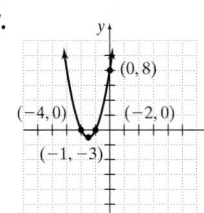   **78.**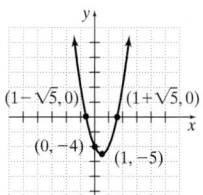

Chapter 16 Test   1. $x = \pm 20$ **2.** $x = -\dfrac{3}{2}, 7$ **3.** $k = \pm 4$ **4.** $m = \dfrac{5 \pm 2\sqrt{2}}{3}$ **5.** $x = 10, 16$ **6.** $x = \dfrac{-6 \pm 4\sqrt{3}}{3}$ **7.** $x = -2, 5$

8. $p = \dfrac{5 \pm \sqrt{37}}{6}$ **9.** $x = 1, -\dfrac{4}{3}$ **10.** $x = -1, \dfrac{5}{3}$ **11.** $x = \dfrac{7 \pm \sqrt{73}}{6}$ **12.** $x = -1, 5$ **13.** $x = 2, \dfrac{1}{3}$ **14.** $x = \dfrac{3 \pm \sqrt{7}}{2}$

15. base: 3 ft; height: 12 ft   **16.** 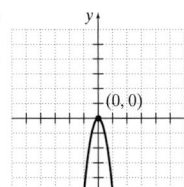   **17.** 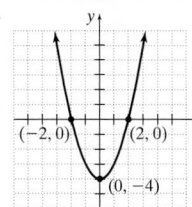   **18.**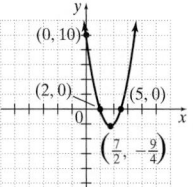

19. 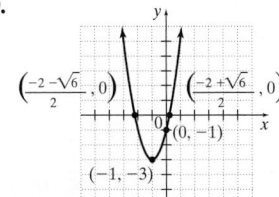   **20.** 6 sides   **21.** 2.7 sec   **22.** 2006

23. domain: $(-\infty, \infty)$; range: $\{5\}$; function

24. domain: $\{-2\}$; range: $(-\infty, \infty)$; not a function

25. domain: $(-\infty, \infty)$; range: $[0, \infty)$; function

26. domain: $(-\infty, \infty)$; range: $(-\infty, \infty)$; function

27. 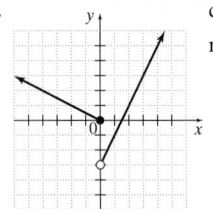   domain: $(-\infty, \infty)$; range: $(-3, \infty)$

Cumulative Review   1. 45% (Sec. 5.3, Ex. 6)   **2.** 106% (Sec. 5.3)   **3.** 150% (Sec. 5.3, Ex. 8)   **4.** 500% (Sec. 5.3)   **5.** 200 (Sec. 5.4, Ex. 10)

6. 242 (Sec. 5.4)   **7.** $\dfrac{101}{200} = \dfrac{p}{100}$ (Sec. 5.5, Ex. 2)   **8.** $101 = n \cdot 200$ (Sec. 5.4)   **9.** $160 (Sec. 5.6, Ex. 2)   **10.** $525 (Sec. 5.6)

11. $73°$ (Sec. 6.1, Ex. 5)   **12.** $56°$ (Sec. 6.1)   **13.** $60°$ (Sec. 6.2, Ex. 2)   **14.** $49°$ (Sec. 6.2)   **15.** $y = -1.6$ (Sec. 9.1, Ex. 2)

16. $x = -3$ (Sec. 9.3)   **17.** $t = \dfrac{16}{3}$ (Sec. 9.3, Ex. 2)   **18.** $\dfrac{29}{8}$ (Sec. 9.3)   **19.** Democratic: 208; Republican: 223 (Sec. 9.4, Ex. 4)

20. 145, 146, 147 (Sec. 9.4)   **21.** 1 (Sec. 12.1, Ex. 28)   **22.** $-\dfrac{216x^3}{y^9}$ (Sec. 12.1)   **23.** 1 (Sec. 12.1, Ex. 29)

24. $\dfrac{a^2}{32b^3}$ (Sec. 12.1)   **25.** -1 (Sec. 12.1, Ex. 30)   **26.** 9 (Sec. 12.1)   **27.** $9y^2 + 12y + 4$ (Sec. 12.6, Ex. 15)   **28.** $x^2y - x^2 + 5y - 5$ (Sec. 12.5)

29. $x + 4$ (Sec. 12.7, Ex. 4)   **30.** $9.1a - 4$ (Sec. 12.3)   **31.** $(r + 6)(r - 7)$ (Sec. 13.2, Ex. 4)   **32. a.** -1 **b.** 30 (Sec. 8.5)

33. $(2x - 3y)(5x + y)$ (Sec. 13.3, Ex. 4)   **34.** $\dfrac{8x + 13}{(x + 2)(x - 1)}$ (Sec. 14.4)   **35.** $(2x - 1)(4x - 5)$ (Sec. 13.4, Ex. 1)   **36.** $\dfrac{2x + 5}{x - 7}$ (Sec. 14.2)

37. a. $x(2x + 7)(2x - 7)$ (Sec. 13.5, Ex. 16)   **b.** $2(9x^2 + 1)(3x + 1)(3x - 1)$ (Sec. 13.5, Ex. 17)   **38.** -32 (Sec. 14.5)

39. $\dfrac{1}{5}, -\dfrac{3}{2}, -6$ (Sec. 13.6, Ex. 8)   **40. a.** $-x + 4$ **b.** $5y - 8$ **c.** $9.1a - 4$ **d.** $2x^2 - 2x$ (Sec. 12.3)   **41.** $\dfrac{x + 7}{x - 5}$ (Sec. 14.1, Ex. 4)

42. $x = -\dfrac{7}{2}, 1$ (Sec. 13.6)   **43.** -5 (Sec. 14.6, Ex. 5)   **44.** $\sqrt{82}$ units; (Ch. 15 Group Activity)   **45. a.** -3 **b.** $0; 0$ **c.** -3 (Sec. 10.1, Ex. 4)

46. a. x-int: $(4, 0)$; y-int: $(0, 1)$ **b.** x-int: $(-2, 0), (0, 0), (3, 0)$; y-int: $(0, 0)$ (Sec. 10.3)   **47. a.** parallel   **b.** perpendicular   **c.** neither (Sec. 10.4, Ex. 7)

48. perpendicular (Sec. 10.4)   **49. a.** function   **b.** not a function (Sec. 10.6, Ex. 2)   **50. a.** $6\sqrt{5}$ **b.** $8\sqrt{2}$ **c.** $11 - 2\sqrt{3} + 4\sqrt{2}$ (Sec. 15.3)

51. $(4, 2)$ (Sec. 11.2, Ex. 1)   **52.** no solution (Sec. 11.2)   **53.** no solution (Sec. 11.3, Ex. 3)   **54.** infinite number of solutions (Sec. 11.3)

55. 6 (Sec. 15.1, Ex. 1)   **56.** $\dfrac{2}{5}$ (Sec. 15.1)   **57.** $\dfrac{3}{10}$ (Sec. 15.1, Ex. 3)   **58.** $\dfrac{4}{11}$ (Sec. 15.1)   **59.** $-1 + \sqrt{3}$ (Sec. 15.4, Ex. 13)   **60.** $\dfrac{5\sqrt{2}}{4}$ (Sec. 15.4)

61. $x = 7, -1$ (Sec. 16.1, Ex. 5)   **62.** $x = 4 \pm \sqrt{3}$ (Sec. 16.1)   **63.** $x = 1 \pm \sqrt{5}$ (Sec. 16.3, Ex. 5)   **64.** $x = -2 \pm 2\sqrt{3}$ (Sec. 16.3)

APPENDIX

Exercise Set Appendix A.1   **1.** $(a + 3)(a^2 - 3a + 9)$ **3.** $(2a + 1)(4a^2 - 2a + 1)$ **5.** $5(k + 2)(k^2 - 2k + 4)$
7. $(xy - 4)(x^2y^2 + 4xy + 16)$ **9.** $(x + 5)(x^2 - 5x + 25)$ **11.** $3x(2x - 3y)(4x^2 + 6xy + 9y^2)$ **13.** $(3 - t)(9 + 3t + t^2)$
15. $8(r - 2)(r^2 + 2r + 4)$ **17.** $(t - 7)(t^2 + 7t + 49)$ **19.** $(s - 4t)(s^2 + 4st + 16t^2)$

Exercise Set Appendix A.2   **1.** $\{2, 3, 4, 5, 6, 7\}$ **3.** $\{4, 6\}$ **5.** $\{\ldots, -2, -1, 0, 1, \ldots\}$ **7.** $\{5, 7\}$
9. $\{x \mid x \text{ is an odd integer or } x = 2 \text{ or } x = 4\}$ **11.** $\{2, 4\}$ **13.**   **15.**   **17.**

19. $[6, \infty)$ **21.** $(-\infty, -3]$ **23.** $(4, 10)$ **25.** $(11, 17)$ **27.** $[1, 4]$ **29.** $\left[-3, \dfrac{3}{2}\right]$ **31.** $\left[-\dfrac{7}{3}, 7\right]$ **33.**

35.   **37.**   **39.** $[2, \infty)$ **41.** $(-\infty, -4) \cup (-2, \infty)$ **43.** $(-\infty, \infty)$ **45.** $\left(-\dfrac{1}{2}, \dfrac{2}{3}\right)$ **47.** $(-\infty, \infty)$

49. $\left[\dfrac{3}{2}, 6\right]$ **51.** $\left(\dfrac{5}{4}, \dfrac{11}{4}\right)$ **53.** $\varnothing$ **55.** $\left(-\infty, -\dfrac{56}{5}\right) \cup \left(\dfrac{5}{3}, \infty\right)$ **57.** $\left(-5, \dfrac{5}{2}\right)$ **59.** $\left(0, \dfrac{14}{3}\right]$ **61.** $(-\infty, -3]$

63. $(-\infty, 1] \cup \left(\dfrac{29}{7}, \infty\right)$ **65.** $\varnothing$ **67.** $\left[-\dfrac{1}{2}, \dfrac{3}{2}\right)$ **69.** $\left(-\dfrac{4}{3}, \dfrac{7}{3}\right)$ **71.** $(6, 12)$ **73.** 1993, 1994, 1995, 1998, 1999, and 2002
75. answers may vary

Mental Math   **1.** d   **3.** c   **5.** a

Exercise Set Appendix A.3   **1.** $\{7, -7\}$ **3.** $\varnothing$ **5.** $\{4.2, -4.2\}$ **7.** $\{-4, 4\}$ **9.** $\{-9, 9\}$ **11.** $\{-5, 23\}$ **13.** $\{7, -2\}$ **15.** $\{8, 4\}$
17. $\{5, -5\}$ **19.** $\{3, -3\}$ **21.** $\{-3, 6\}$ **23.** $\{0\}$ **25.** $\varnothing$ **27.** $\left\{-\dfrac{1}{3}, \dfrac{7}{3}\right\}$ **29.** $\left\{-\dfrac{1}{2}, 9\right\}$ **31.** $\left\{-\dfrac{5}{2}\right\}$ **33.** $\{3, 2\}$

35. $\{-4, 16\}$ **37.** $\{4\}$ **39.** $\left\{\dfrac{3}{2}\right\}$ **41.** $\left\{\dfrac{32}{21}, \dfrac{38}{9}\right\}$ **43.** $\left\{-8, \dfrac{2}{3}\right\}$ **45.** $[-4, 4]$

47. $(-\infty, -3) \cup (3, \infty)$ **49.** $(-5, -1)$ **51.** $(-\infty, -1] \cup [13, \infty)$

53. $(-5, 1)$ **55.** $[-5, 5]$ **57.** $\left\{-\dfrac{3}{2}\right\}$ **59.** $(-\infty, -4) \cup (4, \infty)$

61. $[-10, 3]$ **63.** $\left(1, \dfrac{13}{3}\right)$ **65.** $(-\infty, -24] \cup [4, \infty)$ **67.** $[-2, 9]$

69. $(-\infty, \infty)$ **71.** $\left[-\dfrac{1}{2}, 1\right]$ **73.** $\left(-\infty, \dfrac{2}{3}\right) \cup (2, \infty)$ **75.** $\varnothing$

77. $(-\infty, -12) \cup (0, \infty)$ **79.** $\{-13, 13\}$ **81.** $(-13, 13)$ **83.** $\varnothing$ **85.** $[-10, 10]$ **87.** $\{5, -2\}$

89. $(-\infty, -7] \cup [17, \infty)$ **91.** $\left\{-\dfrac{9}{4}\right\}$ **93.** $(-2, 1)$ **95.** $(-\infty, -18) \cup (12, \infty)$ **97.** $\left\{2, \dfrac{4}{3}\right\}$ **99.** $\varnothing$ **101.** $\left\{-\dfrac{17}{2}, \dfrac{19}{2}\right\}$

103. $\left(-\infty, -\dfrac{25}{3}\right) \cup \left(\dfrac{35}{3}, \infty\right)$ **105.** $\left\{4, -\dfrac{1}{5}\right\}$ **107.** $\left\{-\dfrac{17}{3}, 5\right\}$ **109.** $\varnothing$ **111.** $\{x \mid x \text{ is a real number}\}$ **113.** $|x| = 5$ **115.** $|x| < 7$
117. $|x| \leq 5$, answers may vary

Exercise Set Appendix A.4   **1.** 5 units   **3.** $\sqrt{41}$ units ≈ 6.403 **5.** $\sqrt{5}$ units ≈ 2.236 **7.** $\sqrt{192.58}$ units ≈ 13.877 **9.** $(4, -2)$

11. $\left(-5, \dfrac{5}{2}\right)$ **13.** $\left(-\dfrac{1}{2}, \dfrac{1}{2}\right)$ **15.** $\left(\sqrt{2}, \dfrac{\sqrt{5}}{2}\right)$

Exercise Set Appendix A.5   **1.** $y = 4x - 4$ **3.** $y = -3x + 1$ **5.** $y = 4$ **7.** $y = -\dfrac{3}{2}x - 6$ **9.** $y = -5$ **11.** $y = -4x + 1$
13. $y = -\dfrac{1}{2}x + 1$ **15.** $y = 8x - 47$ **17.** $x = 5$

Exercise Set Appendix A.6 **1.** $(-\infty, -5) \cup (-1, \infty)$ **3.** $[-4, 3]$ **5.** $(-\infty, -5] \cup [-3, \infty)$ **7.** $\left(-5, -\dfrac{1}{3}\right)$ **9.** $(2, 4) \cup (6, \infty)$

11. $(-\infty, -4] \cup [0, 1]$ **13.** $(-\infty, -3) \cup (-2, 2) \cup (3, \infty)$ **15.** $(-7, 2)$ **17.** $(-1, \infty)$ **19.** $(-\infty, -1] \cup (4, \infty)$

21. $(-\infty, 2) \cup \left(\dfrac{11}{4}, \infty\right)$ **23.** $(0, 2] \cup [3, \infty)$ **25.** $(-\infty, 3)$ **27.** $\left[-\dfrac{5}{4}, \dfrac{3}{2}\right]$ **29.** $(-\infty, 0) \cup (1, \infty)$ **31.** $(0, 10)$

33. $(-\infty, -4] \cup [4, 6]$ **35.** $\left(-\infty, -\dfrac{2}{3}\right] \cup \left[\dfrac{3}{2}, \infty\right)$ **37.** $(-\infty, -4) \cup [5, \infty)$ **39.** $(-\infty, 1) \cup (2, \infty)$ **41.** $\left(-4, -\dfrac{3}{2}\right) \cup \left(\dfrac{3}{2}, \infty\right)$

43. $(-\infty, -5] \cup [-1, 1] \cup [5, \infty)$ **45.** $(-\infty, -6] \cup (-1, 0] \cup (7, \infty)$ **47.** $(-\infty, -8] \cup (-4, \infty)$ **49.** $\left(-\infty, -\dfrac{5}{3}\right) \cup \left(\dfrac{7}{2}, \infty\right)$

51. $(-\infty, 0] \cup \left(5, \dfrac{11}{2}\right]$ **53.** $(0, \infty)$ **55.** answers may vary

Exercise Set Appendix A.7 **1.** 7 **3.** 3 **5.** $\dfrac{1}{2}$ **7.** 13 **9.** $2\sqrt[3]{m}$ **11.** $3x^2$ **13.** -3 **15.** -2 **17.** 8 **19.** 16

21. not a real number **23.** $\sqrt[5]{(2x)^3}$ **25.** $\sqrt[3]{(7x + 2)^2}$ **27.** $\dfrac{64}{27}$ **29.** $\dfrac{1}{16}$ **31.** $\dfrac{1}{16}$ **33.** not a real number

35. $\dfrac{1}{x^{1/4}}$ **37.** $a^{2/3}$ **39.** $\dfrac{5x^{3/4}}{7}$ **41.** $a^{7/3}$ **43.** x **45.** $3^{5/8}$ **47.** $y^{1/6}$ **49.** $8u^3$ **51.** $-b$ **53.** $\dfrac{1}{x^2}$ **55.** $27x^{2/3}$ **57.** $\dfrac{y}{z^{1/6}}$

59. $\dfrac{1}{x^{7/4}}$ **61.** $\sqrt{x}$ **63.** $\sqrt[3]{2}$ **65.** $2\sqrt{x}$ **67.** $\sqrt{x + 3}$ **69.** $\sqrt{xy}$ **71.** $\sqrt[3]{a^2 b}$ **73.** $\sqrt[15]{y^{11}}$ **75.** $\sqrt[12]{b^5}$ **77.** $\sqrt[24]{x^{23}}$ **79.** $\sqrt{a}$

81. $\sqrt[6]{432}$ **83.** $\sqrt[15]{343 y^5}$ **85.** $\sqrt[6]{125 r^3 s^2}$ **87.** 1509 calories **89.** answers may vary **91.** $a^{1/3}$ **93.** $x^{1/5}$

Exercise Set Appendix A.8 **1.**
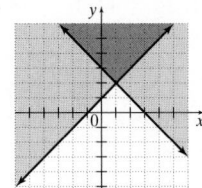
3.
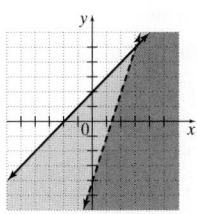
5.
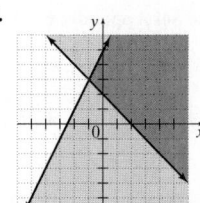
7.

9.
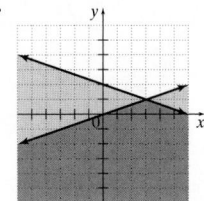
11.
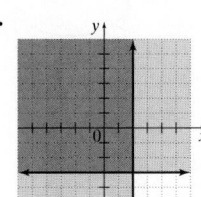
13.
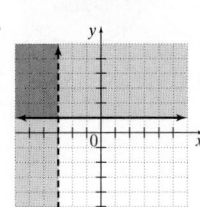
15.
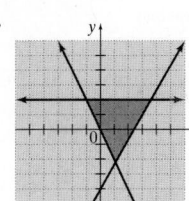
17.
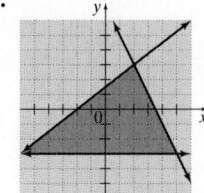

19.
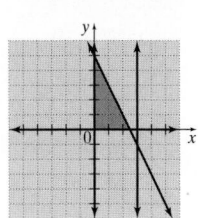
21. C **23.** D **25.** the line $y = 3$

Mental Math **1.** 1 ft **3.** 2 ft **5.** 1 yd **7.** no **9.** yes **11.** no

Exercise Set Appendix D.1 **1.** 5 ft **3.** 36 ft **5.** 8 mi **7.** $8\dfrac{1}{2}$ ft **9.** $3\dfrac{1}{3}$ yd **11.** 33,792 ft **13.** 4.5 yd **15.** 0.25 ft **17.** 13 yd 1 ft
19. 3 ft 5 in. **21.** 1 mi 4720 ft **23.** 62 in. **25.** 23 ft **27.** 84 in. **29.** 12 ft 3 in. **31.** 22 yd 1 ft **33.** 8 ft 5 in. **35.** 5 ft 6 in.
37. 3 ft 4 in. **39.** 50 yd 2 ft **41.** 4000 cm **43.** 4.0 cm **45.** 0.3 km **47.** 1.4 m **49.** 15 m **51.** 42,000 cm **53.** 7000 m
55. 83 mm **57.** 0.201 dm **59.** 40 mm **61.** 8.94 m **63.** 2.94 m or 2940 mm **65.** 1.29 cm or 12.9 mm **67.** 12.640 km or 12,640 m
69. 54.9 m **71.** 1.55 km **73.** $348\dfrac{2}{3}$ yd; 12,552 in. **75.** $11\dfrac{2}{3}$ yd; 140 in. **77.** 5000 mm; 0.005 km; 500 cm **79.** 0.065 m; 65 mm; 0.000065 km
81. 342,000 m; 342,000,000 mm; 34,200,000 cm **83.** 10 ft 6 in. **85.** 13 ft 11 in. **87.** 9.12 m **89.** 26.7 mm **91.** 15 ft 9 in. **93.** 3.35 m
95. Estimate: 13 yd **97.** answers may vary: for example, $1\dfrac{1}{3}$ yd or 48 in. **99.** answers may vary

Mental Math **1.** 1 lb **3.** 2000 lb **5.** 16 oz **7.** 1 ton **9.** no **11.** yes **13.** no

Exercise Set Appendix D.2 **1.** 32 oz **3.** 10,000 lb **5.** 6 tons **7.** $3\dfrac{3}{4}$ lb **9.** $1\dfrac{3}{4}$ tons **11.** 260 oz **13.** 9800 lb **15.** 76 oz

17. 1.5 tons **19.** $\dfrac{1}{20}$ lb **21.** 92 oz **23.** 161 oz **25.** 5 lb 9 oz **27.** 53 lb 10 oz **29.** 9 tons 390 lb **31.** 3 tons 175 lb **33.** 8 lb 11 oz

35. 31 lb 2 oz   **37.** 1 ton 700 lb   **39.** 0.5 kg   **41.** 4000 mg   **43.** 25,000 g   **45.** 0.048 g   **47.** 0.0063 kg   **49.** 15,140 mg
51. 4010 g   **53.** 350,000 cg   **55.** 13.5 mg   **57.** 5.815 g or 5815 mg   **59.** 1850 mg or 1.850 g   **61.** 1360 g or 1.360 kg
63. 13.52 kg   **65.** 2.125 kg   **67.** 200,000 lb; 3,200,000 oz   **69.** $\frac{269}{400}$ or 0.6725 ton; 21,520 oz   **71.** 0.5 g; 0.0005 kg; 50 cg
73. 21,000 g; 21,000,000 mg; 2,100,000 cg   **75.** 8.064 kg   **77.** 30 mg   **79.** 5 lb 8 oz   **81.** 35 lb 14 oz   **83.** 250 mg   **85.** 144 mg
87. 6.12 kg   **89.** 130 lb   **91.** 211 lb   **93.** 850 g or 0.85 kg   **95.** answers may vary   **97.** true   **99.** answers may vary

Mental Math   1. 1 pt   **3.** 1 gal   **5.** 1 qt   **7.** 1 c   **9.** 2 c   **11.** 4 qt   **13.** no   **15.** no

Exercise Set Appendix D.3   1. 4 c   **3.** 16 pt   **5.** $2\frac{1}{2}$ gal   **7.** 5 pt   **9.** 8 c   **11.** $3\frac{3}{4}$ qt   **13.** 768 fl oz   **15.** 9 c   **17.** 23 qt   **19.** $\frac{1}{4}$ pt
21. 14 gal 2 qt   **23.** 4 gal 3 qt 1 pt   **25.** 22 pt   **27.** 10 gal 1 qt   **29.** 4 c 4 fl oz   **31.** 1 gal 1 qt   **33.** 2 gal 3 qt 1 pt   **35.** 2 qt 1 c
37. 17 gal   **39.** 4 gal 3 qt   **41.** 5000 ml   **43.** 4.5 L   **45.** 320 cl   **47.** 0.41 kl   **49.** 0.064 L   **51.** 160 L   **53.** 3600 ml
55. 0.00016 kl   **57.** 22.5 L   **59.** 4.5 L or 4500 ml   **61.** 8410 ml or 8.41 L   **63.** 10,600 ml or 10.6 L   **65.** 3840 ml   **67.** 162.4 L
69. 336 c; 84 qt; 168 pt   **71.** $\frac{1}{4}$ gal; 1 qt; 2 pt   **73.** 2 qt   **75.** 18.954 L   **77.** yes   **79.** answers may vary   **81.** answers may vary
83. 0.6 cc   **85.** 1.9 cc

Exercise Set Appendix D.4   1. $V = 72$ cu in.; $SA = 108$ sq in.   **3.** $V = 512$ cu cm; $SA = 384$ sq cm
5. $V = 4\pi$ cu yd $\approx 12\frac{4}{7}$ cu yd; $SA = (2\sqrt{13}\pi + 4\pi)$ sq yd ≈ 35.23 sq yd   **7.** $V = \frac{500}{3}\pi$ cu in. $\approx 523\frac{17}{21}$ cu in.; $SA = 100\pi$ sq in. $\approx 314\frac{2}{7}$ sq in.
9. $V = 48$ cu cm; $SA = 96$ sq cm   **11.** $2\frac{10}{27}$ cu in.   **13.** 26 sq ft   **15.** $10\frac{5}{6}$ cu in.   **17.** 960 cu cm   **19.** 196π sq in.   **21.** $7\frac{1}{2}$ cu ft
23. $12\frac{4}{7}$ cu cm

Exercise Set Appendix E   1. inductive   **3.** deductive   **5.** inductive   **7.** 81   **9.** C   **11.** 36   **13.** E   **15.** 99999   **17.** 9   **19.** 74
21. 241   **23.**   **25.** 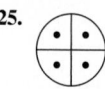   **27.** 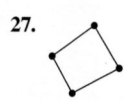   **29.** 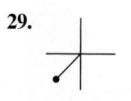   **31.** 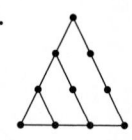   **33.**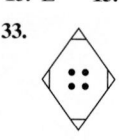

35. answers may vary   **37.** 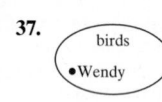   **39.** 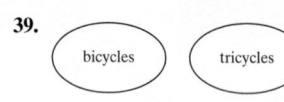   **41.** 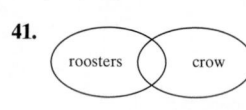   **43.**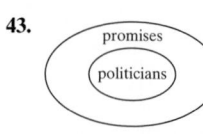

45. Joey   **47.** 15 people   **49.** Donna   **51.** Julio   **53.** 5 people

Exercise Set Appendix F   1. b   **2.** d   **3.** b   **4.** b   **5.** a   **6.** d   **7.** d   **8.** b   **9.** c   **10.** a   **11.** c   **12.** b   **13.** d
14. d   **15.** c   **16.** d   **17.** c   **18.** b   **19.** b   **20.** d   **21.** c   **22.** d   **23.** c   **24.** a   **25.** d   **26.** c   **27.** b   **28.** a
29. c   **30.** d   **31.** d   **32.** b   **33.** a   **34.** b   **35.** c   **36.** a   **37.** b   **38.** d   **39.** c   **40.** b   **41.** d   **42.** c   **43.** a
44. d   **45.** c   **46.** b   **47.** a   **48.** b   **49.** b   **50.** b

INDEX

Photo Credits

I5

$$60$$

$$
\begin{array}{r}
4\,7 \\
17 \\
\hline
119 \\
170 \\
\hline
\boxed{289}
\end{array}
$$

$$
\begin{array}{r}
28 \\
28 \\
\hline
224 \\
560 \\
\hline
\boxed{784}
\end{array}
$$

$$
\begin{array}{r}
784 \\
289 \\
\hline
1073
\end{array}
$$

$$
\begin{array}{r}
20 \\
20 \\
\hline
400
\end{array}
$$

$$
\begin{array}{r}
605 \\
121 \\
+484 \\
\hline
\end{array}
$$

$$
\begin{array}{r}
100 \\
100 \\
\hline
10000
\end{array}
$$

$$
\begin{array}{r}
30 \\
30 \\
\hline
900
\end{array}
$$

$$
\begin{array}{r}
11 \\
11 \\
\hline
110 \\
\boxed{121}
\end{array}
$$

$$
\begin{array}{r}
22 \\
22 \\
\hline
44 \\
440 \\
\boxed{484} \\
121 \\
\hline
605
\end{array}
$$

2^c 2^c

$$
\begin{array}{r}
32 \\
32 \\
\hline
64 \\
960 \\
\hline
1024
\end{array}
$$

$$
\begin{array}{r}
33 \\
33 \\
\hline
99 \\
990 \\
\hline
1089
\end{array}
$$

$h = \sqrt{1073}$

$hyp = 32.757$ ft.

$$
\begin{array}{r}
24 \\
96 \\
480.75 \\
\hline
2355576.75 \\
125 \\
500 \\
\hline
625
\end{array}
$$

$$
\begin{array}{r}
25 \\
150 \\
\hline
225
\end{array}
$$

$-12 = -12$

$12m - 2n$

$$3+16+25$$
$$\frac{9-(-2)}{(-4)+3} = \frac{11}{-1}$$

$$\frac{-3+4}{17} \, \frac{}{17} = \frac{1}{17}$$

$$-\frac{4}{15} \, \frac{3}{15} = \frac{-1}{15}$$

$$\frac{6-5}{3+8} = \frac{1}{11}$$

$$(-1+49-95$$
$$1+49$$
$$1+49$$
$$+36-45$$

$$-8+-3 \qquad -4$$

$$\frac{39}{16} \qquad 3\overline{\smash{)}360}$$

$$\frac{14}{-16}$$

$$-14+\frac{1}{2}$$
$$\frac{11}{12}+\frac{2}{12}=\frac{93}{12}$$

$$29.530$$

$$\frac{57}{0}$$

$$676$$
$$196$$
$$\overline{872}$$

$$\frac{10}{-16} \quad \frac{8}{6} \, \frac{4}{6}$$

$$22)898$$

$$20400 \qquad 151.32$$

$$\frac{1}{2} = 20.2$$
$$\frac{2}{2} = 20.74$$

$$-142.04 \quad \Big| \quad \frac{-9}{14}+\frac{2}{14}=\frac{-9+2}{14}=\frac{-7}{14}$$

Sturdy Memorial Hospital
Emergency Care Center
211 Park Street
P.O. Box 2963
Attleboro, MA 02703-0963
(508) 236-7000

ECC Visit Order Summary

Patient: Jill Lynn Doherty   MR # 257414
Age/Sex: 39/F   DOB: 03/18/73   Date: 03/30/12

Tests & Procedures Ordered This Visit

Order Date/Time	Procedure
03/30/12 - 1448	MICROBIOLOGY - *MIC - STREP SCREEN*

Sturdy Memorial Hospital
Emergency Care Center
211 Park Street
P.O. Box 2963
Attleboro, MA 02703-0963
(508) 236-7000

Medication Reconciliation Discharge Summary

Patient: Jill Lynn Doherty   MR # 257414
Age/Sex: 39/F   DOB: 03/18/73   Date: 03/30/12

Start Taking These Medications

Amoxicillin(Amoxicillin)
500 MG Orally Three-Times A Day
Entered On: 03/30/12

ADDITIONAL MEDICATIONS:

Patient Home Care Instructions

DOHERTY,JILL LYNN   Account # 56288525   VISIT DATE: 03/30/12
DOB: 03/18/73   SEEN BY: TSAI MD,LULU
Chief Complaint: QC-Sore Throat

ICE   SPLINT/SUPPORT/IMMOBILIZER

ELEVATION   AMBULATORY ASSIST DEVICES

REST   PAIN MEDICATION

POSITIONING   HYDRATION

ACTIVITY RESTRICTION   REFERRAL FOR FURTHER FOLLOW-UP

OTHER: _____Strep Screen_____

As uncomfortable as pain can be, it serves an important function and may not be
able to be completely eliminated during your ED visit.

During your recovery period, pain helps you to recognize when you may be
overdoing activity.

Once discharged:

  CONTINUING THE STEPS APPLIED ABOVE, ALONG WITH THE DISCHARGE INSTRUCTIONS
  PROVIDED BY THE PHYSICIAN WILL CONTINUE TO ASSIST IN REDUCING YOUR PAIN.

Healing may take longer than you expect. Once your body has rested sufficiently
the pain should be reduced or eliminated. Please allow yourself the time for
your body to recover.

Patient Home Care Instructions

DOHERTY,JILL LYNN   Account # 56288525   VISIT DATE: 03/30/12
DOB: 03/18/73   SEEN BY: TSAI MD,LULU
Chief Complaint: QC-Sore Throat

SORE THROAT

Sore throats are usually caused by viruses.   Some are caused by bacteria (Strep Throat).

Please follow these instructions carefully:
- Take acetaminophen (Tylenol) or ibuprofen (Advil) for pain or fever.
- Drink plenty of liquids.
- Several throat sprays, gargles and lozenges are available in pharmacies to help with the soreness.
- If you are given an antibiotic (such as penicillin), it is important to finish the whole prescription as directed.

Return to the Emergency Department or see your own doctor right away if any problems develop, including the following:
- You are worse in any way.
- You are not getting better within 3 days.
- Trouble breathing or shortness of breath.
- Trouble talking or swallowing (new or getting worse).
- Drooling.
- Fever over 102 F or fever lasting more than 24 hours.
- Severe headache or neck pain.
- Throwing up.
- Confusion, drowsiness or loss of memory.
- Trouble walking or controlling your arms or legs.
- Anything else that worries you.

For Children (in addition to above):
- Will not drink.
- Does not make urine ("pass water") for 8 hours or if diaper is dry for 8 hours.
- Neck stiffness.
-Change in voice or change in sound of crying.

The Emergency Department is open 24 hours a day for any problems.

PAIN MANAGEMENT

                        PAIN MANAGEMENT
               While in the Emergency Department

You have come to the Emergency Department for a condition that is causing you pain or discomfort. Pain is a warning sign and the body's response to injury or illness.

We recognize and understand how uncomfortable you are. To help you lessen you pain during your visit, we have applied the following pain reducing steps:

                -- circle all that apply --

DOHERTY,JILL LYNN
Amoxicillin

effects to FDA at 1-800-FDA-1088

DOHERTY,JILL LYNN
Amoxicillin

* You may store the oral liquid in the refrigerator. Do not freeze. Throw away any unused medicine after 14 days.
* Ask your pharmacist, doctor, or health caregiver about the best way to dispose of any outdated medicine or medicine no longer needed..
* Keep all medicine away from children and never share your medicine with anyone.

Drugs and Foods to Avoid:

Ask your doctor or pharmacist before using any other medicine, including over-the-counter medicines, vitamins, and herbal products.
* Make sure your doctor knows if you also use allopurinol (Zyloprim(R)), probenecid (Benemid(R)), birth control pills, or a blood thinner (such as warfarin, Coumadin(R)).

Warnings While Using This Medicine:
* Make sure your doctor knows if you are pregnant or breastfeeding or if you have kidney disease or allergies. Tell your doctor if you are on dialysis.
* Tell your doctor if you have a condition called phenylketonuria (PKU). The chewable tablet contains phenylalanine, which can make this condition worse.
* If you have severe diarrhea, ask your doctor before taking any medicine to stop the diarrhea.
* Make sure any doctor or dentist who treats you knows that you are using this medicine. This medicine may affect the results of certain medical tests.
* Birth control pills may not work while you use this medicine. Use another form of birth control along with your birth control pills to avoid pregnancy.
* If your symptoms do not improve or if they get worse, call your doctor.
* Use this medicine only to treat the infection your doctor has prescribed it for. Do not use this medicine for any infection or condition that has not been checked by a doctor. This medicine will not treat the flu or the common cold.

Possible Side Effects While Using This Medicine:

Call your doctor right away if you notice any of these side effects:
* Allergic reaction: Itching or hives, swelling in your face or hands, swelling or tingling in your mouth or throat, chest tightness, trouble breathing
* Blistering, peeling, or red skin rash
* Diarrhea that may contain blood

If you notice these less serious side effects, talk with your doctor:
* Mild diarrhea, nausea, or vomiting
* Mild skin rash

If you notice other side effects that you think are caused by this medicine, tell your doctor.

Call your doctor for medical advice about side effects.   You may report side

DOHERTY,JILL LYNN
Amoxicillin

Amoxicillin (By mouth)

Amoxicillin (a-mox-i-SIL-in)

Treats infections. Also used with other medicines to treat stomach ulcer. This medicine is a penicillin antibiotic.

Brand Name(s):Amoxil, Prevpac, Amoxicot, Trimox, Moxilin, Amoxil Pediatric, Moxatag

There may be other brand names for this medicine.

When This Medicine Should Not Be Used:

You should not use this medicine if you have had an allergic reaction to amoxicillin, any type of penicillin, or a cephalosporin antibiotic, such as cefaclor, cefadroxil, cephalexin, Ceftin(R), or Keflex(R).

How to Use This Medicine:

Capsule, Liquid, Tablet, Chewable Tablet, Long Acting Tablet
* Your doctor will tell you how much of this medicine to use and how often. Do not use more medicine or use it more often than your doctor tells you to.
* The chewable tablet must be chewed before you swallow it. You may crush the tablet and mix the medicine with a small amount of food to make it easier to swallow.
* Shake the oral liquid well just before each use. Measure the oral liquid medicine with a marked measuring spoon, oral syringe, or medicine cup.
* You may mix the oral liquid with a baby formula, milk, fruit juice, water, ginger ale, or another cold drink. Be sure your child drinks all of the mixture right away.
* Place the tablet for suspension in a small drinking glass, and add 2 teaspoons of water to the glass. Do not use any other liquid other than water. Gently stir or swirl the water in the glass until the tablet is completely dissolved. Drink all of this mixture right away. Add more water to the glass and drink all of it to make sure you get all of the medicine.
* Do not chew or swallow the tablet for suspension. The tablet will not dissolve in your mouth.
* Keep using this medicine for the full treatment time, even if you feel better after the first few doses. Your infection may not clear up if you stop using the medicine too soon.

If a dose is missed:
* If you miss a dose or forget to use your medicine, use it as soon as you can. If it is almost time for your next dose, wait until then to use the medicine and skip the missed dose. Do not use extra medicine to make up for a missed dose.

How to Store and Dispose of This Medicine:
* Store the tablets, capsules, and tablets for suspension at room temperature, away from heat, moisture, and direct light.